Statistics
for Management and Economics
Twelfth Edition

Gerald Keller

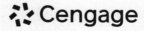
Cengage

Australia • Brazil • Canada • Mexico • Singapore • United Kingdom • United States

Statistics for Management and Economics, **Twelfth Edition**

Gerald Keller

SVP, Higher Education Product Management: Erin Joyner

VP, Product Management, Learning Experiences: Thais Alencar

Product Director: Joe Sabatino

Senior Product Manager: Aaron Arnsparger

Product Assistant: Flannery Cowan

Senior Learning Designer: Brandon Foltz

Senior Content Manager: Conor Allen

Associate Subject-Matter Expert: Nancy Marchant

Digital Delivery Quality Partner: Steven McMillian

Director, Product Marketing: Danae April

IP Analyst: Ashley Maynard

IP Project Manager: Kumaresan Chandrakumar, Integra

Production Service: MPS Limited

Designer: Chris Doughman

Interior image Source: cmillerdesign

Cover Designer: Foo Toon Check

Cover Image:
© iStock.com/Klaus Vedfelt

For product information and technology assistance, contact us at **asia.techsupport@cengage.com**

For permission to use material from this text or product, please email to **asia.permissionrequest@cengage.com**

ISBN: 978-981-5059-43-4

Cengage Learning Asia Pte Ltd
30A Kallang Place #12-06
Singapore 339213

Cengage is a leading provider of customized learning solutions with employees residing in nearly 40 different countries and sales in more than 125 countries around the world. Find your local representative at: **www.cengage.com**.

To learn more about Cengage Solutions, visit **www.cengageasia.com**.

Printed in Singapore
Print Number: 01   Print Year: 2022

BRIEF CONTENTS

CONTENTS

17   Multiple Regression   731

18   Model Building   771

19   Nonparametric Statistics   798

20   Time-Series Analysis and Forecasting   874

PREFACE

Businesses are increasingly using statistical techniques to convert data into information. For students preparing for the business world, it is not enough merely to focus on mastering a diverse set of statistical techniques and calculations. A course and its attendant textbook must provide a complete picture of statistical concepts and their applications to the real world. *Statistics for Management and Economics* is designed to demonstrate that statistical methods are vital tools for today's managers and economists.

Fulfilling this objective requires the several features that I have built into this book. First, I have included data-driven examples, exercises, and cases that demonstrate statistical applications that are and can be used by marketing managers, financial analysts, accountants, economists, operations managers, and others. Many are accompanied by large and genuine data sets. Second, I reinforce the applied nature of the discipline by teaching students how to choose the correct statistical technique. Third, I teach students the concepts that are essential to interpret the statistical results.

Why I Wrote This Book

Business is complex and requires effective management to succeed. Managing complexity requires many skills. There are more competitors, more places to sell products, and more places to locate workers. As a consequence, effective decision making is more crucial than ever before. On the other hand, managers have more access to larger and more detailed data that are potential sources of information. However, to achieve this potential requires that managers know how to convert data into information. This knowledge extends well beyond the arithmetic of calculating statistics. Unfortunately, this is what most textbooks offer—a series of unconnected techniques illustrated mostly with manual calculations. This continues a pattern that goes back many years. What is required now is a complete approach to applying statistical techniques.

When I started teaching statistics in 1971, books demonstrated how to calculate statistics and, in some cases, how various formulas were derived. One reason for doing so was the belief that by doing calculations by hand, students would be able to understand the techniques and concepts. When the first edition of this book was published in 1988, an important goal was to teach students to identify the correct technique. Through the next 10 editions, I refined my approach to emphasize interpretation and decision making equally. I now divide the solution of statistical problems into three stages and include them in every appropriate example: (1) *identify* the technique, (2) *compute* the statistics, and (3) *interpret* the results. The compute stage can be completed in any or all of four ways: manually (with the aid of a calculator), using Excel, XLSTAT, or Stata. For those courses that wish to use the computer extensively, manual calculations can be played down or omitted completely. Conversely, those that wish to emphasize manual calculations may easily do so, and the computer solutions can be selectively introduced or skipped entirely. This approach is designed to provide maximum flexibility, and it leaves to the instructor the decision of if and when to introduce the computer.

I believe that my approach offers several advantages:

- An emphasis on identification and interpretation provides students with practical skills that they can apply to real problems they will face regardless of whether a course uses manual or computer calculations.

- Students learn that statistics is a method of converting data into information. With 1,283 data files and corresponding problems that ask students to interpret statistical results, students are given ample opportunities to practice data analysis and decision making.

- The optional use of the computer allows for larger and more realistic exercises and examples.

Placing calculations in the context of a larger problem allows instructors to focus on more important aspects of the decision problem. For example, more attention needs to be devoted to interpret statistical results. Proper interpretation of statistical results requires an understanding of the probability and statistical concepts that underlie the techniques and an understanding of the context of the problems. An essential aspect of my approach is teaching students the concepts. I do so by providing Excel worksheets that allow students to perform "what-if" analyses. Students can easily see the effect of changing the components of a statistical technique, such as the effect of increasing the sample size.

Efforts to teach statistics as a valuable and necessary tool in business and economics are made more difficult by the positioning of the statistics course in most curricula. The required statistics course in most undergraduate programs appears in the first or second year. In many graduate programs, the statistics course is offered in the first semester of a three-semester program and the first year of a two-year program. Accounting, economics, finance, human resource management, marketing, and operations management are usually taught after the statistics course. Consequently, most students will not be able to understand the general context of the statistical application. This deficiency is addressed in this book by "Applications in …" sections, subsections, and boxes. Illustrations of statistical applications in businesses that students are unfamiliar with are preceded by an explanation of the background material.

- For example, to illustrate graphical techniques, we use an example that compares the histograms of the returns on two different investments. To explain what financial analysts look for in the histograms requires an understanding that risk is measured by the amount of variation in the returns. The example is preceded by an "Applications in Finance" box that discusses how return on investment is computed and used.

- Later when I present the normal distribution, I feature another "Applications in Finance" box to show why the standard deviation of the returns measures the risk of that investment.

- Thirty-five application boxes are scattered throughout the book.

Some applications are so large that I devote an entire section or subsection to the topic. For example, in the chapter that introduces the confidence interval estimator of a proportion, I also present market segmentation. In that section, I show how the confidence interval estimate of a population proportion can yield estimates of the sizes of market segments. In other chapters, I illustrate various statistical techniques by showing how marketing managers can apply these techniques to determine the differences that exist between market segments. There are five such sections and one subsection in this book.

The "Applications in …" segments provide great motivation to the student who asks, "How will I ever use this technique?"

New in This Edition

The use of statistical software has been reorganized. First, Excel can be used for all statistical applications. Second, XLSTAT output and instructions, which were introduced in the 11th edition, have been placed in the appendixes to Chapters 2 to 4, and 10 to 19. Third, Stata has been included for the first time with output and instructions in appendixes similar to the treatment of XLSTAT.

The data from the last 10 General Social Surveys and the last five Surveys of Consumer Finances have been included, which produced hundreds of new exercises. Students will have the opportunity to convert real data into information. Instructors can use these data sets to create hundreds of additional examples and exercises.

Many of the examples, exercises, and cases using real data in the 11th edition have been updated. These include the data on wins, payrolls, and attendance in baseball, basketball, football, and hockey; returns on stocks listed on the New York Stock Exchange, NASDAQ, and Toronto Stock Exchange; and global warming.

I've created many new examples and exercises. Here are the numbers for the 12th edition: 137 solved examples, 2,573 exercises, 32 cases, and 1,283 data sets.

New! MindTap Courseware....

Assign this textbook through MindTap to provide online homework and assessment, study tools, and seamless access to the eBook—inside or outside of your campus Learning Management System. MindTap includes chapter quizzes, Exploring Statistics applets with teaching videos and activities, assignable exercises from the textbook with algorithmic versions and solutions, auto-graded Excel problems, an algorithmic test bank, and more! Contact your Cengage representative for more information about accessing MindTap.

Data Driven: The Big Picture

Solving statistical problems begins with a problem and data. The ability to select the right method by problem objective and data type is **a valuable tool for business**. Because business decisions are driven by data, students will leave this course equipped with the tools they need to make effective, informed decisions in all areas of the business world.

tzf/Shutterstock.com

Identify the Correct Technique

Examples introduce the first crucial step in this three-step (*identify–compute–interpret*) approach. Every example's solution begins by examining the data type and problem objective and then identifying the right technique to solve the problem.

EXAMPLE 13.1*

DATA
Xm13-01

Direct and Broker-Purchased Mutual Funds

Millions of investors buy mutual funds (see page 175 for a description of mutual funds), choosing from thousands of possibilities. Some funds can be purchased directly from banks or other financial institutions whereas others must be purchased through brokers, who charge a fee for this service. This raises the question, Can investors do better by buying mutual funds directly than by purchasing mutual funds through brokers? To help answer this question, a group of researchers randomly sampled the annual returns from mutual funds that can be acquired directly and mutual funds that are bought through brokers and recorded the net annual returns, which are the returns on investment after deducting all relevant fees. These are listed next.

Direct					Broker				
9.33	4.68	4.23	14.69	10.29	3.24	3.71	16.4	4.36	9.43
6.94	3.09	10.28	−2.97	4.39	−6.76	13.15	6.39	−11.07	8.31
16.17	7.26	7.1	10.37	−2.06	12.8	11.05	−1.9	9.24	−3.99
16.97	2.05	−3.09	−0.63	7.66	11.1	−3.12	9.49	−2.67	−4.44
5.94	13.07	5.6	−0.15	10.83	2.73	8.94	6.7	8.97	8.63
12.61	0.59	5.27	0.27	14.48	−0.13	2.74	0.19	1.87	7.06
3.33	13.57	8.09	4.59	4.8	18.22	4.07	12.39	−1.53	1.57
16.13	0.35	15.05	6.38	13.12	−0.8	5.6	6.54	5.23	−8.44
11.2	2.69	13.21	−0.24	−6.54	−5.75	−0.85	10.92	6.87	−5.72
1.14	18.45	1.72	10.32	−1.06	2.59	−0.28	−2.15	−1.69	6.95

Can we conclude at the 5% significance level that directly purchased mutual funds outperform mutual funds bought through brokers?

*Source: D. Bergstresser, J. Chalmers, and P. Tufano, "Assessing the Costs and Benefits of Brokers in the Mutual Fund Industry."

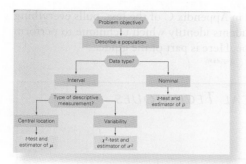

Appendixes 13, 14, 15, 16, 17, and **19** reinforce this problem-solving approach and allow students to hone their skills.

Flowcharts, found within the appendixes, help students develop the logical process for choosing the correct technique, reinforce the learning process, and provide easy review material for students.

APPENDIX 14.C / REVIEW OF CHAPTERS 12 TO 14

The number of techniques introduced in Chapters 12 to 14 is up to 20. As we did in Appendix 13.C, we provide a table of the techniques, a flowchart to help you identify the correct technique, and 34 exercises to give you practice in how to choose the appropriate method. The table and the flowchart have been amended to include the three analysis of variance techniques introduced in this chapter and the three multiple comparison methods.

TABLE **A14.1** **Summary of Statistical Techniques in Chapters 12 to 14**

t-test of μ
Estimator of μ (including estimator of $N\mu$)
χ^2 test of σ^2
Estimator of σ^2
z-test of p
Estimator of p (including estimator of Np)
Equal-variances t-test of $\mu_1 - \mu_2$
Equal-variances estimator of $\mu_1 - \mu_2$
Unequal-variances t-test of $\mu_1 - \mu_2$
Unequal-variances estimator of $\mu_1 - \mu_2$
t-test of μ_D
Estimator of μ_D
F-test of σ_1^2/σ_2^2
Estimator of σ_1^2/σ_2^2
z-test of $p_1 - p_2$ (Case 1)
z-test of $p_1 - p_2$ (Case 2)
Estimator of $p_1 - p_2$
One-way analysis of variance (including multiple comparisons)
Two-way (randomized blocks) analysis of variance
Two-factor analysis of variance

Factors That Identify the t-Test and Estimator of μ_D
1. **Problem objective**: Compare two populations.
2. **Data type**: Interval
3. **Descriptive measurement**: Central location
4. **Experimental design**: Matched pairs

Factors That Identify ... boxes are found in each chapter after a technique or concept has been introduced. These boxes allow students to see a technique's essential requirements and give them a way to easily review their understanding. These essential requirements are revisited in the review chapters, where they are coupled with other concepts illustrated in flowcharts.

A Guide to Statistical Techniques, found in Appendix C of the text, pulls everything together into one useful table that helps students identify which technique to perform based on the problem objective and data type. Here is part of the guide.

A GUIDE TO STATISTICAL TECHNIQUES

Problem Objectives

DATA TYPES		Describe a Population	Compare Two Populations	Compare Two or More Populations
	Interval	Histogram **Section 3-1** Line chart **Section 3-2** Mean, median, and mode **Section 4-1** Range, variance, and standard deviation **Section 4-2** Percentiles and quartiles **Section 4-3** *t*-test and estimator of a mean **Section 12-1** Chi-squared test and estimator of a variance **Section 12-2**	Equal-variances *t*-test and estimator of the difference between two means: independent samples **Section 13-1** Unequal-variances *t*-test and estimator of the difference between two means: independent samples **Section 13-1** *t*-test and estimator of mean difference **Section 13-3** *F*-test and estimator of ratio of two variances **Section 13-4** Wilcoxon rank sum test **Section 19-1** Wilcoxon signed rank sum test **Section 19-2**	One-way analysis of variance **Section 14-1** LSD multiple comparison method **Section 14-2** Tukey's multiple comparison method **Section 14-2** Two-way analysis of variance **Section 14-4** Two-factor analysis of varianc **Section 14-5** Kruskal-Wallis test **Section 19-3** Friedman test **Section 19-3**
	Nominal	Frequency distribution **Section 2-2** Bar chart **Section 2-2** Pie chart **Section 2-2** Z-test and estimator of a proportion **Section 12-3** Chi-squared goodness-of-fit test **Section 15-1**	Z-test and estimator of the difference between two proportions **Section 13-5** Chi-squared test of a contingency table **Section 15-2**	Chi-squared test of a contingency table **Section 15-2**
	Ordinal	Median **Section 4-1** Percentiles and quartiles **Section 4-3**	Wilcoxon rank sum test **Section 19-1** Sign test **Section 19-2**	Kruskal-Wallis test **Section 19-3** Friedman test **Section 19-3**

More Data Sets

A total of 1,283 data sets available to be downloaded provide ample practice. These data sets contain real data, including stock market returns, climate change temperature anomalies and atmospheric carbon dioxide, baseball, basketball, football and hockey team payrolls, wins, and attendance.

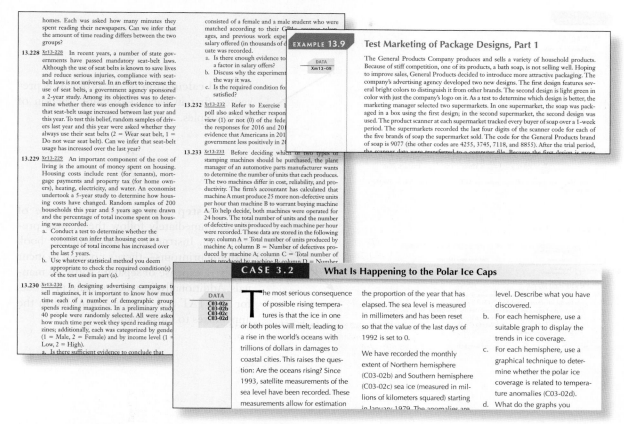

homes. Each was asked how many minutes they spent reading their newspapers. Can we infer that the amount of time reading differs between the two groups?

13.228 Xr13-228 In recent years, a number of state governments have passed mandatory seat-belt laws. Although the use of seat belts is known to save lives and reduce serious injuries, compliance with seat-belt laws is not universal. In an effort to increase the use of seat belts, a government agency sponsored a 2-year study. Among its objectives was to determine whether there was enough evidence to infer that seat-belt usage increased between last year and this year. To test this belief, random samples of drivers last year and this year were asked whether they always use their seat belts (2 = Wear seat belt, 1 = Do not wear seat belt). Can we infer that seat-belt usage has increased over the last year?

13.229 Xr13-229 An important component of the cost of living is the amount of money spent on housing. Housing costs include rent (for tenants), mortgage payments and property tax (for home owners), heating, electricity, and water. An economist undertook a 5-year study to determine how housing costs have changed. Random samples of 200 households this year and 5 years ago were drawn and the percentage of total income spent on housing was recorded.

a. Conduct a test to determine whether the economist can infer that housing cost as a percentage of total income has increased over the last 5 years.

b. Use whatever statistical method you deem appropriate to check the required condition(s) of the test used in part (a).

13.230 Xr13-230 In designing advertising campaigns to sell magazines, it is important to know how much time each of a number of demographic groups spends reading magazines. In a preliminary study, 40 people were randomly selected. All were asked how much time per week they spend reading magazines; additionally, each was categorized by gender (1 = Male, 2 = Female) and by income level (1 = Low, 2 = High).

a. Is there sufficient evidence to conclude that

consisted of a female and a male student who were matched according to their GPAs, courses taken, ages, and previous work experience. The salary offered (in thousands of dollars) to each graduate was recorded.

a. Is there enough evidence to infer that gender is a factor in salary offers?

b. Discuss why the experiment was organized the way it was.

c. Is the required condition for the test satisfied?

13.232 Xr13-232 Refer to Exercise. The poll also asked whether respondents view (1) or not (0) of the federal government. For the responses for 2016 and 2018, is there evidence that Americans in 2018 view the federal government less positively in 2016?

13.233 Xr13-233 Before deciding which of two types of stamping machines should be purchased, the plant manager of an automotive parts manufacturer wants to determine the number of units that each produces. The two machines differ in cost, reliability, and productivity. The firm's accountant has calculated that machine A must produce 25 more non-defective units per hour than machine B to warrant buying machine A. To help decide, both machines were operated for 24 hours. The total number of units and the number of defective units produced by each machine per hour were recorded. These data are stored in the following way: column A = Total number of units produced by machine A; column B = Number of defectives produced by machine A; column C = Total number of units produced by machine B; column D = Number

EXAMPLE 13.9

DATA
Xm13-09

Test Marketing of Package Designs, Part 1

The General Products Company produces and sells a variety of household products. Because of stiff competition, one of its products, a bath soap, is not selling well. Hoping to improve sales, General Products decided to introduce more attractive packaging. The company's advertising agency developed two new designs. The first design features several bright colors to distinguish it from other brands. The second design is light green in color with just the company's logo on it. As a test to determine which design is better, the marketing manager selected two supermarkets. In one supermarket, the soap was packaged in a box using the first design; in the second supermarket, the second design was used. The product scanner at each supermarket tracked every buyer of soap over a 1-week period. The supermarkets recorded the last four digits of the scanner code for each of the five brands of soap the supermarket sold. The code for the General Products brand of soap is 9077 (the other codes are 4255, 3745, 7118, and 8855). After the trial period, the scanner data were transferred to a computer file. Because the first design is more

CASE 3.2 **What Is Happening to the Polar Ice Caps**

DATA
C03-02a
C03-02b
C03-02c
C03-02d

The most serious consequence of possible rising temperatures is that the ice in one or both poles will melt, leading to a rise in the world's oceans with trillions of dollars in damages to coastal cities. This raises the question: Are the oceans rising? Since 1993, satellite measurements of the sea level have been recorded. These measurements allow for estimation

the proportion of the year that has elapsed. The sea level is measured in millimeters and has been reset so that the value of the last days of 1992 is set to 0.

We have recorded the monthly extent of Northern hemisphere (C03-02b) and Southern hemisphere (C03-02c) sea ice (measured in millions of kilometers squared) starting in January 1979. The anomalies are

level. Describe what you have discovered.

b. For each hemisphere, use a suitable graph to display the trends in ice coverage.

c. For each hemisphere, use a graphical technique to determine whether the polar ice coverage is related to temperature anomalies (C03-02d).

d. What do the graphs you

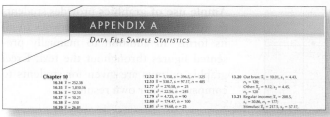

APPENDIX A

DATA FILE SAMPLE STATISTICS

Chapter 10		
10.34 $\bar{x} = 252.38$	12.52 $\bar{x} = 1,158, s = 396.5, n = 325$	13.20 Oat bran: $\bar{x}_1 = 10.01, s_1 = 4.43,$
10.35 $\bar{x} = 1,810.16$	12.53 $\bar{x} = 530.7, s = 97.17, n = 485$	$n_1 = 120;$
10.36 $\bar{x} = 12.10$	12.77 $s^2 = 270.58, n = 25$	Other: $\bar{x}_2 = 9.12, s_2 = 4.45,$
10.37 $\bar{x} = 10.21$	12.78 $s^2 = 22.56, n = 245$	$n_2 = 120$
10.38 $\bar{x} = .510$	12.79 $s^2 = 4.725, n = 90$	13.21 Regular income: $\bar{x}_1 = 208.5,$
10.39 $\bar{x} = 26.81$	12.80 $s^2 = 174.47, n = 100$	$s_1 = 30.86, n_1 = 177;$
	12.81 $s^2 = 19.68, n = 25$	Stimulus: $\bar{x}_2 = 217.5, s_2 = 37.17,$

Appendix A provides summary statistics for many of the exercises with large data sets. This feature offers unparalleled flexibility allowing students to solve most exercises by hand or by computer!

Real Data Sets

The data from the last 10 General Social Surveys and the last five Surveys of Consumer Finances are included. These feature thousands of observations and dozens of selected variables. Solving more than 500 exercises associated with these surveys encourages students to uncover interesting aspects of the society. For example, students can determine the incomes, education, and working hours of people who are self-employed and compare them to people who work for someone else. They can see the effect of education on income, assets, investments, and net worth. Instructors can use the data to create their own examples and exercises.

Compute the Statistics

Once the correct technique has been identified, examples take students to the next level within the solution by asking them to compute the statistics.

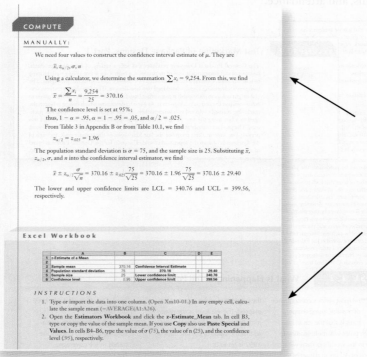

Manual calculation of the problem is presented first in each "Compute" section of the examples.

Step-by-step instructions in the use of **Excel** immediately follow the manual presentation. Instruction appears in the book with the printouts—there's no need to incur the extra expense of separate software manuals. Additionally, instructions and printouts for XLSTAT and Stata are provided in the appendixes to most chapters.

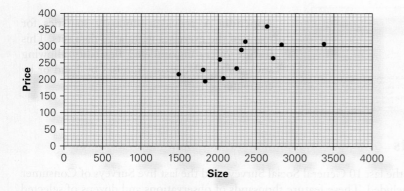

Ample use of graphics provides students many opportunities to see statistics in all its forms. In addition to manually presented figures throughout the text, Excel graphic outputs are given for students to compare to their own results.

Interpret the Results

In the real world, it is not enough to know *how* to generate the statistics. To be truly effective, a business person must also know how to **interpret and articulate** the results. Furthermore, students need a framework to understand and apply statistics **within a realistic setting** by using realistic data in exercises, examples, and case studies.

Examples round out the final component of the identify–compute–interpret approach by asking students to interpret the results in the context of a business-related decision. This final step motivates and shows how statistics is used in everyday business situations.

An Applied Approach

With **Applications in ...** sections and boxes, *Statistics for Management and Economics* now includes 42 **applications** (in finance, marketing, operations management, human resources, economics, and accounting) highlighting how statistics is used in those professions. For example, "Applications in Finance: Portfolio Diversification and Asset Allocation" shows how probability is used to help select stocks to minimize risk. Another optional section, "Applications in Marketing: Market Segmentation" demonstrates how to estimate the size of a market segment.

In addition to sections and boxes, **Applications in ... exercises** can be found within the exercise sections to further reinforce the big picture.

APPLICATIONS in OPERATIONS MANAGEMENT

Quality

A critical aspect of production is quality. The quality of a final product is a function of the quality of the product's components. If the components don't fit, the product will not function as planned and likely cease functioning before its customers expect it to. For example, if a car door is not made to its specifications, it will not fit. As a result, the door will leak both water and air.

Operations managers attempt to maintain and improve the quality of products by ensuring that all components are made so that there is as little variation as possible. As you have already seen, statisticians measure variation by computing the variance. Incidentally, an entire chapter (Chapter 21) is devoted to the topic of quality.

Chapter-opening examples and solutions present compelling discussions of how the techniques and concepts introduced in that chapter are applied to real-world problems. These examples are then revisited with a solution as each chapter unfolds, applying the methodologies introduced in the chapter.

The Number of Unemployed

DATA
GSS2018
One of the most important economic statistics is the unemployment rate. Unfortunately, it is a very poor measure because it is misleading. The United States Bureau of Labor Statistics (BLS) defines the unemployment rate as the percentage of unemployed persons who are currently in the labor force. In order to be in the labor force, a person either must have a job or have looked for work in the last 4 weeks. This leaves out a lot of people. Some are left out because they have not done anything to find work in more than 4 weeks and as a result became discouraged, and some are left out because they are not available for work at the moment. Yet to leave this group out significantly underestimates the unemployment rate.

See page 423 for our answer.

(Continued)

The Number of Unemployed: Solution

IDENTIFY

The problem objective is to describe the population of work status of American adults. The data are nominal. The combination of problem objective and data type make the parameter to be estimated the proportion of the entire population that is unemployed. The confidence interval estimator of the population is

$$\hat{p} \pm z_{\alpha/2} \sqrt{\frac{\hat{p}(1 - \hat{p})}{n}}$$

COMPUTE

MANUALLY:

To solve manually we count the number of 3s and 4s in the WRKSTAT column. They are 53 and 84, respectively. The sample size is 2,346. (There are two blanks representing missing data.) Thus,

$$\hat{p} = \frac{53 + 84}{2,346} = .0584$$

The confidence level is $1 - \alpha = .95$. It follows that $\alpha = .05$, $\alpha/2 = .025$, $z_{\alpha/2} = z_{.025} = 1.96$. The 95% confidence interval estimate of p is

$$\hat{p} \pm z_{\alpha/2} \sqrt{\frac{\hat{p}(1 - \hat{p})}{n}} = .0584 \pm 1.96 \sqrt{\frac{.0584(1 - .0584)}{2,346}} = .0584 \pm .0095$$

LCL = .0489   UCL = .0679

EXCEL Workbook

	A	B	C	D	E
1	z-Estimate of a Proportion				
2					
3	Sample proportion	0.0584	Confidence Interval Estimate		
4	Sample size	2346	0.0584	±	0.0095
5	Confidence level	0.95	Lower confidence limit		0.0489
6			Upper confidence limit		0.0679

INSTRUCTIONS

1. Type or import the data into one column. (Open GSS2018.) (We copied column X into another spreadsheet.) In any empty cell, calculate the number of "successes" (=COUNTIF (A1:A2349,3) and =COUNTIF (A1:A2349,4)). Divide this number (53 + 84) by the sample size (2,346) to obtain the sample proportion.
2. Open the **Estimators Workbook** and click the **z-Estimate_Proportion** tab. Type or copy the sample proportion. Type the value of the sample size and the value of α.

INTERPRET

We estimate that the proportion of unemployed American adults lies between 4.89% and 6.79%. To determine the number of unemployed people, multiply the lower and upper limits by the population size 255,200,373. Thus,

LCL = 255,200,373(.0489) = 12,479,298

UCL = 255,200,373(.0679) = 17,328,105

CASE 12.5   **Bias in Roulette Betting**

The game of roulette consists of a wheel with 38 colored and numbered slots. The numbers are 1 to 36, 0 and 00. Half of the slots numbered 1 to 36 are red and the other half are black. The two "zeros" are green. The wheel is spun and an iron ball is rolled, which eventually comes to rest in one of the slots. Gamblers can make several different kinds of bets. Most players bet on one or more numbers or on

DATA
C12-05

Many of the **examples, exercises, and cases are based on actual studies** performed by statisticians and published in journals, newspapers, and magazines, or presented at conferences. Many data files were recreated to produce the original results.

Chapter summaries briefly review the material and list important terms, symbols, and formulas.

CHAPTER SUMMARY

The inferential methods presented in this chapter address the problem of describing a single population. When the data are interval, the parameters of interest are the population mean μ and the population variance σ^2. The Student t-distribution is used to test and estimate the mean when the population standard deviation is unknown. The chi-squared distribution is used to make inferences about a population variance. When the data are nominal, the parameter to be tested and estimated is the population proportion p. The sample proportion follows an approximate normal distribution, which produces the test statistic and the interval estimator. We also discussed how to determine the sample size required to estimate a population proportion. We introduced market segmentation and described how statistical techniques presented in this chapter can be used to estimate the size of a segment.

IMPORTANT TERMS:

t-statistic 397
Student t-distribution 397

Robust 402
Chi-squared statistic 412

SYMBOLS:

Symbol	Pronounced	Represents
ν	nu	Degrees of freedom
χ^2	chi squared	Chi-squared statistic
$\hat{p}$	p hat	Sample proportion
$\tilde{p}$	p tilde	Wilson estimator

FORMULAS:

Test statistic for μ

$$t = \frac{\bar{x} - \mu}{s/\sqrt{n}}$$

Confidence interval estimator of μ

$$\bar{x} \pm t_{\alpha/2}\frac{s}{\sqrt{n}}$$

Test statistic for σ^2

$$\chi^2 = \frac{(n-1)s^2}{\sigma^2}$$

Confidence interval estimator of σ^2

$$LCL = \frac{(n-1)s^2}{\chi^2_{\alpha/2}}$$

$$UCL = \frac{(n-1)s^2}{\chi^2_{1-\alpha/2}}$$

Test statistic for p

$$z = \frac{\hat{p} - p}{\sqrt{p(1-p)/n}}$$

Confidence interval estimator of p

$$\hat{p} \pm z_{\alpha/2}\sqrt{\hat{p}(1-\hat{p})/n}$$

Sample size to estimate p

$$n = \left(\frac{z_{\alpha/2}\sqrt{\hat{p}(1-\hat{p})}}{B}\right)^2$$

Wilson estimator

$$\tilde{p} = \frac{x+2}{n+4}$$

Confidence interval estimator of p using the Wilson estimator

$$\tilde{p} \pm z_{\alpha/2}\sqrt{\tilde{p}(1-\tilde{p})/(n+4)}$$

Confidence interval estimator of the total of a large finite population

$$N\left[\bar{x} \pm t_{\alpha/2}\frac{s}{\sqrt{n}}\right]$$

Confidence interval estimator of the total number of successes in a large finite population

$$N\left[\hat{p} \pm z_{\alpha/2}\sqrt{\frac{\hat{p}(1-\hat{p})}{n}}\right]$$

Instructor and Student Resources

Additional instructor and student resources for this product are available online. Instructor assets include an Instructor's Manual, Solutions and Answer Guide, Educator's Guide, PowerPoint® slides, and a test bank powered by Cognero®. New to this edition for instructors, Excel solutions files are now available for certain exercises in the book that require computer generated solutions. Student assets include Excel datasets, Excel workbooks, and more. Sign up or sign in at www.cengage.com to search for and access this product and its online resources.

ACKNOWLEDGMENTS

Although there is only one name on the cover of this book, the number of people who made contributions is large. I would like to acknowledge the work of all of them, with particular emphasis on the following: Paul Baum, California State University, Northridge, and John Lawrence, California State University, Fullerton, reviewed the page proofs. Their job was to find errors in presentation, arithmetic, and composition. The following individuals played important roles in the production of this book: Senior Product Manager Aaron Arnsparger, Senior Content Manager Conor Allen, Senior Learning Designer Brandon Foltz, and Associate Subject-Matter Expert Nancy Marchant. (For all remaining errors, place the blame where it belongs—on me.) Their advice and suggestions made my task considerably easier.

Paolo Catasti, Virginia Commonwealth University, produced the Instructor PowerPoint slides and the Instructor's Manual.

The author extends thanks also to the survey participants and reviewers of the previous editions: Roger Bailey, Vanderbilt University; Paul Baum, California State University–Northridge; Nagraj Balakrishnan, Clemson University; Chen-Huei Chou, College of Charleston; Howard Clayton, Auburn University; Philip Cross, Georgetown University; Barry Cuffe, Wingate University; Ernest Demba, Washington University–St. Louis; Michael Douglas, Millersville University; Neal Duffy, State University of New York–Plattsburgh; John Dutton, North Carolina State University; Ehsan Elahi, University of Massachusetts–Boston; Erick Elder, University of Arkansas; Mohammed El-Saidi, Ferris State University; Grace Esimai, University of Texas–Arlington; Leila Farivar, The Ohio State University; Homi Fatemi, Santa Clara University; Abe Feinberg, California State University–Northridge; Samuel Graves, Boston College; Robert Gould, UCLA; Darren Grant, Sam Houston State University; Shane Griffith, Lee University; Paul Hagstrom, Hamilton College; John Hebert, Virginia Tech; James Hightower, California State University, Fullerton; Bo Honore, Princeton University; Ira Horowitz, University of Florida; Onisforos Iordanou, Hunter College; Torsten Jochem, University of Pittsburgh; Gordon Johnson, California State University–Northridge; Hilke Kayser, Hamilton College; Kenneth Klassen, California State University–Northridge; Roger Kleckner, Bowling Green State University–Firelands; Eylem Koca, Fairleigh Dickinson University; Harry Kypraios, Rollins College; John Lawrence, California State University–Fullerton; Tae H. Lee, University of California–Riverside; Dennis Lin, Pennsylvania State University; Jialu Liu, Allegheny College; Chung-Ping Loh, University of North Florida; Neal Long, Stetson University; Jayashree Mahajan, University of Florida; George Marcoulides, California State University–Fullerton; Paul Mason, University of North Florida; Walter Mayer, University of Mississippi; John McDonald, Flinders University; Richard McGowan, Boston College; Richard McGrath, Bowling Green State University; Amy Miko, St. Francis College; Janis

Miller, Clemson University; Glenn Milligan, Ohio State University; James Moran, Oregon State University; Robert G. Morris, University of Texas–Dallas; Patricia Mullins, University of Wisconsin; Adam Munson, University of Florida; David Murphy, Boston College; Kevin Murphy, Oakland University; Pin Ng, University of Illinois; Des Nicholls, Australian National University; Andrew Paizis, Queens College; David Pentico, Duquesne University; Ira Perelle, Mercy College; Nelson Perera, University of Wollongong; Bruce Pietrykowski, University of Michigan–Dearborn; Amy Puelz, Southern Methodist University; Lawrence Ries, University of Missouri; Colleen Quinn, Seneca College; Tony Quon, University of Ottawa; Madhu Rao, Bowling Green State University; Yaron Raviv, Claremont McKenna College; Jason Reed, Wayne State University; Phil Roth, Clemson University; Deb Rumsey, The Ohio State University; Farhad Saboori, Albright College; Don St. Jean, George Brown College; Hedayeh Samavati, Indiana–Purdue University; Sandy Shroeder, Ohio Northern University; Chris Silvia, University of Kansas; Jineshwar Singh, George Brown College; Natalia Smirnova, Queens College; Eric Sowey, University of New South Wales; Cyrus Stanier, Virginia Tech; Stan Stephenson, Southwest Texas State University; Gordon M. Stringer, University of Colorado–Colorado Springs; Arnold Stromberg, University of Kentucky; Pandu Tadikamalla, University of Pittsburgh; Patrick Thompson, University of Florida; Steve Thorpe, University of Northern Iowa; Sheldon Vernon, Houston Baptist University; John J. Wiorkowski, University of Texas–Dallas; and W. F. Younkin, University of Miami.

iStockphoto.com/leluconcepts

WHAT IS STATISTICS?

CHAPTER OUTLINE

INTRODUCTION

Statistics is a way to get information from data. That's it! Most of this textbook is devoted to describing how, when, and why managers and statistics practitioners* conduct statistical procedures. You may ask, "If that's all there is to statistics, why is this book (and most other statistics books) so large?" The answer is that students of applied statistics will be exposed to different kinds of information and data. We demonstrate some of these with a case and two examples that are featured later in this book.

The first may be of particular interest to you.

---

*The term *statistician* is used to describe so many different kinds of occupations that it has ceased to have any meaning. It is used, for example, to describe a person who calculates baseball statistics as well as an individual educated in statistical principles. We will describe the former as a *statistics practitioner* and the

(continued)

1

EXAMPLE 3.3

Business Statistics Marks (See Chapter 3)

Students enrolled in a business program are attending their first class of the required statistics course. The students are somewhat apprehensive because they believe the myth that the course is difficult. To alleviate their anxiety, the professor provides a list of the final marks, which are composed of term work plus the final exam. What information can students obtain from the list?

This is a typical statistics problem. The students have the data (marks) and need to apply statistical techniques to get the information they require. This is a function of **descriptive statistics**.

Descriptive Statistics

Descriptive statistics deals with methods of organizing, summarizing, and presenting data in a convenient and informative way. One form of descriptive statistics uses graphical techniques that allow statistics practitioners to present data in ways that make it easy for the reader to extract useful information. In Chapters 2 and 3 we will present a variety of graphical methods.

Another form of descriptive statistics uses numerical techniques to summarize data. One such method that you have already used frequently calculates the average or mean. In the same way that you calculate the average age of the employees of a company, we can compute the mean mark of last year's statistics course. Chapter 4 introduces several numerical statistical measures that describe different features of the data.

The actual technique we use depends on what specific information we would like to extract. In this example, we can see at least three important pieces of information. The first is the "typical" mark. We call this a *measure of central location*. The average is one such measure. In Chapter 4, we will introduce another useful measure of central location, the median. Suppose that students were told that the average mark last year was 67. Is this enough information to reduce their anxiety? Students would likely respond "No" because they would like to know whether most of the marks were close to 67 or were scattered far below and above the average. They need a *measure of variability*. The simplest such measure is the *range*, which is calculated by subtracting the smallest number from the largest. Suppose the largest mark is 96 and the smallest is 24. Unfortunately, this provides little information since it is based on only two marks. We need other measures—these will be introduced in Chapter 4. Moreover, the students must determine more about the marks. In particular, they need to know how the marks are distributed between 24 and 96. The best way to do this is to use a graphical technique, the histogram, which will be introduced in Chapter 3.

---

latter as a *statistician*. A statistics practitioner is a person who uses statistical techniques properly. Examples of statistics practitioners include the following:

1. a financial analyst who develops stock portfolios based on historical rates of return;

2. an economist who uses statistical models to help explain and predict variables such as inflation rate, unemployment rate, and changes in the gross domestic product; and

3. a market researcher who surveys consumers and converts the responses into useful information.

Our goal in this book is to convert you into one such capable individual.

The term *statistician* refers to individuals who work with the mathematics of statistics. Their work involves research that develops techniques and concepts, which in the future may help the statistics practitioner. Statisticians are also statistics practitioners, frequently conducting empirical research and consulting. If you're taking a statistics course, your instructor is probably a statistician.

Case 12.1 Pepsi's Exclusivity Agreement with a University (see Chapter 12) In the last few years, colleges and universities have signed exclusivity agreements with a variety of private companies. These agreements bind the university to sell these companies' products exclusively on the campus. Many of the agreements involve food and beverage firms.

A large university with a total enrollment of about 50,000 students has offered Pepsi-Cola an exclusivity agreement that would give Pepsi exclusive rights to sell its products at all university facilities for the next year with an option for future years. In return, the university would receive 35% of the on-campus revenues and an additional lump sum of $200,000 per year. Pepsi has been given 2 weeks to respond.

The management at Pepsi quickly reviews what it knows. The market for soft drinks is measured in terms of 12-ounce cans. Pepsi currently sells an average of 22,000 cans per week over the 40 weeks of the year that the university operates. The cans sell for an average of one dollar each. The costs, including labor, total 30 cents per can. Pepsi is unsure of its market share but suspects it is considerably less than 50%. A quick analysis reveals that if its current market share were 25%, then, with an exclusivity agreement, Pepsi would sell 88,000 (22,000 is 25% of 88,000) cans per week or 3,520,000 cans per year. The gross revenue would be computed as follows[†]:

$$\text{Gross revenue} = 3{,}520{,}000 \times \$1.00/\text{can} = \$3{,}520{,}000$$

This figure must be multiplied by 65% because the university would rake in 35% of the gross. Thus,

$$\begin{aligned}&\text{Gross revenue after deducting 35\% university take}\\&= 65\% \times \$3{,}520{,}000 = \$2{,}288{,}000\end{aligned}$$

The total cost of 30 cents per can (or $1,056,000) and the annual payment to the university of $200,000 are subtracted to obtain the net profit:

$$\text{Net profit} = \$2{,}288{,}000 - \$1{,}056{,}000 - \$200{,}000 = \$1{,}032{,}000$$

Pepsi's current annual profit is

$$40 \text{ weeks} \times 22{,}000 \text{ cans/week} \times \$.70 = \$616{,}000$$

If the current market share is 25%, the potential gain from the agreement is

$$\$1{,}032{,}000 - \$616{,}000 = \$416{,}000$$

The only problem with this analysis is that Pepsi does not know how many soft drinks are sold weekly at the university. Coke is not likely to supply Pepsi with information about its sales, which together with Pepsi's line of products constitute virtually the entire market.

Pepsi assigned a recent university graduate to survey the university's students to supply the missing information. Accordingly, the student organizes a survey that asks 500 students to keep track of the number of soft drinks they purchase in the next 7 days. The responses are stored in a file C12-01 available to be downloaded.

Inferential Statistics

The information we would like to acquire in Case 12.1 is an estimate of annual profits from the exclusivity agreement. The data are the numbers of cans of soft drinks consumed in 7 days by the 500 students in the sample. We can use descriptive techniques to

---

[†]We have created an Excel spreadsheet that does the calculations for this case. See Appendix 1 for instructions on how to download this spreadsheet from Cengage's website plus hundreds of data sets and much more.

learn more about the data. In this case, however, we are not so much interested in what the 500 students are reporting as in knowing the mean number of soft drinks consumed by all 50,000 students on campus. To accomplish this goal we need another branch of statistics: **inferential statistics**.

Inferential statistics is a body of methods used to draw conclusions or inferences about characteristics of populations based on sample data. The population in question in this case is the university's 50,000 students. The characteristic of interest is the soft drink consumption of this population. The cost of interviewing each student in the population would be prohibitive and extremely time consuming. Statistical techniques make such endeavors unnecessary. Instead, we can sample a much smaller number of students (the sample size is 500) and infer from the data the number of soft drinks consumed by all 50,000 students. We can then estimate annual profits for Pepsi.

EXAMPLE 12.5	## Exit Polls (See Chapter 12)

When an election for political office takes place, the television networks cancel regular programming to provide election coverage. After the ballots are counted, the results are reported. However, for important offices such as president or senator in large states, the networks actively compete to see which one will be the first to predict a winner. This is done through **exit polls** in which a random sample of voters who exit the polling booth are asked for whom they voted. From the data, the sample proportion of voters supporting the candidates is computed. A statistical technique is applied to determine whether there is enough evidence to infer that the leading candidate will garner enough votes to win. Suppose that the exit poll results from the state of Florida during the year 2000 elections were recorded. Although several candidates were running for president, the exit pollsters recorded only the votes of the two candidates who had any chance of winning: Republican George W. Bush and Democrat Albert Gore. The results (765 people who voted for either Bush or Gore) were stored in file Xm12-05. The network analysts would like to know whether they can conclude that George W. Bush will win the state of Florida.

Example 12.5 describes a common application of statistical inference. The population the television networks wanted to make inferences about is the approximately 5 million Floridians who voted for Bush or Gore for president. The sample consisted of the 765 people randomly selected by the polling company who voted for either of the two main candidates. The characteristic of the population that we would like to know is the proportion of the Florida total electorate that voted for Bush. Specifically, we would like to know whether more than 50% of the electorate voted for Bush (counting only those who voted for either the Republican or Democratic candidate). It must be made clear that we cannot predict the outcome with 100% certainty because we will not ask all 5 million actual voters for whom they voted. This is a fact that statistics practitioners and even students of statistics must understand. A sample that is only a small fraction of the size of the population can lead to correct inferences only a certain percentage of the time. You will find that statistics practitioners can control that fraction and usually set it between 90% and 99%.

Incidentally, on the night of the U.S. election in November 2000, the networks goofed badly. Using exit polls as well as the results of previous elections, all four networks concluded at about 8 P.M. that Al Gore would win Florida. Shortly after 10 P.M., with a large percentage of the actual vote having been counted, the networks reversed course and declared that George W. Bush would win the state. By 2 A.M., another verdict was declared: The result was too close to call. Since then, this experience has likely been used by statistics instructors when teaching how *not* to use statistics.

Notice that, contrary to what you probably believed, data are not necessarily numbers. The marks in Example 3.3 and the number of soft drinks consumed in a week in Case 12.1, of course, are numbers; however, the votes in Example 12.5 are not. In Chapter 2, we will discuss the different types of data you will encounter in statistical applications and how to deal with them.

1-1 / KEY STATISTICAL CONCEPTS

Statistical inference problems involve three key concepts: the population, the sample, and the statistical inference. We now discuss each of these concepts in more detail.

1-1a Population

A **population** is the group of all items of interest to a statistics practitioner. It is frequently very large and may, in fact, be infinitely large. In the language of statistics, *population* does not necessarily refer to a group of people. It may, for example, refer to the population of ball bearings produced at a large plant. In Case 12.1, the population of interest consists of the 50,000 students on campus. In Example 12.5, the population consists of the Floridians who voted for Bush or Gore.

A descriptive measure of a population is called a **parameter**. The parameter of interest in Case 12.1 is the mean number of soft drinks consumed by all the students at the university. The parameter in Example 12.5 is the proportion of the 5 million Florida voters who voted for Bush. In most applications of inferential statistics, the parameter represents the information we need.

1-1b Sample

A **sample** is a set of data drawn from the studied population. A descriptive measure of a sample is called a **statistic**. We use statistics to make inferences about parameters. In Case 12.1, the statistic we would compute is the mean number of soft drinks consumed in the last week by the 500 students in the sample. We would then use the sample mean to infer the value of the population mean, which is the parameter of interest in this problem. In Example 12.5, we compute the proportion of the sample of 765 Floridians who voted for Bush. The sample statistic is then used to make inferences about the population of all 5 million votes—that is, we predict the election results even before the actual count.

1-1c Statistical Inference

Statistical inference is the process of making an estimate, prediction, or decision about a population based on sample data. Because populations are almost always very large, investigating each member of the population would be impractical and expensive. It is far easier and cheaper to take a sample from the population of interest and draw conclusions or make estimates about the population on the basis of information provided by the sample. However, such conclusions and estimates are not always going to be correct. For this reason, we build into the statistical inference a measure of reliability. There are two such measures: the **confidence level** and the **significance level**. The *confidence level* is the proportion of times that an estimating procedure will be correct. For example, in Case 12.1, we will produce an estimate of the average number of soft drinks to be consumed by all 50,000 students that has a confidence level of 95%. In other words, estimates based on this form of statistical inference will be correct 95% of the time. When the purpose of the statistical inference is to draw a conclusion about a population, the *significance level* measures how frequently the conclusion will be wrong. For example, suppose that, as a result of the analysis in Example 12.5, we conclude that more than 50% of the electorate will vote for George W. Bush, and thus he will win the state of Florida. A 5% significance level means that samples that lead us to conclude that Bush wins the election will be wrong 5% of the time.

1-2 / STATISTICAL APPLICATIONS IN BUSINESS

An important function of statistics courses in business and economics programs is to demonstrate that statistical analysis plays an important role in virtually all aspects of business and economics. We intend to do so through examples, exercises, and cases. However, we assume that most students taking their first statistics course have not taken courses in most of the other subjects in management programs. To understand fully how statistics is used in these and other subjects, it is necessary to know something about them. To provide sufficient background to understand the statistical application, we introduce applications in accounting, economics, finance, human resources management, marketing, and operations management. We provide readers with some background of these applications by describing their functions in two ways.

1-2a Application Sections and Subsections

We feature five sections that describe statistical applications in the functional areas of business. In Section 4-5, we discuss an application in finance, the market model, which introduces an important concept in investing. Section 7-3 describes another application in finance that describes a financial analyst's use of probability and statistics to construct portfolios that decrease risk. Section 12-4 is an application in marketing, market segmentation. In Section 14-6, we present an application in operations management, finding and reducing variation. In Section 18-3, we provide an application in human resources, pay equity. A subsection in Section 6-4 presents an application in medical testing (useful in the medical insurance industry).

1-2b Application Boxes

For other topics that require less-detailed description, we provide application boxes with a relatively brief description of the background followed by examples or exercises. These boxes are scattered throughout the book. For example, in Section 4-1, we discuss the geometric mean and why it is used instead of the arithmetic mean to measure variables that are rates of change.

1-3 / LARGE REAL DATA SETS

The author believes that you learn statistics by doing statistics. For their lives after college and university, we expect graduates to have access to large amounts of real data that must be summarized to acquire the information needed to make decisions. We include the data from two sources: the General Social Survey (GSS) and the Survey of Consumer Finances (SCF). We have scattered examples, exercises, and cases for these surveys throughout the book.

1-3a General Social Survey

Since 1972, the GSS has been tracking American attitudes on a wide variety of topics. With the exception of the U.S. Census, the GSS is the most frequently used source of information about American society. The surveys are conducted every second year and feature hundreds of variables and thousands of observations. The data for the 10 most recent surveys are stored in files GSS2000, GSS2002, GSS2004, GSS2006, GSS2008, GSS2010, GSS2012, GSS2014, GSS2016, and GSS2018. The sample sizes are 2,817, 2,765, 2,812, 4,510, 2,023, 2,044, 1,974, 2,538, 2,868, and 2,348, respectively. We downloaded the variables that we think would be of interest to students of business and economics only. We removed the missing data codes representing "No answer," and "Don't know," for most variables and replaced them with blanks.

A list of all the variables and their definitions is available as an online appendix.

1-3b Survey of Consumer Finances

The SCF is conducted every 3 years to provide detailed information on the finances of U.S. households. The study is sponsored by the Federal Reserve Board in cooperation with the Department of the Treasury. Since 1992, data have been collected by the National Opinion Research Center (NORC) at the University of Chicago. The data for the five most recent surveys are stored in folders SCF2007, SCF2010, SCF2013, SCF2016, and SCF2019. The sample sizes are 4,417, 6,482, 6,015, 6,248, and 5,777, respectively. As we did with the General Social Surveys, we downloaded only a fraction of the variables in the original surveys. Because the samples are so large and the range of some of the variables so wide, there are problems summarizing and describing the data. To solve the problem, we have created subsamples based on percentiles of the net worth of the households being sampled. Here is a list of the subsamples.

L20: Lowest 20%

Lower Middle Class (LMC): 20%–40%

Middle Class (MC): 40%–60%

Upper Middle Class (UMC): 60%–80%

Upper Class (UC): 80%–90%

Wealthy (W): 90%–95%

Super Rich (SR): 95%–99%

T1: Top 1%

A complete list of the variables and their definitions is available as an online appendix.

1-4 / STATISTICS AND THE COMPUTER

In virtually all applications of statistics, the statistics practitioner must deal with large amounts of data. For example, Case 12.1 (Pepsi-Cola) involves 500 observations. To estimate annual profits, the statistics practitioner would have to perform computations on the data. Although the calculations do not require any great mathematical skill, the sheer amount of arithmetic makes this aspect of the statistical method time consuming and tedious. Fortunately, numerous commercially prepared computer programs are available to perform the arithmetic. We have chosen to use Microsoft Excel in the belief that virtually all university graduates use it now and will in the future.

Additionally, we have included chapter appendixes (for Chapters 2, 3, 4, 10, 11, 12, 13, 14, 15, 16, 17, and 19) displaying output and step-by-step instructions for two popular statistical software packages, XLSTAT and Stata. This will allow instructors to use any one of Excel, XLSTAT, and Stata without requiring students to acquire instruction manuals.

1-4a Excel

Excel can perform statistical procedures in several ways.

1. **Statistical** (which includes probability) and other functions fx: We use some of these functions to draw graphs and charts in Chapter 2, calculate statistics in Chapters 4 and 15, and to compute probabilities in Chapters 7 and 8.

2. **Analysis ToolPak:** This group of procedures comes with every version of Excel. The techniques are accessed by clicking Data and Data Analysis. One of its drawbacks is that it does not offer a complete set of the statistical techniques we introduce in this book. The methods not included with Data Analysis will be performed by Excel spreadsheets and Do It Yourself Excel.

3. **Spreadsheets:** We use statistical functions to create spreadsheets that calculate statistical inference methods in Chapters 10–16 and 19. These can be downloaded from Cengage's website. Additionally, the spreadsheets can be used to conduct what–if analyses. The rationale for their use is described in subsection 1-4d.

4. **Do It Yourself:** We provide step-by-step instructions on how to use Excel to perform the remaining inference methods.

1-4b File Names and Notation

A large proportion of the examples, exercises, and cases feature large data sets. These are denoted with the file name next to the exercise number. The data sets associated with examples are denoted as Xm. To illustrate, the data for Example 2.2 are stored in file Xm02-02 in the Chapter 2 folder. The data for exercises and cases are stored in files prefixed by Xr and C, respectively. The prefixes GSS and SCF designate data from the General Social Surveys and Surveys of Consumer Finances, respectively.

In many real applications of statistics, additional data are collected. For instance, in Example 12.5, the pollster often records the gender and asks for other information including race, religion, education, and income. In later chapters we will return to these files and require other statistical techniques to extract the needed information. Files that contain additional data are denoted by a plus sign on the file name.

1-4c Our Approach

The approach we prefer to take is to minimize the time spent on manual computations and to focus instead on selecting the appropriate method for dealing with a problem and on interpreting the output after the computer has performed the necessary computations. In this way, we hope to demonstrate that statistics can be as interesting and as practical as any other subject in your curriculum.

1-4d Excel Spreadsheets

Books written for statistics courses taken by mathematics or statistics majors are considerably different from this one. It is not surprising that such courses feature mathematical proofs of theorems and derivations of most procedures. When the material is covered in this way, the underlying concepts that support statistical inference are exposed and relatively easy to see. However, this book was created for an applied course in business and economics statistics. Consequently, we do not address directly the mathematical principles of statistics. However, as we pointed out previously, one of the most important functions of statistics practitioners is to properly interpret statistical results, whether produced manually or by computer. And, to correctly interpret statistics, students require an understanding of the principles of statistics.

To help students understand the basic foundation, we offer readers Excel spreadsheets that allow for *what–if* analyses. By changing some of the input value, students can see for themselves how statistics works. (The term is derived from *what* happens to the statistics *if* I change this value.)

CHAPTER SUMMARY

IMPORTANT TERMS:

Descriptive statistics   2
Inferential statistics   4
Exit polls   4
Population   5
Parameter   5

Sample   5
Statistic   5
Statistical inference   5
Confidence level   5
Significance level   5

CHAPTER EXERCISES

1.1 In your own words, define and give an example of each of the following statistical terms.
a. population
b. sample
c. parameter
d. statistic
e. statistical inference

1.2 Briefly describe the difference between descriptive statistics and inferential statistics.

1.3 A politician who is running for the office of mayor of a city with 25,000 registered voters commissions a survey. In the survey, 48% of the 200 registered voters interviewed say they plan to vote for the politician.
a. What is the population of interest?
b. What is the sample?
c. Is the value 48% a parameter or a statistic? Explain.

1.4 A manufacturer of computer chips claims that less than 10% of its products are defective. When 1,000 chips were drawn from a large production, 7.5% were found to be defective.
a. What is the population of interest?
b. What is the sample?
c. What is the parameter?
d. What is the statistic?
e. Does the value 10% refer to the parameter or to the statistic?
f. Is the value 7.5% a parameter or a statistic?
g. Explain briefly how the statistic can be used to make inferences about the parameter to test the claim.

1.5 Suppose you believe that, in general, graduates who have majored in *your* subject are offered higher salaries upon graduating than are graduates of other programs. Describe a statistical experiment that could help test your belief.

1.6 You are shown a coin that its owner says is fair in the sense that it will produce the same number of heads and tails when flipped a very large number of times.

    a. Describe an experiment to test this claim.

    b. What is the population in your experiment?

    c. What is the sample?

    d. What is the parameter?

    e. What is the statistic?

    f. Describe briefly how statistical inference can be used to test the claim.

1.7 Suppose that in Exercise 1.6 you decide to flip the coin 100 times.

    a. What conclusion would you be likely to draw if you observed 95 heads?

    b. What conclusion would you be likely to draw if you observed 55 heads?

    c. Do you believe that, if you flip a perfectly fair coin 100 times, you will always observe exactly 50 heads? If you answered "no," then what numbers do you think are possible? If you answered "yes," how

many heads would you observe if you flipped the coin twice? Try flipping a coin twice and repeating this experiment 10 times and report the results.

1.8 Xr01-08   The owner of a large fleet of taxis is trying to estimate costs for next year's operations. One major cost is fuel purchase. To estimate fuel purchase, the owner needs to know the total distance the taxis will travel next year, the cost of a gallon of fuel, and the fuel mileage of his taxis. The owner has been provided with the first two figures (distance estimate and cost of a gallon of fuel). However, because of the high cost of gasoline, the owner has recently converted the fleet's taxis to operate on propane. The propane mileage (in miles per gallon) for 50 taxis has been measured and recorded.

    a. What is the population of interest?

    b. What is the parameter the owner needs?

    c. What is the sample?

    d. What is the statistic?

    e. Describe briefly how the statistic will produce the kind of information the owner wants.

APPENDIX 1 / MATERIAL TO DOWNLOAD

Additional Instructor and Student Resources

Additional instructor and student resources for this product are available online. Instructor assets include an Instructor's Manual, Educator's Guide, PowerPoint® slides, and a test bank powered by Cognero®. Student assets include data sets and Excel workbooks. Sign up or sign in at www.cengage.com to search for and access this product and its online resources.

© Steve Cole/Digital Vision/Getty Images

GRAPHICAL DESCRIPTIVE TECHNIQUES I

CHAPTER OUTLINE

Do Male and Female Americans Differ in Their Political Party Affiliation?

DATA
GSS2018

In Chapter 1, we introduced the General Social Survey (GSS), which is conducted every 2 years with the objective to track the experiences, behaviors, and attitudes of Americans. One question that has been asked in all General Social Surveys is "Generally speaking, do you think of yourself as Republican, Democrat, Independent, or what?" The responses are as follows:

On page 40, we will provide our answer.

0. Strong Democrat

1. Not Strong Democrat

2. Independent, Near Democrat

iStockPhoto/hermosawave

3. Independent

4. Independent, Near Republican

5. Not Strong Republican

6. Strong Republican

7. Other Party

Respondents are also identified by sex: 1 = Male, and 2 = Female. The data are stored in the file GSS2018. Note that the file contains other variables that are not needed in this example. The variable SEX is stored in column B and PARTYID is stored in Column AG. Some of the data are listed here.

ID	SEX	PARTYID
62467	1	5
62468	2	2
62469	1	4
⋮	⋮	⋮
64812	2	3
64813	1	4
64814	2	3

Determine whether American males and females differ in their political affiliations. See page 40 for our solution.

INTRODUCTION

In Chapter 1, we pointed out that statistics is divided into two basic areas: descriptive statistics and inferential statistics. The purpose of this chapter, together with the next, is to present the principal methods that fall under the heading of descriptive statistics. In this chapter, we introduce graphical and tabular statistical methods that allow managers to summarize data visually to produce useful information that is often used in decision making. Another class of descriptive techniques, numerical methods, is introduced in Chapter 4.

Managers frequently have access to large masses of potentially useful data. But before the data can be used to support a decision, they must be organized and summarized. Consider, for example, the problems faced by managers who have access to the databases created by the use of debit cards. The database consists of the personal information supplied by customers when they applied for the debit card. This information includes age, gender, residence, and the cardholder's income. In addition, each time the card is used the database grows to include a history of the timing, price, and brand of each product purchased. Using the appropriate statistical technique, managers can determine which segments of the market are buying their company's brands. Specialized marketing campaigns, including telemarketing, can be developed. Both descriptive and inferential statistics would likely be employed in the analysis.

Descriptive statistics involves arranging, summarizing, and presenting a set of data in such a way that useful information is produced. Its methods make use of graphical techniques and numerical descriptive measures (such as averages) to summarize and present the data, allowing managers to make decisions based on the information generated. Although descriptive statistical methods are quite straightforward, their importance should not be underestimated. Most management, business, and economics students will encounter numerous opportunities to make valuable use of graphical and numerical descriptive techniques when preparing reports and presentations in the workplace. According to a Wharton Business School study, top managers reach a consensus 25% more quickly when responding to a presentation in which graphics are used.

In Chapter 1, we introduced the distinction between a population and a sample. Recall that a population is the entire set of observations under study, whereas a sample is a subset of a population. The descriptive methods presented in this chapter and in Chapters 3 and 4 apply to both a set of data constituting a population and a set of data constituting a sample.

In both the preface and Chapter 1, we pointed out that a critical part of your education as statistics practitioners includes an understanding of not only *how* to draw graphs and calculate statistics (manually or by computer) but also *when* to use each technique that we cover. The two most important factors that determine the appropriate method to use are (1) the type of data and (2) the information that is needed. Both are discussed next.

2-1 / TYPES OF DATA AND INFORMATION

The objective of statistics is to extract information from data. There are different types of data and information. To help explain this important principle, we need to define some terms.

A **variable** is some characteristic of a population or sample. For example, the mark on a statistics exam is a characteristic of statistics exams that is certainly of interest to readers of this book. Not all students achieve the same mark. The marks will vary from student to student, thus the name *variable*. The price of a stock is another variable. The prices of most stocks vary daily. We usually represent the name of the variable using uppercase letters such as X, Y, and Z.

The **values** of the variable are the possible observations of the variable. The values of statistics exam marks are the integers between 0 and 100 (assuming the exam is marked out of 100). The values of a stock price are real numbers that are usually measured in dollars and cents (sometimes in fractions of a cent). The values range from 0 to hundreds of dollars.

Data* are the observed values of a variable. For example, suppose that we observe the following midterm test marks of 10 students:

| 67 | 74 | 71 | 83 | 93 | 55 | 48 | 82 | 68 | 62 |

These are the data from which we will extract the information we seek. Incidentally, *data* is plural for **datum**. The mark of one student is a datum.

When most people think of data, they think of sets of numbers. However, there are three types of data: interval, nominal, and ordinal.[†]

---

*Unfortunately, the term *data*, like the term *statistician*, has taken on several different meanings. For example, dictionaries define data as facts, information, or statistics. In the language of computers, data may refer to any piece of information such as this textbook or an essay you have written. Such definitions make it difficult for us to present *statistics* as a method of converting data into *information*. In this book, we carefully distinguish among the three terms.

[†]There are actually four types of data, the fourth being *ratio* data. However, for statistical purposes there is no difference between ratio and interval data. Consequently, we combine the two types.

Interval data are real numbers, such as heights, weights, incomes, and distances. We also refer to this type of data as **quantitative** or **numerical**.

The values of **nominal** data are categories. For example, responses to questions about marital status produce nominal data. The values of this variable are single, married, divorced, and widowed. Notice that the values are not numbers but instead are words that describe the categories. We often record nominal data by arbitrarily assigning a number to each category. For example, we could record marital status using the following codes:

single = 1, married = 2, divorced = 3, widowed = 4

However, any other numbering system is valid provided that each category has a different number assigned to it. Here is another coding system that is just as valid as the previous one.

Single = 7, married = 4, divorced = 13, widowed = 1

Nominal data are also called **qualitative** or **categorical**.

The third type of data is ordinal. **Ordinal** data appear to be nominal, but the difference is that the order of their values has meaning. For example, at the completion of most college and university courses, students are asked to evaluate the course. The variables are the ratings of various aspects of the course, including the professor. Suppose that in a particular college the values are

poor, fair, good, very good, and excellent

The difference between nominal and ordinal types of data is that the order of the values of the latter indicate a higher rating. Consequently, when assigning codes to the values, we should maintain the order of the values. For example, we can record the students' evaluations as

Poor = 1, Fair = 2, Good = 3, Very good = 4, Excellent = 5

Because the only constraint that we impose on our choice of codes is that the order must be maintained, we can use any set of codes that are in order. For example, we can also assign the following codes:

Poor = 6, Fair = 18, Good = 23, Very good = 45, Excellent = 88

As we discuss in Chapter 19, which introduces statistical inference techniques for ordinal data, the use of any code that preserves the order of the data will produce exactly the same result. Thus, it's not the magnitude of the values that is important, it's their order.

Students often have difficulty distinguishing between ordinal and interval data. The critical difference between them is that the intervals or differences between values of interval data are consistent and meaningful (which is why this type of data is called *interval*). For example, the difference between marks of 85 and 80 is the same five-mark difference that exists between 75 and 70—that is, we can calculate the difference and interpret the results.

Because the codes representing ordinal data are arbitrarily assigned except for the order, we cannot calculate and interpret differences. For example, using a 1-2-3-4-5 coding system to represent poor, fair, good, very good, and excellent, we note that the difference between excellent and very good is identical to the difference between good and fair. With a 6-18-23-45-88 coding, the difference between excellent and very good is 43, and the difference between good and fair is 5. Because both coding systems are valid, we cannot use either system to compute and interpret differences.

Here is another example. Suppose that you are given the following list of the most active stocks traded on the NASDAQ in descending order of magnitude:

Order	Most Active Stocks
1	Microsoft
2	Cisco Systems
3	Dell Computer
4	Tesla
5	Oracle

Does this information allow you to conclude that the difference between the number of stocks traded in Microsoft and Cisco Systems is the same as the difference in the number of stocks traded between Dell Computer and Tesla? The answer is "no" because we have information only about the order of the numbers of trades, which are ordinal, and not the numbers of trades themselves, which are interval. In other words, the difference between 1 and 2 is not necessarily the same as the difference between 3 and 4.

2-1a Calculations for Types of Data

Interval Data All calculations are permitted on interval data. We often describe a set of interval data by calculating the average. For example, the average of the 10 marks listed on page 14 is 70.3. As you will discover, there are several other important statistics that we will introduce.

Nominal Data Because the codes of nominal data are completely arbitrary, we cannot perform any calculations on these codes. To understand why, consider a survey that asks people to report their marital status. Suppose that the first 10 people surveyed gave the following responses:

Single, Married, Married, Married, Widowed,
Single, Married, Married, Single, Divorced

Using the codes

Single = 1,   Married = 2,   Divorced = 3,   Widowed = 4

we would record these responses as

1   2   2   2   4   1   2   2   1   3

The average of these numerical codes is 2.0. Does this mean that the average person is married? Now suppose four more persons were interviewed, of whom three are widowed and one is divorced. The data are given here:

1   2   2   2   4   1   2   2   1   3   4   4   4   3

The average of these 14 codes is 2.5. Does this mean that the average person is married—but halfway to getting divorced? The answer to both questions is an emphatic "no." This example illustrates a fundamental truth about nominal data: Calculations based on the codes used to store this type of data are meaningless. All that we are permitted to do with nominal data is count or compute the percentages of the occurrences of each category. Thus, we would describe the 14 observations by counting the number of each marital status category and reporting the frequency as shown in the following table.

Category	Code	Frequency
Single	1	3
Married	2	5
Divorced	3	2
Widowed	4	4

The remainder of this chapter deals with nominal data only. In Chapter 3, we introduce graphical techniques that are used to describe interval data.

Ordinal Data The most important aspect of ordinal data is the order of the values. As a result, the only permissible calculations are those involving a ranking process. For example, we can place all the data in order and select the code that lies in the middle. As we discuss in Chapter 4, this descriptive measurement is called the *median*.

2-1b Hierarchy of Data

The data types can be placed in order of the permissible calculations. At the top of the list, we place the interval data type because virtually *all* computations are allowed. The nominal data type is at the bottom because *no* calculations other than determining frequencies are permitted. (We are permitted to perform calculations using the frequencies of codes, but this differs from performing calculations on the codes themselves.) In between interval and nominal data lies the ordinal data type. Permissible calculations are ones that rank the data.

Higher-level data types may be treated as lower-level ones. For example, in universities and colleges, we convert the marks in a course, which are interval, to letter grades, which are ordinal. Some graduate courses feature only a pass or fail designation. In this case, the interval data are converted to nominal. It is important to point out that when we convert higher-level data as lower-level we lose information. For example, a mark of 89 on an accounting course exam gives far more information about the performance of that student than does a letter grade of B, which might be the letter grade for marks between 80 and 90. As a result, we do not convert data unless it is necessary to do so. We will discuss this later.

It is also important to note that we cannot treat lower-level data types as higher-level types.

The definitions and hierarchy are summarized in the following box.

Types of Data

Interval

  Values are real numbers.

  All calculations are valid.

  Data may be treated as ordinal or nominal.

> ### Ordinal
> Values must represent the ranked order of the data.
>
> Calculations based on an ordering process are valid.
>
> Data may be treated as nominal but not as interval.
>
> ### Nominal
> Values are the arbitrary numbers that represent categories.
>
> Only calculations based on the frequencies or percentages of occurrence are valid.
>
> Data may not be treated as ordinal or interval.

2-1c Interval, Ordinal, and Nominal Variables

The variables whose observations constitute our data will be given the same name as the type of data. Thus, for example, interval data are the observations of an interval variable.

2-1d Problem Objectives and Information

In presenting the different types of data, we introduced a critical factor in deciding which statistical procedure to use. A second factor is the type of information we need to produce from our data. We discuss the different types of information in greater detail in Section 11-4 when we introduce *problem objectives*. However, in this part of the book (Chapters 2–5), we will use statistical techniques to describe a set of data, compare two or more sets of data, and describe the relationship between two variables. In Section 2-2, we introduce graphical and tabular techniques employed to describe a set of nominal data. Section 2-3 shows how to describe the relationship between two nominal variables and compare two or more sets of nominal data.

EXERCISES

2.1 Provide two examples each of nominal, ordinal, and interval data.

2.2 For each of the following examples of data, determine the type.
a. The number of miles joggers run per week
b. The starting salaries of graduates of MBA programs
c. The months in which a firm's employees choose to take their vacations
d. The final letter grades received by students in a statistics course

2.3 For each of the following examples of data, determine the type.
a. The weekly closing price of the stock of Amazon.com
b. The month of highest vacancy rate at a La Quinta motel
c. The size of soft drink (small, medium, or large) ordered by a sample of McDonald's customers
d. The number of Toyotas imported monthly by the United States over the last 5 years
e. The marks achieved by the students in a statistics course final exam marked out of 100

2.4 The placement office at a university regularly surveys the graduates 1 year after graduation and asks for the following information. For each, determine the type of data.
   a. What is your occupation?
   b. What is your income?
   c. What degree did you obtain?
   d. What is the amount of your student loan?
   e. How would you rate the quality of instruction? (excellent, very good, good, fair, poor)

2.5 Residents of condominiums were recently surveyed and asked a series of questions. Identify the type of data for each question.
   a. What is your age?
   b. On what floor is your condominium?
   c. Do you own or rent?
   d. How large is your condominium (in square feet)?
   e. Does your condominium have a pool?

2.6 A sample of shoppers at a mall was asked the following questions. Identify the type of data each question would produce.
   a. What is your age?
   b. How much did you spend?
   c. What is your marital status?
   d. Rate the availability of parking: excellent, good, fair, or poor
   e. How many stores did you enter?

2.7 Information about a magazine's readers is of interest to both the publisher and the magazine's advertisers. A survey of readers asked respondents to complete the following:
   a. Age
   b. Gender
   c. Marital status
   d. Number of magazine subscriptions
   e. Annual income
   f. Rate the quality of our magazine: excellent, good, fair, or poor

   For each item identify the resulting data type.

2.8 Baseball fans are regularly asked to offer their opinions about various aspects of the sport. A survey asked the following questions. Identify the type of data.
   a. How many games do you attend annually?
   b. How would you rate the quality of entertainment? (excellent, very good, good, fair, poor)
   c. Do you have season tickets?
   d. How would you rate the quality of the food? (edible, barely edible, horrible)

2.9 A survey of golfers asked the following questions. Identify the type of data each question produces.
   a. How many rounds of golf do you play annually?
   b. Are you a member of a private club?
   c. What brand of clubs do you own?

2.10 At the end of the term, university and college students often complete questionnaires about their courses. Suppose that in one university, students were asked the following.
   a. Rate the course (highly relevant, relevant, irrelevant)
   b. Rate the professor (very effective, effective, not too effective, not at all effective)
   c. What was your midterm grade (A, B, C, D, F)?

   Determine the type of data each question produces.

2.11 A survey of taxpayers who complete their own tax returns were asked the following questions. Determine the type of data each question produces.
   a. Did you use software?
   b. How long did it take you to complete this year's return?
   c. Rate the ease with which you completed this year's return (very easy, quite easy, neither easy or difficult, quite difficult, very difficult)

2.12 A random sample of car owners was asked these questions. Identify the type of data.
   a. Make of car
   b. Age of your car in months
   c. Amount of annual insurance
   d. Number of miles on odometer

In many surveys, respondents are asked to report variables such as age, income, and education. It is often the case that respondents are reluctant to provide the actual amount (e.g., income). Surveyors have found that providing a list of intervals makes it more likely that the respondent will provide that information. Exercises 2.13 to 2.19 show two ways to record the variable. Briefly describe why the second variable listed provides less information than the first one listed.

2.13 a. Age of adult respondent
   b. Age categories
   1. $21 < x \leq 40$
   2. $41 < x \leq 60$
   3. More than 60

2.14 a. Income
   b. Income categories
   1. $x \leq \$25{,}000$
   2. $\$25{,}000 < x \leq \$50{,}000$
   3. $\$50{,}000 < x \leq \$75{,}000$
   4. More than $75,000

2.15 a. How stressful do you find your job? Select any number between 0 (Not at all stressful) and 100 (Extremely stressful)
   b. Categories
   1. Not at all stressful
   2. Somewhat stressful
   3. Very stressful
   4. Extremely stressful

2.16 a. Years of education
b. Education category

1. No high school diploma
2. High school diploma
3. Some college
4. College degree

2.17 a. Mark on a Statistics course
b. Grades: A, B, C, D, F

2.18 a. Assets
b. Asset categories

1. $x \leq \$100,000$
2. $\$100,000 < x \leq \$500,000$
3. $\$500,000 < x \leq \$1,000,000$
4. More than $\$1,000,000$

2.19 How likely is it that you will vote in the upcoming election?
a. Select any number between 0 (Will not vote) and 100 (Will definitely vote)
b. Categories

1. Not at all likely
2. Somewhat likely
3. Very likely
4. Extremely likely

2.20 Xr02-20   At WLU (a famous Canadian university), suppose that instructors mark exams out of 100 and then must convert that mark to a letter grade using the following conversions.

A: 80–100
B: 70–79.9
C: 60–69.9
D: 50–59.9
F: Less than 50

Student X's marks on each course are 81, 83, 81, 71, 72, 74, 63, 61, 51, 35.

Student Y's marks are 98, 96, 99, 79, 78, 79, 68, 69, 57, 49.

a. Calculate each student's average mark.
b. Convert the individual marks into letter grades and calculate the grade point average where A = 4, B = 3, C = 2, D = 1, and F = 0.

c. Convert the average of all 10 marks into a letter grade for each student. What have you observed?

2.21 Xr02-21   Refer to Exercise 2.20. Another pair of students achieved the following marks.

Student P: 94, 91, 88, 77, 75, 74, 66, 65, 54, 52
Student Q: 93, 91, 88, 75, 75, 73, 67, 66, 55, 51

a. Calculate the average mark and the grade point average for each student.
b. Compare the mark average and the grade point average of this pair of students with the ones in Exercise 2.20.
c. Discuss the differences between the results in Exercises 2.20 and 2.21.

2.22 Xr02-22   Refer to Exercise 2.20. At another university, the marks are converted into letter grades using the following conversions.

A+: 90–100
A: 85–89.9
A−: 80–84.9
B+: 77–79.9
B: 73–76.9
B−: 70–72.9
C+: 67–69.9
C: 63–66.9
C−: 60–62.9
D+: 57–59.9
D: 53–56.9
D−: 50–52.9
F: Less than 50

The marks of two students are listed below. For each, calculate the average mark and the grade point average using a 13-point scale where A+ = 12, A = 11, and so on until F = 0.

Student M: 90, 82, 82, 73, 71, 70, 67, 61, 53, 51

Student N: 98, 84, 84, 76, 72, 72, 69, 62, 56, 52

Describe what you have determined.

2-2 DESCRIBING A SET OF NOMINAL DATA

As we discussed in Section 2-1, the only allowable calculation on nominal data is to count the frequency or compute the percentage that each value of the variable represents. We can summarize the data in a table, which presents the categories and their counts, called a **frequency distribution**. A **relative frequency distribution** lists the categories and the proportion with which each occurs. We can use graphical techniques to present a picture of the data. There are two graphical methods we can use: the bar chart and the pie chart.

DATA
GSS2018

EXAMPLE 2.1

Work Status in the General Social Survey

A major problem with the official unemployment rate is that it excludes people who have given up trying to find a job even though they would like to find employment. In an effort to track the numbers of Americans in the various categories of work status the GSS asked "Last week were you working full time, part time, going to school, keeping house, or what?" The responses are as follows:

1. Working full time
2. Working part time
3. Temporarily not working
4. Unemployed, laid off
5. Retired
6. School
7. Keeping house
8. Other

The responses were recorded using the codes 1, 2, 3, 4, 5, 6, 7, and 8, respectively. The first 150 observations are listed here. The name of the variable is WRKSTAT and is stored in Column X. Construct a frequency and relative frequency distribution for these data and graphically summarize the data by producing a bar chart and a pie chart.

3	1	1	5	1	1	2	1	1	2	1	7	2	1	7
5	2	6	5	5	1	1	7	1	7	5	5	2	1	6
1	5	1	7	3	6	5	1	2	1	3	1	2	1	1
1	1	1	1	7	1	5	1	1	2	1	1	1	1	1
5	7	2	2	2	1	5	1	1	5	1	5	1	6	4
5	2	5	1	2	7	1	1	3	3	3	8	2	1	1
1	4	1	2	7	4	5	7	1	7	2	2	1	1	6
1	7	7	1	5	1	1	7	1	7	7	1	1	1	1
1	1	7	1	5	2	7	5	3	1	1	7	7	1	1
1	1	2	2	1	7	7	1	2	5	2	1	7	2	5

SOLUTION:

Scan the data. Have you learned anything about the responses of these 150 Americans? Unless you have special skills, you have probably learned little about the numbers. If we had listed all 2,348 observations, you would be even less likely to discover anything useful about the data. To extract useful information requires the application of a statistical or graphical technique. To choose the appropriate technique we must first identify the type of data. In this example the data are nominal because the numbers represent categories. The only calculation permitted on nominal data is to count the number of occurrences of each category. Hence, we count the number of 1s, 2s, 3s, 4s, 5s, 6s, 7s, and 8s. The list of the categories and their counts constitute the frequency distribution. The relative frequency distribution is produced by converting the frequencies into proportions. The frequency and the relative frequency distributions are combined in Table 2.1.

There were two individuals who refused to answer resulting in a total of 2,346 observations.

As promised in Chapter 1 (and in the preface) here are the Excel outputs and instructions on how to produce the frequency and the relative frequency distributions and specifically how to get the results shown in Table 2.1.

TABLE **2.1** **Frequency and Relative Frequency Distributions for Example 2.1**

WORK STATUS	CODE	FREQUENCY	RELATIVE FREQUENCY (%)
Working full time	1	1,134	48.34
Working part time	2	259	11.04
Temporarily not working	3	53	2.26
Unemployed, laid off	4	84	3.58
Retired	5	445	18.97
School	6	81	3.45
Keeping house	7	242	10.32
Other	8	48	2.05
Total		2,346	100

EXCEL

INSTRUCTIONS

(Specific commands for this example are highlighted.)

1. Type or import the data into one or more columns. (Open GSS2018)

2. Activate any empty cell and type

$$=\textbf{COUNTIF} \text{ ([Input range], [Criteria])}$$

Input range are the cells containing the data. In this example, the range is X1:X2349. The criteria are the codes you want to count: (1) (2) (3) (4) (5) (6) (7) (8). For example, to count the number of 1s (Working full time), type

$$=\textbf{COUNTIF} \text{ (X1:X2349, 1)}$$

and the frequency will appear in the active cell. Change the criteria to produce the frequency of the remaining seven categories. To produce the results below, we copied the WRKSTAT variable into Column A in a new spreadsheet. We typed the codes 1 to 8 in rows 1 to 8 in Column B and then employed COUNTIF to get the frequencies. Column C calculated the relative frequencies.

INTERPRET

Only 48.34% of respondents were working full time, 18.97% were retired, 11.04% were working part time, 10.32% were keeping house, and the remaining 11.34% were in one of the other four categories.

Bar and Pie Charts

The information contained in the data is summarized well in the table. However, graphical techniques generally catch a reader's eye more quickly than does a table of numbers. Two graphical techniques can be used to display the results shown in the table. A bar chart is often used to display frequencies; a pie chart graphically shows relative frequencies. The bar chart is created by drawing a rectangle representing each category. The height of the rectangle represents the frequency. The base is arbitrary. Figure 2.1 depicts the manually drawn bar chart for Example 2.1.

FIGURE **2.1** Bar Chart for Example 2.1

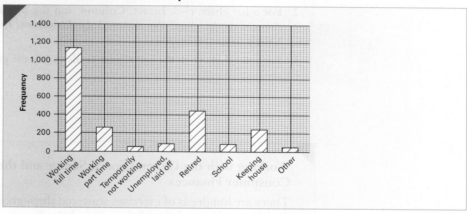

TABLE **2.2** Proportions in Each Category in Example 2.1

WORK STATUS	RELATIVE FREQUENCY (%)	SLICE OF THE PIE (DEGREES)
Working full time	48.34	174.0
Working part time	11.04	39.7
Temporarily not working	2.26	8.1
Unemployed, laid off	3.58	12.9
Retired	18.97	68.3
School	3.45	12.4
Keeping house	10.32	37.1
Other	2.05	7.4
Total	100.0	360

EXCEL

Here is the Excel version of the bar chart and pie chart.

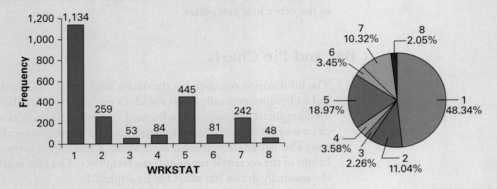

INSTRUCTIONS

1. After creating the frequency distribution, highlight the column of frequencies.

2. For a bar chart, click **Insert**, **Column**, and the first **2-D Column**. You can make changes to the chart. We removed the **Gridlines**, **Legend**, and clicked the **Data Labels** to create the titles.

3. For a pie chart, click **Pie** and **Chart Tools** to edit the graph.

Working with the General Social Survey and the Survey of Consumer Finances

There are hundreds of exercises scattered throughout this book that use the data in the General Social Survey and the Survey of Consumer Finances. Here are some hints on how to work with these data.

1. After you have downloaded all the data sets we recommend that you store them all onto your computer. Make no changes to these files.

2. To work with one or more columns we suggest that you copy the column or columns into a new spreadsheet. For example, in this example we need Column X (WRKSTAT) in the GSS2018 file. Copy the entire column into Column A of another worksheet. Then use the new spreadsheet to conduct any graphical or numerical technique.

3. To take a subset of any column of data use the DATA and SORT commands. Suppose that we are interested in the work status of respondents

who have completed a graduate degree (DEGREE: 4 = graduate). Proceed as follows.

Copy Column T (DEGREE) into Column A of a new worksheet.

Copy Column X (WRKSTAT) into Column B.

Highlight both columns.

Click **DATA** and **SORT**.

Specify **Sort by** Column A (or use the name of the variable).

Scroll down Column A until you reach the rows containing 4s.

Use the data in Column B to conduct your statistical analysis.

2-2a Other Applications of Pie Charts and Bar Charts

Pie and bar charts are used widely in newspapers, magazines, and business and government reports. One reason for this appeal is that they are eye-catching and can attract the reader's interest whereas a table of numbers might not. Perhaps no one understands this better than the newspaper *USA Today*, which typically has a colored graph on the front page and others inside. Pie and bar charts are frequently used to simply present numbers associated with categories. The only reason to use a bar or pie chart in such a situation would be to enhance the reader's ability to grasp the substance of the data. It might, for example, allow the reader to more quickly recognize the relative sizes of the categories, as in the breakdown of a budget. Similarly, treasurers might use pie charts to show the breakdown of a firm's revenues by department, or university students might use pie charts to show the amount of time devoted to daily activities (e.g., eat 10%, sleep 30%, and study statistics 60%).

APPLICATIONS in ECONOMICS

Macroeconomics

Macroeconomics is a major branch of economics that deals with the behavior of the economy as a whole. Macroeconomists develop mathematical models that predict variables such as gross domestic product, unemployment rates, and inflation. These are used by governments and corporations to help develop strategies. For example, central banks attempt to control inflation by lowering or raising interest rates. To do this requires that economists determine the effect of a variety of variables, including the supply and demand for energy.

APPLICATIONS in ECONOMICS

Energy Economics

One variable that has had a large influence on the economies of virtually every country is energy. The 1973 oil crisis in which the price of oil quadrupled over a short period of time is generally considered to be one of the largest financial shocks to our economy. In fact, economists often refer to two different economies: before the 1973 oil crisis and after. Unfortunately, the world will be facing more shocks to our economy because of energy for two primary reasons. The first is the depletion of nonrenewable sources of energy and the resulting price increases. The second is the possibility that burning fossil fuels and the creation of carbon dioxide may be the cause of global warming. One economist predicted that the cost of global warming will be calculated in trillions of dollars. Statistics can play an important role by determining whether Earth's temperature has been increasing and, if so, whether carbon dioxide is the cause. (See Case 3.1.) In this chapter, you will encounter other examples and exercises that involve the issue of energy.

EXAMPLE **2.2**

DATA
Xm02-02

Energy Consumption in the United States in 2019

Table 2.3 lists the total energy consumption of the United States from all sources in 2019 (latest data available at publication). To make it easier to see the details, the table measures the energy in quadrillions of British thermal units (BTUs). Use an appropriate graphical technique to depict these figures.

TABLE **2.3** Energy Consumption in the United States by Source, 2019

ENERGY SOURCES	QUADRILLIONS OF BTUs
Nonrenewable Energy Sources	
Coal	11.31
Natural Gas	32.10
Nuclear	8.862
Petroleum	36.87
Renewable Energy Sources	
Biomass	4.985
Geothermal	.2093
Hydroelectric	2.492
Solar	1.043
Wind	2.732
Total	100.6

Source: U.S. Energy Information Administration

SOLUTION:

We are interested in describing the proportion of total energy consumption from each source. Thus, the appropriate method is the pie chart. The next step is to determine the proportion and sizes of the pie slices from which the Excel pie chart is drawn.

EXCEL Chart

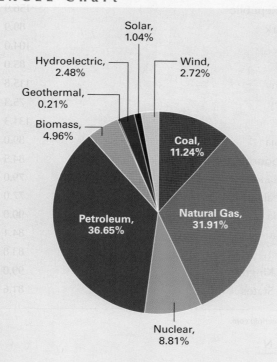

INTERPRET

The United States depends heavily on the three fossil fuels. Coal, natural gas, and petroleum constitute 80% of U.S. consumption. The renewables amount to about 11%, of which about half is biomass (wood, garbage, and crop waste) and a quarter is hydroelectric (mostly from dams). Wind and solar produce a little less than 4% of U.S. consumption. To see if and how the mix has changed since 1960, 1980, and 2000 go to Exercise 2.34.

EXAMPLE 2.3

DATA
Xm02-03

Beer Consumption (Top 20 Countries)

Table 2.4 lists the per capita beer consumption in liters per year for each of the top 20 countries around the world. Graphically present these numbers.

TABLE **2.4** Beer Consumption, Top 20 Countries

COUNTRY	PER CAPITA BEER CONSUMPTION (LITERS/YEAR)
Australia	109.9
Austria	108.3
Belgium	93.0
Croatia	81.2
Czech Republic	156.9
Denmark	89.9
Estonia	104.0
Finland	85.0
Germany	115.8
Hungary	75.3
Ireland	131.3
Lithuania	89.0
Luxembourg	84.5
Netherlands	79.0
New Zealand	77.0
Romania	90.0
Slovakia	84.1
Spain	83.8
United Kingdom	99.0
United States	81.6

Source: www.beerinfo.com.

SOLUTION:

In this example, we are primarily interested in the numbers. There is no use in presenting proportions here. The following is Excel version of the bar chart.

EXCEL Chart

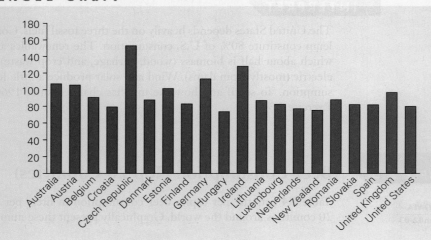

The Czech Republic, Ireland, and Germany head the list. Both the United States and the United Kingdom rank far lower, and Canada did not make it into the top 20 list.

2-2b Describing Ordinal Data

There are no specific graphical techniques for ordinal data. Consequently, when we wish to describe a set of ordinal data, we will treat the data as if they were nominal and use the techniques described in this section. The only criterion is that the bars in bar charts should be arranged in ascending (or descending) ordinal values; in pie charts, the wedges are typically arranged clockwise in ascending or descending order.

We complete this section by describing when bar and pie charts are used to summarize and present data.

Factors That Identify When to Use Frequency and Relative Frequency Tables, and Bar and Pie Charts

1. Objective: Describe a single set of data.
2. Data type: Nominal or ordinal

EXERCISES

2.23 <u>Xr02-23</u> When will the world run out of oil? One way to judge is to determine the oil reserves of the countries around the world. The next table displays the known reserves of the top 15 countries.
  a. Use a bar chart to describe these figures. Describe your findings.
  b. Why is a bar chart a more appropriate graphical technique than a pie chart?
  c. What other figures are needed to make a pie chart a better choice?

Country	Oil Reserves (Millions of Barrels)
Brazil	12,999
Canada	167,896
China	25,620
Iran	155,600
Iraq	145,019
Kazakhstan	30,000
Kuwait	101,500

Country	Oil Reserves (Millions of Barrels)
Libya	48,363
Nigeria	36,972
Qatar	25,244
Russia	80,000
Saudi Arabia	267,026
United Arab Emirates	97,800
United States	47,053
Venezuela	302,809

2.24 <u>Xr02-24</u> The table on the next page lists the number of medals won by the top 15 countries in the 2016 Summer Olympic Games.
  a. Use a bar chart to summarize these figures.
  b. Would a pie chart be a better graphical technique?
  c. What other figure or figures would be necessary to have in order for a pie chart to be a better method?

Country	Number of Medals
Australia	29
Azerbaijan	18
Brazil	19
Canada	22
China	70
France	42
Germany	42
Great Britain	67
Italy	28
Japan	41
Netherlands	19
New Zealand	18
Russia	56
South Korea	21
United States	121

2.25 Xr02-25 In the 2018 midterm election the second most important issue for voters was immigration. (Health care was the most important issue.) To provide more information we have recorded the total number the immigrants in the country and the percentage of the total U.S. population for each decade starting in 1900. Use a bar chart to display both sets of figures. Describe what you have learned.

Decade	Number of Immigrants (Millions)	Percentage: Immigrants
1900	10.3	13.6
1910	13.5	14.7
1920	13.9	13.2
1930	14.2	11.6
1940	11.6	8.8
1950	10.3	6.9
1960	9.7	5.4
1970	9.6	4.7
1980	14.1	6.2
1990	19.8	7.9
2000	31.1	11.1
2010	40.0	12.9
2016	43.7	13.5

Source: Decennial census 1900–2000, American Community Survey 2010 & 2016.

2.26 Xr02-26 Following are the countries with the largest amount of natural gas reserves in the world. Use a graphical technique to summarize and present these figures.

Country	Natural Gas Reserves (Cubic Meters)
Algeria	93,499,998,208
Australia	105,200,001,024
Canada	159,099,994,112
China	145,899,995,136
Iran	214,499,999,744
Norway	123,900,002,304
Qatar	166,400,000,000
Russia	665,600,000,000
Saudi Arabia	109,299,998,720
United States	772,799,987,712

2.27 Xr02-27 The following table lists the average oil consumption per day of the top 20 oil-consuming nations. Use a graphical technique to display this information.

Country	Oil Consumption (Thousands of Barrels per Day)
Australia	1,080
Brazil	3,003
Canada	2,374
China	10,480
France	1,713
Germany	2,435
India	3,660
Indonesia	1,718
Iran	1,885
Italy	1,260
Japan	4,557
Mexico	2,090
Russian Federation	3,493
Saudi Arabia	2,961
Singapore	1,240
South Korea	2,328
Spain	1,208
Thailand	1,171
United Kingdom	1,502
United States	18,961

2.28 Xr02-28 There are 42 gallons in a barrel of oil. The number of products produced and the proportion of the total are listed in the following table. Draw a graph to depict these numbers.

Product	Proportion
Gasoline	51.4
Distillate fuel oil	15.3
Jet fuel	12.6
Still gas	5.4
Marketable coke	5.0
Residual fuel oil	3.3
Liquefied refinery gas	2.8
Asphalt and road oil	1.9
Lubricants	0.9
Other	1.5

Source: California Energy Commission.

2.29 Xr02-29   The table below lists the electricity consumption (in billions of Kilowatt-hours) in the top 20 electricity using countries. Graph the numbers to help describe the figures.

Country	Electricity Consumption (Billion KWH)
Australia	223
Brazil	480
Canada	533
China	4,882
France	453
Germany	534
India	903
Iran	207
Italy	294
Japan	935
South Korea	487
Mexico	232
Russian Federation	878
Saudi Arabia	247
South Africa	212
Spain	235
Taiwan	226
Turkey	195
United Kingdom	319
United States	3,868

2.30 Xr02-30   Here is a list of the 15 largest countries in the world in terms of population. Use a bar chart to display these figures.

Country	Population
Bangladesh	166,368,149
Brazil	210,867,954
China	1,415,045,928
Egypt	99,375,741
Ethiopia	107,534,882
India	1,354,051,854
Indonesia	266,794,980
Japan	127,185,332
Mexico	130,759,074
Nigeria	195,875,237
Pakistan	200,813,818
Philippines	106,512,074
Russia	143,964,709
United States	326,766,748
Viet Nam	96,491,146

2.31 The total population of all countries in the world is 7,632,819,325. Use the population figures in Exercise 2.30 and this figure to draw a pie chart.

2.32 Xr02-32   Here is a list of the top 15 countries in the world in terms of nuclear power consumption. Use a graphical method to display these figures.

Country	Nuclear Energy Consumption (Million Tonnes of Oil Equivalent)
Belgium	9.5
Canada	21.9
China	56.2
Czech Republic	6.4
France	90.1
Germany	17.2
India	8.5
Japan	6.6
Russia	46.0
South Korea	33.6
Spain	13.1
Sweden	14.9
Ukraine	19.4
United Kingdom	15.9
United States	191.7

2.33 Xr02-33 A generally accepted figure to describe the size of a country's economy is the gross domestic product (GDP), which measures the monetary value of final goods and services—produced in a country in a given period of time. The annual GDP ($billions) for the 10 countries with the largest GDPs in 2020 is listed below.

a. Should a bar chart or pie chart be used? Explain.

b. Use the appropriate graphical technique to present these data.

Country	GDP ($Billions)
Brazil	1,893.01
Canada	1,812.46
China	15,269.94
France	2,771.62
Germany	3,982.24
India	3,202.18
Italy	2,013.67
Japan	5,413.05
United Kingdom	2,716.53
United States	22,321.76

2.34 Xr02-34 Refer to Example 2.2. Listed below are the figures for U.S. energy consumption by source (quadrillions of BTUs) for the years 1960, 1980, and 2000. Use a graphical technique to present these figures.

Energy Sources	1960	1980	2000
Nonrenewable Energy Sources			
Coal	9.838	15.42	22.58
Natural Gas	12.39	20.24	23.84
Nuclear	.0006	2.739	7.862
Petroleum	19.87	34.16	38.15
Renewable Energy Sources			
Biomass	1.320	2.476	3.008
Geothermal	.00036	.0527	.1644
Hydroelectric	1.608	2.900	2.811
Solar	0	0	.0635
Wind	0	0	.0571
Total	47.76	77.99	98.54

Source: U.S. Energy Information Administration.

2.35 Xr02-35 The table below lists the total number of medals won by the top 15 countries in the Winter Olympic Games in 2018. Using a graphical method, display these figures.

Country	Medals
Austria	14
Canada	29
China	9
Czech Republic	7
France	15
Germany	31
Italy	10
Japan	13
Netherlands	20
Norway	39
Olympic Athletes from Russia	17
South Korea	17
Sweden	14
Switzerland	15
United States	23

The following exercises require a computer and software.

2.36 Xr02-36 What are the most important characteristics of colleges and universities? This question was asked of a sample of college-bound high school seniors. The responses are as follows:

1. Location
2. Majors
3. Academic reputation
4. Career focus
5. Community
6. Number of students

The results were stored using these codes. Use a graphical technique to summarize and present the data.

2.37 Xr02-37 Where do consumers get information about cars? A sample of recent car buyers was asked to identify the most useful source of information about the cars they purchased. The responses are as follows:

1. Consumer guide
2. Dealership
3. Word of mouth
4. Internet

The responses were stored using these codes. Graphically depict these responses.

Source: Automotive Retailing Today, the Gallup Organization.

2.38 Xr02-38   A survey asked 392 homeowners which area of the home they would most like to renovate. The responses are shown next. Use a graphical technique to present these results. Briefly summarize your findings.

1. Basement
2. Bathroom
3. Bedroom
4. Kitchen
5. Living/dining room

2.39 Xr02-39   Subway train riders frequently pass the time by reading a newspaper. New York City has a subway and four newspapers. A sample of 360 subway riders who regularly read a newspaper was asked to identify that newspaper. The responses are as follows:

1. *New York Daily News*
2. *New York Post*
3. *New York Times*
4. *Wall Street Journal*

The responses were recorded using the numerical codes shown.

a. Produce a frequency distribution and a relative frequency distribution.
b. Draw an appropriate graph to summarize the data. What does the graph tell you?

2.40 Xr02-40   Who applies to MBA programs? To help determine the background of the applicants, a sample of 230 applicants to a university's business school was asked to report their undergraduate degree. The degrees were recorded using these codes.

1. BA
2. BBA
3. B.Eng
4. BSc
5. Other

a. Determine the frequency distribution.
b. Draw a bar chart.
c. Draw a pie chart.
d. What do the charts tell you about the sample of MBA applicants?

2.41 Xr02-41   Many business and economics courses require the use of a computer, so students often must buy their own computers. A survey asks

students to identify which computer brand they have purchased. The responses are as follows:

1. Acer
2. Apple
3. Asus
4. Dell
5. HP
6. Lenovo
7. Other

a. Use a graphical technique that depicts the frequencies.
b. Graphically depict the proportions.
c. What do the charts tell you about the brands of computers used by the students?

2.42 Xr02-42   An increasing number of statistics courses use a computer and software rather than manual calculations. A survey of statistics instructors asked each to report the software their course uses. The responses are as follows:

1. Excel
2. XLSTAT
3. Minitab
4. STATA
5. Other

a. Produce a frequency distribution.
b. Graphically summarize the data so that the proportions are depicted.
c. What do the charts tell you about the software choices?

2.43 Xr02-43+   The total light beer sales in the United States is approximately 3 million gallons annually. With this large a market, breweries often need to know more about who is buying their product. The marketing manager of a major brewery wanted to analyze the light beer sales among college and university students who do drink light beer. A random sample of 285 graduating students was asked to report which of the following is their favorite light beer:

1. Bud Light
2. Busch Light
3. Coors Light
4. Michelob Light
5. Miller Lite
6. Natural Light
7. Other brands

The responses were recorded using the codes 1, 2, 3, 4, 5, 6, and 7, respectively. Use a graphical technique to summarize these data. What can you conclude from the chart?

Opinion Surveys: Pew Research Center, the Gallup Organization, and Abacus Data

There are numerous organizations that conduct surveys for political parties, government agencies, and private corporations. Two of the most famous in the United States are the Pew Research Center and the Gallup Organization. In Canada, Abacus Data conducts surveys and research for public and private enterprises. All three organizations conduct nonpartisan public opinion surveys, which are published in newspapers and discussed on television newscasts. We will use some of their results throughout this book to create exercises whose data sets will produce the same results as the original study.

In the next 17 exercises we specify the date, the population surveyed, the question, and the codes representing the responses. For each exercise, use a graphical technique to summarize and display the data.

2.44 Xr02-44+   Pew Research Center

Date: March 2020

Population: American adults

Question: What is the most common way to get political and election news?

Responses

1. Cable TV
2. Local TV
3. Network TV
4. News website/app
5. Print
6. Radio
7. Social media

2.45 Xr02-45+   Pew Research Center

Date: June 2018

Population: American adults

Question: Should legal immigration to the United States decrease (1), stay the same (2), or increase (3)?

2.46 Xr02-46+   Pew Research Center

Date: August 2017

Population: American adults

Question: Should taxes be lowered (1), stay the same (2), or increased (3) on large businesses and corporations?

2.47 Xr02-47   Pew Research Center

Date: June–July 2017

a. Population: American Millennials (born between 1981 and 1996)

b. Population: American Generation X (born between 1965 and 1980)

Question: Your political values are

1. Consistent conservative
2. Mostly conservative
3. Mixed
4. Mostly liberal
5. Consistent liberal

Use a graphical technique that displays the two populations.

2.48 Xr02-48   Pew Research Center

Date: June–July 2017

Population: American Silent Generation (born between 1928 and 1945)

Question: Your political values are

1. Consistent conservative
2. Mostly conservative
3. Mixed
4. Mostly liberal
5. Consistent liberal

2.49 Xr02-49+   Gallup Organization

Date: August 2018

Population: Americans who commute to work

Question: How stressful do you find your commute?

1. Very or somewhat stressful
2. Not too stressful
3. Not stressful at all

2.50 Xr02-50+ Gallup Organization

Date: July 2018

Population: American adults

Question: Do you think moderate drinking (1 or 2 alcoholic drinks per day) is good for your health (1), makes no difference (2), or is bad for your health (3)?

2.51 Xr02-51 Gallup Organization

Date: September 2018 (Prior to the midterm elections)

Population: American adults

Question: Rate current economic conditions

1. Excellent/good
2. Only fair
3. Poor

2.52 Xr02-52 Gallup Organization

Date: August 2018

Population: American adults with jobs

Question: Do you think you are underpaid for the work you do (1), paid about the right amount (2), or overpaid for the work you do (3)?

2.53 Xr02-53 Gallup Organization

Date: July 2018

Population: American adults

Question: Thinking about the future do you think labor unions in this country will become stronger than they are today (1), stay the same as today (2), or become weaker than they are today (3)?

2.54 Xr02-54 Gallup Organization

Date: August 2018

Population: American adults

Question: How would you rate the U.S. economic system compared to all other modern industrialized countries?

1. Best/Above average
2. Average
3. Worst/Below average

2.55 Xr02-55+ Abacus Data

Date: July 2018

Population: Canadian adults

Question: If a federal election were held tomorrow, which of the following parties would you vote for in your local constituency?

1. Liberal
2. Conservative

3. NDP
4. Green
5. BQ
6. Other

2.56 Xr02-56 Abacus Data

Date: August 2018

Population: Canadian adults

Question: How concerned are you about climate change?

1. Extremely concerned
2. Very concerned
3. A little concerned
4. Not concerned

2.57 Xr02-57 Abacus Data

Date: June 2018

Population: Canadian adults

Question: In early 2018 the Trump administration imposed tariffs on Canadian steel and aluminum. Canada's prime minister responded to this action by announcing that Canada will place tariffs on a number of U.S. products including whiskey, iron and steel, and a variety of food and household products and hardware products. Do you support or oppose this action?

1. Strongly support
2. Support
3. No view
4. Oppose
5. Strongly oppose

2.58 Xr02-58 Abacus Data

Date: August 2018

Population: Canadian adults

Question: Refer to Exercise 2.57. Would you respond by personally not purchasing products made in the United States?

1. Will certainly
2. Will consider
3. Will not consider

2.59 Xr02-59+ Abacus Data

Date: February 2017

Population: Canadian adults

Question: If a major news event occurred, where would you most likely hear it first?

1. Television
2. Radio
3. Word of mouth
4. News website

5. Twitter
6. News alert
7. News app
8. Facebook

1. The economy in general
2. Health care
3. Poverty or income inequality
4. Unemployment
5. The environment or climate change
6. Immigration
7. Housing
8. Education/schools
9. Crime/law and order
10. Terrorism
11. Foreign affairs or defense

2.60 Xr02-60 Abacus Data

Date: November 2016

Population: Canadian adults

Question: What do you see as the most important issue facing Canada today?

2-3 / DESCRIBING THE RELATIONSHIP BETWEEN TWO NOMINAL VARIABLES AND COMPARING TWO OR MORE NOMINAL DATA SETS

In Section 2-2, we presented graphical and tabular techniques used to summarize a set of nominal data. Techniques applied to single sets of data are called **univariate**. There are many situations where we wish to depict the relationship between variables; in such cases, **bivariate** methods are required. A **cross-classification table** (also called a **cross-tabulation table**) is used to describe the relationship between two nominal variables. A variation of the bar chart introduced in Section 2-2 is employed to graphically describe the relationship. The same technique is used to compare two or more sets of nominal data.

2-3a Tabular Method of Describing the Relationship between Two Nominal Variables

To describe the relationship between two nominal variables, we must remember that we are permitted only to determine the frequency of the values. As a first step, we need to produce a cross-classification table that lists the frequency of each combination of the values of the two variables.

EXAMPLE 2.4

DATA
Xm02-04

Newspaper Readership Survey

A major North American city has four competing newspapers: the Globe and Mail (G&M), Post, Star, and Sun. To help design advertising campaigns, the advertising managers of the newspapers need to know which segments of the newspaper market are reading their papers. A survey was conducted to analyze the relationship between newspapers read and occupation. A sample of newspaper readers was asked to report which newspaper they read—Globe and Mail (1), Post (2), Star (3), and Sun (4)—and indicate whether they were blue-collar workers (1), white-collar workers (2), or professionals (3). Some of the data are listed here.

Reader	Occupation	Newspaper
1	2	2
2	1	4
3	2	1

Reader	Occupation	Newspaper
⋮	⋮	⋮
352	3	2
353	1	3
354	2	3

Determine whether the two nominal variables are related.

SOLUTION:

By counting the number of times each of the 12 combinations occurs, we produced Table 2.5.

TABLE **2.5** Cross-Classification Table of Frequencies for Example 2.4

OCCUPATION	NEWSPAPER				
	G&M	POST	STAR	SUN	TOTAL
Blue collar	27	18	38	37	120
White collar	29	43	21	15	108
Professional	33	51	22	20	126
Total	89	112	81	72	354

If occupation and newspaper are related, there will be differences in the newspapers read among the occupations. An easy way to see this is to convert the frequencies in each row (or column) to relative frequencies in each row (or column). That is, compute the row (or column) totals and divide each frequency by its row (or column) total, as shown in Table 2.6. Totals may not equal 1 because of rounding.

TABLE **2.6** Cross-Classification Table of Row proportions for Example 2.4

OCCUPATION	NEWSPAPER				
	G&M	POST	STAR	SUN	TOTAL
Blue collar	.23	.15	.32	.31	1.00
White collar	.27	.40	.19	.14	1.00
Professional	.26	.40	.17	.16	1.00
Total	.25	.32	.23	.20	1.00

EXCEL

Excel can produce the cross-classification table using several methods. We will use and describe the PivotTable in two ways: (1) to create the cross-classification table featuring the counts and (2) to produce a table showing the row relative frequencies.

	A	B	C	D	E	F
1	Count of Reader	Column Labels				
2	Row Labels		1	2	3	4 Grand Total
3	1		27	18	38	37	120
4	2		29	43	21	15	108
5	3		33	51	22	20	126
6	Grand Total		89	112	81	72	354

	A	B	C	D	E	F
	Count of Reader	Column Labels				
	Row Labels		1	2	3	4 Grand Total
	1		0.23	0.15	0.32	0.31	1.00
	2		0.27	0.40	0.19	0.14	1.00
	3		0.26	0.40	0.17	0.16	1.00
	Grand Total		0.25	0.32	0.23	0.20	1.00

INSTRUCTIONS

The data must be stored in (at least) three columns as we have done in Xm02-04. Put the cursor somewhere in the data range.

1. Click **Insert** and **PivotTable**.
2. Make sure that the **Table/Range** is correct. Click **OK**.
3. In the **Pivot Table Fields** check **Reader** and right-click **Add to Values**.
4. Check **Occupation** and right-click **Add to Row Labels**.
5. Check **Newspaper** and right-click **Add to Column Labels**.
6. Place the cursor in the table and right-click **Summarize Values by** and click **Count**.
7. To convert to row percentages, right click any number, click **Show Values As** and click **% of Row Total**.

INTERPRET

Notice that the relative frequencies in the second and third rows are similar and that there are large differences between row 1 and rows 2 and 3. This tells us that blue-collar workers tend to read different newspapers from both white-collar workers and professionals and that white-collar workers and professionals are quite similar in their newspaper choices.

Graphing the Relationship between Two Nominal Variables

We have chosen to draw three bar charts, one for each occupation depicting the four newspapers. We'll use Excel for this purpose. The manually drawn charts are identical.

EXCEL

There are several ways to graphically display the relationship between two nominal variables. We have chosen two-dimensional bar charts for each of the three occupations. The charts can be created from the output of the PivotTable either with counts or with row proportions (as we have done).

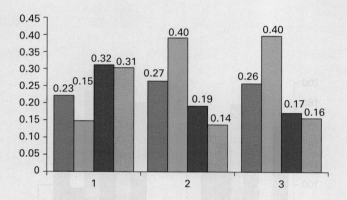

INSTRUCTIONS

From the cross-classification table, click **Insert** and **Column**. You can do the same from any completed cross-classification table.

INTERPRET

If the two variables are unrelated, then the patterns exhibited in the bar charts should be approximately the same. If some relationship exists, then some bar charts will differ from others.

The graphs tell us the same story as did the table. The shapes of the bar charts for occupations 2 and 3 (white collar and professional) are very similar. Both differ considerably from the bar chart for occupation 1 (blue collar).

2-3b Comparing Two or More Sets of Nominal Data

We can interpret the results of the cross-classification table of the bar charts in a different way. In Example 2.4, we can consider the three occupations as defining three different populations. If differences exist between the columns of the frequency distributions (or between the bar charts), then we can conclude that differences exist among the three populations. Alternatively, we can consider the readership of the four newspapers as four different populations. If differences exist among the frequencies or the bar charts, then we conclude that there are differences between the four populations.

Do Male and Female Americans Differ in Their Political Party Affiliation: Solution

DATA GSS2018	Using the technique introduced above, we produced the Excel bar chart.

EXCEL

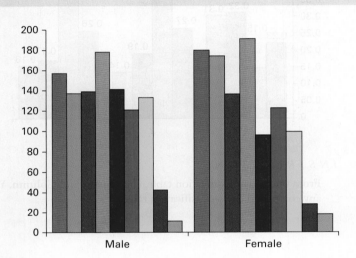

INTERPRET

Because of the way the categories were recorded the bar charts represent the frequencies of (in order from left to right) Strong Democrat, Not Strong Democrat, Independent, Near Democrat, Independent, Independent, Near Republican, Not Strong Republican, Strong Republican, Other Party, and Blank (No answer).

There are some similarities and some differences. For both men and women the most common party affiliation is Independent, followed by Strong Democrat and Not Strong Democrat. Women tend to classify themselves as Democrat more than do men; men tend to be Republican supporters more than do women.

2-3c Data Formats

There are several ways to store the data to be used in this section to produce a table or a bar or pie chart.

1. The data are in two columns. The first column represents the categories of the first nominal variable, and the second column stores the categories for the second. Each row represents one observation of the two variables. The number of observations in each column must be the same. Excel can produce a cross-classification table from these data. (To use Excel's PivotTable, there also must be a third variable representing the observation number.) This is the way the data for Example 2.4 were stored.

2. The data are stored in two or more columns, with each column representing the same variable in a different sample or population. For example, the variable may be the type of undergraduate degree of applicants to an MBA program, and there may be five universities we wish to compare. To produce a cross-classification table, we would have to count the number of observations of each category (undergraduate degree) in each column.

3. The table representing counts in a cross-classification table may have already been created.

We complete this section with the factors that identify the use of the techniques introduced here.

Factors That Identify When to Use a Cross-Classification Table

1. Objective: Describe the relationship between two variables and compare two or more sets of data.
2. Data type: Nominal

EXERCISES

The following exercises require a computer and software.

2.61 Xr02-61 Has the educational level of adults changed over the past 12 years? To help answer this question, a statistics practitioner randomly sampled American adults 25 years of age and older and recorded their educational attainment (for years 2006, 2010, 2014, and 2018): Less than high school (1), High school (2), Some college but less than a Bachelor's degree (3), College (4). Use a graphical technique to present these figures. Briefly describe what the chart tells you.

Source: Adapted from U.S. Census Bureau.

2.62 Xr02-62 The Federal Bureau of Investigation tracks the number of bank robberies for each day of the week. Random samples of bank robberies in the years 2009, 2012, 2015, and 2018 were recorded: Monday (1), Tuesday (2), Wednesday (3), Thursday (4), Friday (5), Saturday (6), Sunday (7). Use a graphical technique to help the FBI determine whether the pattern of bank robberies has changed.

Source: Adapted from FBI Reports.

2.63 Xr02-63 The average loss from robbery in the United States is approximately $1,450. Suppose that an insurance analyst wanted to know whether the type of robbery differs in the years 2006, 2009, 2012, 2015, and 2018. A random sample of robbery reports was taken from each of these years and the types recorded: Street or highway (1), Commercial house (2), Gas station (3), Convenience store (4), Residence (5), Bank (6), and Other (7). Determine whether there are differences in the types of robberies over the 12-year span.

Source: Adapted from FBI Reports.

2.64 Xr02-64 The associate dean of the WLU business school was looking for ways to improve the quality of the applicants to its MBA program. In particular the dean wanted to know whether the undergraduate degree of applicants differed among WLU and the three nearby universities with MBA programs. A random sample of 100 applicants of the WLU program and an equal number from each of the other universities was drawn. Their undergraduate degree was recorded as BA (1), B.Eng (2), BBA (3), and Other (4) as well as the university (codes 1, 2, 3, and 4). Use a graphical technique to determine whether the undergraduate degree and the university each person applied to appear to be related.

2.65 Xr02-65   Is there brand loyalty among car owners in their purchases of gasoline? To help answer the question, a random sample of car owners was asked to record the brand of gasoline in their last two purchases: Exxon (1), Amoco (2), Texaco (3), Other (4). Use a tabular technique to formulate your answer.

2.66 Xr02-66   The costs of smoking for individuals, companies for whom they work, and society in general are in the many billions of dollars. In an effort to reduce smoking, various government and non-government organizations have undertaken information campaigns about the dangers of smoking. Most of these have been directed at young people. This raises the question: Are you more likely to smoke if your parents smoke? To shed light on the issue, a sample of 20- to 40-year-old people was asked whether they smoked [Responses: Do not smoke (1) and Smoke (2)] and whether their parents smoked [Responses: Neither parent smoked (1), Father smoked (2), Mother smoked (3), Both parents smoked (4)]. Use a tabular technique to produce the information you need.

2.67 Xr02-67   In 2018 the unemployment rate in the United States had fallen to lows last seen more than 50 years ago. However, there were still millions of Americans who were unemployed. A statistics practitioner wanted to investigate the reason for that unemployment status and whether the reasons differed by gender. The U.S. Bureau of Labor Statistics randomly sampled people 16 years of age and older. The reasons given for their status are: Lost job (1), Left job (2), Reentrants (3), New entrants (4). Determine whether there are differences between unemployed men and women in terms of the reasons for unemployment.

2.68 Xr02-68   The total number of prescriptions sold in the United States is more than 4 million. (*Source:* National Association of Drug Store Chains.) The sales manager of a chain of drug stores wanted to determine whether there were changes in where the prescriptions were filled. A survey of prescriptions was undertaken in 2006, 2010, 2014, and 2018. The year and type of each prescription were recorded as: Traditional chain store (1), Independent drug store (2), Mass merchant (3), Supermarket (4), Mail order (5). Determine whether there are differences between the years.

2.69 Xr02-43+   Refer to Exercise 2.43. Also recorded was the gender [Male (1) or Female (2)] of the respondents. Use a graphical technique to determine whether the choice of light beers differs between genders.

The following exercises are based on the Pew Research Center, the Gallup Organization, and Abacus Data exercises (Exercises 2.44 to 2.60).

2.70 Xr02-44+   Refer to Exercise 2.44. Another question asked each respondent "Have you seen news and information about COVID-19 that seems to be completely made up?"

1. A lot
2. Some
3. Little or none

Use a graphical technique to determine whether the responses to this question differ between the seven news sources.

2.71 Xr02-49+   In addition to asking American adults to gauge their commuting stress level in Exercise 2.49, drivers were also asked whether they lived in the City (1) or Suburbs (2). Use a graphical method to determine whether stress levels differ between city and suburban drivers.

2.72 Xr02-46+   In Exercise 2.46, a Gallup survey asked American adults whether they believed that taxes should be increased, stay the same, or decreased for large businesses and corporations. Each respondent was also classified Democrat (1) or Republican (2). Present a graphical method to determine whether there are differences between the two political parties in their responses to the issue of higher taxes.

2.73 Xr02-50+   Exercise 2.50 featured a Gallup survey wherein American adults were asked whether they believed that moderate drinking of alcohol was beneficial. The survey also asked whether the respondent drank alcohol [responses: Yes (1), No (2)]. Develop a graph that depicts the differences between the two groups with respect to their responses about the benefits of alcohol.

2.74 Xr02-55+   The Abacus poll in Exercise 2.55 asked Canadians for which party they intended to vote. The survey also recorded the gender of the respondents: Male (1) or Female (2). Use a graphical technique to gauge the differences between the male and female Canadian voters.

2.75 Xr02-59+   Canadians were asked where they received news in Exercise 2.59. Respondents were asked to report their age category: 18–29 (1), 30–44 (2), 45–59 (3), and 60 and over (4). Use a graphical method to display differences between the four age categories.

CHAPTER SUMMARY

Descriptive statistical methods are used to summarize data sets so that we can extract the relevant information. In this chapter, we presented graphical techniques for nominal data.

Bar charts, pie charts, and frequency and relative frequency distributions are employed to summarize single sets of nominal data. Because of the restrictions applied to this type of data, all that we can show is the frequency and proportion of each category.

To describe the relationship between two nominal variables, we produce cross-classification tables and bar charts.

IMPORTANT TERMS:

Variable   14
Values   14
Data   14
Datum   14
Interval   15
Quantitative   15
Numerical   15
Nominal   15

Qualitative   15
Categorical   15
Ordinal   15
Frequency distribution   20
Relative frequency distribution   20
Bar chart   23
Pie chart   23
Univariate   36
Bivariate   36
Cross-classification (cross-tabulation) table   36

EXCEL OUTPUT AND INSTRUCTIONS:

Graphical Technique

Bar chart	23
Pie chart	23

CHAPTER EXERCISES

The following exercises require a computer and software.

2.76 Xr02-76 How has immigration into the United States changed? One way to measure this is to determine the educational attainment of immigrants who came into the country during different periods. The periods are: Before 1970, 1970–1979, 1980–1989, 1990–1999, 2000 and later. The educational attainment responses are: Less than high school (1), High school (2), Some college (3), and College (4). Use a graphical method to compare the five groups of immigrants.

2.77 Xr02-77 As of December 2017, the U.S. government owed $20.5 trillion. To whom did the U.S. government owe money? The list is broken down into two groups, intragovernmental debt, which accounts for 28%, and public debt, which accounts for the remaining 72%. The list of intragovernmental debt is shown below (in $billions). Use a graphical technique to depict these figures.

Category	Amount ($Billions)
Social Security Trust Fund & Federal Disability Insurance	2,820
Medicare	202
Office of Personnel Management Retirement Fund	884
Military Retirement Fund	742
All other retirement funds	415
Cash	606

2.78 Xr02-78 Refer to Exercise 2.77. Following is a list of the top 20 foreign governments that own the U.S. debt. Depict these figures with a graph.

Country	Amount ($Billions)
Belgium	154.5
Bermuda	64.0
Brazil	299.7
Canada	96.0
Cayman Islands	196.3
China	1,171.0
France	111.0
Germany	71.0
Hong Kong	194.4
India	142.6
Ireland	300.2
Japan	1,035.5
Luxembourg	221.5
Saudi Arabia	166.8
Singapore	127.6
South Korea	109.1
Switzerland	233.1
Taiwan	164.2
Thailand	63.0
United Kingdom	271.7

2.79 Xr02-79 June 7 is known as Tax Freedom Day in Canada. The annual taxes paid by an average Canadian family earning $105,236 is $45,167. The breakdown of these taxes is shown in the table below. Use an appropriate graphical technique to present these figures.

Income taxes	14,732
Payroll/health taxes	10,043
Sales taxes	7,013
Property taxes	4,214
Profit taxes	3,895
Liquor and tobacco taxes	2,397
Vehicle and fuel taxes	1,225
Other taxes	1,648

2.80 Xr02-45+ Refer to Exercise 2.45. The Pew Research Center asked American adults whether immigration should decrease, stay the same, or increase. The survey also asked whether the respondent was a Democrat (1) or Republican (2). Use a graphical technique to display the difference between the two political parties.

2.81 Xr02-81 The Wilfrid Laurier University bookstore conducts annual surveys of its customers. One question asks respondents to rate the prices of textbooks. The wording is, "The bookstore's prices of textbooks are reasonable." The responses are: Strongly disagree (1), Disagree (2), Neither agree nor disagree (3), Agree (4), and Strongly agree (5). The responses for a group of 115 students were recorded. Graphically summarize these data and report your findings.

2.82 Xr02-82 A sample of 200 people who had purchased food at the concession stand at Yankee Stadium was asked to rate the quality of the food. The responses are: Poor (1), Fair (2), Good (3), Very good (4), and Excellent (5). Draw a graph that describes the data. What does the graph tell you?

2.83 Xr02-83 There are several ways to teach applied statistics. The most popular approaches are as follows: Emphasize manual calculations (1), Use a computer combined with manual calculations (2), and Use a computer exclusively with no manual calculations (3). A survey of 100 statistics instructors asked them to report their approach. Use a graphical method to extract the most useful information about the teaching approaches.

2.84 Xr02-84 The Red Lobster Restaurant chain conducts regular surveys of its customers to monitor the performance of individual restaurants. One of the questions asks customers to rate the overall quality of their last visit. The listed responses are Poor (1), Fair (2), Good (3), Very good (4), and Excellent (5). The survey also asks respondents whether their children accompanied them [Yes (1) and No (2)] to the restaurant. Graphically depict these data and describe your findings.

2.85 Xr02-85+ A survey of the business school graduates undertaken by a university placement office asked, among other questions, in which area each person was employed. The areas of employment are as follows: Accounting (1), Finance (2), General management (3), Marketing/Sales (4), and Other (5). Additional questions were asked and the responses were recorded in the following way.

Column	Variable
A	Identification number
B	Area
C	Gender: Female (1) and Male (2)
D	Job satisfaction: Very (4), Quite (3), Little (2), and None (1)

The placement office wants to know the following:
a. Do female and male graduates differ in their areas of employment? If so, how?
b. Are area of employment and job satisfaction related?

Exercises 2.86 to 2.96 describe statistics associated with the coronavirus (actual name: SARS-Cov-2, more commonly known as COVID-19). The year 2020 will go down in history as the year of the coronavirus disease. The disease, which started in Wuhan, China, quickly spread across the globe. By October there were 35 million people who contracted the disease and more than a million deaths.

2.86 Xr02-86   Here are the top eight causes (in alphabetical order) and their number of deaths in the United States between February 1 and November 12, 2020.
a. Use a bar chart to graphically present these data.
b. Can you improve the appearance of the bar chart to make it easier to understand?

Cause	Number of Deaths
Alzheimer's	105,780
Cancer	481,935
Chronic low respiratory disease	119,785
COVID-19	248,686
Diabetes	41,953
Heart disease	543,408
Stroke	125,815

2.87 Xr02-87+   How does race affect the death rate from COVID-19? The number of deaths from COVID-19 and the race were recorded as follows.

Race	Number of Deaths
Asian	8,687
Black	46,211
Indigenous	2,251
Latino	46,912
Pacific Islander	344
White	123,429
Unknown/Other	13,873

Use a graphical technique to present these data.

2.88 Xr02-87+   Refer to Exercise 2.87. The number of people in each racial group (excluding Unknown/Other) in the United States was recorded. Calculate the death rate from COVID-19 per 100,000 of population and graphically present these figures.

2.89 Xr02-89   The table below lists the number of cases and deaths of COVID-19 in California for each of 10 age categories and the population. (Cases refer to the number of positive test results.)

Age	Number of Cases	Deaths	Population
5 or less	29,020	0	2,291,580
6–17	112,692	2	6,598,170
18–34	443,645	303	9,600,930
35–49	308,797	1,088	7,625,430
50–59	174,537	2,059	4,938,750
60–64	63,306	1,662	2,331,090
65–69	43,434	1,988	1,975,500
70–74	30,020	2,157	1,619,910
75–79	20,590	2,185	1,066,770
80 or more	37,451	8,036	1,540,890

a. Apply a graphical method to display the number of cases.
b. Repeat part (a) for the number of deaths.
c. Compute the number of cases per million of population and graphically depict these figures.
d. Repeat part (c) for deaths.

2.90 Xr02-90   The table below lists the fatality rate for China, Italy, South Korea, and Spain for each of nine age groups. The figures in this table were produced early in the pandemic (February to March 2020). Produce a graph that depicts the fatality rates for each age category and each country.

	Fatality Rate			
Age	China	Italy	South Korea	Spain
0–9	0.0000	0.0000	0.0000	0.0000
10–19	0.0020	0.0000	0.0000	0.0000
20–29	0.0020	0.0000	0.0000	0.0022
30–39	0.0020	0.0030	0.0011	0.0014
40–49	0.0040	0.0040	0.0008	0.0030
50–59	0.0130	0.0100	0.0050	0.0040
60–69	0.0360	0.0350	0.0180	0.0190
70–79	0.0800	0.1280	0.0630	0.0480
80+	0.1480	0.2020	0.1300	0.1560

2.91 Xr02-91   The figures below were produced from January 25 to May 17, 2020, in the province of Ontario. It shows the population of each of the nine age groups, the number of infected people, the infection rate per 100,000 of population, and the number of deaths.

a. Produce a graph that depicts the cases per 100,000 of population.

b. Use a graphical technique that describes the number of deaths per 100,000 of population.

Age	Cases	Deaths	Population
0 to 9	179	0	1,518,527
9 to 19	465	0	1,617,937
20 to 29	2,729	2	2,100,175
30 to 39	2,838	6	2,056,056
40 to 49	3,179	17	1,876,585
50 to 59	3,841	62	2,060,937
60 to 69	2,824	154	1,795,047
70 to 79	2,018	331	1,159,898
80+	4,869	1,332	679,266

2.92 Xr02-92 A report by the Public Health Agency of Canada in November 26, 2020, listed the number of deaths by age category. (There were an additional 177 deaths where the age was not reported.)

Age	Number of Deaths
0–19	2
20–29	13
30–39	23
40–49	70
50–59	283
60–69	848
70–79	2,148
80+	8,235

Use a graphical method to summarize these figures.

2.93 Refer to Exercises 2.89 to 2.92. Using the information you developed, what advice would you give to

governments about schools and long-term care for the elderly?

2.94 Xr02-94+ Following are the number of deaths in the provinces and territories of Canada.

a. Graphically present these figures.

b. Reorganize the list to improve the presentation of the data.

Province and Territory	Number of Deaths
Alberta	510
British Columbia	384
Manitoba	266
New Brunswick	7
Newfoundland and Labrador	4
Northwest Territories	0
Nova Scotia	65
Ontario	3,575
Prince Edward Island	0
Quebec	6,947
Saskatchewan	40
Yukon	1

2.95 Xr02-94+ Refer to Exercise 2.94. Also recorded are the population figures for each province and territory. Calculate the number of deaths per 100,000. Use a graphical technique to describe these figures.

2.96 Xr02-96 A report from the Johns Hopkins Medicine on October 7, 2020, listed the number of confirmed cases, deaths, fatality rate, and deaths per 100,000 of population for 168 countries and territories. Use Data and Sort to determine the 15 worst countries/territories in terms of confirmed cases, deaths, fatality rate, and deaths per 100,000 of population, and use a graphical method to display the results.

GENERAL SOCIAL SURVEY EXERCISES

DATA
GSS2018

The following exercises are based on the General Social Survey of 2018.

2.97 Use a pie chart to depict the proportion of respondents who worked for the government or worked in the private sector (WRKGOVT: 1 = Government, 2 = Private).

Does this result surprise you? Explain.

2.98 Graphically describe the respondents' highest completed degree (DEGREE: 0 = Left high school, 1 = Graduated high school, 2 = Completed junior college, 3 = Completed Bachelor's degree, 4 = Completed graduate degree). Briefly describe what you have discovered.

2.99 What are the political views (POLVIEWS3: 1 = Liberal, 2 = Moderate, 3 = Conservative) of respondents who work for themselves (WRKSLF: 1 = Self-employed, 2 = Work for someone else)? Use a graphical technique to describe the relationship.

2.100 How does party affiliation (PARTYID3: 1 = Democrat, 2 = Independent, 3 = Republican) affect respondents' opinion of whether Americans should be required to obtain police permit to buy a gun (GUNLAW: 1 = Favor, 2 = Oppose)? Draw a graph that answers the question.

2.101 Do respondents who work for the government (WRKGOVT: 1 = Government, 2 = Private) differ

in their education (DEGREE: 0 = Left high school, 1 = Graduated high school, 2 = Completed junior college, 3 = Completed Bachelor's degree, 4 = Completed graduate degree) from those who work in the private sector? Use a graphical technique to provide an answer.

2.102 Are American women more liberal than their male counterparts (SEX: 1 = Male, 2 = Female; POLVIEWS3: 1 = Liberal, 2 = Moderate, 3 = Conservative)? Apply a graphical technique to determine an answer.

CASE 2.1   Carbon Dioxide Emissions

The planet may be threatened by global warming/climate change, possibly caused by burning fossil fuels (petroleum, natural gas, and coal) that produces carbon dioxide (CO_2). Most of the countries of the world have signed agreements promising to reduce CO_2 emissions. The latest agreement was the Paris Accords, which was signed by most countries in 2015, including the United States when Barack Obama was president. However, President Donald Trump fulfilled one of his campaign promises to withdraw the United States from the Paris Accords. To see how countries have performed in the promises to reduce CO_2, we

have produced a list of 66 countries and their annual emissions between 2007 and 2019 (latest year available). The unit of measurement is millions of tonnes. (A tonne is 1,000 kilograms and a kilogram is about 2.2 pounds.) The carbon emissions reflect only those through consumption of oil, gas, and coal for combustion related activities, and are based on "Default CO_2 Emissions Factors for Combustion" listed by the Intergovernmental Panel on Climate Change (IPCC) in its Guidelines for National Greenhouse Gas Inventories (2006).

a. Use Data and Sort in Excel to put the 66 countries in

descending order of emissions for 2019.

b. Use a bar chart to display the top 15 countries in terms of their emissions. Describe what you have discovered.

c. For all countries, calculate the change from 2007 to 2019. For some countries this will be a negative number representing a decrease in emissions. Draw a bar chart of the top 15 countries that have reduced their emissions the most and the top 15 countries that have increased their emissions the most. Describe your findings.

d. Repeat part (c) to compare 2018 and 2019.

CASE 2.2   Carbon Dioxide Emissions II

We recorded the 2019 emissions, population size (millions), and the gross domestic product (GDP in $billions) for each of the 66 countries listed in Case 2.1.

a. Compute the emissions per capita for each of the 66 countries. Use a bar chart to display the emissions per million of population for the top 15 countries and for the bottom 15 countries.

b. Calculate the emissions per GDP for all 66 countries. Use a bar chart to display the top 15 countries and the bottom 15 countries.

c. Describe your findings for parts (a) and (b).

CASE 2.3   U.S. Political Parties and Political Views

In the United States there are two main political parties, the Democrats and the Republicans. The general consensus holds that Democrats are liberals and Republicans are conservatives. The General Social Survey asks respondents to self-identify on the spectrum. Responses were given to this question:

PARTYID: Generally speaking, do you think of yourself as a Republican, Democrat, Independent, or what?

The responses ranged from 0 = Strong Democrat to 6 = Strong Republican. The responses were grouped to create a new variable PARTYID3 where 1 = Democrat, 2 = Independent, and 3 = Republican.

A second question addressed political views:

POLVIEWS: I'm going to show you a seven-point scale on which the political views that people might hold are arranged from extremely liberal to extremely conservative. Where would you place yourself on this scale?

The responses ranged from 1 = Extremely liberal to 7 = Extremely conservative. The answers were regrouped to create POLVIEWS3: 1 = Liberal, 2 = Moderate, 3 = Conservative. The two variables are stored in columns AH and AK, respectively.

Use the General Social Surveys of 2014, 2016, and 2018 to compute the proportion of respondents in each year who are Democrats, Independents, and Republicans. Compute the proportion of respondents in each year who are liberals, moderates, and conservatives. Describe what you have discovered. What do these results tell you about Democrats and Republicans and their political views?

APPENDIX 2.A / XLSTAT OUTPUT AND INSTRUCTIONS

Frequency Distribution and Bar Chart

Note that the output has been edited.
XLSTAT does not draw pie charts.

Example 2.1

Descriptive statistics for the intervals (WRKSTAT):

Lower Bound	Upper Bound	Frequency	Relative Frequency
1	2	1,134	0.483
2	3	259	0.110
3	4	53	0.023
4	5	84	0.036
5	6	445	0.190
6	7	81	0.035
7	8	242	0.103
8	9	48	0.020

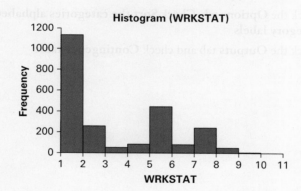

Instructions

1. Type or import the data into one column. (Open GSS2018 and copy column X into another sheet.)

2. Click **XLSTAT**, **Describing data**, and **Histograms**.

3. In the **Data:** dialog box, type the input range: (A1:2349). Check **Variable labels** if the first row of the data contains the name of the variable. Choose **Range:**, **Sheet**, or **Workbook** depending on where you wish the results to appear. Check **Discrete**.

4. Click the **Options** tab and specify the number of **Intervals: 8**.

5. Click the **Missing data** tab and select **Remove the observations**.

6. Click the **Charts** tab, check **Histograms** and **Bars**. Specify **Frequency** in the **Ordinates of the histograms** box.

Cross-Classification Table

Example 2.4

Output has been edited.

Contingency table (Occupation\Newspaper):

Occupation\ Newspaper	Newspaper-1	Newspaper-2	Newspaper-3	Newspaper-4
Occupation-1	27	18	38	37
Occupation-2	29	43	21	15
Occupation-3	33	51	22	20

Instructions

1. Type or import the data into two columns. (Open Xm02-04.)
2. Click **Preparing data** and **Create a contingency table**.
3. Specify **Row variable(s):** (B1:B355). Specify **Column variable(s):** (C1:C355).
4. Check **Variable labels** if the first row of the data contains the name of the variable. Select one of **Range:**, **Sheet**, or **Workbook** depending on where you wish the results to appear.
5. Click the **Options** tab. Check **Sort the categories alphabetically** and **Variable-category labels**.
6. Click the **Outputs** tab and check **Contingency table**.

APPENDIX 2.B / STATA OUTPUT AND INSTRUCTIONS

Frequency Distributions

Example 2.1

WRKSTAT	Freq.	Percent	Cum.
1	1,134	48.34	48.34
2	259	11.04	59.38
3	53	2.26	61.64
4	84	3.58	65.22
5	445	18.97	84.19
6	81	3.45	87.64
7	242	10.32	97.95
8	48	2.05	100.00
Total	2,346	100.00	

Instructions

1. Import the data into one column. (Click File/Import/Excel spreadsheet (*xls,*xlsx)/ GSS2018.)

    Check **Import first row as variable names**.

2. Click **Statistics, Summaries, tables and tests, Frequency tables,** and **One-way table**.

3. Select **WRKSTAT** in the **Categorical variable:** box.

Bar Chart

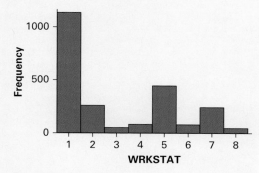

Instructions

Here is the easiest way to draw a bar chart when the data are nominal.

1. Import the data into one column. (Click File/Import/Excel spreadsheet (*xls,*xlsx)/ GSS2018.)

    Check **Import first row as variable names**.

2. Click **Graphics** and **Histogram**. (Histograms will be described in greater detail in Chapter 3.)

3. Select **WRKSTAT** in the **Variable:** box. Check **Bins** and select the number of categories. In this example it is 8. Click **Frequency**.

Cross-classification Table

Example 2.4

Occupation	Newspaper				
	1	2	3	4	Total
1	27	18	38	37	120
2	29	43	21	15	108
3	33	51	22	20	126
Total	89	112	81	72	354

1. Import or type the data into two columns. (Click File/Import /Excel spreadsheet (*xls,*xlsx)/Chapter2/Xm02-04).

   Check **Import first row as variable names**.

2. Click **Statistics, Summaries, tables and tests, Frequency tables**, and **Two-way with measures of association**.

3. Select **Occupation** in the **Row variable:** box and **Newspaper** in the **Column variable:** box.

3

GRAPHICAL DESCRIPTIVE TECHNIQUES II

CHAPTER OUTLINE

What Is the Relationship between the Price of a Gallon of Gasoline and the Price of a Barrel of Oil?

DATA
Xm03-00

In the past three decades, the price of gasoline has been on a roller coaster. In 1991, the average retail price of unleaded regular gasoline in the United States was about $1.20 per gallon. (One U.S. gallon equals 3.79 liters.) Over the next 17 years, the average price rose to over $4.00. It then fell precipitously to less than $1.60 in early 2016. While the lower price is appreciated by all drivers, the rapidly changing price is somewhat bewildering to motorists. When the price was

On page 77, you will find our answer.

(Continued)

rising, we understood there were several reasons. First, oil is a finite resource; the world will eventually run out. In 2019, the world was consuming more than 100 million barrels per day—more than 36 billion barrels per year. The total proven world reserves of oil are 1,779,685,000,000 barrels. At today's consumption levels, the proven reserves will be exhausted in 49 years. (It should be noted, however, that in 2016, the proven reserves of oil amounted to 1,563,350,000,000 and in 2012 the proven reserves were 1,481.5 billion barrels, indicating that new oil discoveries are offsetting increasing usage.) Second, China's and India's industries are rapidly increasing and require ever-increasing amounts of oil. Third, over the last 20 years, hurricanes have threatened the oil rigs in the Gulf of Mexico. In 1995, the price of oil (West Texas intermediate crude) was under $20 per barrel (one barrel equals 42 U.S. gallons). In 2008, the price rose to over $130, and in early 2016 the price fluctuated between $30 and $40. To help understand the gasoline/oil price relationship, we determined the monthly average price of gasoline and the price of a barrel of West Texas intermediate crude for the period 1991 to 2020. Use a graphical technique to describe the relationship. See page 77 for our solution.

INTRODUCTION

Chapter 2 introduced graphical techniques used to summarize and present nominal data. In this chapter, we do the same for interval data. Section 3-1 presents techniques to describe a set of interval data, Section 3-2 introduces time series and the method used to present time-series data, and Section 3-3 describes the technique we use to describe the relationship between two interval variables. We complete this chapter with a discussion of how to properly use graphical methods in Section 3-4.

3-1 / GRAPHICAL TECHNIQUES TO DESCRIBE A SET OF INTERVAL DATA

In this section we introduce the histogram, which is a powerful graphical technique used to summarize a set of interval data. As you will see the histogram is also used to help explain an important aspect of probability (see Chapter 8).

EXAMPLE 3.1

DATA
Xm03-01

Ages of Duplicate Bridge Players

The game of bridge is played all over the world. There are two versions. There is rubber bridge, which is usually played in private and often for money. The second, more popular version is duplicate bridge, which is played in clubs and tournaments around the world. The American Contract Bridge League (ACBL) is the organization that runs duplicate bridge. Anyone who has played in club games will notice that a great majority of players are seniors. The ACBL is concerned about the increasing average age of its members and the relative scarcity of younger players. To help determine whether efforts should be made to encourage younger bridge players to join ACBL, a random sample of 200 ACBL members was drawn, with respondents reporting their age. The results are shown here. What information can be extracted from these data?

73	77	62	35	33	63	68	31	20	93
53	73	94	75	72	66	64	55	60	73
66	68	64	83	62	38	24	25	58	58
82	72	83	26	82	54	68	49	73	27
54	57	24	30	70	75	96	54	52	40

53	30	28	28	32	23	85	69	35	49
78	28	69	61	33	19	64	41	54	54
33	71	62	52	44	65	60	67	50	30
35	30	25	36	30	44	39	28	60	80
40	59	63	37	76	37	32	90	51	62
65	74	81	38	53	25	51	52	56	53
74	28	65	24	60	30	53	49	45	50
55	55	91	22	31	38	16	71	60	36
82	52	26	18	63	27	27	57	46	90
74	75	35	70	69	33	60	82	56	82
76	61	52	71	69	49	61	60	31	60
57	36	83	36	79	42	65	38	72	51
63	37	25	54	65	71	78	76	46	32
65	95	63	48	52	66	45	16	67	22
33	54	99	31	76	42	74	65	27	17

SOLUTION:

Little information can be developed just by casually reading through the 200 observations. If you examine the data more carefully, you may discover that the youngest bridge player in this sample is 16 and the oldest is 99. To gain useful information, we need to know how the ages are distributed between 16 and 99. Are there many old players with few young ones? Are the ages somewhat similar or do they vary considerably? To help answer these questions and others like them, we will construct a frequency distribution from which a histogram can be drawn. In the previous chapter, a frequency distribution was created by counting the number of times each category of the nominal variable occurred. We create a frequency distribution for interval data by counting the number of observations that fall into each of a series of intervals, called **classes** that cover the complete range of observations. We discuss how to decide the number of classes and the upper and lower limits of the intervals later. We have chosen nine classes defined in such a way that each observation falls into one and only one class. These classes are defined as follows:

Classes

Ages that are more than 10 and less than or equal to 20

Ages that are more than 20 but less than or equal to 30

Ages that are more than 30 but less than or equal to 40

Ages that are more than 40 but less than or equal to 50

Ages that are more than 50 but less than or equal to 60

Ages that are more than 60 but less than or equal to 70

Ages that are more than 70 but less than or equal to 80

Ages that are more than 80 but less than or equal to 90

Ages that are more than 90 but less than or equal to 100

Notice that the intervals do not overlap, so there is no uncertainty about which interval to assign to any observation. Moreover, because the smallest number is 16 and the largest is 99, every observation will be assigned to a class. Finally, the intervals are equally wide. Although this is not essential, it makes the task of reading and interpreting the graph easier. To create the frequency distribution manually, we count the number of observations that fall into each interval. Table 3.1 presents the frequency distribution.

TABLE **3.1** Frequency Distribution of ACBL Members' Ages

CLASS LIMITS	FREQUENCY
10–20	6
20–30	27
30–40	30
40–50	16
50–60	40
60–70	36
70–80	27
80–90	12
90–100	6
Total	200

Although the frequency distribution provides information about how the numbers are distributed, the information is more easily understood and imparted by drawing a picture or graph. The graph is called a **histogram**. A histogram is created by drawing rectangles whose bases are the intervals and whose heights are the frequencies. Figure 3.1 exhibits the histogram that was drawn by hand.

FIGURE **3.1** Histogram for Example 3.1

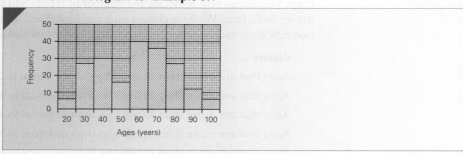

EXCEL Data Analysis

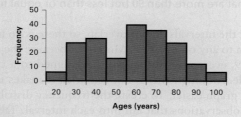

INSTRUCTIONS

1. Type or import the data into one column. (Open Xm03-01) In another column, type the upper limits of the class intervals. Excel calls them bins. (You can put any name in the first row; we typed "Ages.")

2. Click **Data, Data Analysis,** and **Histogram**.

3. Specify the **Input Range** (A1:A201) and the **Bin Range** (B1:B10). Click **Chart Output**. Click **Labels** if the first row contains names.

4. To remove the gaps, place the cursor over one of the rectangles and click the right button of the mouse. Click (with the left button) **Format Data Series . . . .** move the pointer to **Gap Width** and use the slider to change the number from 150 to 0.

Note that except for the first class, Excel counts the number of observations in each class that are greater than the lower limit and less than or equal to the upper limit. Note that the numbers along the horizontal axis represent the upper limits of each class although they appear to be placed in the centers.

INTERPRET

The histogram gives us a clear view of the way the ages are distributed. As expected about 40% of the sample are older than 60. About a sixth are in their teens and twenties. There appears to be a good supply of younger players. However, there is an unexpected gap of players in the 40 to 60 range, particularly in the 40 to 50 range. This group may be individuals who are working and have little time for bridge. Most club games start at 7:00 pm and end after 10:00. Perhaps scheduling shorter games may result in attracting working people to become members of the ACBL.

3-1a Determining the Number of Class Intervals

The number of class intervals we select depends entirely on the number of observations in the data set. The more observations we have, the larger the number of class intervals we need to use to draw a useful histogram. Table 3.2 provides guidelines on choosing the number of classes. In Example 3.1, we had 200 observations. The table tells us to use 7, 8, 9, or 10 classes.

TABLE **3.2** Approximate Number of Classes in Histograms

NUMBER OF OBSERVATIONS	NUMBER OF CLASSES
Less than 50	5–7
50–200	7–9
200–500	9–10
500–1,000	10–11
1,000–5,000	11–13
5,000–50,000	13–17
More than 50,000	17–20

An alternative to the guidelines listed in Table 3.2 is to use Sturges's formula, which recommends that the number of class intervals be determined by the following:

Number of class intervals = 1 + 3.3 log (*n*)

For example, if *n* = 50, Sturges's formula becomes

Number of class intervals = 1 + 3.3 log (50) = 1 + 3.3(1.7) = 6.6

which we round to 7.

Class Interval Widths   We determine the approximate width of the classes by subtracting the smallest observation from the largest and dividing the difference by the number of classes. Thus,

$$Class\ width = \frac{Largest\ Observation - Smallest\ Observation}{Number\ of\ Classes}$$

In Example 3.1, we calculated

$$Class\ width = \frac{99 - 16}{9} = 9.22$$

We often round the result to some convenient value. We then define our class limits by selecting a lower limit for the first class from which all other limits are determined. The only condition we apply is that the first class interval must contain the smallest observation. In Example 3.1, we rounded the class width to 10 and set the lower limit of the first class to 10. Thus, the first class is defined as "Amounts that are greater than or equal to 10 but less than or equal to 20." Table 3.2 and Sturges's formula are guidelines only. It is more important to choose classes that are easy to interpret. For example, suppose that we have recorded the marks on an exam of the 100 students registered in the course where the highest mark is 94 and the lowest is 48. Table 3.2 suggests that we use 7, 8, or 9 classes, and Sturges's formula computes the approximate number of classes as:

Number of class intervals = 1 + 3.3 log (100) = 1 + 3.3(2) = 7.6

which we round to 8. Thus,

$$Class\ width = \frac{94 - 48}{8} = 5.75$$

which we would round to 6. We could then produce a histogram whose upper limits of the class intervals are 50, 56, 62, . . . , 98. Because of the rounding and the way in which we defined the class limits, the number of classes is 9. However, a histogram that is easier to interpret would be produced using classes whose widths are 5; that is, the upper limits would be 50, 55, 60, . . . , 95. The number of classes in this case would be 10.

Exceptions to the Guidelines   In some situations, the guidelines we have just provided may not yield useful results. One such example occurs when there is a wide range of values with very large numbers of observations in some class intervals. This may result in some empty or nearly empty classes in the middle of the histogram. One solution is to create unequal class intervals. Unfortunately, this produces histograms that are more difficult to interpret. Another solution is to allow the last interval to be "more than the upper limit of the previous interval." To see why and how problems occur, see Exercises 3.36 and 3.37.

3-1b Shapes of Histograms

The purpose of drawing histograms, like that of all other statistical techniques, is to acquire information. Once we have the information, we frequently need to describe what we've learned to others. We describe the shape of histograms on the basis of the following characteristics.

Symmetry A histogram is said to be **symmetric** if, when we draw a vertical line down the center of the histogram, the two sides are identical in shape and size. Figure 3.2 depicts three symmetric histograms.

FIGURE **3.2** **Three Symmetric Histograms**

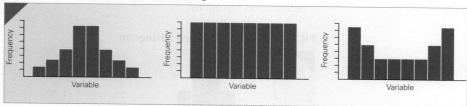

Skewness A skewed histogram is one with a long tail extending to either the right or the left. The former is called **positively skewed**, and the latter is called **negatively skewed**. Figure 3.3 shows examples of both. Incomes of employees in large firms tend to be positively skewed because there is a large number of relatively low-paid workers and a small number of well-paid executives. The time taken by students to write exams is frequently negatively skewed because few students hand in their exams early; most prefer to reread their papers and hand them in near the end of the scheduled test period.

FIGURE **3.3** **Positively and Negatively Skewed Histograms**

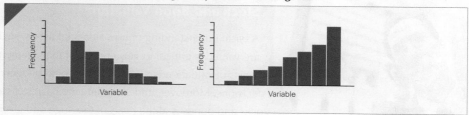

Number of Modal Classes As we discuss in Chapter 4, a *mode* is the observation that occurs with the greatest frequency. A **modal class** is the class with the largest number of observations. A **unimodal histogram** is one with a single peak. The histogram in Figure 3.4 is unimodal. A **bimodal histogram** is one with two peaks, not necessarily equal in height. Bimodal histograms often indicate that two different distributions are present. (See Example 3.4.) Figure 3.5 depicts bimodal histograms.

FIGURE **3.4** **A Unimodal Histogram**

FIGURE **3.5** Bimodal Histograms

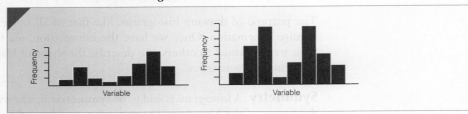

Bell Shape A special type of symmetric unimodal histogram is one that is bell shaped. In Chapter 8, we will explain why this type of histogram is important. Figure 3.6 exhibits a bell-shaped histogram.

FIGURE **3.6** Bell-Shaped Histogram

Now that we know what to look for, let's examine some examples of histograms and see what we can discover.

APPLICATIONS in FINANCE

Return on Investment

The return on an investment is calculated by dividing the gain (or loss) by the value of the investment. For example, a $100 investment that is worth $106 after 1 year has a 6% rate of return. A $100 investment that loses $20 has a −20% rate of return. For many investments, including individual stocks and stock portfolios (combinations of various stocks), the rate of return is a variable. In other words, the investor does not know in advance what the rate of return will be. It could be a positive number, in which case the investor makes money—or negative, and the investor loses money.

Investors are torn between two goals. The first is to maximize the rate of return on investment. The second goal is to reduce risk. If we draw a histogram of the returns for a certain investment, the location of the center of the histogram gives us some information about the return one might expect from that investment. The spread or variation of the histogram provides us with guidance about the risk. If there is little variation, an investor can be quite confident in predicting what the rate of return will be. If there is a great deal of variation, the return becomes much less predictable and thus riskier. Minimizing the risk becomes an important goal for investors and financial analysts.

EXAMPLE 3.2

DATA
Xm03-02

Comparing Returns on Two Investments

Suppose that you are facing a decision about where to invest that small fortune that remains after you have deducted the anticipated expenses for the next year from the earnings from your summer job. A friend has suggested two types of investment, and to help make the decision you acquire some rates of return from each type. You would like to know what you can expect by way of the return on your investment, as well as other types of information, such as whether the rates are spread out over a wide range (making the investment risky) or are grouped tightly together (indicating relatively low risk). Do the data indicate that it is possible that you can do extremely well with little likelihood of a large loss? Is it likely that you could lose money (negative rate of return)?

The returns for the two types of investments are listed here. Draw histograms for each set of returns and report on your findings. Which investment would you choose and why?

Returns on Investment A				Returns on Investment B			
30.00	6.93	13.77	−8.55	30.33	−34.75	30.31	24.3
−2.13	−13.24	22.42	−5.29	−30.37	54.19	6.06	−10.01
4.30	−18.95	34.40	−7.04	−5.61	44.00	14.73	35.24
25.00	9.43	49.87	−12.11	29.00	−20.23	36.13	40.7
12.89	1.21	22.92	12.89	−26.01	4.16	1.53	22.18
−20.24	31.76	20.95	63.00	0.46	10.03	17.61	3.24

Returns on Investment A			
1.20	11.07	43.71	−19.27
−2.59	8.47	−12.83	−9.22
33.00	36.08	0.52	−17.00
14.26	−21.95	61.00	17.30
−15.83	10.33	−11.96	52.00
0.63	12.68	1.94	
38.00	13.09	28.45	

Returns on Investment B			
2.07	10.51	1.2	25.1
29.44	39.04	9.94	−24.24
11	24.76	−33.39	−38.47
−25.93	15.28	58.67	13.44
8.29	34.21	0.25	68.00
61.00	52.00	5.23	
−20.44	−32.17	66	

SOLUTION:

We draw the histograms of the returns on the two investments.

EXCEL Data Analysis

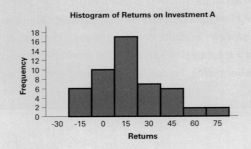
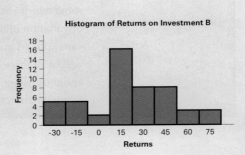

INTERPRET

Comparing the two histograms, we can extract the following information:

1. The center of the histogram of the returns of investment A is slightly lower than that for investment B.

2. The spread of returns for investment A is considerably less than that for investment B.

3. Both histograms are slightly positively skewed.

These findings suggest that investment A is superior. Although the returns for A are slightly less than those for B, the wider spread for B makes it unappealing to most investors. Both investments allow for the possibility of a relatively large return.

The interpretation of the histograms is somewhat subjective. Other viewers may not concur with our conclusion. In such cases, numerical techniques provide the detail and precision lacking in most graphs. We will redo this example in Chapter 4 to illustrate how numerical techniques compare to graphical ones.

EXAMPLE 3.3

DATA
Xm03-03⁺

Business Statistics Marks

A student enrolled in a business program is attending the first class of the required statistics course. The student is somewhat apprehensive because of the myth that the course is difficult. To alleviate anxiety, the student asks the professor about last year's marks. The professor obliges and provides a list of the final marks, which is composed of term work plus the final exam. Draw a histogram and describe the result, based on the following marks:

65	81	72	59
71	53	85	66
66	70	72	71
79	76	77	68
65	73	64	72
82	73	77	75
80	85	89	74
86	83	87	77
67	80	78	69
64	67	79	60
62	78	59	92
74	68	63	69
67	67	84	69
72	62	74	73
68	83	74	65

SOLUTION:

EXCEL Data Analysis

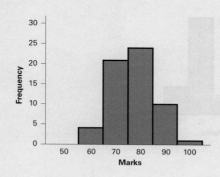

INTERPRET

The histogram is unimodal and approximately symmetric. There are no marks below 50, with the great majority of marks between 60 and 90. The modal class is 70 to 80, and the center of the distribution is approximately 75.

DATA
Xm03-04+

EXAMPLE 3.4

Mathematical Statistics Marks

Suppose the student in Example 3.3 obtained a list of last year's marks in a mathematical statistics course. This course emphasizes derivations and proofs of theorems. Use the accompanying data to draw a histogram and compare it to the one produced in Example 3.3. What does this histogram tell you?

77	67	53	54
74	82	75	44
75	55	76	54
75	73	59	60
67	92	82	50
72	75	82	52
81	75	70	47
76	52	71	46
79	72	75	50
73	78	74	51
59	83	53	44
83	81	49	52
77	73	56	53
74	72	61	56
78	71	61	53

SOLUTION:

EXCEL Data Analysis

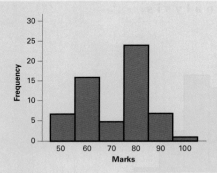

INTERPRET

The histogram is bimodal. The larger modal class is composed of the marks in the 70s. The smaller modal class includes the marks that are in the 50s. There appear to be few marks in the 60s. This histogram suggests that there are two groups of students. Because of the emphasis on mathematics in the course, one may conclude that those who performed poorly in the course are weaker mathematically than those who performed well. The histograms in this example and in Example 3.3 suggest that the courses are quite different from one another and have a completely different distribution of marks.

Here is a summary of this section's technique.

Factors That Identify When to Use a Histogram
1. Objective: Describe a single set of data.
2. Data type: Interval

EXERCISES

3.1 How many classes should a histogram contain if the number of observations is 125?

3.2 Determine the number of classes of a histogram for 1,500 observations.

3.3 A data set consists of 300 observations that range between 147 and 241.
   a. What is an appropriate number of classes to have in the histogram?
   b. What class intervals would you suggest?

3.4 A statistics practitioner would like to draw a histogram of 40 observations that range from 5.2 to 6.1.
   a. How many class intervals should the histogram use?
   b. Define the upper limits of the classes.

3.5 Xr03-05   An Uber driver kept track of the number of calls received over a 28-day period. The data are listed here. Create a histogram.

10	10	7	7	3	8	11
8	10	7	7	7	5	4
9	7	8	4	17	13	9
7	12	8	10	4	7	5

3.6 Xr03-06   There are a number of minor-league baseball players who never make it to the major leagues. A statistics practitioner kept track of the age at which 32 players realized their dream of playing in the majors would never be fulfilled and retired. Draw a histogram of these data.

23	31	31	30	29	28	32	33
29	27	35	32	41	28	30	35
26	25	32	26	30	32	32	28
30	29	24	25	32	35	27	22

3.7 Xr03-07   The 17th hole at the TPC (Tournament Players Club) is an island green that causes even professional players to put their tee shots into the surrounding pond. A statistics practitioner kept track of the number of golf balls put into the pond by amateurs for each of 30 days with the results listed here. Draw a histogram of these data.

81	94	82	79	70	76	70	85	102	91
71	69	95	57	85	85	84	87	67	71
115	102	70	63	81	81	76	99	87	93

3.8 Xr03-08   The numbers of weekly sales calls by a sample of 30 telemarketers are listed here. Draw a histogram of these data and describe it.

14	12	9	17	8	3	10	20	19	15
8	21	3	9	18	17	15	17	7	10
6	4	25	5	16	19	5	14	10	8

3.9 Xr03-09   The amount of time (in seconds) needed to complete a critical task on an assembly line was measured for a sample of 50 assemblies. These data are listed here. Draw a histogram to describe these data.

30.3	34.5	31.1	30.9	33.7
31.9	33.1	31.1	30.0	32.7
34.4	30.1	34.6	31.6	32.4
32.8	31.0	30.2	30.2	32.8
31.1	30.7	33.1	34.4	31.0
32.2	30.9	32.1	34.2	30.7
30.7	30.7	30.6	30.2	33.4
36.8	30.2	31.5	30.1	35.7
30.5	30.6	30.2	31.4	30.7
30.6	37.9	30.3	34.1	30.4

3.10 Xr03-10   A survey of 60 individuals leaving a mall asked how many stores they entered during this visit to the mall. The figures are listed here.

3	2	4	3	3	9
2	4	3	6	2	2
8	7	6	4	5	1
5	2	3	1	1	7
3	4	1	1	4	8
0	2	5	4	4	4
6	2	2	5	3	8
4	3	1	6	9	1
4	4	1	0	4	6
5	5	5	1	4	3

   a. Draw a histogram to summarize these data.
   b. Describe the shape of the histogram.

The following exercises require a computer and statistical software.

3.11 Xr03-11 A survey of 50 baseball fans to report the number of games they attended last year. Draw a histogram and describe its shape.

3.12 Xr03-12 To help determine the need for more golf courses, a survey was undertaken. A sample of 75 self-declared golfers was asked how many rounds of golf they played last year. Draw a histogram and describe what it tells you.

3.13 Xr03-13 The annual incomes for a sample of 200 first-year accountants were recorded. Draw a histogram and describe its shape.

3.14 Xr03-14 Currently Ebay lists over 550,000 U.S. collector coins for sale or auction. An avid collector tracked the number of days it took for 500 coins to be delivered. Create a histogram of these figures. What information can you draw from the shape of the histogram?

3.15 Xr03-15 The number of customers entering a bank in the first hour of operation for each of the last 200 days was recorded. Draw a histogram and describe its shape.

3.16 Xr03-16 Users of previous editions of this book could download an Excel add-in called Data Analysis Plus from our website. We recorded the number of daily downloads during a 78-day period.
a. Draw a histogram.
b. Describe its shape.

3.17 Xr03-17 The marks of 320 students on an economics midterm test were recorded. Use a graphical technique to summarize these data. What does the graph tell you?

3.18 Xr03-18 The lengths (in inches) of 150 newborn babies were recorded. Use whichever graphical technique you judge suitable to describe these data. What have you learned from the graph?

3.19 Xr03-19 The number of copies made by an office copier was recorded for each of the past 75 days. Graph the data using a suitable technique. Describe what the graph tells you.

3.20 Xr03-20 Each of a sample of 240 tomatoes grown with a new type of fertilizer was weighed (in ounces) and recorded. Draw a histogram and describe your findings.

3.21 Xr03-21 The volume of water used by each of a sample of 350 households was measured (in gallons) and recorded. Use a suitable graphical statistical method to summarize the data. What does the graph tell you?

3.22 Xr03-22 The number of books shipped out daily by Amazon.com was recorded for 100 days. Draw a histogram and describe your findings.

3.23 Xr03-23 A survey asked American adults who consume alcohol how many drinks they consume in an average week. Draw a histogram and describe what you have discovered.

3.24 Xr03-34 The net worth of a random sample of households whose heads are Generation X (born between 1965 and 1980) was recorded. Draw a histogram and describe its shape.

3.25 Xr03-25 A professor of statistics recorded the amount of time to complete a 60-minute time limit quiz for each student in a class of 250. Draw a histogram. What does its shape tell you about times to complete the quiz?

3.26 Xr03-26 A random sample of high school students was asked how many minutes a day they spent on their cell phones. Draw a histogram and briefly describe what you have discovered.

GENERAL SOCIAL SURVEY EXERCISES

GSS2018 *The following exercises are based on the General Social Survey of 2018.*

3.27 Draw a histogram of the years of education (EDUC).
a. Is the histogram symmetric or skewed? If skewed, is it positive or negative?
b. What is the modal class? What does this tell you about this variable?
c. Are there other peaks? Is so, what are they?

3.28 Draw a histogram of respondents' incomes (RINCOME). Is the histogram positively skewed? Explain what this means.

3.29 Construct a histogram of the number of hours of work per week (HRS1).
a. Is the histogram symmetric or skewed? If symmetric, is it bell shaped? Explain what this tells you about this variable.

b. What is the modal class? Is this what you would have expected? Explain.

3.30 Create a histogram of the number of hours watched per day (TVHOURS) by Americans.
   a. Describe the shape of the histogram. Is it symmetric or positively skewed?
   b. Is there a modal class? Explain.

3.31 Draw a histogram of the age the respondents were when their first child was born (AGEKDBRN). Describe the shape of the histogram. Is it symmetric or skewed? Is it unimodal? If symmetric and unimodal, is it bell shaped?

SURVEY OF CONSUMER FINANCES EXERCISES

SCF2019:\MC   *Exercises 3.32 to 3.35 are based on the middle-class subsample (defined as net worth between $120,185 and $450,000) in the 2019 Survey of Consumer Finances.*

3.32 Draw a histogram of the total value of mortgages and home equity loans secured by the primary residence held by the household (NH_MORT). What does the shape tell you about this variable?

3.33 For most middle-class households that own their own homes, the house is their biggest investment. Draw a histogram of the unrealized capital gain on their primary residence (KGHOUSE). Describe the shape of the histogram.

3.34 Grocery stores compete with restaurants for the food budget of many middle-class households. Draw histograms of the total annual amounts spent on food at home (FOODHOME) and food away from home (FOODAWAY). Describe the differences and similarities between the two histograms.

3.35 How well are middle-class households doing? To learn more about them, draw a histogram of households' wage and salary incomes (WAGEINC). Is the graph symmetric or skewed? What does this tell you about the variable?

SCF2019:\All   *The following exercises are based on the complete sample of the Survey of Consumer Finances.*

3.36 One of the questions asked respondents to report the total value of assets (ASSET) held by the household. Note that the range is very large. The minimum is $0 and the maximum is $1,967,199,000.
   a. Draw a histogram using the number of class intervals suggested by Table 3.2; that is, between 17 and 20 class intervals. What problems did you encounter?
   b. Try drawing a histogram with the following class intervals 10,000, 20,000, . . . 200,000. What problem do you encounter?
   c. Draw a histogram with the following class intervals 100,000, 200,000, . . . 2,000,000.
   d. Briefly discuss which histogram drawn in (a), (b), and (c) is best.

3.37 Respondents were asked to report their household income (INCOME).
   a. Try drawing histograms with different numbers of class intervals and different upper limits.
   b. What problem do you encounter in drawing the histogram?
   c. Suggest ways of solving the problem of drawing histograms when the range is very large.

3-2 / DESCRIBING TIME-SERIES DATA

Besides classifying data by type, we can also classify them according to whether the observations are measured at the same time or whether they represent measurements at successive points in time. The former are called **cross-sectional data** and the latter **time-series data**.

The technique described in Section 3-1 is applied to cross-sectional data. All the data, for Example 3.1, were probably determined within the same day. We can probably say the same thing for Examples 3.2 to 3.4.

To give another example, consider a real estate consultant who feels that the selling price of a house is a function of its size, age, and lot size. To estimate the specific form of the function, the price, size, age, and lot size for each of 100 homes were recorded. These data are cross-sectional in that they all are observations at the same point in time. The real estate consultant is also working on a separate project to forecast the monthly housing starts in the northeastern United States over the next year. To do so, the consultant collects the monthly housing starts in this region for each of the past 5 years. These 60 values (housing starts) represent time-series data, because they are observations taken over time.

Note that the original data may be interval or nominal. All of these illustrations deal with interval data. A time series can also list the frequencies and relative frequencies of a nominal variable over a number of time periods. For example, a brand-preference survey asks consumers to identify their favorite brand. These data are nominal. If we repeat the survey once a month for several years, the proportion of consumers who prefer a certain company's product each month would constitute a time series.

3-2a Line Chart

Time-series data are often graphically depicted on a **line chart**, which is a plot of the variable over time. It is created by plotting the value of the variable on the vertical axis and the time periods on the horizontal axis.

The chapter-opening example addresses the issue of the relationship between the price of gasoline and the price of oil. We will introduce the technique we need to answer the question in Section 3-3. In discussing the price of gasoline we noted that the price has fluctuated wildly in the last 30 years. The questions that arise are how expensive was gas at its high point (in 2008) and how cheap it became in 2020.

EXAMPLE 3.5	## Price of Gasoline
DATA **Xm03-05**	We recorded the monthly average retail price of gasoline (regular unleaded in dollars per gallon) since 1991. The first four months and the last four months are displayed here. Draw a line chart to describe these figures and describe the results.

Year	Month	Price per Gallon (Dollars)
1991	1	1.180
1991	2	1.094
1991	3	1.040
1991	4	1.076
⋮	⋮	⋮
2020	9	2.095
2020	10	2.091
2020	11	2.093
2020	12	2.225

SOLUTION:

EXCEL Chart

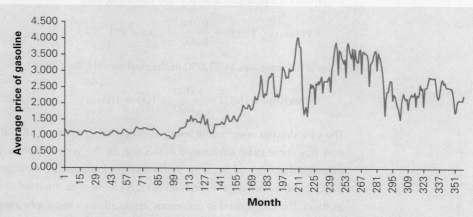

INSTRUCTIONS

1. Type or import the data into one column. (Open Xm03-05.)
2. Highlight the column of data. Click **Insert**, **Line**, and the first **2-D Line**. You can draw two or more line charts (for two or more variables) by highlighting all columns of data you wish to graph.

INTERPRET

The price of gasoline rose from about $1.00 to over $4.00 in 2008 (around month 200) then dropped precipitously in March 2009 (at the end of the housing meltdown) before rising again and then falling to about $2.00.

APPLICATIONS in ECONOMICS

Measuring inflation: Consumer Price Index

Inflation is the increase in the prices for goods and services. In most countries, inflation is measured using the Consumer Price Index (CPI). The CPI works with a basket of some 300 goods and services in the United States (and a similar number in other countries), including such diverse items as food, housing, clothing, transportation, health, and recreation. The basket is defined for the "typical" or "average" middle-income family, and the set of items and their weights are revised periodically (every 10 years in the United States and every 7 years in Canada). Prices for each item in this basket are computed on a monthly basis and the CPI is computed from these prices. Here is how it works. We start by setting a period of time as the base. In the United States, the base is the years 1982–1984. Suppose that the basket of goods and services

(Continued)

cost $1,000 during this period. Thus, the base is $1,000, and the CPI is set at 100. Suppose that in the next month (January 1985) the price increases to $1,010. The CPI for January 1985 is calculated in the following way:

$$CPI(January\ 1985) = \frac{1,010}{1,000} \times 100 = 101$$

If the price increases to $1,050 in the next month, the CPI is

$$CPI(February\ 1985) = \frac{1,050}{1,000} \times 100 = 105$$

The CPI, despite never really being intended to serve as the official measure of inflation, has come to be interpreted in this way by the general public. Pension-plan payments, old-age Social Security, and some labor contracts are automatically linked to the CPI and automatically indexed (so it is claimed) to the level of inflation. Despite its flaws, the CPI is used in numerous applications. One application involves adjusting prices by removing the effect of inflation, making it possible to track the "real" changes in a time series of prices.

In Example 3.5, the figures shown are the actual prices measured in what are called current dollars. To remove the effect of inflation, we divide the monthly prices by the CPI for that month and multiply by 100. These prices are then measured in constant 1982–1984 dollars. This makes it easier to see what has happened to the prices of the goods and services of interest. We created two data sets to help you calculate prices in constant 1982–1984 dollars. File Ch03:\\U.S. CPI Annual and Ch03:\\U.S. CPI Monthly list the values of the CPI where 1982–1984 is set at 100 for annual values and monthly values, respectively.

EXAMPLE 3.6

Price of Gasoline in 1982–1984 Constant Dollars

DATA
Xm03-06

Remove the effect of inflation in Example 3.5 to determine how high gasoline prices were in 2008 and how low they have become.

SOLUTION:

Here are the average monthly prices of gasoline, the CPI, and the adjusted prices for the first four months of 1991.

Year	Month	Price of Gasoline	CPI	Adjusted Price of Gasoline
1991	1	1.18	134.7	0.876
1991	2	1.094	134.8	0.812
1991	3	1.04	134.8	0.772
1991	4	1.076	135.1	0.796

EXCEL Chart

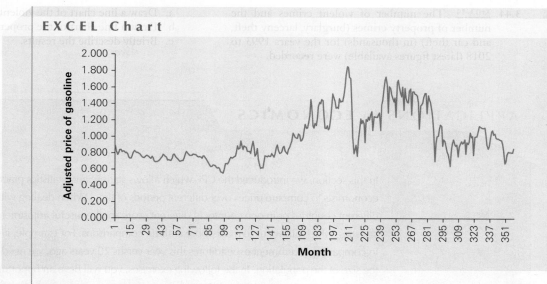

INTERPRET

Using constant 1982–1984 dollars, we can see that the average price of a gallon of gasoline hit its peak in the middle of 2008 (around month 200). From there, it dropped rapidly and then rose and fell. By 2020 the adjusted price was lower than in January 1991.

EXERCISES

3.38 Xr03-38   A city has recently installed a red-light camera to catch drivers who drive through a red light. Following are the monthly totals for the past two years. Use a graphical technique to display these figures. Describe what you have learned.

Red-Light Violations: 14 8 12 9 11 12 10 12 8 13 11 8 6 7 5 5 4 4 2 6 4 3 5 4

3.39 Xr03-39   Following are the monthly sales for the past two years logged by a newly hired used car salesperson. Use a graphical technique to display these figures and describe what you have discovered.

Sales: 2 0 3 1 3 5 2 7 5 6 12 15 10 18 21 25 24 25 23 28 21 25 23 27

3.40 Xr03-40   The monthly number of accidents at a busy intersection in Montreal for 2020 and 2021 is listed next. Draw a line chart and describe what you have learned.

| 2020 | 14 11 9 5 3 2 6 8 5 6 5 13 |
| 2021 | 15 12 13 7 4 4 7 4 5 3 4 12 |

The following exercises require a computer and statistical software.

3.41 Xr03-41   The number of viewers (millions) of the Super Bowl games between 1967 and 2020 was recorded. Use a graphical technique to display these figures. Briefly describe your findings.

3.42 Xr03-42   How well have Canada and the United States performed at the Winter Olympics? We recorded the total number of medals won by the two countries in each year. Draw a chart to describe both time series.

3.43 Xr03-43   It won't come as a surprise to hockey fans that with each passing season, the number of goals scored is decreasing. Many experts blame goalie equipment. The oversized pads and other protection for goalies now make even relatively small goalies look like Sumo wrestlers. To learn more about the problem, a statistics practitioner recorded the save percentage (the percentage of shots that a goalie saves) and the goals against average (the average number of goals allowed) for each season between 1955–1956 and 2018–2019.
a. Draw a line chart of the save percentage.
b. Draw a line chart of the goals against average.
c. Briefly describe your findings.

3.44 Xr03-44   The number of violent crimes and the number of property crimes (burglary, larceny theft, and car theft) (in thousands) for the years 1993 to 2018 (latest figures available) were recorded.

a. Draw a line chart of the violent crimes.
b. Draw a line chart of the property crimes.
c. Briefly describe the results.

APPLICATIONS in ECONOMICS

Per Capita Comparisons

In this section, we introduced the CPI, which allows statisticians, statistics practitioners, and economists to compare prices over different periods of time. When dealing with statistics in different countries or in one country in different years another useful adjustment is per capita statistics, which allows us to make more realistic comparisons. For example, if we're interested in comparing government expenditures this year versus 20 years ago, we need to incorporate the size of the population. In the following exercises, you will have an opportunity to see how and why per capita statistics work. To assist you we have created a file listing the total population of the United States from 1935 to 2020. It is stored in Chapter 3 as U.S. Population.

The following exercises require a computer and statistical software.

Exercises 3.45 to 3.55 deal with various parts of the U.S. federal budget. For each exercise, draw the following line charts and briefly describe what the chart tells you about each variable.
a. Original data
b. Per capita data
c. Per capita in constant 1982–1984 dollars (Use Chapter 3:\US CPI Annual.)

3.45 Xr03-45   The United States spends more money on health care than any other country. To gauge how fast costs are rising, we recorded the total health care costs since 1950.

3.46 Xr03-46   The U.S. government provides Medicare to Americans who are 65 years and older. Medicare Part A pays the costs of hospital and nursing care, but not physicians' bills. The file lists Medicare Part A costs since 1966.

3.47 Xr03-47   Medicare Part B pays for a portion of physicians' visits, medical equipment, outpatient procedures, rehabilitative therapy, laboratory tests, X-rays, ambulance service, and blood. Costs were recorded for 1967 to 2017.

3.48 Xr03-48   Medicaid is a program created by the federal government, but administered by the state, to provide payment for medical services for low-income citizens. The costs were recorded from 1962 to 2017.

3.49 Xr03-49   Social Security Disability Insurance is a program that pays monthly benefits to individuals who have become disabled before reaching retirement age and aren't able to work. SSDI costs were recorded for the years 1958 to 2017.

3.50 Xr03-50   Social Insurance Old Age Survivor Insurance provides a pension for Americans who are over 60 years of age and whose spouse has died. Costs for 1958 to 2017 were recorded.

3.51 Xr03-51   The defense budget for years 1935 to 2017 were recorded.

3.52 Xr03-52   Total federal government spending from 1935 to 2017 is stored.

3.53 Xr03-53   Welfare payments for 1930 to 2017 were recorded.

3.54 Xr03-54   Education spending from 1930 to 2017 was recorded.

3.55 Xr03-55   Interest on federal debt from 1930 to 2017 was recorded.

3.56   Refer to Exercise 3.44.
a. Calculate the violent crime and property crime rates per 100,000 of population.
b. Draw a line chart of the violent crime rate per 100,000 of population.
c. Draw a line chart of the property crime rate per 100,000 of population.
d. Describe your findings.

3.57 Xr03-57 The average daily U.S. oil consumption and production (thousands of barrels) was recorded for the years 1973 to 2019. Draw a line chart for both sets of figures. Describe what you have learned.

3.58 Xr03-58 The gross domestic product (GDP) is the sum total of the economic output of a country. It is an important measure of the wealth of a country. The GDP of the United States from 1935 to 2019 is stored in the file.
a. Draw a line chart of the GDP.
b. Adjust the GDP for inflation and draw a line chart of the adjusted GDP.
c. Briefly describe what the charts tell you.

3.59 Xr03-59 The monthly value of U.S. exports to Canada and imports from Canada from 1985 was recorded ($millions).
a. Draw a line chart of U.S. exports to Canada.
b. Draw a line chart of U.S. imports from Canada.
c. What do all the charts reveal?

3.60 Xr03-60 The monthly value of U.S. exports to Japan and imports from Japan from 1985 was recorded.
a. Draw a line chart of U.S. exports to Japan.
b. Draw a line chart of U.S. imports from Japan.
c. What do all the charts reveal?

3.61 Xr03-61 The monthly value of U.S. exports to China and imports from China from 1985 was recorded.
a. Draw a line chart of U.S. exports to China.
b. Draw a line chart of U.S. imports from China.
c. What do all the charts reveal?

3.62 Xr03-62 The monthly value of U.S. exports to Mexico and imports from Mexico from 1985 was recorded.
a. Draw a line chart of U.S. exports to Mexico.
b. Draw a line chart of U.S. imports from Mexico.
c. What do all the charts reveal?

3.63 Xr03-62 The monthly value of U.S. exports to the United Kingdom and imports from the United Kingdom from 1985 was recorded.
a. Draw a line chart of U.S. exports to the United Kingdom.
b. Draw a line chart of U.S. imports from the United Kingdom.
c. What do all the charts reveal?

3.64 Xr03-64 The exchange rate of the Canadian dollar to one U.S. dollar was recorded monthly from 1971. Draw a graph and briefly describe the information you derived from the graph.

3.65 Xr03-65 The exchange rate of the Japanese yen to one U.S. dollar was recorded monthly from 1971. Draw a graph and briefly describe the information you derived from the graph.

3.66 Xr03-66 The exchange rate of the Chinese yuan to one U.S. dollar was recorded monthly from 1981. Draw a graph and briefly describe the information you derived from the graph.

3.67 Xr03-67 The exchange rate of the Mexican peso to one U.S. dollar was recorded monthly from 1993. Draw a graph and briefly describe the information you derived from the graph.

3.68 Xr03-68 The exchange rate of U.S. dollars to one British pound was recorded monthly from 1971. Draw a graph and briefly describe the information you derived from the graph.

3.69 Xr03-69 The average price of a barrel of oil set by the Organization of Oil Exporting Countries (OPEC) between 1960 and 2018 was recorded. Use a graph to describe these numbers.
Source: OPEC.

3.70 Refer to Exercise 3.69. Use the U.S. CPI annual file to measure the prices in 1982–1984 constant dollars. What have you learned?

3.71 Xr03-71 The Standard & Poor's 500 Index was recorded monthly (close) from 1950 to 2020. Use a graph to describe these numbers.
Source: The Wall Street Journal.

3.72 Refer to Exercise 3.71. Use the U.S. CPI monthly file to measure the Standard & Poor's Stock Index in 1982–1984 constant dollars. What have you learned?

3-3 DESCRIBING THE RELATIONSHIP BETWEEN TWO INTERVAL VARIABLES

Statistics practitioners frequently need to know how two interval variables are related. For example, financial analysts need to understand how the returns of individual stocks are related to the returns of the entire market. Marketing managers need to understand the relationship between sales and advertising. Economists develop statistical techniques to describe the relationship between such variables as unemployment rates and inflation. The technique is called a **scatter diagram**.

To draw a scatter diagram, we need data for two variables. In applications where one variable depends to some degree on the other variable, we label the dependent variable Y and the other, called the *independent variable*, X. For example, an individual's income depends somewhat on the number of years of education. Accordingly, we identify income as the dependent variable and label it Y, and we identify years of education as the independent variable and label it X. In other cases where no dependency is evident, we label the variables arbitrarily.

Analyzing the Relationship between Price and Size of House

A real estate agent wanted to know to what extent the selling price of a home is related to its size. To acquire this information, the price in thousands of dollars and the size in square feet were recorded for a sample of 12 recently sold houses. These data are listed in the accompanying table. Use a graphical technique to describe the relationship between size and price.

Size (ft²)	Price ($1,000)
2,354	315
1,807	229
2,637	355
2,024	261
2,241	234
1,489	216
3,377	308
2,825	306
2,302	289
2,068	204
2,715	265
1,833	195

S O L U T I O N :

Using the guideline just stated, we label the price of the house Y (dependent variable) and the size X (independent variable). Figure 3.7 depicts the manually drawn scatter diagram.

FIGURE **3.7** Scatter Diagram for Example 3.7

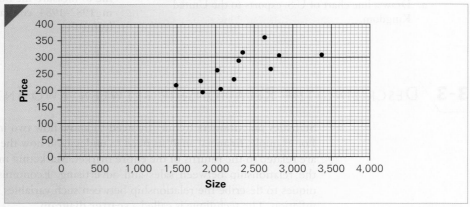

EXCEL Chart

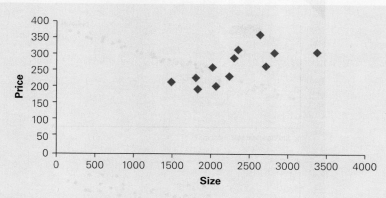

INSTRUCTIONS

1. Type or import the data into two adjacent columns. Store variable *X* in the first column and variable *Y* in the next column. (Open Xm03-07.)
2. Click **Insert** and **Scatter**.

INTERPRET

The scatter diagram reveals that, in general, the greater the size of the house, the greater the price. However, there are other variables that determine price. Further analysis may reveal what these other variables are.

3-3a Patterns of Scatter Diagrams

As was the case with histograms, we frequently need to describe verbally how two variables are related. The two most important characteristics are the strength and direction of the linear relationship.

3-3b Linearity

To determine the strength of the linear relationship, we draw a straight line through the points in such a way that the line represents the relationship. If most of the points fall close to the line, we say that there is a **linear relationship**. If most of the points appear to be scattered randomly with only a semblance of a straight line, there is no, or at best, a weak linear relationship. Figure 3.8 depicts several scatter diagrams that exhibit various levels of linearity.

In drawing the line freehand, we would attempt to draw it so that it passes through the middle of the data. Unfortunately, different people drawing a straight line through the same set of data will produce somewhat different lines. Fortunately, statisticians have produced an objective way to draw the straight line. The method is called the *least squares method*, and it will be presented in Chapter 4 and employed in Chapters 16, 17, and 18.

FIGURE **3.8** **Scatter Diagrams Depicting Linearity**

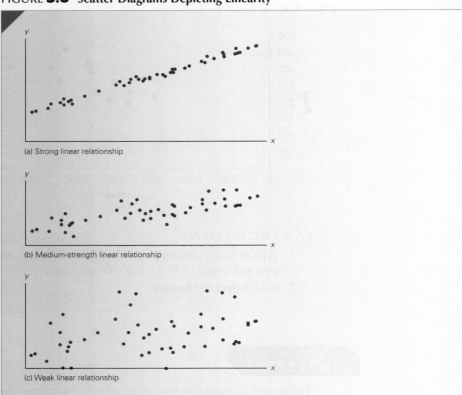

(a) Strong linear relationship

(b) Medium-strength linear relationship

(c) Weak linear relationship

Note that there may well be some other type of relationship, such as a quadratic or exponential one.

3-3c Direction

In general, if one variable increases when the other does, we say that there is a **positive linear relationship**. When the two variables tend to move in opposite directions, we describe the nature of their association as a **negative linear relationship**. (The terms *positive* and *negative* will be explained in Chapter 4.) See Figure 3.9 for examples of scatter diagrams depicting a positive linear relationship, a negative linear relationship, no relationship, and a nonlinear relationship.

3-3d Interpreting a Strong Linear Relationship

In interpreting the results of a scatter diagram it is important to understand that if two variables are linearly related it does not mean that one is causing the other. In fact, we can never conclude that one variable causes another variable. We can express this more eloquently as

Correlation is not causation.

Now that we know what to look for, we can answer the chapter-opening example.

FIGURE **3.9**   **Scatter Diagrams Describing Direction**

(a) Positive linear relationship

(b) Negative linear relationship

(c) No relationship

(d) Nonlinear relationship

What Is the Relationship between the Price of a Gallon of Gasoline and the Price of a Barrel of Oil: Solution

To understand the fluctuations in the price of gasoline, we need to determine the relationship between the prices of gasoline and oil. The appropriate graphical method to display the relationship is the scatter diagram.

We label the price of a gallon of gasoline Y (the dependent variable) and the price of a barrel of oil X (the independent variable).

Comstock Images/Getty Images

(*Continued*)

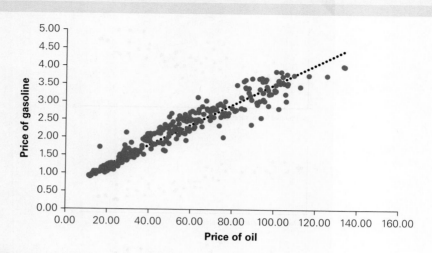

EXCEL Chart

INTERPRET

The scatter diagram reveals that the two prices are strongly linearly related. When the price of oil was below $80, the relationship between the two was stronger than when the price of oil exceeded $80.

We close this section by reviewing the factors that identify the use of a scatter diagram.

> **Factors That Identify When to Use a Scatter Diagram**
> 1. **Objective:** Describe the relationship between two variables.
> 2. **Data type:** Interval

EXERCISES

3.73 <u>Xr03-73</u> A sample of people who use software to complete their tax returns was asked how long it took them to calculate the tax and how many years' experience they had with that software. Draw a scatter diagram and briefly describe what it tells you.

Time to complete (hours)	6.5	6.9	4.1	8.0	11.5	2.5	5.1	6.8	13.2	7.1
Years of experience	1	3	2	1	5	2	4	1	1	3

3.74 <u>Xr03-74</u> Black Friday in the United States is the day after Thanksgiving. Many retailers offer door-crasher specials to induce customers to shop at their stores. The number of door-crasher specials is limited. However, the sale price is so low that people who want to buy that item often line up outside the store to wait for it to open. A random sample of Black Friday shoppers was asked how long they waited outside for the store to open (hours) and the amount they expected to save by buying the door-crasher special. Draw a scatter diagram and describe what you have learned from the graph.

Time	3.0	2.5	1.5	5.0	3.0	4.5	7.0	0.5	6.5	6.0
Savings	325	250	275	150	225	350	375	100	400	350

3.75 <u>Xr03-75</u> An amateur statistician and golf fanatic is concerned about the large number of putts per round. To decide whether practicing putting before each round would help, the statistician recorded the number of practice putts and the number of putts during the round for 10 rounds. Draw a scatter diagram and describe what information you have collected from it.

Practice putts	3	17	5	25	10	15	8	10	12	20
Putts during round	42	39	44	35	38	33	40	34	38	31

3.76 Xr03-76 In a university where calculus is a prerequisite for the statistics course, a sample of 15 students was drawn. The marks for calculus and statistics were recorded for each student. The data are as follows:

Calculus	65	58	93	68	74	81	58	85	88	75	63	79	80	54	72
Statistics	74	72	84	71	68	85	63	73	79	65	62	71	74	68	73

    a. Draw a scatter diagram of the data.
    b. What does the scatter diagram tell you about the relationship between marks in calculus and statistics?

3.77 Xr03-77 The cost of repairing cars involved in collisions is one reason insurance premiums are so high. In an experiment, 10 cars were driven into a wall. The speeds were varied between 2 and 20 mph. The costs of repair were estimated and are listed here. Draw an appropriate graph to analyze the relationship between the two variables. What does the graph tell you?

Speed	2	4	6	8	10	12	14	16	18	20
Cost	88	124	358	519	699	816	905	1,521	1,888	2,201

3.78 Xr03-78 It is well known that mathematicians do their best work before the age of 30. But what happens to them as they grow older? A statistician took a random sample of mathematics professors who were older than 40 and determined their age and the number of top-tier journal publications they produced in the previous five years. Draw a scatter diagram and report what it tells you about the research productivity as mathematicians grow older.

Age	48	71	73	41	66	57	50	42	47	59
Publications	12	4	8	22	7	14	16	8	10	13

3.79 Xr03-79 A statistics professor formed the theory that students who handed in quizzes and exams early outperformed students who handed in their papers later. To develop data to decide whether this theory is valid, the professor recorded the amount of time (in minutes) taken by students to submit their midterm tests (time limit 90 minutes) and the subsequent mark for a sample of 12 students. Draw a scatter diagram and describe what it tells you about the professor's theory.

Time	90	73	86	85	80	87	90	78	84	71	72	88
Mark	68	65	58	94	76	91	62	81	75	83	85	74

The following exercises require the use of a computer and software.

3.80 Xr03-80 In attempt to determine the factors that affect the amount of energy used, 200 households were analyzed. The number of occupants and the amount of electricity used were measured for each household. Produce a scatter diagram. What does the graph tell you about the relationship between number of people in a household and electrical use?

3.81 Xr03-81 Many downhill skiers eagerly look forward to the winter months and fresh snowfalls. However, winter also entails cold days. How does the temperature affect skiers' desire? To answer this question, a local ski resort recorded the temperature for 50 randomly selected days and the number of lift tickets they sold. Use a graphical technique to describe the data and interpret your results.

3.82 Xr03-82 One general belief held by observers of the business world is that taller men earn more money than shorter men. In a University of Pittsburgh study, 250 MBA graduates, all about 30 years old, were polled and asked to report their height (in inches) and their annual income (to the nearest $1,000). Draw a scatter diagram and report whether the general belief holds some validity.

3.83 Xr03-83 Do chief executive officers (CEOs) of publicly traded companies earn their compensation? Every year the *National Post's* Business magazine attempts to answer the question by reporting the CEOs' annual compensation ($1,000), the profit (or loss) ($1,000), and the three-year share return (%) for the top 50 Canadian companies.
    a. Draw a scatter diagram of the CEOs' annual compensation and the profit of the company.
    b. Draw a scatter diagram of the CEOs' annual compensation of the three-year share return.
    c. Based on the scatter diagrams in (a) and (b), report whether the CEOs earn their compensation.

3.84 Xr03-84 Are younger workers less likely to stay with their jobs? To help answer this question, a random sample of workers was selected. All were asked to report their ages and how many months they had been employed with their current employers.
    a. Produce a scatter diagram.
    b. Does your graph produce evidence to indicate that younger workers are less likely to stay with their jobs?

3.85 Xr03-85 A very large contribution to profits for a movie theater is the sales of popcorn, soft drinks, and candy. A movie theater manager speculated that the longer the time between showings of a movie, the greater the sales of concession items. To acquire more information, the manager varied the amount of time between movie showings and calculated the sales.

a. Draw a scatter diagram of the relationship between sales and time between movie showings.

b. Is there a positive relationship between the two variables?

3.86 <u>Xr03-86</u>   Players of duplicate bridge games at clubs and tournaments vie for master points. Top bridge players have tens of thousands of master points in their careers. Points are awarded on the basis of finishes in each game. Usually, the top scores in games are about 60% and the average of every game is 50%. A statistician wondered how the number of masterpoints held by a pair is related to success in games. The score and the total number of master points held by that pair for randomly selected pairs were recorded. Draw a scatter diagram of the two variables and describe what the graph tells you about the relationship between master points and scores.

3.87 <u>Xr03-87</u>   Refer to Exercise 3.86. Online bridge is played on computers whose partner and opponents can be thousands of miles apart. During the pandemic, this form of bridge grew rapidly. One concern is that it is easy to cheat. Players can phone their partner about the hands during bidding and play on defense (e.g., "Partner, play your K doubleton. I have the ace. I'll give you a ruff."). To help shed light on the issue, the statistician recorded the number of master points and scores of randomly selected pairs in online games.

a. Graph the relationship between the two variables.

b. Compare this graph to the one in Exercise 3.86. What have you learned about club games and online games?

3.88 <u>Xr03-88</u>   Coin collecting is big business around the world. As an illustration, there are more than 500,000 American coins and more than 100,000 Canadian coins for sale/auction on eBay. Moreover, there are dozens of other coin auctions every month. There are three critical factors that determine the value of a coin. They are rarity, condition, and demand. Condition is now measured on a 70-point scale where 1 is very poor and 70 is perfect. To determine how condition affects price, a random sample of auction sales of a 1925 Canadian nickel (a relatively rare coin) was drawn. The auction price ($Canadian), including buyer's premium and the condition, were recorded over the past three years.

a. Draw a scatter diagram.

b. What does the graph tell you about condition and price?

3.89 <u>Xr03-89</u>   Does temperature affect the distance that golf balls travel? A Florida golfer decided to try to answer the question. Over the course of a year, the distances of drives on a particular flat 400-yard par 4 were recorded. The temperature (degrees Fahrenheit) was also recorded. Draw a scatter diagram and describe what it tells you.

GENERAL SOCIAL SURVEY EXERCISES

<u>GSS2018</u>   *The following exercises are based on the General Social Survey of 2018.*

3.90 Students reading this book should be particularly interested in determining whether there is a relationship between education and income. Draw a scatter diagram of EDUC and RINCOME to see whether the two variables are related.

3.91 Do educated people tend to marry other educated people? Draw a scatter diagram of EDUC and SPEDUC. What conclusions can you draw from the graph?

3.92 Do more educated people have children who are also more educated? Answer this question by drawing a scatter diagram of the years of education (EDUC) and the years of education of their fathers (PAEDUC).

3.93 It seems reasonable to assume that if someone works longer hours, that should result in higher income. Draw

a scatter diagram of HRS1 and RINCOME to see if the assumption is correct. Describe the graph. Is the relationship positive? How strong is the relationship?

3.94 In order to acquire more education, one often needs to postpone other aspects of life. Draw a scatter diagram of years of education (EDUC) and the age of respondents when their first child was born (AGEKDBRN). Describe the direction and strength of the relationship.

3.95 Do more educated people watch less television? Draw a scatter diagram of EDUC and TVHOURS. Describe what you have discovered.

3.96 Do older Americans watch more television? The easiest way to tell is to draw a scatter diagram with hours of television (TVHOURS) as the dependent variable and ages (AGE) as the independent variable. What information can you extract from the graph?

SURVEY OF CONSUMER FINANCES EXERCISES

SCF2019:\W *Exercises 3.97 to 3.100 are based on the Wealthy category of the Survey of Consumer Finances 2019.*

3.97 Among the wealthy American households, how is household income (INCOME) affected by the age (AGE) of the head of the household? Draw a scatter diagram and explain what it tells you about the relationship.

3.98 Is the total indebtedness of the household (DEBT) affected by household income (INCOME)? In the wealthy category we would expect that as income increases, debt would decrease. Draw an appropriate graph to determine whether the expectation is supported by the data. Describe what the graph tells you.

3.99 Do wealthy Americans buy expensive cars? In particular in this net worth category, does the total value of the vehicles (VEHIC) depend on household income (INCOME). Draw a scatter diagram to answer the question. Describe you findings.

3.100 Does income affect how often wealthy Americans eat in restaurants and how much is spent? Create a scatter diagram of total annual expenditures on food spent away from home (FOODAWAY) and household income (INCOME). Describe the direction and strength of the relationship.

3-4 / ART AND SCIENCE OF GRAPHICAL PRESENTATIONS

In this chapter and in Chapter 2, we introduced a number of graphical techniques. The emphasis was on how to construct each one manually and how to command the computer to draw them. In this section, we discuss how to use graphical techniques effectively. We introduce the concept of **graphical excellence**, which is a term we apply to techniques that are informative and concise and that impart information clearly to their viewers. Additionally, we discuss an equally important concept: graphical integrity and its enemy **graphical deception**.

3-4a Graphical Excellence

Graphical excellence is achieved when the following characteristics apply.

1. **The graph presents large data sets concisely and coherently.** Graphical techniques were created to summarize and describe large data sets. Small data sets are easily summarized with a table. One or two numbers can best be presented in a sentence.

2. **The ideas and concepts the statistics practitioner wants to deliver are clearly understood by the viewer.** The chart is designed to describe what would otherwise be described in words. An excellent chart is one that can replace a thousand words and still be clearly comprehended by its readers.

3. **The graph encourages the viewer to compare two or more variables.** Graphs displaying only one variable provide very little information. Graphs are often best used to depict relationships between two or more variables or to explain how and why the observed results occurred.

4. **The display induces the viewer to address the substance of the data and not the form of the graph.** The form of the graph is supposed to help present the substance. If the form replaces the substance, the chart is not performing its function.

5. **There is no distortion of what the data reveal.** You cannot make statistical techniques say whatever you like. A knowledgeable reader will easily see through distortions and deception. We will endeavor to make you a knowledgeable reader by describing graphical deception later in this section.

Edward Tufte, professor of statistics at Yale University, summarized graphical excellence this way:

1. Graphical excellence is the well-designed presentation of interesting data—a matter of substance, of statistics, and of design.

2. Graphical excellence is that which gives the viewer the greatest number of ideas in the shortest time with the least ink in the smallest space.

3. Graphical excellence is nearly always multivariate.

4. Graphical excellence requires telling the truth about the data.

The chart that has been acclaimed as the best ever is one drawn by Charles Joseph Minard, a French civil engineer. It describes an important historical event, Napoleon Bonaparte's invasion of Russia in 1812.

When Napoleon invaded Russia by crossing the Niemen River on June 21, 1812, he had 422,000 soldiers in his "Grand Armee." Various skirmishes along the way produced a series of losses. For example, shortly after crossing the border a battle was fought leaving 22,000 French soldiers dead. This continued along the way with small battles taking place all the way to Moscow. When Napoleon finally arrived at Moscow in September there were only 100,000 soldiers left. The Russians set fire to Moscow preferring to destroy the city rather than letting it fall into the hands of their enemy. Napoleon had no choice except to retreat. By the time he arrived back at the Niemen River there were only 10,000 soldiers in his army.

Why is the chart so famous? It is because it depicted briefly and clearly what happened to the army and why. Figure 3.10 lists the features of Minard's chart.

FIGURE **3.10** **Statistics Described in Minard's Chart**

1. It is a map of the cities, towns, and rivers between the Niemen River and Moscow.

2. It is a travel itinerary showing the route of the advance and of the retreat.

3. It is a time series of the size of the army at each point in time. The size of the army is illustrated as a wide band getting narrower are as the "Grand Armee" suffers losses.

4. It is a calendar that shows the dates so that the reader can see where the army was and how many soldiers are left at each point in time.

5. It is a time series of the most important statistic, the temperature during the October to December retreat. It was bitterly cold that Autumn and many soldiers died of the exposure to the extreme cold.

The chart displays the five characteristics making the reading of the chart easy to see what happened, when did the events occur, and the reason for the losses.

3-4b Graphical Deception

The use of graphs and charts is pervasive in newspapers, magazines, business and economic reports, and seminars, in large part because of the increasing availability of computers and software that allow the storage, retrieval, manipulation, and summary of large masses of raw data. It is therefore more important than ever to be able to evaluate critically the information presented by means of graphical techniques. In the final analysis, graphical techniques merely create a visual impression, which is easy to distort. In fact, distortion is so easy and commonplace that, the Canadian Institute of Chartered Accountants found it necessary to begin setting guidelines for financial graphics, after a study of hundreds of the annual reports of major corporations found that 8% contained at least one misleading graph that covered up bad results. Although the heading for this section mentions deception, it is quite possible for an inexperienced person inadvertently to create distorted impressions with graphs. In any event, you should be aware of possible methods of graphical deception. This section illustrates a few of them.

The first thing to watch for is a graph without a scale on one axis. The line chart of a firm's sales in Figure 3.11 might represent a growth rate of 100% or 1% over the 5 years depicted, depending on the vertical scale. It is best simply to ignore such graphs.

FIGURE **3.11**   **Graph without Scale**

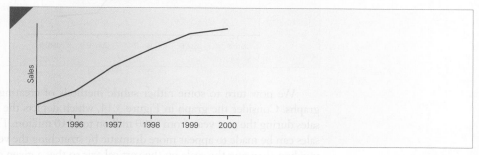

A second trap to avoid is being influenced by a graph's caption. Your impression of the trend in interest rates might be different, depending on whether you read a newspaper carrying caption (a) or caption (b) in Figure 3.12.

FIGURE **3.12**   **Graphs with Different Captions**

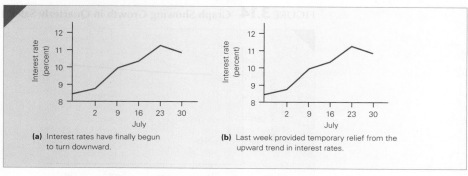

(a) Interest rates have finally begun to turn downward.

(b) Last week provided temporary relief from the upward trend in interest rates.

Perspective is often distorted if only absolute changes in value, rather than percentage changes, are reported. A $1 drop in the price of your $2 stock is relatively more distressing than a $1 drop in the price of your $100 stock. On January 9, 1986, newspapers throughout North America displayed graphs similar to the one shown in Figure 3.13 and reported that the stock market, as measured by the Dow Jones Industrial Average (DJIA), had suffered its worst 1-day loss ever on the previous day. The loss was 39 points, exceeding even the loss of Black Tuesday: October 28, 1929. While the loss was indeed a large one, many news reports failed to mention that the 1986 level of the DJIA was much higher than the 1929 level. A better perspective on the situation could be gained by noticing that the loss on January 8, 1986, represented a 2.5% decline, whereas the decline in 1929 was 12.8%. As a point of interest, we note that the stock market was 12% higher within 2 months of this historic drop and 40% higher 1 year later. The largest 1-day percentage drop in the DJIA is 24.4% (December 12, 1914).

FIGURE 3.13 Graph Showing Drop in the DJIA

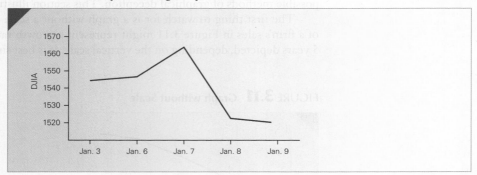

We now turn to some rather subtle methods of creating distorted impressions with graphs. Consider the graph in Figure 3.14, which depicts the growth in a firm's quarterly sales during the past year, from $100 million to $110 million. This 10% growth in quarterly sales can be made to appear more dramatic by stretching the vertical axis—a technique that involves changing the scale on the vertical axis so that a given dollar amount is represented by a greater height than before. As a result, the rise in sales appears to be greater because the slope of the graph is visually (but not numerically) steeper. The expanded scale is usually accommodated by employing a break in the vertical axis, as in Figure 3.15(a), or by truncating the vertical axis, as in Figure 3.15(b), so that the vertical scale begins at a point greater than zero. The effect of making slopes appear steeper can also be created by shrinking the horizontal axis, in which case points on the horizontal axis are moved closer together.

FIGURE 3.14 Graph Showing Growth in Quarterly Sales 1

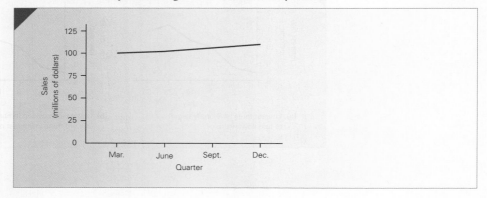

FIGURE **3.15** **Graph Showing Growth in Quarterly Sales 2**

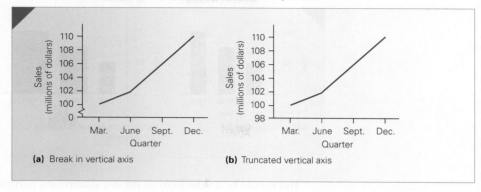

(a) Break in vertical axis   **(b)** Truncated vertical axis

Just the opposite effect is obtained by stretching the horizontal axis; that is, spreading out the points on the horizontal axis to increase the distance between them so that slopes and trends will appear to be less steep. The graph of a firm's profits presented in Figure 3.16(a) shows considerable swings, both upward and downward in the profits from one quarter to the next. However, the firm could convey the impression of reasonable stability in profits from quarter to quarter by stretching the horizontal axis, as shown in Figure 3.16(b).

FIGURE **3.16** **Graph Showing Considerable Swings or Relative Stability**

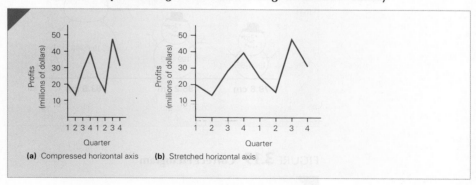

(a) Compressed horizontal axis   **(b)** Stretched horizontal axis

Similar illusions can be created with bar charts by stretching or shrinking the vertical or horizontal axis. Another popular method of creating distorted impressions with bar charts is to construct the bars so that their widths are proportional to their heights. The bar chart in Figure 3.17(a) correctly depicts the average weekly amount spent on food by Canadian families during three particular years. This chart correctly uses bars of equal width so that both the height and the area of each bar are proportional to the expenditures they represent. The growth in food expenditures is exaggerated in Figure 3.17(b), in which the widths of the bars increase with their heights. A quick glance at this bar chart might leave the viewer with the mistaken impression that food expenditures increased fourfold over the decade, because the 1995 bar is four times the size of the 1985 bar.

FIGURE **3.17** Correct and Distorted Bar Charts

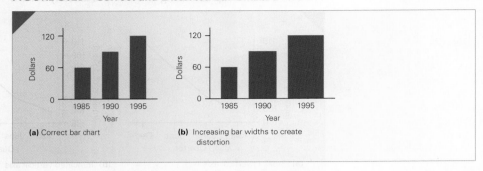

(a) Correct bar chart

(b) Increasing bar widths to create distortion

You should be on the lookout for size distortions, particularly in pictograms, which replace the bars with pictures of objects (such as bags of money, people, or animals) to enhance the visual appeal. Figure 3.18 displays the misuse of a pictogram—the snowman grows in width as well as height. The proper use of a pictogram is shown in Figure 3.19, which effectively uses pictures of Coca-Cola bottles.

FIGURE **3.18** Misuse of Pictogram

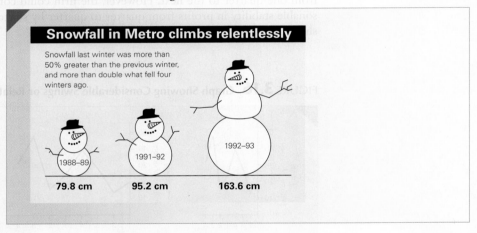

FIGURE **3.19** Correct Pictogram

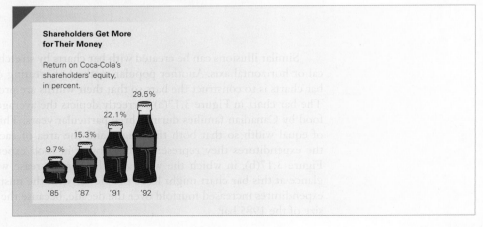

cooling, which seemed to be the consensus among scientists.

3. If the planet is warming, is CO_2 the cause? There are greenhouse gases in the atmosphere without which the earth would be considerably colder. These gases include methane, water vapor, and carbon dioxide. All these gases occur naturally. Carbon dioxide is vital to our life on earth because it is necessary for growing plants. The amount of CO_2 produced by fossil fuels is relatively a small proportion of all the CO_2 in the atmosphere.

The generally accepted procedure is to record monthly temperature anomalies. To do so, we calculate the average for each month over many years. We then calculate any deviations between the latest month's temperature reading and its average. A positive anomaly would represent a month's temperature that is above the average. A negative anomaly indicates a month in which the temperature is less than the average. One key question is how we measure the temperature.

Although there are many different sources of data, we have chosen to provide you with one, the National Climatic Data Center (NCDC), which is affiliated with the National Oceanic and Atmospheric Administration (NOAA). (Other sources tend to agree with the NCDC's data.) C03-01a stores the monthly temperature anomalies from 1880 to 2020.

The best measures of CO_2 levels in the atmosphere come from the Mauna Loa Observatory in Hawaii, which started measuring this variable in March 1958 and continues to do so. However, attempts to estimate CO_2 levels prior to 1958 are as controversial as the methods used to estimate temperatures. These techniques include taking ice-core samples from the arctic and measuring the amount of CO_2 trapped in the ice from which estimates of atmospheric CO_2 are produced. To avoid this controversy, we will use the Mauna Loa Observatory numbers only. These data are stored in file C03-01b. (Note that some of the original data are missing and were replaced by interpolated values.)

a. Use whichever techniques you wish to determine whether there is global warming.

b. Use a graphical technique to determine whether there is a relationship between temperature anomalies and CO_2 levels.

CASE 3.2   What Is Happening to the Polar Ice Caps

The most serious consequence of possible rising temperatures is that the ice in one or both poles will melt, leading to a rise in the world's oceans with trillions of dollars in damages to coastal cities. This raises the question: Are the oceans rising? Since 1993, satellite measurements of the sea level have been recorded. These measurements allow for estimation of global mean sea level changes. These data are stored in C03-02a. Note that the method used to represent the date measures the year and the proportion of the year that has elapsed. The sea level is measured in millimeters and has been reset so that the value of the last days of 1992 is set to 0.

We have recorded the monthly extent of Northern hemisphere (C03-02b) and Southern hemisphere (C03-02c) sea ice (measured in millions of kilometers squared) starting in January 1979. The anomalies are based on the 1981–2010 average.

a. Use a graphical method to show the changes in the sea level. Describe what you have discovered.

b. For each hemisphere, use a suitable graph to display the trends in ice coverage.

c. For each hemisphere, use a graphical technique to determine whether the polar ice coverage is related to temperature anomalies (C03-02d).

d. What do the graphs you produced tell you about ice coverage and temperature anomalies?

CASE 3.3   Does Global Warming Increase the Frequency of Tornadoes?

If the earth is warming, does it mean that we can expect an increase in extreme weather outcomes such as tornadoes? To answer the question we recorded the monthly number of tornadoes that occurred in the United States and monthly temperature anomalies between 2000 and 2020. Use a graphical technique to examine the relationship between temperature and the frequency of tornadoes.

DATA
C03-03a
C03-03b

CASE 3.4   Did Global Warming Cause Canada's Forest Fires?

In the summer of 2016, forest fires burned about a quarter of the homes and businesses in Fort McMurray, Alberta. Some newspapers printed claims by scientists that the forest fires were the result of global warming. To examine this claim, a statistician recorded the number of forest fires and the area burned (in hectares) annually from 1970 to 2019. A hectare is equal to 10,000 square meters. It is about two and half times the size of an acre. Use a graphical technique to graph the number of forest fires and the areas burned. Use annual temperature anomalies from 1970 to 2019 to see if there is a relationship between temperature and forest fires and areas burned. Briefly describe your results.

DATA
C03-04a
C03-04b
C03-04c

CASE 3.5   Economic Freedom, Prosperity, Happiness, and Food Security

Adam Smith published *The Wealth of Nations* in 1776 in which he argued that when institutions protect the liberty of individuals, greater prosperity results for all. Since 1995, *The Wall Street Journal* and the Heritage Foundation, a think tank in Washington D.C., have produced the Index of Economic Freedom for all countries in the world. The index is based on a subjective score for a variety of freedoms including government size, freedom from corruption, and property rights. We recorded the scores for 2017. From the CIA *Factbook*, we determined the per capita gross domestic product (GDP), measured in terms of purchasing power parity (PPP), which makes it possible to compare the GDP for all countries. Use graphical technique to see how freedom is related to prosperity. Briefly describe what the graph informs you.

DATA
C03-05
C03-05a
C03-05b

CASE 3.6   Guns, Firearms Death, and Murder Rates

There is an ongoing debate in the United States concerning guns. The Second Amendment to the Constitution allows American citizens to own guns. However, this does not stop gun control advocates from demanding limits on these rights. To examine this issue, we have recorded for the gun ownership rate, the murder rate per 100,000, and the firearms death rate per 100,000 for all 50 states.

a. Use a graphical technique to display the murder rate.
b. Graphically display the firearms death rate.
c. Conduct an analysis to determine whether gun ownership is related to the murder rate.
d. Graphically depict the relationship between gun ownership and the firearms death rate.
e. Summarize what you have learned about guns, firearms death rate, and the murder rate.

DATA
C03-06a
C03-06b
C03-06c

APPENDIX 3.A / XLSTAT OUTPUT AND INSTRUCTIONS

Histogram

Note that XLSTAT's histogram and Excel's histogram are not the same because of the way each software counts observations that are at the ends of the intervals.

Example 3.1

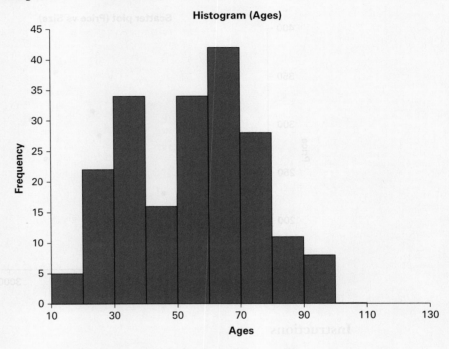

Lower Bound	Upper Bound	Frequency	Relative Frequency
10	20	5	0.025
20	30	22	0.110
30	40	34	0.170
40	50	16	0.080
50	60	34	0.170
60	70	42	0.210
70	80	28	0.140
80	90	11	0.055
90	100	8	0.040

Instructions

1. Type or import the data into one column. (Open Xm03-01.)

2. Click **XLSTAT**, **Describing data**, and **Histograms**.

3. In the **Data:** dialog box type the input range: (A1:A201). In the **Data type** check **Continuous**. Check **Variable labels** if the first row of the data contains the name of the variable. Choose **Range:**, **Sheet**, or **Workbook** depending on where you wish the results to appear.

4. Click the **Options** tab and specify the number of **Intervals:** 9.

5. Click the **Charts** tab, check **Histograms** and **Bars**. Specify **Frequency** in the **Ordinates of the histograms** box.

Scatter Diagram

Example 3.7

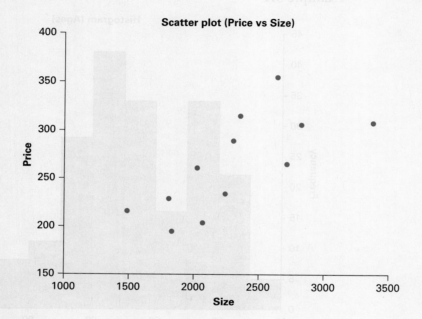

Instructions

1. Type or import the data into two columns. (Open Xm03-07.)

2. Click **XLSTAT**, **Visualizing data**, and **Scatter plots**.

3. Type the input range of the **X:** variable: (A1:A13) and the input range of the **Y:** variable (B1:B13). Check **Variable labels** if the first row of the data contains the name of the variable. Choose **Range:**, **Sheet**, or **Workbook** depending on where you wish the results to appear.

APPENDIX 3.B / STATA OUTPUT AND INSTRUCTIONS

Histograms

Example 3.1

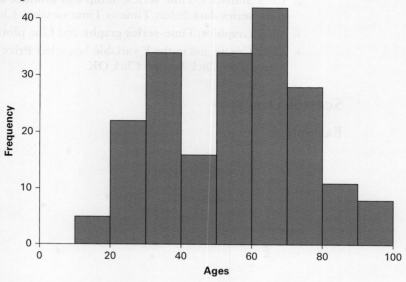

Instructions

1. Import or type the data into one column. (Click File/Import/Excel spreadsheet (*xls,*xlsx)/Xm03-01.) Check **Import first row as variable names**.
2. Click **Graphics**, and **Histogram**.
3. Select **Ages** in the **Variable:** box. Check **Width of bins** and type 10. Check **Lower limit of first bin** and type 10. Select **Frequency**.

Line Charts

Example 3.5

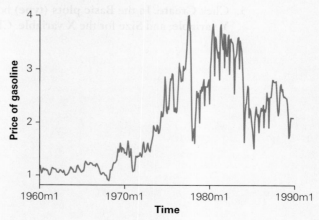

Instructions

1. Import or type the data into one column. (Click **File/Import/Excel** spreadsheet (*xls,*xlsx)/Xm03-05.) Check **Import first row as variable names**. One column must be a time variable. In this data set the variable is Time.
2. Click **Statistics, Time series, Setup and utilities**, and **Declare data set to be time-series data**. Select **Time** as **Time variable**. Check **Monthly**. Click **OK**.
3. Click **Graphics, Time-series graphs**, and **Line plots**.
4. Click **Create** and in the **Y variable** box select **Price of Gasoline**. Click **Time-series plot**. Click **Accept**. Click **OK**.

Scatter Diagram

Example 3.7

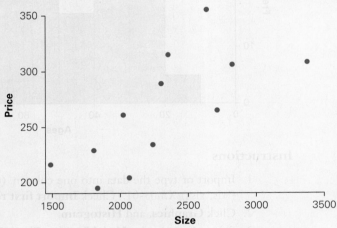

Instructions

1. Import or type the data into one column. (Click **File/Import/Excel** spreadsheet (*xls,*xlsx)/Xm03-07.) Check **Import first row as variable names**.
2. Click **Graphics** and **Twoway graph (scatter, line, etc.)**.
3. Click **Create**. In the **Basic plots (type)** box, select **Scatter**. Select **Price** for the **Y variable**: and **Size** for the **X variable**. Click **Accept**. Click **OK**.

lzf/Shutterstock.com

4

NUMERICAL DESCRIPTIVE TECHNIQUES

CHAPTER OUTLINE

The Cost of One More Win in Major League Baseball

DATA
Xm04-00

In the era of free agency, professional sports teams must compete for the services of the best players. It is generally believed that only teams whose salaries place them in the top quarter have a chance of winning the championship. Efforts have been made to provide balance by establishing salary caps

Andrey Yurlov/Shutterstock.com

(Continued)

97

or some form of equalization. To examine the problem, we gathered data from the 2019 baseball season. For each team in major league baseball, we recorded the number of wins and the team payroll.

To make informed decisions, we need to know how the number of wins and the team payroll are related. After the statistical technique is presented, we return to this problem and solve it.

INTRODUCTION

In Chapters 2 and 3, we presented several graphical techniques that describe data. In this chapter, we introduce numerical descriptive techniques that allow the statistics practitioner to be more precise in describing various characteristics of a sample or population. These techniques are critical to the development of statistical inference.

As we pointed out in Chapter 2, arithmetic calculations can be applied to interval data only. Consequently, most of the techniques introduced here may be used only to numerically describe interval data. However, some of the techniques can be used for ordinal data, and one of the techniques can be employed for nominal data.

When we introduced the histogram, we commented that there are several bits of information that we look for. The first is the location of the center of the data. In Section 4-1, we will present **measures of central location**. Another important characteristic that we seek from a histogram is the spread of the data. The spread will be measured more precisely by measures of variability, which we present in Section 4-2. Section 4-3 introduces measures of relative standing.

In Section 3-3, we introduced the scatter diagram, which is a graphical method that we use to analyze the relationship between two interval variables. The numerical counterparts to the scatter diagram are called *measures of linear relationship*, and they are presented in Section 4-4.

Section 4.5 features an application in finance and in Section 4.6 we compare the information provided by graphical and numerical techniques. Finally, we complete this chapter by providing guidelines on how to explore data and retrieve information.

SAMPLE STATISTIC OR POPULATION PARAMETER

Recall the terms introduced in Chapter 1: population, sample, parameter, and statistic. A parameter is a descriptive measurement about a population, and a statistic is a descriptive measurement about a sample. In this chapter, we introduce a dozen descriptive measurements. For each one, we describe how to calculate both the population parameter and the sample statistic. However, in most realistic applications, populations are very large. The formulas describing the calculation of parameters are not practical and are seldom used. They are provided here primarily to teach the concept and the notation. In Chapter 7, we introduce probability distributions, which describe populations. At that time we show how parameters are calculated from probability distributions. In general, small data sets of the type we feature in this book are samples.

4-1 MEASURES OF CENTRAL LOCATION

4-1a Arithmetic Mean

There are three different measures that we use to describe the center of a set of data. The first is the best known, the *arithmetic mean*, which we'll refer to simply as the **mean**. Students may be more familiar with its other name, the *average*. The mean is computed by summing the observations and dividing by the number of observations. We label the observations in a sample $x_1, x_2, \ldots, x_n$, where x_1 is the first observation, x_2 is the second, and so on until x_n, where n is the sample size. As a result, the sample mean is denoted by $\bar{x}$. In a population, the number of observations is labeled N and the population mean is denoted by μ (Greek letter *mu*).

Mean

$$\text{Population mean: } \mu = \frac{\sum_{i=1}^{N} x_i}{N}$$

$$\text{Sample mean: } \bar{x} = \frac{\sum_{i=1}^{n} x_i}{n}$$

EXAMPLE 4.1

Mean Time Spent on the Internet

A sample of 10 adults was asked to report the number of hours they spent on the Internet the previous month. The results are listed here. Manually calculate the sample mean.

$$0 \quad 7 \quad 12 \quad 5 \quad 33 \quad 14 \quad 8 \quad 0 \quad 9 \quad 22$$

SOLUTION:

Using our notation, we have $x_1 = 0, x_2 = 7, \ldots, x_{10} = 22$, and $n = 10$. The sample mean is

$$\bar{x} = \frac{\sum_{i=1}^{n} x_i}{n} = \frac{0 + 7 + 12 + 5 + 33 + 14 + 8 + 0 + 9 + 22}{10} = \frac{110}{10} = 11.0$$

EXAMPLE 4.2

DATA
Xm03-01

Mean Age of ACBL Members

Refer to Example 3.1. Find the mean age of the sample of ACBL members.

SOLUTION:

To calculate the mean, we add the observations and divide by the size of the sample. Thus,

$$\bar{x} = \frac{\sum_{i=1}^{n} x_i}{n} = \frac{73 + 53 + 66 + \cdots + 17}{200} = \frac{10,753}{200} = 53.765$$

> **EXCEL Function**
>
> There are several ways to command Excel to compute the mean. If we simply want to compute the mean and no other statistics, we can use the AVERAGE function.
>
> *INSTRUCTIONS*
>
> Type or import the data into one or more columns. (Open Xm03-01.) Type into any empty cell
>
> $$= \textbf{AVERAGE}([\text{Input Range}])$$
>
> For Example 4.2, we would type into any empty cell
>
> $$= \textbf{AVERAGE}(A1:A201)$$
>
> The active cell would store the mean as 53.765.

4-1b Median

The second most popular measure of central location is the *median*.

> **Median**
>
> The **median** is calculated by placing all the observations in order (ascending or descending). The observation that falls in the middle is the median. The sample and population medians are computed in the same way. When there is an even number of observations, the median is determined by averaging the two observations in the middle.

EXAMPLE **4.3**

Median Time Spent on Internet

Find the median for the data in Example 4.1.

SOLUTION:

When placed in ascending order, the data appear as follows:

0   0   5   7   8   9   12   14   22   33

The median is the average of the fifth and sixth observations (the middle two), which are 8 and 9, respectively. Thus, the median is 8.5.

EXAMPLE **4.4**

Median Age of Sample of ACBL Members

DATA
Xm03-01

Find the median of the 200 observations in Example 3.1.

SOLUTION:

Because there is an even number of observations, the median is the average of the two middle observations. When all the observations are placed in order, the 100th and 101st observations are 54 and 55, respectively. Thus,

$$\text{Median} = \frac{54 + 55}{2} = 54.5$$

EXCEL Function

To calculate the median use the MEDIAN function. For Example 4.4 we typed into an empty cell

= MEDIAN(A1:201)

The result is 54.5.

INTERPRET

Half the observations are below 54.5 and half are above 54.5.

4-1c Mode

The third and last measure of central location that we present here is the *mode*.

> **Mode**
>
> The **mode** is defined as the observation (or observations) that occurs with the greatest frequency. Both the statistic and parameter are computed in the same way.

For populations and large samples, it is preferable to report the **modal class**, which we defined in Chapter 2. There are several problems with using the mode as a measure of central location. First, in a small sample it may not be a very good measure. Second, it may not be unique.

EXAMPLE 4.5

Mode Time Spent on Internet

Find the mode for the data in Example 4.1.

SOLUTION:

All observations except 0 occur once. There are two 0s. Thus, the mode is 0. As you can see, this is a poor measure of central location. It is nowhere near the center of the data. Compare this with the mean 11.0 and median 8.5 and you can appreciate that in this example the mean and median are superior measures.

EXAMPLE 4.6

Mode of Ages of ACBL Players

DATA
Xm03-01

Determine the mode for Example 3.1.

SOLUTION:

The observation that occurs with the greatest frequency is 60, which occurs 8 times.

EXCEL Function

To compute the mode use the MODE function. Note that if there is more than one mode, Excel prints only the smallest one, without indicating that there are other modes.

Excel Printing All Measures of Central Location Plus Other Statistics Excel can produce the measures of central location and a variety of other statistics that we will introduce in later sections.

EXCEL Data Analysis

Excel Output for Examples 4.2, 4.4, and 4.6

	A	B
1	Ages	
2		
3	Mean	53.765
4	Standard Error	1.40
5	Median	54.5
6	Mode	60
7	Standard Deviation	19.76
8	Sample Variance	390.52
9	Kurtosis	−0.8851
10	Skewness	0.0025
11	Range	83
12	Minimum	16
13	Maximum	99
14	Sum	10753
15	Count	200

INSTRUCTIONS

1. Type or import the data into one column. (Open Xm03-01.)
2. Click **Data, Data Analysis**, and **Descriptive Statistics**.
3. Specify the **Input Range** (A1:A201) and click **Summary Statistics**.

4-1d Mean, Median, Mode: Which Is Best?

With three measures from which to choose, which one should we use? There are several factors to consider when making our choice of measure of central location. The mean is generally our first selection. However, there are several circumstances when the median is better. The mode is seldom the best measure of central location. One advantage the median holds is that it is not as sensitive to extreme values as is the mean. To illustrate, consider the data in Example 4.1. The mean was 11.0, and the median was 8.5. Now suppose that the respondent who reported 33 hours actually reported 133 hours (obviously an Internet addict). The mean becomes

$$\bar{x} = \frac{\sum_{i=1}^{n} x_i}{n} = \frac{0 + 7 + 12 + 5 + 133 + 14 + 8 + 0 + 22}{10} = \frac{210}{10} = 21.0$$

This value is exceeded by only 2 of the 10 observations in the sample, making this statistic a poor measure of central location. The median stays the same. When there is a relatively small number of extreme observations (either very small or very large, but not both), the median usually produces a better measure of the center of the data. To see another advantage of the median over the mean, suppose you and your classmates have written a statistics test and the instructor is returning the graded tests. What piece of information is most important to you? The answer, of course, is your mark. What is the next important bit of information? The answer is how well you performed relative to the class. Most students ask their instructor for the class mean. This is the wrong statistic to request. You want the median because it divides the class into two halves. This information allows you to identify which half of the class your mark falls into. The median provides this information; the mean does not. Nevertheless, the mean can also be useful in this scenario. If there are several sections of the course, the section means can be compared to determine whose class performed best (or worst).

4-1e Measures of Central Location for Ordinal and Nominal Data

When the data are interval, we can use any of the three measures of central location. However, for ordinal and nominal data, the calculation of the mean is not valid. Because the calculation of the median begins by placing the data in order, this statistic is appropriate for ordinal data. The mode, which is determined by counting the frequency of each observation, is appropriate for nominal data. However, nominal data do not have a "center," so we cannot interpret the mode of nominal data in that way. It is generally pointless to compute the mode of nominal data.

APPLICATIONS in **FINANCE**

ProStockStudio/Shutterstock.com

Geometric Mean

The arithmetic mean is the single most popular and useful measure of central location. We noted certain situations, where the median is a better measure of central location. However, there is another circumstance where neither the mean nor the median is the best measure. When the variable is a growth rate or rate of change, such as the value of an investment over periods of time, we need another measure. This will become apparent from the following illustration.

Suppose you make a 2-year investment of $1,000, and it grows by 100% to $2,000 during the first year. During the second year, however, the investment suffers a 50% loss, from $2,000 back to $1,000. The rates of return for years 1 and 2 are $R_1 = 100\%$ and $R_2 = -50\%$, respectively. The arithmetic mean (and the median) is computed as

$$\bar{R} = \frac{R_1 + R_2}{2} = \frac{100 + (-50)}{2} = 25\%$$

But this figure is misleading. Because there was no change in the value of the investment from the beginning to the end of the 2-year period, the "average" compounded rate of return is 0%. As you will see, this is the value of the *geometric mean*.

Let R_i denote the rate of return (in decimal form) in period i ($i = 1, 2, \ldots, n$). The **geometric mean** R_g of the returns $R_1, R_2, \ldots, R_n$ is defined such that

$$(1 + R_g)^n = (1 + R_1)(1 + R_2) \cdots (1 + R_n)$$

(Continued)

Solving for R_g, we produce the following formula:

$$R_g = \sqrt[n]{(1 + R_1)(1 + R_2) \cdots (1 + R_n)} - 1$$

The geometric mean of our investment illustration is

$$R_g = \sqrt[n]{(1 + R_1)(1 + R_2) \cdots (1 + R_n)} - 1 = \sqrt[2]{(1 + 1)(1 + [-.50]} - 1 = 1 - 1 = 0$$

The geometric mean is therefore 0%. This is the single "average" return that allows us to compute the value of the investment at the end of the investment period from the beginning value. Thus, using the formula for compound interest with the rate = 0%, we find

Value at the end of the investment period = $1,000(1 + R_g)^2 = 1,000(1 + 0)^2 = 1,000$

To see how this works, suppose that you invested $1,000 three years ago and the annual rates of return are

Year	1	2	3
Annual rate of return	60%	40%	-20%

The gain after year 1 is 1,000(.60) = 600. Thus, the investment after year 1 is worth 1,000 + 600 = $1,600. The second year produced a return of 40%. The gain in the second year is 1,600(.40) = 640. The investment after year 2 is worth 1,600 + 640 = $2,240. Year 3 resulted in a loss of 20%. The loss in year 3 is 2,240(.20) = 448. The investment at the end of the third year is worth 2,240 − 448 = $1,792. We can produce the same result by multiplying the value of values for each year.

$$1,000(1 + .60)(1 + .40)[1 + (-.20)] = 1,792$$

Or we can compute the geometric mean. It is .2146. Now, instead of the three values, we assume that each year the return is 21.46%. The value after each year is

Year 1: 1,000(1.2146) = 1,214.6
Year 2: 1,214.6(1.2146) = 1,475.3
Year 3: 1,475.3(1.2146) = 1,792

Or more simply

Value at the end of year 3 = $1,000(1.2146^3) = 1,792$

The geometric mean is used whenever we wish to find the "average" growth rate, or rate of change, in a variable *over time*. However, the arithmetic mean of *n* returns (or growth rates) is the appropriate mean to calculate if you wish to estimate the mean rate of return (or growth rate) for any *single* period in the future; that is, in the illustration above if we wanted to estimate the rate of return in year 3, we would use the arithmetic mean of the two annual rates of return, which we found to be 25%.

EXCEL Function

INSTRUCTIONS

1. Type or import the values of $1 + R_i$ into a column.

2. Follow the instructions to produce the mean (page 100) except substitute **GEOMEAN** in place of **AVERAGE**.

3. To determine the geometric mean, subtract 1 from the number produced.

Here is a summary of the numerical techniques introduced in this section and when to use them.

Factors That Identify When to Compute the Mean

1. **Objective**: Describe a single set of data.
2. **Type of data**: Interval
3. **Descriptive measurement**: Central location

Factors That Identify When to Compute the Median

1. **Objective**: Describe a single set of data.
2. **Type of data**: Ordinal or interval (with extreme observations)
3. **Descriptive measurement**: Central location

Factors That Identify When to Compute the Mode

1. **Objective**: Describe a single set of data.
2. **Type of data**: Nominal, ordinal, interval

Factors That Identify When to Compute the Geometric Mean

1. **Objective**: Describe a single set of data.
2. **Type of data**: Interval; growth rates

EXERCISES

4.1 A sample of 12 people was asked how much change they had in their pockets and wallets. The responses (in cents) are

| 52 | 25 | 15 | 0 | 104 | 44 |
| 60 | 30 | 33 | 81 | 40 | 5 |

Determine the mean, median, and mode for these data.

4.2 The number of sick days due to colds and flu last year was recorded by a sample of 15 adults. The data are

| 5 | 7 | 0 | 3 | 15 | 6 | 5 | 9 |
| 3 | 8 | 10 | 5 | 2 | 0 | 12 | |

Compute the mean, median, and mode.

4.3 A random sample of 12 joggers was asked to keep track and report the number of miles they ran last week. The responses are

5.5	7.2	1.6	22.0	8.7	2.8
5.3	3.4	12.5	18.6	8.3	6.6

a. Compute the three statistics that measure central location.
b. Briefly describe what each statistic tells you.

4.4 The midterm test for a statistics course has a time limit of one hour. However, like most statistics exams, this one was quite easy. To assess how easy, the professor recorded the amount of time taken by a sample of nine students to hand in their test papers. The times (rounded to the nearest minute) are

33 29 45 60 42 19 52 38 36

a. Compute the mean, median, and mode.
b. What have you learned from the three statistics calculated in part (a)?

4.5 The professors at Wilfrid Laurier University are required to submit their final exams to the registrar's office 10 days before the end of the semester. The exam coordinator sampled 20 professors and recorded the number of days before the final exam that each submitted their exam. The results are

14	8	3	2	6	4	9	13	10	12
7	4	9	13	15	8	11	12	4	0

a. Compute the mean, median, and mode.
b. Briefly describe what each statistic tells you.

The following are Geometric Mean Exercises.

4.6 Compute the geometric mean of the following rates of return.
a. .25, −.10, .50, .40
b. .50, .30, −.50, −.25
c. .30, .50, .10, .20

4.7 Calculate the geometric mean of the following rates of return.
a. .80, −.50, −.25, .90
b. −.50, −.20, −.10, 0
c. .05, .05, .10, .10

4.8 For the following rates of return, compute the arithmetic mean and the geometric mean.
a. .10, .30, .40
b. −.50, .70, .90

4.9 Calculate the arithmetic mean and the geometric mean for the following rates of return.
a. .20, .60, 0
b. .50, −.40, −.20

4.10 An investment of $1,000 you made 4 years ago was worth $1,200 after the first year, $1,200 after the second year, $1,500 after the third year, and $2,000 today.
a. Compute the annual rates of return.
b. Compute the mean and median of the rates of return.
c. Compute the geometric mean.
d. Discuss whether the mean, median, or geometric mean is the best measure of the performance of the investment.

4.11 Suppose that you bought a stock 6 years ago at $12. The stock's price at the end of each year is shown here.

Year	1	2	3	4	5	6
Price	10	14	15	22	30	25

a. Compute the rate of return for each year.
b. Compute the mean and median of the rates of return.
c. Compute the geometric mean of the rates of return.
d. Explain why the best statistic to use to describe what happened to the price of the stock over the 6-year period is the geometric mean.

4.12 An investment of $1,000 produced the following annual rates of return

Year	1	2	3
Annual rate of return	.10	.50	−.30

a. What is the value of the investment after the first year? After the second year? After the third year?
b. Calculate the geometric mean and the arithmetic mean.
c. If each year's return is equal to the geometric mean, calculate the value of the investment after each year.
d. Repeat part (c) assuming the returns are equal to the arithmetic mean.
e. Briefly discuss why the geometric mean is a better measure of the "average" return than is the arithmetic mean.

4.13 A million dollar investment in the stock market yielded the following annual rates of return:

Year	1	2	2	4	5
Annual rate of return	−.10	−.20	.10	.50	.80

a. What is the value of the investment after each of the 5 years?
b. Compute the arithmetic mean and the geometric mean of the annual rates of return.
c. Assume that each year's return is equal to the geometric mean. Compute the value of the investment after each year.
d. Repeat part (c) assuming the returns are equal to the arithmetic mean.

The following exercises require a computer and software.

4.14 <u>Xr04-14</u> An auction house conducts an auction once every week listing items such as jewelry, furniture, art, coins, and many others. The number of bidders from each of the auctions over the last 3 years was recorded. Determine the mean and median of the weekly number of bidders. What do these statistics tell you about the sample of weekly bidders?

4.15 <u>Xr04-15</u> The starting salaries of a sample of 300 recent Bachelor of Business Administration graduates were recorded. Calculate the mean and median. Interpret the meaning of each statistic.

4.16 <u>Xr04-16</u> The amount of time spent commuting by residents of Washington, D.C., was recorded for a sample of 235 commuters.
  a. Compute the mean and median.
  b. What do the mean and median tell you about this data set?

  Source: U.S. Census Bureau.

4.17 <u>Xr04-17</u> According to a recent National Household Survey (NHS), roughly 15.4 million Canadians commuted to work. Overall, about four out of five Canadian commuters used private vehicles. Specifically, 74.0% of commuters, or 11.4 million workers, drove a vehicle to work. A random sample of these commuters was asked how long their typical commute was. Compute the mean and median and describe what each statistic tells you about these data.

  Source: Statistics Canada.

4.18 <u>Xr04-18</u> In the United States, banks and financial institutions often require buyers to pay fees in order to arrange mortgages. In a survey conducted by the U.S. Federal Housing Finance Board, 400 buyers of new houses who received a mortgage from a bank were asked to report the amount of fees (fees include commissions, discounts, and points) they paid as a percentage of the entire mortgage.
  a. Calculate the mean and the median.
  b. Describe what these statistics tell you about the fees.

4.19 <u>Xr04-19</u> In an effort to slow drivers, traffic engineers painted a solid line 3 feet from the curb over the entire length of a road and filled the space with diagonal lines. The lines made the road look narrower. A sample of car speeds was taken after the lines were drawn.
  a. Compute the mean and median of these data.
  b. Briefly describe what information you acquired from each statistic.

4.20 <u>Xr04-20</u> A random sample of adults whose COVID-19 tests were positive reported their ages.
  a. Calculate the mean and median of these data.

  b. What does the relative position of these statistics tell you about this sample?

4.21 <u>Xr04-21</u> A survey asked single males and single females to calculate their net worth ($thousands). Compute the mean and median for both groups. What do the relative positions of the means and medians tell you about each sample?

4.22 <u>Xr04-22</u> Many graduates of universities and colleges pay their tuition using loans. As a consequence, they leave university with substantial debts. A survey of recent graduates asked them to report the total amount of indebtedness ($thousands).
  a. Compute the mean and median.
  b. What does the relative position of the mean and median tell you about student debts?

The following are Geometric Mean exercises.

4.23 <u>Xr04-23</u> The annual returns of an investment made 18 years ago have been recorded.
  a. Compute the arithmetic mean and the geometric mean.
  b. Should the investor use the arithmetic mean or the geometric mean to gauge how well the investment performed?
  c. Should the investor use the arithmetic mean or the geometric mean to predict the rate of return for the next year?

4.24 <u>Xr04-24</u> The weekly returns of high-risk investment made last year has been recorded.
  a. Which mean (arithmetic or geometric) should the investor use to predict the next period's return? Calculate this mean.
  b. Which mean (arithmetic or geometric) should the investor use to measure how well the investment did? Calculate this mean.

4.25 <u>Xr04-25</u> A successful accountant invested $1,000,000 ten years ago. The annual returns are recorded.
  a. For each year, compute the value of the investment.
  b. Calculate the geometric mean of the annual returns.
  c. For each year, assume that the return is equal to the geometric mean. Compute the value for each year. Describe what you have learned.

4.26 <u>Xr04-26</u> An investor bought stocks worth $100,000. The monthly returns were recorded.
  a. For each month calculate the value of the investment.
  b. Compute the geometric mean of the monthly returns.
  c. Calculate the value of the investment each month assuming that each monthly return is equal to the geometric mean.

4-2 / MEASURES OF VARIABILITY

The statistics introduced in Section 4-1 serve to provide information about the central location of the data. However, as we have already discussed in Chapter 2, there are other characteristics of data that are of interest to practitioners of statistics. One such characteristic is the spread or variability of the data. In this section, we introduce four **measures of variability**. We begin with the simplest.

4-2a Range

> **Range**
>
> Range = Largest observation − Smallest observation

The advantage of the **range** is its simplicity. The disadvantage is also its simplicity. Because the range is calculated from only two observations, it tells us nothing about the other observations. Consider the following two sets of data.

Set 1:   4   4   4   4   4   50
Set 2:   4   8   15   24   39   50

The range of both sets is 46. The two sets of data are completely different, yet their ranges are the same. To measure variability, we need other statistics that incorporate all the data and not just two observations.

4-2b Variance

The **variance** and its related measure, the **standard deviation**, are arguably the most important statistics. They are used to measure variability, but, as you will discover, they play a vital role in almost all statistical inference procedures.

> **Variance**
>
> **Population variance:** $\sigma^2 = \dfrac{\sum\limits_{i=1}^{N} (x_i - \mu)^2}{N}$
>
> **Sample variance:*** $s^2 = \dfrac{\sum\limits_{i=1}^{n} (x_i - \overline{x})^2}{n - 1}$

The population variance is represented by σ^2 (Greek letter *sigma* squared).

Examine the formula for the sample variance s^2. It may appear to be illogical that in calculating s^2 we divide by $n - 1$ rather than by n.[†] However, we do so for the following reason. Population parameters in practical settings are seldom known. One objective of statistical inference is to estimate the parameter from the statistic. For example, we estimate the population mean μ from the sample mean $\bar{x}$. Although it is not obviously logical, the statistic created by dividing $\sum (x_i - \bar{x})^2$ by $n - 1$ is a better estimator than the one created by dividing by n. We will discuss this issue in greater detail in Section 10-1.

To compute the sample variance s^2, we begin by calculating the sample mean $\bar{x}$. Next we compute the difference (also call the **deviation**) between each observation and the mean. We square the deviations and sum. Finally, we divide the sum of squared deviations by $n - 1$.

We'll illustrate with a simple example. Suppose that we have the following observations of the numbers of hours five students spent studying statistics last week:

   8   4   9   11   3

The mean is

$$\bar{x} = \frac{8 + 4 + 9 + 11 + 3}{5} = \frac{35}{5} = 7$$

For each observation, we determine its deviation from the mean. The deviation is squared, and the sum of squares is determined as shown in Table 4.1.

TABLE **4.1** Calculation of Sample Variance

x_i	$(x_i - \bar{x})$	$(x_i - \bar{x})^2$
8	$(8 - 7) = 1$	$(1)^2 = 1$
4	$(4 - 7) = -3$	$(-3)^2 = 9$
9	$(9 - 7) = 2$	$(2)^2 = 4$
11	$(11 - 7) = 4$	$(4)^2 = 16$
3	$(3 - 7) = -4$	$(-4)^2 = 16$
	$\sum\limits_{i=1}^{5} (x_i - \bar{x}) = 0$	$\sum\limits_{i=1}^{5} (x_i - \bar{x})^2 = 46$

The sample variance is

$$s^2 = \frac{\sum\limits_{i=1}^{n} (x_i - \bar{x})^2}{n - 1} = \frac{46}{5 - 1} = 11.5$$

The calculation of this statistic raises several questions. Why do we square the deviations before averaging? If you examine the deviations, you will see that some of the deviations are positive and some are negative. When you add them together, the sum is 0.

[†]Technically, the variance of the sample is calculated by dividing the sum of squared deviations by n. The statistic computed by dividing the sum of squared deviations by $n - 1$ is called the sample variance corrected for the mean. Because this statistic is used extensively, we will shorten its name to sample variance.

This will always be the case because the sum of the positive deviations will always equal the sum of the negative deviations. Consequently, we square the deviations to avoid the "canceling effect."

Is it possible to avoid the canceling effect without squaring? We could average the *absolute* value of the deviations. In fact, such a statistic has already been invented. It is called the **mean absolute deviation** or MAD. However, this statistic has limited utility and is seldom calculated.

What is the unit of measurement of the variance? Because we squared the deviations, we also squared the units. In this illustration the units were hours (of study). Thus, the sample variance is 11.5 hours^2.

EXAMPLE 4.7

Summer Jobs

The following are the number of summer jobs a sample of six students applied for. Find the mean and variance of these data.

17   15   23   7   9   13

SOLUTION:

The mean of the six observations is

$$\bar{x} = \frac{17 + 15 + 23 + 7 + 9 + 13}{6} = \frac{84}{6} = 14 \text{ jobs}$$

The sample variance is

$$s^2 = \frac{\sum_{i=1}^{n}(x_i - \bar{x})^2}{n - 1}$$

$$= \frac{(17 - 14)^2 + (15 - 14)^2 + (23 - 14)^2 + (7 - 14)^2 + (9 - 14)^2 + (13 - 14)^2}{6 - 1}$$

$$= \frac{9 + 1 + 81 + 49 + 25 + 1}{5} = \frac{166}{5} = 33.2 \text{ jobs}^2$$

(Optional) Shortcut Method for Variance The calculations for larger data sets are quite time consuming. The following shortcut for the sample variance may help lighten the load.

Shortcut for Sample Variance

$$s^2 = \frac{1}{n - 1}\left[\sum_{i=1}^{n} x_i^2 - \frac{\left(\sum_{i=1}^{n} x_i\right)^2}{n} \right]$$

To illustrate, we'll do Example 4.7 again.

$$\sum_{i=1}^{n} x_i^2 = 17^2 + 15^2 + 23^2 + 7^2 + 9^2 + 13^2 = 1,342$$

$$\sum_{i=1}^{n} x_i = 17 + 15 + 23 + 7 + 9 + 13 = 84$$

$$\left(\sum_{i=1}^{n} x_i\right)^2 = 84^2 = 7,056$$

$$s^2 = \frac{1}{n-1}\left[\sum_{i=1}^{n} x_i^2 - \frac{\left(\sum_{i=1}^{n} x_i\right)^2}{n}\right] = \frac{1}{6-1}\left[1,342 - \frac{7,056}{6}\right] = 33.2 \text{ jobs}^2$$

Notice that we produced the same exact answer.

EXCEL Function

INSTRUCTIONS

Follow the instructions to compute the mean (page 100) except type VAR instead of AVERAGE.

4-2c Interpreting the Variance

We calculated the variance in Example 4.7 to be 33.2 jobs^2. What does this statistic tell us? Unfortunately, the variance provides us with only a rough idea about the amount of variation in the data. However, this statistic is useful when comparing two or more sets of data of the same type of variable. If the variance of one data set is larger than that of a second data set, we interpret that to mean that the observations in the first set display more variation than the observations in the second set.

The problem of interpretation is caused by the way the variance is computed. Because we squared the deviations from the mean, the unit attached to the variance is the square of the unit attached to the original observations. In other words, in Example 4.7 the unit of the data is jobs; the unit of the variance is jobs squared. This contributes to the problem of interpretation. We resolve this difficulty by calculating another related measure of variability.

4-2d Standard Deviation

Standard Deviation

Population standard deviation: $\sigma = \sqrt{\sigma^2}$

Sample standard deviation: $s = \sqrt{s^2}$

The standard deviation is simply the positive square root of the variance. Thus, in Example 4.7, the sample standard deviation is

$$s = \sqrt{s^2} = \sqrt{33.2} = 5.76 \text{ jobs}$$

Notice that the unit associated with the standard deviation is the unit of the original data set.

EXAMPLE **4.8**

DATA
Xm04-08

Comparing the Consistency of Two Types of Golf Clubs

Consistency is the hallmark of a good golfer. Golf equipment manufacturers are constantly seeking ways to improve their products. Suppose that a recent innovation is designed to improve the consistency of its users. As a test, a golfer was asked to hit 150 shots using a 7 iron, 75 of which were hit with the current club and 75 with the new innovative 7 iron. The distances were measured and recorded. Which 7 iron is more consistent?

S O L U T I O N :

To gauge the consistency, we must determine the standard deviations. (We could also compute the variances, but as we just pointed out, the standard deviation is easier to interpret.) We can get Excel to print the sample standard deviations. Alternatively, we can calculate all the descriptive statistics, a course of action we recommend because we often need several statistics. The printouts for both 7 irons are shown here.

EXCEL Data Analysis

	A	B	C	D	E
1	Current			Innovation	
2					
3	Mean	150.55		Mean	150.15
4	Standard Error	0.67		Standard Error	0.36
5	Median	151		Median	150
6	Mode	150		Mode	149
7	Standard Deviation	5.79		Standard Deviation	3.09
8	Sample Variance	33.55		Sample Variance	9.56
9	Kurtosis	0.13		Kurtosis	−0.89
10	Skewness	−0.43		Skewness	0.18
11	Range	28		Range	12
12	Minimum	134		Minimum	144
13	Maximum	162		Maximum	156
14	Sum	11291		Sum	11261
15	Count	75		Count	75

INTERPRET

The standard deviation of the distances of the current 7 iron is 5.79 yards whereas that of the innovative 7 iron is 3.09 yards. Based on this sample, the innovative club is more consistent. Because the mean distances are similar it would appear that the new club is indeed superior.

Interpreting the Standard Deviation Knowing the mean and standard deviation allows the statistics practitioner to extract useful bits of information. The information depends on the shape of the histogram. If the histogram is bell shaped, we can use the **Empirical Rule**.

> **Empirical Rule**
>
> 1. Approximately 68% of all observations fall within one standard deviation of the mean.
> 2. Approximately 95% of all observations fall within two standard deviations of the mean.
> 3. Approximately 99.7% of all observations fall within three standard deviations of the mean.

EXAMPLE **4.9**

Using the Empirical Rule to Interpret Standard Deviation

After an analysis of the returns on an investment, a statistics practitioner discovered that the histogram is bell shaped and that the mean and standard deviation are 10% and 8%, respectively. What can you say about the way the returns are distributed?

SOLUTION:

Because the histogram is bell shaped, we can apply the Empirical Rule:

1. Approximately 68% of the returns lie between 2% (the mean minus one standard deviation = 10 − 8) and 18% (the mean plus one standard deviation = 10 + 8).
2. Approximately 95% of the returns lie between −6% [the mean minus two standard deviations = 10 − 2(8)] and 26% [the mean plus two standard deviations = 10 + 2(8)].
3. Approximately 99.7% of the returns lie between −14% [the mean minus three standard deviations = 10 − 3(8)] and 34% [the mean plus three standard deviations = 10 + 3(8)].

A more general interpretation of the standard deviation is derived from *Chebysheff's Theorem*, which applies to all shapes of histograms.

> **Chebysheff's Theorem**
>
> The proportion of observations in any sample or population that lie within k standard deviations of the mean is at least
>
> $$1 - \frac{1}{k^2} \quad \text{for} \quad k > 1$$

When $k = 2$, **Chebysheff's Theorem** states that at least three-quarters (75%) of all observations lie within two standard deviations of the mean. With $k = 3$, Chebysheff's Theorem states that at least eight-ninths (88.9%) of all observations lie within three standard deviations of the mean.

Note that the Empirical Rule provides approximate proportions, whereas Chebysheff's Theorem provides lower bounds on the proportions contained in the intervals.

EXAMPLE 4.10

Using Chebysheff's Theorem to Interpret Standard Deviation

The annual salaries of the employees of a chain of computer stores produced a positively **skewed** histogram. The mean and standard deviation are $28,000 and $3,000, respectively. What can you say about the salaries at this chain?

SOLUTION:

Because the histogram is not bell shaped, we cannot use the Empirical Rule. We must employ Chebysheff's Theorem instead.

The intervals created by adding and subtracting two and three standard deviations to and from the mean are as follows:

1. At least 75% of the salaries lie between $22,000 [the mean minus two standard deviations = 28,000 − 2(3,000)] and $34,000 [the mean plus two standard deviations = 28,000 + 2(3,000)].

2. At least 88.9% of the salaries lie between $19,000 [the mean minus three standard deviations = 28,000 − 3(3,000)] and $37,000 [the mean plus three standard deviations = 28,000 + 3(3,000)].

4-2e Coefficient of Variation

Is a standard deviation of 10 a large number indicating great variability or a small number indicating little variability? The answer depends somewhat on the magnitude of the observations in the data set. If the observations are in the millions, then a standard deviation of 10 will probably be considered a small number. On the other hand, if the observations are less than 50, then the standard deviation of 10 would be seen as a large number. This logic lies behind yet another measure of variability, the *coefficient of variation*.

Coefficient of Variation

The **coefficient of variation** of a set of observations is the standard deviation of the observations divided by their mean:

$$\text{Population coefficient of variation: CV} = \frac{\sigma}{\mu}$$

$$\text{Sample coefficient of variation: cv} = \frac{s}{\bar{x}}$$

4-2f Measures of Variability for Ordinal and Nominal Data

The measures of variability introduced in this section can be used only for interval data. The next section will feature a measure that can be used to describe the variability of ordinal data. There are no measures of variability for nominal data.

4-2g Approximating the Mean and Variance from Grouped Data

The statistical methods presented in this chapter are used to compute descriptive statistics from data. However, in some circumstances, the statistics practitioner does not have the raw data but instead has a frequency distribution. This is often the case when data are supplied by government organizations. In the online appendix, Approximating Means and Variances for Grouped Data, we provide the formulas used to approximate the sample mean and variance.

We complete this section by reviewing the factors that identify the use of measures of variability.

Factors That Identify When to Compute the Range, Variance, Standard Deviation, and Coefficient of Variation

1. **Objective**: Describe a single set of data.
2. **Type of Data**: Interval
3. **Descriptive measurement**: Variability

EXERCISES

4.27 Calculate the variance and standard deviation of the following sample.

    6   7   4   3   6   8   8

4.28 Calculate the variance and standard deviation of the sample shown below.

    9   3   7   4   1   7   5   4

4.29 a. Calculate the mean of the sample below.
  b. For each value, compute the deviation between the value and the mean. Calculate the sum of the deviations.
  c. Square each deviation and add these values.
  d. Calculate the variance and standard deviation.

    9   0   6   7   8

4.30 a. Calculate the mean of the following sample.
  b. Compute the deviation between each value and the mean. Calculate the sum of the deviations.
  c. Square each deviation and add these values.
  d. Calculate the sample variance.

    14   20   15   10   11

4.31 a. Calculate the mean of the sample listed next.
  b. For each value, compute the deviation between the value and the mean. Compute the sum of the deviations.

  c. Calculate the absolute value of the deviations and sum these figures.
  d. Calculate the MAD.

    15   19   16   20   11   15

4.32 a. Calculate the mean of the sample below.
  b. For each value, compute the deviation between the value and the mean.
  c. Calculate the sum of the deviations.
  d. Calculate the absolute value of the deviations and sum these figures.
  e. Calculate the MAD.

    25   15   17   26   22

4.33 If a sample has very large deviations, which measure of variance would be larger, the sample standard deviation or MAD? Explain.

4.34 Compute the sample standard deviation and MAD for the following sample.

    6   23   31   14   11

4.35 Calculate the sample standard deviation and MAD for the sample below.

    17   13   19   16   15

4.36 Suppose that you calculated a variance and found it to be –25.0. How should you know that you made a calculation error?

4.37 Create a sample of five observations whose mean is 6 and whose standard deviation is 0.

4.38 A set of data whose histogram is bell shaped yields a mean and standard deviation of 50 and 4, respectively. Approximately what proportion of observations
   a. are between 46 and 54?
   b. are between 42 and 58?
   c. are between 38 and 62?

4.39 Refer to Exercise 4.38. Approximately what proportion of observations
   a. are less than 46?
   b. are less than 58?
   c. are greater than 54?

4.40 A set of data whose histogram is extremely skewed yields a mean and standard deviation of 70 and 12, respectively. What is the minimum proportion of observations that
   a. are between 46 and 94?
   b. are between 34 and 106?

4.41 A statistics practitioner determined that the mean and standard deviation of a data set were 120 and 30, respectively. What can you say about the proportions of observations that lie between each of the following intervals?
   a. 90 and 150
   b. 60 and 180
   c. 30 and 210

The following exercises require a computer and software.

4.42 Xr04-42   There has been much media coverage of the high cost of medicinal drugs in the United States. One concern is the large variation from pharmacy to pharmacy. To investigate, a consumer advocacy group took a random sample of 100 pharmacies around the country and recorded the price (in dollars per 100 pills) of Prozac. Compute the mean and standard deviation. Discuss what these statistics tell you.

4.43 Xr04-43   Many traffic experts argue that the most important factor in accidents is not the average speed of cars but the amount of variation. Suppose that the speeds of a sample of 200 cars were taken over a stretch of highway that has seen numerous accidents and the speeds of 300 cars were taken over a stretch of highway that has seen very few accidents. Compute the mean and standard deviation of both samples and briefly describe what you have learned.

4.44 Xr04-44   Three men are trying to make the football team as punters. The coach had each of them punt the ball 50 times, and the distances were recorded.
   a. Compute the variance and standard deviation for each punter.
   b. What do these statistics tell you about the punters?

4.45 Xr04-45   Variance is often used to measure the quality in production-line products. Suppose that a sample of steel rods that are supposed to be exactly 100 cm long is taken. The length of each is determined, and the results are recorded. Calculate the mean and standard deviation, and briefly describe what these statistics tell you.

4.46 Xr04-46   To learn more about the size of withdrawals at a banking machine, the proprietor took a sample of 75 withdrawals and recorded the amounts. Determine the mean and standard deviation of these data, and describe what these two statistics tell you about the withdrawal amounts.

4.47 Xr04-47   Everyone is familiar with waiting lines or queues. For example, people wait in line at a supermarket to go through the checkout counter. There are two factors that determine how long the queue becomes. One is the speed of service. The other is the number of arrivals at the checkout counter. The mean number of arrivals is an important number, but so is the standard deviation. Suppose that a consultant for the supermarket counts the number of arrivals per hour during a sample of 150 hours.
   a. Compute the mean and standard deviation of the number of arrivals.
   b. Assuming that the histogram is bell shaped, interpret the standard deviation.

4.48 Xr04-48   Flight delays in airplane travel are a fact of life for travelers. Suppose that the time for each of a sample of 125 delays in arriving (in minutes) was recorded. Early arrivals are shown as negative numbers and on-time arrivals are represented by zeroes. Calculate the mean and standard deviation of the times. Assuming that the distribution is approximately bell shaped, describe what the mean and standard deviation tell you.

4.49 Xr04-49   An amateur golfer kept track of the scores of the last 100 rounds. Calculate the mean and standard deviation. Assuming that the distribution of scores is extremely skewed, interpret the mean and standard deviation.

4.50 Xr04-50   A random sample of homeowners was asked to report the amount of money they paid in property taxes last year. Compute the mean and standard deviation. Assuming that the amounts are highly positively skewed, describe what the two statistics tell you.

Source: Adapted from Bureau of Labor Statistics.

4.51 <u>Xr04-51</u> A sample of households was asked to report the amount of money they spend annually for fruits and vegetables. Compute the mean and standard deviation of these data. What do these statistics tell you about the distribution of the amounts?

Source: Adapted from Bureau of Labor Statistics.

4.52 <u>Xr04-52</u> A statistics practitioner working for a major league baseball team recorded the speed of a young pitcher's fastballs in the innings 1–3, innings 4–6, and innings 7–9. Compute the mean and standard deviation for each set of innings. What have you learned from the three sets of statistics?

4.53 <u>Xr04-53</u> Refer to Exercise 4.52. The statistics practitioner conducted the same experiment for an older, more experienced pitcher. Conduct the same analysis and report your findings.

4.54 <u>Xr04-54</u> A management scientist has been asked to help with an assembly line that consists of several

different procedures. The problem occurs with the last two activities. The times (seconds) for each were recorded. Calculate the mean and standard deviation for each activity and describe your results.

4.55 <u>Xr04-55</u> A statistics professor has two quizzes during the semester. The marks for both quizzes were recorded. For each quiz, compute the mean and standard deviation and describe what you have learned.

4.56 <u>Xr04-56</u> A consultant recorded the number of customers who entered two bank branches during their first hour over a 1-year period. Calculate the mean and standard deviation for each branch, and report your findings.

4.57 <u>Xr04-57</u> An assistant dean recorded the number of copies made daily by the printer used by the business professors at a small university during the last two semesters. Calculate the mean and standard deviation. Assuming that the data are bell shaped, describe what the statistics tell you about the number of copies made daily by the printer.

4-3 / MEASURES OF RELATIVE STANDING

Measures of relative standing are designed to provide information about the position of particular values relative to the entire data set. We've already presented one measure of relative standing, the median, which is also a measure of central location. Recall that the median divides the data set into halves, allowing the statistics practitioner to determine which half of the data set each observation lies in. The statistics we're about to introduce will give you much more detailed information.

> **Percentile**
>
> The *P*th **percentile** is the value for which *P*% are less than that value and $(100 - P)$% are greater than that value.

The scores and the percentiles of the Scholastic Achievement Test (SAT) and the Graduate Management Admission Test (GMAT), as well as various other admissions tests, are reported to students taking them. Suppose, for example, that your SAT score is reported to be at the 60th percentile. This means that 60% of all the other scores are below yours and 40% are above it. You now know exactly where you stand relative to the population of SAT scores.

We have special names for the 25th, 50th, and 75th percentiles. Because these three statistics divide the set of data into quarters, these measures of relative standing are also called **quartiles**. The *first* or *lower quartile* is labeled Q_1. It is equal to the 25th percentile. The *second quartile*, Q_2, is equal to the 50th percentile, which is also the median. The *third* or *upper quartile*, Q_3, is equal to the 75th percentile. Incidentally, many people confuse the terms *quartile* and *quarter*. A common error is to state that someone is in the lower *quartile* of a group when they actually mean that someone is in the lower *quarter* of a group.

Besides quartiles, we can also convert percentiles into quintiles and deciles. *Quintiles* divide the data into fifths, and *deciles* divide the data into tenths.

4-3a Locating Percentiles

The following formula allows us to approximate the location of any percentile.

> **Location of a Percentile**
>
> $$L_P = (n+1)\frac{P}{100}$$
>
> where L_P is the location of the Pth percentile.

EXAMPLE 4.11

Percentiles of Time Spent on Internet

Calculate the 25th, 50th, and 75th percentiles (first, second, and third quartiles) of the data in Example 4.1.

SOLUTION:

Placing the 10 observations in ascending order we get

| 0 | 0 | 5 | 7 | 8 | 9 | 12 | 14 | 22 | 33 |

The location of the 25th percentile is

$$L_{25} = (n+1)\frac{25}{100} = (11)(.25) = 2.75$$

The 25th percentile is three-quarters of the distance between the second (which is 0) and the third (which is 5) observations. Three-quarters of the distance is

$$(.75)(5 - 0) = 3.75$$

Because the second observation is 0, the 25th percentile is $0 + 3.75 = 3.75$. To locate the 50th percentile, we substitute $P = 50$ and produce

$$L_{50} = (n+1)\frac{50}{100} = (11)(.50) = 5.5$$

which means that the 50th percentile is halfway between the fifth and sixth observations. The fifth and sixth observations are 8 and 9, respectively. The 50th percentile is 8.5. This is the median calculated in Example 4.3.

The 75th percentile's location is

$$L_{75} = (n+1)\frac{75}{100} = (11)(.75) = 8.25$$

Thus, it is located one-quarter of the distance between the eighth and ninth observations, which are 14 and 22, respectively. One-quarter of the distance is

$$(.25)(22 - 14) = 2$$

which means that the 75th percentile is

$$14 + 2 = 16$$

Set 1

x_i	y_i	$(x_i - \bar{x})$	$(y_i - \bar{y})$	$(x_i - \bar{x})(y_i - \bar{y})$
2	13	-3	-7	21
6	20	1	0	0
7	27	2	7	14
$\bar{x} = 5$	$\bar{y} = 20$			$s_{xy} = 35/2 = 17.5$

Set 2

x_i	y_i	$(x_i - \bar{x})$	$(y_i - \bar{y})$	$(x_i - \bar{x})(y_i - \bar{y})$
2	27	-3	7	-21
6	20	1	0	0
7	13	2	-7	-14
$\bar{x} = 5$	$\bar{y} = 20$			$s_{xy} = -35/2 = -17.5$

Set 3

x_i	y_i	$(x_i - \bar{x})$	$(y_i - \bar{y})$	$(x_i - \bar{x})(y_i - \bar{y})$
2	20	-3	0	0
6	27	1	7	7
7	13	2	-7	-14
$\bar{x} = 5$	$\bar{y} = 20$			$s_{xy} = -7/2 = -3.5$

Notice that the values of x are the same in all three sets and that the values of y are also the same. The only difference is the *order* of the values of y.

In set 1, as x increases so does y. When x is larger than its mean, y is at least as large as its mean. Thus $(x_i - \bar{x})$ and $(y_i - \bar{y})$ have the same sign or 0. Their product is also positive or 0. Consequently, the covariance is a positive number. Generally, when two variables move in the same direction (both increase or both decrease), the covariance will be a large positive number.

If you examine set 2, you will discover that as x increases, y decreases. When x is larger than its mean, y is less than or equal to its mean. As a result when $(x_i - \bar{x})$ is positive, $(y_i - \bar{y})$ is negative or 0. Their products are either negative or 0. It follows that the covariance is a negative number. In general, when two variables move in opposite directions, the covariance is a large negative number.

In set 3, as x increases, y does not exhibit any particular direction. One of the products $(x_i - \bar{x})(y_i - \bar{y})$ is 0, one is positive, and one is negative. The resulting covariance is a small number. In general, when there is no particular pattern, the covariance is a small number.

We would like to extract two pieces of information. The first is the sign of the covariance, which tells us the nature of the relationship. The second is the magnitude, which describes the strength of the association. Unfortunately, the magnitude may be difficult to judge. For example, if you're told that the covariance between two variables is 500, does this mean that there is a strong linear relationship? The answer is that it is impossible to judge without additional statistics. Fortunately, we can improve on the information provided by this statistic by creating another one.

4-4b Coefficient of Correlation

The **coefficient of correlation** is defined as the covariance divided by the standard deviations of the variables.

Coefficient of Correlation

Population coefficient of correlation: $\rho = \dfrac{\sigma_{xy}}{\sigma_x \sigma_y}$

Sample coefficient of correlation: $r = \dfrac{s_{xy}}{s_x s_y}$

The population parameter is denoted by the Greek letter *rho*.

The advantage that the coefficient of correlation has over the covariance is that the former has a set lower and upper limit. The limits are -1 and $+1$, respectively—that is,

$$-1 \le r \le +1 \qquad \text{and} \qquad -1 \le \rho \le +1$$

When the coefficient of correlation equals -1, there is a negative linear relationship and the scatter diagram exhibits a straight line. When the coefficient of correlation equals $+1$, there is a perfect positive relationship. When the coefficient of correlation equals 0, there is no linear relationship. All other values of correlation are judged in relation to these three values. The drawback to the coefficient of correlation is that—except for the three values $-1, 0$, and $+1$—we cannot interpret the correlation. For example, suppose that we calculated the coefficient of correlation to be $-.4$. What does this tell us? It tells us two things. The minus sign tells us the relationship is negative and because .4 is closer to 0 than to 1, we judge that the linear relationship is weak. In many applications, we need a better interpretation than the "linear relationship is weak." Fortunately, there is yet another measure of the strength of a linear relationship, which gives us more information. It is the *coefficient of determination*, which we introduce later in this section.

EXAMPLE 4.14

Calculating the Coefficient of Correlation

Calculate the coefficient of correlation for the three sets of data on page 123.

SOLUTION:

Because we've already calculated the covariances we need to compute only the standard deviations of X and Y.

$$\bar{x} = \frac{2 + 6 + 7}{3} = 5.0$$

$$\bar{y} = \frac{13 + 20 + 27}{3} = 20.0$$

$$s_x^2 = \frac{(2-5)^2 + (6-5)^2 + (7-5)^2}{3-1} = \frac{9 + 1 + 4}{2} = 7.0$$

$$s_y^2 = \frac{(13-20)^2 + (20-20)^2 + (27-20)^2}{3-1} = \frac{49 + 0 + 49}{2} = 49.0$$

The standard deviations are

$$s_x = \sqrt{7.0} = 2.65$$

$$s_y = \sqrt{49.0} = 7.00$$

The coefficients of correlation are:

Set 1: $r = \dfrac{s_{xy}}{s_x s_y} = \dfrac{17.5}{(2.65)(7.0)} = .943$

Set 2: $r = \dfrac{s_{xy}}{s_x s_y} = \dfrac{-17.5}{(2.65)(7.0)} = -.943$

Set 3: $r = \dfrac{s_{xy}}{s_x s_y} = \dfrac{-3.5}{(2.65)(7.0)} = -.189$

It is now easier to see the strength of the linear relationship between X and Y.

4-4c Comparing the Scatter Diagram, Covariance, and Coefficient of Correlation

The scatter diagram depicts relationships graphically; the covariance and the coefficient of correlation describe the linear relationship numerically. Figures 4.1, 4.2, and 4.3 depict three scatter diagrams. To show how the graphical and numerical techniques compare, we calculated the covariance and the coefficient of correlation for each. (The data are stored in files Fig04-01, Fig04-02, and Fig04-03.) As you can see, Figure 4.1 depicts a strong positive relationship between the two variables. The covariance is 36.87, and the coefficient of correlation is .9641. The variables in Figure 4.2 produced a relatively strong negative linear relationship; the covariance and coefficient of correlation are −34.18 and −.8791, respectively. The covariance and coefficient of correlation for the data in Figure 4.3 are 2.07 and .1206, respectively. There is no apparent linear relationship in this figure.

FIGURE **4.1** **Strong Positive Linear Relationship**

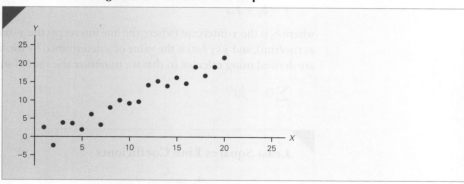

FIGURE **4.2** **Strong Negative Linear Relationship**

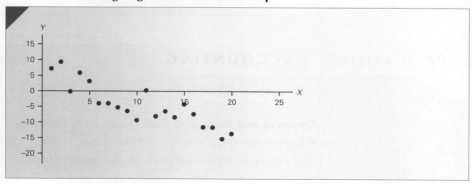

FIGURE **4.3** No Linear Relationship

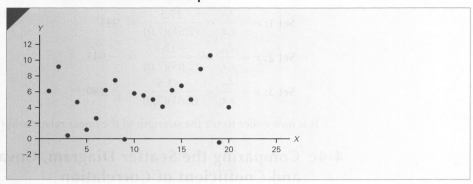

4-4d Least Squares Method

When we presented the scatter diagram in Section 3-3, we pointed out that we were interested in measuring the strength and direction of the linear relationship. Both can be more easily judged by drawing a straight line through the data. However, if different people draw a line through the same data set, it is likely that each person's line will differ from all the others. Moreover, we often need to know the equation of the line. Consequently, we need an objective method of producing a straight line. Such a method has been developed; it is called the **least squares method**.

The least squares method produces a straight line drawn through the points so that the sum of squared deviations between the points and the line is minimized. The line is represented by the equation:

$$\hat{y} = b_0 + b_1 x$$

where b_0 is the y-intercept (where the line intercepts the y-axis), and b_1 is the slope (defined as rise/run), and $\hat{y}$ (y hat) is the value of y determined by the line. The coefficients b_0 and b_1 are derived using calculus so that we minimize the sum of squared deviations:

$$\sum_{i=1}^{n}(y_i - \hat{y}_i)^2$$

Least Squares Line Coefficients

$$b_1 = \frac{s_{xy}}{s_x^2}$$
$$b_0 = \bar{y} - b_1\bar{x}$$

APPLICATIONS in **ACCOUNTING**

Breakeven Analysis

Breakeven analysis is an extremely important business tool, one that you will likely encounter repeatedly in your course of studies. It can be used to determine how much sales volume your business needs to start making a profit.

Breakeven analysis is especially useful when managers are attempting to determine the appropriate price for the company's products and services.

A company's profit can be calculated simply as

Profit = (Price per unit − variable cost per unit) × (Number of units sold) − Fixed costs

The breakeven point is the number of units sold such that the profit is 0. Thus, the breakeven point is calculated as

Number of units sold = Fixed cost/(Price − Variable cost)

Managers can use the formula to help determine the price that will produce a profit. However, to do so requires knowledge of the fixed and variable costs. For example, suppose that a bakery sells only loaves of bread. The bread sells for $1.20, the variable cost is $0.40, and the fixed annual costs are $10,000. The breakeven point is

Number of units sold = 10,000/(1.20 − 0.40) = 12,500

The bakery must sell more than 12,500 loaves per year to make a profit.

In the next application box, we discuss fixed and variable costs.

APPLICATIONS in ACCOUNTING

Fixed and Variable Costs

Fixed costs are costs that must be paid whether or not any units are produced. These costs are "fixed" over a specified period of time or range of production. Variable costs are costs that vary directly with the number of products produced. For the previous bakery example, the fixed costs would include rent and maintenance of the shop, wages paid to employees, advertising costs, telephone, and any other costs that are not related to the number of loaves baked. The variable cost is primarily the cost of ingredients, which rises in relation to the number of loaves baked.

Some expenses are mixed. For the bakery example, one such cost is the cost of electricity. Electricity is needed for lights, which is considered a fixed cost, but also for the ovens and other equipment, which are variable costs.

There are several ways to break the mixed costs into fixed and variable components. One such method is the least squares line; that is, we express the total costs of some component as

$y = b_0 + b_1 x$

where y = total mixed cost, b_0 = fixed cost, b_1 = variable cost, and x is the number of units.

EXAMPLE **4.15**

DATA
Xm04-15

Estimating Fixed and Variable Costs

A tool and die maker operates out of a small shop making specialized tools and is considering increasing the size of the business and needs to know more about costs. One such cost is electricity, which is needed to operate machines and lights. (Some jobs require extra bright lights to illuminate the work.) The daily electricity costs and the number of tools that were made that day were recorded. These data are listed next. Determine the fixed and variable electricity costs.

Day	1	2	3	4	5	6	7	8	9	10
Number of tools	7	3	2	5	8	11	5	15	3	6
Electricity cost	23.80	11.89	15.98	26.11	31.79	39.93	12.27	40.06	21.38	18.65

SOLUTION:

The dependent variable is the daily cost of electricity, and the independent variable is the number of tools. To calculate the coefficients of the least squares line and other statistics (calculated below), we need the sum of X, Y, XY, X^2, and Y^2.

Day	X	Y	XY	X^2	Y^2
1	7	23.80	166.60	49	566.44
2	3	11.89	35.67	9	141.37
3	2	15.98	31.96	4	255.36
4	5	26.11	130.55	25	681.73
5	8	31.79	254.32	64	1,010.60
6	11	39.93	439.23	121	1,594.40
7	5	12.27	61.35	25	150.55
8	15	40.06	600.90	225	1,604.80
9	3	21.38	64.14	9	457.10
10	6	18.65	111.90	36	347.82
Total	65	241.86	1,896.62	567	6,810.20

Covariance:

$$s_{xy} = \frac{1}{n-1}\left[\sum_{i=1}^{n} x_i y_i - \frac{\sum_{i=1}^{n} x_i \sum_{i=1}^{n} y_i}{n}\right] = \frac{1}{10-1}\left[1{,}896.62 - \frac{(65)(241.86)}{10}\right] = 36.06$$

Variance of X:

$$s_x^2 = \frac{1}{n-1}\left[\sum_{i=1}^{n} x_i^2 - \frac{\left(\sum_{i=1}^{n} x_i\right)^2}{n}\right] = \frac{1}{10-1}\left[567 - \frac{(65)^2}{10}\right] = 16.06$$

Sample means

$$\bar{x} = \frac{\sum x_i}{n} = \frac{65}{10} = 6.5$$

$$\bar{y} = \frac{\sum y_i}{n} = \frac{241.86}{10} = 24.19$$

The coefficients of the least squares line are as follows:

Slope:

$$b_1 = \frac{s_{xy}}{s_x^2} = \frac{36.06}{16.06} = 2.25$$

y-intercept:

$$b_0 = \bar{y} - b_1\bar{x} = 24.19 - (2.25)(6.5) = 9.57$$

The least squares line is

$$\hat{y} = 9.57 + 2.25x$$

EXCEL Chart

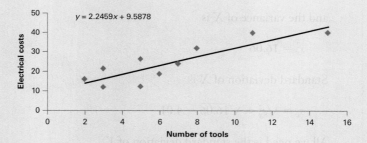

y = 2.2459x + 9.5878

INSTRUCTIONS

1. Type or import the data into two columns where the first column stores the values of X and the second stores Y. (Open Xm04-15.) Highlight the columns containing the variables. Follow the instructions to draw a scatter diagram (page 75).

2. Click the + sign, click **Trendline** and arrow. Click More Options and Display Equation on chart.

INTERPRET

The slope is defined as rise/run, which means that it is the change in y (rise) for a one-unit increase in x (run). Put less mathematically, the slope measures the *marginal* rate of change in the dependent variable. The marginal rate of change refers to the effect of increasing the independent variable by one additional unit. In this example, the slope is 2.25, which means that in this sample, for each one-unit increase in the number of tools, the marginal increase in the electricity cost is $2.25. Thus, the estimated variable cost is $2.25 per tool.

The y-intercept is 9.57; that is, the line strikes the y-axis at 9.57. This is simply the value of $\hat{y}$ when $x = 0$. However, when $x = 0$, we are producing no tools and hence the estimated fixed cost of electricity is $9.57 per day.

Because the costs are estimates based on a straight line, we often need to know how well the line fits the data.

EXAMPLE 4.16

DATA
Xm04-15

Measuring the Strength of the Linear Relationship

Calculate the coefficient of correlation for Example 4.15.

SOLUTION:

To calculate the coefficient of correlation, we need the covariance and the standard deviations of both variables. The covariance and the variance of X were calculated in Example 4.15. The covariance is

$$s_{xy} = 36.06$$

and the variance of X is

$$s_x^2 = 16.06$$

Standard deviation of X is

$$s_x = \sqrt{s_x^2} = \sqrt{16.06} = 4.01$$

All we need is the standard deviation of Y.

$$s_y^2 = \frac{1}{n-1}\left[\sum_{i=1}^{n}y_i^2 - \frac{\left(\sum_{i=1}^{n}y_i\right)^2}{n}\right] = \frac{1}{10-1}\left[6{,}810.20 - \frac{(241.86)^2}{10}\right] = 106.73$$

$$s_y = \sqrt{s_y^2} = \sqrt{106.73} = 10.33$$

The coefficient of correlation is

$$r = \frac{s_{xy}}{s_x s_y} = \frac{36.06}{(4.01)(10.33)} = .8705$$

EXCEL Function and Data Analysis

As with the other statistics introduced in this chapter, there is more than one way to calculate the coefficient of correlation and the covariance. Here are the instructions for both.

INSTRUCTIONS

1. Type or import the data into two columns. (Open Xm04-15.) Type the following into any empty cell.

   = **CORREL**([Input range of one variable], [Input range of second variable])

In this example, we would enter

   = **CORREL**(B1:B11, C1:C11)

To calculate the covariance, replace **CORREL** with **COVAR**.

Another method, which is also useful if you have more than two variables and would like to compute the coefficient of correlation or the covariance for each pair of variables, is to produce the correlation matrix and the variance–covariance matrix. We do the correlation matrix first.

	A	B	C
1		Number of tools	Electrical costs
2	Number of tools	1	
3	Electrical costs	0.8711	1

INSTRUCTIONS

1. Type or import the data into adjacent columns. (Open Xm04-15.)
2. Click **Data, Data Analysis**, and **Correlation**.
3. Specify the **Input Range (B1:C11)**.

The coefficient of correlation between number of tools and electrical costs is .8711 (slightly different from the manually calculated value). (The two 1s on the diagonal of the matrix are the coefficients of number of tools and number of tools, and electrical costs and electrical costs, telling you the obvious.)

Incidentally, the formulas for the population parameter ρ (Greek letter *rho*) and for the sample statistic r produce exactly the same value.

The variance–covariance matrix is shown next.

	A	B	C
1		Number of tools	Electrical costs
2	Number of tools	14.45	
3	Electrical costs	32.45	96.06

INSTRUCTIONS

1. Type or import the data into adjacent columns. (Open Xm04-15.)
2. Click **Data, Data Analysis**, and **Covariance**.
3. Specify the **Input Range (B1:C11)**.

Unfortunately, Excel computes the population parameters. In other words, the variance of the number of tools is $\sigma_x^2 = 14.45$, the variance of the electrical costs is $\sigma_y^2 = 96.06$, and the covariance is $\sigma_{xy} = 32.45$. You can convert these parameters to statistics by multiplying each by $n/(n-1)$.

	D	E	F
1		Number of tools	Electrical costs
2	Number of tools	16.06	
3	Electrical costs	36.06	106.73

The coefficient of correlation is .8711, which tells us that there is a positive linear relationship between the number of tools and the electricity cost. The coefficient of correlation tells us that the linear relationship is quite strong and thus the estimates of the fixed and variable costs should be good.

4-4e Coefficient of Determination

When we introduced the coefficient of correlation (page 124), we pointed out that except for -1, 0, and $+1$ we cannot precisely interpret its meaning. We can judge the coefficient of correlation in relation to its proximity to only -1, 0, and $+1$. Fortunately, we have another measure that can be precisely interpreted. It is the coefficient of determination, which is calculated by squaring the coefficient of correlation. For this reason, we denote it R^2.

The coefficient of determination measures the amount of variation in the dependent variable that is explained by the variation in the independent variable. For example, if the coefficient of correlation is -1 or $+1$, a scatter diagram would display all the points lining up in a straight line. The coefficient of determination is 1, which we interpret to mean that 100% of the variation in the dependent variable Y is explained by the variation in the independent variable X. If the coefficient of correlation is 0, then there is no linear relationship between the two variables, $R^2 = 0$, and none of the variation in Y is explained by the variation in X. In Example 4.16, the coefficient of correlation was calculated to be $r = .8711$. Thus, the coefficient of determination is

$$r^2 = (.8711)^2 = .7588$$

This tells us that 75.88% of the variation in electrical costs is explained by the number of tools. The remaining 24.12% is unexplained.

EXCEL

You can use Excel to calculate the coefficient of correlation and then square the result. Alternatively, use Excel to draw the least squares line. After doing so, click **Trendline**, **More Options**, and **Display R-squared value on chart**.

The concept of explained variation is an extremely important one in statistics. We return to this idea repeatedly in Chapters 13, 14, 16, 17, and 18. In Chapter 16, we explain why we interpret the coefficient of determination in the way that we do.

Cost of One More Win: Solution

To determine the cost of an additional win, we must describe the relationship between two variables. To do so, we use the least squares method to produce a straight line through the data. Because we believe that the number of games a baseball team wins depends to some extent on its team payroll, we label Wins as the dependent variable and Payroll as the independent variable. Because of rounding problems, we expressed the payroll in the number of millions of dollars.

EXCEL Chart

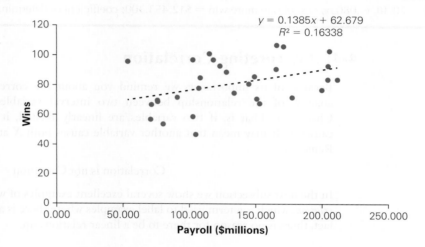

As you can see, Excel outputs the least squares line and the coefficient of determination.

INTERPRET

The least squares line is

$$\hat{y} = 62.679 + .1385x$$

The slope is equal to .1385, which is the marginal rate of change in games won for each 1-unit increase in payroll. Because payroll is measured in millions of dollars, we estimate that for each $1 million increase in the payroll, the number of games won increases on average by .1385. Thus, to win one more game requires on average an additional expenditure of $7,220,217 (calculated as 1 million/.1385). In addition to analyzing the least squares line, we should determine the strength of the linear relationship. The coefficient of determination is .1634, which means that the variation in the teams' payroll explains 16.34% of the variation in the teams' number of games won. This tells us that there is a weak positive linear relationship between team payroll and the number of wins in the 2019 season. This suggests that there are some teams that win a small number of games with large payrolls (e.g., San Francisco Giants, $199 million payroll and 77 wins), whereas others win a large number of wins with small payrolls (e.g., Tampa Bay Rays, $53 million payroll and 96 wins).

(Continued)

Here are the results of the 2006, 2009, 2012, 2015, and 2018 seasons.

2006:
$\hat{y} = 68.31 + .163x$; cost of one more win = \$6,134,969; coefficient of determination = 28.27%

2009:
$\hat{y} = 65.76 + .1725x$; cost of one more win = \$5,797,101; coefficient of determination = 25.12%

2012:
$\hat{y} = 74.77 + .0636x$; cost of one more win = \$15,723,270; coefficient of determination = 3.85%

2015:
$\hat{y} = 75.04 + .0474x$; cost of one more win = \$21,097,705; coefficient of determination = 4.18%

2018:
$\hat{y} = 70.38 + .0803x$; cost of one more win = \$12,453,300; coefficient of determination = 5.52%

4-4f Interpreting Correlation

Because of its importance, we remind you about the correct interpretation of the analysis of the relationship between two interval variables that we discussed in Chapter 3. That is, if two variables are linearly related, it does not mean that X causes Y. It may mean that another variable causes both X and Y or that Y causes X. Remember:

Correlation is not Causation

In the next subsection we show several excellent examples of what is called *spurious correlation*, which is a term used to label examples where there is a large correlation, but in fact, there is no reason for there to be a linear relationship.

4-4g Spurious Correlation

Here are three examples.

Example 1

Variable X: Millions of pounds of uranium stored annually in the United States (years 1996–2008)

Variable Y: Number of Mathematics doctorates awarded annually in the United States

X	66.1	65.9	65.8	58.3	54.8	55.6	53.5	45.6	57.7	64.7	77.5	81.2	81.9
Y	1,122	1,123	1,177	1,083	1,050	1,010	919	993	1,076	1,205	1,325	1,393	1,399

Coefficient of correlation: .9523

Example 2

Variable X: Per capita consumption of margarines annually in the United States (years 2000–2008)

Variable Y: Divorce rate in Maine (per 1,000)

X	7.0	6.5	5.3	5.2	4.0	4.6	4.5	4.2	4.7
Y	4.7	4.6	4.4	4.3	4.1	4.2	4.2	4.2	4.1

Coefficient of correlation: .9926

Example 3

Variable X: Total U.S. imports of crude oil annually (billions of barrels) (years 2000–2009)

Variable Y: Per capita consumption of chicken (pounds)

| X | 3.311 | 3.405 | 3.336 | 3.521 | 3.674 | 3.670 | 3.685 | 3.656 | 3.571 | 3.307 |
| Y | 54.2 | 54.0 | 56.8 | 57.5 | 59.3 | 60.5 | 60.9 | 59.9 | 58.7 | 56.0 |

Coefficient of correlation: .8999

As you can see, the coefficients of correlation in all three examples are large enough to infer that there is a linear relationship between each pair of variables. However, common sense tells us that no such relationship actually exists. Here is how to avoid concluding that a relationship exists when there is spurious correlation.

The first step is to start with a theory of the relationship between two variables. For example, it is logical to believe that there is a linear relationship between the price of gasoline and the price of oil. After an analysis of the values of both variables, a large coefficient of correlation would confirm our belief.

We complete this section with a review of when to use the techniques introduced in this section.

Factors That Identify When to Compute Covariance, Coefficient of Correlation, Coefficient of Determination, and Least Squares Line

1. **Objective**: Describe the relationship between two variables.

2. **Type of data**: Interval

EXERCISES

4.78 Find the coefficient of correlation given these statistics.

$$s_{xy} = 50 \qquad s_x = 20 \qquad s_y = 6$$

4.79 Suppose that you calculated the statistics below. How do you know that you have made a calculation error?

$$s_{xy} = 1895 \qquad s_x = 40 \qquad s_y = 30$$

4.80 A statistics practitioner calculated the covariance between two variables as $-13,576$. Does this statistic indicate that there is a strong negative relationship between the two variables? Explain.

4.81 Refer to Exercise 4.80. The two sample standard deviations of the two variables are 105 and 155. What do the covariance calculated in Exercise 4.80

and these two standard deviations tell you about the relationship between the two variables?

4.82 The covariance between two variables was calculated as 1.35. Can we conclude that there is a weak positive linear relationship between the two variables? Explain.

4.83 Refer to Exercise 4.82. The two sample standard deviations were calculated as 1.05 and 1.31. What do the covariance calculated in Exercise 4.82 and these two standard deviations tell you about the relationship between the two variables? Explain.

4.84 Xr04-84 A retailer wanted to estimate the monthly fixed and variable selling expenses. The total selling expenses ($1,000) and the total sales ($1,000) were recorded and are listed below.

Total Sales	Selling Expenses
20	14
40	16
60	18
50	17
50	18
55	18
60	18
70	20

a. Compute the covariance, the coefficient of correlation, and the coefficient of determination, and describe what these statistics tell you.

b. Determine the least squares line and use it to produce the estimates the retailer wants.

4.85 Xr04-85 Are the marks one receives in a course related to the amount of time spent studying the subject? To investigate this mysterious possibility, a student took a random sample of 10 students who had enrolled in an accounting class last semester. They were asked to report their marks in the course and the total number of hours spent studying accounting. These data are listed here.

Study time	40	42	37	47	25	44	41	48	35	28
Marks	77	63	79	86	51	78	83	90	65	47

a. Calculate the covariance.
b. Calculate the coefficient of correlation.
c. Calculate the coefficient of determination.
d. Determine the least squares line.
e. What do these statistics tell you about the relationship between marks and study time?

4.86 Xr04-86 Students who apply to MBA programs must take the Graduate Management Admission Test (GMAT). University admissions committees use the GMAT score as one of the critical indicators of how well a student is likely to perform in the MBA program. However, the GMAT may not be a very strong indicator for all MBA programs. Suppose that an MBA program designed for middle managers who wish to upgrade their skills was launched three years ago. To judge how well the GMAT score predicts MBA performance, a sample of 12 graduates was taken. Their grade point averages in the MBA program (values from 0 to 12) and their GMAT score (values range from 200 to 800) are listed here. Compute the covariance, the coefficient of correlation, and the coefficient of determination. Interpret your findings.

GMAT	599	689	584	631	594	643
GPA	9.6	8.8	7.4	10.0	7.8	9.2

GMAT	656	594	710	611	593	683
GPA	9.6	8.4	11.2	7.6	8.8	8.0

The following exercises require a computer and software.

4.87 Xr04-87 The unemployment rate is an important measure of a country's economic health. The unemployment rate measures the percentage of people who are looking for work and who are without jobs. Unfortunately, it can be a misleading statistic because it does not include people who are unemployed and would like to find work but have tried and failed and have become discouraged and are no longer looking for a job. Another way of measuring this economic variable is to calculate the labor participation rate, which is the percentage of adults who are employed. We have recorded the labor participation rates and the official unemployment rates for the largest economies. Calculate the coefficient of determination and describe what you have learned.

4.88 Xr04-88 All Canadians have government-funded health insurance, which pays for any medical care they require. However, when traveling out of the country, Canadians usually acquire supplementary health insurance to cover the difference between the costs incurred for emergency treatment and what the government program pays. In the United States, this cost differential can be prohibitive. Until recently, private insurance companies (such as BlueCross BlueShield) charged everyone the same weekly rate, regardless of age. However, because of rising costs and the realization that older people frequently incur greater medical emergency expenses, insurers had to change their premium plans. They decided to offer rates that depend on the age of the customer. To help determine the new rates, one insurance company gathered data concerning the age and mean daily medical expenses of a random sample of 1,348 Canadians during the previous 12-month period.

a. Calculate the coefficient of determination.
b. What does the statistic calculated in part (a) tell you?
c. Determine the least squares line.
d. Interpret the coefficients.
e. What rate plan would you suggest?

4.89 Xr04-89 A real estate developer of single-family dwellings across the country is in the process of developing plans for the next several years. An analyst for the company believes that interest rates are likely to increase but remain at low levels. To help make decisions about the number of homes to build, the developer acquired the monthly bank prime rate and the number of new single-family homes sold monthly (thousands) from 1963 to 2020. Calculate the coefficient of determination. Explain what this statistic tells you about the relationship between the prime bank rate and the number of single-family homes sold.

Source: Federal Reserve Statistics and U.S. Census Bureau.

4.90 Xr04-90 When the price of crude oil increases, do oil companies drill more oil wells? To determine the strength and nature of the relationship, an economist recorded the price of a barrel of domestic crude oil (West Texas crude) and the number of exploratory oil wells drilled for each month from 1973 to 2010 (latest year available). Analyze the data and explain what you have discovered.

Source: U.S. Department of Energy.

4.91 Xr04-91 One way of measuring the extent of unemployment is through the help wanted index, which measures the number of want ads in the nation's newspapers. The higher the index, the greater is the demand for workers. Another measure is the unemployment rate among insured workers. An economist wanted to know whether these two variables are related, and if so, how. The help wanted index and unemployment rates for each month between 1951 and 2006 (last year available) were recorded. Determine the strength and direction of the relationship.

Source: U.S. Department of Labor Statistics.

4.92 Xr04-92 A manufacturing firm produces its products in batches using sophisticated machines and equipment. The general manager wanted to investigate the relationship between direct labor costs and the number of units produced per batch. The data from the last 30 batches were recorded. Determine the fixed and variable labor costs.

4.93 Xr04-93 A manufacturer has recorded its cost of electricity and the total number of hours of machine time for each of 52 weeks. Estimate the fixed and variable electricity costs.

4.94 Xr04-94 The U.S. Census Bureau in conjunction with the Bureau of Labor Statistics conducts surveys that record a wide variety of subjects. In a Consumer Expenditure Survey, respondents were asked their age and the amount of money spent in the previous year on alcoholic beverages. Compute whatever statistics you need to determine whether age and alcoholic expenditures are related.

4.95 Xr04-96 Refer to Exercise 4.94. In another survey by the Bureau of Labor Statistics, respondents who reported that they rent their dwelling were asked their age and how much they spend annually on rent. Use a statistical analysis to determine whether the data indicate that as renters grow older, they spend less on rent.

4.96 Xr04-96 To determine the relationship between age of cars and annual repair costs, a random sample of car owners was drawn and the two variables were recorded. Calculate statistics to determine whether cost of repairs increase as the car ages, and on average, what is the cost.

4.97 Xr04-97 A professional income tax preparer recorded the amount of tax rebate and the total taxable amount of a sample of 80 customers. Compute whichever statistics you need to determine whether tax rebates increase as the taxable income increases.

4.98 Xr04-98 Carbon monoxide (CO) in the home is caused by faulty furnaces burning natural gas or heating oil. Concentrations above 35 parts per million (ppm) are considered dangerous. Suppose that a municipal home inspector randomly samples 180 houses around the city and records the age of the furnace and the CO concentration during 1 day in the winter heating season. Conduct a statistical analysis to determine whether the age of the furnace and CO concentrations are related.

4.99 Xr04-99 The U.S.–Canada exchange rate has fluctuated over the past 30 years. Can any single commodity explain these fluctuations? Is it oil, for example? Canada sells a lot of oil to the United States. It may be lumber or gold. A statistician set out to investigate the U.S.–Canada exchange rate and its underlying causes. We have stored the monthly exchange rate (the ratio of the value of the U.S. dollar to the value of the Canadian dollar) from January 1991 to August 2018. The other prices we recorded are listed below. For each, compute the coefficient of correlation with the U.S.–Canada exchange rate and briefly describe what the statistic tells you.

Price of gold (U.S. dollars per troy ounce)
Price of copper (U.S. dollars per metric ton)
Price of silver (U.S. cents per troy ounce)
Price of beef (U.S. cents per pound)
Price of West Texas crude oil (U.S. dollars per barrel)

4.100 Xr04-100 The chapter-opening example showed that there is a weak linear relationship between a baseball teams' payroll and the number of wins. This raises the question: Are success on the field and attendance related? If the answer is no, then profit-driven owners may not be inclined to spend money to improve their teams. We recorded the number of wins and the total home attendance for the 2019 baseball season.
a. Calculate the least squares line and the coefficient of determination.
b. Estimate the marginal number of tickets sold for each additional game won.
c. What does the coefficient of determination tell you about the relationship between the number of wins and attendance?

4.101 Xr04-101 Refer to Exercise 4.100. The practitioner also recorded the road attendance for each team in the 2019 season. Since visiting teams take a share of the gate, owners should be interested in this analysis.

a. Is visiting team attendance related to number of wins?

b. Estimate the marginal number of tickets sold for each additional game won.

4.102 Xr04-102   Repeat Exercise 4.100 for the National Hockey League. Analyze the relationship between points attained (2 points for a win and 1 point for an overtime loss) and home attendance.

4.103 Xr04-103   A statistics practitioner recorded the number of wins and the home attendance for the 2018–2019 National Football League. Conduct an analysis of the data to determine whether there is a relationship between the two variables.

4.104 Xr04-104   Repeat Exercise 4.103 for the 2018–2019 National Basketball Association season.

4.105 Xr04-105   In hockey, winning faceoffs is important because losing a faceoff in your own defensive zone increases the probability of having a goal scored on your team. We recorded the number of wins and the percentage of faceoffs won for the 2017–2018 season of the NHL. Determine if winning faceoffs increases team wins.

4-5 / (OPTIONAL) APPLICATIONS IN FINANCE: MARKET MODEL

In the Applications in Finance box on page 61, we introduced the terms *return on investment* and *risk*. We described two goals of investing. The first is to maximize the expected or mean return and the second is to minimize the risk. Financial analysts use a variety of statistical techniques to achieve these goals. Most investors are risk-averse, which means that for them minimizing risk is of paramount importance. Analysts use the variance and standard deviation to measure the risk associated with investments.

APPLICATIONS in FINANCE

Stock Market Indexes

Stock markets such as the New York Stock Exchange (NYSE), NASDAQ, Toronto Stock Exchange (TSE), and many others around the world calculate indexes to provide information about the prices of stocks on their exchanges. A stock market index is composed of a number of stocks that more or less represent the entire market. For example, the Dow Jones Industrial Average (DJIA) is the average price of a group of 30 NYSE stocks of large publicly traded companies. The Standard and Poor's 500 (S&P) is the average price of 500 NYSE stocks. These indexes represent their stock exchanges and give readers a quick view of how well the exchange is doing as well the economy of the country as a whole. The NASDAQ 100 is the average price of the 100 largest nonfinancial companies on the NASDAQ exchange. The S&P/TSX Composite Index is composed of 60 large companies on the TSE.

In this section, we describe one of the most important applications of the use of a least squares line. It is the well-known and often applied *market model*. This model assumes that the rate of return on a stock is linearly related to the rate of return on the stock market index. The return on the index is calculated in the same way the return on a single stock is computed. For example, if the index at the end of last year was 10,000 and the value at the end of this year is 11,000, the market index annual return is 10%. The return on the stock is the dependent variable Y and the return on the index is the independent variable X.

We use the least squares line to represent the linear relationship between X and Y. The coefficient b_1 is called the stock's *beta coefficient*, which measures how sensitive the stock's rate of return is to changes in the level of the overall market. For example, if b_1 is greater than 1, the stock's rate of return is more sensitive to changes in the level of the overall market than is the average stock. To illustrate, suppose that $b_1 = 2$. Then a 1% increase in the index results in an average increase of 2% in the stock's return. A 1% decrease in the index produces an average 2% decrease in the stock's return. Thus, a stock with a beta coefficient greater than 1 will tend to be more volatile than the market.

EXAMPLE 4.17   Market Model for Home Depot

DATA
Xm04-17

The monthly rates of returns for Home Depot (Symbol HD) and the Standard and Poor's index (a measure of the NYSE stock market) were recorded for each month between January 2016 and December 2019. Some of these data are shown here. Estimate the market model and analyze the results.

Year	Month	S&P 500	HD
2016	January	−0.00413	−0.01304
	February	0.06599	0.07501
	March	0.00270	0.00897
	April	0.01532	−0.01322
2019	September	0.02043	0.01721
	October	0.03405	−0.05998
	November	0.02859	−0.00966
	December	−0.00163	0.05119

SOLUTION:

Excel's scatter diagram and least squares line are shown here. We included the equation and the coefficient of determination on the graph.

EXCEL Chart

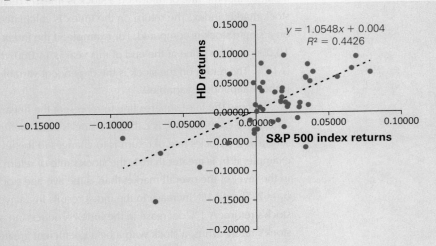

We note that the slope coefficient for Home Depot is 1.0548. We interpret this to mean that in this sample for each 1% increase in the S&P 500 index's return, the average increase in Home Depot's return is 1.0548%. Because b_1 is greater than 1, we conclude that the return on investing in Home Depot stock is (slightly) more volatile and therefore (slightly) riskier than the Standard & Poor's index.

4-5a Systematic and Firm-Specific Risk

The coefficient of determination measures the proportion of the total risk that is market related. In this case we see that 44.26% of Home Depot's total risk is market related. That is, 44.26% of the variation in HD's returns is explained by the variation in the returns of the S&P 500 index. The remaining 55.74% is the proportion of the risk that is associated with events specific to Home Depot, rather than the market. Financial analysts (and most everyone else) call this the *firm-specific* (or *nonsystematic*) *risk*. The firm-specific risk is attributable to variables and events not included in the market model, such as effectiveness of Home Depot's advertising or the need for Home Depot's products. For example, after a hurricane does damage to houses, the demand for many of Home Depot's products increases. This is part of the risk that cannot be "diversified away" by creating a portfolio of stocks as discussed in Section 7-3. We cannot, however, diversify away the part of the risk that is market related.

When a portfolio has been created, we can estimate its beta by averaging the betas of the stocks that compose the portfolio. If an investor believes that the market is likely to rise, a portfolio with a beta coefficient greater than 1 is desirable. Risk-averse investors or ones who believe that the market will fall will seek out portfolios with betas less than 1.

EXERCISES

The following exercises require the use of a computer and software.

<u>Xr04-NYSE</u> We have recorded the 48 monthly returns for the S&P 500 index and the following 23 of the 30 Dow Jones Industrial stocks listed on the New York Stock Exchange (six others are on the NASDAQ and one has been around since 2019 only) for the period January 2016–December 2019.

> 3M (MMM)
> American Express (AXP)
> Boeing (BA)
> Caterpillar (CAT)
> Chevron (CVX)
> Coca-Cola (KO)
> Goldman Sachs (GS)
> Home Depot (HD)
> Honeywell (HON)
> International Business Machines (IBM)
> Johnson & Johnson (JNJ)
> JP Morgan Chase (JPM)
> McDonald's (MCD)
> Merck (MRK)
> Nike (NKE)
> Procter & Gamble (PG)
> Salesforce (CRM)
> Travelers (TRV)
> United Health (UNH)
> Verizon Communications (VZ)
> Visa (V)
> Wal-Mart Stores (WMT)
> Walt Disney (DIS)

For the following exercises, calculate the beta coefficient and the coefficient of determination for the listed stock and interpret their values. (Excel users: Note that to use the scatter diagram to compute the beta coefficient, the data must be stored in two adjacent columns. The first must contain the returns on the index and the second stores the returns for whichever stock whose coefficient you wish to calculate.)

4.106 Procter and Gamble (PG)

4.107 American Express (AXP)

4.108 3M (MMM)

4.109 McDonald's (MCD)

4.110 Nike (NKE)

4.111 Visa (V)

For the following exercises, determine the average beta coefficient for the stocks in the listed portfolio.

4.112 Boeing (BA), Caterpillar (CAT), and JP Morgan Chase (JPM)

4.113 Travelers (TRV), Chevron (CVX), and McDonald's (MCD)

4.114 Merck (MRK), Visa (V), and United Health (UNH)

<u>Xr04-TSE</u> Monthly returns for the Toronto Stock Exchange Index and the following selected stocks on the Toronto Stock Exchange were recorded for the period January 2016–December 2019.

> Agnico Eagle (AEM)
> Barrick Gold (ABX)
> Bell Canada Enterprises (BCE)
> Bank of Montreal (BMO)
> Bank of Nova Scotia (BNS)
> Canadian Imperial Bank of Commerce (CM)
> Canadian National Railways (CNR)
> Canadian Tire (CTC)
> Enbridge (ENB)
> Fortis (FTS)
> Great West Life (GWO)
> Manulife Financial (MFC)
> Magna International (MG)
> Open Text (OTEX)
> Power Corporation of Canada (POW)
> Rogers Communication (RCI.B)
> Royal Bank of Canada (RY)
> Suncor Energy (SU)
> Telus (T)
> George Weston (WN)

Calculate the beta coefficient and the coefficient of determination for the listed stock and interpret their values.

4.115 Barrick Gold (ABX)

4.116 Enbridge (ENB)

4.117 Telus (T)

Determine the average beta coefficient for the stocks in the listed portfolios.

4.118 Bank of Montreal (BMO), Bank of Nova Scotia (BNS), and Royal Bank of Canada (RY)

4.119 Fortis (FTS), Enbridge (ENB), and Suncor Energy (SU)

4.120 Rogers Communication (RCI.B) and Telus (T)

Xr04-NASDAQ   We calculated the returns on the NASDAQ Index and the following selected stocks on the NASDAQ Exchange for the period January 2016–December 2019.

Adobe Systems (ADBE)
Amazon (AMZN)
Amgen (AMGN)
Apple (AAPL)
Bed Bath & Beyond (BBBY)
Cisco Systems (CSCO)
Comcast (CMCSA)
Costco Wholesale (COST)
Dollar Tree (DLTR)
Expedia (EXPE)
Garmin (GRMN)
Intel (INTC)
Mattel (MAT)
Microsoft (MSFT)
Netflix (NFLX)

Oracle (ORCL)
Sirius XM Radio (SIRI)
Starbucks (SBUX)
Tesla (TSLA)
Vertex Pharmaceuticals (VRTX)

Calculate the beta coefficient and the coefficient of determination for the listed stocks and interpret their values.

4.121 Amazon (AMZN)

4.122 Expedia (EXPE)

4.123 Netflix (NFLX)

Determine the average beta coefficient for the stocks in the listed portfolios.

4.124 Apple (AAPL), Cisco Systems (CSCO), and Oracle (ORCL)

4.125 Costco Wholesale (COST), Dollar Tree (DLTR), and Starbucks (SBUX)

4.126 Adobe System (ADBE) and Microsoft (MSFT)

4-6 / COMPARING GRAPHICAL AND NUMERICAL TECHNIQUES

As we mentioned before, graphical techniques are useful in producing a quick picture of the data. For example, you learn something about the location, spread, and shape of a set of interval data when you examine its histogram. Numerical techniques provide the same approximate information. We have measures of central location, measures of variability, and measures of relative standing that do what the histogram does. The scatter diagram graphically describes the relationship between two interval variables. But so do the numerical measures covariance, coefficient of correlation, coefficient of determination, and least squares line. Why then do we need to learn both categories of techniques? The answer is that they differ in the information each provides. We illustrate the difference between graphical and numerical methods by redoing four examples we used to illustrate graphical techniques in Chapter 3.

EXAMPLE 3.2

Comparing Returns on Two Investments

In Example 3.2, we wanted to judge which investment appeared to be better. As we discussed in the Applications in Finance: Return on Investment (page 61), we judge investments in terms of the return we can expect and its risk. We drew histograms and attempted to interpret them. The centers of the histograms provided us with information about the expected return and their spreads gauged the risk. However, the histograms were not clear. Fortunately, we can use numerical measures. The mean and median provide us with information about the return we can expect, and the variance or standard deviation tell us about the risk associated with each investment.

Here are the descriptive statistics produced by Excel.

Excel Output for Example 3.2

	A	B	C	D	E
1	Return A			Return B	
2					
3	Mean	10.95		Mean	12.76
4	Standard Error	3.10		Standard Error	3.97
5	Median	9.88		Median	10.76
6	Mode	12.89		Mode	#N/A
7	Standard Deviation	21.89		Standard Deviation	28.05
8	Sample Variance	479.35		Sample Variance	786.62
9	Kurtosis	−0.32		Kurtosis	−0.62
10	Skewness	0.54		Skewness	0.01
11	Range	84.95		Range	106.47
12	Minimum	−21.95		Minimum	−38.47
13	Maximum	63		Maximum	68
14	Sum	547.27		Sum	638.01
15	Count	50		Count	50

We can now see that investment B has a larger mean and median, but that investment A has a smaller variance and standard deviation. If investors were interested in low-risk investments, they would choose investment A. If you reexamine the histograms from Example 3.2 (page 61), you will see that the precision provided by the numerical techniques (mean, median, and standard deviation) provides more useful information than did the histograms.

EXAMPLES 3.3 AND 3.4

Business Statistics Marks; Mathematical Statistical Marks

In these examples, we wanted to see what differences existed between the marks in the two statistics classes. Here are the descriptive statistics. (We combined the two printouts in one worksheet.)

Excel Output for Examples 3.3 and 3.4

	A	B	C	D	E
1	Marks (Example 3.3)			Marks (Example 3.4)	
2					
3	Mean	72.67		Mean	66.40
4	Standard Error	1.07		Standard Error	1.610
5	Median	72		Median	71.5
6	Mode	67		Mode	75
7	Standard Deviation	8.29		Standard Deviation	12.470
8	Sample Variance	68.77		Sample Variance	155.498
9	Kurtosis	−0.36		Kurtosis	−1.241
10	Skewness	0.16		Skewness	−0.217
11	Range	39		Range	48
12	Minimum	53		Minimum	44
13	Maximum	92		Maximum	92
14	Sum	4360		Sum	3984
15	Count	60		Count	60
16	Largest(15)	79		Largest(15)	76
17	Smallest(15)	67		Smallest(15)	53

The statistics tell us that the mean and median of the marks in the business statistics course (Example 3.3) are higher than in the mathematical statistics course (Example 3.4). We found that the histogram of the mathematical statistics marks was bimodal, which we interpreted to mean that this type of approach created differences between students. The unimodal histogram of the business statistics marks informed us that this approach eliminated those differences.

Chapter 3 Opening Example

In this example, we wanted to know whether the prices of gasoline and oil were related. The scatter diagram did reveal a strong positive linear relationship. We can improve upon the quality of this information by computing the coefficient of correlation and drawing the least squares line.

Excel Output for Chapter 3 Opening Example: Coefficient of Correlation

	A	B	C
1		Price of Oil	Price of Gasoline
2	Price of Oil	1	
3	Price of Gasoline	0.9677	1

The coefficient of correlation confirms what we learned from the scatter diagram. That is, there is strong positive linear relationship between the price of oil and the price of gasoline.

Excel Output for Chapter 3 Opening Example: Least Squares line

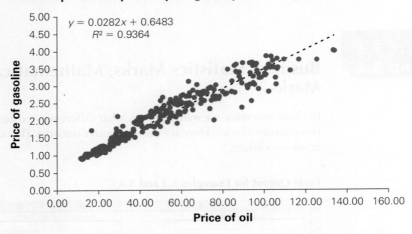

The slope coefficient tells us that for each dollar increase in the price of a barrel of oil, the price of a (U.S.) gallon of gasoline increases on average by 2.82 cents. However, because there are 42 gallons per barrel, we would expect a dollar increase in a barrel of oil to yield a 2.4* cents per gallon (calculated as \$1.00/42) increase. It does appear that the oil companies are taking some small advantage by adding an extra half cent per gallon. The coefficient of determination is .9364, which indicates that 93.64% of the variation in gasoline prices is explained by the variation in oil prices.

---

*This is a simplification. In fact, a barrel of oil yields a variety of other profitable products. See Exercise 2.28.

EXERCISES

4.127 Xr03-76 Calculate the coefficient of determination for Exercise 3.76. What does this statistic tell you about the relationship between marks in calculus and statistics that the scatter diagram did not?

4.128 Xr03-80 Refer to Exercise 3.80.
a. Compute the coefficients of the least squares line.
b. What do the coefficients tell you about the number of occupants and electricity use?

4.129 Xr03-79 Refer to Exercise 3.79.
a. Compute the coefficient of determination and the least squares line.
b. Briefly discuss what the coefficients of the least squares line and the coefficient of

determination tell you about the relationship between time to complete the quiz and the mark that the scatter diagram could not.

4.130 Xr03-82 Refer to Exercise 3.82. Calculate the coefficient of determination and the least squares line. What do these statistics tell you about the relationship between heights and annual incomes? Is this more informative than the scatter diagram? Explain.

4.131 Xm03-07 Refer to Example 3.7.
a. Calculate the coefficients of the least squares line relating house size and price.
b. Interpret the coefficients.
c. Are these statistics more useful than the scatter diagram? Explain.

4-7 GENERAL GUIDELINES FOR EXPLORING DATA

The purpose of applying graphical and numerical techniques is to describe and summarize data. Statisticians usually apply graphical techniques as a first step because we need to know the shape of the distribution. The shape of the distribution helps answer the following questions:

1. Where is the approximate center of the distribution?

2. Are the observations close to one another, or are they widely dispersed?

3. Is the distribution unimodal, bimodal, or multimodal? If there is more than one mode, where are the peaks, and where are the valleys?

4. Is the distribution symmetric? If not, is it skewed? If symmetric, is it bell shaped?

Histograms provide most of the answers. We can frequently make several inferences about the nature of the data from the shape. For example, we can assess the relative risk of investments by noting their spreads. We can attempt to improve the teaching of a course by examining whether the distribution of final grades is bimodal or skewed.

The shape can also provide some guidance on which numerical techniques to use. As we noted in this chapter, the central location of highly skewed data may be more appropriately measured by the median. We may also choose to use the interquartile range instead of the standard deviation to describe the spread of skewed data.

When we have an understanding of the structure of the data, we may do additional analysis. For example, we often want to determine how one variable, or several variables, affects another. Scatter diagrams, covariance, and the coefficient of correlation are useful techniques for detecting relationships between variables. A number of techniques to be introduced later in this book will help uncover the nature of these associations.

CHAPTER SUMMARY

This chapter extended our discussion of descriptive statistics, which deals with methods of summarizing and presenting the essential information contained in a set of data. After constructing a frequency distribution to obtain a general idea about the distribution of a data set, we can use numerical measures to describe the central location and variability of interval data. Three popular measures of central location, or averages, are the mean, the median, and the mode. Taken by themselves, these measures provide an inadequate description of the data because they say nothing about the extent to which the data vary. Information regarding the variability of interval data is conveyed by such numerical measures as the range, variance, and standard deviation.

For the special case in which a sample of measurements has a mound-shaped distribution, the Empirical Rule provides a good approximation of the percentages of measurements that fall within one, two, and three standard deviations of the mean. Chebysheff's Theorem applies to all sets of data no matter the shape of the histogram.

Measures of relative standing that were presented in this chapter are percentiles and quartiles. The linear relationship between two interval variables is measured by the covariance, the coefficient of correlation, the coefficient of determination, and the least squares line.

IMPORTANT TERMS:

Measures of central location   98
Mean   99
Median   100
Mode   101
Modal class   101
Geometric mean   103
Measures of variability   108
Range   108
Variance   108
Standard deviation   108
Deviation   109

Mean absolute deviation   110
Empirical Rule   112
Chebysheff's Theorem   113
Skewed   114
Coefficient of variation   114
Percentiles   117
Quartiles   117
Interquartile range   120
Covariance   122
Coefficient of correlation   124
Least squares method   126

SYMBOLS:

Symbol	Pronounced	Represents
μ	mu	Population mean
σ^2	sigma squared	Population variance
σ	sigma	Population standard deviation
ρ	rho	Population coefficient of correlation
$\sum$	Sum of	Summation
$\sum_{i=1}^{n} x_i$	Sum of x_i from 1 to n	Summation of n numbers
$\hat{y}$	y hat	Fitted or calculated value of y
b_0	b zero	y-Intercept
b_1	b one	Slope coefficient

FORMULAS:

Population mean

$$\mu = \frac{\sum_{i=1}^{N} x_i}{N}$$

Sample mean

$$\bar{x} = \frac{\sum_{i=1}^{n} x_i}{n}$$

Range

Largest observation − Smallest observation

Population variance

$$\sigma^2 = \frac{\sum_{i=1}^{N}(x_i - \mu)^2}{N}$$

Sample variance

$$s^2 = \frac{\sum_{i=1}^{n}(x_i - \bar{x})^2}{n - 1}$$

Population standard deviation

$$\sigma = \sqrt{\sigma^2}$$

Sample standard deviation

$$s = \sqrt{s^2}$$

Population covariance

$$\sigma_{xy} = \frac{\sum_{i=1}^{N}(x_i - \mu_x)(y_i - \mu_y)}{N}$$

Sample covariance

$$s_{xy} = \frac{\sum_{i=1}^{n}(x_i - \bar{x})(y_i - \bar{y})}{n - 1}$$

Population coefficient of correlation

$$\rho = \frac{\sigma_{xy}}{\sigma_x \sigma_y}$$

Sample coefficient of correlation

$$r = \frac{s_{xy}}{s_x s_y}$$

Coefficient of determination

$$R^2 = r^2$$

Slope coefficient

$$b_1 = \frac{s_{xy}}{s_x^2}$$

y-intercept

$$b_0 = \bar{y} - b_1\bar{x}$$

EXCEL OUTPUT AND INSTRUCTIONS

Technique	
Mean	100
Median	101
Mode	102
Descriptive statistics	102
Variance	111
Quartiles	119
Percentiles	119
Least squares line	129
Covariance	131
Correlation	131
Coefficient of determination	132

CHAPTER EXERCISES

GENERAL SOCIAL SURVEY EXERCISES

DATA
GSS2018

The following exercises are based on the General Social Survey of 2018.

4.132 Compute the mean, standard deviation, and the quartiles of the annual income (RINCOME) of

respondents. Briefly describe what the statistics tell you about annual incomes.

4.133 Exercise 3.90 analyzed the relationship between years of education (EDUC) and annual income

(RINCOME) by drawing a scatter diagram. We looked at the scatter diagram to see the direction and the strength of the relationship. Calculate the least squares line and the coefficients of correlation and determination. Describe what these statistics tell you that the scatter diagram could not.

4.134 Compute the mean, standard deviation, and quartiles for years of education (EDUC). Briefly describe what these statistics inform us about this variable.

4.135 Exercise 3.93 examined the relationship between annual income (RINCOME) and hours of work per week (HRS1) using a scatter diagram. Calculate the least squares line and the coefficients of correlation and determination. Interpret their meaning.

4.136 Calculate the mean, standard deviations, and the quartiles of the hours of watching television (TVHOURS). Briefly describe what each statistic tells you about this variable.

4.137 Exercise 3.95 analyzed the relationship between years of education (EDUC) and number of hours of television watching (TVHOURS). The only technique you had at that time was the scatter diagram. Determine the coefficients of the least squares line and the coefficient of correlation. Describe what they tell you about the relationship.

4.138 To learn more about hours of work per week (HRS1), compute the mean, standard deviation, and the quartiles. Interpret each statistic.

4.139 Exercise 3.96 asked whether older (AGE) Americans watch more television (TVHOURS). The scatter diagram did not provide any precision. Answer the question by determining the least squares line and the coefficient of determination. Briefly explain what information you draw from the statistics.

CASE 4.1   Return to the Global Warming Question

Now that we have presented techniques that allow us to conduct more precise analyses, we'll return to Case 3.1. Recall that there are two issues in this discussion. First, is there global warming and, second, if so, is carbon dioxide the cause? The only tools available at the end of Chapter 3 were graphical techniques including line charts and scatter diagrams. You are now invited to apply the more precise techniques used in this chapter to answer the same questions.

Here are the data sets you can work with:

C04-01a: Column 1: Months numbered 1 to 1688
Column 2: Temperature anomalies produced by the National Climatic Data Center

C04-01b: Column 1: Year
Column 2: Month
Column 3: Monthly carbon dioxide levels measured by the Mauna Loa Observatory

Column 4: Temperature anomalies produced by the National Climatic Data Center

a. Use the least squares method to estimate average monthly changes in temperature anomalies.

b. Calculate the least squares line and the coefficient of correlation between CO_2 levels and temperature anomalies and describe your findings.

APPENDIX 4.A / XLSTAT OUTPUT AND INSTRUCTIONS

Descriptive Statistics

Examples 4.2, 4.4, and 4.6 (using the data from Example 3.1)

Descriptive Statistics (Quantitative data):	
Statistic	*Ages*
Nbr. Of observations	200
Minimum	16.000
Maximum	99.000
Range	83.000
1st Quartile	36.000
Median	54.500
3rd Quartile	69.000
Mean	53.765
Variance (n-1)	390.522
Standard deviation (n-1)	19.762

Instructions

1. Type or import the data into one column. (Open Xm03-01.)

2. Click **XLSTAT**, **Describing data**, and **Descriptive statistics**.

3. Check **Quantitative data** and type the input range; (A1:A201). Check **Variable labels** if the first row of the data contains the name of the variable. Choose **Range:**, **Sheet**, or **Workbook** depending on where you wish the results to appear.

4. Click the **Outputs** tab and check the following (Scroll down as necessary): **Nbr. Of observations, Minimum, Maximum, Range, 1st Quartile, Median, 3rd Quartile, Mean, Variance (n-1)**, and **Standard deviation (n-1)**.

Coefficient of Correlation and Least Squares Line

Example 4.15

	B	C	D	E
10	Correlation matrix:			
11				
12		Number of tools	Electrical costs	
13	Number of tools	1	0.8711	
14	Electrical costs	0.8711	1	
15				
38	Equation of the model (Electrical costs):			
39				
40	Electrical costs = 9.58776+2.24588*Number of tools			

The output has been edited by hiding rows and columns.

Instructions

1. Type or import the data into two columns. (Open Xm04-15.)

2. Click **Modeling data** and **Linear regression**.

3. Type the range of the **Y/Dependent variable(s)** (C1:C11). Type the range of the **X/Explanatory variable(s)** (B1:B11).

4. Click the **Outputs** tab and check **Correlations**.

APPENDIX 4.B / STATA OUTPUT AND INSTRUCTIONS

Descriptive Statistics

Examples 4.2, 4.4, and 4.6 (using data from Example 3.1)

Ages

	Percentiles	Smallest		
1%	16.5	16		
5%	24	16		
10%	27	17	Obs	200
25%	36	18	Sum of Wgt.	200
50%	54.5		Mean	53.765
		Largest	Std. Dev.	19.76164
75%	69	94		
90%	78.5	95	Variance	390.5224
95%	83	96	Skewness	.0025145
99%	95.5	99	Kurtosis	2.107035

STATA prints a variety of statistics.

Mean = 53.765; variance = 390.5224; standard deviation = 19.76164; first quartile = 25th percentile = 36, second quartile = 50th percentile = median = 54.5; third quartile = 75th percentile = 69.

Instructions

1. Import or type the data into one column. (Click File/Import/Excel spreadsheet (*xls,*xlsx)/Xm03-01.) Check **Import first row as variable names**.

2. Click **Statistics, Summary, tables, and tests, Summary and descriptive statistics,** and **Summary statistics**.

3. In the **Variables (leave empty for all variables)** select **Ages**. Under **Options** select **Display additional statistics**.

Least Squares Line

Examples 4.15

Electricalc~s	Coef.	Std. Err.	t	P>|t|	[95% Conf. Interval]	
Numberoftools	2.245882	.4477112	5.02	0.001	1.213458	3.278306
_cons	9.587765	3.371239	2.84	0.022	1.813674	17.36186

The least squares line is $\hat{y} = 9.587765 + 2.245882 \times$ Number of tools

Instructions

1. Import or type the data into one column. (Click File/Import/Excel spreadsheet (*xls,*xlsx)/Xm04-15.) Check **Import first row as variable names**.
2. Click **Statistics, Linear models and related**, and **Linear regression**.
3. Select **Electrical costs** as the **Dependent variable:** and in the **Independent variables:** box select **Number of tools**.

Covariance and Coefficient of Correlation

Example 4.15

	Number~s	Electr~s
Numberofto~s	1.0000	
Electrical~s	0.8711	1.0000

	Number~s	Electr~s
Numberofto~s	16.0556	
Electrical~s	36.0589	106.73

Instructions

1. Import or type the data into one column. (Click File/Import/Excel spreadsheet (*xls,*xlsx)/Xm04-15.) Check **Import first row as variable names**.
2. Click **Statistics, Summaries, tables and tests, Summary and descriptive statistics**, and **Correlations and Covariances**.
3. In the **Variables (leave empty for all):** box select **Number of tools Electrical costs**. Click **OK**.
4. To output the covariance, repeat steps 1–3 and click **Options** and check **Display covariances**.

APPENDIX 4.C / REVIEW OF DESCRIPTIVE TECHNIQUES

Here is a list of the statistical techniques introduced in Chapters 2, 3, and 4. This is followed by a flowchart designed to help you select the most appropriate method to use to address any problem requiring a descriptive method.

Graphical Techniques

Histogram

Bar chart

Pie chart

Scatter diagram

Line chart (time series)

Numerical Techniques

Measures of central location

Mean

Median

Mode

Geometric mean (growth rates)

Measures of variability

Range

Variance

Standard deviation

Coefficient of variation

Interquartile range

Measures of relative standing

Percentiles

Quartiles

Measures of linear relationship

Covariance

Coefficient of correlation

Coefficient of determination

Least squares line

Flowchart: Graphical and Numerical Techniques

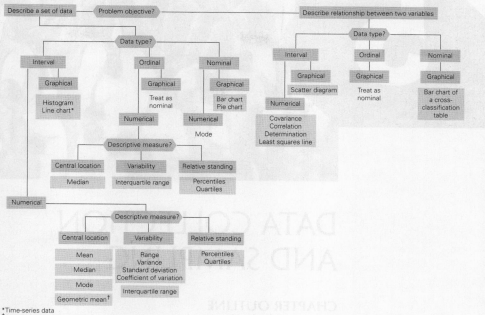

*Time-series data
†Growth rates

5

DATA COLLECTION AND SAMPLING

CHAPTER OUTLINE

Sampling and the Census

The census, which is conducted every 10 years in the United States, serves an important function. It is the basis for deciding how many congressional representatives and how many votes in the electoral college each state will have. Businesses often use the information derived from the census to help make decisions about products, advertising, and plant locations.

Spencer Grant/Age Fotostock

On page 164, you will find our answer.

One of the problems with the census is the issue of undercounting, which occurs when some people are not included. For example, the 1990 census reported that 12.05% of adults were African American; the true value was 12.41%. To address undercounting, the Census Bureau adjusts the numbers it gets from the census. The adjustment is based on another survey. The mechanism is called the Accuracy and Coverage Evaluation. Using sampling methods described in this chapter, the Census Bureau is able to adjust the numbers in American subgroups. For example, the Bureau may discover that the number of Hispanics has been undercounted or that the number of people living in California has not been accurately counted.

Later in this chapter we'll discuss how the sampling is conducted and how the adjustments are made.

INTRODUCTION

In Chapter 1, we briefly introduced the concept of statistical inference—the process of inferring information about a population from a sample. Because information about populations can usually be described by parameters, the statistical technique used generally deals with drawing inferences about population parameters from sample statistics. (Recall that a parameter is a measurement about a population, and a statistic is a measurement about a sample.)

Working within the covers of a statistics textbook, we can assume that population parameters are known. In real life, however, calculating parameters is virtually impossible because populations tend to be very large. As a result, most population parameters are not only unknown but also unknowable. The problem that motivates the subject of statistical inference is that we often need information about the value of parameters in order to make decisions. For example, to make decisions about whether to expand a line of clothing, we may need to know the mean annual expenditure on clothing by North American adults. Because the size of this population is approximately 200 million, determining the mean is prohibitive. However, if we are willing to accept less than 100% accuracy, we can use statistical inference to obtain an estimate. Rather than investigating the entire population, we select a sample of people, determine the annual expenditures on clothing in this group, and calculate the sample mean. Although the probability that the sample mean will equal the population mean is very small, we would expect them to be close. For many decisions, we need to know how close. We postpone that discussion until Chapters 10 and 11. In this chapter, we will discuss the basic concepts and techniques of sampling itself. But first we take a look at various sources for collecting data.

5-1 / METHODS OF COLLECTING DATA

Most of this book addresses the problem of converting data into information. The question arises, where do data come from? The answer is that a large number of methods produce data. Before we proceed, however, we'll remind you of the definition of data introduced in Section 2-1. Data are the observed values of a variable; that is, we define a variable or variables that are of interest to us and then proceed to collect observations of those variables.

5-1a Direct Observation

The simplest method of obtaining data is by direct observation. When data are gathered in this way, they are said to be **observational**. For example, suppose that a researcher for a pharmaceutical company wants to determine whether aspirin actually reduces the incidence of heart attacks. Observational data may be gathered by selecting a sample of adults and asking whether they had taken aspirin regularly over the past 2 years. Each person would be asked whether they had suffered a heart attack over the same period. The proportions reporting heart attacks would be compared and a statistical technique that is introduced in Chapter 13 would be used to determine whether aspirin is effective in reducing the likelihood of heart attacks. There are many drawbacks to this method. One of the most critical is that it is difficult to produce useful information in this way. For example, if the statistics practitioner concludes that people who take aspirin suffer fewer heart attacks, can we conclude that aspirin is effective? It may be that people who take aspirin tend to be more health conscious, and health-conscious people tend to have fewer heart attacks. The one advantage of direct observation is that it is relatively inexpensive.

5-1b Experiments

A more expensive but better way to produce data is through experiments. Data produced in this manner are called **experimental**. In the aspirin illustration, a statistics practitioner can randomly select men and women. The sample would be divided into two groups. One group would take aspirin regularly, and the other would not. After 2 years, the statistics practitioner would determine the proportion of people in each group who had suffered heart attacks, and statistical methods again would be used to determine whether aspirin works. If we find that the aspirin group suffered fewer heart attacks, then we may more confidently conclude that taking aspirin regularly is a healthy decision.

5-1c Surveys

One of the most familiar methods of collecting data is the **survey**, which solicits information from people concerning such things as their income, family size, and opinions on various issues. We're all familiar, for example, with opinion polls that accompany each political election. The Gallup Poll and the Harris Survey are two well-known surveys of public opinion whose results are often reported by the media. But the majority of surveys are conducted for private use. Private surveys are used extensively by market researchers to determine the preferences and attitudes of consumers and voters. The results can be used for a variety of purposes, from helping to determine the target market for an advertising campaign to modifying a candidate's platform in an election campaign. As an illustration, consider a television network that has hired a market research firm to provide the network with a profile of owners of luxury automobiles, including what they watch on television and at what times. The network could then use this information to develop a package of recommended time slots for Cadillac commercials, including costs, which it would present to General Motors. It is quite likely that many students reading this book will one day be marketing executives who will "live and die" by such market research data.

An important aspect of surveys is the **response rate**. The response rate is the proportion of all people who were selected who complete the survey. As we discuss in the next section, a low response rate can destroy the validity of any conclusion resulting from the statistical analysis. Statistics practitioners need to ensure that data are reliable.

Personal Interview Many researchers feel that the best way to survey people is by means of a personal interview, which involves an interviewer soliciting information from a respondent by asking prepared questions. A personal interview has the advantage of having a higher expected response rate than other methods of data collection. In addition, there will probably be fewer incorrect responses resulting from respondents misunderstanding some questions because the interviewer can clarify misunderstandings when asked to. But the interviewer must also be careful not to say too much for fear of biasing the response. To avoid introducing such biases, as well as to reap the potential benefits of a personal interview, the interviewer must be well trained in proper interviewing techniques and well informed on the purpose of the study. The main disadvantage of personal interviews is that they are expensive, especially when travel is involved.

Telephone Interview A telephone interview is usually less expensive, but it is also less personal and has a lower expected response rate. Unless the issue is of interest, many people will refuse to respond to telephone surveys. This problem is exacerbated by telemarketers trying to sell something. Moreover, many people do not have land lines and use cell phones instead, making it difficult to include them in surveys.

Self-Administered Survey A third popular method of data collection is the self-administered questionnaire, which is usually mailed to a sample of people. This is an inexpensive method of conducting a survey and is therefore attractive when the number of people to be surveyed is large. But self-administered questionnaires usually have a low response rate and may have a relatively high number of incorrect responses due to respondents misunderstanding some questions.

Questionnaire Design Whether a questionnaire is self-administered or completed by an interviewer, it must be well designed. Proper questionnaire design takes knowledge, experience, time, and money. Some basic points to consider regarding questionnaire design follow.

1. First and foremost, the questionnaire should be kept as short as possible to encourage respondents to complete it. Most people are unwilling to spend much time filling out a questionnaire.

2. The questions themselves should also be short, as well as simply and clearly worded, to enable respondents to answer quickly, correctly, and without ambiguity. Even familiar terms such as "*unemployed*" and "*family*" must be defined carefully because several interpretations are possible.

3. Questionnaires often begin with simple demographic questions to help respondents get started and become comfortable quickly.

4. Dichotomous questions (questions with only two possible responses such as "yes" and "no" and multiple-choice questions) are useful and popular because of their simplicity, but they also have possible shortcomings. For example, a respondent's choice of yes or no to a question may depend on certain assumptions not stated in the question. In the case of a multiple-choice question, a respondent may feel that none of the choices offered is suitable.

5. Open-ended questions provide an opportunity for respondents to express opinions more fully, but they are time consuming and more difficult to tabulate and analyze.

6. Avoid using leading questions, such as "Wouldn't you agree that the statistics exam was too difficult?" These types of questions tend to lead the respondent to a particular answer.

7. Time permitting, it is useful to pretest a questionnaire on a small number of people in order to uncover potential problems such as ambiguous wording.

8. Finally, when preparing the questions, think about how you intend to tabulate and analyze the responses. First, determine whether you are soliciting values (i.e., responses) for an interval variable or a nominal variable. Then consider which type of statistical techniques—descriptive or inferential—you intend to apply to the data to be collected, and note the requirements of the specific techniques to be used. Thinking about these questions will help ensure that the questionnaire is designed to collect the data you need.

Whatever method is used to collect primary data, we need to know something about sampling, the subject of the next section.

EXERCISES

5.1 Briefly describe the difference between observational and experimental data.

5.2 A soft drink manufacturer has been supplying its cola drink in bottles to grocery stores and in cans to small convenience stores. The company is analyzing sales of this cola drink to determine which type of packaging is preferred by consumers.
a. Is this study observational or experimental? Explain your answer.
b. Outline a better method for determining whether a store will be supplied with cola in bottles or in cans so that future sales data will be more helpful in assessing the preferred type of packaging.

5.3 a. Briefly describe how you might design a study to investigate the relationship between smoking and lung cancer.
b. Is your study in part (a) observational or experimental? Explain why.

5.4 a. List three methods of conducting a survey of people.
b. Give an important advantage and disadvantage of each of the methods listed in part (a).

5.5 List five important points to consider when designing a questionnaire.

5-2 / SAMPLING

The chief motive for examining a sample rather than a population is cost. Statistical inference permits us to draw conclusions about a population parameter based on a sample that is quite small in comparison to the size of the population. For example, television executives want to know the proportion of television viewers who watch a network's programs. Because 100 million people may be watching television in the United States on a given evening, determining the actual proportion of the population that is watching certain programs is impractical and prohibitively expensive. The Nielsen ratings provide approximations of the desired information by observing what is watched by a sample of 5,000 television viewers. The proportion of households watching a particular program can be calculated for the households in the Nielsen sample. This sample proportion is then used as an **estimate** of the proportion of all households (the population proportion) that watched the program.

Another illustration of sampling can be taken from the field of quality management. To ensure that a production process is operating properly, the operations manager needs to know what proportion of items being produced is defective. If the quality technician must destroy the item to determine whether it is defective, then there is no alternative to sampling: A complete inspection of the product population would destroy the entire output of the production process.

We know that the sample proportion of television viewers or of defective items is probably not exactly equal to the population proportion we want to estimate. Nonetheless, the sample statistic can come quite close to the parameter it is designed to estimate if the **target population** (the population about which we want to draw inferences) and the **sampled population** (the actual population from which the sample has been taken) are the same. In practice, these may not be the same. One of statistics' most famous failures illustrates this phenomenon.

The *Literary Digest* was a popular magazine of the 1920s and 1930s that had correctly predicted the outcomes of several presidential elections. In 1936, the *Digest* predicted that the Republican candidate, Alfred Landon, would defeat the Democratic incumbent, Franklin D. Roosevelt, by a 3 to 2 margin. But in that election, Roosevelt defeated Landon in a landslide victory, garnering the support of 62% of the electorate. The source of this blunder was the sampling procedure, and there were two distinct mistakes.* First, the *Digest* sent out 10 million sample ballots to prospective voters. However, most of the names of these people were taken from the *Digest*'s subscription list and from telephone directories. Subscribers to the magazine and people who owned telephones tended to be wealthier than average and such people then, as today, tended to vote Republican. In addition, only 2.3 million ballots were returned resulting in a self-selected sample.

Self-selected samples are almost always biased because the individuals who participate in them are more keenly interested in the issue than are the other members of the population. You often find similar surveys conducted today when radio and television stations ask people to call and give their opinion on an issue of interest. Again, only listeners who are concerned about the topic and have enough patience to get through to the station will be included in the sample. Hence, the sampled population is composed entirely of people who are interested in the issue, whereas the target population is made up of all the people within the listening radius of the radio station. As a result, the conclusions drawn from such surveys are frequently wrong.

An excellent example of this phenomenon occurred on ABC's *Nightline* in 1984. Viewers were given a 900 telephone number (cost: 50 cents) and asked to phone in their responses to the question of whether the United Nations should continue to be located in the United States. More than 186,000 people called, with 67% responding "no." At the same time, a (more scientific) market research poll of 500 people revealed that 72% wanted the United Nations to remain in the United States. In general, because the true value of the parameter being estimated is never known, these surveys give the impression of providing useful information. In fact, the results of such surveys are likely to be no more accurate than the results of the 1936 *Literary Digest* poll or *Nightline*'s phone-in show. Statisticians have coined two terms to describe these polls: SLOP (self-selected opinion poll) and *Oy vey* (from the Yiddish lament), both of which convey the contempt that statisticians have for such data-gathering processes.

---

*Many statisticians ascribe the *Literary Digest*'s statistical debacle to the wrong causes. For an understanding of what really happened, read Maurice C. Bryson, "The Literary Digest Poll: Making of a Statistical Myth," *American Statistician* 30(4) (November 1976): 184–185.

EXERCISES

5.6 For each of the following sampling plans, indicate why the target population and the sampled population are not the same.

a. To determine the opinions and attitudes of customers who regularly shop at a particular mall, a surveyor stands outside a large department store in the mall and randomly selects people to participate in the survey.

b. A library wants to estimate the proportion of its books that have been damaged. The librarians decide to select one book per shelf as a sample by measuring 12 inches from the left edge of each shelf and selecting the book in that location.

c. Political surveyors visit 200 residences during one afternoon to ask eligible voters present in the house at the time whom they intend to vote for.

5.7 a. Describe why the *Literary Digest* poll of 1936 has become infamous.

b. What caused this poll to be so wrong?

5.8 a. What is meant by *self-selected sample*?

b. Give an example of a recent poll that involved a self-selected sample.

c. Why are self-selected samples not desirable?

5.9 A regular feature in a newspaper asks readers to respond via e-mail to a survey that requires a yes or no response. In the following day's newspaper, the percentage of yes and no responses are reported. Discuss why we should ignore these statistics.

5.10 Suppose your statistics professor distributes a questionnaire about the course. One of the questions asks, "Would you recommend this course to a friend?" Can the professor use the results to infer something about all statistics courses? Explain.

5-3 / SAMPLING PLANS

Our objective in this section is to introduce three different sampling plans: simple random sampling, stratified random sampling, and cluster sampling. We begin our presentation with the most basic design.

5-3a Simple Random Sampling

Simple Random Sample

A **simple random sample** is a sample selected in such a way that every possible sample with the same number of observations is equally likely to be chosen.

One way to conduct a simple random sample is to assign a number to each element in the population, write these numbers on individual slips of paper, toss them into a hat, and draw the required number of slips (the sample size, n) from the hat. This is the kind of procedure that occurs in raffles, when all the ticket stubs go into a large rotating drum from which the winners are selected.

Sometimes the elements of the population are already numbered. For example, virtually all adults have Social Security numbers (in the United States) or Social Insurance numbers (in Canada); all employees of large corporations have employee numbers; many people have driver's license numbers, medical plan numbers, student numbers, and so on. In such cases, choosing which sampling procedure to use is simply a matter of deciding how to select from among these numbers.

In other cases, the existing form of numbering has built-in flaws that make it inappropriate as a source of samples. Not everyone has a phone number, for example, so the telephone book does not list all the people in a given area. Many households have two (or more) adults but only one phone listing. It seems that everyone in the world has a cell phone. Many of these people have no land phone, so they do not appear on any list. Some people do not have phones, some have unlisted phone numbers, and some have more than one phone; these differences mean that each element of the population does not have an equal probability of being selected.

After each element of the chosen population has been assigned a unique number, sample numbers can be selected at random. We can use Excel to perform this function.

| EXAMPLE 5.1 | **Random Sample of Income Tax Returns** |

A government income tax auditor has been given responsibility for 1,000 tax returns. A computer is used to check the arithmetic of each return. However, to determine whether the returns have been completed honestly, the auditor must check each entry and confirm its veracity. Because it takes, on average, 1 hour to completely audit a return and has only 1 week to complete the task, the auditor has decided to randomly select 40 returns. The returns are numbered from 1 to 1,000. Use a computer random-number generator to select the sample for the auditor.

SOLUTION:

We generated 50 numbers between 1 and 1,000 even though we needed only 40 numbers. We did so because it is likely that there will be some duplicates. We will use the first 40 unique random numbers to select our sample. The following numbers were generated by Excel. The instructions are provided here. [Notice that the 24th and 36th (counting down the columns) numbers generated were the same—467.]

Computer-Generated Random Numbers

383	246	372	952	75
101	46	356	54	199
597	33	911	706	65
900	165	467	817	359
885	220	427	973	488
959	18	304	467	512
15	286	976	301	374
408	344	807	751	986
864	554	992	352	41
139	358	257	776	231

EXCEL Data Analysis

INSTRUCTIONS

1. Click **Data, Data Analysis**, and **Random Number Generation**.
2. Specify the **Number of Variables** (1) and the **Number of Random Numbers** (50).
3. Select **Uniform Distribution.**
4. Specify the range of the uniform distribution (**Parameters**) (0 and 1).
5. Click **OK**. Column A will fill with 50 numbers that range between 0 and 1.
6. Multiply column A by 1,000 and store the products in column B.

7. Make cell C1 active, and click f_x, **Math & Trig, ROUNDUP**, and **OK**.

8. Specify the first number to be rounded (B1).

9. Type the **number of digits** (decimal places) (0). Click **OK**.

10. Complete column C.

The first five steps command Excel to generate 50 uniformly distributed random numbers between 0 and 1 to be stored in column A. Steps 6 through 10 convert these random numbers to integers between 1 and 1,000. Each tax return has the same probability $(1/1{,}000 = .001)$ of being selected. Thus, each member of the population is equally likely to be included in the sample.

INTERPRET

The auditor would examine the tax returns numbered 383, 101, 597, ..., 352, 776, and 75 (the first 40 unique numbers). Each of these returns would be audited to determine whether it is fraudulent. If the objective is to audit these 40 returns, no statistical procedure would be employed. However, if the objective is to estimate the proportion of all 1,000 returns that are dishonest, then the auditor would use one of the inferential techniques presented later in this book.

5-3b Stratified Random Sampling

In making inferences about a population, we attempt to extract as much information as possible from a sample. The basic sampling plan, simple random sampling, often accomplishes this goal at low cost. Other methods, however, can be used to increase the amount of information about the population. One such procedure is *stratified random sampling*.

> **Stratified Random Sample**
>
> A **stratified random sample** is obtained by separating the population into mutually exclusive sets, or strata, and then drawing simple random samples from each stratum.

Examples of criteria for separating a population into strata (and of the strata themselves) follow.

1. Gender
   male
   female

2. Age
   under 20
   20–30
   31–40
   41–50
   51–60
   over 60

3. Occupation
   professional
   clerical
   blue-collar
   other

4. Household income
   under $25,000
   $25,000–$39,999
   $40,000–$60,000
   over $60,000

To illustrate, suppose a public opinion survey is to be conducted to determine how many people favor a tax increase. A stratified random sample could be obtained by selecting a random sample of people from each of the four income groups we just described. We usually stratify in a way that enables us to obtain particular kinds of information. In this example, we would like to know whether people in the different income categories differ in their opinions about the proposed tax increase, because the tax increase will affect the strata differently. We avoid stratifying when there is no connection between the survey and the strata. For example, little purpose is served in trying to determine whether people within religious strata have divergent opinions about the tax increase.

One advantage of stratification is that, besides acquiring information about the entire population, we can also make inferences within each stratum or compare strata. For instance, we can estimate what proportion of the lowest income group favors the tax increase, or we can compare the highest and lowest income groups to determine whether they differ in their support of the tax increase.

Any stratification must be done in such a way that the strata are mutually exclusive: Each member of the population must be assigned to exactly one stratum. After the population has been stratified in this way, we can use simple random sampling to generate the complete sample. There are several ways to do this. For example, we can draw random samples from each of the four income groups according to their proportions in the population. Thus, if in the population the relative frequencies of the four groups are as listed here, our sample will be stratified in the same proportions. If a total sample of 1,000 is to be drawn, then we will randomly select 250 from stratum 1, 400 from stratum 2, 300 from stratum 3, and 50 from stratum 4.

Stratum	Income Categories ($)	Population Proportions (%)
1	Less than 25,000	25
2	25,000–39,999	40
3	40,000–60,000	30
4	More than 60,000	5

The problem with this approach, however, is that if we want to make inferences about the last stratum, a sample of 50 may be too small to produce useful information. In such cases, we usually increase the sample size of the smallest stratum to ensure that the sample data provide enough information for our purposes. An adjustment must then be made before we attempt to draw inferences about the entire population. The required procedure is beyond the level of this book. We recommend that anyone planning such a survey consult an expert statistician or a reference book on the subject. Better still, become an expert statistician yourself by taking additional statistics courses.

5-3c Cluster Sampling

> **Cluster Sample**
> A **cluster sample** is a simple random sample of groups or clusters of elements.

Cluster sampling is particularly useful when it is difficult or costly to develop a complete list of the population members (making it difficult and costly to generate a simple random sample). It is also useful whenever the population elements are widely dispersed geographically. For example, suppose we wanted to estimate the average annual household income in a large city. To use simple random sampling, we would need a complete list of households in the city from which to sample. To use stratified random sampling, we would need the list of households, and we would also need to have each household categorized by some other variable (such as age of household head) in order to develop the strata. A less-expensive alternative would be to let each block within the city represent a cluster. A sample of clusters could then be randomly selected, and every household within these clusters could be questioned to determine income. By reducing the distances the surveyor must cover to gather data, cluster sampling reduces the cost.

But cluster sampling also increases sampling error (see Section 5-4) because households belonging to the same cluster are likely to be similar in many respects, including household income. This can be partially offset by using some of the cost savings to choose a larger sample than would be used for a simple random sample.

5-3d Sample Size

Whichever type of sampling plan you select, you still have to decide what size sample to use. Determining the appropriate sample size will be addressed in detail in Chapters 10 and 12. Until then, we can rely on our intuition, which tells us that the larger the sample size is, the more accurate we can expect the estimates to be.

Sampling and the Census

To adjust for undercounting, the Census Bureau conducts cluster sampling. The clusters are geographic blocks. For the year 2000 census, the bureau randomly sampled 11,800 blocks, which contained 314,000 housing units. Each unit was intensively revisited to ensure that all residents were counted. From the results of this survey, the Census Bureau estimated the number of people missed by the first census in various subgroups, defined by several variables including gender, race, and age. Because of the importance of determining state populations, adjustments were made to state totals. For example, by comparing the results of the census and of the sampling, the Bureau determined that the undercount in the state of Texas was 1.7087. The official census produced a state population of 20,851,820. Taking 1.7087% of this total produced an adjustment of 356,295. Using this method changed the population of the state of Texas to 21,208,115.

It should be noted that this process is contentious. The controversy concerns the way in which subgroups are defined. Changing the definition alters the undercounts, making this statistical technique subject to politicking.

Spencer Grant/Age Fotostock

EXERCISES

5.11 A statistics practitioner would like to conduct a survey to ask people their views on a proposed new shopping mall in their community. According to the latest census, there are 500 households in the community. The statistician has numbered each household (from 1 to 500), and would like to randomly select 25 of these households to participate in the study. Use Excel to generate the sample.

5.12 A safety expert wants to determine the proportion of cars in his state with worn tire treads. The state license plate contains six digits. Use Excel to generate a sample of 20 cars to be examined.

5.13 A large university campus has 60,000 students. The president of the students' association wants to conduct a survey of the students to determine their views on an increase in the student activity fee. The president would like to acquire information about all the students but would also like to compare the school of business, the faculty of arts and sciences, and the graduate school. Describe a sampling plan that accomplishes these goals.

5.14 A telemarketing firm has recorded the households that have purchased one or more of the company's products. These number in the millions. The firm would like to conduct a survey of purchasers to acquire information about their attitude concerning the timing of the telephone calls. The president of the company would like to know the views of all purchasers but would also like to compare the attitudes of people in the West, South, North, and East. Describe a suitable sampling plan.

5.15 The operations manager of a large plant with four departments wants to estimate the person-hours lost per month from accidents. Describe a sampling plan that would be suitable for estimating the plant-wide loss and for comparing departments.

5.16 A statistics practitioner wants to estimate the mean age of children in his city. Describe a sampling plan that would be suitable for his purposes.

5-4 / SAMPLING AND NONSAMPLING ERRORS

Two major types of error can arise when a sample of observations is taken from a population: *sampling error* and *nonsampling error*. Anyone reviewing the results of sample surveys and studies, as well as statistics practitioners conducting surveys and applying statistical techniques, should understand the sources of these errors.

5-4a Sampling Error

Sampling error refers to differences between the sample and the population that exists only because of the observations that happened to be selected for the sample. Sampling error is an error that we expect to occur when we make a statement about a population that is based only on the observations contained in a sample taken from the population.

To illustrate, suppose that we wish to determine the mean annual income of North American blue-collar workers. To determine this parameter we would have to ask all North American blue-collar workers for their incomes and then calculate the mean of all the responses. Because the size of this population is several million, the task is both expensive and impractical. We can use statistical inference to estimate the mean income μ of the population if we are willing to accept less than 100% accuracy. We record the incomes of a sample of the workers and find the mean $\bar{x}$ of this sample of incomes. This sample mean is an estimate of the desired population mean. But the value of the sample mean will deviate from the population mean simply by chance because the value of the sample mean depends on which incomes just happened to be selected for the sample. The difference between the true (unknown) value of the population mean and its estimate, the sample mean, is the sampling error. The size of this deviation may be large simply because of bad luck—bad luck that a particularly unrepresentative sample happened to be selected. The only way we can reduce the expected size of this error is to take a larger sample.

Given a fixed sample size, the best we can do is to state the probability that the sampling error is less than a certain amount (as we will discuss in Chapter 10). It is common today for such a statement to accompany the results of an opinion poll. If an opinion poll states that, based on sample results, the incumbent candidate for mayor has the support of 54% of eligible voters in an upcoming election, the statement may be accompanied by the following explanatory note: "This percentage is correct to within three percentage points, 19 times out of 20." This statement means that we estimate that the actual level of support for the candidate is between 51% and 57%, and that in the long run this type of procedure is correct 95% of the time.

5-4b Nonsampling Error

Nonsampling error is more serious than sampling error because taking a larger sample won't diminish the size, or the possibility of occurrence, of this error. Even a census can (and probably will) contain nonsampling errors. **Nonsampling errors** result from mistakes made in the acquisition of data or from the sample observations being selected improperly.

1. *Errors in data acquisition.* This type of error arises from the recording of incorrect responses. Incorrect responses may be the result of incorrect measurements being taken because of faulty equipment, mistakes made during transcription from primary sources, inaccurate recording of data because terms were misinterpreted, or inaccurate responses were given to questions concerning sensitive issues such as sexual activity or possible tax evasion.

2. *Nonresponse error.* **Nonresponse error** refers to error (or **bias**) introduced when responses are not obtained from some members of the sample. When this happens, the sample observations that are collected may not be representative of the target population, resulting in biased results (as was discussed in Section 5-2). Nonresponse can occur for a number of reasons. An interviewer may be unable to contact a person listed in the sample, or the sampled person may refuse to respond for some reason. In either case, responses are not obtained from a sampled person, and bias is introduced. The problem of nonresponse is even greater when self-administered questionnaires are used rather than an interviewer, who can attempt to reduce the nonresponse rate by means of callbacks. As noted previously, the *Literary Digest* fiasco was largely the result of a high nonresponse rate, resulting in a biased, self-selected sample.

3. *Selection bias.* **Selection bias** occurs when the sampling plan is such that some members of the target population cannot possibly be selected for inclusion in the sample. Together with nonresponse error, selection bias played a role in the *Literary Digest* poll being so wrong, as voters without telephones or without a subscription to *Literary Digest* were excluded from possible inclusion in the sample taken.

EXERCISES

5.17 a. Explain the difference between sampling error and nonsampling error.

b. Which type of error in part (a) is more serious? Why?

5.18 Briefly describe three types of nonsampling error.

5.19 Is it possible for a sample to yield better results than a census? Explain.

probabilities of heads and tails in the flip of a balanced coin are equal to each other. Because the sum of the probabilities must be 1, the probability of heads and the probability of tails are both 50%. Similarly, the six possible outcomes of the toss of a balanced die have the same probability; each is assigned a probability of 1/6. In some experiments, it is necessary to develop mathematical ways to count the number of outcomes. For example, to determine the probability of winning a lottery, we need to determine the number of possible combinations. For details on how to count events, see the online appendix Counting Formulas.

The **relative frequency approach** defines probability as the long-run relative frequency with which an outcome occurs. For example, suppose that we know that of the last 1,000 students who took the statistics course you're now taking, 200 received a grade of *A*. The relative frequency of *A*'s is then 200/1,000 or 20%. This figure represents an estimate of the probability of obtaining a grade of *A* in the course. It is only an estimate because the relative frequency approach defines probability as the "long-run" relative frequency. One thousand students do not constitute the long run. The larger the number of students whose grades we have observed, the better the estimate becomes. In theory, we would have to observe an infinite number of grades to determine the exact probability.

When it is not reasonable to use the classical approach and there is no history of the outcomes, we have no alternative but to employ the **subjective approach**. In the subjective approach, we define probability as the degree of belief that we hold in the occurrence of an event. An excellent example is derived from the field of investment. An investor would like to know the probability that a particular stock will increase in value. Using the subjective approach, the investor would analyze a number of factors associated with the stock and the stock market in general and, using experience and judgment, assign a probability to the outcomes of interest.

6-1b Defining Events

An individual outcome of a sample space is called a *simple event*. All other events are composed of the simple events in a sample space.

> **Event**
>
> An **event** is a collection or set of one or more simple events in a sample space.

In illustration 2, we can define the event, achieve a grade of *A*, as the set of numbers that lie between 80 and 100, inclusive. Using set notation, we have

$$A = \{80, 81, 82, \ldots, 99, 100\}$$

Similarly,

$$F = \{0, 1, 2, \ldots, 48, 49\}$$

6-1c Probability of Events

We can now define the probability of any event.

> ### Probability of an Event
> The probability of an event is the sum of the probabilities of the simple events that constitute the event.

For example, suppose that in illustration 3, we employed the relative frequency approach to assign probabilities to the simple events as follows:

$$P(A) = .20$$
$$P(B) = .30$$
$$P(C) = .25$$
$$P(D) = .15$$
$$P(F) = .10$$

The probability of the event, pass the course, is

$$P(\text{Pass the course}) = P(A) + P(B) + P(C) + P(D) = .20 + .30 + .25 + .15 = .90$$

6-1d Interpreting Probability

No matter what method was used to assign probability, we interpret it using the relative frequency approach for an infinite number of experiments. For example, an investor may have used the subjective approach to determine that there is a 65% probability that a particular stock's price will increase over the next month. However, we interpret the 65% figure to mean that if we had an infinite number of stocks with exactly the same economic and market characteristics as the one the investor will buy, 65% of them will increase in price over the next month. Similarly, we can determine that the probability of throwing a 5 with a balanced die is 1/6. We may have used the classical approach to determine this probability. However, we interpret the number as the proportion of times that a 5 is observed on a balanced die thrown an infinite number of times.

This relative frequency approach is useful to interpret probability statements such as those heard from weather forecasters or scientists. You will also discover that this is the way we link the population and the sample in statistical inference.

EXERCISES

6.1 The weather forecaster reports that the probability of rain tomorrow is 10%.
  a. Which approach was used to arrive at this number?
  b. How do you interpret the probability?

6.2 A sportscaster states that he believes that the probability that the New York Yankees will win the World Series this year is 25%.
  a. Which method was used to assign that probability?
  b. How would you interpret the probability?

6.3 A quiz contains a multiple-choice question with five possible answers, only one of which is correct. A student who knows absolutely nothing about the subject plans to guess the answers.
  a. Produce the sample space for each question.
  b. Assign probabilities to the simple events in the sample space you produced.
  c. Which approach did you use to answer part (b)?
  d. Interpret the probabilities you assigned in part (b).

6.4 An investor estimates that there is a 60% probability that the Dow Jones Industrial Averages index will increase tomorrow.
   a. Which approach was used to produce this figure?
   b. Interpret the 60% probability.

6.5 The sample space of the toss of a fair die is

$$S = \{1, 2, 3, 4, 5, 6\}$$

If the die is balanced each simple event has the same probability. Find the probability of the following events.
   a. An even number
   b. A number less than or equal to 4
   c. A number greater than or equal to 5

6.6 Four candidates are running for mayor. The four candidates are Adams, Brown, Collins, and Dalton. Determine the sample space of the results of the election.

6.7 Refer to Exercise 6.6. Employing the subjective approach a political scientist has assigned the following probabilities:

$$P(\text{Adams wins}) = .42$$
$$P(\text{Brown wins}) = .09$$
$$P(\text{Collins wins}) = .27$$
$$P(\text{Dalton wins}) = .22$$

Determine the probabilities of the following events.
   a. Adams loses.
   b. Either Brown or Dalton wins.
   c. Adams, Brown, or Collins wins.

6.8 The manager of a computer store has kept track of the number of computers sold per day. On the basis of this information, the manager produced the following list of the number of daily sales.

Number of Computers Sold	Probability
0	.08
1	.17
2	.26
3	.21
4	.18
5	.10

   a. If we define the experiment as observing the number of computers sold tomorrow, determine the sample space.
   b. Use set notation to define the event, sell more than three computers.
   c. What is the probability of selling five computers?
   d. What is the probability of selling two, three, or four computers?
   e. What is the probability of selling six computers?

6.9 Three contractors (call them contractors 1, 2, and 3) bid on a project to build a new bridge. What is the sample space?

6.10 Refer to Exercise 6.9. Suppose that you believe that contractor 1 is twice as likely to win as contractor 3 and that contractor 2 is three times as likely to win as contactor 3. What are the probabilities of winning for each contractor?

6.11 Shoppers can pay for their purchases with cash, a credit card, or a debit card. Suppose that the proprietor of a shop determines that 60% of customers use a credit card, 30% pay with cash, and the rest use a debit card.
   a. Determine the sample space for this experiment.
   b. Assign probabilities to the simple events.
   c. Which method did you use in part (b)?

6.12 Refer to Exercise 6.11.
   a. What is the probability that a customer does not use a credit card?
   b. What is the probability that a customer pays in cash or with a credit card?

6.13 A survey asks adults to report their marital status. The sample space is

$$S = \{\text{single, married, divorced, widowed}\}$$

Use set notation to represent the event the adult is not married.

6.14 Refer to Exercise 6.13. Suppose that in the city in which the survey is conducted, 50% of adults are married, 15% are single, 25% are divorced, and 10% are widowed.
   a. Assign probabilities to each simple event in the sample space.
   b. Which approach did you use in part (a)?

6.15 Refer to Exercises 6.13 and 6.14. Find the probability of each of the following events.
   a. The adult is single.
   b. The adult is not divorced.
   c. The adult is either widowed or divorced.

6.16 There are 62 million Americans who speak a language other than English at home. The languages are Spanish, Chinese Tagalog (Philippines language), Vietnamese, French, Korean, and others. Suppose that one of these individuals is selected at random. Use set notation to list the sample space.

6.17 Refer to Exercise 6.16. The numbers (in millions) of Americans speaking non-English languages at home are listed next.

Language Spoken at Home	Millions of Americans
Spanish	38.4
Chinese	3.0
Tagalog	1.6
Vietnamese	1.4
French	1.3
Korean	1.1
Other	15.2

Source: Center for Immigration Studies.

If one individual is selected at random, find the probability of the following events.
a. Individual speaks Spanish.
b. Individual speaks a language other than Spanish.
c. Individual speaks Vietnamese or French.
d. Individual speaks one of the other languages.

6.18   Uber, the ride-sharing service has been encountering protests mostly from taxi drivers. The taxi industry claims that Uber is more dangerous than other taxis because of the lack of government scrutiny. A survey was conducted where people were asked, "In your opinion how safe is Uber?" The responses are

Very safe; Somewhat safe; Somewhat unsafe; Very unsafe; Not sure

Create the sample space for this survey.

6.19   Refer to Exercise 6.18. The results of the survey are listed next.

How Safe Is Uber?	Responses (%)
Very safe	17
Somewhat safe	28
Somewhat unsafe	21
Very unsafe	12
Not sure	22

If one person surveyed is selected at random, find the following probabilities
a. Person selected said Very safe
b. Person selected said Very safe or Somewhat safe
c. Person said it was Very unsafe

6-2 / JOINT, MARGINAL, AND CONDITIONAL PROBABILITY

In the previous section, we described how to produce a sample space and assign probabilities to the simple events in the sample space. Although this method of determining probability is useful, we need to develop more sophisticated methods. In this section, we discuss how to calculate the probability of more complicated events from the probability of related events. Here is an illustration of the process.

The sample space for the toss of a die is

$$S = \{1, 2, 3, 4, 5, 6\}$$

If the die is balanced, the probability of each simple event is 1/6. In most parlor games and casinos, players toss two dice. To determine playing and wagering strategies, players need to compute the probabilities of various totals of the two dice. For example, the probability of tossing a total of 3 with two dice is 2/36. This probability was derived by creating combinations of the simple events. There are several different types of combinations. One of the most important types is the *intersection* of two events.

6-2a Intersection

Intersection of Events _A_ and _B_

The **intersection** of events _A_ and _B_ is the event that occurs when both _A_ and _B_ occur. It is denoted as

_A_ and _B_

The probability of the intersection is called the **joint probability**.

For example, one way to toss a 3 with two dice is to toss a 1 on the first die *and* a 2 on the second die, which is the intersection of two simple events. Incidentally, to compute the probability of a total of 3, we need to combine this intersection with another intersection, namely, a 2 on the first die and a 1 on the second die. This type of combination is called a *union* of two events, and it will be described later in this section. Here is another illustration.

APPLICATIONS in FINANCE

Mutual Funds

A mutual fund is a pool of investments made on behalf of people who share similar objectives. In most cases, a professional manager who has been educated in finance and statistics manages the fund. The manager makes decisions to buy and sell individual stocks and bonds in accordance with a specified investment philosophy. For example, there are funds that concentrate on other publicly traded mutual fund companies. Other mutual funds specialize in Internet stocks, whereas others buy stocks of biotechnology firms. Surprisingly, most mutual funds do not outperform the market; that is, the increase in the net asset value (NAV) of the mutual fund is often less than the increase in the value of stock indexes that represent their stock markets. One reason for this is the management expense ratio (MER), which is a measure of the costs charged to the fund by the manager to cover expenses, including the salary and bonus of the managers. The MERs for most funds range from .5% to more than 4%. The ultimate success of the fund depends on the skill and knowledge of the fund manager. This raises the question, Which managers do best?

EXAMPLE **6.1**

Determinants of Success among Mutual Fund Managers—Part 1[*]

Why are some mutual fund managers more successful than others? One possible factor is the university where the managers earned their master of business administration (MBA) degree. Suppose that a potential investor examined the relationship between how well the mutual fund performs and which university awarded the manager's MBA. After the analysis, Table 6.1, a table of joint probabilities, was developed. Analyze these probabilities and interpret the results.

TABLE **6.1** Joint Probabilities

	MUTUAL FUND OUTPERFORMS MARKET	MUTUAL FUND DOES NOT OUTPERFORM MARKET
Top-20 MBA program	.11	.29
Not top-20 MBA program	.06	.54

Table 6.1 tells us that the joint probability that a mutual fund outperforms the market *and* that its manager graduated from a top-20 MBA program is .11; that is,

[*]This example is adapted from "Are Some Mutual Fund Managers Better than Others? Cross-Sectional Patterns in Behavior and Performance" by Judith Chevalier and Glenn Ellison, Working paper 5852, National Bureau of Economic Research.

11% of all mutual funds outperform the market and their managers graduated from a top-20 MBA program. The other three joint probabilities are defined similarly:

The probability that a mutual fund outperforms the market and its manager did not graduate from a top-20 MBA program is .06.

The probability that a mutual fund does not outperform the market and its manager graduated from a top-20 MBA program is .29.

The probability that a mutual fund does not outperform the market and its manager did not graduate from a top-20 MBA program is .54.

To help make our task easier, we'll use notation to represent the events. Let

A_1 = Fund manager graduated from a top-20 MBA program

A_2 = Fund manager did not graduate from a top-20 MBA program

B_1 = Fund outperforms the market

B_2 = Fund does not outperform the market

Thus,

$$P(A_1 \text{ and } B_1) = .11$$
$$P(A_2 \text{ and } B_1) = .06$$
$$P(A_1 \text{ and } B_2) = .29$$
$$P(A_2 \text{ and } B_2) = .54$$

6-2b Marginal Probability

The joint probabilities in Table 6.1 allow us to compute various probabilities. **Marginal probabilities**, computed by adding across rows or down columns, are so named because they are calculated in the margins of the table.

Adding across the first row produces

$$P(A_1 \text{ and } B_1) + P(A_1 \text{ and } B_2) = .11 + .29 = .40$$

Notice that both intersections state that the manager graduated from a top-20 MBA program (represented by A_1). Thus, when randomly selecting mutual funds, the probability that its manager graduated from a top-20 MBA program is .40. Expressed as relative frequency, 40% of all mutual fund managers graduated from a top-20 MBA program.

Adding across the second row:

$$P(A_2 \text{ and } B_1) + P(A_2 \text{ and } B_2) = .06 + .54 = .60$$

This probability tells us that 60% of all mutual fund managers did not graduate from a top-20 MBA program (represented by A_2). Notice that the probability that a mutual fund manager graduated from a top-20 MBA program and the probability that the manager did not graduate from a top-20 MBA program add to 1.

Adding down the columns produces the following marginal probabilities.

Column 1: $P(A_1 \text{ and } B_1) + P(A_2 \text{ and } B_1) = .11 + .06 = .17$

Column 2: $P(A_1 \text{ and } B_2) + P(A_2 \text{ and } B_2) = .29 + .54 = .83$

These marginal probabilities tell us that 17% of all mutual funds outperform the market and that 83% of mutual funds do not outperform the market.

Table 6.2 lists all the joint and marginal probabilities.

TABLE **6.2** Joint and Marginal Probabilities

	MUTUAL FUND OUTPERFORMS MARKET	MUTUAL FUND DOES NOT OUTPERFORM MARKET	TOTALS
Top-20 MBA program	$P(A_1 \text{ and } B_1) = .11$	$P(A_1 \text{ and } B_2) = .29$	$P(A_1) = .40$
Not top-20 MBA program	$P(A_2 \text{ and } B_1) = .06$	$P(A_2 \text{ and } B_2) = .54$	$P(A_2) = .60$
Totals	$P(B_1) = .17$	$P(B_2) = .83$	1.00

6-2c Conditional Probability

We frequently need to know how two events are related. In particular, we would like to know the probability of one event given the occurrence of another related event. For example, we would certainly like to know the probability that a fund managed by a graduate of a top-20 MBA program will outperform the market. Such a probability will allow us to make an informed decision about where to invest our money. This probability is called a **conditional probability** because we want to know the probability that a fund will outperform the market *given* the condition that the manager graduated from a top-20 MBA program. The conditional probability that we seek is represented by

$$P(B_1|A_1)$$

where the "|" represents the word *given*. Here is how we compute this conditional probability.

The marginal probability that a manager graduated from a top-20 MBA program is .40, which is made up of two joint probabilities. They are (1) the probability that the mutual fund outperforms the market and the manager graduated from a top-20 MBA program [$P(A_1 \text{ and } B_1)$] and (2) the probability that the fund does not outperform the market and the manager graduated from a top-20 MBA program [$P(A_1 \text{ and } B_2)$]. Their joint probabilities are .11 and .29, respectively. We can interpret these numbers in the following way. On average, for every 100 mutual funds, 40 will be managed by a graduate of a top-20 MBA program. Of these 40 managers, on average 11 of them will manage a mutual fund that will outperform the market. Thus, the conditional probability is 11/40 = .275. Notice that this ratio is the same as the ratio of the joint probability to the marginal probability .11/.40. All conditional probabilities can be computed this way.

Conditional Probability

The probability of event A given event B is

$$P(A|B) = \frac{P(A \text{ and } B)}{P(B)}$$

The probability of event B given event A is

$$P(B|A) = \frac{P(A \text{ and } B)}{P(A)}$$

| EXAMPLE 6.2 | **Determinants of Success among Mutual Fund Managers—Part 2** |

Suppose that in Example 6.1 we select one mutual fund at random and discover that it did not outperform the market. What is the probability that a graduate of a top-20 MBA program manages it?

SOLUTION:

We wish to find a conditional probability. The condition is that the fund did not outperform the market (event B_2), and the event whose probability we seek is that the fund is managed by a graduate of a top-20 MBA program (event A_1). Thus, we want to compute the following probability:

$$P(A_1|B_2)$$

Using the conditional probability formula, we find

$$P(A_1|B_2) = \frac{P(A_1 \text{ and } B_2)}{P(B_2)} = \frac{.29}{.83} = .349$$

Thus, 34.9% of all mutual funds that do not outperform the market are managed by top-20 MBA program graduates.

The calculation of conditional probabilities raises the question of whether the two events, the fund outperformed the market and the manager graduated from a top-20 MBA program, are related, a subject we tackle next.

6-2d Independence

One of the objectives of calculating conditional probability is to determine whether two events are related. In particular, we would like to know whether they are **independent events**.

Independent Events

Two events A and B are said to be independent if

$$P(A|B) = P(A)$$

or

$$P(B|A) = P(B)$$

Put another way, two events are independent if the probability of one event is not affected by the occurrence of the other event.

EXAMPLE **6.3**

Determinants of Success among Mutual Fund Managers—Part 3

Determine whether the event that the manager graduated from a top-20 MBA program and the event the fund outperforms the market are independent events.

SOLUTION:

We wish to determine whether A_1 and B_1 are independent. To do so, we must calculate the probability of A_1 given B_1; that is,

$$P(A_1|B_1) = \frac{P(A_1 \text{ and } B_1)}{P(B_1)} = \frac{.11}{.17} = .647$$

The marginal probability that a manager graduated from a top-20 MBA program is

$$P(A_1) = .40$$

Since the two probabilities are not equal, we conclude that the two events are dependent.

Incidentally, we could have made the decision by calculating $P(B_1|A_1) = .275$ and observing that it is not equal to $P(B_1) = .17$.

Note that there are three other combinations of events in this problem. They are (A_1 and B_2), (A_2 and B_1), (A_2 and B_2) [ignoring mutually exclusive combinations (A_1 and A_2) and (B_1 and B_2), which are dependent]. In each combination, the two events are dependent. In this type of problem, where there are only four combinations, if one combination is dependent, then all four will be dependent. Similarly, if one combination is independent, then all four will be independent. This rule does not apply to any other situation.

6-2e Union

Another event that is the combination of other events is the *union*.

Union of Events A and B

The **union** of events A and B is the event that occurs when either A or B or both occur. It is denoted as

$$A \text{ or } B$$

EXAMPLE **6.4**

Determinants of Success among Mutual Fund Managers—Part 4

Determine the probability that a randomly selected fund outperforms the market or the manager graduated from a top-20 MBA program.

SOLUTION:

We want to compute the probability of the union of two events

$$P(A_1 \text{ or } B_1)$$

The union A_1 or B_1 consists of three events; That is, the union occurs whenever any of the following joint events occurs:

1. Fund outperforms the market and the manager graduated from a top-20 MBA program.
2. Fund outperforms the market and the manager did not graduate from a top-20 MBA program.
3. Fund does not outperform the market and the manager graduated from a top-20 MBA program.

Their probabilities are

$$P(A_1 \text{ and } B_1) = .11$$
$$P(A_2 \text{ and } B_1) = .06$$
$$P(A_1 \text{ and } B_2) = .29$$

Thus, the probability of the union—the fund outperforms the market or the manager graduated from a top-20 MBA program—is the sum of the three probabilities. That is,

$$P(A_1 \text{ or } B_1) = P(A_1 \text{ and } B_1) + P(A_2 \text{ and } B_1) + P(A_1 \text{ and } B_2) = .11 + .06 + .29 = .46$$

Notice that there is another way to produce this probability. Of the four probabilities in Table 6.1, the only one representing an event that is not part of the union is the probability of the event the fund does not outperform the market and the manager did not graduate from a top-20 MBA program. That probability is

$$P(A_2 \text{ and } B_2) = .54$$

which is the probability that the union *does not* occur. Thus, the probability of the union is

$$P(A_1 \text{ or } B_1) = 1 - P(A_2 \text{ and } B_2) = 1 - .54 = .46.$$

Thus, we determined that 46% of mutual funds either outperform the market or are managed by a top-20 MBA program graduate or have both characteristics.

EXERCISES

6.20 Given the following table of joint probabilities, calculate the marginal probabilities.

	A_1	A_2	A_3
B_1	.1	.3	.2
B_2	.2	.1	.1

6.21 Calculate the marginal probabilities from the following table of joint probabilities.

	A_1	A_2
B_1	.4	.3
B_2	.2	.1

6.22 Refer to Exercise 6.21.
a. Determine $P(A_1|B_1)$.
b. Determine $P(A_2|B_1)$.
c. Did your answers to parts (a) and (b) sum to 1? Is this a coincidence? Explain.

6.23 Refer to Exercise 6.21.
a. Determine $P(A_1|B_2)$.
b. Determine $P(B_2|A_1)$.
c. Did you expect the answers to parts (a) and (b) to be reciprocals? In other words, did you expect that $P(A_1|B_2) = 1/P(B_2|A_1)$? Why is this impossible (unless both probabilities are 1)?

6.24 Are the events in Exercise 6.21 independent? Explain.

6.25 Refer to Exercise 6.21. Compute the following.
  a. $P(A_1$ or $B_1)$
  b. $P(A_1$ or $B_2)$
  c. $P(A_1$ or $A_2)$

6.26 Suppose that you have been given the following joint probabilities. Are the events independent? Explain.

	A_1	A_2
B_1	.20	.60
B_2	.05	.15

6.27 Determine whether the events are independent from the following joint probabilities.

	A_1	A_2
B_1	.20	.15
B_2	.60	.05

6.28 Suppose we have the following joint probabilities.

	A_1	A_2	A_3
B_1	.15	.20	.10
B_2	.25	.25	.05

Compute the marginal probabilities.

6.29 Refer to Exercise 6.28.
  a. Compute $P(A_2|B_2)$.
  b. Compute $P(B_2|A_2)$.
  c. Compute $P(B_1|A_2)$.

6.30 Refer to Exercise 6.28.
  a. Compute $P(A_1$ or $A_2)$.
  b. Compute $P(A_2$ or $B_2)$.
  c. Compute $P(A_3$ or $B_1)$.

6.31 Discrimination in the workplace is illegal, and companies that discriminate are often sued. The female instructors at a large university recently lodged a complaint about the most recent round of promotions from assistant professor to associate professor. An analysis of the relationship between gender and promotion produced the following joint probabilities.

	Promoted	Not Promoted
Female	.03	.12
Male	.17	.68

  a. What is the rate of promotion among female assistant professors?
  b. What is the rate of promotion among male assistant professors?
  c. Is it reasonable to accuse the university of gender bias?

6.32 A department store analyzed its most recent sales and determined the relationship between the way the customer paid for the item and the price category of the item. The joint probabilities in the following table were calculated.

	Cash	Credit Card	Debit Card
Less than $20	.09	.03	.04
$20–$100	.05	.21	.18
More than $100	.03	.23	.14

  a. What proportion of purchases was paid by debit card?
  b. Find the probability that a credit card purchase was more than $100.
  c. Determine the proportion of purchases made by credit card or by debit card.

6.33 The following table lists the probabilities of unemployed females and males and their educational attainment.

	Female	Male
Less than high school	.057	.104
High school graduate	.136	.224
Some college/university—no degree	.132	.150
College/university graduate	.095	.103

Source: Statistical Abstract of the United States.

  a. If one unemployed person is selected at random, what is the probability that that person did not finish high school?
  b. If an unemployed female is selected at random, what is the probability that she has a college or university degree?
  c. If an unemployed high school graduate is selected at random, what is the probability that he is a male?

6.34 The costs of medical care in North America are increasing faster than inflation, and with the baby boom generation soon to need health care, it becomes imperative that countries find ways to reduce both costs and demand. The following table lists the joint probabilities associated with smoking and lung disease among 60- to 65-year-old men.

	He Is a Smoker	He Is a Nonsmoker
He has lung disease	.12	.03
He does not have lung disease	.19	.66

One 60- to 65-year-old man is selected at random. What is the probability of the following events?
  a. He is a smoker.
  b. He does not have lung disease.
  c. He has lung disease given that he is a smoker.
  d. He has lung disease given that he does not smoke.

6.35 Refer to Exercise 6.34. Are smoking and lung disease among 60- to 65-year-old men related? Explain.

6.36 The method of instruction in college and university applied statistics courses is changing. Historically, most courses were taught with an emphasis on manual calculation. The alternative is to employ a computer and a software package to perform the calculations. An analysis of applied statistics courses investigated whether the instructor's educational background is primarily mathematics (or statistics) or some other field. The result of this analysis is the accompanying table of joint probabilities.

Education of Instructor	Emphasizes Manual Calculations	Emphasizes Computer and Software
Mathematics or statistics education	.23	.36
Other education	.11	.30

a. What is the probability that a randomly selected applied statistics course instructor whose education was in statistics emphasizes manual calculations?

b. What proportion of applied statistics courses employs a computer and software?

c. Are the educational background of the instructor and the way the course is taught independent?

6.37 A restaurant chain routinely surveys its customers. Among other questions, the survey asks customers whether they would return and to rate the quality of food. Summarizing hundreds of thousands of questionnaires produced this table of joint probabilities.

Rating	Customer Will Return	Customer Will Not Return
Poor	.02	.10
Fair	.08	.09
Good	.35	.14
Excellent	.20	.02

a. What proportion of customers say that they will return and rate the restaurant's food as good?

b. What proportion of customers who say that they will return rate the restaurant's food as good?

c. What proportion of customers who rate the restaurant's food as good say that they will return?

d. Discuss the differences in your answers to parts (a), (b), and (c).

6.38 To determine whether drinking alcoholic beverages has an effect on the bacteria that cause ulcers, researchers developed the following table of joint probabilities.

Number of Alcoholic Drinks per Day	Ulcer	No Ulcer
None	.01	.22
One	.03	.19
Two	.03	.32
More than two	.04	.16

a. What proportion of people have ulcers?

b. What is the probability that a teetotaler (no alcoholic beverages) develops an ulcer?

c. What is the probability that someone who has an ulcer does not drink alcohol?

d. What is the probability that someone who has an ulcer drinks alcohol?

6.39 An analysis of fired or laid-off workers, their age, and the reasons for their departure produced the following table of joint probabilities.

Reason for job loss	Age Category			
	20–24	25–54	55–64	65 and older
Plant or company closed or moved	.015	.320	.089	.029
Insufficient work	.014	.180	.034	.011
Position or shift abolished	.006	.214	.071	.016

Source: Statistical Abstract of the United States.

a. What is the probability that a 25- to 54-year-old employee was laid off or fired because of insufficient work?

b. What proportion of laid-off or fired workers is age 65 and older?

c. What is the probability that a laid-off or fired worker because the plant or company closed is 65 or older?

6.40 Many critics of television claim that there is too much violence and that it has a negative effect on society. There may also be a negative effect on advertisers. To examine this issue, researchers developed two versions of a cops-and-robbers made-for-television movie. One version depicted several violent crimes, and the other removed these scenes. In the middle of the movie, one 60-second commercial was shown advertising a new product and brand name. At the end of the movie, viewers were asked to name the brand. After observing the results, the researchers produced the following table of joint probabilities.

	Watch Violent Movie	Watch Nonviolent Movie
Remember brand name	.15	.18
Do not remember brand name	.35	.32

a. What proportion of viewers remember the brand name?

b. What proportion of viewers who watch the violent movie remember the brand name?

c. Does watching a violent movie affect whether the viewer will remember the brand name? Explain.

6.41 Is there a relationship between the male hormone testosterone and criminal behavior? To answer this question, medical researchers measured the testosterone level of penitentiary inmates and recorded whether they were convicted of murder. After analyzing the results, the researchers produced the following table of joint probabilities.

Testosterone Level	Murderer	Other Felon
Above average	.27	.24
Below average	.21	.28

a. What proportion of murderers have above-average testosterone levels?

b. Are levels of testosterone and the crime committed independent? Explain.

6.42 The issue of health care coverage in the United States is becoming a critical issue in American politics. A large-scale study was undertaken to determine who is and is not covered. From this study, the following table of joint probabilities was produced.

Age Category	Has Health Insurance	Does Not Have Health Insurance
25–34	.167	.085
35–44	.209	.061
45–54	.225	.049
55–64	.177	.026

Source: U.S. Department of Health and Human Services.

If one person is selected at random, find the following probabilities.

a. P(Person has health insurance)

b. P(Person 55−64 has no health insurance)

c. P(Person without health insurance is between 25 and 34 years old)

6.43 Violent crime in many American schools is an unfortunate fact of life. An analysis of schools and violent crime yielded the table of joint probabilities shown next.

Level	Violent Crime Committed This Year	No Violent Crime Committed This Year
Primary	.393	.191
Middle	.176	.010
High School	.134	.007
Combined	.074	.015

Source: Statistical Abstract of the United States.

If one school is randomly selected, find the following probabilities.

a. Probability of at least one incident of violent crime during the year in a primary school

b. Probability of no violent crime during the year

6.44 Refer to Exercise 6.43. A similar analysis produced these joint probabilities.

Enrollment	Violent Crime Committed This Year	No Violent Crime Committed This Year
Less than 300	.159	.091
300 to 499	.221	.065
500 to 999	.289	.063
1,000 or more	.108	.004

Source: Statistical Abstract of the United States.

a. What is the probability that a school with an enrollment of less than 300 had at least one violent crime during the year?

b. What is the probability that a school that has at least one violent crime had an enrollment of less than 300?

6.45 A firm has classified its customers in two ways: (1) according to whether the account is overdue and (2) whether the account is new (less than 12 months) or old. An analysis of the firm's records provided the input for the following table of joint probabilities.

Account	Overdue	Not Overdue
New	.06	.13
Old	.52	.29

One account is randomly selected.

a. If the account is overdue, what is the probability that it is new?

b. If the account is new, what is the probability that it is overdue?

c. Is the age of the account related to whether it is overdue? Explain.

6.46 How are the size of a firm (measured in terms of the number of employees) and the type of firm related? To help answer the question, an analyst referred to the U.S. Census and developed the following.

Employees	Construction	Manufacturing	Retail
Fewer than 20	.464	.147	.237
20 to 99	.039	.049	.035
100 or more	.005	.019	.005

Source: Statistical Abstract of the United States.

If one firm is selected at random, find the probability of the following events.

a. The firm employs fewer than 20 employees.
b. The firm is in the retail industry.
c. A firm in the construction industry employs between 20 and 99 workers.

6.47 Credit scorecards are used by financial institutions to help decide to whom loans should be granted. An analysis of the records of one bank produced the following probabilities.

	Score	
Loan Performance	**Under 400**	**400 or More**
Fully repaid	.19	.64
Defaulted	.13	.04

a. What proportion of loans are fully repaid?
b. What proportion of loans given to scorers of less than 400 fully repay?
c. What proportion of loans given to scorers of 400 or more fully repay?
d. Are score and whether the loan is fully repaid independent? Explain.

6.48 A retail outlet wanted to know whether its weekly advertisement in the daily newspaper works. To acquire this critical information, the store manager surveyed the people who entered the store and determined whether each individual saw the ad and whether a purchase was made. From the information developed, the manager produced the following table of joint probabilities. Are the ads effective? Explain.

	Purchase	**No Purchase**
See ad	.18	.42
Do not see ad	.12	.28

6.49 To gauge the relationship between education and unemployment, an economist turned to the U.S. Census from which the following table of joint probabilities was produced:

Education	**Employed**	**Unemployed**
Not a high school graduate	.075	.015
High school graduate	.257	.035
Some college, no degree	.155	.016
Associate's degree	.096	.008
Bachelor's degree	.211	.012
Advanced degree	.118	.004

Source: Statistical Abstract of the United States.

a. What is the probability that a high school graduate is unemployed?

b. Determine the probability that a randomly selected individual is employed.
c. Find the probability that an unemployed person possesses an advanced degree.
d. What is the probability that a randomly selected person did not finish high school?

6.50 The decision about where to build a new plant is a major one for most companies. One of the factors that is often considered is the education level of the location's residents. Census information may be useful in this regard. After analyzing a recent census, a company produced the following joint probabilities:

Education	**Northeast**	**Midwest**	**South**	**West**
Not a high school graduate	.021	.022	.053	.032
High school graduate	.062	.075	.118	.058
Some college, no degree	.024	.038	.062	.044
Associate's degree	.015	.022	.032	.022
Bachelor's degree	.038	.040	.067	.050
Advanced degree	.024	.021	.036	.025

Source: Statistical Abstract of the United States.

a. Determine the probability that a person living in the West has a bachelor's degree.
b. Find the probability that a high school graduate lives in the Northeast.
c. What is the probability that a person selected at random lives in the South?
d. What is the probability that a person selected at random does not live in the South?

6.51 A Gallup survey asked a sample of Americans how much confidence they had in the criminal justice system. After recording the responses as well as the race of the respondent, the following table of joint probabilities was created.

Confidence in Justice System	**White**	**Black**
A great deal or quite a lot	.240	.041
Some	.356	.048
Very little or none	.255	.060

a. Calculate the probability that a white person had some confidence in the justice system.
b. Find the probability that a black person would have very little or no confidence in the justice system
c. What is the probability that a person who has some confidence is white?

6.52 Arthritis is an inflammation of one or more joints. The symptoms are pain and stiffness, which usually worsen with age. Suppose that an analysis of age and incidence of arthritis produced the following table of joint probabilities.

Age Categories	Has Arthritis	Does Not Have Arthritis
50–60	.040	.360
60–70	.075	.225
70–80	.072	.088
Over 80	.105	.035

a. What is the probability that a person who is over 80 has arthritis?
b. Determine the probability that a person who is 55 years old does not have arthritis.
c. What is the probability that someone who has arthritis is between 60 and 70 years old?

6.53 There are three major political parties in Canada. They are Conservatives, Liberals, and New Democrats. Suppose that in one city the breakdown of the party preferences and gender produced the following table of joint probabilities.

Party	Men	Women
Conservative	.255	.215
Liberal	.191	.224
New Democrat	.044	.071

a. Find the probability that a man would support the New Democrats.
b. Calculate the probability that a Liberal supporter is a woman.
c. If we select one person at random, what is the probability that person is a Conservative supporter?

6.54 The generally accepted definitions of Generation X and Millennials is that the former was born between 1965 and 1980 and the latter born after 1981. Baby Boomers are defined as people born between 1946 and 1964. An analysis conducted by the Pew Research Center produced the following table of joint probabilities relating marital status of the three groups defined here.

Marital Status	Millennial	Gen X	Boomer
Single, never married	0.195	0.058	0.030
Married	0.089	0.223	0.201
Living with not married	0.030	0.025	0.009
Divorced, separated, widowed	0.017	0.054	0.070

a. Find the probability that a Millennial is married.
b. Compute the probability that a Baby Boomer is single, never married.

c. Suppose that one person is selected at random. What is the probability that that person is married?
d. What is the probability that someone who is living with a partner but not married is a Generation Xer?

6.55 In a large city, an analysis of unemployment and education reveals the following joint probabilities.

	Employed	Unemployed
No university degree	.45	.07
University degree	.34	.03
Post-graduate degree	.11	0

a. What is the probability that a person with no university degree is unemployed?
b. What is the probability that an employed person has a post-graduate degree?
c. What proportion of this population has a university degree?

6.56 The following table lists the joint probabilities associated with gender and cigarette smoking.

Gender	Never Smoked	Former Smoker	Current Smoker
Male	.23	.05	.20
Female	.29	.16	.07

a. Find the probability that a male is a current smoker.
b. Compute the probability that a former smoker is female.

In Chapter 2 (page 34), we introduced the Pew Research Center. The next four exercises are based on several Pew Research Center surveys. Pew investigated political polarization and media habits. A sample of Americans was selected and each person was placed in one of the following political categories: Consistent liberal, Mostly liberal, Mixed, Mostly conservative, Consistent conservative. Each was also asked to what degree they trusted a variety of television networks for news about government and politics.

6.57 After tabulating the results for NBC News, the table of joint probabilities was created.

NBC News	Consistent Liberal	Mostly Liberal	Mixed	Mostly Conservative	Consistent Conservative
Trust	0.090	0.139	0.194	0.063	0.014
Distrust	0.010	0.015	0.054	0.060	0.056
Neither trust nor distrust	0.057	0.051	0.086	0.039	0.015
Don't know	0.003	0.015	0.025	0.009	0.005

a. Find the probability that one respondent selected at random would trust NBC News.
b. What is the probability that a consistent conservative would distrust NBC News?

c. What is the probability that a consistent liberal neither trusts nor distrusts NBC News?

d. If one person is randomly chosen, what is the probability that that person is a consistent liberal?

6.58 Here are the joint probabilities for MSNBC.

MSNBC	Consistent Liberal	Mostly Liberal	Mixed	Mostly Conservative	Consistent Conservative
Trust	0.083	0.106	0.140	0.044	0.006
Distrust	0.015	0.020	0.054	0.068	0.068
Neither trust nor distrust	0.056	0.068	0.112	0.044	0.011
Don't know	0.006	0.026	0.054	0.014	0.005

a. Compute the probability that a mostly conservative would distrust MSNBC.

b. Find the probability that a mixed liberal–conservative would neither trust nor distrust MSNBC.

c. If one person is selected at random, what is the probability that that person trusts MSNBC?

d. If one person is chosen at random, what is the probability that that person is a mostly conservative?

6.59 Following are the joint probabilities for Fox News.

Fox News	Consistent Liberal	Mostly Liberal	Mixed	Mostly Conservative	Consistent Conservative
Trust	0.009	0.062	0.169	0.122	0.079
Distrust	0.129	0.119	0.101	0.019	0.003
Neither trust nor distrust	0.013	0.026	0.054	0.019	0.005
Don't know	0.008	0.013	0.036	0.010	0.004

a. Determine the probability that a consistent liberal would distrust Fox News.

b. Find the probability that a mostly conservative trusts Fox News.

c. Find the probability that a consistent conservative neither trusts nor distrusts Fox News.

d. If one person is chosen at random, find the probability that that person is a consistent conservative.

6.60 Following are the joint probabilities for CNN.

CNN	Consistent Liberal	Mostly Liberal	Mixed	Mostly Conservative	Consistent Conservative
Trust	0.090	0.145	0.220	0.066	0.013
Distrust	0.019	0.024	0.050	0.056	0.055
Neither trust nor distrust	0.048	0.040	0.061	0.041	0.017
Don't know	0.003	0.011	0.029	0.007	0.005

a. If one person is selected at random, what is the probability that that person distrusts CNN?

b. Find the probability that a consistent conservative trusts CNN.

c. Compute the probability that a mostly liberal neither trusts nor distrusts CNN.

d. If one person is selected at random, determine the probability that that person is a mixed liberal–conservative.

6-3 / PROBABILITY RULES AND TREES

In Section 6-2, we introduced intersection and union and described how to determine the probability of the intersection and the union of two events. In this section, we present other methods of determining these probabilities. We introduce three rules that enable us to calculate the probability of more complex events from the probability of simpler events.

6-3a Complement Rule

The **complement** of event A is the event that occurs when event A does not occur. The complement of event A is denoted by A^C. The **complement rule** defined here derives from the fact that the probability of an event and the probability of the event's complement must sum to 1.

> **Complement Rule**
>
> $$P(A^C) = 1 - P(A)$$
>
> for any event A.

We will demonstrate the use of this rule after we introduce the next rule.

6-3b Multiplication Rule

The **multiplication rule** is used to calculate the joint probability of two events. It is based on the formula for conditional probability supplied in the previous section; that is, from the following formula

$$P(A|B) = \frac{P(A \text{ and } B)}{P(B)}$$

we derive the multiplication rule simply by multiplying both sides by $P(B)$.

> **Multiplication Rule**
>
> The joint probability of any two events A and B is
>
> $$P(A \text{ and } B) = P(B)P(A|B)$$
>
> or, altering the notation,
>
> $$P(A \text{ and } B) = P(A)P(B|A)$$

If A and B are independent events, $P(A|B) = P(A)$ and $P(B|A) = P(B)$. It follows that the joint probability of two independent events is simply the product of the probabilities of the two events. We can express this as a special form of the multiplication rule.

> **Multiplication Rule for Independent Events**
>
> The joint probability of any two independent events A and B is
>
> $$P(A \text{ and } B) = P(A)P(B)$$

EXAMPLE 6.5*

Selecting Two Students without Replacement

A graduate statistics course has seven male and three female students. The professor wants to select two students at random to help conduct a research project. What is the probability that the two students chosen are female?

---

*This example can be solved using the Hypergeometric distribution, which is described in the online appendix of the same name.

SOLUTION:

Let A represent the event that the first student chosen is female and B represent the event that the second student chosen is also female. We want the joint probability $P(A \text{ and } B)$. Consequently, we apply the multiplication rule:

$$P(A \text{ and } B) = P(A)P(B|A)$$

Because there are 3 female students in a class of 10, the probability that the first student chosen is female is

$$P(A) = 3/10$$

After the first student is chosen, there are only 9 students left. Given that the first student chosen was female, there are only 2 female students left. It follows that

$$P(B|A) = 2/9$$

Thus, the joint probability is

$$P(A \text{ and } B) = P(A)P(B|A) = \left(\frac{3}{10}\right)\left(\frac{2}{9}\right) = \frac{6}{90} = .067$$

EXAMPLE 6.6

Selecting Two Students with Replacement

Refer to Example 6.5. The professor who teaches the course is suffering from flu and will be unavailable for two classes. The professor's replacement will teach the next two classes. The replacement's style is to select one student at random and pick on that student to answer questions during that class. What is the probability that the two students chosen are female?

SOLUTION:

The form of the question is the same as in Example 6.5: We wish to compute the probability of choosing two female students. However, the experiment is slightly different. It is now possible to choose the *same* student in each of the two classes taught by the replacement. Thus, A and B are independent events, and we apply the multiplication rule for independent events:

$$P(A \text{ and } B) = P(A)P(B)$$

The probability of choosing a female student in each of the two classes is the same; that is,

$$P(A) = 3/10 \text{ and } P(B) = 3/10$$

Hence,

$$P(A \text{ and } B) = P(A)P(B) = \left(\frac{3}{10}\right)\left(\frac{3}{10}\right) = \frac{9}{100} = .09$$

6-3c Addition Rule

The **addition rule** enables us to calculate the probability of the union of two events.

Addition Rule

The probability that event A, or event B, or both occur is

$$P(A \text{ or } B) = P(A) + P(B) - P(A \text{ and } B)$$

If you're like most students, you're wondering why we subtract the joint probability from the sum of the probabilities of A and B. To understand why this is necessary, examine Table 6.2 (page 177), which we have reproduced here as Table 6.3.

TABLE **6.3** Joint and Marginal Probabilities

	B_1	B_2	TOTALS
A_1	$P(A_1 \text{ and } B_1) = .11$	$P(A_1 \text{ and } B_2) = .29$	$P(A_1) = .40$
A_2	$P(A_2 \text{ and } B_1) = .06$	$P(A_2 \text{ and } B_2) = .54$	$P(A_2) = .60$
Totals	$P(B_1) = .17$	$P(B_2) = .83$	1.00

This table summarizes how the marginal probabilities were computed. For example, the marginal probability of A_1 and the marginal probability of B_1 were calculated as

$$P(A_1) = P(A_1 \text{ and } B_1) + P(A_1 \text{ and } B_2) = .11 + .29 = .40$$
$$P(B_1) = P(A_1 \text{ and } B_1) + P(A_2 \text{ and } B_1) = .11 + .06 = .17$$

If we now attempt to calculate the probability of the union of A_1 and B_1 by summing their probabilities, we find

$$P(A_1) + P(B_1) = .11 + .29 + .11 + .06$$

Notice that we added the joint probability of A_1 and B_1 (which is .11) twice. To correct the double counting, we subtract the joint probability from the sum of the probabilities of A_1 and B_1. Thus,

$$P(A_1 \text{ or } B_1) = P(A_1) + P(B_1) - P(A_1 \text{ and } B_1)$$
$$= [.11 + .29] + [.11 + .06] - .11$$
$$= .40 + .17 - .11 = .46$$

This is the probability of the union of A_1 and B_1, which we calculated in Example 6.4 (page 179).

As was the case with the multiplication rule, there is a special form of the addition rule. When two events are mutually exclusive (which means that the two events cannot occur together), their joint probability is 0.

> **Addition Rule for Mutually Exclusive Events**
>
> The probability of the union of two mutually exclusive events A and B is
>
> $$P(A \text{ or } B) = P(A) + P(B)$$

EXAMPLE 6.7

Applying the Addition Rule

In a large city, two newspapers are published, the *Sun* and the *Post*. The circulation departments report that 22% of the city's households have a subscription to the *Sun* and 35% subscribe to the *Post*. A survey reveals that 6% of all households subscribe to both newspapers. What proportion of the city's households subscribe to either newspaper?

S O L U T I O N :

We can express this question as, What is the probability of selecting a household at random that subscribes to the *Sun*, the *Post*, or both? Another way of asking the question is, What is the probability that a randomly selected household subscribes to *at least one* of the newspapers? It is now clear that we seek the probability of the union, and we must apply the addition rule. Let A = household that subscribes to the *Sun* and B = the household that subscribes to the *Post*. We perform the following calculation:

$$P(A \text{ or } B) = P(A) + P(B) - P(A \text{ and } B) = .22 + .35 - .06 = .51$$

The probability that a randomly selected household subscribes to either newspaper is .51. Expressed as relative frequency, 51% of the city's households subscribe to either newspaper.

6-3d Probability Trees

An effective and simpler method of applying the probability rules is the probability tree, wherein the events in an experiment are represented by lines. The resulting figure resembles a tree, hence the name. We will illustrate the probability tree with several examples, including two that we addressed using the probability rules alone.

In Example 6.5, we wanted to find the probability of choosing two female students, where the two choices had to be different. The tree diagram in Figure 6.1 describes this experiment. Notice that the first two branches represent the two possibilities, female and male students, on the first choice. The second set of branches represents the two possibilities on the second choice. The probabilities of female and male student chosen first are 3/10 and 7/10, respectively. The probabilities for the second set of branches are conditional probabilities based on the choice of the first student selected.

We calculate the joint probabilities by multiplying the probabilities on the linked branches. Thus, the probability of choosing two female students is $P(F \text{ and } F) = (3/10)(2/9) = 6/90$. The remaining joint probabilities are computed similarly.

FIGURE **6.1** Probability Tree for Exercise 6.5

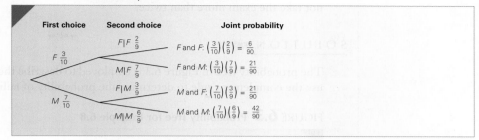

In Example 6.6, the experiment was similar to that of Example 6.5. However, the student selected on the first choice was returned to the pool of students and was eligible to be chosen again. Thus, the probabilities on the second set of branches remain the same as the probabilities on the first set, and the probability tree is drawn with these changes, as shown in Figure 6.2.

FIGURE **6.2** Probability Tree for Exercise 6.6

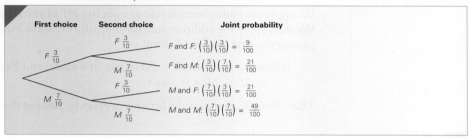

The advantage of a probability tree on this type of problem is that it restrains its users from making the wrong calculation. Once the tree is drawn and the probabilities of the branches inserted, virtually the only allowable calculation is the multiplication of the probabilities of linked branches. An easy check on those calculations is available. The joint probabilities at the ends of the branches must sum to 1 because all possible events are listed. In both figures, notice that the joint probabilities do indeed sum to 1.

The special form of the addition rule for mutually exclusive events can be applied to the joint probabilities. In both probability trees, we can compute the probability that one student chosen is female and one is male simply by adding the joint probabilities. For the tree in Example 6.5, we have

$$P(F \text{ and } M) + P(M \text{ and } F) = 21/90 + 21/90 = 42/90$$

In the probability tree in Example 6.6, we find

$$P(F \text{ and } M) + P(M \text{ and } F) = 21/100 + 21/100 = 42/100$$

EXAMPLE **6.8**

Probability of Passing the Bar Exam

Students who graduate from law schools must still pass a bar exam before becoming lawyers. Suppose that in a particular jurisdiction the pass rate for first-time test takers is 72%. Candidates who fail the first exam may take it again several months later. Of those who fail their first test, 88% pass their second attempt. Find the probability that a randomly selected law school graduate becomes a lawyer. Assume that candidates cannot take the exam more than twice.

SOLUTION:

The probability tree in Figure 6.3 is employed to describe the experiment. Note that we use the complement rule to determine the probability of failing each exam.

FIGURE **6.3** Probability Tree for Example 6.8

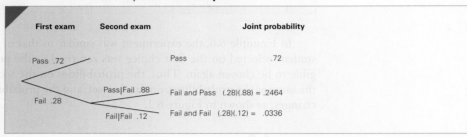

We apply the multiplication rule to calculate P(Fail and Pass), which we find to be .2464. We then apply the addition rule for mutually exclusive events to find the probability of passing the first or second exam:

$$P(\text{Pass [on first exam]}) + P(\text{Fail [on first exam] and Pass [on second exam]})$$
$$= .72 + .2464 = .9664$$

Thus, 96.64% of applicants become lawyers by passing the first or second exam.

EXERCISES

6.61 Given the following probabilities, compute all joint probabilities.

$P(A) = .9$ $P(A^C) = .1$
$P(B|A) = .4$ $P(B|A^C) = .7$

6.62 Determine all joint probabilities from the following.

$P(A) = .8$ $P(A^C) = .2$
$P(B|A) = .4$ $P(B|A^C) = .7$

6.63 Draw a probability tree to compute the joint probabilities from the following probabilities.

$P(A) = .5$ $P(A^C) = .5$
$P(B|A) = .4$ $P(B|A^C) = .7$

6.64 Given the following probabilities, draw a tree to compute the joint probabilities.

$P(A) = .8$ $P(A^C) = .2$
$P(B|A) = .3$ $P(B|A^C) = .3$

6.65 Given the following probabilities, find the joint probability $P(A \text{ and } B)$.

$P(A) = .7$ $P(B|A) = .3$

6.66 Approximately 10% of people are left-handed. If two people are selected at random, what is the probability of the following events?
 a. Both are right-handed.
 b. Both are left-handed.
 c. One is right-handed and the other is left-handed.
 d. At least one is right-handed.

6.67 Refer to Exercise 6.66. Suppose that three people are selected at random.
 a. Draw a probability tree to depict the experiment.
 b. If we use the notation RRR to describe the selection of three right-handed people, what are the descriptions of the remaining seven events? (Use L for left-hander.)
 c. How many of the events yield no right-handers, one right-hander, two right-handers, and three right-handers?
 d. Find the probability of no right-handers, one right-hander, two right-handers, and three right-handers.

6.68 Suppose there are 100 students in your accounting class, 10 of whom are left-handed. Two students are selected at random.

    a. Draw a probability tree and insert the probabilities for each branch.

    What is the probability of the following events?

    b. Both are right-handed.

    c. Both are left-handed.

    d. One is right-handed and the other is left-handed.

    e. At least one is right-handed.

6.69 Refer to Exercise 6.68. Suppose that three people are selected at random.

    a. Draw a probability tree and insert the probabilities of each branch.

    b. What is the probability of no right-handers, one right-hander, two right-handers, and three right-handers?

6.70 An aerospace company has submitted bids on two separate federal government defense contracts. The company president believes that there is a 40% probability of winning the first contract. If they win the first contract, the probability of winning the second is 70%. However, if they lose the first contract, the president thinks that the probability of winning the second contract decreases to 50%.

    a. What is the probability that they win both contracts?

    b. What is the probability that they lose both contracts?

    c. What is the probability that they win only one contract?

6.71 A telemarketer calls people and tries to sell them a subscription to a daily newspaper. On 20% of calls, there is no answer or the line is busy. The telemarketer sells subscriptions to 5% of the remaining calls. What proportion of calls results in a sale?

6.72 The operations manager for an injection-molding firm admits that on 10% of shifts, the manager forgets to shut off the injection machine. This causes the machine to overheat, increasing the probability from 2% to 20% that a defective molding will be produced during the early morning run. What proportion of moldings from the early morning run is defective?

6.73 A study undertaken by the Miami-Dade Supervisor of Elections revealed that 44% of registered voters are Democrats, 37% are Republicans, and 19% are others. If two registered voters are selected at random, what is the probability that both of them have the same party affiliation?

6.74 Among many other pieces of information, the U.S. Census Bureau records the race or ethnicity of the residents of every county in every state. From these results, the bureau calculated a "diversity index" that measures the probability that two people chosen at random are of different races or ethnicities. Suppose that the census determined that in a county in Wisconsin 80% of its residents are white, 15% are black, and 5% are Asian. Calculate the diversity index for this county.

6.75 A survey of middle-aged men reveals that 28% of them are balding at the crown of their heads. Moreover, it is known that such men have an 18% probability of suffering a heart attack in the next 10 years. Men who are not balding in this way have an 11% probability of a heart attack. Find the probability that a middle-aged man will suffer a heart attack sometime in the next 10 years.

6.76 The chartered financial analyst (CFA) is a designation earned after a candidate has taken three annual exams (CFA I, II, and III). The exams are taken in early June. Candidates who pass an exam are eligible to take the exam for the next level in the following year. The pass rates for levels I, II, and III are .57, .73, and .85, respectively. Suppose that 3,000 candidates take the level I exam, 2,500 take the level II exam, and 2,000 take the level III exam. Suppose that one student is selected at random. What is the probability that the candidate has passed the exam?

Source: Institute of Financial Analysts.

6.77 The Nickels restaurant chain regularly conducts surveys of its customers. Respondents are asked to assess food quality, service, and price. The responses are

    Excellent   Good   Fair

Surveyed customers are also asked whether they would come back. After analyzing the responses, an expert in probability determined that 87% of customers say that they will return. Of those who so indicate, 57% rate the restaurant as excellent, 36% rate it as good, and the remainder rate it as fair. Of those who say that they won't return, the probabilities are 14%, 32%, and 54%, respectively. What proportion of customers rate the restaurant as good?

6.78 Researchers at the University of Pennsylvania School of Medicine have determined that children under 2 years old who sleep with the lights on have a 36% chance of becoming myopic before they are 16. Children who sleep in darkness have a 21% chance of becoming myopic. A survey indicates that 28% of children under 2 sleep with some light on. Find the probability that a child under 16 is myopic.

6.79 All printed circuit boards (PCBs) that are manufactured at a certain plant are inspected. An analysis of the company's records indicates that 22% are flawed in some way. Of those that are flawed, 84% are reparable and the rest must be discarded. If a newly produced PCB is randomly selected, what is the probability that it does not have to be discarded?

6.80 A financial analyst has determined that there is a 22% probability that a mutual fund will outperform the market over a 1-year period provided that it outperformed the market the previous year. If only 15% of mutual funds outperform the market during any year, what is the probability that a mutual fund will outperform the market 2 years in a row?

6.81 An investor believes that on a day when the Dow Jones Industrial Average (DJIA) increases, the probability that the NASDAQ also increases is 77%. If the investor believes that there is a 60% probability that the DJIA will increase tomorrow, what is the probability that the NASDAQ will increase as well?

6.82 The controls of an airplane have several backup systems or redundancies so that if one fails the plane will continue to operate. Suppose that the mechanism that controls the flaps has two backups. If the probability that the main control fails is .0001 and the probability that each backup will fail is .01, what is the probability that all three fail to operate?

6.83 From the U.S. Census we learn that in the United States, 65% of people who are over 85 are women. The census also tells us that 53% of women over 85 live alone and that 30% of men over 85 live alone. Calculate the probability that an American who is over 85 is living alone.

6.84 A financial analyst estimates that the probability that the economy will experience a recession in the next 12 months is 25% and that if the economy encounters a recession, the probability that the mutual fund the analyst owns will increase in value is 20%. If there is no recession, the probability that the mutual fund will increase in value is 75%. Find the probability that the mutual fund's value will increase.

6.85 In June 2016, Britons were heading to the polls to vote in a referendum to decide whether the United Kingdom would leave the European Union. Pew Research Center conducted surveys in European countries to determine opinions about the possible "Brexit." Respondents were asked what the U.K.'s departure would mean for the EU. Responses were "Bad thing" or "Good thing." The number of respondents in each of the countries and the proportions who said it would be a bad thing are listed in the following table.

Country	Number of Respondents	Probability of Responding "Bad Thing"
France	630	62%
Germany	590	74%
Italy	480	57%

What is the probability that if we select one respondent at random the respondent would say the U.K. leaving the EU is a bad thing?

6.86 Refer to Exercise 6.85. Respondents in Greece, Hungary, and Poland were asked whether they approved or disapproved of the way the EU was dealing with the refugee issue. The number of respondents and the percentage opting for disapprove are listed here.

Country	Number of Respondents	Probability of Disapprove (%)
Greece	385	94
Hungary	420	70
Poland	475	66

What is the probability that if we select one respondent at random that respondent disapproves of the way the EU is handling the refugee issue?

6.87 How many Americans under the age of 40 have student debts? A Pew Research Center attempted to answer the question by asking whether respondents had student debt and in what was their occupation. The following probabilities were determined.

Occupation	Proportion (%)	Has Student Debt (%)
Managerial/ Professional	32	45
Technical, Sales, or Services	15	39
Other	53	27

Calculate the probability that a randomly selected respondent has student debt.

6.88 A statistics professor was in the process of comparing the pass rates (the percentage of entering students who graduate in 5 years or less) for B.A.'s, B.B.A.'s, B.Sc.'s, and B.Eng.'s. Delving into the record the professor finds the following probabilities.

Degree	Proportion of Entering Class (%)	Pass Rate (%)
B.A.	38	79
B.B.A.	41	74
B.Sc.	13	68
B.Eng.	8	57

What is the probability that a student graduates in 5 years or less?

6.89 In Ontario, Canada's largest province, beer can only be sold in the Beer Stores or in Liquor Control Board of Ontario stores, and liquor and wine can only be sold in LCBO stores. Some Ontarians want the choice expanded to any grocery store. Surveys of Ontarians asked whether they support or oppose letting grocery stores sell beer, wine, and liquor. The results generated the following probabilities. It is known that support for the Liberal Party, New Democratic Party, and the Progressive Conservative Party stands at 22%, 35%, and 43%, respectively.

Party Support	Strongly Support	Somewhat Support	Somewhat Oppose	Strongly Oppose
Liberal	.24	.47	.19	.10
New Democratic	.24	.41	.22	.14
Progressive Conservative	.27	.47	.15	.11

a. Find the probability that a randomly selected Ontarian strongly opposes the proposal.

b. What is the probability that a randomly selected Ontarian somewhat opposes the proposal?

6.90 A census of Americans over 60 years of age who have a post-graduate degree examined the relationship between age and type of post-graduate degree produced the following table of probabilities.

Age	P(Master's Degree)	P(Professional Degree)	P(Doctorate Degree)
60–64	.72	.18	.10
65–74	.68	.17	.15
75+	.60	.20	.20

The proportion of Americans 60 years of age and older in each of the age categories is listed next.

$P(60–64) = 33\%, P(65–74) = 44\%, P(75 \text{ and older}) = 23\%$

a. What is the probability that a randomly selected American who is older than 60 and possesses a post-graduate degree has a doctorate?

b. Find the probability that an American who is 60 years old with a post-graduate degree has a Master's degree.

6.91 In the population of adults who consume alcohol, 22% are between 18 and 29, 33% are between 30 and 49, 25% are between 50 and 64, and 20% are 60 and over. Surveys of adults who consume alcohol produced the following table of probabilities that an adult who consumes alcohol prefers beer by age category.

	P(Prefer beer)
18–29	.45
30–49	.47
50–64	.42
65+	.29

Find the probability that a randomly selected individual who consumes alcohol does not prefer beer.

6.92 Of grocery shoppers who have a shopping cart, 55% pay cash, 30% pay by debit card, and 15% pay by check. Of shoppers without a shopping cart, 70% pay cash, 20% pay by debit card, and 10% pay by check. It is known that 80% of grocery shoppers use a shopping cart. What is the probability that a shopper will pay by cash?

6.93 An analysis of children between the ages of 6 and 17 and their participation in after-school sports produced the following information. Proportion of students participating in sports in School Districts 1, 2, and 3 are .36, .55, and .42, respectively. The number of students in School Districts 1, 2, and 3 are 11,000, 8,000, and 21,000 respectively. If a student is selected at random, what is the probability that the student participates in sports?

6.94 There are four major parties in Canada: Conservative, Green, Liberal, and New Democrat. A survey asked a random sample of Canadians which party they support. From their responses, the following table of probabilities was produced. The Canadian census gives us the proportion of Canadians in each of the four age categories:

$P(18–29) = 18\%, P(30–44) = 27\%, P(45–59) = 26\%, P(60 \text{ and over}) = 29\%$

	Conservative	Green	Liberal	NDP	Other
18–29	.24	.11	.37	.24	.04
30–44	.31	.07	.36	.23	.03
45–59	.35	.07	.35	.17	.06
60+	.43	.03	.35	.14	.05

a. Find the probability that a Canadian prefers the Conservative party.

b. Calculate the probability that a Canadian prefers a party that is not the NDP.

6.95 High school calculus is a requirement to be admitted to WLU's undergraduate business program. Suppose that last year 53% of those admitted achieved a mark in calculus between 80 and 100, 27% received a mark between 60 and 79, and the rest achieved a mark between 50 and 59. Of those who received a mark between 80 and 100, 85% achieved a grade of A in the first year required mathematics course, Math 130; 64% of students whose calculus mark fell between 60 and 79 achieved a grade of A in Math 130; and no student whose calculus mark fell between 50 and 59 achieved a grade of A in Math 130. One student was selected at random. What is the probability that the student achieved a grade of A in Math 130?

6.96   The most recent U.S. Census reveals that 17.6% of Americans live in the Northeast, 21.3% live in the Midwest, 23.5% live in the West, and 37.6% live in the South. A survey asked American adults whether they approve of unions. From the survey, the probabilities below were generated.

	P(Approve unions)
Northeast	.69
Midwest	.65
West	.60
South	.58

Find the probability that a randomly selected person would not approve of unions.

6.97   According to Environment Canada, 60% of Canadians check the weather on radio, television, or the Internet so they can dress appropriately before leaving the house. These people always dress appropriately. Among people who don't check the weather 2 in 5 "under-dress" for the weather, 2 in 5 "over-dress" for the weather, and the rest dress appropriately. Given that it's raining, what is the chance that the first person you spot on University Avenue is wearing appropriate rain gear?

6.98   At WLU, newly hired faculty members have 5 years before they are required to apply for tenure. An analysis of past tenure decisions reveals that after 5 years, 35% have published more than five papers, 45% have published between three and five papers, and the rest published less than three papers. Tenure was granted to 95% of professors who published more than five papers, 65% of those who published between three and five papers, and 5% of those who published less than three papers. A young instructor has just been hired. What is the probability that tenure will be granted after 5 years?

6-4 / BAYES'S LAW

Conditional probability is often used to gauge the relationship between two events. In many of the examples and exercises you've already encountered, conditional probability measures the probability that an event occurs given that a possible cause of the event has occurred. In Example 6.2, we calculated the probability that a mutual fund outperforms the market (the effect) given that the fund manager graduated from a top-20 MBA program (the possible cause). There are situations, however, where we witness a particular event and we need to compute the probability of one of its possible causes. **Bayes's Law** is the technique we use.

EXAMPLE 6.9

Should an MBA Applicant Take a Preparatory Course?

The Graduate Management Admission Test (GMAT) is a requirement for all applicants of MBA programs. A variety of preparatory courses are designed to help applicants improve their GMAT scores, which range from 200 to 800. Suppose that a survey of MBA students reveals that among GMAT scorers above 650, 52% took a preparatory course; whereas among GMAT scorers of less than 650, only 23% took a preparatory course. An applicant to an MBA program has determined that one needs a score of more than 650 to get into a certain MBA program, but feels that the probability of getting that high a score is quite low—10%. The applicant is considering taking a preparatory course that costs $500 and is willing to do so only if the probability of achieving 650 or more doubles. What should the applicant do?

S O L U T I O N :

The easiest way to address this problem is to draw a tree diagram. The following notation will be used:

A = GMAT score is 650 or more

A^C = GMAT score less than 650

B = Took preparatory course

B^C = Did not take preparatory course

The probability of scoring 650 or more is

$P(A) = .10$

The complement rule gives us

$P(A^C) = 1 - .10 = .90$

Conditional probabilities are

$P(B|A) = .52$

and

$P(B|A^C) = .23$

Again using the complement rule, we find the following conditional probabilities:

$P(B^C|A) = 1 - .52 = .48$

and

$P(B^C|A^C) = 1 - .23 = .77$

We would like to determine the probability of achieving a GMAT score of 650 or more given that the applicant took the preparatory course; that is, we need to compute

$P(A|B)$

Using the definition of conditional probability (page 177), we have

$$P(A|B) = \frac{P(A \text{ and } B)}{P(B)}$$

Neither the numerator nor the denominator is known. The probability tree (Figure 6.4) will provide us with the probabilities.

FIGURE **6.4** Probability Tree for Example 6.9

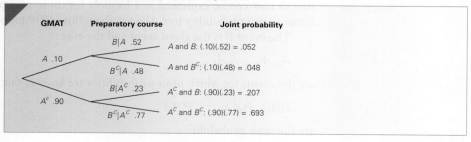

As you can see,

$$P(A \text{ and } B) = (.10)(.52) = .052$$
$$P(A^C \text{ and } B) = (.90)(.23) = .207$$

and

$$P(B) = P(A \text{ and } B) + P(A^C \text{ and } B) = .052 + .207 = .259$$

Thus,

$$P(A|B) = \frac{P(A \text{ and } B)}{P(B)} = \frac{.052}{.259} = .201$$

The probability of scoring 650 or more on the GMAT doubles when the preparatory course is taken.

Thomas Bayes first employed the calculation of conditional probability as shown in Example 6.9 during the eighteenth century. Accordingly, it is called Bayes's Law.

The probabilities $P(A)$ and $P(A^C)$ are called **prior probabilities** because they are determined *prior* to the decision about taking the preparatory course. The conditional probabilities are called **likelihood probabilities** for reasons that are beyond the mathematics in this book. Finally, the conditional probability $P(A|B)$ and similar conditional probabilities $P(A^C|B)$, $P(A|B^C)$, and $P(A^C|B^C)$ are called **posterior probabilities** or **revised probabilities** because the prior probabilities are revised *after* the decision about taking the preparatory course.

You may be wondering why we did not get $P(A|B)$ directly. In other words, why not survey people who took the preparatory course and ask whether they received a score of 650 or more? The answer is that using the likelihood probabilities and using Bayes's Law allows individuals to set their own prior probabilities, which can then be revised. For example, another MBA applicant may assess the probability of scoring 650 or more as .40. Inputting the new prior probabilities produces the following probabilities:

$$P(A \text{ and } B) = (.40)(.52) = .208$$
$$P(A^C \text{ and } B) = (.60)(.23) = .138$$
$$P(B) = P(A \text{ and } B) + P(A^C \text{ and } B) = .208 + .138 = .346$$
$$P(A|B) = \frac{P(A \text{ and } B)}{P(B)} = \frac{.208}{.346} = .601$$

The probability of achieving a GMAT score of 650 or more increases by a more modest 50% (from .40 to .601).

6-4a (Optional) Bayes's Law Formula

Bayes's Law can be expressed as a formula for those who prefer an algebraic approach rather than a probability tree. We use the following notation.

The event B is the given event and the events

$$A_1, A_2, \ldots, A_k$$

are the events for which prior probabilities are known; that is,

$$P(A_1), \ P(A_2), \ldots, P(A_k)$$

are the prior probabilities.

The following table lists the proportion of each age category wherein the PSA test is positive [$P(PT)$].

Age	Proportion of Tests That Are Positive	Number of Biopsies Performed per Million	Number of Cancers Detected	Number of Biopsies per Cancer Detected
40–49	.1407	140,700	.0498(140,700) = 7,007	20.10
50–59	.1474	147,400	.1045(147,400) = 15,403	9.57
60–79	.1610	161,000	.2000(161,000) = 32,200	5.00
70 and older	.1796	179,600	.3078(179,600) = 55,281	3.25

If we assume a cost of $1,000 per biopsy, the cost per cancer detected is $20,100 for 40 to 50, $9,570 for 50 to 60, $5,000 for 60 to 70, and $3,250 for over 70.

We have created an Excel spreadsheet to help you perform the calculations in Example 6.10. Open the **Excel Workbooks** folder and select **Medical screening**. There are three cells that you may alter. In cell B5, enter a new prior probability for prostate cancer. Its complement will be calculated in cell B15. In cells D6 and D15, type new values for the false-negative and false-positive rates, respectively. Excel will do the rest. We will use this spreadsheet to demonstrate some terminology standard in medical testing.

Terminology We will illustrate the terms using the probabilities calculated for the 40 to 50 age category.

The false-negative rate is .300. Its complement is the likelihood probability $P(PT|C)$, called the *sensitivity*. It is equal to $1 - .300 = .700$. Among men with prostate cancer, this is the proportion of men who will get a positive test result.

The complement of the false-positive rate (.135) is $P(NT|C^C)$, which is called the *specificity*. This likelihood probability is $1 - .135 = .865$.

The posterior probability that someone has prostate cancer given a positive test result [$P(C|PT) = .0498$] is called the *positive predictive value*. Using Bayes's Law, we can compute the other three posterior probabilities.

The probability that the patient does not have prostate cancer given a positive test result is

$$P(C^C|PT) = .9502$$

The probability that the patient has prostate cancer given a negative test result is

$$P(C|NT) = .0035$$

The probability that the patient does not have prostate cancer given a negative test result is

$$P(C^C|NT) = .9965$$

This revised probability is called the *negative predictive value*.

6-4c Developing an Understanding of Probability Concepts

If you review the computations made previously, you'll realize that the prior probabilities are as important as the probabilities associated with the test results (the likelihood probabilities) in determining the posterior probabilities. The following table shows the prior probabilities and the revised probabilities.

Age	Prior Probabilities for Prostate Cancer	Posterior Probabilities Given a Positive PSA Test
40–49	.010	.0498
50–59	.022	.1045
60–69	.046	.2000
70 and older	.079	.3078

As you can see, if the prior probability is low, then unless the screening test is quite accurate, the revised probability will still be quite low.

To see the effects of different likelihood probabilities, suppose the PSA test is a perfect predictor. In other words, the false-positive and false-negative rates are 0. Figure 6.7 displays the probability tree.

FIGURE **6.7** Probability Tree for Example 6.10 with a Perfect Predictor Test

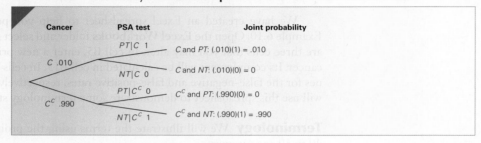

We find

$$P(PT) = P(C \text{ and } PT) + P(C^C \text{ and } PT) = .01 + 0 = .01$$

$$P(C|PT) = \frac{P(C \text{ and } PT)}{P(PT)} = \frac{.01}{.01} = 1.00$$

Now we calculate the probability of prostate cancer when the test is negative.

$$P(NT) = P(C \text{ and } NT) + P(C^C \text{ and } NT) = 0 + .99 = .99$$

$$P(C|NT) = \frac{P(C \text{ and } NT)}{P(NT)} = \frac{0}{.99} = 0$$

Thus, if the test is a perfect predictor and a man has a positive test, then as expected the probability that he has prostate cancer is 1.0. The probability that he does not have cancer when the test is negative is 0.

Now suppose that the test is always wrong; that is, the false-positive and false-negative rates are 100%. The probability tree is shown in Figure 6.8.

FIGURE **6.8** Probability Tree for Example 6.10 with a Test That Is Always Wrong

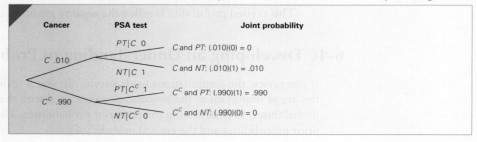

$$P(PT) = P(C \text{ and } PT) + P(C^C \text{ and } PT) = 0 + .99 = .99$$

$$P(C|PT) = \frac{P(C \text{ and } PT)}{P(PT)} \quad \frac{0}{.99} = 0$$

and

$$P(NT) = P(C \text{ and } NT) + P(C^C \text{ and } NT) = .01 + 0 = .01$$

$$P(C|NT) = \frac{P(C \text{ and } NT)}{P(NT)} = \frac{.01}{.01} = 1.00$$

Notice we have another perfect predictor except that it is reversed. The probability of prostate cancer given a positive test result is 0, but the probability becomes 1.00 when the test is negative.

Finally we consider the situation when the set of likelihood probabilities are the same. Figure 6.9 depicts the probability tree for a 40- to 50-year-old male and the probability of a positive test is (say) .3 and the probability of a negative test is .7.

FIGURE **6.9** **Probability Tree for Example 6.10 with Identical Likelihood Probabilities**

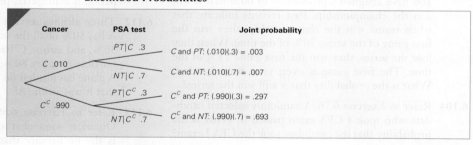

$$P(PT) = P(C \text{ and } PT) + P(C^C \text{ and } PT) = .003 + .297 = .300$$

$$P(C|PT) = \frac{P(C \text{ and } PT)}{P(PT)} = \frac{.003}{.300} = .01$$

and

$$P(NT) = P(C \text{ and } NT) + P(C^C \text{ and } NT) = .007 + .693 = .700$$

$$P(C|NT) = \frac{P(C \text{ and } NT)}{P(NT)} = .007/.700 = .01$$

As you can see, the posterior and prior probabilities are the same. That is, the PSA test does not change the prior probabilities. Obviously, the test is useless.

We could have used any probability for the false-positive and false-negative rates, including .5. If we had used .5, then one way of performing this PSA test is to flip a fair coin. One side would be interpreted as positive and the other side as negative. It is clear that such a test has no predictive power.

The exercises and Case 6.4 offer the probabilities for several other screening tests.

EXERCISES

6.99 Refer to Exercise 6.61. Determine $P(A|B)$.

6.100 Refer to Exercise 6.62. Find the following.
a. $P(A|B)$
b. $P(A^C|B)$
c. $P(A|B^C)$
d. $P(A^C|B^C)$

6.101 Refer to Example 6.9. An MBA applicant believes that the probability of scoring more than 650 on the GMAT without the preparatory course is .95. What is the probability of attaining that level after taking the preparatory course?

6.102 Refer to Exercise 6.72. The operations manager randomly selects a molding from the early morning run and discovers it is defective. What is the probability that the operations manager forgot to shut off the machine the previous night?

6.103 Your favorite baseball team is in the final playoffs. You have assigned a probability of 60% that it will win the championship. Past records indicate that when teams win the championship, they win the first game of the series 70% of the time. When they lose the series, they win the first game 25% of the time. The first game is over; your team has lost. What is the probability that it will win the series?

6.104 Refer to Exercise 6.76. A randomly selected candidate who took a CFA exam passed it. What is the probability that the candidate took the CFA I exam?

6.105 Bad gums may mean a bad heart. Researchers discovered that 85% of people who have suffered a heart attack had periodontal disease, an inflammation of the gums. Only 29% of people who have not had a heart attack have this disease. Suppose that in a certain community, heart attacks are quite rare, occurring with only 10% probability. If someone has periodontal disease, what is the probability that that person will have a heart attack?

6.106 Refer to Exercise 6.105. If 40% of the people in a community will have a heart attack, what is the probability that a person with periodontal disease will have a heart attack?

6.107 Refer to Exercise 6.85. A respondent who said that the U.K. leaving the EU is a bad thing was selected. What is the probability that the respondent is from Italy?

6.108 Refer to Exercise 6.78. The researchers examined a child under 16 and discovered that the child is myopic. What is the probability that the child slept with the lights when under the age of 2?

6.109 Data from the Office on Smoking and Health, Centers for Disease Control and Prevention, indicate that 40% of adults who did not finish high school, 34% of high school graduates, 24% of adults who completed some college, and 14% of college graduates smoke. In a particular community among adults, 15% did not finish high school, 20% are high school graduates, 30% completed some college, and 35% are college graduates. Suppose that one individual is selected at random, and it is discovered that the individual smokes. What is the probability that the individual is a college graduate?

6.110 Refer to Exercise 6.86. A respondent who disapproved of the way the EU handled the refugee issue was selected. Calculate the probability that the respondent is from Greece.

6.111 Refer to Exercise 6.87. An American under 40 has student debt. What is the probability that the occupation is managerial/professional?

6.112 Three airlines serve a small town in Ohio. Airline A has 50% of all the scheduled flights, airline B has 30%, and airline C has the remaining 20%. Their on-time rates are 80%, 65%, and 40%, respectively. A plane has just left on time. What is the probability that it was airline A?

6.113 Refer to Exercise 6.89. If the randomly selected Ontarian somewhat opposes the proposal, what is the probability that the Ontarian supports the Liberals?

6.114 Refer to Exercise 6.90. What is the probability that someone who is older than 60 and has a doctorate degree is 75 years of age or older?

6.115 Where do people get their news? These probabilities were generated by answers to this question as well as questions about ages. In this population, 18% are between 18 and 29, 27% are between 30 and 44, 26% are between 45 and 59, and 29% are 60 and older.

	Television	Facebook	Other
18–29	.12	.43	.45
30–44	.20	.30	.50
45–59	.33	.13	.54
60+	.50	.05	.45

You meet someone from this population who gets news from television. What is the probability that that person is between 30 and 44?

6.116 Refer to Exercise 6.92. A shopper is wheeling a shopping cart. What is the probability that the shopper paid in cash?

6.117 There are three shifts at an automobile plant. Shift 1 makes 50%, shift 2 makes 40%, and shift 3 makes 10% of the vans produced in the plant. It is known that shift 1 has a defective rate of 1%, shift 2's defective rate is 2%, and shift 3's defective rate is 6%. A customer recently purchased a van made at the plant and complains that it is defective. Calculate the probability that the van was made in shift 2.

6.118 Refer to Exercise 6.94. What is the probability that a Canadian who supports the Conservative party is 60 years of age or older?

6.119 Refer to Exercise 6.91. A randomly selected adult who consumes alcohol does not prefer beer. Compute the probability that the person is between 30 and 49 years old.

6.120 An airport luggage scanner can detect a weapon in suitcases with a false-positive rate of 2% and a false-negative rate of 3%. In a particular airport, about 4 passengers in 10,000 carry a weapon (accidentally or on purpose) in their luggage. If the scanner triggers an alarm (indicating that the scanner "thinks" it saw a weapon), what is the probability that there really is a weapon?

6.121 Refer to Exercise 6.93. What is the probability that a child who is 10 years old and participates in after-school sports goes to school 1?

6.122 Bank managers sometimes make decisions about whether to grant a loan simply on outward appearances. However, banks also use a technique called credit scoring to help make the decision. A credit scorecard assigns scores to applicants based on their credit history. The higher the score, the higher is the probability that an applicant will repay the loan. An analysis of credit scores reveals that among people who repay loans, 85% score more than 700. Only 60% of loan defaulters score more than 700. Suppose that a manager has subjectively assigned a probability of 80% that a loan applicant will repay the loan. You now determine that the credit score is more than 700. Determine the probability the applicant will repay the loan.

6.123 Refer to exercise 6.95. A WLU business student achieved a grade of A in Math 130. What is the probability that the student's high school calculus mark was between 60 and 79?

6.124 Refer to Exercise 6.96. You meet a stranger who is vacationing in Florida who does not support unions. What is the probability that the stranger is from the Northeast?

6.125 Refer to Exercise 6.97. What is the probability that someone is dressed appropriately does not check the weather?

The following exercises are based on Subsection 6-4b and 6-4c.

6.126 Transplant operations have become routine. One common transplant operation is for kidneys. The most dangerous aspect of the procedure is the possibility that the body may reject the new organ. Several new drugs are available for such circumstances, and the earlier the drug is administered, the higher the probability of averting rejection. The *New England Journal of Medicine* recently reported the development of a new urine test to detect early warning signs that the body is rejecting a transplanted kidney. However, like most other tests, the new test is not perfect. When the test is conducted on someone whose kidney will be rejected, approximately one out of five tests will be negative (i.e., the test is wrong). When the test is conducted on a person whose kidney will not be rejected, 8% will show a positive test result (i.e., another incorrect result). Physicians know that in about 35% of kidney transplants, the body tries to reject the organ. Suppose that the test was performed and the test is positive (indicating early warning of rejection). What is the probability that the body is attempting to reject the kidney?

6.127 The Rapid Test is used to determine whether someone has HIV (the virus that causes AIDS). The false-positive and false-negative rates are .027 and .080, respectively. A physician has just received the Rapid Test report that the patient tested positive. Before receiving the result, the physician assigned the patient to the low-risk group (defined on the basis of several variables) with only a 0.5% probability of having HIV. What is the probability that the patient actually has HIV?

6.128 What are the sensitivity, specificity, positive predictive value, and negative predictive value in the previous exercise?

6.129 The Pap smear is the standard test for cervical cancer. The false-positive rate is .636; the false-negative rate is .180. Family history and age are factors that must be considered when assigning a probability of cervical cancer. Suppose that, after obtaining a medical history, a physician determines that 2% of women of this patient's age and with similar family histories have cervical cancer. Determine the effects a positive and a negative Pap smear test have on the probability that the patient has cervical cancer.

6-5 / IDENTIFYING THE CORRECT METHOD

As we've previously pointed out, the emphasis in this book will be on identifying the correct statistical technique to use. In Chapters 2 and 4, we showed how to summarize data by first identifying the appropriate method to use. Although it is difficult to offer strict rules on which probability method to use, we can still provide some general guidelines.

In the examples and exercises in this text (and most other introductory statistics books), the key issue is whether joint probabilities are provided or are required.

6-5a Joint Probabilities Are Given

In Section 6-2, we addressed problems where the joint probabilities were given. In these problems, we can compute marginal probabilities by adding across rows and down columns. We can use the joint and marginal probabilities to compute conditional probabilities, for which a formula is available. This allows us to determine whether the events described by the table are independent or dependent.

We can also apply the addition rule to compute the probability that either of two events occur.

6-5b Joint Probabilities Are Required

The previous section introduced three probability rules and probability trees. We need to apply some or all of these rules in circumstances where one or more joint probabilities are required. We apply the multiplication rule (either by formula or through a probability tree) to calculate the probability of intersections. In some problems, we're interested in adding these joint probabilities. We're actually applying the addition rule for mutually exclusive events here. We also frequently use the complement rule. In addition, we can also calculate new conditional probabilities using Bayes's Law.

CHAPTER SUMMARY

The first step in assigning probability is to create an **exhaustive** and **mutually exclusive** list of outcomes. The second step is to use the **classical, relative frequency**, or **subjective approach** and assign probability to the outcomes. A variety of methods are available to compute the probability of other events. These methods include **probability rules** and **trees**.

An important application of these rules is **Bayes's Law**, which allows us to compute conditional probabilities from other forms of probability.

IMPORTANT TERMS:

Random experiment   169
Exhaustive   169
Mutually exclusive   169
Sample space   170
Classical approach   170
Relative frequency approach   171
Subjective approach   171
Event   171
Intersection   174
Joint probability   174
Marginal probability   176
Conditional probability   177
Independent events   178

Union   179
Complement   186
Complement rule   186
Multiplication rule   187
Addition rule   189
Bayes's Law   196
Prior probability   198
Likelihood probability   198
Posterior probability   198
Revised probability   198
False-positive   200
False-negative   200

FORMULAS:

Conditional probability

$$P(A|B) = \frac{P(A \text{ and } B)}{P(B)}$$

Complement rule

$$P(A^C) = 1 - P(A)$$

Multiplication rule

$$P(A \text{ and } B) = P(A|B)P(B)$$

Addition rule

$$P(A \text{ or } B) = P(A) + P(B) - P(A \text{ and } B)$$

CHAPTER EXERCISES

6.130 In one Midwest city, an analysis of educational attainment and housing status yielded the following conditional probabilities.

	Owned with No Mortgage	Owned with a Mortgage	Renter
Less than high school	.30	.15	.55
High school	.40	.25	.35
College	.48	.30	.22

In this city, 5% of the population did not complete high school, 30% completed high school only, and 65% completed a college degree.
   a. What is the probability that a randomly selected individual who owns a home with no mortgage did not finish high school?
   b. Calculate the probability that a randomly selected resident of the Midwest city who is a renter graduated college.

6.131 According to the U.S. Census, there are 25,135,165 people aged between 65 and 74, 13,541,560 between 75 and 84, and 5,938,750 age 85 and over. The census also provided these conditional probabilities of individuals who did not complete any education beyond high school.

	Less Than Grade 5	Grades 5–8	Grades 9–12 (no diploma)	High School
65–74	.07	.09	.18	.66
75–84	.08	.12	.19	.61
85+	.10	.18	.22	.50

You encounter a person who is obviously older than 65 and who is a high school graduate. Find the probability that the person is at least 85.

6.132 The following table lists the joint probabilities of achieving grades of A and not achieving A's in two MBA courses.

	Marketing: A	Marketing: Not A
Statistics: A	.053	.130
Statistics: Not A	.237	.580

   a. What is the probability that a student achieves a grade of A in marketing?
   b. What is the probability that a student achieves a grade of A in marketing, given that the student does not achieve a grade of A in statistics?
   c. Are achieving grades of A in marketing and statistics independent events? Explain.

6.133 A construction company has bid on two contracts. The probability of winning contract A is .3. If the company wins contract A, then the probability of winning contract B is .4. If the company loses contract A, then the probability of winning contract B decreases to .2. Find the probability of the following events.
   a. Winning both contracts
   b. Winning exactly one contract
   c. Winning at least one contract

6.134 Laser surgery to fix shortsightedness is becoming more popular. However, for some people, a second procedure is necessary. The following table lists the joint probabilities of needing a second procedure and whether the patient has a corrective lens with a factor (diopter) of minus 8 or less.

	More Than Minus 8	Minus 8 or Less
First procedure is successful	.66	.15
Second procedure is required	.05	.14

   a. Find the probability that a second procedure is required.
   b. Determine the probability that someone whose corrective lens factor is minus 8 or less does not require a second procedure.
   c. Are the events independent? Explain your answer.

6.135 An examination of the U.S. Census reveals that 40% of citizens have a high school education or less, 29% have some college, 20% completed a college degree only, and 11% have a post-graduate degree. A survey of American workers asked whether they were worried about their jobs. The results yielded the following conditional probabilities.

	Completely Satisfied	Worried	Other
High school or less	.64	.24	.12
Some college	.60	.17	.23
College graduate only	.57	.18	.25
Post-graduate degree	.59	.15	.26

a. A person is selected at random who is worried about their job. Calculate the probability that the person has a post-graduate degree.
b. What is the probability that a randomly selected American who is completely satisfied did not finish high school?

6.136 How do Millennials, Generation Xers, and Baby Boomers feel about the direction the province of Ontario is heading? After surveying Ontarians, the following table of conditional probabilities was produced.

	Right Direction	Wrong Direction	Unsure
Baby Boom	.20	.55	.25
Generation X	.21	.51	.28
Millennial	.29	.40	.31

In Ontario 36% of residents are Baby Boomers, 31% are Generation X, and 33% are Millennials. What is the probability that someone who believes that the province is headed in the wrong direction is a Millennial?

6.137 The effect of an antidepressant drug varies from person to person. Suppose that the drug is effective on 80% of women and 65% of men. It is known that 66% of the people who take the drug are women. What is the probability that the drug is effective for a person taking the drug?

6.138 Refer to Exercise 6.137. Suppose that you are told that the drug is effective. What is the probability that the drug taker is a man?

6.139 In a four-cylinder engine, there are four spark plugs. If any one of them malfunctions, the car will idle roughly and power will be lost. Suppose that for a certain brand of spark plugs, the probability that a spark plug will function properly after 5,000 miles is .90. Assuming that the spark plugs operate independently, what is the probability that the car will idle roughly after 5,000 miles?

6.140 A telemarketer sells magazine subscriptions over the telephone. The probability of a busy signal or no answer is 65%. If the telemarketer does make contact, the probability of 0, 1, 2, or 3 magazine subscriptions is .5, .25, .20, and .05, respectively. Find the probability that in one call the telemarketer sells no magazines.

6.141 A statistics professor believes that there is a relationship between the number of missed classes and the grade on the midterm test. After examining records, the following table of joint probabilities was produced.

	Student Fails the Test	Student Passes the Test
Student misses fewer than five classes	.02	.86
Student misses five or more classes	.09	.03

a. What is the pass rate on the midterm test?
b. What proportion of students who miss five or more classes passes the midterm test?
c. What proportion of students who miss fewer than five classes passes the midterm test?
d. Are the events independent?

6.142 In Canada, criminals are entitled to parole after serving only one-third of their sentence. Virtually all prisoners, with several exceptions including murderers, are released after serving two-thirds of their sentence. The government has proposed a new law that would create a special category of inmates based on whether they had committed crimes involving violence or drugs. Such criminals would be subject to additional detention if the Correction Services judges them highly likely to reoffend. Currently, 27% of prisoners who are released commit another crime within 2 years of release. Among those who have reoffended, 41% would have been detained under the new law, whereas 31% of those who have not reoffended would have been detained.

a. What is the probability that a prisoner who would have been detained under the new law does commit another crime within 2 years?
b. What is the probability that a prisoner who would not have been detained under the new law does commit another crime within 2 years?

6.143 Casino Windsor conducts surveys to determine the opinions of its customers. Among other questions, respondents are asked to give their opinion about "Your overall impression of Casino Windsor." The responses are

    Excellent   Good   Average   Poor

In addition, the gender of the respondent is noted. After analyzing the results, the following table of joint probabilities was produced.

Rating	Women	Men
Excellent	.27	.22
Good	.14	.10
Average	.06	.12
Poor	.03	.06

a. What proportion of customers rate Casino Windsor as excellent?
b. Determine the probability that a male customer rates Casino Windsor as excellent.
c. Find the probability that a customer who rates Casino Windsor as excellent is a man.
d. Are gender and rating independent? Explain your answer.

6.144 A customer-service supervisor regularly conducts a survey of customer satisfaction. The results of the latest survey indicate that 8% of customers were not satisfied with the service they received at their last visit to the store. Of those who are not satisfied, only 22% return to the store within a year. Of those who are satisfied, 64% return within a year. A customer has just entered the store. In response to your question, the customer informs you that it is less than 1 year since the last visit to the store. What is the probability that the customer was satisfied with the service?

6.145 How does level of affluence affect health care? To address one dimension of the problem, a group of heart attack victims was selected. Each was categorized as a low-, medium-, or high-income earner. Each was also categorized as having survived or died. A demographer notes that in our society, 21% fall into the low-income group, 49% are in the medium-income group, and 30% are in the high-income group. Furthermore, an analysis of heart attack victims reveals that 12% of low-income people, 9% of medium-income people, and 7% of high-income people die of heart attacks. Find the probability that a survivor of a heart attack is in the low-income group.

6.146 A couple are planning to take a two-week vacation in Hawaii, but they can't decide whether to spend 1 week on each of the islands of Maui and Oahu, 2 weeks on Maui, or 2 weeks on Oahu. Placing their faith in random chance, they insert two Maui brochures in one envelope, two Oahu brochures in a second envelope, and one brochure from each island in a third envelope. They will select one envelope at random, and their vacation schedule will be based on the brochures of the islands so selected. After randomly selecting an envelope, they remove one brochure from the envelope (without looking at the second brochure) and observe that it is a Maui brochure. What is the probability that the other brochure in the envelope is a Maui brochure? (Proceed with caution: The problem is more difficult than it appears.)

6.147 The owner of an appliance store is interested in the relationship between the price at which an item is sold (regular or sale price) and the customer's decision on whether to purchase an extended warranty. After analyzing records, the following joint probabilities were calculated.

	Purchased Extended Warranty	Did Not Purchase Extended Warranty
Regular price	.21	.57
Sale price	.14	.08

a. What is the probability that a customer who bought an item at the regular price purchased the extended warranty?
b. What proportion of customers buy an extended warranty?
c. Are the events independent? Explain.

6.148 Researchers have developed statistical models based on financial ratios that predict whether a company will go bankrupt over the next 12 months. In a test of one such model, the model correctly predicted the bankruptcy of 85% of firms that did in fact fail, and it correctly predicted non-bankruptcy for 74% of firms that did not fail. Suppose that we expect 8% of the firms in a particular city to fail over the next year. Suppose that the model predicts bankruptcy for a firm that you own. What is the probability that your firm will fail within the next 12 months?

6.149 A union's executive conducted a survey of its members to determine what the membership felt were the important issues to be resolved during upcoming negotiations with management. The results indicate that 74% of members felt that job security was an important issue, whereas 65% identified pension benefits as an important issue. Of those who felt that pension benefits were important, 60% also felt that job security was an important issue. One member is selected at random.

a. What is the probability the member felt that both job security and pension benefits were important?

b. What is the probability that the member felt that at least one of these two issues was important?

6.150 In a class on probability, a statistics professor flips a dime and a quarter. Both fall to the floor and roll under the desk. A student in the first row informs the professor that one coin shows tails but cannot determine the denomination. What is the probability that the other coin is also tails? (Beware the obvious.)

6.151 Refer to Exercise 6.150. Suppose the student informs the professor that the dime shows tails. What is the probability that the other coin is also tails?

CASE 6.1   Let's Make a Deal

Everett Collection Inc / Alamy Stock Photo

A number of years ago, there was a popular television game show called *Let's Make a Deal*. The host, Monty Hall, would randomly select contestants from the audience and, as the title suggests, he would make deals for prizes. Contestants would be given relatively modest prizes and would then be offered the opportunity to risk those prizes to win better ones.

Suppose that you are a contestant on this show. Monty has just given you a free trip touring toxic waste sites around the country. He now offers you a trade: Give up the trip in exchange for a gamble. On the stage are three curtains, A, B, and C. Behind one of them is a brand new car worth $50,000. Behind the other two curtains, the stage is empty. You decide to gamble and select curtain A. In an attempt to make things more interesting, Monty then exposes an empty stage by opening curtain C (he knows there is nothing behind curtain C). He then offers you the free trip again if you quit now or, if you like, he will propose another deal (i.e., you can keep your choice of curtain A or perhaps switch to curtain B). What do you do?

To help you answer that question, try first answering these questions.

1. Before Monty shows you what's behind curtain C, what is the probability that the car is behind curtain A? What is the probability that the car is behind curtain B?

2. After Monty shows you what's behind curtain C, what is the probability that the car is behind curtain A? What is the probability that the car is behind curtain B?

CASE 6.2   To Bunt or Not to Bunt, That Is the Question

Kyodo News/Getty Images

No sport generates as many statistics as baseball. Reporters, managers, and fans argue and discuss strategies on the basis of these statistics. An article in *Chance* ("A Statistician Reads the Sports Page," Hal S. Stern, Vol. 1, Winter 1997) offers baseball lovers another opportunity to analyze numbers associated with the game. Table 1 lists the probabilities of scoring at least one run in situations that are defined by the number of outs and the bases occupied. For example, the probability of scoring at least one run when there are no outs and a man is on first base is .39. If the bases are loaded with one out, then the probability of scoring any runs is .67. (Probabilities are based on results from the American League during the 1989 season. The results for the National League are also shown in the article and are similar.)

TABLE **1** **Probability of Scoring Any Runs**

Bases Occupied	0 Outs	1 Out	2 Outs
Bases empty	.26	.16	.07
First base	.39	.26	.13
Second base	.57	.42	.24
Third base	.72	.55	.28
First base and second base	.59	.45	.24
First base and third base	.76	.61	.37
Second base and third base	.83	.74	.37
Bases loaded	.81	.67	.43

Table 1 allows us to determine the best strategy in a variety of circumstances. This case will concentrate on the strategy of the sacrifice bunt. The purpose of the sacrifice bunt is to sacrifice the batter to move base runners to the next base. It can be employed when there are fewer than two outs and men on base. Ignoring the suicide squeeze, any of four outcomes can occur:

1. The bunt is successful. The runner (or runners) advances one base, and the batter is out.
2. The batter is out but fails to advance the runner.
3. The batter bunts into a double play.
4. The batter is safe (hit or error), and the runner advances.

Suppose that you are an American League manager. The game is tied in the middle innings of a game, and there is a runner on first base with no one out. Given the following probabilities of the four outcomes of a bunt for the batter at the plate, should you signal the batter to sacrifice bunt?

P(Outcome 1) = .75
P(Outcome 2) = .10
P(Outcome 3) = .10
P(Outcome 4) = .05

Assume for simplicity that after the hit or error in outcome 4, there will be men on first and second base and no one out.

CASE 6.3 Should He Attempt to Steal a Base?

Otto Greule Jr/Getty Images

Refer to Case 6.2. Another baseball strategy is to attempt to steal second base. Historically the probability of a successful steal of second base is approximately 68%. The probability of being thrown out is 32%. (We'll ignore the relatively rare event wherein the catcher throws the ball into center field allowing the base runner to advance to third base.) Suppose there is a runner on first base. For each of the possible number of outs (0, 1, or 2), determine whether it is advisable to have the runner attempt to steal second base.

CASE 6.4 Maternal Serum Screening Test for Down Syndrome

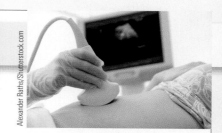

Alexander Raths/Shutterstock.com

Pregnant women are screened for a birth defect called Down syndrome. Down syndrome babies are mentally and physically challenged. Some mothers choose to abort the fetus when they are certain that their baby will be born with the syndrome. The most common screening is maternal serum screening, a blood test that looks for markers in the blood to indicate whether the birth defect may occur. The false-positive and false-negative rates vary according to the age of the mother.

Mother's Age	False-Positive Rate	False-Negative Rate
Under 30	.04	.376
30–34	.082	.290
35–37	.178	.269
Over 38	.343	.029

The probability that a baby has Down syndrome is primarily a function of the mother's age. The probabilities are listed here.

Age	Probability of Down Syndrome
25	1/1,300
30	1/900
35	1/350
40	1/100
45	1/25
49	1/12

a. For each of the ages 25, 30, 35, 40, 45, and 49, determine the probability of Down syndrome if the maternity serum screening produces a positive result.

b. Repeat for a negative result.

CASE 6.5 — Probability That at Least Two People in the Same Room Have the Same Birthday

Anna Jurkovska/Shutterstock.com

Suppose that there are two people in a room. The probability that they share the same birthday (date, not necessarily year) is 1/365, and the probability that they have different birthdays is 364/365. To illustrate, suppose that you're in a room with one other person and that your birthday is July 1. The probability that the other person does not have the same birthday is 364/365 because there are 364 days in the year that are not July 1. If a third person now enters the room, the probability that that person has a different birthday from the first two people in the room is 363/365. Thus, the probability that three people in a room having different birthdays is (364/365)(363/365). You can continue this process for any number of people.

Find the number of people in a room so that there is about a 50% probability that at least two have the same birthday.

Hint 1: Calculate the probability that they don't have the same birthday.

Hint 2: Excel users can employ the **product** function to calculate joint probabilities.

Baloncici/Shutterstock.com

RANDOM VARIABLES AND DISCRETE PROBABILITY DISTRIBUTIONS

CHAPTER OUTLINE

Investing to Maximize Returns and Minimize Risk

DATA
Xm07-00

A finance professor has $100,000 to invest in the stock market. The professor is interested in developing a stock portfolio made up of stocks on the New York Exchange (NYSE), the Toronto Stock Exchange (TSE), and the NASDAQ. The stocks chosen are Home Depot (HD) and Nike (NKE) on the NYSE, Canadian National Railway (CNR) on the TSE, and Expedia (EXPE) on the NASDAQ. The professor would like to maximize returns while minimizing risk. The monthly returns for all four stocks during a 48-month period (January 2016 to December 2019) were recorded. After some consideration, the professor has narrowed the choices down to the following three. What would you recommend?

1. Invest $25,000 in each stock
2. Home Depot: $10,000, Nike: $20,000, Canadian National Railway: $30,000, Expedia: $40,000
3. Home Depot: $10,000, Nike: $10,000, Canadian National Railway: $50,000, Expedia: $30,000

Terry Vine/Blend/Getty Images

We will provide our answer after we've developed the necessary tools in Section 7-3.

215

INTRODUCTION

In this chapter, we extend the concepts and techniques of probability introduced in Chapter 6. We present random variables and probability distributions, which are essential in the development of statistical inference.

Here is a brief glimpse into the wonderful world of statistical inference. Suppose that you flip a coin 100 times and count the number of heads. The objective is to determine whether we can infer from the count that the coin is not balanced. It is reasonable to believe that observing a large number of heads (say, 90) or a small number (say, 15) would be a statistical indication of an unbalanced coin. However, where do we draw the line? At 75 or 65 or 55? Without knowing the probability of the frequency of the number of heads from a balanced coin, we cannot draw any conclusions from the sample of 100 coin flips.

The concepts and techniques of probability introduced in this chapter will allow us to calculate the probability we seek. As a first step, we introduce random variables and probability distributions.

7-1 / RANDOM VARIABLES AND PROBABILITY DISTRIBUTIONS

Consider an experiment where we flip two balanced coins and observe the results. We can represent the events as

Heads on the first coin and heads on the second coin

Heads on the first coin and tails on the second coin

Tails on the first coin and heads on the second coin

Tails on the first coin and tails on the second coin

However, we can list the events in a different way. Instead of defining the events by describing the outcome of each coin, we can count the number of heads (or, if we wish, the number of tails). Thus, the events are now

2 heads

1 heads

1 heads

0 heads

The number of heads is called the **random variable**. We often label the random variable X, and we're interested in the probability of each value of X. Thus, in this illustration, the values of X are 0, 1, and 2.

Here is another example. In many parlor games as well as in the game of craps played in casinos, the player tosses two dice. One way of listing the events is to describe the number on the first die and the number on the second die as follows.

1, 1	1, 2	1, 3	1, 4	1, 5	1, 6
2, 1	2, 2	2, 3	2, 4	2, 5	2, 6
3, 1	3, 2	3, 3	3, 4	3, 5	3, 6
4, 1	4, 2	4, 3	4, 4	4, 5	4, 6
5, 1	5, 2	5, 3	5, 4	5, 5	5, 6
6, 1	6, 2	6, 3	6, 4	6, 5	6, 6

However, in almost all games, the player is primarily interested in the total. Accordingly, we can list the totals of the two dice instead of the individual numbers.

2	3	4	5	6	7
3	4	5	6	7	8
4	5	6	7	8	9
5	6	7	8	9	10
6	7	8	9	10	11
7	8	9	10	11	12

If we define the random variable X as the total of the two dice, then X can equal 2, 3, 4, 5, 6, 7, 8, 9, 10, 11, and 12.

Random Variable

A **random variable** is a function or rule that assigns a number to each outcome of an experiment.

In some experiments, the outcomes are numbers. For example, when we observe the return on an investment or measure the amount of time to assemble a computer, the experiment produces events that are numbers. Simply stated, the value of a random variable is a numerical event.

There are two types of random variables, discrete and continuous. A **discrete random variable** is one that can take on a countable number of values. For example, if we define X as the number of heads observed in an experiment that flips a coin 10 times, then the values of X are 0, 1, 2, . . . , 10. The variable X can assume a total of 11 values. Obviously, we counted the number of values; hence, X is discrete.

A **continuous random variable** is one whose values are uncountable. An excellent example of a continuous random variable is the amount of time to complete a task. For example, let X = time to write a statistics exam in a university where the time limit is 3 hours and students cannot leave before 30 minutes. The smallest value of X is 30 minutes. If we attempt to count the number of values that X can take on, we need to identify the next value. Is it 30.1 minutes? 30.01 minutes? 30.001 minutes? None of these is the second possible value of X because there exist numbers larger than 30 and smaller than 30.001. It becomes clear that we cannot identify the second, or third, or any other values of X (except for the largest value 180 minutes). Thus, we cannot count the number of values, and X is continuous.

A **probability distribution** is a table, formula, or graph that describes the values of a random variable and the probability associated with these values. We will address discrete probability distributions in the rest of this chapter and cover continuous distributions in Chapter 8.

As we noted earlier, an uppercase letter will represent the *name* of the random variable, usually X. Its lowercase counterpart will represent the value of the random variable. Thus, we represent the probability that the random variable X will equal x as

$P(X = x)$

or more simply

$P(x)$

7-1a Discrete Probability Distributions

The probabilities of the values of a discrete random variable may be derived by means of probability tools such as tree diagrams or by applying one of the definitions of probability. However, two fundamental requirements apply as stated in the box.

Requirements for a Distribution of a Discrete Random Variable

1. $0 \leq P(x) \leq 1$ for all x

2. $\sum_{\text{all } x} P(x) = 1$

where the random variable can assume values x and $P(x)$ is the probability that the random variable is equal to x.

These requirements are equivalent to the rules of probability provided in Chapter 6. To illustrate, consider the following example.

EXAMPLE 7.1

Probability Distribution of Persons per Household

The U.S. Census contains a wide variety of information. The objective is to provide information about different aspects of the lives of the country's residents. One of the questions asks households to report the number of persons living in the household. The following table summarizes the data. Develop the probability distribution of the random variable defined as the number of persons per household.
(*Source:* U.S. Census)

Number of Persons	Number of Households (Millions)
1	35.2
2	43.5
3	19.5
4	16.2
5	7.3
6	2.8
7 or more	1.6
Total	126.1

SOLUTION:

The probability of each value of X, the number of persons per household, is computed as the relative frequency. We divide the frequency for each value of X by the total number of households, producing the following probability distribution.

x	$P(X)$
1	35.2/126.1 = .279
2	43.5/126.1 = .345
3	19.5/126.1 = .155
4	16.2/126.1 = .128
5	7.3/126.1 = .058
6	2.8/126.1 = .022
7 or more	1.6/126.1 = .013
Total	1.000

As you can see, the requirements are satisfied. Each probability lies between 0 and 1, and the total is 1.

We interpret the probabilities in the same way we did in Chapter 6. For example, if we select one household at random, the probability that it has three persons is

$$P(3) = .155$$

We can also apply the addition rule for mutually exclusive events. (The values of X are mutually exclusive; a household can have 1, 2, 3, 4, 5, 6, or 7 or more persons.) The probability that a randomly selected household has four or more persons is

$$P(X \geq 4) = P(4) + P(5) + P(6) + P(7 \text{ or more})$$
$$= .128 + .058 + .022 + .013 = .221$$

In Example 7.1, we calculated the probabilities using census information about the entire population. The next example illustrates the use of the techniques introduced in Chapter 6 to develop a probability distribution.

EXAMPLE 7.2   ## Probability Distribution of the Number of Sales

A mutual fund salesperson has arranged to call on three people tomorrow. Based on past experience, the salesperson knows there is a 20% chance of closing a sale on each call. Determine the probability distribution of the number of sales the salesperson will make.

SOLUTION:

We can use the probability rules and trees introduced in Section 6-3. Figure 7.1 displays the probability tree for this example. Let X = the number of sales.

FIGURE **7.1** **Probability Tree for Example 7.2**

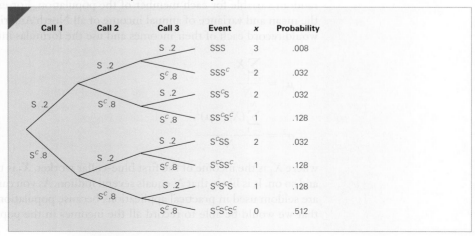

The tree exhibits each of the eight possible outcomes and their probabilities. We see that there is one outcome that represents no sales, and its probability is $P(0) = .512$. There are three outcomes representing one sale, each with probability .128, so we add these probabilities. Thus,

$$P(1) = .128 + .128 + .128 = 3(.128) = .384$$

The probability of two sales is computed similarly:

$$P(X) = 3(.032) = .096$$

There is one outcome where there are three sales:

$$P(3) = .008$$

The probability distribution of X is listed in Table 7.1.

TABLE **7.1** **Probability Distribution of the Number of Sales in Example 7.2**

x	P(x)
0	.512
1	.384
2	.096
3	.008

7-1b Probability Distributions and Populations

The importance of probability distributions derives from their use as representatives of populations. In Example 7.1, the distribution provided us with information about the population of numbers of persons per household. In Example 7.2, the population was the number of sales made in three calls by the salesperson. And as we noted before, statistical inference deals with inference about populations.

7-1c Describing the Population/Probability Distribution

In Chapter 4, we showed how to calculate the mean, variance, and standard deviation of a population. The formulas we provided were based on knowing the value of the random variable for each member of the population. For example, if we want to know the mean and variance of annual income of all North American blue-collar workers, we would record each of their incomes and use the formulas introduced in Chapter 4:

$$\mu = \frac{\sum_{i=1}^{N} X_i}{N}$$

$$\sigma^2 = \frac{\sum_{i=1}^{N} (X_i - \mu)^2}{N}$$

where X_1 is the income of the first blue-collar worker, X_2 is the second worker's income, and so on. It is likely that N equals several million. As you can appreciate, these formulas are seldom used in practical applications because populations are so large. It is unlikely that we would be able to record all the incomes in the population of North American blue-collar workers. However, probability distributions often represent populations. Rather than record each of the many observations in a population, we list the values and their associated probabilities as we did in deriving the probability distribution of the number of persons per household in Example 7.1 and the number of successes in three calls by the mutual fund salesperson. These can be used to compute the mean and variance of the population.

The population mean is the weighted average of all of its values. The weights are the probabilities. This parameter is also called the **expected value** of X and is represented by $E(X)$.

Population Mean

$$E(X) = \mu = \sum_{\text{all } x} xP(x)$$

The population variance is calculated similarly. It is the weighted average of the squared deviations from the mean.

Population Variance

$$V(X) = \sigma^2 = \sum_{\text{all } x} (x - \mu)^2 P(x)$$

There is a shortcut calculation that simplifies the calculations for the population variance. This formula is not an approximation; it will yield the same value as the formula above.

Shortcut Calculation for Population Variance

$$V(X) = \sigma^2 = \sum_{\text{all } x} x^2 P(x) - \mu^2$$

The standard deviation is defined as in Chapter 4.

Population Standard Deviation

$$\sigma = \sqrt{\sigma^2}$$

EXAMPLE **7.3** ## Describing the Population of the Number of Persons per Household

Find the mean, variance, and standard deviation for the population of the number of persons per household in Example 7.1.

S O L U T I O N :

For this example, we will assume that the last category is exactly seven persons. The mean of X is

$$E(X) = \mu = \sum_{\text{all } x} xP(x) = 1P(1) + 2P(2) + 3P(3) + 4P(4) + 5P(5) + 6P(6) + 7P(7)$$

$$= 1(.279) + 2(.345) + 3(.155) + 4(.128) + 5(.058) + 6(.022) + 7(.013)$$

$$= 2.46$$

Notice that the random variable can assume integer values only, yet the mean is 2.46.

The variance of X is

$$V(x) = \sigma^2 = \sum_{\text{all } x} (x - \mu)^2 P(x)$$

$$= (1 - 2.46)^2(.279) + (2 - 2.46)^2(.345) + (3 - 2.46)^2(.155)$$

$$+ (4 - 2.46)^2(.128) + (5 - 2.46)^2(.058) + (6 - 2.46)^2(.022)$$

$$+ (7 - 2.46)^2(.013)$$

$$= 1.93$$

The standard deviation is

$$\sigma = \sqrt{\sigma^2} \sqrt{1.93} = 1.39$$

These parameters tell us that the mean and standard deviation of the number of persons per household is 2.46 and 1.39, respectively.

7-1d Laws of Expected Value and Variance

As you will discover, we often create new variables that are functions of other random variables. The formulas given in the next two boxes allow us to quickly determine the expected value and variance of these new variables. In the notation used here, X is the random variable and c is a constant.

Laws of Expected Value

1. $E(c) = c$
2. $E(X + c) = E(X) + c$
3. $E(cX) = cE(X)$

Laws of Variance

1. $V(c) = 0$
2. $V(X + c) = V(X)$
3. $V(cX) = c^2 V(X)$

EXAMPLE 7.4

Describing the Population of Monthly Profits

The monthly sales at a computer store have a mean of $25,000 and a standard deviation of $4,000. Profits are calculated by multiplying sales by 30% and subtracting fixed costs of $6,000. Find the mean and standard deviation of monthly profits.

SOLUTION:

We can describe the relationship between profits and sales by the following equation:

$$\text{Profit} = .30(\text{Sales}) - 6,000$$

The expected or mean profit is

$$E(\text{Profit}) = E[.30(\text{Sales}) - 6,000]$$

Applying the second law of expected value, we produce

$$E(\text{Profit}) = E[.30(\text{Sales})] - 6,000$$

Applying law 3 yields

$$E(\text{Profit}) = .30E(\text{Sales}) - 6,000 = .30(25,000) - 6,000 = 1,500$$

Thus, the mean monthly profit is $1,500.

The variance is

$$V(\text{Profit}) = V[.30(\text{Sales}) - 6,000]$$

The second law of variance states that

$$V(\text{Profit}) = V[.30(\text{Sales})]$$

and law 3 yields

$$V(\text{Profit}) = (.30)^2 V(\text{Sales}) = .09(4,000)^2 = 1,440,000$$

Thus, the standard deviation of monthly profits is

$$\sigma_{\text{Profit}} = \sqrt{1,440,000} = \$1,200$$

EXERCISES

7.1 The number of accidents that occur on a busy stretch of highway is a random variable.
  a. What are the possible values of this random variable?
  b. Are the values countable? Explain.
  c. Is there a finite number of values? Explain.
  d. Is the random variable discrete or continuous? Explain.

7.2 The distance a car travels on a tank of gasoline is a random variable.
  a. What are the possible values of this random variable?
  b. Are the values countable? Explain.
  c. Is there a finite number of values? Explain.

  d. Is the random variable discrete or continuous? Explain.

7.3 The amount of money students earn on their summer jobs is a random variable.
  a. What are the possible values of this random variable?
  b. Are the values countable? Explain.
  c. Is there a finite number of values? Explain.
  d. Is the random variable discrete or continuous? Explain.

7.4 The mark on a statistics exam that consists of 100 multiple-choice questions is a random variable.
  a. What are the possible values of this random variable?

b. Are the values countable? Explain.

c. Is there a finite number of values? Explain.

d. Is the random variable discrete or continuous? Explain.

7.5 Determine whether each of the following is a valid probability distribution.

a.
x	0	1	2	3
P(x)	.1	.3	.4	.1

b.
x	5	−6	10	0
P(x)	.01	.01	.01	.97

c.
x	14	12	−7	13
P(x)	.25	.46	.04	.24

7.6 Let X be the random variable designating the number of spots that turn up when a balanced die is rolled. What is the probability distribution of X?

7.7 In a recent census, the number of color televisions per household was recorded.

Number of color televisions	0	1	2	3	4	5
Number of households (thousands)	1,218	32,379	37,961	19,387	7,714	2,842

a. Develop the probability distribution of X, the number of color televisions per household.

b. Determine the following probabilities.

$$P(X \leq 2)$$
$$P(X > 2)$$
$$P(X \geq 4)$$

7.8 Using historical records, the personnel manager of a plant has determined the probability distribution of X, the number of employees absent per day. It is

x	0	1	2	3	4	5	6	7
P(x)	.005	.025	.310	.340	.220	.080	.019	.001

a. Find the following probabilities.

$$P(2 \leq X \leq 5)$$
$$P(X > 5)$$
$$P(X < 4)$$

b. Calculate the mean of the population.

c. Calculate the standard deviation of the population.

7.9 Second-year business students at many universities are required to take 10 one-semester courses. The number of courses that result in a grade of A is a discrete random variable. Suppose that each value

of this random variable has the same probability. Determine the probability distribution.

7.10 The random variable X has the following probability distribution.

x	−3	2	6	8
P(x)	.2	.3	.4	.1

Find the following probabilities.

a. $P(X > 0)$

b. $P(X \geq 1)$

c. $P(X \geq 2)$

d. $P(2 \leq X \leq 5)$

7.11 An Internet pharmacy advertises that it will deliver the over-the-counter products that customers purchase in 3–6 days. The manager of the company wanted to be more precise in its advertising. Accordingly, the number of days it took to deliver to customers was recorded. From the data, the following probability distribution was developed.

Number of days	0	1	2	3	4	5	6	7	8
Probability	0	0	.01	.04	.28	.42	.21	.02	.02

a. What is the probability that a delivery will be made within the advertised 3- to 6-day period?

b. What is the probability that a delivery will be late?

c. What is the probability that a delivery will be early?

7.12 A number of gamblers believe that a strategy called "doubling down" is an effective way to gamble. The method requires them to double the stake after each loss. Thus, if the initial bet is $1, after losing they will double the bet until they win. After a win, the gamblers resort back to a $1 bet. The result is that they will net $1 for every win. The problem, however, is that they will eventually run out of money or bump up against the table limit. Suppose that for a certain game the probability of winning is .5 and that losing six in a row will result in bankrupting the gambler. A gambler just won. Find the probability of losing the next six times in a row.

7.13 The probability that a university graduate will be offered no jobs within a month of graduation is estimated to be 5%. The probability of receiving one, two, and three job offers has similarly been estimated to be 43%, 31%, and 21%, respectively. Determine the following probabilities.

a. A graduate is offered fewer than two jobs.

b. A graduate is offered more than one job.

7.14 Use a probability tree to compute the probability of the following events when flipping two fair coins.
   a. Heads on the first coin and heads on the second coin
   b. Heads on the first coin and tails on the second coin
   c. Tails on the first coin and heads on the second coin
   d. Tails on the first coin and tails on the second coin

7.15 Refer to Exercise 7.14. Find the following probabilities.
   a. No heads
   b. One head
   c. Two heads
   d. At least one head

7.16 Draw a probability tree to describe the flipping of three fair coins.

7.17 Refer to Exercise 7.16. Find the following probabilities.
   a. Two heads
   b. One head
   c. At least one head
   d. At least two heads

7.18 The random variable X has the following distribution.

x	−2	5	7	8
$P(x)$	.59	.15	.25	.01

   a. Find the mean and variance for the probability distribution below.
   b. Determine the probability distribution of Y where $Y = 5X$.
   c. Use the probability distribution in part (b) to compute the mean and variance of Y.
   d. Use the laws of expected value and variance to find the expected value and variance of Y from the parameters of X.

7.19 We are given the following probability distribution.

x	0	1	2	3
$P(x)$	.4	.3	.2	.1

   a. Calculate the mean, variance, and standard deviation.
   b. Suppose that $Y = 3X + 2$. For each value of X, determine the value of Y. What is the probability distribution of Y?
   c. Calculate the mean, variance, and standard deviation from the probability distribution of Y.
   d. Use the laws of expected value and variance to calculate the mean, variance, and standard deviation of Y from the mean, variance, and standard deviation of X. Compare your answers in parts (c) and (d). Are they the same (except for rounding)?

7.20 The number of pizzas delivered to university students each month is a random variable with the following probability distribution.

x	0	1	2	3
$P(x)$	.1	.3	.4	.2

   a. Find the probability that a student has received delivery of two or more pizzas this month.
   b. Determine the mean and variance of the number of pizzas delivered to students each month.

7.21 Refer to Exercise 7.20. If the pizzeria makes a profit of $3 per pizza, determine the mean and variance of the profits per student.

7.22 After watching a number of children playing games at a video arcade, a statistics practitioner estimated the following probability distribution of X, the number of games per visit.

x	1	2	3	4	5	6	7
$P(x)$	.05	.15	.15	.25	.20	.10	.10

   a. What is the probability that a child will play more than four games?
   b. What is the probability that a child will play at least two games?

7.23 Refer to Exercise 7.22. Determine the mean and variance of the number of games played.

7.24 Refer to Exercise 7.22. Suppose that each game costs the player 25 cents. Use the laws of expected value and variance to determine the expected value and variance of the amount of money the arcade takes in.

7.25 Refer to Exercise 7.22.
   a. Determine the probability distribution of the amount of money the arcade takes in per child.
   b. Use the probability distribution to calculate the mean and variance of the amount of money the arcade takes in.
   c. Compare the answers in part (b) with those of Exercise 7.24. Are they identical (except for rounding errors)?

7.26 A survey of Amazon.com shoppers reveals the following probability distribution of the number of books purchased per hit.

x	0	1	2	3	4	5	6	7
$P(x)$	.35	.25	.20	.08	.06	.03	.02	.01

   a. What is the probability that an Amazon.com visitor will buy four books?
   b. What is the probability that an Amazon.com visitor will buy eight books?
   c. What is the probability that an Amazon.com visitor will not buy any books?
   d. What is the probability that an Amazon.com visitor will buy at least one book?

7.27 A university librarian produced the following probability distribution of the number of times a student walks into the library over the period of a semester.

x	0	5	10	15	20	25	30	40	50	75	100
P(x)	.22	.29	.12	.09	.08	.05	.04	.04	.03	.03	.01

Find the following probabilities.
a. $P(X \geq 20)$
b. $P(X = 60)$
c. $P(X > 50)$
d. $P(X > 100)$

7.28 After analyzing the frequency with which cross-country skiers participate in their sport, a sportswriter created the following probability distribution for X = number of times per year cross-country skiers ski.

x	0	1	2	3	4	5	6	7	8
P(x)	.04	.09	.19	.21	.16	.12	.08	.06	.05

Find the following.
a. $P(3)$
b. $P(X \geq 5)$
c. $P(5 \leq X \leq 7)$

7.29 The natural remedy Echinacea is reputed to boost the immune system, which will reduce the number of flu and colds. A 6-month study was undertaken to determine whether the remedy works. From this study, the following probability distribution of the number of respiratory infections per year (X) for Echinacea users was produced.

x	0	1	2	3	4
P(x)	.45	.31	.17	.06	.01

Find the following probabilities.
a. An Echinacea user has more than one infection per year.
b. An Echinacea user has no infections per year.
c. An Echinacea user has between one and three (inclusive) infections per year.

7.30 A shopping mall estimates the probability distribution of the number of stores mall customers actually enter, as shown in the table.

x	0	1	2	3	4	5	6
P(x)	.04	.19	.22	.28	.12	.09	.06

Find the mean and standard deviation of the number of stores entered.

7.31 Refer to Exercise 7.30. Suppose that, on average, customers spend 10 minutes in each store they enter. Find the mean and standard deviation of the total amount of time customers spend in stores.

7.32 When parking a car in a downtown parking lot, drivers pay according to the number of hours or parts thereof. The probability distribution of the number of hours cars are parked has been estimated as follows.

x	1	2	3	4	5	6	7	8
P(x)	.24	.18	.13	.10	.07	.04	.04	.20

Find the mean and standard deviation of the number of hours cars are parked in the lot.

7.33 Refer to Exercise 7.32. The cost of parking is $2.50 per hour. Calculate the mean and standard deviation of the amount of revenue each car generates.

7.34 You have been given the choice of receiving $500 in cash or receiving a gold coin that has a face value of $100. However, the actual value of the gold coin depends on its gold content. You are told that the coin has a 40% probability of being worth $400, a 30% probability of being worth $900, and a 30% probability of being worth its face value. Basing your decision on expected value, should you choose the coin?

7.35 The manager of a bookstore recorded the number of customers who arrive at a checkout counter every 5 minutes from which the following distribution was calculated. Calculate the mean and standard deviation of the random variable.

x	0	1	2	3	4
P(x)	.10	.20	.25	.25	.20

7.36 A student has just purchased a personal computer. It has been suggested that the student buy a surge suppressor to provide protection for the new hardware against possible surges or variations in the electrical current, which have the capacity to damage the computer. The amount of damage depends on the strength of the surge. It has been estimated that there is a 1% chance of incurring $400 damage, a 2% chance of incurring $200 damage, and 10% chance of $100 damage. An inexpensive suppressor, which would provide protection for only one surge can be purchased. How much should the student be willing to pay if the decision is based on expected value?

7.37 It cost one dollar to buy a lottery ticket, which has five prizes. The prizes and the probability that a player wins the prize are listed here. Calculate the expected value of the payoff.

Prize ($)	1 million	200,000	50,000
Probability	1/10 million	1/1 million	1/500,000

Prize ($)	10,000	1,000
Probability	1/50,000	1/10,000

7.38 After an analysis of incoming faxes, the manager of an accounting firm determined the probability distribution of the number of pages per facsimile as follows:

x	1	2	3	4	5	6	7
P(x)	.05	.12	.20	.30	.15	.10	.08

Compute the mean and variance of the number of pages per fax.

7.39 Refer to Exercise 7.38. Further analysis by the manager revealed that the cost of processing each page of a fax is $.25. Determine the mean and variance of the cost per fax.

7.40 To examine the effectiveness of its four annual advertising promotions, a mail-order company has sent a questionnaire to each of its customers, asking how many of the previous year's promotions prompted orders that would not otherwise have been made. The table lists the probabilities that were derived from the questionnaire, where X is the random variable representing the number of promotions that prompted orders. If we assume that overall customer behavior next year will be the same as last year, what is the expected number of promotions that each customer will take advantage of next year by ordering goods that otherwise would not be purchased?

x	0	1	2	3	4
$P(x)$	.10	.25	.40	.20	.05

7.41 Refer to Exercise 7.40. A previous analysis of historical records found that the mean value of orders for promotional goods is $20, with the company earning a gross profit of 20% on each order. Calculate the expected value of the profit contribution next year.

7.42 An expensive restaurant conducted an analysis of the number of people at tables from which the probability distribution was developed.

x	1	2	3	4	5	6	7	8
$P(x)$	.03	.32	.05	.28	.04	.15	.03	.10

If one table is selected at random, determine the probability of the following events.
a. Table has more than 4 people
b. Table has fewer than 5 people
c. Table has between 4 and 6 people (inclusive)

7.43 Refer to Exercise 7.42. Compute the mean, variance, and standard deviation of the population.

7.44 At a private golf course known for its excellent golfers a statistician quizzed the members to determine how many holes in one each made in their lifetime. From this work the following probability distribution of the number of career holes in one was produced.

x	0	1	2	3	4	5	6	7 or more
$P(x)$	.78	.10	.05	.03	.02	.01	.01	0

One member was selected at random. Find the following probabilities.
a. The member has more than 3 holes in one.
b. The member never had a hole in one.
c. The member has between 3 and 5 (inclusive) holes in one.

7-2 / (OPTIONAL) BIVARIATE DISTRIBUTIONS

Thus far, we have dealt with the distribution of a *single* variable. However, there are circumstances where we need to know about the relationship between two variables. Recall that we have addressed this problem statistically in Chapter 3 by drawing the scatter diagram and in Chapter 4 by calculating the covariance and the coefficient of correlation. In this section, we present the **bivariate distribution**, which provides probabilities of combinations of two variables. Incidentally, when we need to distinguish between the bivariate distributions and the distributions of one variable, we'll refer to the latter as *univariate* distributions.

The joint probability that two variables will assume the values x and y is denoted $P(x, y)$. A bivariate (or joint) probability distribution of X and Y is a table or formula that lists the joint probabilities for all pairs of values of x and y. As was the case with univariate distributions, the joint probability must satisfy two requirements.

Requirements for a Discrete Bivariate Distribution

1. $0 \leq P(x, y) \leq 1$ for all pairs of values (x, y)

2. $\displaystyle\sum_{\text{all } x}\sum_{\text{all } y} P(x, y) = 1$

EXAMPLE 7.5

Bivariate Distribution of the Number of House Sales

Xavier and Yvette are real estate agents. Let X denote the number of houses that Xavier will sell in a month and let Y denote the number of houses Yvette will sell in a month. An analysis of their past monthly performances has the following joint probabilities.

Bivariate Probability Distribution

		X		
		0	1	2
	0	.12	.42	.06
Y	1	.21	.06	.03
	2	.07	.02	.01

We interpret these joint probabilities in the same way we did in Chapter 6. For example, the probability that Xavier sells 0 houses and Yvette sells 1 house in the month is $P(0, 1) = .21$.

7-2a Marginal Probabilities

As we did in Chapter 6, we can calculate the marginal probabilities by summing across rows or down columns.

Marginal Probability Distribution of X in Example 7.5

$$P(X = 0) = P(0, 0) + P(0, 1) + P(0, 2) = .12 + .21 + .07 = .4$$
$$P(X = 1) = P(1, 0) + P(1, 1) + P(1, 2) = .42 + .06 + .02 = .5$$
$$P(X = 2) = P(2, 0) + P(2, 1) + P(2, 2) = .06 + .03 + .01 = .1$$

The marginal probability distribution of X is

x	P(x)
0	.4
1	.5
2	.1

Marginal Probability Distribution of Y in Example 7.5

$$P(Y = 0) = P(0, 0) + P(1, 0) + P(2, 0) = .12 + .42 + .06 = .6$$
$$P(Y = 1) = P(0, 1) + P(1, 1) + P(2, 1) = .21 + .06 + .03 = .3$$
$$P(Y = 2) = P(0, 2) + P(1, 2) + P(2, 2) = .07 + .02 + .01 = .1$$

The marginal probability distribution of Y is

y	P(y)
0	.6
1	.3
2	.1

Notice that both marginal probability distributions meet the requirements; the probabilities are between 0 and 1, and they add to 1.

7-2b Describing the Bivariate Distribution

As we did with the univariate distribution, we often describe the bivariate distribution by computing the mean, variance, and standard deviation of each variable. We do so by utilizing the marginal probabilities.

Expected Value, Variance, and Standard Deviation of X in Example 7.5

$$E(X) = \mu_X = \sum xP(x) = 0(.4) + 1(.5) + 2(.1) = .7$$

$$V(X) = \sigma_X^2 = \sum (x - \mu_X)^2 P(x) = (0 - .7)^2(.4) + (1 - .7)^2(.5) + (2 - .7)^2(.1) = .41$$

$$\sigma_X = \sqrt{\sigma_X^2} = \sqrt{.41} = .64$$

Expected Value, Variance, and Standard Deviation of Y in Example 7.5

$$E(Y) = \mu_Y = \sum yP(y) = 0(.6) + 1(.3) + 2(.1) = .5$$

$$V(Y) = \sigma_Y^2 = \sum (y - \mu_Y)^2 P(y) = (0 - .5)^2(.6) + (1 - .5)^2(.3) + (2 - .5)^2(.1) = .45$$

$$\sigma_Y = \sqrt{\sigma_Y^2} = \sqrt{.45} = .67$$

There are two more parameters we can and need to compute. Both deal with the relationship between the two variables. They are the covariance and the coefficient of correlation. Recall that both were introduced in Chapter 4, where the formulas were based on the assumption that we knew each of the N observations of the population. In this chapter, we compute parameters like the covariance and the coefficient of correlation from the bivariate distribution.

Covariance

The covariance of two discrete variables is defined as

$$COV(X, Y) = \sigma_{xy} = \sum_{\text{all } x} \sum_{\text{all } y} (x - \mu_X)(y - \mu_Y)P(x, y)$$

Notice that we multiply the deviations from the mean for both X and Y and then multiply by the joint probability.

The calculations are simplified by the following shortcut method.

Shortcut Calculation for Covariance

$$COV(X, Y) = \sigma_{xy} = \sum_{\text{all } x} \sum_{\text{all } y} xyP(x, y) - \mu_X\mu_Y$$

The coefficient of correlation is calculated in the same way as in Chapter 4.

Coefficient of Correlation

$$\rho = \frac{\sigma_{xy}}{\sigma_x \sigma_y}$$

EXAMPLE 7.6

Describing the Bivariate Distribution

Compute the covariance and the coefficient of correlation between the numbers of houses sold by the two agents in Example 7.5.

SOLUTION:

We start by computing the covariance.

$$
\begin{aligned}
\sigma_{xy} &= \sum_{\text{all } x} \sum_{\text{all } y} (x - \mu_X)(y - \mu_Y) P(x, y) \\
&= (0 - .7)(0 - .5)(.12) + (1 - .7)(0 - .5)(.42) + (2 - .7)(0 - .5)(.06) \\
&\quad + (0 - .7)(1 - .5)(.21) + (1 - .7)(1 - .5)(.06) + (2 - .7)(1 - .5)(.03) \\
&\quad + (0 - .7)(2 - .5)(.07) + (1 - .7)(2 - .5)(.02) + (2 - .7)(2 - .5)(.01) \\
&= -.15
\end{aligned}
$$

As we did with the shortcut method for the variance, we'll recalculate the covariance using its shortcut method.

$$
\begin{aligned}
\sum_{\text{all } x} \sum_{\text{all } y} xy P(x, y) &= (0)(0)(.12) + (1)(0)(.42) + (2)(0)(.06) \\
&\quad + (0)(1)(.21) + (1)(1)(.06) + (2)(1)(.03) \\
&\quad + (0)(2)(.07) + (1)(2)(.02) + (2)(2)(.01) \\
&= .2
\end{aligned}
$$

Using the expected values computed above, we find

$$\sigma_{xy} = \sum_{\text{all } x} \sum_{\text{all } y} xy P(x, y) - \mu_X \mu_Y = .2 - (.7)(.5) = -.15$$

We also computed the standard deviations above. Thus, the coefficient of correlation is

$$\rho = \frac{\sigma_{xy}}{\sigma_x \sigma_y} = \frac{-.15}{(.64)(.67)} = -.35$$

There is a weak negative relationship between the two variables: the number of houses Xavier will sell in a month (X) and the number of houses Yvette will sell in a month (Y).

7-2c Sum of Two Variables

The bivariate distribution allows us to develop the probability distribution of any combination of the two variables. Of particular interest to us is the sum of two variables. The analysis of this type of distribution leads to an important statistical application in finance, which we present in the next section.

To see how to develop the probability distribution of the sum of two variables from their bivariate distribution, return to Example 7.5. The sum of the two variables X and Y is the total number of houses sold per month. The possible values of $X + Y$ are 0, 1, 2, 3, and 4. The probability that $X + Y = 2$, for example, is obtained by summing the joint probabilities of all pairs of values of X and Y that sum to 2:

$$P(X + Y = 2) = P(0, 2) + P(1, 1) + P(2, 0) = .07 + .06 + .06 = .19$$

We calculate the probabilities of the other values of $X + Y$ similarly, producing the following table.

Probability Distribution of $X + Y$ in Example 7.5

$x + y$	0	1	2	3	4
$P(x + y)$	.12	.63	.19	.05	.01

We can compute the expected value, variance, and standard deviation of $X + Y$ in the usual way.

$$E(X + Y) = 0(.12) + 1(.63) + 2(.19) + 3(.05) + 4(.01) = 1.2$$

$$\begin{aligned}
V(X + Y) = \sigma_{X+Y}^2 &= (0 - 1.2)^2(.12) + (1 - 1.2)^2(.63) + (2 - 1.2)^2(.19) \\
&\quad + (3 - 1.2)^2(.05) + (4 - 1.2)^2(.01) \\
&= .56
\end{aligned}$$

$$\sigma_{X+Y} = \sqrt{.56} = .75$$

We can derive a number of laws that enable us to compute the expected value and variance of the sum of two variables.

Laws of Expected Value and Variance of the Sum of Two Variables

1. $E(X + Y) = E(X) + E(Y)$

2. $V(X + Y) = V(X) + V(Y) + 2\text{COV}(X, Y)$

If X and Y are independent, $\text{COV}(X, Y) = 0$ and thus $V(X + Y) = V(X) + V(Y)$.

EXAMPLE 7.7

Describing the Population of the Total Number of House Sales

Use the rules of expected value and variance of the sum of two variables to calculate the mean and variance of the total number of houses sold per month in Example 7.5.

SOLUTION:

Using law 1 we compute the expected value of $X + Y$:

$$E(X + Y) = E(X) + E(Y) = .7 + .5 = 1.2$$

which is the same value we produced directly from the probability distribution of $X + Y$. We apply law 3 to determine the variance:

$$V(X + Y) = V(X) + V(Y) + 2COV(X, Y) = .41 + .45 + 2(-.15) = .56$$

This is the same value we obtained from the probability distribution of $X + Y$.

We will encounter several applications where we need the laws of expected value and variance for the sum of two variables. Additionally, we will demonstrate an important application in operations management where we need the formulas for the expected value and variance of the sum of more than two variables. See Exercises 7.57–7.60.

EXERCISES

7.45 The following table lists the bivariate distribution of X and Y.

	x	
y	1	2
1	.5	.1
2	.1	.3

a. Find the marginal probability distribution of X.
b. Find the marginal probability distribution of Y.
c. Compute the mean and variance of X.
d. Compute the mean and variance of Y.

7.46 Refer to Exercise 7.45. Compute the covariance and the coefficient of correlation.

7.47 Refer to Exercise 7.45. Use the laws of expected value and variance of the sum of two variables to compute the mean and variance of $X + Y$.

7.48 Refer to Exercise 7.45.
a. Determine the distribution of $X + Y$.
b. Determine the mean and variance of $X + Y$.
c. Does your answer to part (b) equal the answer to Exercise 7.45?

7.49 The bivariate distribution of X and Y is described here.

	x	
y	1	2
1	.28	.42
2	.12	.18

a. Find the marginal probability distribution of X.

b. Find the marginal probability distribution of Y.
c. Compute the mean and variance of X.
d. Compute the mean and variance of Y.

7.50 Refer to Exercise 7.49. Compute the covariance and the coefficient of correlation.

7.51 Refer to Exercise 7.49. Use the laws of expected value and variance of the sum of two variables to compute the mean and variance of $X + Y$.

7.52 Refer to Exercise 7.49.
a. Determine the distribution of $X + Y$.
b. Determine the mean and variance of $X + Y$.
c. Does your answer to part (b) equal the answer to Exercise 7.49?

7.53 The joint probability distribution of X and Y is shown in the following table.

	x		
y	1	2	3
1	.42	.12	.06
2	.28	.08	.04

a. Determine the marginal distributions of X and Y.
b. Compute the covariance and coefficient of correlation between X and Y.
c. Develop the probability distribution of $X + Y$.

7.54 The following distributions of X and of Y have been developed. If X and Y are independent, determine the joint probability distribution of X and Y.

x	0	1	2
p(x)	.6	.3	.1

y	1	2
p(y)	.7	.3

7.55 The distributions of X and of Y are described here. If X and Y are independent, determine the joint probability distribution of X and Y.

x	0	1	y	1	2	3
$p(x)$	.2	.8	$p(y)$	.2	.4	.4

7.56 After analyzing several months of sales data, the owner of an appliance store produced the following joint probability distribution of the number of refrigerators and stoves sold daily.

	Refrigerators		
Stoves	0	1	2
0	.08	.14	.12
1	.09	.17	.13
2	.05	.18	.04

a. Find the marginal probability distribution of the number of refrigerators sold daily.
b. Find the marginal probability distribution of the number of stoves sold daily.
c. Compute the mean and variance of the number of refrigerators sold daily.
d. Compute the mean and variance of the number of stoves sold daily.
e. Compute the covariance and the coefficient of correlation.

7.57 Canadians who visit the United States often buy liquor and cigarettes, which are much cheaper in the United States. However, there are limitations. Canadians visiting the United States for more than 2 days are allowed to bring into Canada one bottle of liquor and one carton of cigarettes. A Canada customs agent has produced the following joint probability distribution of the number of bottles of liquor and the number of cartons of cigarettes imported by Canadians who have visited the United States for 2 or more days.

	Bottles of Liquor	
Cartons of Cigarettes	0	1
0	.63	.18
1	.09	.10

a. Find the marginal probability distribution of the number of bottles imported.
b. Find the marginal probability distribution of the number of cigarette cartons imported.
c. Compute the mean and variance of the number of bottles imported.

d. Compute the mean and variance of the number of cigarette cartons imported.
e. Compute the covariance and the coefficient of correlation.

7.58 Refer to Exercise 7.56. Find the following conditional probabilities.
a. $P(1$ refrigerator $|0$ stoves$)$
b. $P(0$ stoves $|1$ refrigerator$)$
c. $P(2$ refrigerators $|2$ stoves$)$

7.59 A fire inspector has conducted an extensive analysis of the number of smoke detectors and the number of carbon monoxide detectors in the homes in a large city. The analysis led to the creation of the following bivariate probability distribution.

	Carbon Monoxide Detectors		
Smoke Detectors	0	1	2
0	.42	.03	0
1	.15	.07	.01
2	.06	.10	.15
3	.05	.04	.02

a. What proportion of homes have no carbon monoxide detectors and two smoke detectors?
b. What proportion of homes have two carbon monoxide detectors and no smoke detectors?
c. What proportion of homes have at least one carbon monoxide detector and at least one smoke detector?

7.60 Refer to Exercise 7.59. (*Hint:* The answers to parts (a), (b), and (c) are all different.)
a. What proportions of homes have one carbon monoxide detector and two smoke detectors?
b. What proportion of homes with one carbon monoxide detector have two smoke detectors?
c. What proportion of homes with two smoke detectors have one carbon monoxide detector?

7.61 Refer to Exercise 7.59.
a. Determine the probability distribution of carbon monoxide detectors.
b. What is the mean, variance, and standard deviation of the number of carbon monoxide detectors?

7.62 Refer to Exercise 7.59.
a. Determine the probability distribution of smoke detectors.
b. What is the mean, variance, and standard deviation of the number of smoke detectors?

7.63 After watching several seasons of soccer a statistician produced the following bivariate distribution of scores.

Visiting team	Home team			
	0	**1**	**2**	**3**
0	.14	.11	.09	.10
1	.12	.10	.05	.02
2	.09	.07	.04	.01
3	.03	.02	.01	0

a. What is the probability that the home team wins?
b. What is the probability of a tie?
c. What is the probability that the visiting team wins?

7.64 Refer to Exercise 7.63.
a. Determine the probability distribution of the home team scores.
b. Calculate the mean, variance, and standard deviation of the home team scores.

7.65 Refer to Exercise 7.63.
a. Determine the probability distribution of the visiting team scores.
b. Calculate the mean, variance, and standard deviation of the visiting team scores.

7.66 Refer to Exercise 7.63.
a. Determine the probability distribution of the total scores for both teams.
b. Calculate the mean, variance, and standard deviation of the total scores for both teams.
c. Calculate the covariance and coefficient of correlation of the two variables.

APPLICATIONS in OPERATIONS MANAGEMENT

PERT/CPM

The Project Evaluation and Review Technique (**PERT**) and the Critical Path Method (**CPM**) are related management-science techniques that help operations managers control the activities and the amount of time it takes to complete a project. Both techniques are based on the order in which the activities must be performed. For example, in building a house the excavation of the foundation must precede the pouring of the foundation, which in turn precedes the framing. A **path** is defined as a sequence of related activities that leads from the starting point to the completion of a project. In most projects, there are several paths with differing amounts of time needed for their completion. The longest path is called the **critical path** because any delay in the activities along this path will result in a delay in the completion of the project. In some versions of PERT/CPM, the activity completion times are fixed and the chief task of the operations manager is to determine the critical path. In other versions, each activity's completion time is considered to be a random variable, where the mean and variance can be estimated. By extending the laws of expected value and variance for the sum of two variables to more than two variables, we produce the following, where $X_1, X_2, \ldots, X_k$ are the times for the completion of activities $1, 2, \ldots, k$, respectively. These times are independent random variables.

Laws of Expected Value and Variance for the Sum of More Than Two Independent Variables

1. $E(X_1 + X_2 + \cdots + X_k) = E(X_1) + E(X_2) + \cdots + E(X_K)$
2. $V(X_1 + X_2 + \cdots + X_k) = V(X_1) + V(X_2) + g + V(X_K)$

Using these laws, we can then produce the expected value and variance for the complete project. Exercises 7.67–7.70 address this problem.

7.67 There are four activities along the critical path for a project. The expected values and variances of the completion times of the activities are listed here. Determine the expected value and variance of the completion time of the project.

Activity	Expected Completion Time (Days)	Variance
1	18	8
2	12	5
3	27	6
4	8	2

7.68 The operations manager of a large plant wishes to overhaul a machine. After conducting a PERT/CPM analysis he has developed the following critical path.
1. Disassemble machine
2. Determine parts that need replacing
3. Find needed parts in inventory
4. Reassemble machine
5. Test machine

He has estimated the mean (in minutes) and variances of the completion times as follows.

Activity	Mean	Variance
1	35	8
2	20	5
3	20	4
4	50	12
5	20	2

Determine the mean and variance of the completion time of the project.

7.69 In preparing to launch a new product, a marketing manager has determined the critical path for the department. The activities and the mean and variance of the completion time for each activity along the critical path are shown in the accompanying table. Determine the mean and variance of the completion time of the project.

Activity	Expected Completion Time (Days)	Variance
Develop survey questionnaire	8	2
Pretest the questionnaire	14	5
Revise the questionnaire	5	1
Hire survey company	3	1
Conduct survey analyze data	30	8
Analyze data	30	10
Prepare report	10	3

7.70 A professor of business statistics is about to begin work on a new research project. The professor has developed a PERT/CPM critical path, which consists of the following activities:
1. Conduct a search for relevant research articles.
2. Write a proposal for a research grant.
3. Perform the analysis.
4. Write the article and send to journal.

(Continued)

5. Wait for reviews.
6. Revise on the basis of the reviews and resubmit.

The mean (in days) and variance of the completion times are as follows:

Activity	Mean	Variance
1	10	9
2	3	0
3	30	100
4	5	1
5	100	400
6	20	64

Compute the mean and variance of the completion time of the entire project.

7-3 / (OPTIONAL) APPLICATIONS IN FINANCE: PORTFOLIO DIVERSIFICATION AND ASSET ALLOCATION

In this section, we introduce an important application in finance that is based on the previous section.

In Example 3.2 (page 61) we described what we look for in a histogram of investment returns to gauge the risk associated with that investment. Most investors tend to be risk averse, which means that they prefer to have lower risk associated with their investments. One of the ways in which financial analysts lower the risk that is associated with the stock market is through **diversification**. This strategy was first mathematically developed by Harry Markowitz in 1952. His model paved the way for the development of modern portfolio theory (MPT), which is the concept underlying mutual funds (see page 175).

To illustrate the basics of portfolio diversification, consider an investor who forms a portfolio, consisting of only two stocks, by investing $4,000 in one stock and $6,000 in a second stock. Suppose that the results after 1 year are as listed here. (We've previously defined return on investment. See Applications in Finance: Return on Investment on page 61.)

One-Year Results

Stock	Initial Investment ($)	Value of Investment after One Year ($)	Rate of Return on Investment
1	4,000	5,000	$R_1 = .25\ (25\%)$
2	6,000	5,400	$R_2 = -.10\ (-10\%)$
Total	10,000	10,400	$R_p = .04\ (4\%)$

Another way of calculating the portfolio return R_p is to compute the weighted average of the individual stock returns R_1 and R_2, where the weights w_1 and w_2 are the proportions of the initial $10,000 invested in stocks 1 and 2, respectively. In this illustration, $w_1 = .4$ and $w_2 = .6$. (Note that w_1 and w_2 must always sum to 1 because the two stocks constitute the entire portfolio.) The weighted average of the two returns is

$$R_p = w_1R_1 + w_2R_2$$
$$= (.4)(.25) + (.6)(-.10) = .04$$

This is how portfolio returns are calculated. However, when the initial investments are made, the investor does not know what the returns will be. In fact, the returns are random variables. We are interested in determining the expected value and variance of the portfolio. The formulas in the box were derived from the laws of expected value and variance introduced in the two previous sections.

Mean and Variance of a Portfolio of Two Stocks

$$E(R_p) = w_1E(R_1) + w_2E(R_2)$$
$$V(R_p) = w_1^2V(R_1) + w_2^2V(R_2) + 2w_1w_2\text{COV}(R_1, R_2)$$
$$= w_1^2\sigma_1^2 + w_2^2\sigma_2^2 + 2w_1w_2\rho\sigma_1\sigma_2$$

where w_1 and w_2 are the proportions or weights of investments 1 and 2, $E(R_1)$ and $E(R_2)$ are their expected values, σ_1 and σ_2 are their standard deviations, $\text{COV}(R_1, R_2)$ is the covariance, and ρ is the coefficient of correlation.

[Recall that $\rho = \dfrac{\text{COV}(R_1, R_2)}{\sigma_1\sigma_2}$, which means that $\text{COV}(R_1, R_2) = \rho\sigma_1\sigma_2$.]

EXAMPLE 7.8

Describing the Population of the Returns on a Portfolio

An investor has decided to form a portfolio by putting 25% into McDonald's stock and 75% into Cisco Systems stock. The investor assumes that the expected returns will be 8% and 15%, respectively, and that the standard deviations will be 12% and 22%, respectively.

a. Find the expected return on the portfolio.

b. Compute the standard deviation of the returns on the portfolio assuming that

   i. the two stocks' returns are perfectly positively correlated.

   ii. the coefficient of correlation is .5.

   iii. the two stocks' returns are uncorrelated.

SOLUTION:

a. The expected values of the two stocks are

$$E(R_1) = .08 \quad \text{and} \quad E(R_2) = .15$$

The weights are $w_1 = .25$ and $w_2 = .75$.

Thus,

$$E(R_p) = w_1E(R_1) + w_2E(R_2) = .25(.08) + .75(.15) = .1325$$

b. The standard deviations are

$$\sigma_1 = .12 \text{ and } \sigma_2 = .22$$

Thus,

$$V(R_p) = w_1^2\sigma_1^2 + w_2^2\sigma_2^2 + 2w_1w_2\rho\sigma_1\sigma_2$$
$$= (.25^2)(.12^2) + (.75^2)(.22^2) + 2(.25)(.75)\rho(.12)(.22)$$
$$= .0281 + .0099\rho$$

When $\rho = 1$

$$V(R_p) = .0281 + .0099(1) = .0380$$

$$\text{Standard deviation} = \sqrt{V(R_p)} = \sqrt{.0380} = .1949$$

When $\rho = .5$

$$V(R_p) = .0281 + .0099(.5) = .0331$$

$$\text{Standard deviation} = \sqrt{V(R_p)} = \sqrt{.0331} = .1819$$

When $\rho = 0$

$$V(R_p) = .0281 + .0099(0) = .0281$$

$$\text{Standard deviation} = \sqrt{V(R_p)} = \sqrt{.0281} = .1676$$

Notice that the variance and standard deviation of the portfolio returns decrease as the coefficient of correlation decreases.

7-3a Portfolio Diversification in Practice

The formulas introduced in this section require that we know the expected values, variances, and covariance (or coefficient of correlation) of the investments we're interested in. The question arises, How do we determine these parameters? (Incidentally, this question is rarely addressed in finance textbooks!) The most common procedure is to estimate the parameters from historical data, using sample statistics.

7-3b Portfolios with More Than Two Stocks

We can extend the formulas that describe the mean and variance of the returns of a portfolio of two stocks to a portfolio of any number of stocks.

Mean and Variance of a Portfolio of k Stocks

$$E(R_p) = \sum_{i=1}^{k} w_i E(R_i)$$

$$V(R_p) = \sum_{i=1}^{k} w_i^2\sigma_i^2 + 2\sum_{i=1}^{k}\sum_{j=i+1}^{k} w_i w_j \text{COV}(R_i, R_j)$$

where R_i is the return of the ith stock, w_i is the proportion of the portfolio invested in stock i, and k is the number of stocks in the portfolio.

When k is greater than 2, the calculations can be tedious and time consuming. For example, when $k = 3$, we need to know the values of the three weights, three expected values, three variances, and three covariances. When $k = 4$, there are four expected values, four variances, and six covariances. [The number of covariances required in general is $k(k − 1)/2$.] To assist you, we have created an Excel worksheet to perform the computations when $k = 2$, 3, or 4. To demonstrate, we'll return to the problem described in this chapter's introduction.

Investing to Maximize Returns and Minimize Risk: Solution

Because of the large number of calculations, we will solve this problem using only Excel. From the file, we compute the means of each stock's returns.

Excel Means

	A	B	C	D
50	0.01575	0.01203	0.01257	0.00530

Next we compute the variance-covariance matrix. (The commands are the same as those described in Chapter 4—simply include all the columns of the returns of the investments you wish to include in the portfolio.)

Excel Variance-Covariance Matrix

	G	H	I	J	K
1		*HD*	*NKE*	*CNR*	*EXPE*
2	HD	0.00257			
3	NKE	0.00144	0.00356		
4	CNR	0.00074	0.00004	0.00178	
5	EXPE	0.00149	0.00059	0.00057	0.00566

Notice that the variances of the returns are listed on the diagonal. Thus, for example, the variance of the 48 monthly returns of Nike is .00356. The covariances appear below the diagonal. The covariance between the returns of Home Depot and Nike is .00144.

The means and the variance-covariance matrix are copied to the spreadsheet using the commands described here. The weights are typed producing the accompanying output.

Excel Worksheet: Portfolio Diversification-Plan 1

	A	B	C	D	E	F	G
1	Portfolio of 4 Stocks						
2			HD	NKE	CNR	EXPE	
3	Variance-Covariance Matrix	HD	0.002569				
4		NKE	0.001444	0.003556			
5		CNR	0.000738	0.000037	0.001785		
6		EXPE	0.001490	0.000591	0.000571	0.005661	
7							
8	Expected Returns		0.015751	0.012032	0.012569	0.005297	
9							
10	Weights		0.250000	0.250000	0.250000	0.250000	1.000000
11							
12	Portfolio Return						
13	Expected Value	0.0114					
14	Variance	0.0015					
15	Standard Deviation	0.0382					

The expected return on the portfolio is .0114 and the variance is .0015.

(Continued)

INSTRUCTIONS

1. Open the file containing the returns. In this example, open file **Ch7:\ Xm07-00**.

2. Compute the means of the columns containing the returns of the stocks in the portfolio.

3. Using the commands described in Chapter 4 (page 131) compute the variance-covariance matrix.

4. Open the **Portfolio Diversification** workbook. Use the tab to select the **4 Stocks** worksheet. DO NOT CHANGE ANY CELLS THAT APPEAR IN BOLD PRINT. DO NOT SAVE ANY WORKSHEETS.

5. Copy the means into cells C8 to F8. (Use **Copy, Paste Special** with **Values and number formats**.)

6. Copy the variance-covariance matrix (including row and column labels) into columns B, C, D, E, and F.

7. Type the weights into cells C10 to F10.

The mean, variance, and standard deviation of the portfolio will be printed. Use similar commands for 2 stock and 3 stock portfolios.

The results for Plan 2 are:

	A	B
12	Portfolio Return	
13	Expected Value	0.0099
14	Variance	0.0017
15	Standard Deviation	0.0411

The results for Plan 3 are:

	A	B
12	Portfolio Return	
13	Expected Value	0.0107
14	Variance	0.0014
15	Standard Deviation	0.0377

Plan 1 has the largest expected value and the second smallest variance. Plan 2 has the smallest expected value and the largest variance. Plan 3's expected value is the second largest and has the smallest variance. Most investors are conservative and likely would select Plan 3 because of its lower risk. Other more daring investors may choose Plan 1 to take advantage of its higher expected value.

In this example, we showed how to compute the expected return, variance, and standard deviation from a sample of returns on the investments for any combination of weights. (We illustrated the process with three sets of weights.) It is possible to determine the "optimal" weights that minimize risk for a given expected value or maximize expected return for a given standard deviation. This is an extremely important function of financial analysts and investment advisors. Solutions can be determined using a management science technique called *linear programming*, a subject taught by most schools of business and faculties of management.

EXERCISES

7.71 Describe what happens to the expected value and standard deviation of the portfolio returns when the coefficient of correlation decreases.

7.72 A portfolio is composed of two stocks. The proportion of each stock, their expected values, and standard deviations are listed next.

Stock	1	2
Proportion of portfolio	.30	.70
Mean	.12	.25
Standard deviation	.02	.15

For each of the following coefficients of correlation, calculate the expected value and standard deviation of the portfolio:

a. $\rho = .5$

b. $\rho = .2$

c. $\rho = 0$

7.73 An investor is given the following information about the returns on two stocks:

Stock	1	2
Mean	.09	.13
Standard deviation	.15	.21

a. If the goal is to maximize returns, which stock should be selected?

b. If minimizing risk is the goal, which stock should be chosen?

7.74 Refer to Exercise 7.73. Compute the expected value and standard deviation of the portfolio composed of 60% stock 1 and 40% stock 2. The coefficient of correlation is .4.

7.75 Refer to Exercise 7.73. Compute the expected value and standard deviation of the portfolio composed of 30% stock 1 and 70% stock 2.

The following exercises require the use of a computer.

[Xr07-NYSE] *We have recorded the 48 monthly returns for the following 23 of the 30 Dow Jones Industrials stocks listed on the New York Stock Exchange (six others are on the NASDAQ and one has been around since 2019 only) for the period January 2016–December 2019.*

3M (MMM), American Express (AXP), Boeing (BA), Caterpillar (CAT), Chevron (CVX), Coca-Cola (KO), Goldman Sachs (GS), Home Depot (HD), Honeywell (HON), International Business Machines (IBM), Johnson & Johnson (JNJ), JP Morgan Chase (JPM), McDonald's (MCD), Merck (MRK), Nike (NKE), Procter & Gamble (PG), Salesforce (CRM), Travelers (TRV), United Health (UNH), Verizon Communications (VZ), Visa (V), Wal-Mart Stores (WMT), Walt Disney (DIS)

For Exercises 7.76 to 7.82, calculate the mean and standard deviation of the portfolio. The proportions invested in each stock are shown.

7.76 a. American Express (AXP): 30%, Boeing (BA): 50%, Caterpillar (CAT): 20%

b. AXP: 60%, BA: 20%, CAT: 20%

c. AXP: 10%, BA: 80%, CAT: 10%

d. Which portfolio would an investor who likes to gamble choose? Explain.

e. Which portfolio would a risk-averse investor choose? Explain.

7.77 a. Coca-Cola (KO): 30%, Honeywell (HON): 40%, Johnson & Johnson (JNJ): 30%

b. KO: 50%, HON: 25%, JNJ: 25%

c. KO: 20%, HON: 70%, JNJ: 10%

d. Which portfolio would a gambler choose? Explain.

e. Which portfolio would a risk-averse investor choose? Explain.

7.78 a. Goldman Sachs (GS): 25%, Home Depot (HD): 25%, Nike (NKE): 25%, Salesforce (CRM): 25%

b. GS: 40%, HD: 30%, NKE: 20%, CRM: 10%

c. GS: 10%, HD: 20%, NKE: 50%, CRM: 20%

d. Explain why the choice of which portfolio to invest in is obvious.

7.79 a. Coca-Cola (KO): 40%, McDonald's (MCD): 10%, Procter and Gamble (PG): 40%, Visa (V): 10%

b. KO: 25%, MCD: 25%, PG: 25%, V: 25%

c. KO: 20%, MCD: 20%, PG: 20%, V: 40%

d. Which portfolio would an investor who likes to gamble choose? Explain.

e. Which portfolio would a risk-averse investor choose? Explain.

7.80 a. Boeing (BA): 25%, Caterpillar (CAT): 25%, International Business Machines (IBM): 25%, Wal-Mart Stores (WMT): 25%

b. BA: 10%, CAT: 20%, IBM: 30%, WMT: 40%

c. BA: 50%, CAT: 30%, IBM: 10%, WMT: 10%

d. Which portfolio would an investor who likes to gamble choose? Explain.

e. Which portfolio would a risk-averse investor choose? Explain.

7.81 a. 3M (MMM): 25%, Travelers (TRV): 25%, Verizon Communications (VZ): 25%, Walt Disney (DIS): 25%

b. MMM: 50%, TRV: 30%, VZ: 10%, DIS: 10%

c. MMM: 20%, TRV: 60%, VZ: 10%, DIS: 10%

d. Explain why the choice of which portfolio to not invest in is obvious.

7.82 a. Goldman Sachs (GS): 50%, JP Morgan Chase (JPM): 30%, Merck (MRK): 10%, United Health (UNH): 10%

b. GS: 10%, JPM: 20%, MRK: 20%, UNH: 50%

c. GS: 10%, JPM: 40%, MRK: 40%, UNH: 10%

d. Which portfolio would an investor who likes to gamble choose? Explain.

e. Which portfolio would a risk-averse investor choose? Explain.

7.83 Refer to Exercise 7.82.

a. Try to find weights that produce an expected return of at least .0150.

b. Using trial and error, find weights that produce an expected value of at least .0150 and the smallest variance.

7.84   Refer to Exercises 7.82 and 7.83.
a. Compute the expected value and variance of this portfolio:
GS: 10.4%, JPM: 16.0%, MRK: 52.0%, UNH: 21.6%
b. Can you do better? That is, can you find a portfolio whose expected value is at least .0150 and whose variance is less than the one you calculated in part (a)? *Hint*: Don't spend too much time at this. You won't be able to do better. If you want to learn how we produced the portfolio above, take a course that teaches linear and nonlinear programming.

[Xr07-TSE]   *Monthly returns for the following selected stocks on the Toronto Stock Exchange were recorded for the years 2016 to 2019:*

Agnico Eagle (AEM), Barrick Gold (ABX), Bell Canada Enterprises (BCE), Bank of Montreal (BMO), Bank of Nova Scotia (BNS), Canadian Imperial Bank of Commerce (CM), Canadian National Railways (CNR), Canadian Tire (CTC), Enbridge (ENB), Fortis (FTS), Great West Life (GWO), Manulife Financial (MFC), Magna International (MG), Open Text (OTEX), Power Corporation of Canada (POW), Rogers Communication (RCI), Royal Bank of Canada (RY), Suncor Energy (SU), Telus (T), George Weston (WN)

7.85   An analyst recommends that you invest in a portfolio made up of Bank of Montreal (BMO), Bank of Nova Scotia (BNS), Canadian Imperial Bank of Commerce (CM), and Royal Bank (RY). Why would it not be useful in diversification?

7.86   Refer to Exercise 7.85. Compute the correlation matrix of the returns of the four banks. Briefly describe what the correlations tell you.

For Exercises 7.87 to 7.91, calculate the mean and standard deviation of the portfolio. The proportions invested in each stock are shown.

7.87   a. Agnico Eagle (AEM): 20%, Bank of Montreal (BMO): 50%, Canadian Tire (CTC): 30%
b. AEM: 20%, BMO: 20%, CTC: 60%
c. AEM: 40%, BMO: 40%, CTC: 20%
d. Which portfolio would an investor who likes to gamble choose? Explain.
e. Which portfolio would a risk-averse investor choose? Explain.

7.88   a. Barrick Gold (ABX): 50%, Bell Canada Enterprises (BCE): 30%, Suncor Energy (SU): 20%
b. ABX: 20%, BCE: 60%, SU: 20%
c. ABX: 30%, BCE: 30%, SU: 40%

d. Which portfolio would a gambler choose? Explain.
e. Which portfolio would a risk-averse investor choose? Explain.

7.89   a. Bank of Nova Scotia (BNS): 25%, Canadian National Railways (CNR): 25%, Fortis (FTS): 25%, George Weston (WN): 25%
b. BNS: 10%, CNR: 40%, FTS: 30%, WN: 20%
c. BNS: 30%, CNR: 30%, FTS: 20%, WN: 20%
d. Which portfolio would an investor who likes to gamble choose? Explain.
e. Which portfolio would a risk-averse investor choose? Explain.

7.90   a. Enbridge (ENB): 10%, Magna International (MG): 20%, Open Text (OTEX): 30%, Telus (T): 40%
b. ENB: 30%, MG: 10%, OTEX: 50%, T: 10%
c. ENB: 10%, MG: 10%, OTEX: 30%, T: 50%
d. Which portfolio would a gambler choose? Explain.
e. Which portfolio would a risk-averse investor choose? Explain.

7.91   a. Great West Life (GWO): 25%, Manulife Financial (MFC): 25%, Power Corporation of Canada (POW): 25%, Rogers Communication (RCI): 25%
b. GWO: 10%, MFC: 20%, POW: 30%, RCI: 40%
c. GWO: 15%, MFC: 15%, POW: 15%, RCI: 55%
d. Explain why the choice of which portfolio to invest in is obvious.

7.92   You have decided to invest in a portfolio made up of these four stocks: Agnico Eagle (AEM), Barrick Gold (ABX), Open Text (OTEX), and Telus (T). You need the expected monthly return to exceed .0150. Try several different proportions of the four stocks to see if you can find the portfolio with the smallest variance.

7.93   Refer to Exercise 7.92.
a. Compute the expected value and variance of this portfolio:
AEM: 2.93%, ABX: 15.5%, OTEX: 71.4%, T: 10.1%
b. Can you do better? That is, can you find a portfolio whose expected value is at least .0150 and whose variance is less than the one you calculated in part (a)? *Hint:* Don't spend too much time at this. You won't be able to do better. If you want to learn how we produced the portfolio above, take a course that teaches linear and nonlinear programming.

[Xr07-NASDAQ] *We calculated the returns for the following selected stocks on the NASDAQ Exchange for the period January 2016–December 2019.*

Adobe Systems (ADBE), Amazon (AMZN), Amgen (AMGN), Apple (AAPL), Bed Bath & Beyond (BBBY), Cisco Systems (CSCO), Comcast (CMCSA), Costco Wholesale (COST), Dollar Tree (DLTR), Expedia (EXPE), Garmin (GRMN), Intel (INTC), Mattel (MAT), Microsoft (MSFT), Netflix (NFLX), Oracle (ORCL), Sirius XM Radio (SIRI), Starbucks (SBUX), Tesla (TSLA), Vertex Pharmaceuticals (VRTX)

For Exercises 7.94 to 7.99, calculate the mean and standard deviation of the portfolio. The proportions invested in each stock are shown.

7.94 a. Adobe Systems (ADBE): 25%, Amgen (AMGN): 25%, Dollar Tree (DLTR): 25%, Garmin (GRMN): 25%

b. ADBE: 10%, AMGN: 20%, DLTR: 30%, GRMN: 40%

c. ADBE: 40%, AMGN: 10%, DLTR: 40%, GRMN: 10%

d. Explain why the choice of which portfolio to invest in is obvious.

7.95 a. Cisco Systems (CSCO): 40%, Costco Wholesale (COST): 30%, Expedia (EXPE): 20%, Microsoft (MSFT): 10%

b. CSCO: 10%, COST: 30%, EXPE: 30%, MSFT: 30%

c. CSCO: 25%, COST: 25%, EXPE: 25%, MSFT: 25%

d. In choosing which portfolio to invest in, explain why the choice is obvious.

7.96 a. Comcast (CMCSA): 25%, Intel (INTC): 25%, Oracle (ORCL): 25%, Sirius XM Radio (SIRI): 25%

b. CMCSA: 40%, INTC: 10%, ORCL: 40%, SIRI: 10%

c. CMCSA: 10%, INTC: 50%, ORCL: 10%, SIRI: 30%

d. Which portfolio would a gambler choose? Explain.

e. Which portfolio would a risk-averse investor choose? Explain.

7.97 a. Netflix (NFLX): 10%, Starbucks (SBUX): 20%, Tesla (TSLA): 30%, Vertex Pharmaceuticals (VRTX): 40%

b. NFLX: 30%, SBUX: 10%, TSLA: 30%, VRTX: 30%

c. NFLX: 50%, SBUX: 10%, TSLA: 20%, VRTX: 20%

d. Which portfolio would an investor who likes to gamble choose? Explain.

e. Which portfolio would a risk-averse investor choose? Explain.

7.98 You have decided to invest in a portfolio made up of these four stocks: Amazon (AMZN), Apple (AAPL), Netflix (NFLX), Tesla (TSLA). You need the expected monthly return to exceed .0300. Try several different proportions of the four stocks to see if you can find the portfolio with the smallest variance.

7.99 Refer to Exercise 7.98.

a. Compute the expected value and variance of this portfolio: AMZN: 41.8%, AAPL: 36.6%, NFLX: 8.7%, TSLA: 12.9%

b. Can you do better? That is, can you find a portfolio whose expected value is at least .0300 and whose variance is less than the one you calculated in part (a)? *Hint:* Don't spend too much time at this. You won't be able to do better. If you want to learn how we produced the portfolio above, take a course that teaches linear and nonlinear programming.

7-4 / BINOMIAL DISTRIBUTION

Now that we've introduced probability distributions in general, we need to introduce several specific probability distributions. In this section, we present the *binomial distribution*.

The binomial distribution is the result of a *binomial experiment*, which has the following properties.

> **Binomial Experiment**
>
> 1. The **binomial experiment** consists of a fixed number of trials. We represent the number of trials by n.
> 2. Each trial has two possible outcomes. We label one outcome a *success*, and the other a *failure*.
> 3. The probability of success is p. The probability of failure is $1 - p$.
> 4. The trials are independent, which means that the outcome of one trial does not affect the outcomes of any other trials.

If properties 2, 3, and 4 are satisfied, we say that each trial is a **Bernoulli process**. Adding property 1 yields the binomial experiment. The random variable of a binomial experiment is defined as the number of successes in the n trials. It is called the **binomial random variable**. Here are several examples of binomial experiments.

1. Flip a coin 10 times. The two outcomes per trial are heads and tails. The terms *success* and *failure* are arbitrary. We can label either outcome success. However, generally, we call success anything we're looking for. For example, if we were betting on heads, we would label heads a success. If the coin is fair, the probability of heads is 50%. Thus, $p = .5$. Finally, we can see that the trials are independent because the outcome of one coin flip cannot possibly affect the outcomes of other flips.

2. Draw five cards out of a shuffled deck. We can label as success whatever card we seek. For example, if we wish to know the probability of receiving five clubs, a club is labeled a success. On the first draw, the probability of a club is $13/52 = .25$. However, if we draw a second card without replacing the first card and shuffling, the trials are not independent. To see why, suppose that the first draw is a club. If we draw again without replacement, the probability of drawing a second club is $12/51$, which is not .25. In this experiment, the trials are *not* independent.[*] Hence, this is not a binomial experiment. However, if we replace the card and shuffle before drawing again, the experiment is binomial. Note that in most card games, we do not replace the card, and as a result the experiment is not binomial.

3. A political survey asks 1,500 voters who they intend to vote for in an approaching election. In most elections in the United States, there are only two candidates, the Republican and Democratic nominees. Thus, we have two outcomes per trial. The trials are independent because the choice of one voter does not affect the choice of other voters. In Canada, and in other countries with parliamentary systems of government, there are usually several candidates in the race. However, we can label a vote for our favored candidate (or the party that is paying us to do the survey) a success and all the others are failures.

As you will discover, the third example is a very common application of statistical inference. The actual value of p is unknown, and the job of the statistics practitioner is to estimate its value. By understanding the probability distribution that uses p, we will be able to develop the statistical tools to estimate p.

---

[*]The hypergeometric distribution described in the online appendix of the same name is used to calculate probabilities in such cases.

7-4a Binomial Random Variable

The binomial random variable is the number of successes in the experiment's n trials. It can take on values 0, 1, 2, . . . , n. Thus, the random variable is discrete. To proceed, we must be capable of calculating the probability associated with each value.

Using a probability tree, we draw a series of branches as depicted in Figure 7.2. The stages represent the outcomes for each of the n trials. At each stage, there are two branches representing success and failure. To calculate the probability that there are X successes in n trials, we note that for each success in the sequence, we must multiply by p. And if there are X successes, there must be $n - X$ failures. For each failure in the sequence, we multiply by $1 - p$. Thus, the probability for each sequence of branches that represent x successes and $n - x$ failures has probability

$$p^x(1 - p)^{n-x}$$

FIGURE 7.2 Probability Tree for a Binomial Experiment

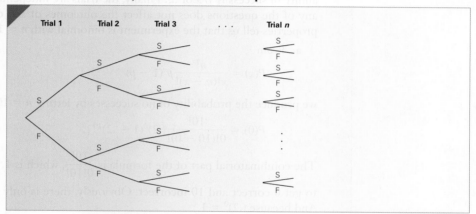

There are a number of branches that yield x successes and $n - x$ failures. For example, there are two ways to produce exactly one success and one failure in two trials: SF and FS. To count the number of branch sequences that produce x successes and $n - x$ failures, we use the combinatorial formula

$$C_x^n = \frac{n!}{x!(n - x)!}$$

where $n! = n(n - 1)(n - 2) \ldots (2)(1)$. For example, $3! = 3(2)(1) = 6$. Incidentally, although it may not appear to be logical $0! = 1$.

Pulling together the two components of the probability distribution yields the following.

Binomial Probability Distribution

The probability of x successes in a binomial experiment with n trials and probability of success $= p$ is

$$P(x) = \frac{n!}{x!(n - x)!} \, p^x(1 - p)^{n - x} \quad \text{for} \quad x = 0, 1, 2, \ldots, n$$

EXAMPLE 7.9

Pat Statsdud and the Statistics Quiz

Pat Statsdud is a student taking a statistics course. Unfortunately, Pat is not a good student. Pat does not read the textbook before class, does not do homework, and regularly misses class. Pat intends to rely on luck to pass the next quiz. The quiz consists of 10 multiple-choice questions. Each question has five possible answers, only one of which is correct. Pat plans to guess the answer to each question.

a. What is the probability that Pat gets no answers correct?

b. What is the probability that Pat gets two answers correct?

SOLUTION:

The experiment consists of 10 identical trials, each with two possible outcomes and where success is defined as a correct answer. Because Pat intends to guess, the probability of success is 1/5 or .2. Finally, the trials are independent because the outcome of any of the questions does not affect the outcomes of any other questions. These four properties tell us that the experiment is binomial with $n = 10$ and $p = .2$.

a. From

$$P(x) = \frac{n!}{x!(n-x)!}p^x(1-p)^{n-x}$$

we produce the probability of no successes by letting $n = 10$, $p = .2$, and $x = 0$. Hence,

$$P(0) = \frac{10!}{0!(10-0)!}(.2)^0(1-.2)^{10-0}$$

The combinatorial part of the formula is $\frac{10!}{0!10!}$, which is 1. This is the number of ways to get 0 correct and 10 incorrect. Obviously, there is only one way to produce $X = 0$. And because $(.2)^0 = 1$,

$$P(X = 0) = 1(1)(.8)^{10} = .1074$$

b. The probability of two correct answers is computed similarly by substituting $n = 10$, $p = .2$, and $x = 2$:

$$P(x) = \frac{n!}{x!(n-x)!}p^x(1-p)^{n-x}$$

$$P(0) = \frac{10!}{2!(10-2)!}(.2)^2(1-.2)^{10-2}$$

$$= \frac{(10)(9)(8)(7)(6)(5)(4)(3)(2)(1)}{(2)(1)(8)(7)(6)(5)(4)(3)(2)(1)}(.04)(.1678)$$

$$= 45(.006712)$$

$$= .3020$$

In this calculation, we discovered that there are 45 ways to get exactly two correct and eight incorrect answers, and that each such outcome has probability .006712. Multiplying the two numbers produces a probability of .3020.

7-4b Cumulative Probability

The formula of the binomial distribution allows us to determine the probability that X equals individual values. In Example 7.9, the values of interest were 0 and 2. There are

7.124 According to a Gallup poll, 52% of American adults think that protecting the environment should be given priority over developing U.S. energy supplies. Thirty-six percent think that developing energy supplies is more important, and 6% believe the two are equally important. The rest had no opinion. Suppose that a sample of 100 American adults is quizzed on the subject. What is the probability of the following events?
  a. Fifty or more think that protecting the environment should be given priority.
  b. Thirty or fewer think that developing energy supplies is more important.
  c. Five or fewer have no opinion.

7.125 Power and Associates survey new car owners and ask a variety of questions. In a recent report they note that 60% of car buyers use the Internet for research and price comparisons. Find the probability that in a random sample of 10 new car buyers, 6 or more used the Internet to help make a decision.

7.126 The statistics practitioner in Exercise 7.116 also determined that if a batter hits a line drive, the probability of an out is 23%. Determine the following probabilities.
  a. In a game with 10 line drives, at least 5 are outs.
  b. In a game with 25 line drives, there are 5 outs or less.

7.127 In a *Bon Appetit* poll, 38% of people said that chocolate was their favorite flavor of ice cream. A sample of 100 people was asked to name their favorite flavor of ice cream. What is the probability that more than half of them prefer chocolate?

7.128 Refer to Exercise 7.127. Suppose you discover that more than half of your sample prefers chocolate. What does that tell you about the *Bon Appetit* poll results?

7.129 In a recent Gallup poll, 53% of American adults believed that Congress is doing a poor or bad job. Suppose that you randomly choose 100 American adults and ask their opinion about Congress.
  a. Determine the probability that less than half say that Congress is doing a poor or bad job.
  b. Compute the probability more than 60% say that Congress is doing a poor or bad job.
  c. What is the expected number of American adults in your sample who would say that Congress is doing a poor or bad job?

7.130 Refer to Exercise 7.129. You find that more than 70% of your sample of 100 say that Congress is doing a poor or bad job. What does that tell you about the Gallup poll?

7.131 A financial analyst believes that the percentage of Millennials who do not own any stocks is 19%. A survey of 500 Millennials is conducted, which asks whether they own stocks. Find the probability that less than 110 own stocks.

7.132 In his career, Babe Ruth hit an average of one home run per 11.76 at bats. If the Babe were cloned, what is the probability that the clone would hit more than 60 home runs in a season with 800 at bats?

7.133 In an Abacus poll, 40% of Millennials believe that the province of Ontario is on the wrong track. To confirm these results, you take a sample of 200 Ontario Millennials and ask their opinion on the subject. Find the probability that between 35% and 45% (inclusive) say that the province is headed in the wrong direction.

7.134 A financial analyst reports that 7% of women between 35 and 45 are self-employed. A survey of 250 women between 35 and 45 was conducted. Compute the probability that more than 10% are self-employed.

7.135 A Canadian politician tells you that 10% of the population supports conventional and offshore oil but opposes development of the oil sands. As a properly educated statistics practitioner, you conduct your own survey of 300 Canadians. Using the politician's figure, calculate the probability that more than 15% supports conventional and offshore oil but opposes development of the oil sands.

7.136 Refer to Exercise 7.135. You discover that more than 15% support conventional and offshore oil but oppose the development of oil sands. Does this confirm or reject the politician's claim? Explain.

7.137 A management consultant claims that 4% of American workers actually believe that they are overpaid. A Gallup survey was planned in which American workers were asked, among other questions, whether they were overpaid. If the sample size is 1,000 and assuming the consultant is correct, find the probability that in the survey less than 3% think they are overpaid.

7.138 An environmentalist claims that 20% of people would participate in a protest about climate change. You organize a survey wherein you plan to ask people about the issue. If the sample size is 400 and the environmentalist is correct, compute the probability that less than 15% would participate in a protest.

7.139 A neighborhood group has complained that at an intersection near a school, half of all cars roll through the stop sign without coming to a complete halt. A statistics practitioner plans to observe a random sample of 200 cars. If the neighborhood group is correct, what is the probability that between 40% and 60% of the cars roll through the stop sign?

7.140 A school board claims that 80% of its grade 10 students pass the state's reading comprehension test. An auditor randomly selects 100 grade 10 students and determines whether each passed the test. If the claim is true, what is the probability that less than 75% of the sample passed the test?

7.141 When two fair dice are used in a Las Vegas casino, the probability that the total equals 7 is 1/6. Find the probability that in next 100 tosses of the dice, the 7 occurs less than 12% of the time.

7-5 / (OPTIONAL) POISSON DISTRIBUTION

Another useful discrete probability distribution is the **Poisson distribution**, named after its French creator. Like the binomial random variable, the **Poisson random variable** is the number of occurrences of events, which we'll continue to call *successes*. The difference between the two random variables is that a binomial random variable is the number of successes in a set number of trials, whereas a Poisson random variable is the number of successes in an interval of time or specific region of space. Here are several examples of Poisson random variables.

1. The number of cars arriving at a service station in 1 hour. (The interval of time is 1 hour.)

2. The number of flaws in a bolt of cloth. (The specific region is a bolt of cloth.)

3. The number of accidents in 1 day on a particular stretch of highway. (The interval is defined by both time, 1 day, and space, the particular stretch of highway.)

The Poisson experiment is described in the box.

Poisson Experiment

A **Poisson experiment** is characterized by the following properties:

1. The number of successes that occur in any interval is independent of the number of successes that occur in any other interval.

2. The probability of a success in an interval is the same for all equal-size intervals.

3. The probability of a success in an interval is proportional to the size of the interval.

4. The probability of more than one success in an interval approaches 0 as the interval becomes smaller.

Poisson Random Variable

The **Poisson random variable** is the number of successes that occur in a period of time or an interval of space in a Poisson experiment.

There are several ways to derive the probability distribution of a Poisson random variable. However, all are beyond the mathematical level of this book. We simply provide the formula and illustrate how it is used.

Poisson Probability Distribution

The probability that a Poisson random variable assumes a value of x in a specific interval is

$$P(x) = \frac{e^{-\mu}\mu^x}{x!} \quad \text{for} \quad x = 0, 1, 2, \ldots$$

where μ is the mean number of successes in the interval or region and e is the base of the natural logarithm (approximately 2.71828). Incidentally, the variance of a Poisson random variable is equal to its mean; that is, $\sigma^2 = \mu$.

EXAMPLE 7.12

Probability of the Number of Typographical Errors in Textbooks

A statistics instructor has observed that the number of typographical errors in new editions of textbooks varies considerably from book to book and that the number of errors is Poisson distributed with a mean of 1.5 per 100 pages. The instructor randomly selects 100 pages of a new book. What is the probability that there are no typographical errors?

SOLUTION:

We want to determine the probability that a Poisson random variable with a mean of 1.5 is equal to 0. Using the formula

$$P(x) = \frac{e^{-\mu}\mu^x}{x!}$$

and substituting $x = 0$ and $\mu = 1.5$, we get

$$P(0) = \frac{e^{-1.5}1.5^0}{0!} = \frac{(2.71828)^{-1.5}(1)}{1} = .2231$$

The probability that in the 100 pages selected there are no errors is .2231.

Notice that in Example 7.12, we wanted to find the probability of 0 typographical errors in 100 pages given a mean of 1.5 typos in 100 pages. The next example illustrates how we calculate the probability of events where the intervals or regions do not match.

EXAMPLE 7.13

Probability of the Number of Typographical Errors in 400 Pages

Refer to Example 7.12. Suppose that the instructor has just received a copy of a new statistics book and notices that there are 400 pages.

a. What is the probability that there are no typos?

b. What is the probability that there are five or fewer typos?

SOLUTION:

The specific region that we're interested in is 400 pages. To calculate Poisson probabilities associated with this region, we must determine the mean number of typos per 400 pages. Because the mean is specified as 1.5 per 100 pages, we multiply this figure by 4 to convert to 400 pages. Thus, $\mu = 6$ typos per 400 pages.

a. The probability of no typos is

$$P(0) = \frac{e^{-6}6^0}{0!} = \frac{(2.71828)^{-6}(1)}{1} = .002479$$

b. We want to determine the probability that a Poisson random variable with a mean of 6 is 5 or less; that is, we want to calculate

$$P(X \le 5) = P(0) + P(1) + P(2) + P(3) + P(4) + P(5)$$

To produce this probability, we need to compute the six probabilities in the summation.

$$P(0) = .002479$$

$$P(1) = \frac{e^{-\mu}\mu^x}{x!} = \frac{e^{-6}6^1}{1!} = \frac{(2.71828)^{-6}(6)}{1} = .01487$$

$$P(2) = \frac{e^{-\mu}\mu^x}{x!} = \frac{e^{-6}6^2}{2!} = \frac{(2.71828)^{-6}(36)}{2} = .04462$$

$$P(3) = \frac{e^{-\mu}\mu^x}{x!} = \frac{e^{-6}6^3}{3!} = \frac{(2.71828)^{-6}(216)}{6} = .08924$$

$$P(4) = \frac{e^{-\mu}\mu^x}{x!} = \frac{e^{-6}6^4}{4!} = \frac{(2.71828)^{-6}(1296)}{24} = .1339$$

$$P(5) = \frac{e^{-\mu}\mu^x}{x!} = \frac{e^{-6}6^5}{5!} = \frac{(2.71828)^{-6}(7776)}{120} = .1606$$

Thus,

$$P(X \le 5) = .002479 + .01487 + .04462 + .08924 + .1339 + .1606$$
$$= .4457$$

The probability of observing 5 or fewer typos in this book is .4457.

7-5a Poisson Table

As was the case with the binomial distribution, a table is available that makes it easier to compute Poisson probabilities of individual values of x as well as cumulative and related probabilities.

Table 2 in Appendix B provides cumulative Poisson probabilities for selected values of μ. This table makes it easy to find cumulative probabilities like those in Example 7.13, part (b), where we found $P(X \le 5)$.

To do so, find $\mu = 6$ in Table 2. The values in that column are $P(X \le x)$ for $x = 0, 1, 2, \ldots, 18$, which are shown in Table 7.3.

TABLE **7.3** Cumulative Poisson Probabilities for $\mu = 6$

x	$P(X \le x)$
0	.0025
1	.0174
2	.0620
3	.1512
4	.2851
5	.4457
6	.6063
7	.7440
8	.8472
9	.9161
10	.9574
11	.9799
12	.9912
13	.9964
14	.9986
15	.9995
16	.9998
17	.9999
18	1.0000

Theoretically, a Poisson random variable has no upper limit. The table provides cumulative probabilities until the sum is 1.0000 (using four decimal places).

The first cumulative probability is $P(X \le 0)$, which is $P(0) = .0025$. The probability we need for Example 7.13, part (b), is $P(X \le 5) = .4457$, which is the same value we obtained manually.

Like Table 1 for binomial probabilities, Table 2 can be used to determine probabilities of the type $P(X \ge x)$. For example, to find the probability that in Example 7.13 there are 6 or more typos, we note that $P(X \le 5) + P(X \ge 6) = 1$. Thus,

$$P(X \ge 6) = 1 - P(X \le 5) = 1 - .4457 = .5543$$

Using Table 2 to Find the Poisson Probability $P(X \ge x)$

$$P(X \ge x) = 1 - P(X \le [x - 1])$$

We can also use the table to determine the probability of one individual value of X. For example, to find the probability that the book contains exactly 10 typos, we note that

$$P(X \le 10) = P(0) + P(1) + \cdots + P(9) + P(10)$$

and

$$P(X \le 9) = P(0) + P(1) + \cdots + P(9)$$

The difference between these two cumulative probabilities is $P(10)$. Thus,

$$P(10) = P(X \le 10) - P(X \le 9) = .9574 - .9161 = .0413$$

> ### Using Table 2 to Find the Poisson Probability $P(X = x)$
>
> $$P(x) = P(X \le x) - P(X \le [x - 1])$$

EXCEL Function

INSTRUCTIONS

Type the following into any empty cell:

$$= \textbf{POISSON}([x], [\mu], [\text{True}] \text{ or } [\text{False}])$$

We calculate the probability in Example 7.12 by typing

$$= \textbf{POISSON}(0, 1.5, \text{False})$$

For Example 7.13, we type

$$= \textbf{POISSON}(5, 6, \text{True})$$

EXERCISES

7.142 Given a Poisson random variable with $\mu = 2$, use the formula to find the following probabilities.
a. $P(X = 0)$
b. $P(X = 3)$
c. $P(X = 5)$

7.143 Given that X is a Poisson random variable with $\mu = .5$, use the formula to determine the following probabilities.
a. $P(X = 0)$
b. $P(X = 1)$
c. $P(X = 2)$

7.144 The number of accidents that occur at a busy intersection is Poisson distributed with a mean of 3.5 per week. Find the probability of the following events.
a. No accidents in 1 week
b. Five or more accidents in 1 week
c. One accident today

7.145 Snowfalls occur randomly and independently over the course of winter in a Minnesota city. The average is one snowfall every 3 days.
a. What is the probability of five snowfalls in 2 weeks?
b. Find the probability of a snowfall today.

7.146 The number of students who seek assistance with their statistics assignments is Poisson distributed with a mean of two per day.
a. What is the probability that no students seek assistance tomorrow?
b. Find the probability that 10 students seek assistance in a week.

7.147 Hits on a personal website occur quite infrequently. They occur randomly and independently with an average of five per week.
a. Find the probability that the site gets 10 or more hits in a week.
b. Determine the probability that the site gets 20 or more hits in 2 weeks.

7.148 In older cities across North America, infrastructure is deteriorating, including water lines that supply homes and businesses. A report to the Toronto city council stated that there are on average 30 water line breaks per 100 kilometers per year in the city of Toronto. Outside of Toronto, the average number of breaks is 15 per 100 kilometers per year.

a. Find the probability that in a stretch of 100 kilometers in Toronto there are 35 or more breaks next year.

b. Find the probability that there are 12 or fewer breaks in a stretch of 100 kilometers outside of Toronto next year.

7.149 The number of bank robberies that occur in a large North American city is Poisson distributed with a mean of 1.8 per day. Find the probabilities of the following events.
  a. Three or more bank robberies in a day.
  b. Between 10 and 15 (inclusive) robberies during a 5-day period.

7.150 Flaws in a carpet tend to occur randomly and independently at a rate of one every 200 square feet. What is the probability that a carpet that is 8 feet by 10 feet contains no flaws?

7.151 At an auction of antique furniture a statistician kept track of the number of bids for each item and concludes that the number of bids is Poisson distributed with a mean of 2.5.
  a. Calculate the probability that on any item the number of bids is 5 or more.
  b. Compute the probability that there are no bids.
  c. What is the probability that there are 3 bids or less?

7.152 The random variable in Exercise 7.30 was the number of stores entered by customers at a mall. Suppose that the random variable is Poisson distributed with a mean of 4.
  a. What proportion of mall customers enter 5 stores or more?
  b. Compute the probability that a customer enters 3 or fewer stores.
  c. Calculate the probability that a customer enters exactly 4 stores.

7.153 At a public library one of the librarians surveys individuals reading online newspapers and concludes that the number of newspapers read online is Poisson distributed with a mean of 5.
  a. What proportion of library patrons read 3 or fewer newspapers online?
  b. What proportion of library patrons read 6 or more newspapers online?
  c. What proportion of library patrons read 8 or fewer newspapers online?

7.154 The random variable in Exercise 7.44 was the number of holes in one by the members of a private golf course. In fact, the number of holes in one is Poisson distributed with a mean of 1.
  a. What proportion of members never have had a hole in one?
  b. What proportion have 5 or more holes in one?

7.155 After conducting a survey of golfers a statistician concludes that the number of lost balls in a round is Poisson distributed with a mean of 2. Find the probability of the following events.
  a. A golfer loses no golf balls
  b. A golfer loses 4 or more golf balls
  c. A golfer loses 2 or fewer golf balls

7.156 According to J.D. Power and Associates, the mean defect rate in a new Jaguar convertible is 2.4. What is the probability that a randomly selected new Jaguar convertible has 3 or more defects?

7.157 The mean number of accidents that occur daily on a stretch of highway is 12. Find the probability that there will be 12 accidents on this stretch of highway tomorrow.

APPLICATIONS in **OPERATIONS MANAGEMENT**

Galina Barskaya /Shutterstock.com

Waiting Lines

Everyone is familiar with waiting lines. We wait in line at banks, groceries, and fast-food restaurants. There are also waiting lines in firms where trucks wait to load and unload and on assembly lines where stations wait for new parts. Management scientists have developed mathematical models that allow managers to determine the operating characteristics of waiting lines. Some of the operating characteristics are:

The probability that there are no units in the system

The average number of units in the waiting line

The average time a unit spends in the waiting line

The probability that an arriving unit must wait for service

(Continued)

The Poisson probability distribution is used extensively in waiting-line (also called *queuing*) models. Many models assume that the arrival of units for service is Poisson distributed with a specific value of μ. Exercises 7.158 to 7.160 require the calculation of the probability of a number of arrivals.

7.158 The number of trucks crossing at the Ambassador Bridge connecting Detroit, Michigan, and Windsor, Ontario, is Poisson distributed with a mean of 1.5 per minute.
a. What is the probability that in any 1-minute time span two or more trucks will cross the bridge?
b. What is the probability that fewer than four trucks will cross the bridge over the next 4 minutes?

7.159 Cars arriving for gasoline at a particular gas station follow a Poisson distribution with a mean of 5 per hour.
a. Determine the probability that over the next hour only one car will arrive.
b. Compute the probability that in the next 3 hours more than 20 cars will arrive.

7.160 The number of users of an automatic banking machine is Poisson distributed. The mean number of users per 5-minute interval is 1.5. Find the probability of the following events.
a. No users in the next 5 minutes
b. Five or fewer users in the next 15 minutes
c. Three or more users in the next 10 minutes

CHAPTER SUMMARY

There are two types of random variables. A **discrete random variable** is one whose values are countable. A **continuous random variable** can assume an uncountable number of values. In this chapter, we discussed discrete random variables and their **probability distributions**. We defined the **expected value**, **variance**, and **standard deviation** of a population represented by a discrete probability distribution. Also introduced in this chapter were **bivariate discrete distributions** on which an important application in finance was based. Finally, the two most important discrete distributions—the **binomial** and the **Poisson**—were presented.

IMPORTANT TERMS:

Random variable   216
Discrete random variable   217
Continuous random variable   217
Probability distribution   217
Expected value   221
Bivariate distribution   227
PERT (Project Evaluation and Review Technique)   234
CPM (Critical Path Method)   234
Path   234
Critical path   234

Diversification   236
Binomial experiment   244
Bernoulli process   244
Binomial random variable   244
Binomial probability distribution   245
Cumulative probability   247
Poisson distribution   252
Poisson random variable   252
Poisson experiment   252

SYMBOLS:

Symbol	Pronounced	Represents
$\sum_{\text{all } x} x$	Sum of x for all values of x	Summation
C_x^n	n choose x	Number of combinations
$n!$	n factorial	$n(n-1)(n-2) \cdots (3)(2)(1)$
e		$2.71828\ldots$

FORMULAS:

Expected value (mean)

$$E(X) = \mu = \sum_{\text{all } x} xP(x)$$

Variance

$$V(x) = \sigma^2 = \sum_{\text{all } x} (x - \mu)^2 P(x)$$

Standard deviation

$$\sigma = \sqrt{\sigma^2}$$

Covariance

$$\text{COV}(X, Y) = \sigma_{xy} = \sum (x - \mu_x)(y - \mu_y)P(x, y)$$

Coefficient of Correlation

$$\rho = \frac{\text{COV}(X, Y)}{\sigma_x \sigma_y} = \frac{\sigma_{xy}}{\sigma_x \sigma_y}$$

Laws of expected value

1. $E(c) = c$
2. $E(X + c) = E(X) + c$
3. $E(cX) = cE(X)$

Laws of variance

1. $V(c) = 0$
2. $V(X + c) = V(X)$
3. $V(cX) = c^2 V(X)$

Laws of expected value and variance of the sum of two variables

1. $E(X + Y) = E(X) + E(Y)$
2. $V(X + Y) = V(X) + V(Y) + 2\text{COV}(X, Y)$

Laws of expected value and variance for the sum of k variables, where $k \geq 2$

1. $E(X_1 + X_2 + \cdots + X_k)$
   $$= E(X_1) + E(X_2) + \cdots + E(X_k)$$

2. $V(X_1 + X_2 + \cdots + X_k)$
   $$= V(X_1) + V(X_2) + \cdots + V(X_k)$$

   if the variables are independent

Mean and variance of a portfolio of two stocks

$$E(R_p) = w_1 E(R_1) + w_2 E(R_2)$$
$$V(R_p) = w_1^2 V(R_1) + w_2^2 V(R_2)$$
$$+ 2w_1 w_2 \text{COV}(R_1, R_2)$$
$$= w_1^2 \sigma_1^2 + w_2^2 \sigma_2^2 + 2w_1 w_2 \rho \sigma_1 \sigma_2$$

Mean and variance of a portfolio of k stocks

$$E(R_p) = \sum_{i=1}^{k} w_i E(R_i)$$

$$V(R_p) = \sum_{i=1}^{k} w_i^2 \sigma_i^2 + 2 \sum_{i=1}^{k} \sum_{j=i+1}^{k} w_i w_j \text{COV}(R_i, R_j)$$

Binomial probability

$$P(X = x) = \frac{n!}{x!(n - x)!} p^x (1 - p)^{n-x}$$

$$\mu = np$$
$$\sigma^2 = np(1 - p)$$
$$\sigma = \sqrt{np(1 - p)}$$

Poisson probability

$$P(X = x) = \frac{e^{-\mu} \mu^x}{x!}$$

EXCEL INSTRUCTIONS:

Probability Distribution

Binomial	230
Poisson	236

CHAPTER EXERCISES

7.161 In a Gallup poll 20% of adults said that they had a great deal or quite a lot of confidence in newspapers. If we take a random sample of 25 adults and ask each whether they had a great deal or quite a lot of confidence in newspapers, determine probability of each of these events.
  a. 5 or fewer have confidence
  b. 7 or more have confidence
  c. Exactly 5 have confidence

7.162 A recent Pew Center Research survey revealed that 15% of American adults have used an online dating service. Suppose a statistician randomly selected 20 American adults.
  a. What is the probability that exactly 3 used an online dating service?
  b. What is the probability that 5 or fewer used an online dating service?
  c. What is the probability that 3 or more used an online dating service?

7.163 An airline boasts that 77.4% of its flights were on time. If we select five flights at random, what is the probability that all five are on time?

7.164 The final exam in a one-term statistics course is taken in the December exam period. Students who are sick or have other legitimate reasons for missing the exam are allowed to write a deferred exam scheduled for the first week in January. A statistics professor has observed that only 2% of all students legitimately miss the December final exam. Suppose that the professor has 40 students registered this term.
  a. How many students can the professor expect to miss the December exam?
  b. What is the probability that the professor will not have to create a deferred exam?

7.165 The number of magazine subscriptions per household is represented by the following probability distribution.

Magazine subscriptions per household	0	1	2	3	4
Probability	.48	.35	.08	.05	.04

  a. Calculate the mean number of magazine subscriptions per household.
  b. Find the standard deviation.

7.166 The number of arrivals at a car wash is Poisson distributed with a mean of eight per hour.
  a. What is the probability that 10 cars will arrive in the next hour?
  b. What is the probability that more than 5 cars will arrive in the next hour?
  c. What is the probability that fewer than 12 cars will arrive in the next hour?

7.167 Hikers and other outdoor enthusiasts have a new concern, the Zika virus. Physicians are recommending that people use a mosquito repellant while in areas where mosquitoes are present. A statistician estimated that 80% of hikers would be spraying themselves with mosquito repellant. Suppose that a sample of 10 hikers is asked whether they are using repellant. Find the following probabilities.
  a. 9 or more are using repellant
  b. Exactly 8 are using repellant
  c. 7 or fewer are using repellant

7.168 Lotteries are an important income source for various governments around the world. However, the availability of lotteries and other forms of gambling has created a social problem: gambling addicts. A critic of government-controlled gambling contends that 30% of people who buy tickets are gambling addicts. If we randomly select 10 people among those who report that they regularly buy lottery tickets, what is the probability that more than 5 of them are addicts?

7.169 The distribution of the number of home runs in soft-ball games is shown here.

Number of home runs	0	1	2	3	4	5
Probability	.05	.16	.41	.27	.07	.04

  a. Calculate the mean number of home runs.
  b. Find the standard deviation.

7.170 The Powerball lottery is one of the most popular lotteries in the United States. From time to time, the jackpot exceeds $100 million. As a result so many more people buy Powerball tickets that there are frequent lineups at convenience stores. A statistician interviews hundreds of people in queues and asks how many tickets each person intends to buy. He concludes that the number of tickets is a Poisson random variable with a mean of 5.
  a. What proportion of people will buy only 1 ticket?
  b. What proportion of people will buy 5 or fewer tickets?
  c. What proportion of people will buy 8 or more tickets?

7.171 Ten percent of American adults devote so much time to playing video games either on a console, computer, or cell phone that they consider themselves to be "gamers" according to a Pew Research Center report. Suppose that a random sample of 25 American adults is drawn and each is asked whether they consider themselves to be gamers. Determine the probability of the following events.

a. 3 or more consider themselves to be gamers

b. Exactly 2 consider themselves to be gamers

c. 3 or fewer consider themselves to be gamers

7.172 University and college students are relatively confident about finding a job after graduation.

According to a Gallup survey, 50% of students say now is a good time to find a quality job. Suppose you randomly select 10 students and ask about their future job prospects.

a. What is the probability that 6 of them believe that now is a good time to find a quality job?

b. Calculate the probability that at least 8 believe that now is a good time to find a quality job?

c. Calculate the probability that 4 or fewer believe that now is a good time to find a quality job?

7.173 Many cell phone service providers offer family plans wherein parents who subscribe can get discounts for other family members. Suppose that the number of cell phones per family is Poisson distributed with a mean of 1.5. If one family is randomly selected, calculate the following probabilities.

a. Family has only 1 cell phone.

b. Family has 3 or more cell phones.

c. Family has 4 or fewer cell phones.

7.174 An auditor is preparing for a physical count of inventory as a means of verifying its value. Items counted are reconciled with a list prepared by the storeroom supervisor. In one particular firm, 20% of the items counted cannot be reconciled without reviewing invoices. The auditor selects 10 items. Find the probability that 6 or more cannot be reconciled.

7.175 Shutouts in the National Hockey League occur randomly and independently at a rate of 1 every 20 games. Calculate the probability of the following events.

a. 2 shutouts in the next 10 games

b. 25 shutouts in 400 games

c. A shutout in tonight's game

7.176 Most Miami Beach restaurants offer "early-bird" specials. These are lower-priced meals that are available only from 4 to 6 P.M. However, not all

customers who arrive between 4 and 6 P.M. order the special. In fact, only 70% do.

a. Find the probability that of 80 customers between 4 and 6 P.M., more than 65 order the special.

b. What is the expected number of customers who order the special?

c. What is the standard deviation?

7.177 According to climatologists, the long-term average for Atlantic storms is 9.6 per season (June 1 to November 30), with 6 becoming hurricanes and 2.3 becoming intense hurricanes. Find the probability of the following events.

a. Ten or more Atlantic storms

b. Five or fewer hurricanes

c. Three or more intense hurricanes

7.178 Researchers at the University of Pennsylvania School of Medicine theorized that children under 2 years old who sleep in rooms with the light on have a 40% probability of becoming myopic by age 16. Suppose that researchers found 25 children who slept with the light on before they were 2.

a. What is the probability that 10 of them will become myopic before age 16?

b. What is the probability that fewer than 5 of them will become myopic before age 16?

c. What is the probability that more than 15 of them will become myopic before age 16?

7.179 A pharmaceutical researcher working on a cure for baldness noticed that middle-aged men who are balding at the crown of their head have a 45% probability of suffering a heart attack over the next decade. In a sample of 100 middle-age balding men, what are the following probabilities?

a. More than 50 will suffer a heart attack in the next decade.

b. Fewer than 44 will suffer a heart attack in the next decade.

c. Exactly 45 will suffer a heart attack in the next decade.

7.180 Advertising researchers have developed a theory that states that commercials that appear in violent television shows are less likely to be remembered and will thus be less effective. After examining samples of viewers who watch violent and nonviolent programs and asking them a series of five questions about the commercials, the researchers produced the following probability distributions of the number of correct answers.

Viewers of violent shows

x	0	1	2	3	4	5
P(x)	.36	.22	.20	.09	.08	.05

Viewers of nonviolent shows

x	0	1	2	3	4	5
P(x)	.15	.18	.23	.26	.10	.08

a. Calculate the mean and standard deviation of the number of correct answers among viewers of violent television programs.

b. Calculate the mean and standard deviation of the number of correct answers among viewers of nonviolent television programs.

7.181 In 1941 Joe DiMaggio hit in 56 consecutive games, a record that is predicted to never be broken. To see how unlikely this streak was, assume that a player batting .350 gets to bat 5 times in a game (with no walks and hit by pitch).

a. What is the probability that the player will get at least one hit in a game?

b. Use the probability calculated in part (a) to determine the probability that a player can hit in 56 consecutive games.

7.182 In Basketball players are awarded free throw when they are fouled. Suppose that a player has a career percentage of making free throws 80% of the time. If the player is awarded 10 free throws, determine the probability of the following events.

a. He makes all 10.

b. He makes 8 or more.

c. He makes 8 or fewer.

7.183 An investor hears a radio report that says 60% of the stocks on the New York Stock Exchange increased in value. The investor owns 20 stocks on the NYSE. Determine the probability of the following events.

a. 15 or more stocks increased in value.

b. 12 or fewer stocks increased in value.

c. 12 stocks increased in value.

7.184 When Earth traveled through the storm of meteorites trailing the comet Tempel-Tuttle on November 17, 1998, the storm was 1,000 times as intense as the average meteor storm. Before the comet arrived, telecommunication companies worried about the potential damage that might be inflicted on the approximately 650 satellites in orbit. It was estimated that each satellite had a 1% chance of being hit, causing damage to the satellite's electronic system. One company had five satellites in orbit at the time. Determine the probability distribution of the number of the company's satellites that would be damaged.

7.185 According to a Gallup poll conducted in 2015, only 1% of Russians approved of U.S. leadership. To evaluate whether this claim has any merit a statistician took a random sample of 100 Russians. Determine the probability of these events.

a. Noone approved of U.S. leadership.

b. One Russian approved of U.S. leadership.

c. Two Russians approved of U.S. leadership.

7.186 It is recommended that women age 40 and older have a mammogram annually. A recent report indicated that if a woman has annual mammograms over a 10-year period, there is a 60% probability that there will be at least one false-positive result. (A false-positive mammogram test result is one that indicates the presence of cancer when, in fact, there is no cancer.) If the annual test results are independent, what is the probability that in any one year a mammogram will produce a false-positive result? (*Hint:* Find the value of p such that the probability that a binomial random variable with $n = 10$ is greater than or equal to 1 is .60.)

7.187 A teacher's union president claims that more than 90% of parents are satisfied with their children's school. A group of unsatisfied parents hires a polling company to test the claim. If the sample size is 400 and 90% of parents are satisfied, what is the probability that 85% or less of the sample are satisfied?

7.188 It is estimated that one in five Americans owns a smartphone. If this figure is correct, what is the probability that in a random sample of 100 between 15 and 25 inclusive people own a smartphone?

7.189 A statistics professor has observed that the number of errors in a softball game averages 3 per game.

a. What is the probability that there will be no errors in the next game?

b. Find the probability that the next game will have 6 or more errors.

7.190 The Internal Revenue Service (IRS) is attempting to change their image. After an advertising campaign showing how friendly and cooperative IRS auditors are, the commissioner of the IRS claims that half of the population has a favorable opinion of the IRS. A taxpayer who does not believe the claim is in the process of conducting a survey wherein a sample of 200 people will be asked if they have a favorable opinion of the IRS. What is the probability that less than 45% of the sample has a favorable opinion?

7.191 In Major League Baseball, team managers can appeal an umpire's call on the field. If umpire calls are overturned 55% of the time, what is the probability that in the next 10 calls umpires' decisions will be overturned 7 or more times?

7.192 A statistician working for Major League Baseball counted the number of foul balls hit into the stands and calculated that the number averages 7.2 per inning. What is the probability that in one inning there will be fewer than 6 foul balls hit into the stands?

7.193 A survey asked Americans whether they think that taxes on large corporations should be increased, decreased, or stay the same. If 24% believe that taxes should be decreased, what is the probability that in a sample of 200, less than 20% think that taxes should be decreased?

7.194 The average number of goals in a National Hockey League (NHL) game is 5.35. Determine the probability that there are 3 goals in a game.

CASE 7.1 To Bunt or Not to Bunt, That Is the Question—Part 2

Debby Wong/Shutterstock.com

In Case 6.2, we presented the probabilities of scoring at least one run and asked you to determine whether the manager should signal for the batter to sacrifice bunt. The decision was made on the basis of comparing the probability of scoring at least one run when the manager signaled for the bunt and when he signaled the batter to swing away. Another factor that should be incorporated into the decision is the *number* of runs the manager expects his team to score. In the same article referred to in Case 6.2, the author also computed the expected number of runs scored for each situation. Table 1 lists the expected number of runs in situations that are defined by the number of outs and the bases occupied.

TABLE 1 Expected Number of Runs Scored

Bases Occupied	0 Out	1 Out	2 Outs
Bases empty	.49	.27	.10
First base	.85	.52	.23
Second base	1.06	.69	.34
Third base	1.21	.82	.38
First base and second base	1.46	1.00	.48
First base and third base	1.65	1.10	.51
Second base and third base	1.94	1.50	.62
Bases loaded	2.31	1.62	.82

Assume that the manager wishes to score as many runs as possible. Using the same probabilities of the four outcomes of a bunt listed in Case 6.2, determine whether the manager should signal the batter to sacrifice bunt.

Wavebreakmedia/Shutterstock.com

8

CONTINUOUS PROBABILITY DISTRIBUTIONS

CHAPTER OUTLINE

Minimum GMAT Score to Enter Executive MBA Program

A university has just approved a new Executive MBA Program. The new director believes that to maintain the prestigious image of the business school, the new program must be seen as having high standards. Accordingly, the Faculty Council decides that one of the entrance requirements will be that applicants must score in the top 1% of Graduate Management Admission Test (GMAT) scores. The director knows that GMAT scores are normally distributed with a mean of 490 and a standard deviation of 61. The only thing the director doesn't know is what the minimum GMAT score for admission should be.

After introducing the normal distribution, we will return to this question and answer it.

wavebreakmedia/Shutterstock.com

See page 281.

INTRODUCTION

This chapter completes our presentation of probability by introducing continuous random variables and their distributions. In Chapter 7, we introduced discrete probability distributions that are employed to calculate the probability associated with discrete random variables. In Section 7-4, we introduced the binomial distribution, which allows us to determine the probability that the random variable equals a particular value (the number of successes). In this way we connected the population represented by the probability distribution with a sample of nominal data. In this chapter, we introduce continuous probability distributions, which are used to calculate the probability associated with an interval variable. By doing so, we develop the link between a population and a sample of interval data.

Section 8-1 introduces probability density functions and uses the uniform density function to demonstrate how probability is calculated. In Section 8-2, we focus on the normal distribution, one of the most important distributions because of its role in the development of statistical inference. Section 8-3 introduces the exponential distribution, a distribution that has proven to be useful in various management-science applications. Finally, in Section 8-4 we introduce three additional continuous distributions. They will be used in statistical inference throughout the book.

8-1 / PROBABILITY DENSITY FUNCTIONS

A continuous random variable is one that can assume an uncountable number of values. Because this type of random variable is so different from a discrete variable, we need to treat it completely differently. First, we cannot list the possible values because there is an infinite number of them. Second, because there is an infinite number of values, the probability of each individual value is virtually 0. Consequently, we can determine the probability of only a range of values. To illustrate how this is done, consider the histogram we created for the ages of ACBL members (Example 3.1), which is depicted in Figure 8.1.

FIGURE **8.1** Histogram for Example 3.1

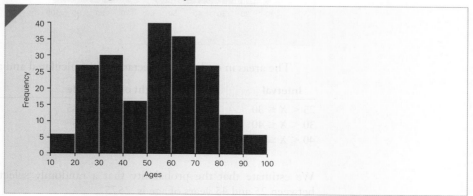

We found, for example, that the relative frequency of the interval 10–20 was 6/200. Using the relative frequency approach, we estimate that the probability that a randomly selected ACBL member will be between 10 and 20 years of age is 6/200 = .030. We can similarly estimate the probabilities of the other intervals in the histogram.

Interval	Relative Frequency
$10 \leq X \leq 20$	6/200
$20 < X \leq 30$	27/200
$30 < X \leq 40$	30/200
$40 < X \leq 50$	16/200
$50 < X \leq 60$	40/200
$60 < X \leq 70$	36/200
$70 < X \leq 80$	27/200
$80 < X \leq 90$	12/200
$90 < X \leq 100$	6/200
Total	200/200 = 1

Notice that the sum of the probabilities equals 1. To proceed, we set the values along the vertical axis so that the *area* in all the rectangles together adds to 1. We accomplish this by dividing each relative frequency by the width of the interval, which is 10. The result is a rectangle over each interval whose *area* equals the probability that the random variable will fall into that interval.

To determine probabilities of ranges other than the ones created when we drew the histogram, we apply the same approach. For example, the probability that an ACBL member is between 25 and 45 years of age is equal to the area between 25 and 45 as shown in Figure 8.2.

FIGURE **8.2** **Estimated Probability That an ACBL Member Will Be between 25 and 45**

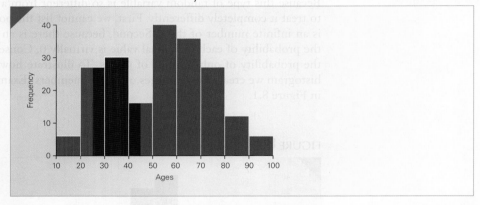

The areas in each shaded rectangle are calculated and added together as follows:

Interval	Height of Rectangle	Base Multiplied by Height
$25 < X \leq 30$	27/(200 × 10) = .0135	(30 − 25) × .0135 = .0675
$30 < X \leq 40$	30/(200 × 10) = .015	(40 − 30) × .015 = .150
$40 < X \leq 45$	16/(200 × 10) = .008	(45 − 40) × .008 = .040
		Total = .2575

We estimate that the probability that a randomly selected ACBL member will be between 25 and 45 years of age is .2575.

If the histogram is drawn with a large number of small intervals, we can smooth the edges of the rectangles to produce a smooth curve as shown in Figure 8.3. In many cases, it is possible to determine a function $f(x)$ that approximates the curve. The function is called a **probability density function**. Its requirements are stated in the following box.

FIGURE **8.3** Density Function for Example 3.1

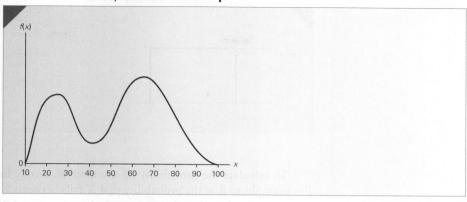

Requirements for a Probability Density Function

The following requirements apply to a probability density function $f(x)$ whose range is $a \leq x \leq b$.

1. $f(x) \geq 0$ for all x between a and b.
2. The total area under the curve between a and b is 1.0.

Integral calculus* can often be used to calculate the area under a curve. Fortunately, the probabilities corresponding to continuous probability distributions that we deal with do not require this mathematical tool. The distributions will be either simple or too complex for calculus. Let's start with the simplest continuous distribution.

8-1a Uniform Distribution

To illustrate how we find the area under the curve that describes a probability density function, consider the **uniform probability distribution**, also called the **rectangular probability distribution**.

Uniform Probability Density Function

The uniform distribution is described by the function

$$f(x) = \frac{1}{b - a} \quad \text{where } a \leq x \leq b$$

The function is graphed in Figure 8.4. You can see why the distribution is called *rectangular*.

---

*The online appendix Continuous Probability Distributions: Calculus Approach demonstrates how to use integral calculus to determine probabilities and parameters for continuous random variables.

FIGURE **8.4**   Uniform Distribution

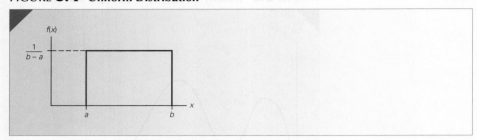

To calculate the probability of any interval, simply find the area under the curve. For example, to find the probability that X falls between x_1 and x_2 determine the area in the rectangle whose base is $x_2 - x_1$ and whose height is $1/(b - a)$. Figure 8.5 depicts the area we wish to find. As you can see, it is a rectangle and the area of a rectangle is found by multiplying the base times the height.

FIGURE **8.5** $P(x_1 < X < x_2)$

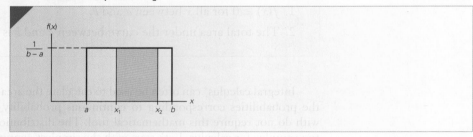

Thus,

$$P(x_1 < X < x_2) = \text{Base} \times \text{Height} = (x_2 - x_1) \times \frac{1}{b - a}$$

EXAMPLE **8.1**

Uniformly Distributed Gasoline Sales

The amount of gasoline sold daily at a service station is uniformly distributed with a minimum of 2,000 gallons and a maximum of 5,000 gallons.

   a. Find the probability that daily sales will fall between 2,500 and 3,000 gallons.
   b. What is the probability that the service station will sell at least 4,000 gallons?
   c. What is the probability that the station will sell exactly 2,500 gallons?

SOLUTION:

The probability density function is

$$f(x) = \frac{1}{5{,}000 - 2{,}000} = \frac{1}{3{,}000} \quad 2{,}000 \leq x \leq 5{,}000$$

a. The probability that X falls between 2,500 and 3,000 is the area under the curve between 2,500 and 3,000 as depicted in Figure 8.6a. The area of a rectangle is the base times the height. Thus,

$$P(2,500 \leq X \leq 3,000) = (3,000 - 2,500) \times \left(\frac{1}{3,000}\right) = .1667$$

b. $P(X \geq 4,000) = (5,000 - 4,000) \times \left(\dfrac{1}{3,000}\right) = .3333$ [See Figure 8.6b.]

c. $P(X = 2,500) = 0$

Because there is an uncountable infinite number of values of X, the probability of each individual value is zero. Moreover, as you can see from Figure 8.6c, the area of a line is 0.

Because the probability that a continuous random variable equals any individual value is 0, there is no difference between $P(2,500 \leq X \leq 3,000)$ and $P(2,500 < X < 3,000)$. Of course, we cannot say the same thing about discrete random variables.

FIGURE **8.6** **Density Functions for Example 8.1**

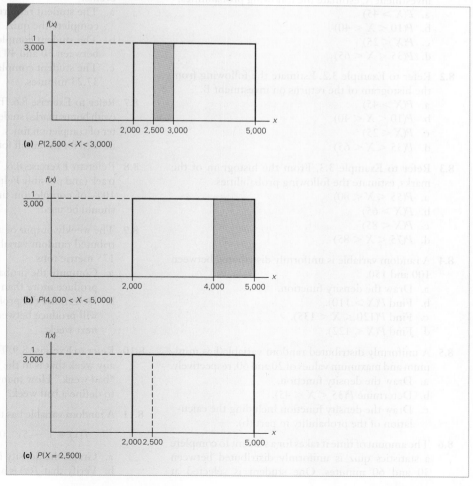

(a) $P(2,500 < X < 3,000)$

(b) $P(4,000 < X < 5,000)$

(c) $P(X = 2,500)$

8-1b Using a Continuous Distribution to Approximate a Discrete Distribution

In our definition of discrete and continuous random variables, we distinguish between them by noting whether the number of possible values is countable or uncountable. However, in practice, we frequently use a continuous distribution to approximate a discrete one when the number of values the variable can assume is countable but large. For example, the number of possible values of weekly income is countable. The values of weekly income expressed in dollars are 0, .01, .02, …. Although there is no set upper limit, we can easily identify (and thus count) all the possible values. Consequently, weekly income is a discrete random variable. However, because it can assume such a large number of values, we prefer to employ a continuous probability distribution to determine the probability associated with such variables. In the next section, we introduce the normal distribution, which is often used to describe discrete random variables that can assume a large number of values.

EXERCISES

8.1 Refer to Example 3.2. From the histogram for investment A, estimate the following probabilities.
   a. $P(X > 45)$
   b. $P(10 < X < 40)$
   c. $P(X < 25)$
   d. $P(35 < X < 65)$

8.2 Refer to Example 3.2. Estimate the following from the histogram of the returns on investment B.
   a. $P(X > 45)$
   b. $P(10 < X < 40)$
   c. $P(X < 25)$
   d. $P(35 < X < 65)$

8.3 Refer to Example 3.3. From the histogram of the marks, estimate the following probabilities.
   a. $P(55 < X < 80)$
   b. $P(X > 65)$
   c. $P(X < 85)$
   d. $P(75 < X < 85)$

8.4 A random variable is uniformly distributed between 100 and 150.
   a. Draw the density function.
   b. Find $P(X > 110)$.
   c. Find $P(120 < X < 135)$.
   d. Find $P(X < 122)$.

8.5 A uniformly distributed random variable has minimum and maximum values of 20 and 60, respectively.
   a. Draw the density function.
   b. Determine $P(35 < X < 45)$.
   c. Draw the density function including the calculation of the probability in part (b).

8.6 The amount of time it takes for a student to complete a statistics quiz is uniformly distributed between 30 and 60 minutes. One student is selected at random. Find the probability of the following events.
   a. The student requires more than 55 minutes to complete the quiz.
   b. The student completes the quiz in a time between 30 and 40 minutes.
   c. The student completes the quiz in exactly 37.23 minutes.

8.7 Refer to Exercise 8.6. The professor wants to reward (with bonus marks) students who are in the lowest quarter of completion times. What completion time should be used for the cutoff for awarding bonus marks?

8.8 Refer to Exercise 8.6. The professor would like to track (and possibly help) students who are in the top 10% of completion times. What completion time should be used?

8.9 The weekly output of a steel mill is a uniformly distributed random variable that lies between 110 and 175 metric tons.
   a. Compute the probability that the steel mill will produce more than 150 metric tons next week.
   b. Determine the probability that the steel mill will produce between 120 and 160 metric tons next week.

8.10 Refer to Exercise 8.9. The operations manager labels any week that is in the bottom 20% of production a "bad week." How many metric tons should be used to define a bad week?

8.11 A random variable has the following density function.

$$f(x) = 1 - .5x \quad 0 < x < 2$$

   a. Graph the density function.
   b. Verify that $f(x)$ is a density function.

c. Find $P(X > 1)$.
d. Find $P(X < .5)$.
e. Find $P(X = 1.5)$.

8.12 The following function is the density function for the random variable X:

$$f(x) = \frac{x - 1}{8} \quad 1 < x < 5$$

a. Graph the density function.
b. Find the probability that X lies between 2 and 4.
c. What is the probability that X is less than 3?

8.13 The following density function describes the random variable X.

$$f(x) = \begin{cases} \dfrac{x}{25} & 0 < x < 5 \\ \dfrac{10 - x}{25} & 5 < x < 10 \end{cases}$$

a. Graph the density function.
b. Find the probability that X lies between 1 and 3.
c. What is the probability that X lies between 4 and 8?
d. Compute the probability that X is less than 7.
e. Find the probability that X is greater than 3.

8.14 The following is a graph of a density function.

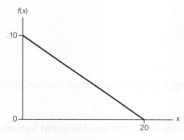

a. Determine the density function.
b. Find the probability that X is greater than 10.
c. Find the probability that X lies between 6 and 12.

8.15 Here is another density function.

$$f(x) = .40 \quad 0 < x < 1$$
$$ = .05 \quad 1 < x < 13$$

a. Graph the density function.
b. Determine the probability that X is less than 8.
c. What is the probability that X lies between .4 and 10?

8.16 The following density function describes the random variable X.

$$f(x) = .10 \quad 0 < x < 2$$
$$ = .20 \quad 2 < x < 5$$
$$ = .15 \quad 5 < x < 6$$
$$ = .05 \quad 6 < x < 7$$

a. Graph the density function.
b. Calculate the probability that X is less than 5.5.
c. Calculate the probability that X is greater than 3.5.
d. What is the probability that X lies between 1 and 6.5?

8.17 Here is another function.

$$f(x) = .2x \quad 0 < x < 2$$
$$ = .4 \quad 2 < x < 3.5$$

a. Confirm that it is a density function.
b. Graph the function.
c. Determine the probability that X is less than 2.
d. Find the probability that X is less than 3.
e. What is the probability that X lies between 1 and 2.5?

8.18 The following density function describes the random variable X.

$$f(x) = .40 - .10x \quad 0 < x < 4$$
$$ = .10x - .40 \quad 4 < x < 6$$

a. Graph the density function.
b. What is the probability that X is less than 2?
c. Find the probability that X is greater than 5.
d. Find the probability that X lies between 2.5 and 5.5.

8-2 / NORMAL DISTRIBUTION

The **normal distribution** is the most important of all probability distributions because of its crucial role in statistical inference.

> **Normal Density Function**
>
> The probability density function of a **normal random variable** is
>
> $$f(x) = \frac{1}{\sigma\sqrt{2\pi}} e^{-\frac{1}{2}\left(\frac{x - \mu}{\sigma}\right)^2} \quad -\infty < x < \infty$$
>
> where $e = 2.71828\ldots$ and $\pi = 3.14159\ldots$

Figure 8.7 depicts a normal distribution. Notice that the curve is symmetric about its mean and the random variable ranges between $-\infty$ and $+\infty$.

FIGURE **8.7** Normal Distribution

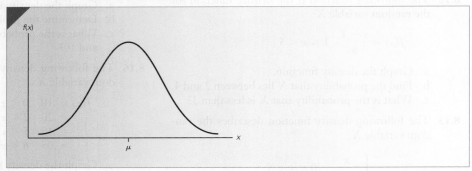

The normal distribution is described by two parameters, the mean μ and the standard deviation σ. In Figure 8.8, we demonstrate the effect of changing the value of μ. Obviously, increasing μ shifts the curve to the right and decreasing μ shifts it to the left.

FIGURE **8.8** Normal Distributions with the Same Variance but Different Means

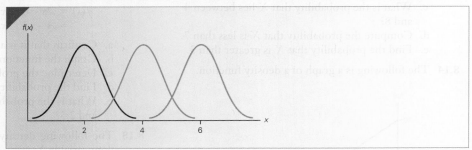

Figure 8.9 describes the effect of σ. Larger values of σ widen the curve and smaller ones narrow it.

FIGURE **8.9** Normal Distributions with the Same Means but Different Variances

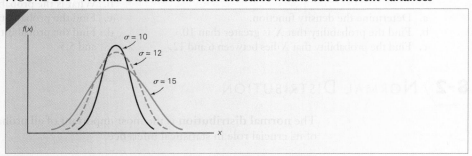

8-2a Calculating Normal Probabilities

To calculate the probability that a normal random variable falls into any interval, we must compute the area in the interval under the curve. Unfortunately, the function is not as simple as the uniform probability distribution, precluding the use of simple mathematics or even integral calculus. Instead we will resort to using a probability table similar to Tables 1 and 2 in Appendix B, which are used to calculate binomial and Poisson probabilities, respectively. Recall that to determine binomial probabilities from Table 1 we needed probabilities for selected values of n and p. Similarly, to find Poisson probabilities we needed probabilities for each value of μ that we chose to include in Table 2. It would appear then that we will need a separate table for normal probabilities for a selected set of values of μ and σ. Fortunately, this won't be necessary. Instead, we reduce the number of tables needed to one by standardizing the random variable. We standardize a random variable by subtracting its mean and dividing by its standard deviation. When the variable is normal, the transformed variable is called a **standard normal random variable** and denoted by Z; that is,

$$Z = \frac{X - \mu}{\sigma}$$

The probability statement about X is transformed by this formula into a statement about Z. To illustrate how we proceed, consider the following example.

EXAMPLE 8.2

Normally Distributed Gasoline Sales

Suppose that the daily demand for regular gasoline at another gas station is normally distributed with a mean of 1,000 gallons and a standard deviation of 100 gallons. The station manager has just opened the station for business and notes that there is exactly 1,100 gallons of regular gasoline in storage. The next delivery is scheduled later today at the close of business. The manager would like to know the probability that there will be enough regular gasoline to satisfy today's demands.

SOLUTION:

The amount of gasoline on hand will be sufficient to satisfy the demand if the demand is less than the supply. We label the demand for regular gasoline as X, and we want to find the probability:

$$P(X \le 1,100)$$

Note that because X is a continuous random variable, we can also express the probability as

$$P(X < 1,100)$$

because the area for $X = 1,100$ is 0.

Figure 8.10 describes a normal curve with mean of 1,000 and standard deviation of 100, and the area we want to find.

FIGURE **8.10** $P(X < 1,100)$

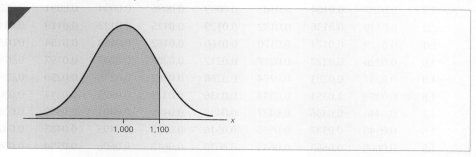

The first step is to standardize X. However, if we perform any operations on X, we must perform the same operations on 1,100. Thus,

$$P(X < 1,100) = P\left(\frac{X - \mu}{\sigma} < \frac{1,100 - 1,000}{100}\right) = P(Z < 1.00)$$

Figure 8.11 describes the transformation that has taken place. Notice that the variable X was transformed into Z, and 1,100 was transformed into 1.00. However, the area has not changed. In other words, the probability that we wish to compute $P(X < 1,100)$ is identical to $P(Z < 1.00)$.

FIGURE **8.11** $P(Z < 1.00)$

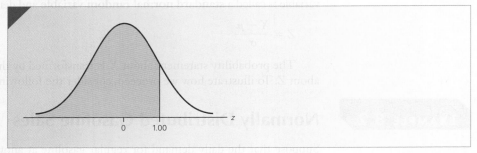

The values of Z specify the location of the corresponding value of X. A value of $Z = 1$ corresponds to a value of X that is 1 standard deviation above the mean. Notice as well that the mean of Z, which is 0, corresponds to the mean of X.

If we know the mean and standard deviation of a normally distributed random variable, we can always transform the probability statement about X into a probability statement about Z. Consequently, we need only one table, Table 3 in Appendix B, the standard normal probability table, which is reproduced here as Table 8.1.

TABLE **8.1**   Normal Probabilities (Table 3 in Appendix B)

Z	0.00	0.01	0.02	0.03	0.04	0.05	0.06	0.07	0.08	0.09
−3.0	0.0013	0.0013	0.0013	0.0012	0.0012	0.0011	0.0011	0.0011	0.0010	0.0010
−2.9	0.0019	0.0018	0.0018	0.0017	0.0016	0.0016	0.0015	0.0015	0.0014	0.0014
−2.8	0.0026	0.0025	0.0024	0.0023	0.0023	0.0022	0.0021	0.0021	0.0020	0.0019
−2.7	0.0035	0.0034	0.0033	0.0032	0.0031	0.0030	0.0029	0.0028	0.0027	0.0026
−2.6	0.0047	0.0045	0.0044	0.0043	0.0041	0.0040	0.0039	0.0038	0.0037	0.0036
−2.5	0.0062	0.0060	0.0059	0.0057	0.0055	0.0054	0.0052	0.0051	0.0049	0.0048
−2.4	0.0082	0.0080	0.0078	0.0075	0.0073	0.0071	0.0069	0.0068	0.0066	0.0064
−2.3	0.0107	0.0104	0.0102	0.0099	0.0096	0.0094	0.0091	0.0089	0.0087	0.0084
−2.2	0.0139	0.0136	0.0132	0.0129	0.0125	0.0122	0.0119	0.0116	0.0113	0.0110
−2.1	0.0179	0.0174	0.0170	0.0166	0.0162	0.0158	0.0154	0.0150	0.0146	0.0143
−2.0	0.0228	0.0222	0.0217	0.0212	0.0207	0.0202	0.0197	0.0192	0.0188	0.0183
−1.9	0.0287	0.0281	0.0274	0.0268	0.0262	0.0256	0.0250	0.0244	0.0239	0.0233
−1.8	0.0359	0.0351	0.0344	0.0336	0.0329	0.0322	0.0314	0.0307	0.0301	0.0294
−1.7	0.0446	0.0436	0.0427	0.0418	0.0409	0.0401	0.0392	0.0384	0.0375	0.0367
−1.6	0.0548	0.0537	0.0526	0.0516	0.0505	0.0495	0.0485	0.0475	0.0465	0.0455
−1.5	0.0668	0.0655	0.0643	0.0630	0.0618	0.0606	0.0594	0.0582	0.0571	0.0559
−1.4	0.0808	0.0793	0.0778	0.0764	0.0749	0.0735	0.0721	0.0708	0.0694	0.0681
−1.3	0.0968	0.0951	0.0934	0.0918	0.0901	0.0885	0.0869	0.0853	0.0838	0.0823
−1.2	0.1151	0.1131	0.1112	0.1093	0.1075	0.1056	0.1038	0.1020	0.1003	0.0985

Z	0.00	0.01	0.02	0.03	0.04	0.05	0.06	0.07	0.08	0.09
−1.1	0.1357	0.1335	0.1314	0.1292	0.1271	0.1251	0.1230	0.1210	0.1190	0.1170
−1.0	0.1587	0.1562	0.1539	0.1515	0.1492	0.1469	0.1446	0.1423	0.1401	0.1379
−0.9	0.1841	0.1814	0.1788	0.1762	0.1736	0.1711	0.1685	0.1660	0.1635	0.1611
−0.8	0.2119	0.2090	0.2061	0.2033	0.2005	0.1977	0.1949	0.1922	0.1894	0.1867
−0.7	0.2420	0.2389	0.2358	0.2327	0.2296	0.2266	0.2236	0.2206	0.2177	0.2148
−0.6	0.2743	0.2709	0.2676	0.2643	0.2611	0.2578	0.2546	0.2514	0.2483	0.2451
−0.5	0.3085	0.3050	0.3015	0.2981	0.2946	0.2912	0.2877	0.2843	0.2810	0.2776
−0.4	0.3446	0.3409	0.3372	0.3336	0.3300	0.3264	0.3228	0.3192	0.3156	0.3121
−0.3	0.3821	0.3783	0.3745	0.3707	0.3669	0.3632	0.3594	0.3557	0.3520	0.3483
−0.2	0.4207	0.4168	0.4129	0.4090	0.4052	0.4013	0.3974	0.3936	0.3897	0.3859
−0.1	0.4602	0.4562	0.4522	0.4483	0.4443	0.4404	0.4364	0.4325	0.4286	0.4247
−0.0	0.5000	0.4960	0.4920	0.4880	0.4840	0.4801	0.4761	0.4721	0.4681	0.4641
0.0	0.5000	0.5040	0.5080	0.5120	0.5160	0.5199	0.5239	0.5279	0.5319	0.5359
0.1	0.5398	0.5438	0.5478	0.5517	0.5557	0.5596	0.5636	0.5675	0.5714	0.5753
0.2	0.5793	0.5832	0.5871	0.5910	0.5948	0.5987	0.6026	0.6064	0.6103	0.6141
0.3	0.6179	0.6217	0.6255	0.6293	0.6331	0.6368	0.6406	0.6443	0.6480	0.6517
0.4	0.6554	0.6591	0.6628	0.6664	0.6700	0.6736	0.6772	0.6808	0.6844	0.6879
0.5	0.6915	0.6950	0.6985	0.7019	0.7054	0.7088	0.7123	0.7157	0.7190	0.7224
0.6	0.7257	0.7291	0.7324	0.7357	0.7389	0.7422	0.7454	0.7486	0.7517	0.7549
0.7	0.7580	0.7611	0.7642	0.7673	0.7704	0.7734	0.7764	0.7794	0.7823	0.7852
0.8	0.7881	0.7910	0.7939	0.7967	0.7995	0.8023	0.8051	0.8078	0.8106	0.8133
0.9	0.8159	0.8186	0.8212	0.8238	0.8264	0.8289	0.8315	0.8340	0.8365	0.8389
1.0	0.8413	0.8438	0.8461	0.8485	0.8508	0.8531	0.8554	0.8577	0.8599	0.8621
1.1	0.8643	0.8665	0.8686	0.8708	0.8729	0.8749	0.8770	0.8790	0.8810	0.8830
1.2	0.8849	0.8869	0.8888	0.8907	0.8925	0.8944	0.8962	0.8980	0.8997	0.9015
1.3	0.9032	0.9049	0.9066	0.9082	0.9099	0.9115	0.9131	0.9147	0.9162	0.9177
1.4	0.9192	0.9207	0.9222	0.9236	0.9251	0.9265	0.9279	0.9292	0.9306	0.9319
1.5	0.9332	0.9345	0.9357	0.9370	0.9382	0.9394	0.9406	0.9418	0.9429	0.9441
1.6	0.9452	0.9463	0.9474	0.9484	0.9495	0.9505	0.9515	0.9525	0.9535	0.9545
1.7	0.9554	0.9564	0.9573	0.9582	0.9591	0.9599	0.9608	0.9616	0.9625	0.9633
1.8	0.9641	0.9649	0.9656	0.9664	0.9671	0.9678	0.9686	0.9693	0.9699	0.9706
1.9	0.9713	0.9719	0.9726	0.9732	0.9738	0.9744	0.9750	0.9756	0.9761	0.9767
2.0	0.9772	0.9778	0.9783	0.9788	0.9793	0.9798	0.9803	0.9808	0.9812	0.9817
2.1	0.9821	0.9826	0.9830	0.9834	0.9838	0.9842	0.9846	0.9850	0.9854	0.9857
2.2	0.9861	0.9864	0.9868	0.9871	0.9875	0.9878	0.9881	0.9884	0.9887	0.9890
2.3	0.9893	0.9896	0.9898	0.9901	0.9904	0.9906	0.9909	0.9911	0.9913	0.9916
2.4	0.9918	0.9920	0.9922	0.9925	0.9927	0.9929	0.9931	0.9932	0.9934	0.9936
2.5	0.9938	0.9940	0.9941	0.9943	0.9945	0.9946	0.9948	0.9949	0.9951	0.9952
2.6	0.9953	0.9955	0.9956	0.9957	0.9959	0.9960	0.9961	0.9962	0.9963	0.9964
2.7	0.9965	0.9966	0.9967	0.9968	0.9969	0.9970	0.9971	0.9972	0.9973	0.9974
2.8	0.9974	0.9975	0.9976	0.9977	0.9977	0.9978	0.9979	0.9979	0.9980	0.9981
2.9	0.9981	0.9982	0.9982	0.9983	0.9984	0.9984	0.9985	0.9985	0.9986	0.9986
3.0	0.9987	0.9987	0.9987	0.9988	0.9988	0.9989	0.9989	0.9989	0.9990	0.9990

This table is similar to the ones we used for the binomial and Poisson distributions; that is, this table lists cumulative probabilities

$$P(Z < z)$$

for values of z ranging from -3.09 to $+3.09$.

To use the table, we simply find the value of z and read the probability. For example, the probability $P(Z < 2.00)$ is found by finding 2.0 in the left margin and under the heading 0.00 finding 0.9772. The probability $P(Z < 2.01)$ is found in the same row but under the heading 0.01. It is .9778.

Returning to Example 8.2, the probability we seek is found in Table 8.1 by finding 1.0 in the left margin. The number to its right under the heading 0.00 is .8413. See Figure 8.12.

FIGURE **8.12** $P(Z < 1.00)$

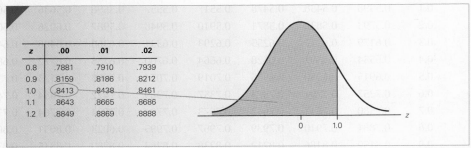

As was the case with Tables 1 and 2, we can also determine the probability that the standard normal random variable is greater than some value of z. For example, we find the probability that Z is greater than 1.80 by determining the probability that Z is less than 1.80 and subtracting that value from 1. By applying the complement rule, we get

$$P(Z > 1.80) = 1 - P(Z < 1.80) = 1 - .9641 = .0359$$

See Figure 8.13.

FIGURE **8.13** $P(Z > 1.80)$

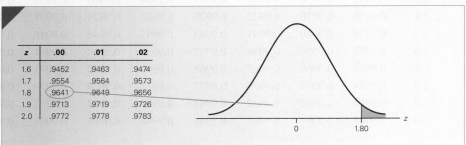

We can also easily determine the probability that a standard normal random variable lies between two values of z. For example, we find the probability

$$P(-0.71 < Z < 0.92)$$

by finding the two cumulative probabilities and calculating their difference; that is,

$$P(Z < -0.71) = .2389$$

and

$$P(Z < 0.92) = .8212$$

Hence,

$$P(-0.71 < Z < 0.92) = P(Z < 92) - P(Z < -0.71) = .8212 - .2389 = .5823$$

Figure 8.14 depicts this calculation.

FIGURE **8.14** $P(-0.71 < Z < 0.92)$

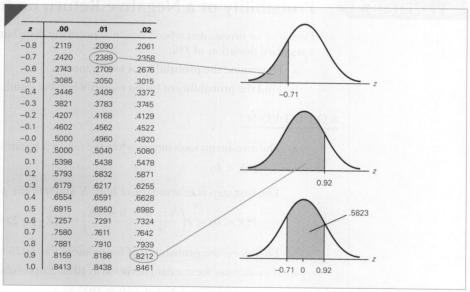

Notice that the largest value of z in the table is 3.09 and that $P(Z < 3.09) = .9990$. This means that

$$P(Z > 3.09) = 1 - .9990 = .0010$$

However, because the table lists no values beyond 3.09, we approximate any area beyond 3.10 as 0. In other words,

$$P(Z > 3.10) = P(Z < -3.10) \approx 0$$

Recall that in Tables 1 and 2 we were able to use the table to find the probability that X is *equal* to some value of x, but we won't do the same with the normal table. Remember that the normal random variable is continuous and the probability that a continuous random variable is equal to any single value is 0.

APPLICATIONS in FINANCE

Measuring Risk

In previous chapters, we discussed several probability and statistical applications in finance where we wanted to measure and perhaps reduce the risk associated with investments. In Example 3.2, we drew histograms to gauge the spread of the histogram of the returns on two investments. We repeated this example in Chapter 4, where we computed the standard deviation and variance as numerical measures of risk. In Section 7-3, we developed an important application in finance in which we emphasized reducing the variance of the returns on a portfolio. However, we have not demonstrated why risk is measured by the variance and standard deviation. The following example corrects this deficiency.

Zhukovvlad/Shutterstock.com

EXAMPLE 8.3

Probability of a Negative Return on Investment

Consider an investment whose return is normally distributed with a mean of 10% and a standard deviation of 5%.

   a. Determine the probability of losing money.

   b. Find the probability of losing money when the standard deviation is equal to 10%.

S O L U T I O N :

   a. The investment loses money when the return is negative. Thus, we wish to determine

$$P(X < 0)$$

The first step is to standardize both X and 0 in the probability statement:

$$P(X < 0) = P\left(\frac{X - \mu}{\sigma} < \frac{0 - 10}{5}\right) = P(Z < -2.00) = .0228$$

Therefore, the probability of losing money is .0228.

   b. If we increase the standard deviation to 10%, the probability of suffering a loss becomes

$$P(X < 0) = P\left(\frac{X - \mu}{\sigma} < \frac{0 - 10}{10}\right) = P(Z < -1.00) = .1587$$

As you can see, increasing the standard deviation increases the probability of losing money. Note that increasing the standard deviation will also increase the probability that the return will exceed some relatively large amount. However, because investors tend to be risk averse, we emphasize the increased probability of negative returns when discussing the effect of increasing the standard deviation.

8-2b Finding Values of Z

There is a family of problems that require us to determine the value of Z given a probability. We use the notation Z_A to represent the value of z such that the area to its right under the standard normal curve is A; that is, Z_A is the value of a standard normal random variable such that

$$P(Z > Z_A) = A$$

To calculate a value of x given the probability $P(X > x) = A$, enter

$$= \mathbf{NORMINV}(1 - A, \mu, \sigma)$$

The chapter-opening example would be solved by typing

$$= \mathbf{NORMINV}(.99, 490, 61)$$

which yields 632.

APPLICATIONS in OPERATIONS MANAGEMENT

Kzenon/Shutterstock.com

Inventory Management

Every organization maintains some inventory, which is defined as a stock of items. For example, grocery stores hold inventories of almost all the products they sell. When the total number of products drops to a specified level, the manager arranges for the delivery of more products. An automobile repair shop keeps an inventory of a large number of replacement parts. A school keeps stock of items that it uses regularly, including chalk, pens, envelopes, file folders, and paper clips. There are costs associated with inventories.

These include the cost of capital, losses (theft and obsolescence), and warehouse space, as well as maintenance and record keeping. Management scientists have developed many models to help determine the optimum inventory level that balances the cost of inventory with the cost of shortages and the cost of making many small orders. Several of these models are deterministic—that is, they assume that the demand for the product is constant. However, in most realistic situations, the demand is a random variable. One commonly applied probabilistic model assumes that the demand during lead time is a normally distributed random variable. *Lead time* is defined as the amount of time between when the order is placed and when it is delivered.

The quantity ordered is usually calculated by attempting to minimize the total costs, including the cost of ordering and the cost of maintaining inventory. (This topic is discussed in most management-science courses.) Another critical decision involves the *reorder point*, which is the level of inventory at which an order is issued to its supplier. If the reorder point is too low, the company will run out of product, suffering the loss of sales and potentially customers who will go to a competitor. If the reorder point is too high, the company will be carrying too much inventory, which costs money to buy and store. In some companies, inventory has a tendency to walk out the back door or become obsolete. As a result, managers create a *safety stock*, which is the extra amount of inventory to reduce the times when the company has a shortage. They do so by setting a service level, which is the probability that the company will not experience a shortage. The method used to determine the reorder point will be demonstrated with Example 8.6.

EXAMPLE 8.6

Determining the Reorder Point

During the spring, the demand for electric fans at a large home-improvement store is quite strong. The company tracks inventory using a computer system so that it knows how many fans are in the inventory at any time. The policy is to order a new shipment of 250 fans when the inventory level falls to the reorder point, which is 150. However, this policy has resulted in frequent shortages and thus lost sales because both lead time and demand are highly variable. The manager would like to reduce the incidence of shortages so that only 5% of orders will arrive after inventory drops to 0 (resulting in a shortage). This policy is expressed as a 95% service level. From previous periods, the company has determined that demand during lead time is normally distributed with a mean of 200 and a standard deviation of 50. Find the reorder point.

S O L U T I O N :

The reorder point is set so that the probability that demand during lead time exceeds this quantity is 5%. Figure 8.20 depicts demand during lead time and the reorder point. As we did in the solution to the chapter-opening example, we find the standard normal value such that the area to its right is .05. The standardized value of the reorder point (ROP) is $Z_{.05} = 1.645$. To find ROP, we must unstandardize $Z_{.05}$.

$$Z_{.05} = \frac{\text{ROP} - \mu}{\sigma}$$

$$1.645 = \frac{\text{ROP} - 200}{50}$$

$$\text{ROP} = 50(1.645) + 200 = 282.25$$

which we round up to 283. The policy is to order a new batch of fans when there are 283 fans left in inventory.

FIGURE **8.20** Distribution of Demand during Lead Time

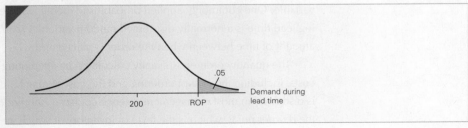

EXERCISES

In Exercises 8.19 to 8.34, find the probabilities.

8.19 $P(Z < 1.60)$

8.20 $P(Z < 1.61)$

8.21 $P(Z < 1.65)$

8.22 $P(Z < -1.39)$

8.23 $P(Z < -1.80)$

8.24 $P(Z < -2.16)$

8.25 $P(-1.30 < Z < .70)$

8.26 $P(Z > -1.24)$

8.27 $P(Z < 2.23)$

8.28 $P(Z > 1.87)$

8.29 $P(Z < 2.57)$

8.30 $P(1.04 < Z < 2.03)$

8.31 $P(-0.71 < Z < -0.33)$

8.32 $P(Z > 3.09)$

8.33 $P(Z > 0)$

8.34 $P(Z > 4.0)$

8.35 Find $z_{.03}$.

8.36 Find $z_{.065}$.

8.37 Find $z_{.28}$.

8.38 X is normally distributed with mean 100 and standard deviation 20. What is the probability that X is greater than 145?

8.39 X is normally distributed with mean 250 and standard deviation 40. What value of X does only the top 15% exceed?

8.40 X is normally distributed with mean 1,000 and standard deviation 250. What is the probability that X lies between 800 and 1,100?

8.41 X is normally distributed with mean 50 and standard deviation 8. What value of X is such that only 8% of values are below it?

8.42 The long-distance calls made by the employees of a company are normally distributed with a mean of 6.3 minutes and a standard deviation of 2.2 minutes. Find the probability that a call
a. lasts between 5 and 10 minutes.
b. lasts more than 7 minutes.
c. lasts less than 4 minutes.

8.43 Refer to Exercise 8.42. How long do the longest 10% of calls last?

8.44 The lifetimes of lightbulbs that are advertised to last for 5,000 hours are normally distributed with a mean of 5,100 hours and a standard deviation of 200 hours. What is the probability that a bulb lasts longer than the advertised figure?

8.45 Refer to Exercise 8.44. If we wanted to be sure that 98% of all bulbs last longer than the advertised figure, what figure should be advertised?

8.46 SAT scores are normally distributed with a mean of 1,000 and a standard deviation of 300. Find the quartiles.

8.47 According to a Pew Research Center survey, the mean student loan at graduation is $25,000. Suppose that student loans are normally distributed with a standard deviation of $5,000. A graduate with a student loan is selected at random. Find the following probabilities.

a. The loan is greater than $30,000.
b. The loan is less than $22,500.
c. The loan falls between $20,000 and $32,000.

8.48 The Tesla Model S 85D is an electric car that the manufacturer claims can travel 270 miles on a single charge. However, the actual distance depends on a number of factors including speed and whether the car is driven in the city or on highways. Suppose that the distance is a normally distributed random variable with a mean of 200 miles and a standard deviation of 20 miles. An owner of this model intends to travel to a nearby city and return on the same charge. If the total distance is 210 miles, what is the probability that car makes it without running out of power?

8.49 Exercise 4.67 addressed the problem of setting an appropriate speed limit on highways. Automotive experts believe that the "correct" speed is the 85th percentile. Suppose that the speeds on a highway are normally distributed with a mean of 68 and a standard deviation of 5. Find the "correct" speed.

8.50 Economists frequently make use of quintiles (i.e., the 20th, 40th, 60th, and 80th percentiles) particularly when discussing incomes. Suppose that in a large city household incomes are normally distributed with a mean of $50,000 and a standard deviation of $10,000. An economist wishes to identify the quintiles but did not pass the required statistics course. Help the economist by providing the quintiles.

8.51 The top-selling Red and Voss tire is rated 70,000 miles, which means nothing. In fact, the distance the tires can run until they wear out is a normally distributed random variable with a mean of 82,000 miles and a standard deviation of 6,400 miles.
a. What is the probability that a tire wears out before 70,000 miles?
b. What is the probability that a tire lasts more than 100,000 miles?

8.52 The heights of 2-year-old children are normally distributed with a mean of 32 inches and a standard deviation of 1.5 inches. Pediatricians regularly measure the heights of toddlers to determine whether there is a problem. There may be a problem when a child is in the top or bottom 5% of heights. Determine the heights of 2-year-old children that could be a problem.

8.53 Refer to Exercise 8.52. Find the probability of these events.
a. A 2-year-old child is taller than 36 inches.
b. A 2-year-old child is shorter than 34 inches.
c. A 2-year-old child is between 30 and 33 inches tall.

8.54 University and college students average 7.2 hours of sleep per night, with a standard deviation of 40 minutes. If the amount of sleep is normally distributed, what proportion of university and college students sleep for more than 8 hours?

8.55 Refer to Exercise 8.54. Find the amount of sleep that is exceeded by only 25% of students.

8.56 The amount of time devoted to studying statistics each week by students who achieve a grade of A in the course is a normally distributed random variable with a mean of 7.5 hours and a standard deviation of 2.1 hours.
   a. What proportion of A students study for more than 10 hours per week?
   b. Find the probability that an A student spends between 7 and 9 hours studying.
   c. What proportion of A students spend fewer than 3 hours studying?
   d. What is the amount of time below which only 5% of all A students spend studying?

8.57 The number of pages printed before replacing the cartridge in a laser printer is normally distributed with a mean of 11,500 pages and a standard deviation of 800 pages. A new cartridge has just been installed.
   a. What is the probability that the printer produces more than 12,000 pages before this cartridge must be replaced?
   b. What is the probability that the printer produces fewer than 10,000 pages?

8.58 Refer to Exercise 8.57. The manufacturer wants to provide guidelines to potential customers advising them of the minimum number of pages they can expect from each cartridge. How many pages should it advertise if the company wants to be correct 99% of the time?

8.59 The mean monthly income of graduates of professional and Ph.D. degrees is $6,000 according to a recent Pew Research Center survey. If these incomes are normally distributed with a standard deviation of $1,200,
   a. What proportion of incomes is greater than $4,900?
   b. Calculate the proportion of incomes that fall between $3,800 and $5,700.
   c. Calculate the proportion of incomes that are less than $6,500.

8.60 In a large city, the annual amount of money households spend on food away from home is normally distributed. The mean and standard deviation are $2,200 and $700, respectively. Compute the probability that a household spends less than $2,500 on food away from home.

8.61 Battery manufacturers compete on the basis of the amount of time their products last in cameras and toys. A manufacturer of alkaline batteries has observed that its batteries last for an average of 26 hours when used in a toy racing car. The amount of time is normally distributed with a standard deviation of 2.5 hours.
   a. What is the probability that the battery lasts between 24 and 28 hours?
   b. What is the probability that the battery lasts longer than 28 hours?
   c. What is the probability that the battery lasts less than 24 hours?

8.62 Because of the relatively high interest rates, most consumers attempt to pay off their credit card bills promptly. However, this is not always possible. An analysis of the amount of interest paid monthly by a bank's Visa cardholders reveals that the amount is normally distributed with a mean of $27 and a standard deviation of $7.
   a. What proportion of the bank's Visa cardholders pay more than $30 in interest?
   b. What proportion of the bank's Visa cardholders pay more than $40 in interest?
   c. What proportion of the bank's Visa cardholders pay less than $15 in interest?
   d. What interest payment is exceeded by only 20% of the bank's Visa cardholders?

8.63 It is said that sufferers of a cold virus experience symptoms for 7 days. However, the amount of time is actually a normally distributed random variable whose mean is 7.5 days and whose standard deviation is 1.2 days.
   a. What proportion of cold sufferers experience fewer than 4 days of symptoms?
   b. What proportion of cold sufferers experience symptoms for between 7 and 10 days?

8.64 How much money does a typical family of four spend at a McDonald's restaurant per visit? The amount is a normally distributed random variable with a mean of $16.40 and a standard deviation of $2.75.
   a. Find the probability that a family of four spends less than $10.
   b. What is the amount below which only 10% of families of four spend at McDonald's?

8.65 The final marks in a statistics course are normally distributed with a mean of 70 and a standard deviation of 10. The professor must convert all marks to letter grades. The professor wants 10% A's, 30% B's, 40% C's, 15% D's, and 5% F's. Determine the cutoffs for each letter grade.

8.66 Mensa is an organization whose members possess IQs that are in the top 2% of the population. It is known that IQs are normally distributed with a mean of 100 and a standard deviation of 16. Find the minimum IQ needed to be a Mensa member.

8.67 The daily withdrawals from an ATM located at a service station is normally distributed with a mean of $50,000 and a standard deviation of $8,000. The operator of the ATM puts $64,000 in cash at the beginning of the day. What is the probability that the ATM will run out of money?

8.68 According to the U.S. Census, the mean family net worth of families whose head is between 55 and 64 years old is approximately $110,600. If family net worth is normally distributed with a standard deviation of $22,000, find the probability that a randomly selected family whose head is between 55 and 64 years old has a net worth greater than $150,000.

8.69 A retailer of computing products sells a variety of computer-related products. One of the most popular products is an HP laser printer. The average weekly demand is 200. Lead time for a new order from the manufacturer to arrive is 1 week. If the demand for printers were constant, the retailer would reorder when there were exactly 200 printers in inventory. However, the demand is a random variable. An analysis of previous weeks reveals that the weekly demand standard deviation is 30. The retailer wants the probability of running short in any week to be no more than 6%. How many HP laser printers should be in stock when the retailer reorders from the manufacturer?

8.70 The demand for a daily newspaper at a newsstand at a busy intersection is known to be normally distributed with a mean of 150 and a standard deviation of 25. How many newspapers should the newsstand operator order to ensure that it runs short on no more than 20% of days?

8.71 Every day a bakery prepares its famous marble rye. A statistically savvy customer determined that daily demand is normally distributed with a mean of 850 and a standard deviation of 90. How many loaves should the bakery make if it wants the probability of running short on any day to be no more than 30%?

8.72 Refer to Exercise 8.71. Any marble ryes that are unsold at the end of the day are marked down and sold for half-price. How many loaves should the bakery prepare so that the proportion of days that result in unsold loaves is no more than 60%?

8.73 The annual rate of return on a mutual fund is normally distributed with a mean of 14% and a standard deviation of 18%.
a. What is the probability that the fund returns more than 25% next year?
b. What is the probability that the fund loses money next year?

8.74 In a survey of consumer finances, it was determined that the average household debt is $250,000. If household debt is normally distributed with a standard deviation of $30,000, determine the quintiles.

8.75 The Bureau of Labor Statistics gathers data about a variety of subjects. One of them is the Consumer Expenditures Survey. From this survey we learn that the mean annual expenditure of an American family on dairy products is $450. For the following questions, assume that the expenditure is normally distributed with a standard deviation of $80.
a. What is the probability that a family spends more than $600 per year on dairy products?
b. What is the amount above which only 10% of the population spend?

8.76 In 2018, the amount of time it takes to play an average major league baseball game is 3 hours and 5 minutes (or 185 minutes). Assume that the game completion times are normally distributed with a standard deviation of 20 minutes.
a. Compute the probability that a game lasts less than 3 hours.
b. What is the length of games whose completion times are at the first quartile?

8.77 The U.S. Census states that the average net worth of a family that rents (rather than owns) their residence is $2,381. Assume that this variable is normally distributed with a standard deviation of $800.
a. What is the probability that a randomly selected family that rents their home has a negative net worth?
b. Compute the proportion of families that rent their home that have a net worth of more than $4,000.

8.78 The number of emails that are received by an executive in a week is normally distributed with a mean and standard deviation of 220 and 40, respectively. Compute the probability that the executive gets 220 emails next week.

8.79 The amount of money spent by cruise passengers on land excursions is a normal random variable with a mean and standard deviation of $650 and $150, respectively. Find the three quartiles for this variable.

8.80 Most restaurants suggest that tips should exceed 18%. In fact, tips are a normally distributed random variable with a mean of 15% and a standard deviation of 2%. Determine the tip amount that is exceeded only by the top 1%.

8.81 In middle class homes, the food budget is a normally distributed random variable with a mean of $5,800 and a standard deviation of $1,400.

a. What is the probability that a randomly selected middle-class home spends between $5,000 and $6,000 per year on food?

b. Find the amount that is exceed by 20% of the population.

8.82 The debt-to-income ratio is an important economic indicator. A large ratio may indicate that a particular household's debt is unsustainable. Assume that this ratio is normally distributed with a mean and standard deviation of 1.5 and .5, respectively. Determine the 90th and 99th percentiles.

8.83 In the United States, capital gains on homes is taxable if the amount exceeds a set amount. In one large American city the amount of capital gains on houses was studied. It turns out that the variable is normally distributed with a mean of $41,000 and a standard deviation of $19,000. What is the probability that a house has a negative capital gain?

8.84 A golfer playing a new course encounters a hole that requires a shot of 111 yards to successfully clear a pond and land on the green. The golfer's 7-iron shots are normally distributed with a mean of 115 yards and a standard deviation of 8 yards. The golfer's playing partner suggested to take an extra club or an extra ball. What is the probability that the golfer should have heeded that advice? That is, calculate the probability that the golf ball will be at the bottom of the pond.

8.85 The weekly demand for a popular software sold by Business Depot is normally distributed with a mean of 42 and a standard deviation of 10. At the beginning of this week the store has on hand 46 packages. What is the probability that the store will have enough supply to satisfy the demand?

8.86 The marks on the statistics midterm test are normally distributed with a mean of 72 and a standard deviation of 9. Pat Statsdud plans to do just enough work so that the midterm mark is better than 25% of the class. What midterm mark should Pat aim for?

8.87 The monthly balances of the checking accounts of a bank's customers are normally distributed with an average balance of $1,200 and a standard deviation of $250. If the bank wants to launch an advertisement targeting the customers with the top 15% of monthly balances, what is the minimum monthly balance of these customers?

8.88 The amount of time it takes statistics students to complete a midterm test is normally distributed with a mean of 80 minutes and a standard deviation of 12 minutes. How long should the professor make the exam so that 77% of the class can complete the test?

8.89 The lengths of full-term newborn babies are normally distributed with a mean of 50 cm and a standard deviation of 2 cm. Physicians express concern if a full-term newborn baby is in the bottom 20% in lengths. Determine the length below which physicians should be concerned.

8.90 The coffee shop in the business school is open until 9:00 P.M. each week day. The amount of coffee sold after 8:00 P.M. each day is normally distributed with a mean of 15 cups and a standard deviation of 3 cups. At 8:00 P.M., two new pots of coffee are prepared, each containing 10 cups. If demand exceeds supply, more coffee will have to be prepared. What is the probability that they will not have to prepare more coffee?

APPLICATIONS in OPERATIONS MANAGEMENT

PERT/CPM

In the Applications in Operations Management box on page 234, we introduced PERT/CPM. The purpose of this powerful management-science procedure is to determine the critical path of a project. The expected value and variance of the completion time of the project are based on the expected values and variances of the completion times of the activities on the critical path. Once we have the expected value and variance of the completion time of the project, we can use these figures to determine the probability that the project will be completed by a certain date. Statisticians have established that the completion time of the project is approximately normally distributed, enabling us to compute the needed probabilities.

8.91 Refer to Exercise 7.67. Find the probability that the project will take more than 60 days to complete.

8.92 The mean and variance of the time to complete the project in Exercise 7.68 was 145 minutes and 31 minutes^2. What is the probability that it will take less than 2.5 hours to overhaul the machine?

8.93 Refer to Exercise 7.69. Find the probability of the following events.
   a. The launch of the new product takes more than 105 days.
   b. The launch of the new product takes more than 92 days.
   c. The launch of the new product takes between 95 and 112 days.

8.94 Refer to Exercise 7.70. Find the quartiles of the time to complete the research project.

8-3 / (OPTIONAL) EXPONENTIAL DISTRIBUTION

Another important continuous distribution is the **exponential distribution**.

> **Exponential Probability Density Function**
>
> A random variable X is exponentially distributed if its probability density function is given by
>
> $$f(x) = \lambda e^{-\lambda x}, \quad x \geq 0$$
>
> where $e = 2.71828 \ldots$ and λ is the parameter of the distribution.

Statisticians have shown that the mean and standard deviation of an exponential random variable are equal to each other:

$$\mu = \sigma = 1/\lambda$$

Recall that the normal distribution is a two-parameter distribution. The distribution is completely specified once the values of the two parameters μ and σ are known. In contrast, the exponential distribution is a one-parameter distribution. The distribution is completely specified once the value of the parameter λ is known. Figure 8.21 depicts three exponential distributions, corresponding to three different values of the parameter λ. Notice that for any exponential density function $f(x)$, $f(0) = \lambda$ and $f(x)$ approaches 0 as x approaches infinity.

FIGURE **8.21** Exponential Distributions

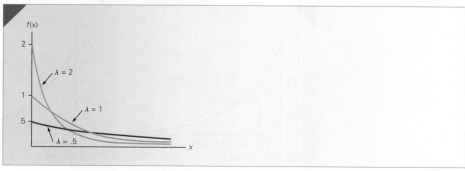

The exponential density function is easier to work with than the normal. As a result, we can develop formulas for the calculation of the probability of any range of values. Using integral calculus, we can determine the following probability statements.

Probability Associated with an Exponential Random Variable

If X is an exponential random variable,

$$P(X > x) = e^{-\lambda x}$$
$$P(X < x) = 1 - e^{-\lambda x}$$
$$P(x_1 < X < x_2) = P(X < x_2) - P(X < x_1) = e^{-\lambda x_1} - e^{-\lambda x_2}$$

The value of $e^{-\lambda x}$ can be obtained with the aid of a calculator.

EXAMPLE 8.7

Lifetimes of Alkaline Batteries

The lifetime of an alkaline battery (measured in hours) is exponentially distributed with $\lambda = .05$.

    a. What is the mean and standard deviation of the battery's lifetime?

    b. Find the probability that a battery will last between 10 and 15 hours.

    c. What is the probability that a battery will last for more than 20 hours?

SOLUTION:

    a. The mean and standard deviation are equal to $1/\lambda$. Thus,

$$\mu = \sigma = 1/\lambda = 1/.05 = 20 \text{ hours}$$

    b. Let X denote the lifetime of a battery. The required probability is

$$
\begin{aligned}
P(10 < X < 15) &= e^{-.05(10)} - e^{-.05(15)} \\
&= e^{-.5} - e^{-.75} \\
&= .6065 - .4724 \\
&= .1341
\end{aligned}
$$

    c.
$$
\begin{aligned}
P(X > 20) &= e^{-.05(20)} \\
&= e^{-1} \\
&= .3679
\end{aligned}
$$

Figure 8.22 depicts these probabilities.

FIGURE **8.22** Probabilities for Example 8.7

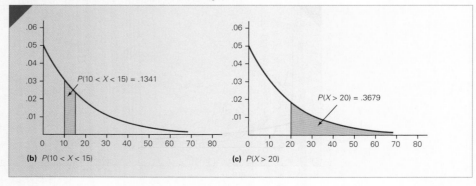

(b) $P(10 < X < 15)$ **(c)** $P(X > 20)$

random variable is 1, whereas the variance of a Student t random variable is $\nu/(\nu - 2)$, which is greater than 1 for all ν.]

FIGURE **8.24** **Student t and Normal Distributions**

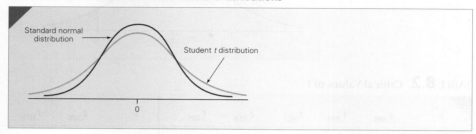

Figure 8.25 depicts Student t distributions with several different degrees of freedom. Notice that for larger degrees of freedom the Student t distribution's dispersion is smaller. For example, when $\nu = 10$, $V(t) = 1.25$; when $\nu = 50$, $V(t) = 1.042$; and when $\nu = 200$, $V(t) = 1.010$. As ν grows larger, the Student t distribution approaches the standard normal distribution.

FIGURE **8.25** **Student t Distribution with $\nu = 2, 10$, and 30**

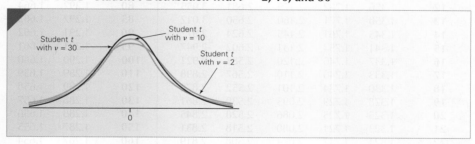

Student t Probabilities For each value of ν (the number of degrees of freedom), there is a different Student t distribution. If we wanted to calculate probabilities of the Student t random variable manually as we did for the normal random variable, then we would need a different table for each ν, which is not practical. Alternatively, we can use Microsoft Excel. The instructions are given later in this section.

Determining Student t Values As you will discover later in this book, the Student t distribution is used extensively in statistical inference. And for inferential methods, we often need to find values of the random variable. To determine values of a normal random variable, we used Table 3 backward. Finding values of a Student t random variable is considerably easier. Table 4 in Appendix B (reproduced here as Table 8.2) lists values of $t_{A,\nu}$, which are the values of a Student t random variable with ν degrees of freedom such that

$$P(t > t_{A,\nu}) = A$$

Figure 8.26 depicts this notation.

FIGURE **8.26** Student t Distribution with t_A

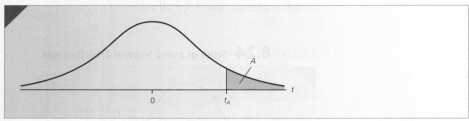

TABLE **8.2** Critical Values of t

ν	$t_{.100}$	$t_{.050}$	$t_{.025}$	$t_{.010}$	$t_{.005}$	ν	$t_{.100}$	$t_{.050}$	$t_{.025}$	$t_{.010}$	$t_{.005}$
1	3.078	6.314	12.71	31.82	63.66	29	1.311	1.699	2.045	2.462	2.756
2	1.886	2.920	4.303	6.965	9.925	30	1.310	1.697	2.042	2.457	2.750
3	1.638	2.353	3.182	4.541	5.841	35	1.306	1.690	2.030	2.438	2.724
4	1.533	2.132	2.776	3.747	4.604	40	1.303	1.684	2.021	2.423	2.704
5	1.476	2.015	2.571	3.365	4.032	45	1.301	1.679	2.014	2.412	2.690
6	1.440	1.943	2.447	3.143	3.707	50	1.299	1.676	2.009	2.403	2.678
7	1.415	1.895	2.365	2.998	3.499	55	1.297	1.673	2.004	2.396	2.668
8	1.397	1.860	2.306	2.896	3.355	60	1.296	1.671	2.000	2.390	2.660
9	1.383	1.833	2.262	2.821	3.250	65	1.295	1.669	1.997	2.385	2.654
10	1.372	1.812	2.228	2.764	3.169	70	1.294	1.667	1.994	2.381	2.648
11	1.363	1.796	2.201	2.718	3.106	75	1.293	1.665	1.992	2.377	2.643
12	1.356	1.782	2.179	2.681	3.055	80	1.292	1.664	1.990	2.374	2.639
13	1.350	1.771	2.160	2.650	3.012	85	1.292	1.663	1.988	2.371	2.635
14	1.345	1.761	2.145	2.624	2.977	90	1.291	1.662	1.987	2.368	2.632
15	1.341	1.753	2.131	2.602	2.947	95	1.291	1.661	1.985	2.366	2.629
16	1.337	1.746	2.120	2.583	2.921	100	1.290	1.660	1.984	2.364	2.626
17	1.333	1.740	2.110	2.567	2.898	110	1.289	1.659	1.982	2.361	2.621
18	1.330	1.734	2.101	2.552	2.878	120	1.289	1.658	1.980	2.358	2.617
19	1.328	1.729	2.093	2.539	2.861	130	1.288	1.657	1.978	2.355	2.614
20	1.325	1.725	2.086	2.528	2.845	140	1.288	1.656	1.977	2.353	2.611
21	1.323	1.721	2.080	2.518	2.831	150	1.287	1.655	1.976	2.351	2.609
22	1.321	1.717	2.074	2.508	2.819	160	1.287	1.654	1.975	2.350	2.607
23	1.319	1.714	2.069	2.500	2.807	170	1.287	1.654	1.974	2.348	2.605
24	1.318	1.711	2.064	2.492	2.797	180	1.286	1.653	1.973	2.347	2.603
25	1.316	1.708	2.060	2.485	2.787	190	1.286	1.653	1.973	2.346	2.602
26	1.315	1.706	2.056	2.479	2.779	200	1.286	1.653	1.972	2.345	2.601
27	1.314	1.703	2.052	2.473	2.771	∞	1.282	1.645	1.960	2.326	2.576
28	1.313	1.701	2.048	2.467	2.763						

Observe that $t_{A,\nu}$ is provided for degrees of freedom ranging from 1 to 200 and ∞. To read this table, simply identify the degrees of freedom and find that value or the closest number to it if it is not listed. Then locate the column representing the t_A value you wish. For example, if we want the value of t with 10 degrees of freedom such that the area under the Student t curve is .05, we locate 10 in the first column and move across this row until we locate the number under the heading $t_{.05}$. From Table 8.3, we find

$$t_{.05,10} = 1.812$$

If the number of degrees of freedom is not shown, find its closest value. For example, suppose we wanted to find $t_{.025,32}$. Because 32 degrees of freedom is not listed, we find the closest number of degrees of freedom, which is 30, and use $t_{.025,30} = 2.042$ as an approximation.

TABLE **8.3** Finding $t_{.05,10}$

DEGREES OF FREEDOM	$t_{.10}$	$t_{.05}$	$t_{.025}$	$t_{.01}$	$t_{.005}$
1	3.078	6.314	12.706	31.821	63.657
2	1.886	2.920	4.303	6.965	9.925
3	1.638	2.353	3.182	4.541	5.841
4	1.533	2.132	2.776	3.747	4.604
5	1.476	2.015	2.571	3.365	4.032
6	1.440	1.943	2.447	3.143	3.707
7	1.415	1.895	2.365	2.998	3.499
8	1.397	1.860	2.306	2.896	3.355
9	1.383	1.833	2.262	2.821	3.250
10	1.372	1.812	2.228	2.764	3.169
11	1.363	1.796	2.201	2.718	3.106
12	1.356	1.782	2.179	2.681	3.055

Because the Student t distribution is symmetric about 0, the value of t such that the area to its *left* is A is $-t_{A,v}$. For example, the value of t with 10 degrees of freedom such that the area to its left is .05 is

$$-t_{.05,10} = -1.812$$

Notice the last row in the Student t table. The number of degrees of freedom is infinite, and the t values are identical (except for the number of decimal places) to the values of z. For example,

$t_{.10,\infty} = 1.282$
$t_{.05,\infty} = 1.645$
$t_{.025,\infty} = 1.960$
$t_{.01,\infty} = 2.326$
$t_{.005,\infty} = 2.576$

In the previous section, we showed (or showed how we determine) that

$z_{.10} = 1.28$
$z_{.05} = 1.645$
$z_{.025} = 1.96$
$z_{.01} = 2.23$
$z_{.005} = 2.575$

EXCEL Function

To compute Student t probabilities, type

$$= \textbf{TDIST}([x], [v], [\text{Tails}])$$

where x must be positive, ν is the number of degrees of freedom, and "Tails" is 1 or 2. Typing 1 for "Tails" produces the area to the right of x. Typing 2 for "Tails" produces the area to the right of x plus the area to the left of $-x$. For example,

$$= \mathbf{TDIST}(2, 50, 1) = .02547$$

and

$$= \mathbf{TDIST}(2, 50, 2) = .05095$$

To determine t_A, type

$$= \mathbf{TINV}([2A], [\nu])$$

For example, to find $t_{.05, 200}$ enter

$$= \mathbf{TINV}(.10, 200)$$

yielding 1.6525.

Chi-Squared Distribution The density function of another very useful random variable is exhibited next.

Chi-Squared Density Function

The chi-squared density function is

$$f(\chi^2) = \frac{1}{\Gamma(\nu/2)} \frac{1}{2^{\nu/2}} (\chi^2)^{(\nu/2)-1} e^{-\chi^2/2} \quad \chi^2 > 0$$

The parameter ν is the number of degrees of freedom, which like the degrees of freedom of the Student t distribution affects the shape.

Figure 8.27 depicts a **chi-squared distribution**. As you can see, it is positively skewed ranging between 0 and ∞. Like that of the Student t distribution, its shape depends on its number of degrees of freedom. The effect of increasing the degrees of freedom is seen in Figure 8.28.

FIGURE **8.27** Chi-Squared Distribution

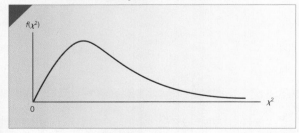

FIGURE **8.28** Chi-Squared Distribution with $\nu = 1$, 5, and 10

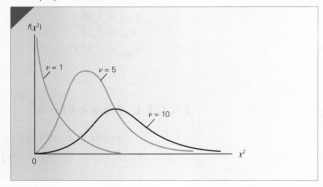

The mean and variance of a chi-squared random variable are

$$E(\chi^2) = \nu$$

and

$$V(\chi^2) = 2\nu$$

Determining Chi-Squared Values The value of χ^2 with ν degrees of freedom such that the area to its right under the chi-squared curve is equal to A is denoted by $\chi^2_{A,\nu}$. We cannot use $-\chi^2_{A,\nu}$ to represent the point such that the area to its *left* is A (as we did with the standard normal and Student t values) because χ^2 is always greater than 0. To represent left-tail critical values, we note that if the area to the left of a point is A, the area to its right must be $1 - A$ because the entire area under the chi-squared curve (as well as all continuous distributions) must equal 1. Thus, $\chi^2_{1-A,\nu}$ denotes the point such that the area to its left is A. See Figure 8.29.

FIGURE **8.29** χ^2_A and χ^2_{1-A}

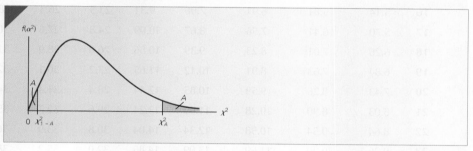

Table 5 in Appendix B (reproduced here as Table 8.4) lists critical values of the chi-squared distribution for degrees of freedom equal to 1 to 30, 40, 50, 60, 70, 80, 90, and 100. For example, to find the point in a chi-squared distribution with 8 degrees of freedom such that the area to its right is .05, locate 8 degrees of freedom in the left column and $\chi^2_{.050}$ across the top. The intersection of the row and column contains the number we seek as shown in Table 8.5; that is,

$$\chi^2_{.050,8} = 15.5$$

To find the point in the same distribution such that the area to its *left* is .05, find the point such that the area to its *right* is .95. Locate $\chi^2_{.950}$ across the top row and 8 degrees of freedom down the left column (also shown in Table 8.5). You should see that

$$\chi^2_{.950,8} = 2.73$$

TABLE **8.4** Critical Values of χ^2

ν	$\chi^2_{.995}$	$\chi^2_{.990}$	$\chi^2_{.975}$	$\chi^2_{.950}$	$\chi^2_{.900}$	$\chi^2_{.100}$	$\chi^2_{.050}$	$\chi^2_{.025}$	$\chi^2_{.010}$	$\chi^2_{.005}$
1	0.000039	0.000157	0.000982	0.00393	0.0158	2.71	3.84	5.02	6.63	7.88
2	0.0100	0.0201	0.0506	0.103	0.211	4.61	5.99	7.38	9.21	10.6
3	0.072	0.115	0.216	0.352	0.584	6.25	7.81	9.35	11.3	12.8

(Continued)

ν	$\chi^2_{.995}$	$\chi^2_{.990}$	$\chi^2_{.975}$	$\chi^2_{.950}$	$\chi^2_{.900}$	$\chi^2_{.100}$	$\chi^2_{.050}$	$\chi^2_{.025}$	$\chi^2_{.010}$	$\chi^2_{.005}$
4	0.207	0.297	0.484	0.711	1.06	7.78	9.49	11.1	13.3	14.9
5	0.412	0.554	0.831	1.15	1.61	9.24	11.1	12.8	15.1	16.7
6	0.676	0.872	1.24	1.64	2.20	10.6	12.6	14.4	16.8	18.5
7	0.989	1.24	1.69	2.17	2.83	12.0	14.1	16.0	18.5	20.3
8	1.34	1.65	2.18	2.73	3.49	13.4	15.5	17.5	20.1	22.0
9	1.73	2.09	2.70	3.33	4.17	14.7	16.9	19.0	21.7	23.6
10	2.16	2.56	3.25	3.94	4.87	16.0	18.3	20.5	23.2	25.2
11	2.60	3.05	3.82	4.57	5.58	17.3	19.7	21.9	24.7	26.8
12	3.07	3.57	4.40	5.23	6.30	18.5	21.0	23.3	26.2	28.3
13	3.57	4.11	5.01	5.89	7.04	19.8	22.4	24.7	27.7	29.8
14	4.07	4.66	5.63	6.57	7.79	21.1	23.7	26.1	29.1	31.3
15	4.60	5.23	6.26	7.26	8.55	22.3	25.0	27.5	30.6	32.8
16	5.14	5.81	6.91	7.96	9.31	23.5	26.3	28.8	32.0	34.3
17	5.70	6.41	7.56	8.67	10.09	24.8	27.6	30.2	33.4	35.7
18	6.26	7.01	8.23	9.39	10.86	26.0	28.9	31.5	34.8	37.2
19	6.84	7.63	8.91	10.12	11.65	27.2	30.1	32.9	36.2	38.6
20	7.43	8.26	9.59	10.85	12.44	28.4	31.4	34.2	37.6	40.0
21	8.03	8.90	10.28	11.59	13.24	29.6	32.7	35.5	38.9	41.4
22	8.64	9.54	10.98	12.34	14.04	30.8	33.9	36.8	40.3	42.8
23	9.26	10.20	11.69	13.09	14.85	32.0	35.2	38.1	41.6	44.2
24	9.89	10.86	12.40	13.85	15.66	33.2	36.4	39.4	43.0	45.6
25	10.52	11.52	13.12	14.61	16.47	34.4	37.7	40.6	44.3	46.9
26	11.16	12.20	13.84	15.38	17.29	35.6	38.9	41.9	45.6	48.3
27	11.81	12.88	14.57	16.15	18.11	36.7	40.1	43.2	47.0	49.6
28	12.46	13.56	15.31	16.93	18.94	37.9	41.3	44.5	48.3	51.0
29	13.12	14.26	16.05	17.71	19.77	39.1	42.6	45.7	49.6	52.3
30	13.79	14.95	16.79	18.49	20.60	40.3	43.8	47.0	50.9	53.7
40	20.71	22.16	24.43	26.51	29.05	51.8	55.8	59.3	63.7	66.8
50	27.99	29.71	32.36	34.76	37.69	63.2	67.5	71.4	76.2	79.5
60	35.53	37.48	40.48	43.19	46.46	74.4	79.1	83.3	88.4	92.0
70	43.28	45.44	48.76	51.74	55.33	85.5	90.5	95.0	100	104
80	51.17	53.54	57.15	60.39	64.28	96.6	102	107	112	116
90	59.20	61.75	65.65	69.13	73.29	108	113	118	124	128
100	67.33	70.06	74.22	77.93	82.36	118	124	130	136	140

TABLE **8.5** Critical Values of $\chi^2_{.05,8}$ and $\chi^2_{.950,8}$

DEGREES OF FREEDOM	$\chi^2_{.995}$	$\chi^2_{.990}$	$\chi^2_{.975}$	$\chi^2_{.950}$	$\chi^2_{.900}$	$\chi^2_{.100}$	$\chi^2_{.050}$	$\chi^2_{.025}$	$\chi^2_{.010}$	$\chi^2_{.005}$
1	0.000039	0.000157	0.000982	0.00393	0.0158	2.71	3.84	5.02	6.63	7.88
2	0.0100	0.0201	0.0506	0.103	0.211	4.61	5.99	7.38	9.21	10.6
3	0.072	0.115	0.216	0.352	0.584	6.25	7.81	9.35	11.3	12.8
4	0.207	0.297	0.484	0.711	1.06	7.78	9.49	11.1	13.3	14.9
5	0.412	0.554	0.831	1.15	1.61	9.24	11.1	12.8	15.1	16.7
6	0.676	0.872	1.24	1.64	2.20	10.6	12.6	14.4	16.8	18.5
7	0.989	1.24	1.69	2.17	2.83	12.0	14.1	16.0	18.5	20.3
8	1.34	1.65	2.18	2.73	3.49	13.4	15.5	17.5	20.1	22.0
9	1.73	2.09	2.70	3.33	4.17	14.7	16.9	19.0	21.7	23.6
10	2.16	2.56	3.25	3.94	4.87	16.0	18.3	20.5	23.2	25.2
11	2.60	3.05	3.82	4.57	5.58	17.3	19.7	21.9	24.7	26.8

For values of degrees of freedom greater than 100, the chi-squared distribution can be approximated by a normal distribution with $\mu = \nu$ and $\sigma = \sqrt{2\nu}$.

EXCEL Function

To calculate $P(\chi^2 > x)$, type into any cell

$$= \textbf{CHIDIST}([x], [\nu])$$

For example, **CHIDIST**$(6.25, 3) = .100$.

To determine $\chi_{A,\nu}$, type

$$= \textbf{CHIINV}([A], [\nu])$$

For example, $= \textbf{CHIINV}(.10, 3) = 6.25$

8-4b *F* Distribution

The density function of the *F* distribution is given in the following box.

F Density Function

$$f(F) = \frac{\Gamma\left(\dfrac{\nu_1 + \nu_2}{2}\right)}{\Gamma\left(\dfrac{\nu_1}{2}\right)\Gamma\left(\dfrac{\nu_2}{2}\right)} \left(\frac{\nu_1}{\nu_2}\right)^{\frac{\nu_1}{2}} \frac{F^{\frac{\nu_1-2}{2}}}{\left(1 + \dfrac{\nu_1 F}{\nu_2}\right)^{\frac{\nu_2+\nu_2}{2}}} \quad F > 0$$

where F ranges from 0 to ∞ and ν_1 and ν_2 are the parameters of the distribution called degrees of freedom. For reasons that are clearer in Chapter 13, we call ν_1 the *numerator degrees of freedom* and ν_2 the *denominator degrees of freedom*.

The mean and variance of an F random variable are

$$E(F) = \frac{\nu_2}{\nu_2 - 2} \quad \nu_2 > 2$$

and

$$V(F) = \frac{2\nu_2^2(\nu_1 + \nu_2 - 2)}{\nu_1(\nu_2 - 2)^2(\nu_2 - 4)} \quad \nu_2 > 4$$

Notice that the mean depends only on the denominator degrees of freedom and that for large ν_2 the mean of the F distribution is approximately 1. Figure 8.30 describes the density function when it is graphed. As you can see, the F distribution is positively skewed. Its actual shape depends on the two numbers of degrees of freedom.

FIGURE **8.30** *F* Distribution

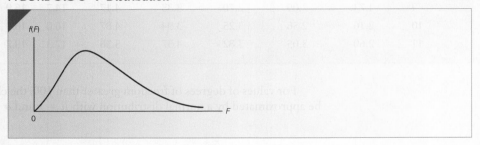

Determining Values of *F* We define F_{A,ν_1,ν_2} as the value of F with ν_1 and ν_2 degrees of freedom such that the area to its right under the curve is A; that is,

$$P(F > F_{A,\nu_1,\nu_2}) = A$$

Because the F random variable like the chi-squared can equal only positive values, we define F_{1-A,ν_1,ν_2} as the value such that the area to its left is A. Figure 8.31 depicts this notation. Table 6 in Appendix B provides values of F_{A,ν_1,ν_2} for $A = .05, .025, .01,$ and .005. Part of Table 6 is reproduced here as Table 8.6.

Values of F_{1-A,ν_1,ν_2} are unavailable. However, we do not need them because we can determine F_{1-A,ν_1,ν_2} from F_{A,ν_1,ν_2}. Statisticians can show that

$$F_{1-A,\nu_1,\nu_2} = \frac{1}{F_{A,\nu_2,\nu_1}}.$$

FIGURE **8.31** F_{1-A} and F_A

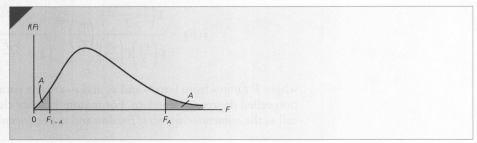

TABLE **8.6** Critical Values of F_A for $A = .05$

ν_2	ν_1 1	2	3	4	5	6	7	8	9	10
1	161	199	216	225	230	234	237	239	241	242
2	18.5	19.0	19.2	19.2	19.3	19.3	19.4	19.4	19.4	19.4
3	10.1	9.55	9.28	9.12	9.01	8.94	8.89	8.85	8.81	8.79
4	7.71	6.94	6.59	6.39	6.26	6.16	6.09	6.04	6.00	5.96
5	6.61	5.79	5.41	5.19	5.05	4.95	4.88	4.82	4.77	4.74
6	5.99	5.14	4.76	4.53	4.39	4.28	4.21	4.15	4.10	4.06
7	5.59	4.74	4.35	4.12	3.97	3.87	3.79	3.73	3.68	3.64
8	5.32	4.46	4.07	3.84	3.69	3.58	3.50	3.44	3.39	3.35
9	5.12	4.26	3.86	3.63	3.48	3.37	3.29	3.23	3.18	3.14
10	4.96	4.10	3.71	3.48	3.33	3.22	3.14	3.07	3.02	2.98
11	4.84	3.98	3.59	3.36	3.20	3.09	3.01	2.95	2.90	2.85
12	4.75	3.89	3.49	3.26	3.11	3.00	2.91	2.85	2.80	2.75
13	4.67	3.81	3.41	3.18	3.03	2.92	2.83	2.77	2.71	2.67
14	4.60	3.74	3.34	3.11	2.96	2.85	2.76	2.70	2.65	2.60
15	4.54	3.68	3.29	3.06	2.90	2.79	2.71	2.64	2.59	2.54
16	4.49	3.63	3.24	3.01	2.85	2.74	2.66	2.59	2.54	2.49
17	4.45	3.59	3.20	2.96	2.81	2.70	2.61	2.55	2.49	2.45
18	4.41	3.55	3.16	2.93	2.77	2.66	2.58	2.51	2.46	2.41
19	4.38	3.52	3.13	2.90	2.74	2.63	2.54	2.48	2.42	2.38
20	4.35	3.49	3.10	2.87	2.71	2.60	2.51	2.45	2.39	2.35
22	4.30	3.44	3.05	2.82	2.66	2.55	2.46	2.40	2.34	2.30
24	4.26	3.40	3.01	2.78	2.62	2.51	2.42	2.36	2.30	2.25
26	4.23	3.37	2.98	2.74	2.59	2.47	2.39	2.32	2.27	2.22
28	4.20	3.34	2.95	2.71	2.56	2.45	2.36	2.29	2.24	2.19
30	4.17	3.32	2.92	2.69	2.53	2.42	2.33	2.27	2.21	2.16
35	4.12	3.27	2.87	2.64	2.49	2.37	2.29	2.22	2.16	2.11
40	4.08	3.23	2.84	2.61	2.45	2.34	2.25	2.18	2.12	2.08
45	4.06	3.20	2.81	2.58	2.42	2.31	2.22	2.15	2.10	2.05
50	4.03	3.18	2.79	2.56	2.40	2.29	2.20	2.13	2.07	2.03
60	4.00	3.15	2.76	2.53	2.37	2.25	2.17	2.10	2.04	1.99
70	3.98	3.13	2.74	2.50	2.35	2.23	2.14	2.07	2.02	1.97
80	3.96	3.11	2.72	2.49	2.33	2.21	2.13	2.06	2.00	1.95
90	3.95	3.10	2.71	2.47	2.32	2.20	2.11	2.04	1.99	1.94
100	3.94	3.09	2.70	2.46	2.31	2.19	2.10	2.03	1.97	1.93
120	3.92	3.07	2.68	2.45	2.29	2.18	2.09	2.02	1.96	1.91
140	3.91	3.06	2.67	2.44	2.28	2.16	2.08	2.01	1.95	1.90
160	3.90	3.05	2.66	2.43	2.27	2.16	2.07	2.00	1.94	1.89
180	3.89	3.05	2.65	2.42	2.26	2.15	2.06	1.99	1.93	1.88
200	3.89	3.04	2.65	2.42	2.26	2.14	2.06	1.98	1.93	1.88
∞	3.84	3.00	2.61	2.37	2.21	2.10	2.01	1.94	1.88	1.83

To determine any critical value, find the numerator degrees of freedom ν_1 across the top of Table 6 and the denominator degrees of freedom ν_2 down the left column. The intersection of the row and column contains the number we seek. To illustrate, suppose that we want to find $F_{.05,5,7}$. Table 8.7 shows how this point is found. Locate the numerator degrees of freedom, 5, across the top and the denominator degrees of freedom, 7, down the left column. The intersection is 3.97. Thus, $F_{.05,5,7} = 3.97$.

TABLE **8.7** $F_{.05,5,7}$

ν_1 / ν_2	NUMERATOR DEGREES OF FREEDOM								
	1	2	3	4	5	6	7	8	9
1	161	199	216	225	230	234	237	239	241
2	18.5	19.0	19.2	19.2	19.3	19.3	19.4	19.4	19.4
3	10.1	9.55	9.28	9.12	9.01	8.94	8.89	8.85	8.81
4	7.71	6.94	6.59	6.39	6.26	6.16	6.09	6.04	6.00
5	6.61	5.79	5.41	5.19	5.05	4.95	4.88	4.82	4.77
6	5.99	5.14	4.76	4.53	4.39	4.28	4.21	4.15	4.1
7	5.59	4.74	4.35	4.12	3.97	3.87	3.79	3.73	3.68
8	5.32	4.46	4.07	3.84	3.69	3.58	3.5	3.44	3.39
9	5.12	4.26	3.86	3.63	3.48	3.37	3.29	3.23	3.18
10	4.96	4.10	3.71	3.48	3.33	3.22	3.14	3.07	3.02

Denominator Degrees of Freedom

Note that the order in which the degrees of freedom appear is important. To find $F_{.05,7,5}$ (numerator degrees of freedom = 7 and denominator degrees of freedom = 5), we locate 7 across the top and 5 down the side. The intersection is $F_{.05,7,5} = 4.88$.

Suppose that we want to determine the point in an F distribution with $\nu_1 = 4$ and $\nu_2 = 8$ such that the area to its right is .95. Thus,

$$F_{.95,4,8} = \frac{1}{F_{.05,8,4}} = \frac{1}{6.04} = .166$$

EXCEL Function

For probabilities, type

$$= \textbf{FDIST}([X], [\nu_1], [\nu_2])$$

For example, $= \textbf{FDIST}(3.97, 5, 7) = .05$.

To determine F_{A,ν_1,ν_2}, type

$$= \textbf{FINV}([A], [\nu_1], [\nu_2])$$

For example, $= \textbf{FINV}(.05, 5, 7) = 3.97$.

EXERCISES

Some of the following exercises require the use of a computer and software.

8.111 Use the t table (Table 4) to find the following values of t.
 a. $t_{.10,15}$ b. $t_{.10,23}$ c. $t_{.025,83}$ d. $t_{.05,195}$

8.112 Use the t table (Table 4) to find the following values of t.
 a. $t_{.005,33}$ b. $t_{.10,600}$ c. $t_{.05,4}$ d. $t_{.01,20}$

8.113 Use a computer to find the following values of t.
 a. $t_{.10,15}$ b. $t_{.10,23}$ c. $t_{.025,83}$ d. $t_{.05,195}$

8.114 Use a computer to find the following values of t.
 a. $t_{.05,143}$ b. $t_{.01,12}$ c. $t_{.025,\infty}$ d. $t_{.05,100}$

8.115 Use a computer to find the following probabilities.
 a. $P(t_{64} > 2.12)$ c. $P(t_{159} > 1.33)$
 b. $P(t_{27} > 1.90)$ d. $P(t_{550} > 1.85)$

8.116 Use a computer to find the following probabilities.
 a. $P(t_{141} > .94)$ c. $P(t_{1000} > 1.96)$
 b. $P(t_{421} > 2.00)$ d. $P(t_{82} > 1.96)$

8.117 Use the χ^2 table (Table 5) to find the following values of χ^2.
 a. $\chi^2_{.10,5}$ b. $\chi^2_{.01,100}$ c. $\chi^2_{.95,18}$ d. $\chi^2_{.99,60}$

8.118 Use the χ^2 table (Table 5) to find the following values of χ^2.
 a. $\chi^2_{.90,26}$ b. $\chi^2_{.01,30}$ c. $\chi^2_{.10,1}$ d. $\chi^2_{.99,80}$

8.119 Use a computer to find the following values of χ^2.
 a. $\chi^2_{.25,66}$ b. $\chi^2_{.40,100}$ c. $\chi^2_{.50,17}$ d. $\chi^2_{.10,17}$

8.120 Use a computer to find the following values of χ^2.
 a. $\chi^2_{.99,55}$ b. $\chi^2_{.05,800}$ c. $\chi^2_{.99,43}$ d. $\chi^2_{.10,233}$

8.121 Use a computer to find the following probabilities.
 a. $P(\chi^2_{73} > 80)$
 b. $P(\chi^2_{200} > 125)$
 c. $P(\chi^2_{88} > 60)$
 d. $P(\chi^2_{1000} > 450)$

8.122 Use a computer to find the following probabilities.
 a. $P(\chi^2_{250} > 250)$ c. $P(\chi^2_{600} > 500)$
 b. $P(\chi^2_{36} > 25)$ d. $P(\chi^2_{120} > 100)$

8.123 Use the F table (Table 6) to find the following values of F.
 a. $F_{.05,3,7}$ b. $F_{.05,7,3}$ c. $F_{.025,5,20}$ d. $F_{.01,12,60}$

8.124 Use the F table (Table 6) to find the following values of F.
 a. $F_{.025,8,22}$ c. $F_{.01,9,18}$
 b. $F_{.05,20,30}$ d. $F_{.025,24,10}$

8.125 Use a computer to find the following values of F.
 a. $F_{.05,70,70}$ c. $F_{.025,36,50}$
 b. $F_{.01,45,100}$ d. $F_{.05,500,500}$

8.126 Use a computer to find the following values of F.
 a. $F_{.01,100,150}$ c. $F_{.01,11,33}$
 b. $F_{.05,25,125}$ d. $F_{.05,300,800}$

8.127 Use a computer to find the following probabilities.
 a. $P(F_{7,20} > 2.5)$ c. $P(F_{34,62} > 1.8)$
 b. $P(F_{18,63} > 1.4)$ d. $P(F_{200,400} > 1.1)$

8.128 Use a computer to find the following probabilities.
 a. $P(F_{600,800} > 1.1)$
 b. $P(F_{35,100} > 1.3)$
 c. $P(F_{66,148} > 2.1)$
 d. $P(F_{17,37} > 2.8)$

CHAPTER SUMMARY

This chapter dealt with **continuous random variables** and their distributions. Because a continuous random variable can assume an infinite number of values, the probability that the random variable equals any single value is 0. Consequently, we addressed the problem of computing the probability of a range of values. We showed that the probability of any interval is the area in the interval under the curve representing the **density function**.

  We introduced the most important distribution in statistics and showed how to compute the probability that a normal random variable falls into any interval. Additionally, we demonstrated how to use the normal table backward to find values of a normal random variable given a probability. Next we introduced the **exponential distribution**, a distribution that is particularly useful in several management-science applications. Finally, we presented three more continuous random variables and their probability density functions. The **Student t, chi-squared,** and **F distributions** will be used extensively in statistical inference.

IMPORTANT TERMS:

Probability density function   266
Uniform probability distribution   267
Rectangular probability distribution   267
Normal distribution   271
Normal random variable   271
Standard normal random variable   273

Exponential distribution   289
Student t distribution   294
Degrees of freedom   294
Chi-squared distribution   298
F distribution   301

SYMBOLS:

Symbol	Pronounced	Represents
π	pi	$3.14159\dots$
z_A	z-sub-A or z-A	Value of Z such that area to its right is A
ν	nu	Degrees of freedom
t_A	t-sub-A or t-A	Value of t such that area to its right is A
χ^2_A	chi-squared-sub-A or chi-squared-A	Value of chi-squared such that area to its right is A
F_A	F-sub-A or F-A	Value of F such that area to its right is A
ν_1	nu-sub-one or nu-one	Numerator degrees of freedom
ν_2	nu-sub-two or nu-two	Denominator degrees of freedom

EXCEL OUTPUT AND INSTRUCTIONS:

Probability/Random Variable	
Normal probability	282
Normal random variable	283
Exponential probability	291
Student t probability	297
Student t random variable	298
Chi-squared probability	301
Chi-squared random variable	301
F probability	304
F random variable	304

George Rudy/Shutterstock.com

9

SAMPLING DISTRIBUTIONS

CHAPTER OUTLINE

Salaries of a Business School's Graduates

Deans and other faculty members in professional schools often monitor how well the graduates of their programs fare in the job market. Information about the types of jobs and their salaries may provide useful information about the success of a program.

In the advertisements for a large university, the dean of the School of Business claims that the average salary of the school's graduates 1 year after graduation is $800 per week, with a standard deviation of $100. A second-year student in the business school who has just completed the statistics course would like to check whether the claim about the mean is correct. The student does a survey of 25 people who graduated 1 year earlier and determines their weekly salary and calculates the sample mean to be $750. To interpret this result, the student needs to calculate the probability that a sample of 25 graduates would have a mean of $750 or less when the population mean is $800 and the standard deviation is $100. After calculating the probability, what conclusion should be drawn?

Anton Gvozdikov/Shutterstock.com

See page 315 for the answer.

INTRODUCTION

This chapter introduces the *sampling distribution*, a fundamental element in statistical inference. We remind you that statistical inference is the process of converting data into information. Here are the parts of the process we have thus far discussed:

1. Parameters describe populations.

2. Parameters are almost always unknown.

3. We take a random sample of a population to obtain the necessary data.

4. We calculate one or more statistics from the data.

For example, to estimate a population mean, we compute the sample mean. Although there is very little chance that the sample mean and the population mean are identical, we would expect them to be quite close. However, for the purposes of statistical inference, we need to be able to measure *how* close. The sampling distribution provides this service. It plays a crucial role in the process because the measure of proximity it provides is the key to statistical inference.

9-1 / SAMPLING DISTRIBUTION OF THE MEAN

A **sampling distribution** is created by, as the name suggests, sampling. There are two ways to create a sampling distribution. The first is to actually draw samples of the same size from a population, calculate the statistic of interest, and then use descriptive techniques to learn more about the sampling distribution. The second method relies on the rules of probability and the laws of expected value and variance to derive the sampling distribution. We'll demonstrate the latter approach by developing the sampling distribution of the mean of two dice.

9-1a Sampling Distribution of the Mean of Two Dice

The population is created by throwing a fair die infinitely many times, with the random variable X indicating the number of spots showing on any one throw. The probability distribution of the random variable X is as follows:

x	1	2	3	4	5	6
$P(x)$	1/6	1/6	1/6	1/6	1/6	1/6

The population is infinitely large because we can throw the die infinitely many times (or at least imagine doing so). From the definitions of expected value and variance presented in Section 7-1, we calculate the population mean, variance, and standard deviation.

Population mean:

$$\mu = \sum xP(x)$$

$$= 1(1/6) + 2(1/6) + 3(1/6) + 4(1/6) + 5(1/6) + 6(1/6)$$

$$= 3.5$$

Population variance:

$$\sigma^2 = \sum (x - \mu)^2 P(x)$$
$$= (1 - 3.5)^2(1/6) + (2 - 3.5)^2(1/6) + (3 - 3.5)^2(1/6) + (4 - 3.5)^2(1/6)$$
$$+ (5 - 3.5)^2(1/6) + (6 - 3.5)^2(1/6)$$
$$= 2.92$$

Population standard deviation:

$$\sigma = \sqrt{\sigma^2} = \sqrt{2.92} = 1.71$$

The sampling distribution is created by drawing samples of size 2 from the population. In other words, we toss two dice. Figure 9.1 depicts this process in which we compute the mean for each sample. Because the value of the sample mean varies randomly from sample to sample, we can regard $\overline{X}$ as a new random variable created by sampling. Table 9.1 lists all the possible samples and their corresponding values of $\bar{x}$.

FIGURE **9.1** Drawing Samples of Size 2 from a Population

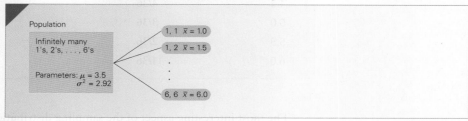

TABLE **9.1** All Samples of Size 2 and Their Means

SAMPLE	$\overline{X}$	SAMPLE	$\overline{X}$	SAMPLE	$\overline{X}$
1, 1	1.0	3, 1	2.0	5, 1	3.0
1, 2	1.5	3, 2	2.5	5, 2	3.5
1, 3	2.0	3, 3	3.0	5, 3	4.0
1, 4	2.5	3, 4	3.5	5, 4	4.5
1, 5	3.0	3, 5	4.0	5, 5	5.0
1, 6	3.5	3, 6	4.5	5, 6	5.5
2, 1	1.5	4, 1	2.5	6, 1	3.5
2, 2	2.0	4, 2	3.0	6, 2	4.0
2, 3	2.5	4, 3	3.5	6, 3	4.5
2, 4	3.0	4, 4	4.0	6, 4	5.0
2, 5	3.5	4, 5	4.5	6, 5	5.5
2, 6	4.0	4, 6	5.0	6, 6	6.0

There are 36 different possible samples of size 2; because each sample is equally likely, the probability of any one sample being selected is 1/36. However, $\bar{x}$ can assume only 11 different possible values: 1.0, 1.5, 2.0, ..., 6.0, with certain values of $\bar{x}$ occurring more frequently than others. The value $\bar{x} = 1.0$ occurs only once, so its probability is $1/36$. The value $\bar{x} = 1.5$ can occur in two ways—(1, 2) and (2, 1)—each having the same probability (1/36). Thus, $P(\bar{x} = 1.5) = 2/36$. The probabilities of the other values of $\bar{x}$ are determined in similar fashion, and the resulting **sampling distribution of the sample mean** is shown in Table 9.2.

TABLE **9.2** Sampling Distribution of $\bar{X}$

$\bar{X}$	$P(\bar{X})$
1.0	1/36
1.5	2/36
2.0	3/36
2.5	4/36
3.0	5/36
3.5	6/36
4.0	5/36
4.5	4/36
5.0	3/36
5.5	2/36
6.0	1/36

The most interesting aspect of the sampling distribution of $\bar{X}$ is how different it is from the distribution of X, as can be seen in Figure 9.2.

FIGURE **9.2** Distributions of X and $\bar{X}$

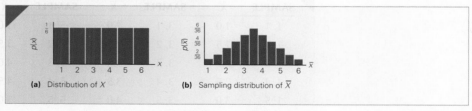

(a) Distribution of X (b) Sampling distribution of $\bar{X}$

We can also compute the mean, variance, and standard deviation of the sampling distribution. Once again using the definitions of expected value and variance, we determine the following parameters of the sampling distribution.

Mean of the sampling distribution of $\bar{X}$:

$$\mu_{\bar{x}} = \sum \bar{x}P(\bar{x})$$
$$= 1.0(1/36) + 1.5(2/36) + \cdots + 6.0(1/36)$$
$$= 3.5$$

Notice that the mean of the sampling distribution of $\bar{X}$ is equal to the mean of the population of the toss of a die computed previously.

FIGURE **9.4** Distribution of X and Sampling Distribution of $\bar{X}$

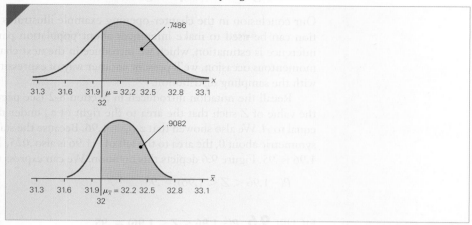

In Example 9.1(b), we began with the assumption that both μ and σ were known. Then, using the sampling distribution, we made a probability statement about $\bar{X}$. Unfortunately, the values of μ and σ are not usually known, so an analysis such as that in Example 9.1 cannot usually be conducted. However, we can use the sampling distribution to infer something about an unknown value of μ on the basis of a sample mean.

Salaries of a Business School's Graduates: Solution

We want to find the probability that the sample mean is less than $750. Thus, we seek

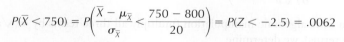

$$P(\bar{X} < 750)$$

The distribution of X, the weekly income, is likely to be positively skewed, but not sufficiently so to make the distribution of $\bar{X}$ nonnormal. As a result, we may assume that $\bar{X}$ is normal with mean $\mu_{\bar{X}} = \mu = 800$ and standard deviation $\sigma_{\bar{X}} = \sigma/\sqrt{n} = 100/\sqrt{25} = 20$. Thus,

$$P(\bar{X} < 750) = P\left(\frac{\bar{X} - \mu_{\bar{X}}}{\sigma_{\bar{X}}} < \frac{750 - 800}{20}\right) = P(Z < -2.5) = .0062$$

Figure 9.5 illustrates the distribution.

FIGURE **9.5** $P(\bar{X} < 750)$

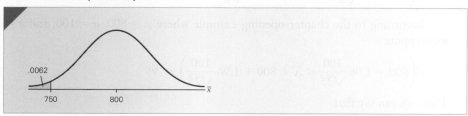

The probability of observing a sample mean as low as $750 when the population mean is $800 is extremely small. Because this event is quite unlikely, we would have to conclude that the dean's claim is not justified.

9-1c Using the Sampling Distribution for Inference

Our conclusion in the chapter-opening example illustrates how the sampling distribution can be used to make inferences about population parameters. The first form of inference is estimation, which we introduce in the next chapter. In preparation for this momentous occasion, we'll present another way of expressing the probability associated with the sampling distribution.

Recall the notation introduced in Section 8-2 (see page 278). We defined z_A to be the value of Z such that the area to the right of z_A under the standard normal curve is equal to A. We also showed that $z_{.025} = 1.96$. Because the standard normal distribution is symmetric about 0, the area to the left of -1.96 is also .025. The area between -1.96 and 1.96 is .95. Figure 9.6 depicts this notation. We can express the notation algebraically as

$$P(-1.96 < Z < 1.96) = .95$$

FIGURE **9.6** $P(-1.96 < Z < 1.96) = .95$

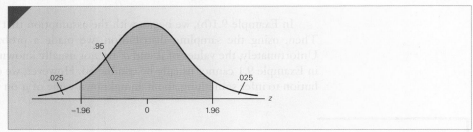

In this section, we established that

$$Z = \frac{\overline{X} - \mu}{\sigma/\sqrt{n}}$$

is standard normally distributed. Substituting this form of Z into the previous probability statement, we produce

$$P\left(-1.96 < \frac{\overline{X} - \mu}{\sigma/\sqrt{n}} < 1.96\right) = .95$$

With a little algebraic manipulation (multiply all three terms by $\sigma/\sqrt{n}$ and add μ to all three terms), we determine

$$P\left(\mu - 1.96\frac{\sigma}{\sqrt{n}} < \overline{X} < \mu + 1.96\frac{\sigma}{\sqrt{n}}\right) = .95$$

Returning to the chapter-opening example where $\mu = 800$, $\sigma = 100$, and $n = 25$, we compute

$$P\left(800 - 1.96\frac{100}{\sqrt{25}} < \overline{X} < 800 + 1.96\frac{100}{\sqrt{25}}\right) = .95$$

Thus, we can say that

$$P(760.8 < \overline{X} < 839.2) = .95$$

This tells us that there is a 95% probability that a sample mean will fall between 760.8 and 839.2. Because the sample mean was computed to be $750, we would have to conclude that the dean's claim is not supported by the statistic.

Changing the probability from .95 to .90 changes the probability statement to

$$P\left(\mu - 1.645 \frac{\sigma}{\sqrt{n}} < \overline{X} < \mu + 1.645 \frac{\sigma}{\sqrt{n}}\right) = .90$$

We can also produce a general form of this statement:

$$P\left(\mu - z_{\alpha/2}\frac{\sigma}{\sqrt{n}} < \overline{X} < \mu + z_{\alpha/2}\frac{\sigma}{\sqrt{n}}\right) = 1 - \alpha$$

In this formula α (Greek letter *alpha*) is the probability that $\overline{X}$ does not fall into the interval. To apply this formula, all we need to do is substitute the values for μ, σ, n, and α. For example, with $\mu = 800$, $\sigma = 100$, $n = 25$, and $\alpha = .01$, we produce

$$P\left(\mu - z_{.005}\frac{\sigma}{\sqrt{n}} < \overline{X} < \mu + z_{.005}\frac{\sigma}{\sqrt{n}}\right) = 1 - .01$$

$$P\left(800 - 2.575 \frac{100}{\sqrt{25}} < \overline{X} < 800 + 2.575 \frac{100}{\sqrt{25}}\right) = .99$$

$$P(748.5 < \overline{X} < 851.5) = .99$$

which is another probability statement about $\overline{X}$. In Section 10-2, we will use a similar type of probability statement to derive the first statistical inference technique.

9-1d Creating the Sampling Distribution Empirically by Computer Simulation

We can use Excel to approximate the theoretical sampling distribution. We'll start with the sampling distribution of the mean of the toss of two dice.

1. Set up the distribution of the toss of one die. In Column A, store the numbers 1, 2, 3, 4, 5, 6 and in Cell B1 type

   = 1/6

   (Do not type .1667 or any other version of 1/6 since the sum of the probabilities will not equal 1 causing Excel to issue an error warning at step 4.) Drag to fill cells B2–B6.

2. Click **Data, Data Analysis**, and **Random Number Generation**.

3. Type 2 to specify the **Number of Variables** and type 10000 to specify the **Number of Random Numbers**.

4. Click **Discrete** distribution and in the **Parameters** box type A1:B6 to specify the **Value and Probability Input Range**.

5. Specify **New Worksheet Ply** and click **OK**. Columns A and B of the new worksheet ply will fill with the random numbers.

6. In column C row 1, type

   = AVERAGE(A1:B1)

7. Drag to fill the rest of Column C. Column C will now contain the values of the sample means.

It is important to understand that sampling distributions created in this way are only approximations of the theoretical sampling distributions. As a result, the histogram of the sample means will not look exactly like Figure 9.2 and the mean and standard deviation of the sample means will only approximate the theoretical values 3.5 and 1.21, respectively. Of course, if we increase the number of simulated tosses of the two dice to (say) a million, the approximations will be better.

COMPUTER SIMULATION EXERCISES

Exercises 9.1 to 9.8 are based on the simulation described in Subsection 9-1d.

9.1 Draw the histogram of the sample means using bins 1.0, 1.5, 2.0, . . ., 6.0. Does it appear to be bell shaped? Explain.

9.2 Calculate the mean and standard deviation of the sample means stored in Column C. These are the mean and standard deviation of the simulated sampling distribution. Are they close to the theoretical values of 3.5 and 1.21?

9.3 Repeat the simulation using the sample size $n = 10$. Draw the histogram using bins 1.0, 1.5, 2.0, . . ., 6.0. Compare this histogram with the one you created in Exercise 9.1. Describe the differences between the two histograms.

9.4 Refer to Exercise 9.3. Compute the mean and standard deviation of the simulated sampling distribution. Compare them with the theoretical values of

$$\mu_{\bar{x}} = \mu = 3.5$$

$$\sigma_{\bar{x}} = \frac{\sigma}{\sqrt{n}} = \frac{1.71}{\sqrt{10}} = .54$$

9.5 Repeat the simulation described above with the following changes. At step 3, specify 1 for the Number of Variables and 10000 for the Number of Random Numbers. At step 4, change the distribution to Normal and type the Parameters Mean 100 and Standard Deviation 20. Calculate the mean and standard deviation of these numbers and draw a histogram. Describe your results.

9.6 Refer to Exercise 9.5. Create the sampling distribution of the mean from a normal population with mean 100 and standard deviation of 20 and a sample of size 9. Calculate the mean and standard deviation of these numbers and draw a histogram. Compare these results with those in Exercise 9.5.

9.7 Refer to Exercise 9.6. Determine the sampling distribution of the sample median. Draw the histogram and compute the mean and standard deviation

of the sampling distribution. Compare the results of Exercise 9.6.

9.8 Repeat Exercise 9.6 calculating the sampling distribution of the sample variance. Describe its shape.

9.9 Let X represent the result of the toss of a fair die. Find the following probabilities.

a. $P(X = 1)$
b. $P(X = 6)$

9.10 Let $\bar{X}$ represent the mean of the toss of two fair dice. Use the probabilities listed in Table 9.2 to determine the following probabilities.

a. $P(\bar{X} = 1)$
b. $P(\bar{X} = 6)$

9.11 An experiment consists of tossing five balanced dice. Find the following probabilities. (Determine the exact probabilities as we did in Tables 9.1 and 9.2 for two dice.)

a. $P(\bar{X} = 1)$
b. $P(\bar{X} = 6)$

9.12 Refer to Exercises 9.9–9.11. What do the probabilities tell you about the variances of X and $\bar{X}$?

9.13 A normally distributed population has a mean of 40 and a standard deviation of 12. What does the central limit theorem say about the sampling distribution of the mean if samples of size 100 are drawn from this population?

9.14 Refer to Exercise 9.13. Suppose that the population is not normally distributed. Does this change your answer? Explain.

9.15 A sample of $n = 16$ observations is drawn from a normal population with $\mu = 1,000$ and $\sigma = 200$. Find the following.

a. $P(\bar{X} > 1,050)$
b. $P(\bar{X} < 960)$
c. $P(\bar{X} > 1,100)$

9.16 Repeat Exercise 9.15 with $n = 25$.

9.17 Repeat Exercise 9.15 with $n = 100$.

9.18 Given a normal population whose mean is 50 and whose standard deviation is 5, find the probability that a random sample of
a. 4 has a mean between 49 and 52.
b. 16 has a mean between 49 and 52.
c. 25 has a mean between 49 and 52.

9.19 Repeat Exercise 9.18 for a standard deviation of 10.

9.20 Repeat Exercise 9.18 for a standard deviation of 20.

9.21 a. Calculate the finite population correction factor when the population size is $N = 1,000$ and the sample size is $n = 100$.
b. Repeat part (a) when $N = 3,000$.
c. Repeat part (a) when $N = 5,000$.
d. What have you learned about the finite population correction factor when N is large relative to n?

9.22 a. Suppose that the standard deviation of a population with $N = 10,000$ members is 500. Determine the standard error of the sampling distribution of the mean when the sample size is 1,000.
b. Repeat part (a) when $n = 500$.
c. Repeat part (a) when $n = 100$.

9.23 The heights of North American women are normally distributed with a mean of 64 inches and a standard deviation of 2 inches.
a. What is the probability that a randomly selected woman is taller than 66 inches?
b. A random sample of four women is selected. What is the probability that the sample mean height is greater than 66 inches?
c. What is the probability that the mean height of a random sample of 100 women is greater than 66 inches?

9.24 Refer to Exercise 9.23. If the population of women's heights is not normally distributed, which, if any, of the questions can you answer? Explain.

9.25 An automatic machine in a manufacturing process is operating properly if the lengths of an important subcomponent are normally distributed with mean = 117 cm and standard deviation = 5.2 cm.
a. Find the probability that one selected subcomponent is longer than 120 cm.
b. Find the probability that if four subcomponents are randomly selected, their mean length exceeds 120 cm.
c. Find the probability that if four subcomponents are randomly selected, all four have lengths that exceed 120 cm.

9.26 Statisticians determined that the mortgages of homeowners in a city is normally distributed with a mean of $250,000 and a standard deviation of $50,000. A random sample of 100 homeowners was drawn.

What is the probability that the mean is greater than $262,000?

9.27 Refer to Exercise 9.26. Does your answer change if you discover that mortgages are not normally distributed?

9.28 The amount of time the university professors devote to their jobs per week is normally distributed with a mean of 52 hours and a standard deviation of 6 hours.
a. What is the probability that a professor works for more than 60 hours per week?
b. Find the probability that the mean amount of work per week for three randomly selected professors is more than 60 hours.
c. Find the probability that if three professors are randomly selected all three work for more than 60 hours per week.

9.29 The number of pizzas consumed per month by university students is normally distributed with a mean of 10 and a standard deviation of 3.
a. What proportion of students consume more than 12 pizzas per month?
b. What is the probability that in a random sample of 25 students more than 275 pizzas are consumed? (*Hint:* What is the mean number of pizzas consumed by the sample of 25 students?)

9.30 The marks on a statistics midterm test are normally distributed with a mean of 78 and a standard deviation of 6.
a. What proportion of the class has a midterm mark of less than 75?
b. What is the probability that a class of 50 has an average midterm mark that is less than 75?

9.31 The amount of time spent by North American adults watching television per day is normally distributed with a mean of 6 hours and a standard deviation of 1.5 hours.
a. What is the probability that a randomly selected North American adult watches television for more than 7 hours per day?
b. What is the probability that the average time watching television by a random sample of five North American adults is more than 7 hours?
c. What is the probability that in a random sample of five North American adults, all watch television for more than 7 hours per day?

9.32 The manufacturer of cans of salmon that are supposed to have a net weight of 6 ounces tells you that the net weight is actually a normal random variable with a mean of 6.05 ounces and a standard deviation of .18 ounces. Suppose that you draw a random sample of 36 cans.

a. Find the probability that the mean weight of the sample is less than 5.97 ounces.

b. Suppose your random sample of 36 cans of salmon produced a mean weight that is less than 5.97 ounces. Comment on the statement made by the manufacturer.

9.33 The number of customers who enter a supermarket each hour is normally distributed with a mean of 600 and a standard deviation of 200. The supermarket is open 16 hours per day. What is the probability that the total number of customers who enter the supermarket in 1 day is greater than 10,000? (*Hint:* Calculate the average hourly number of customers necessary to exceed 10,000 in one 16-hour day.)

9.34 The sign on the elevator in an office tower states, "Maximum Capacity 1,140 kilograms (2,500 pounds) or 16 Persons." A professor of statistics wonders what the probability is that 16 persons would weigh more than 1,140 kilograms. Discuss what the professor needs (besides the ability to perform the calculations) in order to answer the question.

9.35 Refer to Exercise 9.34. Suppose that the professor discovers that the weights of people who use the elevator are normally distributed with an average of 75 kilograms and a standard deviation of 10 kilograms. Calculate the probability that the professor seeks.

9.36 The time it takes for a statistics professor to mark the midterm test is normally distributed with a mean of 4.8 minutes and a standard deviation of 1.3 minutes. There are 60 students in the professor's class. What is the probability that more than 5 hours are needed to mark all the midterm tests? (The 60 midterm tests of the students in this year's class can be considered a random sample of the many thousands of midterm tests the professor has marked and will mark.)

9.37 Refer to Exercise 9.36. Does your answer change if you discover that the times needed to mark a midterm test are not normally distributed?

9.38 The restaurant in a large commercial building provides coffee for the occupants in the building. The restaurateur has determined that the mean number of cups of coffee consumed in a day by all

the occupants is 2.0 with a standard deviation of .6. A new tenant of the building intends to have a total of 125 new employees. What is the probability that the new employees will consume more than 240 cups per day?

9.39 The number of pages produced by a fax machine in a busy office is normally distributed with a mean of 275 and a standard deviation of 75. Determine the probability that in 1 week (5 days) more than 1,500 faxes will be received?

9.40 The property tax paid by homeowners in a large city was determined to be normally distributed with a mean of $2,800 and a standard deviation of $400. A random sample of four homes was drawn.
a. What is the probability distribution of the mean of the sample of four homes?
b. Determine the probability that the sample mean falls between $2,500 and $2,900.

9.41 How would you answer Exercise 9.40 if property tax is not normally distributed?

9.42 A factory's worker daily productivity is normally distributed with a mean of 70 units and a standard deviation of 20 units. What is the probability that in 1 week (5 working days), the number of units produced is greater than 400?

9.43 A professor of statistics noticed that marks in the course are normally distributed with a mean and standard deviation of 73 and 12, respectively. What is the probability that the mean mark of four randomly selected students is greater than 75?

9.44 A brewery sells cans of beer that are supposed to contain 355 ml. However, there is some variation in the amount of beer dispensed into each can. The mean amount is 356 ml with a standard deviation of 2 ml. What is the probability that a randomly selected case of 24 cans contains less beer in total than is indicated on the can of beer?

9.45 Every morning before your first class, you line up for a cup of coffee at a coffee shop. You observe that the waiting times are normally distributed with a mean of 3.8 minutes and a standard deviation of 1 minute. You have calculated that the number of days that you line up for coffee during the fall semester is 64. What is the probability that your average wait is longer than 4 minutes?

9-2 / SAMPLING DISTRIBUTION OF A PROPORTION

In Section 7-4, we introduced the binomial distribution whose parameter is *p*, the probability of success in any trial. In order to compute binomial probabilities, we assumed that *p* was known. However, in the real world *p* is unknown, requiring the statistics practitioner to estimate its value from a sample. The estimator of a population proportion of successes is the sample proportion; that is, we count the number of successes in a sample and compute

$$\hat{P} = \frac{X}{n}$$

($\hat{P}$ is read as *p hat*) where X is the number of successes and n is the sample size. When we take a sample of size n, we're actually conducting a binomial experiment; as a result, X is binomially distributed. Thus, the probability of any value of $\hat{P}$ can be calculated from its value of X. For example, suppose that we have a binomial experiment with $n = 10$ and $p = .4$. To find the probability that the sample proportion $\hat{P}$ is less than or equal to .50, we find the probability that X is less than or equal to 5 (because $5/10 = .50$). From Table 1 in Appendix B we find with $n = 10$ and $p = .4$

$$P(\hat{P} \le .50) = P(X \le 5) = .8338$$

We can calculate the probability associated with other values of $\hat{P}$ similarly.

Discrete distributions such as the binomial do not lend themselves easily to the kinds of calculation needed for inference. And inference is the reason we need sampling distributions. Fortunately, we can approximate the binomial distribution by a normal distribution.

What follows is an explanation of how and why the normal distribution can be used to approximate a binomial distribution. Disinterested readers can skip to page 324, where we present the approximate **sampling distribution of a sample proportion**.

9-2a (Optional) Normal Approximation to the Binomial Distribution

Recall how we introduced continuous probability distributions in Chapter 8. We developed the density function by converting a histogram so that the total area in the rectangles equaled 1. We can do the same for a binomial distribution. To illustrate, let X be a binomial random variable with $n = 20$ and $p = .5$. We can easily determine the probability of each value of X, where $X = 0, 1, 2, \ldots, 19, 20$. A rectangle representing a value of x is drawn so that its area equals the probability. We accomplish this by letting the height of the rectangle equal the probability and the base of the rectangle equal 1. Thus, the base of each rectangle for x is the interval $x - .5$ to $x + .5$. Figure 9.7 depicts this graph. As you can see, the rectangle representing $x = 10$ is the rectangle whose base is the interval 9.5 to 10.5 and whose height is $P(X = 10) = .1762$.

If we now smooth the ends of the rectangles, we produce a bell-shaped curve as seen in Figure 9.8. Thus, to use the normal approximation, all we need to do is find the area under the *normal* curve between 9.5 and 10.5.

To find normal probabilities it is required to first standardize x by subtracting the mean and dividing by the standard deviation. The values for μ and σ are derived from the binomial distribution being approximated. In Section 7-4 we pointed out that

$$\mu = np$$

and

$$\sigma = \sqrt{np(1 - p)}$$

For $n = 20$ and $p = .5$, we have

$$\mu = np = 20(.5) = 10$$

FIGURE **9.7**   Binomial Distribution with *n* = 20 and *p* = .5

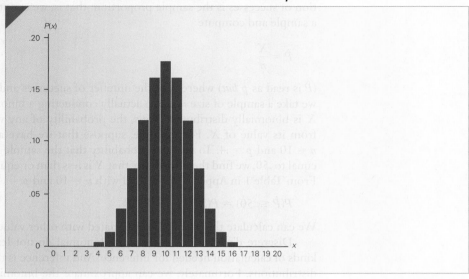

FIGURE **9.8**   Binomial Distribution with *n* = 20 and *p* = .5 and Normal Approximation

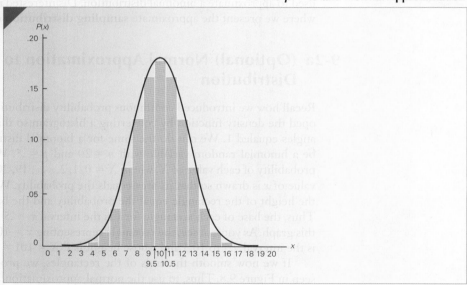

and

$$\sigma = \sqrt{np(1 - p)} = \sqrt{20(.5)(1 - .5)} = 2.24$$

To calculate the probability that $X = 10$ using the normal distribution requires that we find the area under the normal curve between 9.5 and 10.5; that is,

$$P(X = 10) \approx P(9.5 < Y < 10.5)$$

where Y is a normal random variable approximating the binomial random variable X. We standardize Y and use Table 3 of Appendix B to find

$$P(9.5 < Y < 10.5) = P\left(\frac{9.5 - 10}{2.24} < \frac{Y - \mu}{\sigma} < \frac{10.5 - 10}{2.24}\right)$$
$$= P(-.22 < Z < .22) = (Z < .22) - P(Z < -.22)$$
$$= .5871 - .4129 = .1742$$

The actual probability that X equals 10 is

$$P(X = 10) = .1762$$

As you can see, the approximation is quite good.

Notice that to draw a binomial distribution, which is discrete, it was necessary to draw rectangles whose bases were constructed by adding and subtracting .5 to the values of X. The .5 is called the **continuity correction factor**.

The approximation for any other value of X would proceed in the same manner. In general, the binomial probability $P(X = x)$ is approximated by the area under a normal curve between $x - .5$ and $x + .5$. To find the binomial probability $P(X \leq x)$, we calculate the area under the normal curve to the left of $x + .5$. For the same binomial random variable, the probability that its value is less than or equal to 8 is $P(X \leq 8) = .2517$. The normal approximation is

$$P(X \leq 8) \approx P(Y < 8.5) = P\left(\frac{Y - \mu}{\sigma} < \frac{8.5 - 10}{2.24}\right) = P(Z < -.67) = .2514$$

We find the area under the normal curve to the right of $x - .5$ to determine the binomial probability $P(X \geq x)$. To illustrate, the probability that the binomial random variable (with $n = 20$ and $p = .5$) is greater than or equal to 14 is $P(X \geq 14) = .0577$. The normal approximation is

$$P(X \geq 14) \approx P(Y > 13.5) = P\left(\frac{Y - \mu}{\sigma} > \frac{13.5 - 10}{2.24}\right) = P(Z > 1.56) = .0594$$

9-2b Omitting the Correction Factor for Continuity

When calculating the probability of *individual* values of X as we did when we computed the probability that X equals 10 earlier, the correction factor *must* be used. If we don't, we are left with finding the area in a line, which is 0. When computing the probability of a *range* of values of X, we can omit the correction factor. However, the omission of the correction factor will decrease the accuracy of the approximation. For example, if we approximate $P(X \leq 8)$ as we did previously except without the correction factor, we find

$$P(X \leq 8) \approx P(Y < 8) = P\left(\frac{Y - \mu}{\sigma} < \frac{8 - 10}{2.24}\right) = P(Z < -.89) = .1867$$

The absolute size of the error between the actual cumulative binomial probability and its normal approximation is quite small when the values of x are in the tail regions of the distribution. For example, the probability that a binomial random variable with $n = 20$ and $p = .5$ is less than or equal to 3 is

$$P(X \leq 3) = .0013$$

The normal approximation with the correction factor is

$$P(X \leq 3) \approx P(Y < 3.5) = P\left(\frac{Y-\mu}{\sigma} < \frac{3.5-10}{2.24}\right) = P(Z < -2.90) = .0019$$

The normal approximation without the correction factor is (using Excel)

$$P(X \leq 3) \approx P(Y < 3) = P\left(\frac{Y-\mu}{\sigma} < \frac{3-10}{2.24}\right) = P(Z < -3.13) = .0009$$

For larger values of n, the differences between the normal approximation with and without the correction factor are small even for values of X near the center of the distribution. For example, the probability that a binomial random variable with $n = 1,000$ and $p = .3$ is less than or equal to 260 is

$$P(X \leq 260) = .0029 \text{ (using Excel)}$$

The normal approximation with the correction factor is

$$P(X \leq 260) \approx P(Y < 260.5) = P\left(\frac{Y-\mu}{\sigma} < \frac{260.5-300}{14.49}\right) = P(Z < -2.73) = .0032$$

The normal approximation without the correction factor is

$$P(X \leq 260) \approx P(Y < 260) = P\left(\frac{Y-\mu}{\sigma} < \frac{260-300}{14.49}\right) = P(Z < -2.76) = .0029$$

As we pointed out, the normal approximation of the binomial distribution is made necessary by the needs of statistical inference. As you will discover, statistical inference generally involves the use of large values of n, and the part of the sampling distribution that is of greatest interest lies in the tail regions. The correction factor was a temporary tool that allowed us to convince you that a binomial distribution can be approximated by a normal distribution. Now that we have done so, we will use the normal approximation of the binomial distribution to approximate the sampling distribution of a sample proportion, and in such applications the correction factor will be omitted.

9-2c Approximate Sampling Distribution of a Sample Proportion

Using the laws of expected value and variance (see the online appendix Using the Laws of Expected Value and Variance to Derive the Parameters of Sampling Distributions), we can determine the mean, variance, and standard deviation of $\hat{P}$. We will summarize what we have learned.

Sampling Distribution of a Sample Proportion

1. $\hat{P}$ is approximately normally distributed provided that np and $n(1 - p)$ are greater than or equal to 5.

2. The expected value: $E(\hat{P}) = p$

3. The variance: $V(\hat{P}) = \sigma_{\hat{p}}^2 = \dfrac{p(1 - p)}{n}$

4. The standard deviation: $\sigma_{\hat{p}} = \sqrt{p(1 - p)/n}$*

(The standard deviation of $\hat{P}$ is called the **standard error of the proportion**.)

---

*As was the case with the standard error of the mean (page 311), the standard error of a proportion is $\sqrt{p(1 - p)/n}$ when sampling from infinitely large populations. When the population is finite, the standard error of the proportion must include the finite population correction factor, which can be omitted when the population is large relative to the sample size, a very common occurrence in practice.

The sample size requirement is theoretical because, in practice, much larger sample sizes are needed for the normal approximation to be useful.

EXAMPLE 9.2 Political Survey

In the last election, a state representative received 52% of the votes cast. One year after the election, the representative organized a survey that asked a random sample of 300 people how they would vote in the next election. If we assume that the representative's popularity has not changed, what is the probability that more than half of the sample would vote to re-elect?

SOLUTION:

The number of respondents who would vote for the representative is a binomial random variable with $n = 300$ and $p = .52$. We want to determine the probability that the sample proportion is greater than 50%. In other words, we want to find $P(\hat{P} > .50)$.

We now know that the sample proportion $\hat{P}$ is approximately normally distributed with mean $p = .52$ and standard deviation $= \sqrt{p(1 - p)/n} = \sqrt{(.52)(.48)/300} = .0288$. Thus, we calculate

$$P(\hat{P} > .50) = \left(\frac{\hat{P} - p}{\sqrt{p(1 - p)/n}} > \frac{.50 - .52}{.0288} \right)$$

$$= P(Z > -.69) = 1 - P(Z < -.69) = 1 - .2451 = .7549$$

If we assume that the level of support remains at 52%, the probability that more than half the sample of 300 people would vote for the representative is .7549.

EXERCISES

Use the normal approximation without the correction factor to find the probabilities in the following exercises.

9.46 a. In a binomial experiment with $n = 300$ and $p = .5$, find the probability that $\hat{P}$ is greater than 60%.
  b. Repeat part (a) with $p = .55$.
  c. Repeat part (a) with $p = .6$.

9.47 a. The probability of success on any trial of a binomial experiment is 25%. Find the probability that the proportion of successes in a sample of 500 is less than 22%.
  b. Repeat part (a) with $n = .800$.
  c. Repeat part (a) with $p = 1,000$.

9.48 Determine the probability that in a sample of 100 the sample proportion is less than .75 if $p = .80$.

9.49 A binomial experiment where $p = .4$ is conducted. Find the probability that in a sample of 60 the proportion of successes exceeds .35.

9.50 The proportion of eligible voters in the next election who will vote for the incumbent is assumed to be 55%. What is the probability that in a random sample of 500 voters less than 49% say they will vote for the incumbent?

9.51 The assembly line that produces an electronic component of a missile system has historically resulted in a 2% defective rate. A random sample of 800 components is drawn. What is the probability that the defective rate is greater than 4%? Suppose that in the random sample the defective rate is 4%. What does that suggest about the defective rate on the assembly line?

9.52 a. The manufacturer of aspirin claims that the proportion of headache sufferers who get relief with just two aspirins is 53%. What is the probability that in a random sample of 400 headache sufferers, less than 50% obtain relief? If 50% of the sample actually obtained relief, what does this suggest about the manufacturer's claim?

b. Repeat part (a) using a sample of 1,000.

9.53 The manager of a restaurant in a commercial building has determined that the proportion of customers who drink tea is 14%. What is the probability that in the next 100 customers at least 10% will be tea drinkers?

9.54 A commercial for a manufacturer of household appliances claims that 3% of all its products require a service call in the first year. A consumer protection association wants to check the claim by surveying 400 households that recently purchased one of the company's appliances. What is the probability that more than 5% require a service call within the first year? What would you say about the commercial's honesty if in a random sample of 400 households 5% report at least one service call?

9.55 The Laurier Company's brand has a market share of 30%. Suppose that 1,000 consumers of the product are asked in a survey which brand they prefer. What is the probability that more than 32% of the respondents say they prefer the Laurier brand?

9.56 A university bookstore claims that 50% of its customers are satisfied with the service and prices.

a. If this claim is true, what is the probability that in a random sample of 600 customers less than 45% are satisfied?

b. Suppose that in a random sample of 600 customers, 270 express satisfaction with the bookstore. What does this tell you about the bookstore's claim?

9.57 A psychologist believes that 80% of male drivers when lost continue to drive hoping to find the location they seek rather than ask directions. To examine this belief, the psychologist took a random sample of 350 male drivers and asked each what they did when lost. If the belief is true, determine the probability that less than 75% said they continue driving.

9.58 The Red Lobster restaurant chain regularly surveys its customers. On the basis of these surveys, the management of the chain claims that 75% of its customers rate the food as excellent. A consumer testing service wants to examine the claim by asking 460 customers to rate the food. What is the probability that less than 70% rate the food as excellent?

9.59 An accounting professor claims that no more than one-quarter of undergraduate business students will major in accounting. What is the probability that in a random sample of 1,200 undergraduate business students, 336 or more will major in accounting?

9.60 Refer to Exercise 9.59. A survey of a random sample of 1,200 undergraduate business students indicates that 336 students plan to major in accounting. What does this tell you about the professor's claim?

9.61 In 2014, approximately 13% of nonelderly American adults had no health insurance. Suppose that a random sample of 400 such individuals was drawn. What is the probability that 15% or more had no health insurance?

9.62 In a Gallup survey, Americans were asked about their main source of news about current events around the world. If 20% of the population report that their main source is television news, find the probability that in a sample of 500 at least 22% say that their source of news is television.

9.63 Most televised baseball games display a pitch tracker that shows whether the pitch was in the strike zone, which in turn shows whether the umpire made the correct call. Major League Baseball keeps track of how well each umpire calls games. Batters swing at approximately 47% of all pitches. As a result umpires need to make calls on the other 53%. The best umpires get 10% of their calls wrong and the worst get 15% wrong. Suppose that in an average game the best umpire makes calls on 150 pitches. If we assume that the calls in a game are random, what is the probability that the umpire gets less than 8% wrong?

9.64 Repeat Exercise 9.63 for the worst umpire.

9-3 / FROM HERE TO INFERENCE

The primary function of the sampling distribution is statistical inference. To see how the sampling distribution contributes to the development of inferential methods, we need to briefly review how we got to this point.

In Chapters 7 and 8, we introduced probability distributions, which allowed us to make probability statements about values of the random variable. A prerequisite of this calculation is knowledge of the distribution and the relevant parameters. In Example 7.9, we needed to know that the probability that Pat Statsdud guesses the correct answer is 20% ($p = .2$) and that the number of correct answers (successes) in 10 questions (trials) is a binomial random variable. We could then compute the probability of any number of successes. In Example 8.3, we needed to know that the return on investment is normally distributed with a mean of 10% and a standard deviation of 5%. These three bits of information allowed us to calculate the probability of various values of the random variable.

Figure 9.9 symbolically represents the use of probability distributions. Simply put, knowledge of the population and its parameter(s) allows us to use the probability distribution to make probability statements about individual members of the population. The direction of the arrows indicates the direction of the flow of information.

FIGURE **9.9** **Probability Distribution**

In this chapter, we developed the sampling distribution, wherein knowledge of the parameter(s) and some information about the distribution allow us to make probability statements about a sample statistic. In Example 9.1(b), knowing the population mean and standard deviation and assuming that the population is not extremely non-normal enabled us to calculate a probability statement about a sample mean. Figure 9.10 describes the application of sampling distributions.

FIGURE **9.10** **Sampling Distribution**

Notice that in applying both probability distributions and sampling distributions, we must know the value of the relevant parameters, a highly unlikely circumstance. In the real world, parameters are almost always unknown because they represent descriptive measurements about extremely large populations. Statistical inference addresses this problem. It does so by reversing the direction of the flow of knowledge in Figure 9.10. In Figure 9.11, we display the character of statistical inference. Starting in Chapter 10, we will assume that most population parameters are unknown. The statistics practitioner will sample from the population and compute the required statistic. The sampling distribution of that statistic will enable us to draw inferences about the parameter.

FIGURE **9.11** **Sampling Distribution in Inference**

You may be surprised to learn that, by and large, that is all we do in the remainder of this book. Why then do we need another 14 chapters? They are necessary because there are many more parameter and sampling distribution combinations that define the inferential procedures to be presented in an introductory statistics course. However, they all work in the same way. If you understand how one procedure is developed, then you will likely understand all of them. Our task in the next two chapters is to ensure that you understand the first inferential method. Your job is identical.

CHAPTER SUMMARY

The sampling distribution of a statistic is created by repeated sampling from one population. In this chapter, we introduced the sampling distribution of the mean, the proportion, and the difference between two means. We described how these distributions are created theoretically and empirically.

IMPORTANT TERMS:

Sampling distribution   308
Sampling distribution of the sample mean   310
Standard error of the mean   311
Central limit theorem   311

Finite population correction factor   313
Sampling distribution of a sample proportion   321
Continuity correction factor   323
Standard error of the proportion   324

SYMBOLS:

Symbol	Pronounced	Represents
$\mu_{\bar{x}}$	mu x bar	Mean of the sampling distribution of the sample mean
$\sigma_{\bar{x}}^2$	sigma squared x bar	Variance of the sampling distribution of the sample mean
$\sigma_{\bar{x}}$	sigma x bar	Standard deviation (standard error) of the sampling distribution of the sample mean
α	alpha	Probability
$\hat{P}$	p hat	Sample proportion
$\sigma_{\hat{p}}^2$	sigma squared p hat	Variance of the sampling distribution of the sample proportion
$\sigma_{\hat{p}}$	sigma p hat	Standard deviation (standard error) of the sampling distribution of the sample proportion

FORMULAS:

Expected value of the sample mean

$$E(\overline{X}) = \mu_{\bar{x}} = \mu$$

Variance of the sample mean

$$V(\overline{X}) = \sigma_{\bar{x}}^2 = \frac{\sigma^2}{n}$$

Standard error of the sample mean

$$\sigma_{\bar{x}} = \frac{\sigma}{\sqrt{n}}$$

Standardizing the sample mean

$$Z = \frac{\overline{X} - \mu}{\sigma/\sqrt{n}}$$

Expected value of the sample proportion

$$E(\hat{P}) = \mu_{\hat{p}} = p$$

Variance of the sample proportion

$$V(\hat{P}) = \sigma_{\hat{p}}^2 = \frac{p(1 - p)}{n}$$

Standard error of the sample proportion

$$\sigma_{\hat{p}} = \sqrt{\frac{p(1 - p)}{n}}$$

Standardizing the sample proportion

$$Z = \frac{\hat{P} - p}{\sqrt{p(1 - p)/n}}$$

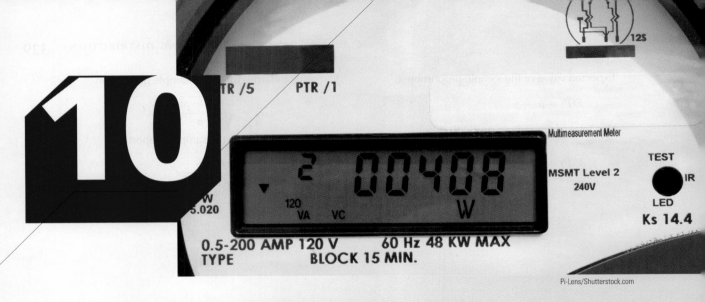

Pi-Lens/Shutterstock.com

INTRODUCTION TO ESTIMATION

CHAPTER OUTLINE

Determining the Sample Size to Estimate the Mean Tree Diameter

A lumber company has just acquired the rights to a large tract of land containing thousands of trees.

A lumber company needs to be able to estimate the amount of lumber it can harvest in a tract of land to determine whether the effort will be profitable. To do so, it must estimate the mean diameter of the trees. It decides to estimate that parameter to within 1 inch with 90% confidence. A forester familiar with the territory guesses that the diameters of the trees are normally distributed with a standard deviation of

Image.Art/Shutterstock.com

See page 349 for the solution.

6 inches. The formula on page 349 indicates that 98 trees should be sampled. The forester then calculates the sample mean to be 25 inches and discovers that the standard deviation is actually 12 inches. Will the forester be satisfied with the result?

INTRODUCTION

Having discussed descriptive statistics (Chapter 4), probability distributions (Chapters 7 and 8), and sampling distributions (Chapter 9), we are ready to tackle statistical inference. As we explained in Chapter 1, *statistical inference* is the process by which we acquire information and draw conclusions about populations from samples. There are two general procedures for making inferences about populations: *estimation* and *hypothesis testing*. In this chapter, we introduce the concepts and foundations of estimation and demonstrate them with simple examples. In Chapter 11, we describe the fundamentals of hypothesis testing. Because most of what we do in the remainder of this book applies the concepts of estimation and hypothesis testing, understanding Chapters 10 and 11 is vital to your development as a statistics practitioner.

10-1 / CONCEPTS OF ESTIMATION

As its name suggests, the objective of estimation is to determine the approximate value of a population parameter on the basis of a sample statistic. For example, the sample mean is employed to estimate the population mean. We refer to the sample mean as the *estimator* of the population mean. Once the sample mean has been computed, its value is called the *estimate*. In this chapter, we will introduce the statistical process whereby we estimate a population mean using sample data. In the rest of the book, we use the concepts and techniques introduced here for other parameters.

10-1a Point and Interval Estimators

We can use sample data to estimate a population parameter in two ways. First, we can compute the value of the estimator and consider that value as the estimate of the parameter. Such an estimator is called a *point estimator*.

> **Point Estimator**
>
> A **point estimator** draws inferences about a population by estimating the value of an unknown parameter using a single value or point.

There are three drawbacks to using point estimators. First, it is virtually certain that the estimate will be wrong. (The probability that a continuous random variable will equal a specific value is 0; that is, the probability that $\bar{x}$ will exactly equal μ is 0.) Second, we often need to know how close the estimator is to the parameter. Third, in drawing inferences about a population, it is intuitively reasonable to expect that a large sample will produce more accurate results because it contains more information than a smaller sample does. But point estimators don't have the capacity to reflect the effects of larger sample sizes. As a consequence, we use the second method of estimating a population parameter, the *interval estimator*.

Interval Estimator

An **interval estimator** draws inferences about a population by estimating the value of an unknown parameter using an interval.

As you will see, the interval estimator is affected by the sample size; because it possesses this feature, we will deal mostly with interval estimators in this text.

To illustrate the difference between point and interval estimators, suppose that a statistics professor wants to estimate the mean summer income of second-year business students. Selecting 25 students at random, the sample mean weekly income is calculated to be $400. The point estimate is the sample mean. In other words, the professor estimates the mean weekly summer income of all second-year business students to be $400. Using the techniques introduced below, the professor may instead estimate that the mean weekly summer income lies between $380 and $420.

Numerous applications of estimation occur in the real world. For example, television network executives want to know the proportion of television viewers who are tuned in to their networks; an economist wants to know the mean income of university graduates; and a medical researcher wishes to estimate the recovery rate of heart attack victims treated with a new drug. In each of these cases, to accomplish the objective exactly, the statistics practitioner would have to examine each member of the population and then calculate the parameter of interest. For instance, network executives would have to ask all people in the country what they are watching to determine the proportion of people who are watching their shows. Because there are millions of television viewers, the task is both impractical and prohibitively expensive. An alternative would be to take a random sample from this population, calculate the sample proportion, and use that as an estimator of the population proportion. The use of the sample proportion to estimate the population proportion seems logical. The selection of the sample statistic to be used as an estimator, however, depends on the characteristics of that statistic. Naturally, we want to use the statistic with the most desirable qualities for our purposes.

One desirable quality of an estimator is *unbiasedness*.

Unbiased Estimator

An **unbiased estimator** of a population parameter is an estimator whose expected value is equal to that parameter.

This means that if you were to take an infinite number of samples and calculate the value of the estimator in each sample, the average value of the estimators would equal the parameter. This amounts to saying that, on average, the sample statistic is equal to the parameter.

We know that the sample mean $\overline{X}$ is an unbiased estimator of the population mean μ. In presenting the sampling distribution of $\overline{X}$ in Section 9-1, we stated that $E(\overline{X}) = \mu$. We also know that the sample proportion is an unbiased estimator of the population proportion because $E(\hat{P}) = p$.

Recall that in Chapter 4 we defined the sample variance as

$$s^2 = \sum \frac{(x_i - \overline{x})^2}{n - 1}$$

At the time, it seemed odd that we divided by $n - 1$ rather than by n. The reason for choosing $n - 1$ was to make $E(s^2) = \sigma^2$ so that this definition makes the sample variance an unbiased estimator of the population variance. (The proof of this statement requires about a page of algebraic manipulation, which is more than we would be comfortable presenting here.) Had we defined the sample variance using n in the denominator, the resulting statistic would be a biased estimator of the population variance, one whose expected value is less than the parameter.

Knowing that an estimator is unbiased only assures us that its expected value equals the parameter; it does not tell us how close the estimator is to the parameter. Another desirable quality is that as the sample size grows larger, the sample statistic should come closer to the population parameter. This quality is called *consistency*.

Consistency

An unbiased estimator is said to be **consistent** if the difference between the estimator and the parameter grows smaller as the sample size grows larger.

The measure we use to gauge closeness is the variance (or the standard deviation). Thus, $\overline{X}$ is a consistent estimator of μ because the variance of $\overline{X}$ is σ^2/n. This implies that as n grows larger, the variance of $\overline{X}$ grows smaller. As a consequence, an increasing proportion of sample means falls close to μ.

Figure 10.1 depicts two sampling distributions of $\overline{X}$. One sampling distribution is based on samples of size 25, and the other is based on samples of size 100. The former is more spread out than the latter.

FIGURE **10.1** Sampling Distribution of $\overline{X}$ with $n = 25$ and $n = 100$

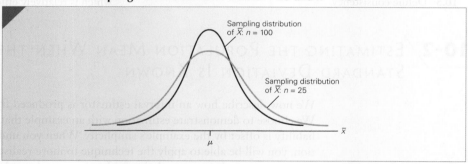

Similarly, $\hat{P}$ is a consistent estimator of p because it is unbiased and the variance of $\hat{P}$ is $p(1 - p)/n$, which grows smaller as n grows larger.

A third desirable quality is *relative efficiency*, which compares two unbiased estimators of a parameter.

Relative Efficiency

If there are two unbiased estimators of a parameter, the one whose variance is smaller is said to have **relative efficiency**.

We have already seen that the sample mean is an unbiased estimator of the population mean and that its variance is σ^2/n. In the next section, we will discuss the use of the sample median as an estimator of the population mean. Statisticians have established that the sample median is an unbiased estimator but that its variance is greater than that of the sample mean (when the population is normal). As a consequence, the sample mean is relatively more efficient than the sample median when estimating the population mean.

In the remaining chapters of this book, we will present the statistical inference of a number of different population parameters. In each case, we will select a sample statistic that is unbiased and consistent. When there is more than one such statistic, we will choose the one that is relatively efficient to serve as the estimator.

10-1b Developing an Understanding of Statistical Concepts

In this section, we described three desirable characteristics of estimators: unbiasedness, consistency, and relative efficiency. An understanding of statistics requires that you know that there are several potential estimators for each parameter, but that we choose the estimators used in this book because they possess these characteristics.

EXERCISES

10.1 How do point estimators and interval estimators differ?

10.2 Define unbiasedness.

10.3 Draw a sampling distribution of an unbiased estimator.

10.4 Draw a sampling distribution of a biased estimator.

10.5 Define consistency.

10.6 Draw diagrams representing what happens to the sampling distribution of a consistent estimator when the sample size increases.

10.7 Define relative efficiency.

10.8 Draw a diagram that shows the sampling distribution representing two unbiased estimators, one of which is relatively efficient.

10-2 / ESTIMATING THE POPULATION MEAN WHEN THE POPULATION STANDARD DEVIATION IS KNOWN

We now describe how an interval estimator is produced from a sampling distribution. We choose to demonstrate estimation with an example that is unrealistic. However, this liability is offset by the example's simplicity. When you understand more about estimation, you will be able to apply the technique to more realistic situations.

Suppose we have a population with mean μ and standard deviation σ. The population mean is assumed to be unknown, and our task is to estimate its value. As we just discussed, the estimation procedure requires the statistics practitioner to draw a random sample of size n and calculate the sample mean $\bar{x}$.

The central limit theorem presented in Section 9-1 stated that $\overline{X}$ is normally distributed if X is normally distributed, or approximately normally distributed if X is non-normal and n is sufficiently large. This means that the variable

$$Z = \frac{\overline{X} - \mu}{\sigma / \sqrt{n}}$$

is standard normally distributed (or approximately so). In Section 9-1 (page 317) we developed the following probability statement associated with the sampling distribution of the mean:

$$P\left(\mu - Z_{\alpha/2}\frac{\sigma}{\sqrt{n}} < \overline{X} < \mu + Z_{\alpha/2}\frac{\sigma}{\sqrt{n}}\right) = 1 - \alpha$$

which was derived from

$$P\left(-Z_{\alpha/2} < \frac{\overline{X} - \mu}{\sigma/\sqrt{n}} < Z_{\alpha/2}\right) = 1 - \alpha$$

Using a similar algebraic manipulation, we can express the probability in a slightly different form:

$$P\left(\overline{X} - Z_{\alpha/2}\frac{\sigma}{\sqrt{n}} < \mu < \overline{X} + Z_{\alpha/2}\frac{\sigma}{\sqrt{n}}\right) = 1 - \alpha$$

Notice that in this form the population mean is in the center of the interval created by adding and subtracting $Z_{\alpha/2}$ standard errors to and from the sample mean. It is important for you to understand that this is merely another form of probability statement about the sample mean. This equation says that, with repeated sampling from this population, the proportion of values of $\overline{X}$ for which the interval

$$\overline{X} - Z_{\alpha/2}\frac{\sigma}{\sqrt{n}}, \ \ \overline{X} + Z_{\alpha/2}\frac{\sigma}{\sqrt{n}}$$

includes the population mean μ is equal to $1 - \alpha$. This form of probability statement is very useful to us because it is the **confidence interval estimator of μ**.

Confidence Interval Estimator of μ*

$$\overline{x} - z_{\alpha/2}\frac{\sigma}{\sqrt{n}}, \ \ \overline{x} + z_{\alpha/2}\frac{\sigma}{\sqrt{n}}$$

The probability $1 - \alpha$ is called the **confidence level**.

$\overline{x} - z_{\alpha/2}\dfrac{\sigma}{\sqrt{n}}$ is called the **lower confidence limit (LCL)**.

$\overline{x} + z_{\alpha/2}\dfrac{\sigma}{\sqrt{n}}$ is called the **upper confidence limit (UCL)**.

We often represent the confidence interval estimator as

$$\overline{x} \pm z_{\alpha/2}\frac{\sigma}{\sqrt{n}}$$

where the minus sign defines the lower confidence limit and the plus sign defines the upper confidence limit.

To apply this formula, we specify the confidence level $1 - \alpha$, from which we determine α, $\alpha/2$, $z_{\alpha/2}$ (from Table 3 in Appendix B). Because the confidence level is the probability that the interval includes the actual value of μ, we generally set $1 - \alpha$ close to 1 (usually between .90 and .99).

In Table 10.1, we list four commonly used confidence levels and their associated values of $z_{\alpha/2}$. For example, if the confidence level is $1 - \alpha = .95$, $\alpha = .05$, $\alpha/2 = .025$,

---

*Since Chapter 7, we've been using the convention whereby an uppercase letter (usually X) represents a random variable and a lowercase letter (usually x) represents one of its values. However, in the formulas used in statistical inference, the distinction between the variable and its value becomes blurred. Accordingly, we will discontinue the notational convention and simply use lowercase letters except when we wish to make a probability statement.

and $z_{\alpha/2} = z_{.025} = 1.96$. The resulting confidence interval estimator is then called the **95% confidence interval estimator of μ**.

TABLE **10.1** Four Commonly Used Confidence Levels and $z_{\alpha/2}$

$1 - \alpha$	α	$\alpha/2$	$z_{\alpha/2}$
.90	.10	.05	$z_{.05} = 1.645$
.95	.05	.025	$z_{.025} = 1.96$
.98	.02	.01	$z_{.01} = 2.33$
.99	.01	.005	$z_{.005} = 2.575$

10-2a Identify-Compute-Interpret System

The following example illustrates how statistical techniques are applied. It also illustrates how we intend to solve problems in the rest of this book. The solution process we advocate and use throughout this book is by and large the same one that statistics practitioners use to apply their skills in the real world. The process is divided into three stages. Simply stated, the stages are (1) the activities we perform before the calculations, (2) the calculations, and (3) the activities we perform after the calculations. The approach is called the **Identify-Compute-Interpret System** or simply ICI.

Stage 1: To begin we *identify* the appropriate statistical method to employ. Of course, for the following example you will have no difficulty in determining the technique because you will know only one, the confidence interval estimate of a population mean. Don't underestimate the importance of this stage. Over the next nine chapters we will introduce about three dozen statistical techniques, making the task of recognizing which one to use quite challenging. We will provide more details on the identify stage in Chapter 11.

Stage 2: Next, we *compute* the statistics. Where practicable, we will conduct the computations manually with the assistance of a calculator only. Doing the arithmetic by hand often provides insights into how the statistical technique works. However, at some point the arithmetic becomes so tedious we intend to use the computer exclusively. We have chosen to use Microsoft Excel (as well as XLSTAT and Stata in the appendixes of most of the following chapters). The four components of Excel were described in Chapter 1. They are:

1. **Statistical** functions
2. **Analysis ToolPak:** The techniques are accessed by clicking **Data** and **Data Analysis**.
3. **Spreadsheets:** These were created by the author and can be downloaded from Cengage's website.
4. **Do It Yourself:** We provide step-by-step instructions on how to use Excel to perform the remaining inference methods.

Stage 3: And finally, we *interpret* the results. To be capable of properly interpreting, one needs to have an understanding of the fundamental principles underlying statistical inference.

APPLICATIONS in **OPERATIONS MANAGEMENT**

Inventory Management

Operations managers use inventory models to determine the stock level that minimizes total costs. In Section 8-2, we showed how the probabilistic model is used to make the inventory level decision (see page 283). One component of that model is the mean demand during lead time. Recall that *lead time* refers to the interval between the time an order is made and when it is delivered. Demand during lead time is a random variable that is often assumed to be normally distributed. There are several ways to determine mean demand during lead time, but the simplest is to estimate that quantity from a sample.

EXAMPLE 10.1

DATA
Xm 10-01

GK Computer Company

The GK Computer Company makes its own computers and delivers them directly to customers who order them via the Internet. It competes primarily on price and speed of delivery. To achieve its objective of speed, GK makes each of its five most popular computers and transports them to warehouses across the country. The computers are stored in the warehouses from which it generally takes 1 day to deliver a computer to the customer. This strategy requires high levels of inventory that add considerably to the cost. To lower these costs, the operations manager wants to use an inventory model. It is known that demand during lead time is normally distributed. The manager needs to determine the mean demand during lead time to compute the optimum inventory level. A sample of 25 lead times is taken, and the demand during each period was recorded. These data are listed here. The manager would like a 95% confidence interval estimate of the mean demand during lead time. From long experience, the manager knows that the standard deviation is 75 computers.

Demand During Lead Time

235	374	309	499	253
421	361	514	462	369
394	439	348	344	330
261	374	302	466	535
386	316	296	332	334

SOLUTION:

IDENTIFY

To ultimately determine the optimum inventory level, the manager must know the mean demand during lead time. Thus, the parameter to be estimated is μ. At this point, we have described only one interval estimator. Thus, the confidence interval estimator that we intend to use is

$$\bar{x} \pm z_{\alpha/2}\frac{\sigma}{\sqrt{n}}$$

The next step is to perform the calculations. As we discussed previously, we will perform the calculations manually and using Excel.

COMPUTE

MANUALLY:

We need four values to construct the confidence interval estimate of μ. They are

$$\bar{x}, z_{\alpha/2}, \sigma, n$$

Using a calculator, we determine the summation $\sum x_i = 9{,}254$. From this, we find

$$\bar{x} = \frac{\sum x_i}{n} = \frac{9{,}254}{25} = 370.16$$

The confidence level is set at 95%;

thus, $1 - \alpha = .95, \alpha = 1 - .95 = .05$, and $\alpha/2 = .025$.

From Table 3 in Appendix B or from Table 10.1, we find

$$z_{\alpha/2} = z_{.025} = 1.96$$

The population standard deviation is $\sigma = 75$, and the sample size is 25. Substituting $\bar{x}$, $z_{\alpha/2}, \sigma$, and n into the confidence interval estimator, we find

$$\bar{x} \pm z_{\alpha/2}\frac{\sigma}{\sqrt{n}} = 370.16 \pm z_{.025}\frac{75}{\sqrt{25}} = 370.16 \pm 1.96\frac{75}{\sqrt{25}} = 370.16 \pm 29.40$$

The lower and upper confidence limits are LCL = 340.76 and UCL = 399.56, respectively.

Excel Workbook

	A	B	C	D	E
1	z-Estimate of a Mean				
2					
3	Sample mean	370.16	Confidence Interval Estimate		
4	Population standard deviation	75	370.16	±	29.40
5	Sample size	25	Lower confidence limit		340.76
6	Confidence level	0.95	Upper confidence limit		399.56

INSTRUCTIONS

1. Type or import the data into one column. (Open Xm10-01.) In any empty cell, calculate the sample mean (=AVERAGE(A1:A26).

2. Open the **Estimators Workbook** and click the **z-Estimate_Mean** tab. In cell B3, type or copy the value of the sample mean. If you use **Copy** also use **Paste Special** and **Values**. In cells B4–B6, type the value of σ (75), the value of n (25), and the confidence level (.95), respectively.

Using the same algebraic steps that we used on page 335, we derive the confidence interval estimator of a population mean using the sample median

$$m \pm z_{\alpha/2} \frac{1.2533\sigma}{\sqrt{n}}$$

To illustrate, suppose that we have drawn the following random sample from a normal population whose standard deviation is 2.

$$1 \quad 1 \quad 1 \quad 3 \quad 4 \quad 5 \quad 6 \quad 7 \quad 8$$

The sample mean is $\bar{x} = 4$, and the sample median is $m = 4$.

The 95% confidence interval estimates using the sample mean and the sample median are

$$\bar{x} \pm z_{\alpha/2} \frac{\sigma}{\sqrt{n}} = 4.0 \pm 1.96 \frac{2}{\sqrt{9}} = 4 \pm 1.307$$

$$m \pm z_{\alpha/2} \frac{1.2533\sigma}{\sqrt{n}} = 4.0 \pm 1.96 \frac{(1.2533)(2)}{\sqrt{9}} = 4 \pm 1.638$$

As you can see, the interval based on the sample mean is narrower; as we pointed out previously, narrower intervals provide more precise information. To understand why the sample mean produces better estimators than the sample median, recall how the median is calculated. We simply put the data in order and select the observation that falls in the middle. Thus, as far as the median is concerned the data appear as

$$1 \quad 2 \quad 3 \quad 4 \quad 5 \quad 6 \quad 7 \quad 8 \quad 9$$

By ignoring the actual observations and using their ranks instead, we lose information. With less information, we have less precision in the interval estimators and so ultimately make poorer decisions.

10-2e Computer Simulation of a Confidence Interval Estimator of μ

This simulation is similar to the computer simulations described in Subsection 9-1d (page 317).

We'll simulate drawing 1,000 samples with sample size $n = 9$ from a normal population with mean $\mu = 5$ and standard deviation $\sigma = 1$. The simulation will produce 95% confidence interval estimates of the population mean.

1. Click **Data**, **Data Analysis**, and **Random Number Generation**.

2. Type 9 to specify the **Number of Variables** and type 1000 to specify the **Number of Random Numbers**.

3. Click **Normal** in the **Distribution** box and in the **Parameters** box type **Mean** 5 and **Standard Deviation** 1.

4. Specify **New Worksheet Ply** and click **OK**. Columns A to I of the new worksheet ply will fill with the random numbers.

5. In Cell J1, type

=AVERAGE(A1:I1)

6. Drag to fill the rest of Column J. Column J will now contain the values of the sample means.

7. In Cell K1, calculate the lower limit of the 95% confidence interval estimate

$$\bar{x} - z_{\alpha/2}\frac{\sigma}{\sqrt{n}} = \bar{x} - 1.96\frac{1}{\sqrt{9}} = \bar{x} - .6533$$

Drag to fill the rest of Column K, which will contain the lower limits of the 1,000 samples.

8. In Cell L1, calculate the upper limit of the 95% confidence interval estimate

$$\bar{x} + z_{\alpha/2}\frac{\sigma}{\sqrt{n}} = \bar{x} + 1.96\frac{1}{\sqrt{9}} = \bar{x} + .6533$$

and drag to fill in the rest of Column L.

9. Some of the intervals will contain the value of the population mean μ, which is 5, and some will not. To instruct Excel to determine which intervals contain μ in Cell M1, type

=AND(K1 < = 5, L1 > = 5)

This tells Excel that if the lower limit (K1) is less than or equal to 5 and the upper limit is greater than or equal to 5 (that is the interval contains the value of the population mean 5); the word TRUE will appear in Cell M1. Drag to complete Column M.

10. There are several ways to count the number of intervals that exclude the population mean 5. Here is one. In Cell N1, type

=IF(M1 = TRUE,0,1)

and drag to fill Column N. In each row where the interval contains the value of the population mean (where Column M shows TRUE), the value 0 will appear. If the interval excludes the population mean, a 1 will appear. Sum Column N and you will have the total number of 95% confidence interval estimates that are "wrong."

COMPUTER SIMULATION EXERCISES

10.9 Conduct the simulation described above. What proportion of intervals excluded the mean $\mu = 5$? How many did you expect?

10.10 Repeat Exercise 10.9 using a 90% confidence interval estimator.

10.11 Repeat Exercise 10.9 with a 99% confidence level.

10.12 Would your answers to Exercises 10.9 to 10.11 change substantially if the sample size changed from 9 to 100? Explain.

EXERCISES

Developing an Understanding of Statistical Concepts

Exercises 10.13 to 10.20 are "what-if" analyses designed to determine what happens to the interval estimate when the confidence level, sample size, and standard deviation change. These problems can be solved manually or using the z-Estimate_Mean spreadsheet in the Estimators workbook.

10.13 a. A statistics practitioner took a random sample of 50 observations from a population with a standard deviation of 25 and computed the sample mean to be 100. Estimate the population mean with 90% confidence.

b. Repeat part (a) using a 95% confidence level.

c. Repeat part (a) using a 99% confidence level.

d. Describe the effect on the confidence interval estimate of increasing the confidence level.

10.14 a. The mean of a random sample of 25 observations from a normal population with a standard deviation of 50 is 200. Estimate the population mean with 95% confidence.

b. Repeat part (a) changing the population standard deviation to 25.

c. Repeat part (a) changing the population standard deviation to 10.

d. Describe what happens to the confidence interval estimate when the standard deviation is decreased.

10.15 a. A random sample of 25 was drawn from a normal distribution with a standard deviation of 5. The sample mean is 80. Determine the 95% confidence interval estimate of the population mean.

b. Repeat part (a) with a sample size of 100.

c. Repeat part (a) with a sample size of 400.

d. Describe what happens to the confidence interval estimate when the sample size increases.

10.16 a. Given the following information, determine the 98% confidence interval estimate of the population mean:

$\bar{x} = 500$ $\sigma = 12$ $n = 50$

b. Repeat part (a) using a 95% confidence level.

c. Repeat part (a) using a 90% confidence level.

d. Review parts (a)–(c) and discuss the effect on the confidence interval estimator of decreasing the confidence level.

10.17 a. A statistics practitioner took a random sample of 100 observations from a population with a standard deviation of 25 and computed the sample mean to be 50. Estimate the population mean with 95% confidence.

b. Repeat part (a) changing the standard deviation to 50.

c. Repeat part (a) changing the standard deviation to 100.

d. Describe the effect on the confidence interval estimate of increasing the standard deviation.

10.18 a. The mean of a random sample of 400 observations from a normal population with a standard deviation of 100 is 1,000. Estimate the population mean with 95% confidence.

b. Repeat part (a) changing the sample size to 225.

c. Repeat part (a) changing the sample size to 100.

d. Describe what happens to the confidence interval estimate when the sample size is decreased.

10.19 a. A sample of 25 observations produced a mean of 300. The sample was randomly drawn from a population with a standard deviation of 15. Estimate the population mean with 99% confidence.

b. Repeat part (a) changing the population standard deviation to 30.

c. Repeat part (a) changing the population standard deviation to 60.

d. Describe what happens to the confidence interval estimate when the standard deviation is increased.

10.20 a. A statistics practitioner randomly sampled 100 observations from a population with a standard deviation of 5 and found the mean to be 10. Estimate the population mean with 90% confidence.

b. Repeat part (a) with a sample size of 25.

c. Repeat part (a) with a sample size of 10.

d. Describe what happens to the confidence interval estimate when the sample size decreases.

Exercises 10.21 to 10.24 are based on the optional subsection "Estimating the Population Mean Using the Sample Median." All exercises assume that the population is normal.

10.21 Is the sample median an unbiased estimator of the population mean? Explain.

10.22 Is the sample median a consistent estimator of the population mean? Explain.

10.23 Show that the sample mean is relatively more efficient than the sample median when estimating the population mean.

10.24 a. Given the following information, determine the 90% confidence interval estimate of the population mean using the sample median.

Sample median = 500, $\sigma = 12$, and $n = 50$

b. Compare your answer in part (a) to that produced in part (c) of Exercise 10.16. Why is the confidence interval estimate based on the sample median wider than that based on the sample mean?

Applications

The following exercises may be answered manually or with the assistance of a computer. The names of the files containing the data are shown.

10.25 <u>Xr10-25</u>   The following data represent a random sample of 9 marks on a statistics quiz. (A perfect score is 10.) The marks are normally distributed with a standard deviation of 2. Estimate the population mean with 90% confidence.

7 9 7 5 4 8 3 10 9

10.26 <u>Xr10-26</u>   The following observations are the ages of a random sample of 8 men in a bar. It is known that the ages are normally distributed with a standard deviation of 10. Determine the 95% confidence interval estimate of the population mean. Interpret the interval estimate.

52 68 22 35 30 56 39 48

10.27 <u>Xr10-27</u>   How many rounds of golf do physicians (who play golf) play per year? A survey of 12 physicians revealed the following numbers:

3 41 17 1 33 37 18 15 17 12 29 51

Estimate with 95% confidence the mean number of rounds per year played by physicians, assuming that the number of rounds is normally distributed with a standard deviation of 12.

10.28 <u>Xr10-28</u>   Among the most exciting aspects of a university professor's life are the departmental meetings where such critical issues as the color of the walls will be painted and who gets a new desk are decided. A sample of 20 professors was asked how many hours per year are devoted to these meetings. The responses are listed here. Assuming that the variable is normally distributed with a standard deviation of 8 hours, estimate the mean number of hours spent at departmental meetings by all professors. Use a confidence level of 90%.

14 17 3 6 17 3 8 4 20 15
7 9 0 5 11 15 18 13 8 4

10.29 <u>Xr10-29</u>   The number of cars sold annually by used car salespeople is normally distributed with a standard deviation of 15. A random sample of 15 salespeople was taken, and the number of cars each sold is listed here. Find the 95% confidence interval estimate of the population mean. Interpret the interval estimate.

79 43 58 66 101 63 79 33 58
71 60 101 74 55 88

10.30 <u>Xr10-30</u>   It is known that the amount of time needed to change the oil on a car is normally distributed with a standard deviation of 5 minutes. The amount of time to complete a random sample of 10 oil changes was recorded and listed here. Compute the 99% confidence interval estimate of the mean of the population.

11 10 16 15 18 12 25 20 18 24

10.31 <u>Xr10-31</u>   Suppose that the amount of time teenagers spend weekly working at part-time jobs is normally distributed with a standard deviation of 40 minutes. A random sample of 15 teenagers was drawn, and each reported the amount of time spent at part-time jobs (in minutes). These are listed here. Determine the 95% confidence interval estimate of the population mean.

180 130 150 165 90 130 120 60 200
180 80 240 210 150 125

10.32 <u>Xr10-32</u>   One of the few negative side effects of quitting smoking is weight gain. Suppose that the weight gain in the 12 months following a cessation in smoking is normally distributed with a standard deviation of 6 pounds. To estimate the mean weight gain, a random sample of 13 quitters was drawn; their recorded weights are listed here. Determine the 90% confidence interval estimate of the mean 12-month weight gain for all quitters.

16 23 8 2 14 22 18 11 10 19 5 8 15

10.33 <u>Xr10-33</u>   Because of different sales ability, experience, and devotion, the incomes of real estate agents vary considerably. Suppose that in a large city the annual income is normally distributed with a standard deviation of $15,000. A random sample of 16 real estate agents was asked to report their annual income (in $1,000). The responses are listed here. Determine the 99% confidence interval estimate of the mean annual income of all real estate agents in the city.

65 94 57 111 83 61 50 73 68 80
93 84 113 41 60 77

The following exercises require the use of a computer and software. The answers may be calculated manually. See Appendix A for the sample statistics.

10.34 <u>Xr10-34</u>   A survey of 400 statistics professors was undertaken. Each professor was asked how much time was devoted to teaching graphical techniques. We believe that the times are normally distributed with a standard deviation of 30 minutes. Estimate the population mean with 95% confidence.

10.35 Xr10-35 In a survey conducted to determine, among other things, the cost of vacations, 64 individuals were randomly sampled. All were asked to compute the costs of their most recent vacations. Assuming that the standard deviation is $400, estimate with 95% confidence the average cost of all vacations.

10.36 Xr10-36 In an article about *disinflation*, various investments were examined. The investments included stocks, bonds, and real estate. Suppose that a random sample of 200 rates of return on real estate investments was computed and recorded. Assuming that the standard deviation of all rates of return on real estate investments is 2.1%, estimate the mean rate of return on all real estate investments with 90% confidence. Interpret the estimate.

10.37 Xr10-37 A statistics professor is in the process of investigating how many classes university students miss each semester. A random sample of 100 university students were asked to report how many classes they missed in the previous semester. Estimate the mean number of classes missed by all students at the university. Use a 99% confidence level and assume that the population standard deviation is known to be 2.2 classes.

10.38 Xr10-38 As part of a project to develop better lawn fertilizers, a research chemist wanted to determine the mean weekly growth rate of Kentucky bluegrass, a common type of grass. A sample of 250 blades of grass was measured, and the amount of growth in 1 week was recorded. Assuming that weekly growth is normally distributed with a standard deviation of .10 inch, estimate with 99% confidence the mean weekly growth of Kentucky bluegrass. Briefly describe what the interval estimate tells you about the growth of Kentucky bluegrass.

10.39 Xr10-39 A time study of a large production facility was undertaken to determine the mean time required to assemble a cell phone. A random sample of the times to assemble 50 cell phones was recorded. An analysis of the assembly times reveals that they are normally distributed with a standard deviation of 1.3 minutes. Estimate with 95% confidence the mean assembly time for all cell phones. What do your results tell you about the assembly times?

10.40 Xr10-40 The image of the Japanese manager is that of a workaholic with little or no leisure time. In a survey, a random sample of 250 Japanese middle managers was asked how many hours per week they spent in leisure activities (e.g., sports, movies, television). The results of the survey were recorded. Assuming that the population standard deviation is 6 hours, estimate with 90% confidence the mean leisure time per week for all Japanese middle managers. What do these results tell you?

10.41 Xr10-41 One measure of physical fitness is the amount of time it takes for the pulse rate to return to normal after exercise. A random sample of 100 women age 40 to 50 exercised on stationary bicycles for 30 minutes. The amount of time it took for their pulse rates to return to pre-exercise levels was measured and recorded. If the times are normally distributed with a standard deviation of 2.3 minutes, estimate with 99% confidence the true mean pulse-recovery time for all 40- to 50-year-old women. Interpret the results.

10.42 Xr10-42 A survey of 80 randomly selected companies asked them to report the annual income of their presidents. Assuming that incomes are normally distributed with a standard deviation of $30,000, determine the 90% confidence interval estimate of the mean annual income of all company presidents. Interpret the statistical results.

10.43 Xr10-43 The rising cost of electricity is a concern for homeowners. An economist wanted to determine how much electricity has increased over the past 5 years. A survey was conducted with the percentage increase recorded. Assuming that the population standard deviation is known to be 20% estimate the mean percentage increase with 95% confidence.

10.44 Xr10-44 How much do American families spend on entertainment each month. A survey was conducted and the amounts spent on entertainment in the previous month were recorded. Assuming that the population standard deviation is $50 determine the 99% confidence interval estimate of the mean monthly amount of money spent by American families.

10.45 Xr10-45 Registered Retirement Savings Plan are retirement plans that defer taxes. Many Canadians rely on these plans for their retirement. To measure how these are doing, a random sample of 60-year-old Canadians was drawn and asked to report the total value of their RRSPs. If the population standard deviation is known to be $75,000, estimate the mean with 90% confidence.

10.46 Xr10-46 The sponsors of television shows targeted at the children's market wanted to know the amount of time children spend watching television because the types and number of programs and commercials are greatly influenced by this information. As a result, it was decided to survey 100 North American children and ask them to keep track of the number of hours of television they watch each week. From past experience, it is known that the population standard deviation of the weekly amount of television watched is $\sigma = 8.0$ hours. The television sponsors want an estimate of the amount of television watched by the average North American child. A confidence level of 95% is judged to be appropriate.

10-3 / SELECTING THE SAMPLE SIZE

As we discussed in the previous section, if the interval estimate is too wide, it provides little information. In Example 10.1 the interval estimate was 340.76 to 399.56. If the manager is to use this estimate as input for an inventory model, greater precision is needed. Fortunately, statistics practitioners can control the width of the interval by determining the sample size necessary to produce narrow intervals.

To understand how and why we can determine the sample size, we discuss the error of estimation.

10-3a Error of Estimation

In Chapter 5, we pointed out that sampling error is the difference between the sample and the population that exists only because of the observations that happened to be selected for the sample. Now that we have discussed estimation, we can define the sampling error as the difference between an estimator and a parameter. We can also define this difference as the **error of estimation**. In this chapter, this can be expressed as the difference between $\overline{X}$ and μ. In our derivation of the confidence interval estimator of μ (see page 335), we expressed the following probability,

$$P\left(-Z_{\alpha/2} < \frac{\overline{X} - \mu}{\sigma/\sqrt{n}} < Z_{\alpha/2}\right) = 1 - \alpha$$

which can also be expressed as

$$P\left(-Z_{\alpha/2}\frac{\sigma}{\sqrt{n}} < \overline{X} - \mu < + Z_{\alpha/2}\frac{\sigma}{\sqrt{n}}\right) = 1 - \alpha$$

This tells us that the difference between $\overline{X}$ and μ lies between $-Z_{\alpha/2}\sigma/\sqrt{n}$ and $+Z_{\alpha/2}\sigma/\sqrt{n}$ with probability $1 - \alpha$. Expressed another way, we have with probability $1 - \alpha$,

$$|\overline{X} - \mu| < Z_{\alpha/2}\frac{\sigma}{\sqrt{n}}$$

In other words, the error of estimation is less than $Z_{\alpha/2}\sigma/\sqrt{n}$. We interpret this to mean that $Z_{\alpha/2}\sigma/\sqrt{n}$ is the maximum error of estimation that we are willing to tolerate. We label this value B, which stands for the **bound on the error of estimation**; that is,

$$B = Z_{\alpha/2}\frac{\sigma}{\sqrt{n}}$$

10-3b Determining the Sample Size

We can solve the equation for n if the population standard deviation σ, the confidence level $1 - \alpha$, and the bound on the error of estimation B are known. Solving for n, we produce the following.

Sample Size to Estimate a Mean

$$n = \left(\frac{z_{\alpha/2}\sigma}{B} \right)^2$$

To illustrate, suppose that in Example 10.1, before gathering the data, the manager needed to estimate the mean demand during lead time to within 16 units, which is the bound on the error of estimation. We also have $1 - \alpha = .95$ and $\sigma = 75$. We calculate

$$n = \left(\frac{z_{\alpha/2}\sigma}{B} \right)^2 = \left(\frac{(1.96)(75)}{16} \right)^2 = 84.41$$

Because n must be an integer and because we want the bound on the error of estimation to be *no more* than 16, any noninteger value must be rounded up. Thus, the value of n is rounded to 85, which means that to be 95% confident that the error of estimation will be no larger than 16, we need to randomly sample 85 lead time intervals.

In this chapter, we have assumed that we know the value of the population standard deviation. In practice, this is seldom the case. (In Chapter 12, we introduce a more realistic confidence interval estimator of the population mean.) It is frequently necessary to "guesstimate" the value of σ to calculate the sample size; that is, we must use our knowledge of the variable with which we're dealing to assign some value to σ.

Unfortunately, we cannot be very precise in this guess. However, in guesstimating the value of σ, we prefer to err on the high side. The result of guessing wrong is shown in the solution to the chapter-opening example.

Determining the Sample Size to Estimate the Mean Tree Diameter: Solution

Before the sample was taken, the forester determined the sample size as follows.

The bound on the error of estimation is $B = 1$. The confidence level is 90% ($1 - \alpha = .90$). Thus $\alpha = .10$ and $\alpha/2 = .05$. It follows that $z_{\alpha/2} = 1.645$. The population standard deviation is assumed to be $\sigma = 6$. Thus,

$$n = \left(\frac{z_{\alpha/2}\sigma}{B} \right)^2 = \left(\frac{1.645 \times 6}{1} \right)^2 = 97.42$$

which is rounded to 98.

(*Continued*)

However, after the sample is taken the forester discovered that $\sigma = 12$. The 90% confidence interval estimate is

$$\bar{x} \pm z_{\alpha/2} \frac{\sigma}{\sqrt{n}} = 25 \pm z_{.05} \frac{12}{\sqrt{98}} = 25 \pm 1.645 \frac{12}{\sqrt{98}} = 25 \pm 2$$

As you can see, the bound on the error of estimation is 2 and not 1. The interval is twice as wide as it was designed to be. The resulting estimate will not be as precise as needed.

What happens if the standard deviation is *smaller* than assumed? If we discover that the standard deviation is less than we assumed when we determined the sample size, the confidence interval estimator will be narrower and therefore more precise. Suppose that after the sample of 98 trees was taken (assuming again that $\sigma = 6$), the forester discovers that $\sigma = 3$. The confidence interval estimate is

$$\bar{x} \pm z_{\alpha/2} \frac{\sigma}{\sqrt{n}} = 25 \pm 1.645 \frac{3}{\sqrt{98}} = 25 \pm 0.5$$

which is narrower than the forester wanted. Although this means that more trees were sampled than needed, the additional cost is relatively low when compared to the value of the information derived.

EXERCISES

Developing an Understanding of Statistical Concepts

10.47 a. Determine the sample size required to estimate a population mean to within 10 units given that the population standard deviation is 50. A confidence level of 90% is judged to be appropriate.

b. Repeat part (a) changing the standard deviation to 100.

c. Re-do part (a) using a 95% confidence level.

d. Repeat part (a) wherein we wish to estimate the population mean to within 20 units.

10.48 Review Exercise 10.47. Describe what happens to the sample size when

a. the population standard deviation increases.

b. the confidence level increases.

c. the bound on the error of estimation increases.

10.49 a. A statistics practitioner would like to estimate a population mean to within 50 units with 99% confidence given that the population standard deviation is 250. What sample size should be used?

b. Re-do part (a) changing the standard deviation to 50.

c. Re-do part (a) using a 95% confidence level.

d. Re-do part (a) wherein we wish to estimate the population mean to within 10 units.

10.50 Review the results of Exercise 10.49. Describe what happens to the sample size when

a. the population standard deviation decreases.

b. the confidence level decreases.

c. the bound on the error of estimation decreases.

10.51 a. Determine the sample size necessary to estimate a population mean to within 1 with 90% confidence given that the population standard deviation is 10.

b. Suppose that the sample mean was calculated as 150. Estimate the population mean with 90% confidence.

10.52 a. Repeat part (b) in Exercise 10.51 after discovering that the population standard deviation is actually 5.

b. Repeat part (b) in Exercise 10.51 after discovering that the population standard deviation is actually 20.

10.53 Review Exercises 10.51 and 10.52. Describe what happens to the confidence interval estimate when

a. the standard deviation is equal to the value used to determine the sample size.

b. the standard deviation is smaller than the one used to determine the sample size.

c. the standard deviation is larger than the one used to determine the sample size.

10.54 a. A statistics practitioner would like to estimate a population mean to within 10 units. The confidence level has been set at 95% and $\sigma = 200$. Determine the sample size.

b. Suppose that the sample mean was calculated as 500. Estimate the population mean with 95% confidence.

10.55 a. Repeat part (b) of Exercise 10.54 after discovering that the population standard deviation is actually 100.

b. Repeat part (b) of Exercise 10.54 after discovering that the population standard deviation is actually 400.

10.56 Review Exercises 10.54 and 10.55. Describe what happens to the confidence interval estimate when

a. the standard deviation is equal to the value used to determine the sample size.

b. the standard deviation is smaller than the one used to determine the sample size.

c. the standard deviation is larger than the one used to determine the sample size.

Applications

10.57 A medical statistician wants to estimate the average weight loss of people who are on a new diet plan. In a preliminary study, the statistician guesses that the standard deviation of the population of weight losses is about 10 pounds. How large a sample should be taken to estimate the mean weight loss to within 2 pounds, with 90% confidence?

10.58 The operations manager of a large production plant would like to estimate the average amount of time workers take to assemble a new electronic component. After observing a number of workers assembling similar devices, the manager guesses that the standard deviation is 6 minutes. How large a sample of workers should be taken to estimate the mean assembly time to within 20 seconds? Assume that the confidence level is to be 99%.

10.59 A statistics professor wants to compare today's students with those 25 years ago. All current students' marks are stored on a computer so that the population mean can be determined. However, the marks 25 years ago reside only in musty files. The professor does not want to retrieve all the marks and will be satisfied with a 95% confidence interval estimate of the mean mark 25 years ago. If we assume that the population standard deviation is 12, how large a sample should be taken to estimate the mean to within 2 marks?

10.60 A medical researcher wants to investigate the amount of time it takes for patients' headache to be relieved after taking a new prescription painkiller. The researcher plans to use statistical methods to estimate the mean of the population of relief times. It is known that the population is normally distributed with a standard deviation of 20 minutes. How large a sample should be taken to estimate the mean time to within 1 minute with 90% confidence?

10.61 The label on 1-gallon cans of paint states that the amount of paint in the can is sufficient to paint 400 square feet. However, this number is quite variable. In fact, the amount of coverage is known to be approximately normally distributed with a standard deviation of 25 square feet. How large a sample should be taken to estimate the true mean coverage of all 1-gallon cans to within 5 square feet with 95% confidence?

10.62 The operations manager of a plant making cellular telephones has proposed rearranging the production process to be more efficient. The manager wants to estimate the time to assemble the telephone using the new arrangement and believes that the population standard deviation is 15 seconds. How large a sample of workers should the manager take to estimate the mean assembly time to within 2 seconds with 95% confidence?

CHAPTER SUMMARY

This chapter introduced the concepts of **estimation** and the **estimator** of a population mean when the population variance is known. It also presented a formula to calculate the sample size necessary to estimate a population mean.

IMPORTANT TERMS:

Point estimator   331
Interval estimator   332
Unbiased estimator   332
Consistency   333
Relative efficiency   333
Confidence interval estimator of μ 335
Confidence level   335

Lower confidence limit (LCL)   335
Upper confidence limit (UCL)   335
95% confidence interval estimator of μ 336
Identify-Compute-Interpret System   336
Error of estimation   348
Bound on the error of estimation   348

SYMBOLS:

Symbol	Pronounced	Represents
$1 - \alpha$	One minus alpha	Confidence level
B		Bound on the error of estimation
$z_{\alpha/2}$	z alpha by 2	Value of Z such that the area to its right is equal to $\alpha/2$

FORMULAS:

Confidence interval estimator of μ with σ known

$$\bar{x} \pm z_{\alpha/2}\frac{\sigma}{\sqrt{n}}$$

Sample size to estimate μ

$$n = \left(\frac{z_{\alpha/2}\sigma}{B}\right)^2$$

EXCEL OUTPUT AND INSTRUCTIONS:

Technique	
Confidence interval estimate of μ	335

APPENDIX 10.A / XLSTAT OUTPUT AND INSTRUCTIONS

Confidence Interval Estimate of a Mean

Example 10.1

	B	C	D	E	F	G
9	Summary statistics:					
10						
11	Variable	Observations	Minimum	Maximum	Mean	Std. deviation
12	Demand	25	235	535	370.16	80.783
13						
15	**One-sample z-test / Two-tailed test:**					
16						
17	95% confidence interval on the mean:					
18	(340.76, 399.56)					

Note: the output has been edited.

Instructions

1. Type or import the data into one column. (Open Xm10-01.)

2. Click **XLSTAT, Parametric tests**, and **One-sample t-test and z-test**.

3. Check **One sample** under **Data format:** In the **Data** dialog box, type the input range (A1:A26). Check **Column labels** if the first row of the data contains the name of the variable. Choose **Range:, Sheet,** or **Workbook** depending on where you wish the results to appear. Under Tests click **z-test**.

4. Click **Options** and choose **Mean ≠ Theoretical mean** in the **Alternative hypothesis** box. Type any number since you're not conducting a test here. Under **Variance for the z-test:**, check **User defined** and type the value of σ^2 (5625). Specify the value of α in percent (5) in the **Significance level (%)** box.

5. Click **Outputs** and check **Descriptive statistics, Detailed results,** and **Confidence interval**.

APPENDIX 10.B / STATA OUTPUT AND INSTRUCTIONS

Estimating a Population Mean: Standard Deviation Known

Example 10.1

```
One-sample z test

Variable      Obs        Mean     Std. Err.    Std. Dev.    [95% Conf. Interval]

Demand         25      370.16           15           75      340.7605    399.5595

    mean = mean(Demand)                                               z =   24.6773
Ho: mean = 0

    Ha: mean < 0                  Ha: mean != 0                      Ha: mean > 0
 Pr(Z < z) = 1.0000          Pr(|Z| > |z|) = 0.0000            Pr(Z > z) = 0.0000
```

The 95% confidence interval estimate: LCL = 340.7605 and UCL = 399.5595.

Instructions

1. Import the data into one column. (Click File/Import/Excel spreadsheet (*xls,*xlsx)/Chapter10/Xm10-01.) Check **Import first row as variable names**.

2. Click **Statistics, Summaries, tables and tests, Classical tests of hypotheses**, and **z-test (mean-comparison test known variance)**.

3. Select **One-sample**, select **Demand** in the **Variable name**: box, and type any number in the **Hypothesized mean**: box. Type the value of the **Confidence level** 95, and the **Standard deviation** 75.

Wavebreakmedia/Shutterstock.com

INTRODUCTION TO HYPOTHESIS TESTING

CHAPTER OUTLINE

SSA Envelope Plan

Data
Xm11-00

Federal Express (FedEx) sends invoices to customers requesting payment within 30 days. Each bill lists an address, and customers are expected to use their own envelopes to return their payments. Currently, the mean and standard deviation of the amount of time taken to pay bills are 24 days and 6 days, respectively. The chief financial officer (CFO) believes that including a stamped self-addressed (SSA) envelope would decrease the amount of time and calculates that the improved cash flow from a 2-day decrease in the payment period would pay for the costs of the envelopes and stamps. Any further decrease in the payment period would generate a profit. To test this belief, the CFO randomly selects 220 customers and includes an SSA envelope with their invoices. The numbers of days until payment is received were recorded. Can the CFO conclude that the plan will be profitable?

Franck Boston/Shutterstock.com

After we've introduced the required tools, we'll return to this question and answer it (see page 368).

355

INTRODUCTION

In Chapter 10, we introduced estimation and showed how it is used. Now we're going to present the second general procedure of making inferences about a population—hypothesis testing. The purpose of this type of inference is to determine whether enough statistical evidence exists to enable us to conclude that a belief or hypothesis about a parameter is supported by the data. You will discover that hypothesis testing has a wide variety of applications in business and economics, as well as many other fields. This chapter will lay the foundation upon which the rest of the book is based. As such it represents a critical contribution to your development as a statistics practitioner.

In the next section, we will introduce the concepts of hypothesis testing, and in Section 11-2 we will develop the method employed to test a hypothesis about a population mean when the population standard deviation is known. The rest of the chapter deals with related topics.

11-1 / CONCEPTS OF HYPOTHESIS TESTING

The term **hypothesis testing** is likely new to most readers, but the concepts underlying hypothesis testing are quite familiar. There are a variety of nonstatistical applications of hypothesis testing, the best known of which is a criminal trial.

When someone is accused of a crime, that person faces a trial. The prosecution presents its case, and a jury must make a decision on the basis of the evidence presented. In fact, the jury conducts a test of hypothesis. There are actually two hypotheses that are tested. The first is called the **null hypothesis** and is represented by H_0 (pronounced *H nought*—*nought* is a British term for zero). It is

H_0:   The defendant is innocent.

The second is called the **alternative hypothesis** (or **research hypothesis**) and is denoted H_1. In a criminal trial it is

H_1:   The defendant is guilty.

Of course, the jury does not know which hypothesis is correct. The members must make a decision on the basis of the evidence presented by both the prosecution and the defense. There are only two possible decisions. Convict or acquit the defendant. In statistical parlance, convicting the defendant is equivalent to *rejecting the null hypothesis in favor of the alternative*; that is, the jury is saying that there was enough evidence to conclude that the defendant was guilty. Acquitting a defendant is phrased as *not rejecting the null hypothesis in favor of the alternative*, which means that the jury decided that there was not enough evidence to conclude that the defendant was guilty. Notice that we do not say that we accept the null hypothesis. In a criminal trial, that would be interpreted as finding the defendant *innocent*. Our justice system does not allow this decision.

There are two possible errors. A **Type I error** occurs when we reject a true null hypothesis. A **Type II error** is defined as not rejecting a false null hypothesis. In the criminal trial, a Type I error is made when an innocent person is wrongly convicted. A Type II error occurs when a guilty defendant is acquitted. The probability of a Type I error is denoted by α which is also called the **significance level**. The probability of a Type II error is denoted by β (Greek letter *beta*). The error probabilities α and β are inversely related, meaning that any attempt to reduce one will increase the other. Table 11.1 summarizes the terminology and the concepts.

TABLE **11.1** Terminology of Hypothesis Testing

DECISION	H_0 IS TRUE Defendant is innocent	H_0 IS FALSE Defendant is guilty
REJECT H_0 Convict defendant	TYPE I ERROR $P(\text{TYPE I ERROR}) = \alpha$	CORRECT DECISION
DO NOT REJECT H_0 Acquit defendant	CORRECT DECISION	TYPE II ERROR $P(\text{TYPE II ERROR}) = \beta$

In our justice system, Type I errors are regarded as more serious. As a consequence, the system is set up so that the probability of a Type I error is small. This is arranged by placing the burden of proof on the prosecution (the prosecution must prove guilt—the defense need not prove anything) and by having judges instruct the jury to find the defendant guilty only if there is "evidence beyond a reasonable doubt." In the absence of enough evidence, the jury must acquit even though there may be some evidence of guilt. The consequence of this arrangement is that the probability of acquitting guilty people is relatively large. Sir William Blackstone (1723–1780), an English legal scholar, phrased the relationship between the probabilities of Type I and Type II errors in the following way: "Better for 10 guilty persons escape than that one innocent suffers." In Sir William's opinion, the probability of a Type I error should be one-tenth of the probability of a Type II error. The ratio of the two probabilities is called the *Blackstone ratio*. Benjamin Franklin (1706–1790) thought that the 1 to 10 ratio was not the prevailing view in the eighteenth century. He stated that "it is better 100 guilty persons should escape than that one innocent person should suffer, is a maxim that has been long and generally approved."

The critical concepts in hypothesis testing follow.

1. There are two hypotheses. One is called the null hypothesis, and the other the alternative or research hypothesis.

2. The testing procedure begins with the assumption that the null hypothesis is true.

3. The goal of the process is to determine whether there is enough evidence to infer that the alternative hypothesis is true.

4. There are two possible decisions:

   Conclude that there is enough evidence to support the alternative hypothesis.

   Conclude that there is not enough evidence to support the alternative hypothesis.

5. Two possible errors can be made in any test. A Type I error occurs when we reject a true null hypothesis, and a Type II error occurs when we don't reject a false null hypothesis. The probabilities of Type I and Type II errors are

$P(\text{Type I error}) = \alpha$

$P(\text{Type II error}) = \beta$

Let's extend these concepts to statistical hypothesis testing.

In statistics we frequently test hypotheses about parameters. The hypotheses we test are generated by questions that managers need to answer. To illustrate, suppose that in Example 10.1 (page 337) the operations manager did not want to estimate the mean demand during lead time but instead wanted to know whether the mean is different from 350, which may be the point at which the current inventory policy needs to be altered. In other words, we want to determine whether we can infer that μ is not equal to 350. We can rephrase the question so that it now reads, Is there enough evidence to conclude that μ is not equal to 350? This wording is analogous to the criminal trial wherein the jury is asked to determine whether there is enough evidence to conclude that the defendant is guilty. Thus, the alternative (research) hypothesis is

$$H_1: \quad \mu \neq 350$$

In a criminal trial, the process begins with the assumption that the defendant is innocent. In a similar fashion, we start with the assumption that the parameter equals the value we're testing. Consequently, the operations manager would assume that $\mu = 350$, and the null hypothesis is expressed as

$$H_0: \quad \mu = 350$$

When we state the hypotheses, we list the null first followed by the alternative hypothesis. To determine whether the mean is different from 350, we test

$$H_0: \quad \mu = 350$$
$$H_1: \quad \mu \neq 350$$

Now suppose that in this illustration the current inventory policy is based on an analysis that revealed that the actual mean demand during lead time is 350. After a vigorous advertising campaign, the manager suspects that there has been an increase in demand and thus an increase in mean demand during lead time. To test whether there is evidence of an increase, the manager would specify the alternative hypothesis as

$$H_1: \quad \mu > 350$$

Because the manager knew that the mean was (and maybe still is) 350, the null hypothesis would state

$$H_0: \quad \mu = 350$$

Further suppose that the manager does not know the actual mean demand during lead time, but the current inventory policy is based on the assumption that the mean is *less than or equal to* 350. If the advertising campaign increases the mean to a quantity larger than 350, a new inventory plan will have to be instituted. In this scenario, the hypotheses become

$$H_0: \quad \mu \leq 350$$
$$H_1: \quad \mu > 350$$

Notice that in both illustrations the alternative hypothesis is designed to determine whether there is enough evidence to conclude that the mean is greater than 350. Although the two null hypotheses are different (one states that the mean is equal to 350, and the other states that the mean is less than or equal to 350), when the test is conducted, the process begins by assuming that the mean is *equal to* 350. In other words, no matter the form of the null hypothesis, we use the equal sign in the null hypothesis. Here is the reason. If there is enough evidence to conclude that the alternative hypothesis (the mean is greater than 350) is true when we assume that the mean is *equal to* 350, we would certainly draw the same conclusion when we assume that the mean is a value that is *less than* 350. As a result, the null hypothesis will always state that the parameter equals the value specified in the alternative hypothesis.

To emphasize this point, suppose the manager now wanted to determine whether there has been a decrease in the mean demand during lead time. We express the null and alternative hypotheses as

$$H_0: \quad \mu = 350$$

$$H_1: \quad \mu < 350$$

The hypotheses are often set up to reflect a manager's decision problem wherein the null hypothesis represents the *status quo*. Often this takes the form of some course of action such as maintaining a particular inventory policy. If there is evidence of an increase or decrease in the value of the parameter, a new course of action will be taken. Examples include deciding to produce a new product, switching to a better drug to treat an illness, or sentencing a defendant to prison.

The next element in the procedure is to randomly sample the population and calculate the sample mean. This is called the **test statistic**. The test statistic is the criterion on which we base our decision about the hypotheses. (In the criminal trial analogy, this is equivalent to the evidence presented in the case.) The test statistic is based on the best estimator of the parameter. In Chapter 10, we stated that the best estimator of a population mean is the sample mean.

If the test statistic's value is inconsistent with the null hypothesis, we reject the null hypothesis and infer that the alternative hypothesis is true. For example, if we're trying to decide whether the mean is greater than 350, a large value of $\bar{x}$ (say, 600) would provide enough evidence. If $\bar{x}$ is close to 350 (say, 355), we would say that this does not provide much evidence to infer that the mean is greater than 350. In the absence of sufficient evidence, we do not reject the null hypothesis in favor of the alternative. (In the absence of sufficient evidence of guilt, a jury finds the defendant not guilty.)

In a criminal trial, "sufficient evidence" is defined as "evidence beyond a reasonable doubt." In statistics, we need to use the test statistic's sampling distribution to define "sufficient evidence." We will do so in the next section.

EXERCISES

Exercises 11.1–11.5 feature nonstatistical applications of hypothesis testing. For each, identify the hypotheses, define Type I and Type II errors, and discuss the consequences of each error. In setting up the hypotheses, you will have to consider where to place the "burden of proof."

11.1 It is the responsibility of the federal government to judge the safety and effectiveness of new drugs. There are two possible decisions: approve the drug or disapprove the drug.

11.2 You are contemplating a Ph.D. in business or economics. If you succeed, a life of fame, fortune, and happiness awaits you. If you fail, you've wasted 5 years of your life. Should you go for it?

11.3 You are the centerfielder of the New York Yankees. It is the bottom of the ninth inning of the seventh game of the World Series. The Yanks lead by 2 with 2 outs and men on second and third. The batter is known to hit for high average and runs very well

but only has mediocre power. A single will tie the game, and a hit over your head will likely result in the Yanks losing. Do you play shallow?

11.4 You are faced with two investments. One is very risky, but the potential returns are high. The other is safe, but the potential is quite limited. Pick one.

11.5 You are the pilot of a jumbo jet. You smell smoke in the cockpit. The nearest airport is less than 5 minutes away. Should you land the plane immediately?

11.6 Several years ago in a high-profile case, a defendant was acquitted in a double-murder trial but was subsequently found responsible for the deaths in a civil trial. (Guess the name of the defendant—the answer is in Appendix C.) In a civil trial the plaintiff (the victims' relatives) are required only to show that the preponderance of evidence points to the guilt of the defendant. Aside from the other issues in the cases, discuss why these results are logical.

11-2 TESTING THE POPULATION MEAN WHEN THE POPULATION STANDARD DEVIATION IS KNOWN

To illustrate the process, consider the following example.

EXAMPLE 11.1

Data
Xm11-01

Department Store's New Billing System

The manager of a department store is thinking about establishing a new billing system for the store's credit customers. After a thorough financial analysis, it has been determined that the new system will be cost-effective only if the mean monthly account is more than $170. A random sample of 400 monthly accounts is drawn, for which the sample mean is $178. The manager knows that the accounts are approximately normally distributed with a standard deviation of $65. Can the manager conclude from this that the new system will be cost-effective?

SOLUTION:

IDENTIFY

This example deals with the population of the credit accounts at the store. To conclude that the system will be cost-effective requires the manager to show that the mean account for all customers is greater than $170. Consequently, we set up the alternative hypothesis to express this circumstance:

H_1: $\mu > 170$ (Install new system)

If the mean is less than or equal to 170, then the system will not be cost-effective. The null hypothesis can be expressed as

H_0: $\mu \leq 170$ (Do not install new system)

However, as was discussed in Section 11-1, we will actually test $\mu = 170$, which is how we specify the null hypothesis:

H_0: $\mu = 170$

As we previously pointed out, the test statistic is the best estimator of the parameter. In Chapter 10, we used the sample mean to estimate the population mean. To conduct this test, we ask and answer the following question: Is a sample mean of 178 sufficiently greater than 170 to allow us to confidently infer that the population mean is greater than 170?

There are two approaches to answering this question. The first is called the *rejection region method*. It can be used in conjunction with the computer, but it is mandatory for those computing statistics manually. The second is the *p-value approach*, which in general can be employed only in conjunction with a computer and statistical software. We recommend, however, that users of statistical software be familiar with both approaches.

11-2a Rejection Region

It seems reasonable to reject the null hypothesis in favor of the alternative if the value of the sample mean is large relative to 170. If we had calculated the sample mean to be say, 500, it would be quite apparent that the null hypothesis is false and we would reject it.

On the other hand, values of $\bar{x}$ close to 170, such as 171, do not allow us to reject the null hypothesis because it is entirely possible to observe a sample mean of 171 from a population whose mean is 170. Unfortunately, the decision is not always so obvious. In this example, the sample mean was calculated to be 178, a value apparently neither very far away from nor very close to 170. To make a decision about this sample mean, we set up the *rejection region*.

> **Rejection Region**
>
> The **rejection region** is a range of values such that if the test statistic falls into that range, we decide to reject the null hypothesis in favor of the alternative hypothesis.

Suppose we define the value of the sample mean that is just large enough to reject the null hypothesis as $\bar{x}_L$. The rejection region is

$$\bar{x} > \bar{x}_L$$

Because a Type I error is defined as rejecting a true null hypothesis, and the probability of committing a Type I error is α, it follows that

$$\alpha = P(\text{rejecting } H_0 \text{ given that } H_0 \text{ is true})$$
$$= P(\bar{x} > \bar{x}_L \text{ given that } H_0 \text{ is true})$$

Figure 11.1 depicts the sampling distribution and the rejection region.

FIGURE **11.1** **Sampling Distribution for Example 11.1**

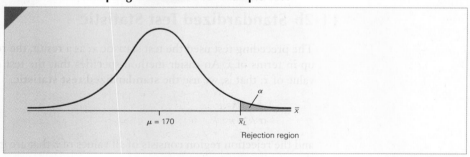

From Section 9-1, we know that the sampling distribution of $\bar{x}$ is normal or approximately normal, with mean μ and standard deviation $\sigma/\sqrt{n}$. As a result, we can standardize $\bar{x}$ and obtain the following probability:

$$P\left(\frac{\bar{x} - \mu}{\sigma/\sqrt{n}} > \frac{\bar{x}_L - \mu}{\sigma/\sqrt{n}}\right) = P\left(Z > \frac{\bar{x}_L - \mu}{\sigma/\sqrt{n}}\right) = \alpha$$

From Section 8-2, we defined z_α to be the value of a standard normal random variable such that

$$P(Z > z_\alpha) = \alpha$$

Because both probability statements involve the same distribution (standard normal) and the same probability (α), it follows that the limits are identical. Thus,

$$\frac{\bar{x}_L - \mu}{\sigma / \sqrt{n}} = z_\alpha$$

We know that $\sigma = 65$ and $n = 400$. Because the probabilities defined earlier are conditional on the null hypothesis being true, we have $\mu = 170$. To calculate the rejection region, we need a value of α at the significance level. Suppose that the manager chose α to be 5%. It follows that $z_\alpha = z_{.05} = 1.645$. We can now calculate the value of $\bar{x}_L$:

$$\frac{\bar{x}_L - \mu}{\sigma / \sqrt{n}} = z_\alpha$$

$$\frac{\bar{x}_L - 170}{65 / \sqrt{400}} = 1.645$$

$$\bar{x}_L = 175.34$$

Therefore, the rejection region is

$$\bar{x} > 175.34$$

The sample mean was computed to be 178. Because the test statistic (sample mean) is in the rejection region (it is greater than 175.34), we reject the null hypothesis. Thus, there is sufficient evidence to infer that the mean monthly account is greater than $170.

Our calculations determined that any value of $\bar{x}$ above 175.34 represents an event that is quite unlikely when sampling (with $n = 400$) from a population whose mean is 170 (and whose standard deviation is 65). This suggests that the assumption that the null hypothesis is true is incorrect, and consequently we reject the null hypothesis in favor of the alternative hypothesis.

11-2b Standardized Test Statistic

The preceding test used the test statistic $\bar{x}$; as a result, the rejection region had to be set up in terms of $\bar{x}$. An easier method specifies that the test statistic be the standardized value of $\bar{x}$; that is, we use the **standardized test statistic**.

$$z = \frac{\bar{x} - \mu}{\sigma / \sqrt{n}}$$

and the rejection region consists of all values of z that are greater than z_α. Algebraically, the rejection region is

$$z > z_\alpha$$

We can redo Example 11.1 using the standardized test statistic. The rejection region is

$$z > z_\alpha = z_{.05} = 1.645$$

The value of the test statistic is calculated next:

$$z = \frac{\bar{x} - \mu}{\sigma / \sqrt{n}} = \frac{178 - 170}{65 / \sqrt{400}} = 2.46$$

Because 2.46 is greater than 1.645, reject the null hypothesis and conclude that there is enough evidence to infer that the mean monthly account is greater than $170.

As you can see, the conclusions we draw from using the test statistic $\bar{x}$ and the standardized test statistic z are identical. Figures 11.2 and 11.3 depict the two sampling distributions, highlighting the equivalence of the two tests.

FIGURE **11.2** Sampling Distribution of $\bar{X}$ for Example 11.1

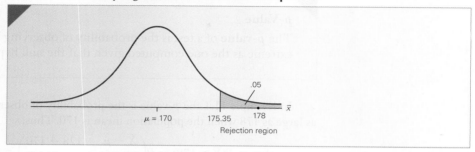

FIGURE **11.3** Sampling Distribution of Z for Example 11.1

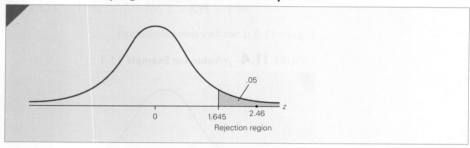

Because it is convenient and because statistical software packages employ it, the standardized test statistic will be used throughout this book. For simplicity, we will refer to the *standardized test statistic* simply as the *test statistic*.

Incidentally, when a null hypothesis is rejected, the test is said to be **statistically significant** at whatever significance level the test was conducted. Summarizing Example 11.1, we would say that the test was significant at the 5% significance level.

11-2c *p*-Value

There are several drawbacks to the rejection region method. Foremost among them is the type of information provided by the result of the test. The rejection region method produces a yes or no response to the question, Is there sufficient statistical evidence to infer that the alternative hypothesis is true? The implication is that the result of the test of hypothesis will be converted automatically into one of two possible courses of action: one action as a result of rejecting the null hypothesis in favor of the alternative and another as a result of not rejecting the null hypothesis in favor of the alternative. In Example 11.1, the rejection of the null hypothesis seems to imply that the new billing system will be installed.

In fact, this is not the way in which the result of a statistical analysis is utilized. The statistical procedure is only one of several factors considered by a manager when making a decision. In Example 11.1, the manager discovered that there was enough statistical evidence to conclude that the mean monthly account is greater than $170. However, before taking any action, the manager would like to consider a number of factors including the cost and feasibility of restructuring the billing system and the possibility of making an error, in this case a Type I error.

What is needed to take full advantage of the information available from the test result and make a better decision is a measure of the amount of statistical evidence supporting the alternative hypothesis so that it can be weighed in relation to the other factors, especially the financial ones. The *p-value of a test* provides this measure.

---

p-Value

The **p-value** of a test is the probability of observing a test statistic at least as extreme as the one computed given that the null hypothesis is true.

In Example 11.1 the *p*-value is the probability of observing a sample mean at least as large as 178 when the population mean is 170. Thus,

$$p\text{-value} = P(\overline{X} > 178) = P\left(\frac{\overline{X} - \mu}{\sigma / \sqrt{n}} > \frac{178 - 170}{65 / \sqrt{400}}\right) = P(Z > 2.46)$$

$$= 1 - P(Z < 2.46) = 1 - .9931 = .0069$$

Figure 11.4 describes this calculation.

FIGURE **11.4** *p*-Value for Example 11.1

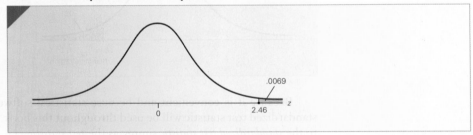

11-2d Interpreting the *p*-Value

To properly interpret the results of an inferential procedure, you must remember that the technique is based on the sampling distribution. The sampling distribution allows us to make probability statements about a sample statistic assuming knowledge of the population parameter. Thus, the probability of observing a sample mean at least as large as 178 from a population whose mean is 170 is .0069, which is very small. In other words, we have just observed an unlikely event, an event so unlikely that we seriously doubt the assumption that began the process—that the null hypothesis is true. Consequently, we have reason to reject the null hypothesis and support the alternative.

Students may be tempted to simplify the interpretation by stating that the *p*-value is the probability that the null hypothesis is true. Don't! As was the case with interpreting the confidence interval estimator, you cannot make a probability statement about a parameter. It is not a random variable.

The *p*-value of a test provides valuable information because it is a measure of the amount of statistical evidence that supports the alternative hypothesis. To understand this interpretation fully, refer to Table 11.2 where we list several values of $\overline{x}$, their *z*-statistics, and *p*-values for Example 11.1. Notice that the closer $\overline{x}$ is to the hypothesized mean, 170, the larger the *p*-value is. The farther $\overline{x}$ is above 170, the smaller the *p*-value is. Values of $\overline{x}$ far above 170 tend to indicate that the alternative hypothesis is true. Thus, the smaller the p-value, the more the statistical evidence supports the alternative hypothesis. Figure 11.5 graphically depicts the information in Table 11.2.

TABLE **11.2** Test Statistics and p-Values for Example 11.1

SAMPLE MEAN $\bar{x}$	TEST STATISTIC $z = \dfrac{\bar{x} - \mu}{\sigma / \sqrt{n}} = \dfrac{\bar{x} - 170}{65 / \sqrt{400}}$	p-VALUE
170	0	.5000
172	0.62	.2676
174	1.23	.1093
176	1.85	.0322
178	2.46	.0069
180	3.08	.0010

FIGURE **11.5** p-Values for Example 11.1

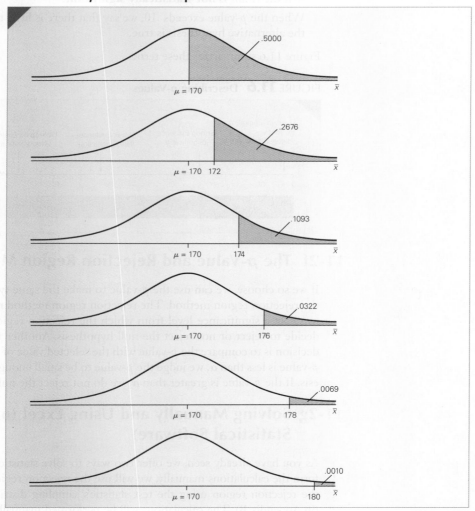

This raises the question, How small does the *p*-value have to be to infer that the alternative hypothesis is true? In general, the answer depends on a number of factors, including the costs of making Type I and Type II errors. In Example 11.1, a Type I error would occur if the manager adopts the new billing system when it is not cost-effective. If the cost of this error is high, we attempt to minimize its probability. In the rejection region method, we do so by setting the significance level quite low—say, 1%. Using the *p*-value method, we would insist that the *p*-value be quite small, providing sufficient evidence to infer that the mean monthly account is greater than $170 before proceeding with the new billing system.

11-2e Describing the *p*-Value

Statistics practitioners can translate *p*-values using the following descriptive terms:

If the *p*-value is less than .01, we say that there is *overwhelming* evidence to infer that the alternative hypothesis is true. We also say that the test is **highly significant**.

If the *p*-value lies between .01 and .05, there is *strong* evidence to infer that the alternative hypothesis is true. The result is deemed to be **significant**.

If the *p*-value is between .05 and .10, we say that there is *weak* evidence to indicate that the alternative hypothesis is true. When the *p*-value is greater than 5%, we say that the result is **not statistically significant**.

When the *p*-value exceeds .10, we say that there is little to no evidence to infer that the alternative hypothesis is true.

Figure 11.6 summarizes these terms.

FIGURE **11.6** Describing *p*-Values

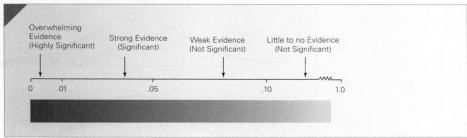

11-2f The *p*-Value and Rejection Region Methods

If we so choose, we can use the *p*-value to make the same type of decisions we make in the rejection region method. The rejection region method requires the decision maker to select a significance level from which the rejection region is constructed. We then decide to reject or not reject the null hypothesis. Another way of making that type of decision is to compare the *p*-value with the selected value of the significance level. If the *p*-value is less than α, we judge the *p*-value to be small enough to reject the null hypothesis. If the *p*-value is greater than α, we do not reject the null hypothesis.

11-2g Solving Manually and Using Excel (or Other Statistical Software)

As you have already seen, we offer two ways to solve statistical problems. When we perform the calculations manually, we will use the rejection region approach. We will set up the rejection region using the test statistic's sampling distribution and associated table (in Appendix B). The calculations will be performed manually and a reject–do not reject decision will be made. In this chapter, it is possible to compute the *p*-value of the test manually. However, in later chapters we will be using test statistics that are not normally distributed, making it impossible to calculate the *p*-values manually. In these instances, manual calculations require the decision to be made via the rejection region method only. However, when we use a computer to perform the calculations, we will make the decision on the basis of the *p*-value, which Excel's Data Analysis and our workbooks output (as do most statistical software).

EXCEL Workbook

	A	B	C	D
1	z-Test of a Mean			
2				
3	Sample mean	178	z Stat	2.46
4	Population standard deviation	65	P(Z<=z) one-tail	0.0069
5	Sample size	400	z Critical one-tail	1.6449
6	Hypothesized mean	170	P(Z<=z) two-tail	0.0138
7	Alpha	0.05	z Critical two-tail	1.9600

INSTRUCTIONS

1. Type or import the data into one column. (Open Xm11-01.) In any empty cell, calculate the sample mean (=AVERAGE(A1:A401).)

2. Open the **Test Statistics Workbook** and click the **z-Test_Mean** tab. In Cell B3, type or copy the value of the sample mean. In cells B4–B7, type the value of σ (65), the value of n (400), the value of μ under the null hypothesis (170), and the value of α (.05), respectively.

The spreadsheet reports the value of the test statistic, z = 2.46. The *p*-value* of the test is .0069. Excel reports this probability as

P(Z <= z) one-tail

*Excel provides two probabilities in its printout. The way in which we determine the *p*-value of the test from the printout is somewhat more complicated. Interested students are advised to read the online appendix Converting Excel's Probabilities to *p*-Values.

11-2h Interpreting the Results of a Test

In Example 11.1, we rejected the null hypothesis. Does this prove that the alternative hypothesis is true? The answer is no; because our conclusion is based on sample data (and not on the entire population), we can never *prove* anything by using statistical inference. Consequently, we summarize the test by stating that there is enough statistical evidence to infer that the null hypothesis is false and that the alternative hypothesis is true.

Now suppose that $\bar{x}$ had equaled 174 instead of 178. We would then have calculated z = 1.23 (*p*-value = .1093), which is not in the rejection region. Could we conclude on this basis that there is enough statistical evidence to infer that the null hypothesis is true and hence that $\mu = 170$? Again the answer is "no" because it is absurd to suggest that a sample mean of 174 provides enough evidence to infer that the population mean is 170. (If it proved anything, it would prove that the population mean is 174.) Because we're testing a single value of the parameter under the null hypothesis, we can never have enough statistical evidence to establish that the null hypothesis is true (unless we sample the entire population). (The same argument is valid if you set up the null hypothesis as H_0: $\mu \leq 170$. It would be illogical to conclude that a sample mean of 174 provides enough evidence to conclude that the population mean is *less than or equal to* 170.)

Consequently, if the value of the test statistic does not fall into the rejection region (or the *p*-value is large), rather than say we accept the null hypothesis (which implies that we're stating that the null hypothesis is true), we state that we do not reject the null hypothesis, and we conclude that not enough evidence exists to show that the alternative hypothesis is true. Although it may appear to be the case, we are not being overly technical. Your ability to set up tests of hypotheses properly and to interpret their results correctly very much depends on your understanding of this point. The point is that the conclusion is based on the alternative hypothesis. In the final analysis, there are only two possible conclusions of a test of hypothesis.

Conclusions of a Test of Hypothesis

If we reject the null hypothesis, we conclude that there is enough statistical evidence to infer that the alternative hypothesis is true.

If we do *not* reject the null hypothesis, we conclude that there is *not* enough statistical evidence to infer that the alternative hypothesis is true.

Observe that the alternative hypothesis is the focus of the conclusion. It represents what we are investigating, which is why it is also called the *research hypothesis*. Whatever you're trying to show statistically must be represented by the alternative hypothesis (bearing in mind that you have only three choices for the alternative hypothesis—the parameter is greater than, less than, or not equal to the value specified in the null hypothesis).

When we introduced statistical inference in Chapter 10, we pointed out that the first step in the solution is to identify the technique. When the problem involves hypothesis testing, part of this process is the specification of the hypotheses. Because the alternative hypothesis represents the condition we're researching, we will identify it first. The null hypothesis automatically follows because the null hypothesis must specify equality. However, by tradition, when we list the two hypotheses, the null hypothesis comes first, followed by the alternative hypothesis. All examples in this book will follow that format.

SSA Envelope Plan: Solution

Franck Boston/Shutterstock.com

IDENTIFY

The objective of the study is to draw a conclusion about the mean payment period. Thus, the parameter to be tested is the population mean μ. We want to know whether there is enough statistical evidence to show that the population mean is less than 22 days. Thus, the alternative hypothesis is

$$H_1: \quad \mu < 22$$

The null hypothesis is

$$H_0: \quad \mu = 22$$

The test statistic is the only one we've presented thus far. It is

$$z = \frac{\bar{x} - \mu}{\sigma / \sqrt{n}}$$

COMPUTE

MANUALLY:

To solve this problem manually, we need to define the rejection region, which requires us to specify a significance level. A 10% significance level is deemed to be appropriate. (We'll discuss our choice later.)

We wish to reject the null hypothesis in favor of the alternative only if the sample mean and hence the value of the test statistic is small enough. As a result, we locate the rejection region in the left tail of the sampling distribution. To understand why, remember that we're trying to decide whether there is enough statistical evidence to infer that the mean is less than 22 (which is the alternative hypothesis). If we observe a large sample mean (and hence a large value of z), do we want to reject the null hypothesis in favor of the alternative? The answer is an emphatic "no." It is illogical to think that if the sample mean is, say, 30, there is enough evidence to conclude that the mean payment period for all customers would be less than 22.

Consequently, we want to reject the null hypothesis only if the sample mean (and hence the value of the test statistic z) is small. How small is small enough? The answer is determined by the significance level and the rejection region. Thus, we set up the rejection region as

$$z < -z_\alpha = -z_{.10} = -1.28$$

Note that the direction of the inequality in the rejection region ($z < -z_\alpha$) matches the direction of the inequality in the alternative hypothesis ($\mu < 22$). Also note that we use the negative sign, because the rejection region is in the left tail (containing values of z less than 0) of the sampling distribution.

From the data, we compute the sum and the sample mean. They are

$$\sum x_i = 4{,}759$$

$$\bar{x} = \frac{\sum x_i}{220} = \frac{4{,}759}{220} = 21.63$$

We will assume that the standard deviation of the payment periods for the SSA plan is unchanged from its current value of $\sigma = 6$. The sample size is $n = 220$, and the value of μ is hypothesized to be 22. We compute the value of the test statistic as

$$z = \frac{\bar{x} - \mu}{\sigma/\sqrt{n}} = \frac{21.63 - 22}{6/\sqrt{220}} = -.91$$

Because the value of the test statistic, $z = -.91$, is not less than -1.28, we do not reject the null hypothesis and we do not conclude that the alternative hypothesis is true. There is insufficient evidence to infer that the mean is less than 22 days.

We can determine the p-value of the test as follows:

$$p\text{-value} = P(Z < -.91) = .1814$$

In this type of one-tail (left-tail) test of hypothesis, we calculate the p-value as $P(Z < z)$, where z is the actual value of the test statistic. Figure 11.7 depicts the sampling distribution, rejection region, and p-value.

(Continued)

EXCEL Workbook

	A	B	C	D
1	z-Test of a Mean			
2				
3	Sample mean	21.63	z Stat	-0.91
4	Population standard deviation	6	P(Z<=z) one-tail	0.1802
5	Sample size	220	z Critical one-tail	1.6449
6	Hypothesized mean	22	P(Z<=z) two-tail	0.3604
7	Alpha	0.05	z Critical two-tail	1.9600

INTERPRET

The value of the test statistic is −.91, and its *p*-value is .1814 (Excel's p-value = .1802), a figure that does not allow us to reject the null hypothesis. Because we were not able to reject the null hypothesis, we say that there is not enough evidence to infer that the mean payment period is less than 22 days. Note that there was some evidence to indicate that the mean of the entire population of payment periods is less than 22 days. We did calculate the sample mean to be 21.63. However, to reject the null hypothesis we need *enough* statistical evidence—and in this case we simply did not have enough reason to reject the null hypothesis in favor of the alternative. In the absence of evidence to show that the mean payment period for all customers sent a stamped self-addressed envelope would be less than 22 days, we cannot infer that the plan would be profitable.

A Type I error occurs when we conclude that the plan works when it actually does not. The cost of this mistake is not high. A Type II error occurs when we don't adopt the SSA envelope plan when it would reduce costs. The cost of this mistake can be high. As a consequence, we would like to minimize the probability of a Type II error. Thus, we chose a large value for the probability of a Type I error; we set

$$\alpha = .10$$

Figure 11.7 exhibits the sampling distribution for this example.

FIGURE **11.7** **Sampling Distribution for SSA Envelope Example**

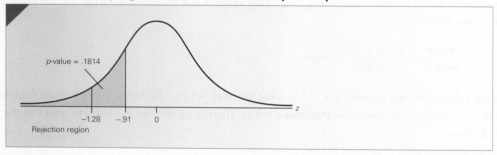

11-2i One- and Two-Tail Tests

The statistical tests conducted in Example 11.1 and the SSA envelope example are called **one-tail tests** because the rejection region is located in only one tail of the sampling distribution. The *p*-value is also computed by finding the area in one tail of the sampling distribution. The right tail in Example 11.1 is the important one because the alternative hypothesis specifies that the mean is *greater than* 170. In the SSA envelope example, the left tail is emphasized because the alternative hypothesis specifies that the mean is *less than* 22.

We now present an example that requires a **two-tail test**.

EXAMPLE 11.2

DATA
Xm 11-02

The Effects of Kiosks on Sales in Fast-Food Restaurants

A number of states have recently passed legislation that substantially raises the minimum wage. Many minimum wage earners work for fast-food restaurants. To deal with rising labor costs, some companies have replaced workers with self-serve kiosks wherein the customer makes a selection and pays using a credit or debit card. A small-chain of fast-food restaurants is considering replacing the cashiers with kiosks. To help plan, a franchisee takes a random sample of individual customers who use the new machines at McDonald's. It is known that before the advent of the kiosks, the average individual customer at McDonald's spent $6.03 with a standard deviation of $0.91. The franchisee is concerned about possible changes in the sales. Do the data provide enough evidence at the 5% significance level of a change in the size of the transaction for individual customer?

SOLUTION:

IDENTIFY

In this problem we want to know whether the mean expenditure has changed from the mean of $6.03. Consequently, we set up the alternative hypothesis to express this condition.

$$H_1: \quad \mu \neq 6.03$$

The null hypothesis specifies that the mean is equal to the value specified in the alternative hypothesis. Hence,

$$H_0: \quad \mu = 6.03$$

COMPUTE

MANUALLY:

To set up the rejection region, we realize that we can reject the null hypothesis when the test statistic is large or when it is small. Because the total area in the rejection region must be α, we divide this probability by 2. Thus, the rejection region is

$$z < -z_{\alpha/2} \quad \text{or} \quad z > z_{\alpha/2}$$

For $\alpha = .05$, $\alpha/2 = .05/2 = .025$ and $z_{\alpha/2} = z_{.025} = 1.96$, the rejection region is

$$z < -196 \quad \text{or} \quad z > 1.96$$

From the data we calculate

$$\sum x_i = 591$$

$$\bar{x} = \frac{\displaystyle\sum_{i=1}^{n} x_i}{n} = \frac{591}{100} = 5.91$$

The value of the test statistic is

$$z = \frac{\bar{x} - \mu}{\sigma/\sqrt{n}} = \frac{5.91 - 6.03}{.91/\sqrt{100}} = -1.32$$

Because -1.32 is not less than -1.96 nor greater than 1.96, we cannot reject the null hypothesis.

We can calculate the p-value of the test. Because it is a two-tail test, we determine the p-value by finding the area in both tails; that is,

$$p\text{-value} = P(Z < -1.32) + P(Z > 1.32) = .0934 + .0934 = .1868.$$

EXCEL Workbook

	A	B	C	D
1	z-Test of a Mean			
2				
3	Sample mean	5.91	z Stat	-1.32
4	Population standard deviation	0.91	P(Z<=z) one-tail	0.0936
5	Sample size	100	z Critical one-tail	1.6449
6	Hypothesized mean	6.03	P(Z<=z) two-tail	0.1873
7	Alpha	0.05	z Critical two-tail	1.9600

INTERPRET

The value of the test statistic is $z = -1.32$ and the p-value $= .1868$ (Excel's p-value $= .1873$). There is not enough evidence to conclude that the self-serve kiosks result in a change from the amounts incurred with a cashier.

FIGURE **11.8** Sampling Distribution for Example 11.2

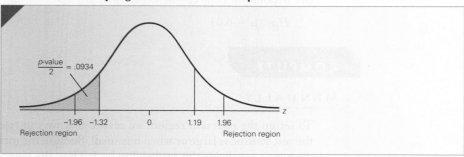

11-2j When Do We Conduct One- and Two-Tail Tests?

A **two-tail test** is conducted whenever the alternative hypothesis specifies that the mean is *not equal* to the value stated in the null hypothesis—that is, when the hypotheses assume the following form:

$$H_0: \quad \mu = \mu_0$$
$$H_1: \quad \mu \neq \mu_0$$

There are two one-tail tests. We conduct a one-tail test that focuses on the right tail of the sampling distribution whenever we want to know whether there is enough evidence to infer that the mean is greater than the quantity specified by the null hypothesis—that is, when the hypotheses are

$$H_0: \quad \mu = \mu_0$$
$$H_1: \quad \mu > \mu_0$$

The second one-tail test involves the left tail of the sampling distribution. It is used when the statistics practitioner wants to determine whether there is enough evidence to infer that the mean is less than the value of the mean stated in the null hypothesis. The resulting hypotheses appear in this form:

$$H_0: \quad \mu = \mu_0$$
$$H_1: \quad \mu < \mu_0$$

The techniques introduced in Chapters 12, 13, 16, 17, 18, and 19 require you to decide which of the three forms of the test to employ. Make your decision in the same way as we described the process.

11-2k Testing Hypotheses and Confidence Interval Estimators

The test statistic and the confidence interval estimator are both derived from the sampling distribution. It shouldn't be a surprise then that we can use the confidence interval estimator to test hypotheses. To illustrate, consider Example 11.2. The 95% confidence interval estimate of the population mean is

$$\bar{x} \pm z_{\alpha/2}\frac{\sigma}{\sqrt{n}} = 5.91 \pm 1.96\frac{.91}{\sqrt{100}} = 5.91 \pm .18$$

$$LCL = 5.73 \text{ and } UCL = 6.09$$

We estimate that μ lies between 5.73 and 6.09. Because this interval includes 6.03, we cannot conclude that there is sufficient evidence to infer that the mean has changed.

In Example 11.1, the 95% confidence interval estimate is LCL = 171.63 and UCL = 184.37. The interval estimate excludes 170, allowing us to conclude that the population mean account is not equal to $170.

As you can see, the confidence interval estimator can be used to conduct tests of hypotheses. This process is equivalent to the rejection region approach. However, instead of finding the critical values of the rejection region and determining whether the test statistic falls into the rejection region, we compute the interval estimate and determine whether the hypothesized value of the mean falls into the interval.

Using the interval estimator to test hypotheses has the advantage of simplicity. Apparently, we don't need the formula for the test statistic; we need only the interval estimator. However, there are two serious drawbacks.

First, when conducting a one-tail test, our conclusion may not answer the original question. In Example 11.1, we wanted to know whether there was enough evidence to infer that the mean is *greater than* 170. The estimate concludes that the mean *differs from* 170. You may be tempted to say that because the entire interval is greater than 170, there is enough statistical evidence to infer that the population mean is greater than 170. However, in attempting to draw this conclusion, we run into the problem of determining the procedure's significance level. Is it 5% or is it 2.5%? We may be able to overcome this problem through the use of **one-sided confidence interval estimators**.

However, if the purpose of using confidence interval estimators instead of test statistics is simplicity, one-sided estimators are a contradiction.

Second, the confidence interval estimator does not yield a *p*-value, which we have argued is the better way to draw inferences about a parameter. Using the confidence interval estimator to test hypotheses forces the decision maker into making a reject–don't reject decision rather than providing information about how much statistical evidence exists to be judged with other factors in the decision process. Furthermore, we only postpone the point in time when a test of hypothesis must be used. In later chapters, we will present problems where only a test produces the information we need to make decisions.

11-2l   Developing an Understanding of Statistical Concepts 1

As is the case with the confidence interval estimator, the test of hypothesis is based on the sampling distribution of the sample statistic. The result of a test of hypothesis is a probability statement about the sample statistic. We assume that the population mean is specified by the null hypothesis. We then compute the test statistic and determine how likely it is to observe this large (or small) a value when the null hypothesis is true. If the probability is small, we conclude that the assumption that the null hypothesis is true is unfounded and we reject it.

11-2m   Developing an Understanding of Statistical Concepts 2

When we (or the computer) calculate the value of the test statistic

$$z = \frac{\bar{x} - \mu}{\sigma/\sqrt{n}}$$

we're also measuring the difference between the sample statistic $\bar{x}$ and the hypothesized value of the parameter μ in terms of the standard error $\sigma/\sqrt{n}$. In Example 11.2, we found that the value of the test statistic was $z = -1.32$. This means that the sample mean was 1.32 standard errors below the hypothesized value of μ. The standard normal probability table told us that this value is not considered unlikely. As a result, we did not reject the null hypothesis.

The concept of measuring the difference between the sample statistic and the hypothesized value of the parameter in terms of the standard errors is one that will be used throughout this book.

EXERCISES

Developing an Understanding of Statistical Concepts

In Exercises 11.7–11.12, calculate the value of the test statistic, set up the rejection region, determine the p-value, interpret the result, and draw the sampling distribution.

11.7 H_0: $\mu = 1{,}000$
H_1: $\mu \neq 1{,}000$
$\sigma = 200, n = 100, \bar{x} = 980, \alpha = .01$

11.8 H_0: $\mu = 50$
H_1: $\mu > 50$
$\sigma = 5, n = 9, \bar{x} = 51, \alpha = .03$

11.9 H_0: $\mu = 15$
H_1: $\mu < 15$
$\sigma = 2, n = 25, \bar{x} = 14.3, \alpha = .10$

11.10 H_0: $\mu = 100$
H_1: $\mu \neq 100$
$\sigma = 10, n = 100, \bar{x} = 100, \alpha = .05$

11.11 H_0: $\mu = 70$
H_1: $\mu > 70$
$\sigma = 20, n = 100, \bar{x} = 80, \alpha = .01$

11.12 H_0: $\mu = 50$
H_1: $\mu < 50$
$\sigma = 15, n = 100, \bar{x} = 48, \alpha = .05$

For Exercises 11.13–11.19, calculate the p-value of the test to determine that there is sufficient evidence to infer each research objective.

11.13 Research objective: The population mean is less than 250.

$\sigma = 40, n = 70, \bar{x} = 240$

11.14 Research objective: The population mean is not equal to 1,500.

$\sigma = 220, n = 125, \bar{x} = 1,525$

11.15 Research objective: The population mean is greater than 7.5.

$\sigma = 1.5, n = 30, \bar{x} = 8.5$

11.16 Research objective: The population mean is greater than 0.

$\sigma = 10, n = 100, \bar{x} = 1.5$

11.17 Research objective: The population mean is less than 0.

$\sigma = 25, n = 400, \bar{x} = -2.3$

11.18 Research objective: The population mean is not equal to 0.

$\sigma = 50, n = 90, \bar{x} = -5.5$

11.19 Research objective: The population mean is not equal to −5.

$\sigma = 5, n = 25, \bar{x} = -4.0$

11.20 You are conducting a test to determine whether there is enough statistical evidence to infer that a population mean is greater than 100. You discover that the sample mean is 95.
a. Is it necessary to do any further calculations? Explain.
b. If you did calculate the p-value would it be smaller or larger than .5? Explain.

Exercises 11.21 to 11.35 are "what-if analyses" designed to determine what happens to the test statistic and p-value when the sample size, standard deviation, and sample mean change.

These problems can be solved manually or by using the Excel spreadsheet.

11.21 a. Compute the p-value in order to test the following hypotheses given that $\bar{x} = 52, n = 9$, and $\sigma = 5$.

H_0: $\mu = 50$
H_1: $\mu > 50$
b. Repeat part (a) with $n = 25$.
c. Repeat part (a) with $n = 100$.
d. Describe what happens to the value of the test statistic and its p-value when the sample size increases.

11.22 a. A statistics practitioner formulated the following hypotheses

H_0: $\mu = 200$
H_1: $\mu < 200$
and learned that $\bar{x} = 190, n = 9$, and $\sigma = 50$ Compute the p-value of the test.
b. Repeat part (a) with $\sigma = 30$.
c. Repeat part (a) with $\sigma = 10$.
d. Discuss what happens to the value of the test statistic and its p-value when the standard deviation decreases.

11.23 a. Given the following hypotheses, determine the p-value when $\bar{x} = 21, n = 25$, and $\sigma = 5$.

H_0: $\mu = 20$
H_1: $\mu \neq 20$
b. Repeat part (a) with $\bar{x} = 22$.
c. Repeat part (a) with $\bar{x} = 23$.
d. Describe what happens to the value of the test statistic and its p-value when the value of $\bar{x}$ increases.

11.24 a. Test these hypotheses by calculating the p-value given that $\bar{x} = 99, n = 100$, and $\sigma = 8$.

H_0: $\mu = 100$
H_1: $\mu \neq 100$
b. Repeat part (a) with $n = 50$.
c. Repeat part (a) with $n = 20$.
d. What is the effect on the value of the test statistic and the p-value of the test when the sample size decreases?

11.25 a. Find the p-value of the following test given that $\bar{x} = 990, n = 100$, and $\sigma = 25$.

H_0: $\mu = 1,000$
H_1: $\mu < 1,000$
b. Repeat part (a) with $\sigma = 50$.
c. Repeat part (a) with $\sigma = 100$.
d. Describe what happens to the value of the test statistic and its p-value when the standard deviation increases.

11.26 a. Calculate the p-value of the test described here.

H_0: $\mu = 60$

H_1: $\mu > 60$

$\bar{x} = 72, n = 25, \sigma = 20$

b. Repeat part (a) with $\bar{x} = 68$.

c. Repeat part (a) with $\bar{x} = 64$.

d. Describe the effect on the test statistic and the p-value of the test when the value of $\bar{x}$ decreases.

11.27 Redo Example 11.1 with

a. $n = 200$

b. $n = 100$

c. Describe the effect on the test statistic and the p-value when n increases.

11.28 Redo Example 11.1 with

a. $\sigma = 35$

b. $\sigma = 100$

c. Describe the effect on the test statistic and the p-value when σ increases.

11.29 While conducting a test to determine whether a population mean is less than 900, you find that the sample mean is 1,050.

a. Can you make a decision on this information alone? Explain.

b. If you did calculate the p-value, would it be smaller or larger than .5? Explain.

11.30 Redo the SSA example with

a. $n = 100$

b. $n = 500$

c. What is the effect on the test statistic and the p-value when n increases?

11.31 Redo the SSA example with

a. $\sigma = 3$

b. $\sigma = 12$

c. Discuss the effect on the test statistic and the p-value when σ increases.

11.32 For the SSA example, create a table that shows the effect on the test statistic and the p-value of decreasing the value of the sample mean. Use $\bar{x} = 22.0, 21.8, 21.6, 21.4, 21.2, 21.0, 20.8, 20.6,$ and 20.4.

11.33 Redo Example 11.2 with

a. $n = 50$

b. $n = 400$

c. Briefly describe the effect on the test statistic and the p-value when n increases.

11.34 Redo Example 11.2 with

a. $\sigma = 2$

b. $\sigma = 3$

c. What happens to the test statistic and the p-value when σ increases?

11.35 Refer to Example 11.2. Create a table that shows the effect on the test statistic and the p-value

of changing the value of the sample mean. Use $\bar{x} = 6.05, 6.10, 6.15, 6.20, 6.25, 6.30, 6.35,$ and 6.40.

Applications

The following exercises may be answered manually or with the assistance of a computer. The files containing the data are given.

11.36 <u>Xr11-36</u> A business student claims that, on average, an MBA student is required to prepare more than five cases per week. To examine the claim, a statistics professor asks a random sample of 10 MBA students to report the number of cases they prepare weekly. The results are exhibited here. Can the professor conclude at the 5% significance level that the claim is true, assuming that the number of cases is normally distributed with a standard deviation of 1.5?

| 2 | 7 | 4 | 8 | 9 | 5 | 11 | 3 | 7 | 4 |

11.37 <u>Xr11-37</u> A random sample of 18 young adult men (20–30 years old) was sampled. Each person was asked how many minutes of sports he watched on television daily. The responses are listed here. It is known that $\sigma = 10$. Test to determine at the 5% significance level whether there is enough statistical evidence to infer that the mean amount of television watched daily by all young adult men is greater than 50 minutes.

| 50 | 48 | 65 | 74 | 66 | 37 | 45 | 68 | 64 |
| 65 | 58 | 55 | 52 | 63 | 59 | 57 | 74 | 65 |

11.38 <u>Xr11-38</u> The club professional at a difficult public course boasts that the course is so tough that the average golfer loses a dozen or more golf balls during a round of golf. A dubious golfer sets out to show that the pro is fibbing. A random sample of 15 golfers are asked to report the number of golf balls lost during the round they just completed. Assuming that the number of golf balls lost is normally distributed with a standard deviation of 3, can we infer at the 10% significance level that the average number of golf balls lost is less than 12?

| 1 | 14 | 8 | 15 | 17 | 10 | 12 | 6 |
| 14 | 21 | 15 | 9 | 11 | 4 | 8 | |

11.39 <u>Xr11-39</u> A random sample of 12 second-year university students enrolled in a business statistics course was drawn. At the course's completion, the students were asked how many hours they spent doing homework in statistics. The data are listed here. It is known that the population standard deviation is $\sigma = 8.0$. The instructor has recommended that students devote 3 hours per week for the duration of the 12-week semester, for a total of 36 hours. Test to determine whether there is evidence that the average student spent less than the recommended amount of time. Compute the p-value of the test.

31 40 26 30 36 38 29 40 38 30 35 38

11.40 Xr11-40 The owner of a public golf course is concerned about slow play, which clogs the course and results in selling fewer rounds. The owner believes the problem lies in the amount of time taken to sink putts on the green. To investigate the problem, random samples of 10 foursomes were drawn and the amount of time taken on the 18th green was recorded. The data are listed here. Assuming that the times are normally distributed with a standard deviation of 2 minutes, test to determine whether the owner can infer at the 5% significance level that the mean amount of time spent putting on the 18th green is greater than 6 minutes.

8 11 5 6 7 8 6 4 8 3

11.41 Xr11-41 A machine that produces ball bearings is set so that the average diameter is .50 inch. A sample of 10 ball bearings was measured, with the results shown here. Assuming that the standard deviation is .05 inch, can we conclude at the 5% significance level that the mean diameter is not .50 inch?

.48 .50 .49 .52 .53 .48 .49 .47 .46 .51

11.42 Xr11-42 Spam e-mail has become a serious and costly nuisance. An office manager believes that the average amount of time spent by office workers reading and deleting spam exceeds 25 minutes per day. To test this belief, a random sample of 18 workers was drawn and the amount of time each spent reading and deleting spam was measured. The results are listed here. If the population of times is normal with a standard deviation of 12 minutes, can the manager infer at the 1% significance level that he is correct?

35 48 29 44 17 21 32 28 34
23 13 9 11 30 42 37 43 48

The following exercises require the use of a computer and software. The answers may be calculated manually. See Appendix A for the sample statistics.

11.43 Xr11-43 A manufacturer of lightbulbs advertises that, on average, its long-life bulb will last more than 5,000 hours. To test the claim, a statistician took a random sample of 100 bulbs and measured the amount of time until each bulb burned out. If we assume that the lifetime of this type of bulb has a standard deviation of 400 hours, can we conclude at the 5% significance level that the claim is true?

11.44 Xr11-44 In the midst of labor–management negotiations, the president of a company argues that the company's blue-collar workers, who are paid an average of $50,000 per year, are well paid because the mean annual income of all blue-collar workers in the country is less than $50,000. That figure is disputed by the union, which does not believe that the mean blue-collar income is less than $50,000. To test the company president's belief, an arbitrator draws a random sample of 350 blue-collar workers from across the country and asks each to report their annual income. If the arbitrator assumes that the blue-collar incomes are normally distributed with a standard deviation of $15,000, can it be inferred at the 5% significance level that the company president is correct?

11.45 Xr11-45 A dean of a business school claims that the Graduate Management Admission Test (GMAT) scores of applicants to the school's MBA program have increased during the past 5 years. Five years ago, the mean and standard deviation of GMAT scores of MBA applicants were 560 and 50, respectively. Twenty applications for this year's program were randomly selected and the GMAT scores recorded. If we assume that the distribution of GMAT scores of this year's applicants is the same as that of 5 years ago, with the possible exception of the mean, can we conclude at the 5% significance level that the dean's claim is true?

11.46 Xr11-46 At the start of the COVID-19 pandemic in March 2020, Americans stocked up on goods that they thought might experience shortages. The one product that everyone seemed to buy was toilet paper. A mathematician did a quick calculation and concluded that the average household would have more than 30 rolls of toilet paper on hand. To test the claim, a random sample of households was polled and asked to report their inventory.

a. Assuming the population standard deviation is 6, is there sufficient evidence at the 10% significance level to confirm the claim?

b. What assumption must you make to answer part (a)?

11.47 Xr11-47 In an attempt to reduce the number of person-hours lost as a result of industrial accidents, a large production plant installed new safety equipment. In a test of the effectiveness of the equipment, a random sample of 50 departments was chosen. The number of person-hours lost in the month before and the month after the installation of the safety equipment was recorded. The percentage change was calculated and recorded. Assume that the population standard deviation is $\sigma = 6$. Can we infer at the 10% significance level that the new safety equipment is effective?

11.48 Xr11-48 A highway patrol officer believes that the average speed of cars traveling over a certain stretch of highway exceeds the posted limit of 55 mph. The speeds of a random sample of 200 cars were recorded.

Do these data provide sufficient evidence at the 1% significance level to support the officer's belief? What is the *p*-value of the test? (Assume that the standard deviation is known to be 5.)

11.49 Xr11-49   An automotive expert claims that the large number of self-serve gasoline stations has resulted in poor automobile maintenance, and that the average tire pressure is more than 4 pounds per square inch (psi) below its manufacturer's specification. As a quick test, 50 tires are examined, and the number of psi each tire is below specification is recorded. If we assume that tire pressure is normally distributed with $\sigma = 1.5$ psi, can we infer at the 10% significance level that the expert is correct? What is the *p*-value?

11.50 Xr11-50   For the past few years, the number of customers of a drive-up bank in New York has averaged 20 per hour, with a standard deviation of 3 per hour. This year, another bank 1 mile away opened a drive-up window. The manager of the first bank believes that this will result in a decrease in the number of customers. The number of customers who arrived during 36 randomly selected hours was recorded. Can we conclude at the 5% significance level that the manager is correct?

11.51 Xr11-51   A fast-food franchiser is considering building a restaurant at a certain location. Based on financial analyses, a site is acceptable only if the number of pedestrians passing the location averages more than 100 per hour. The number of pedestrians observed for each of 40 hours was recorded. Assuming that the population standard deviation is known to be 16, can we conclude at the 1% significance level that the site is acceptable?

11.52 Xr11-52   Many Alpine ski centers base their projections of revenues and profits on the assumption that the average Alpine skier skis four times per year. To investigate the validity of this assumption, a random sample of 63 skiers is drawn and all were asked to report the number of times they skied the previous year. If we assume that the standard deviation is 2, can we infer at the 10% significance level that the assumption is wrong?

11.53 Xr11-53   The golf professional at a private course claims that members who have taken lessons lowered their handicap by more than five strokes. The club manager decides to test the claim by randomly sampling 25 members who have had lessons and asking each to report the reduction in handicap, where a negative number indicates an increase in the handicap. Assuming that the reduction in handicap is approximately normally distributed with a standard deviation of two strokes, test the golf professional's claim using a 10% significance level.

11.54 Xr11-54   The current no-smoking regulations in office buildings require workers who smoke to take breaks and leave the building in order to satisfy their habits. A study indicates that such workers average 32 minutes per day taking smoking breaks. The standard deviation is 8 minutes. To help reduce the average break, rooms with powerful exhausts were installed in the buildings. To see whether these rooms serve their designed purpose, a random sample of 110 smokers was taken. The total amount of time away from their desks was measured for 1 day. Test to determine whether there has been a decrease in the mean time away from their desks. Compute the *p*-value and interpret it relative to the costs of Type I and Type II errors.

11.55 Xr11-55   A low-handicap golfer who uses Titleist brand golf balls observed that his average drive is 230 yards and the standard deviation is 10 yards. Nike has just introduced a new ball, which has been endorsed by Tiger Woods. Nike claims that the ball will travel farther than Titleist. To test the claim, the golfer hits 100 drives with a Nike ball and measures the distances. Conduct a test to determine whether Nike is correct. Use a 5% significance level.

11.56 Xr11-56   An economist surveyed homeowners in a large city to determine the percentage increase in their heating bills over the last 5 years. The economist particularly wanted to know if there was enough evidence to infer that heating cost increases were greater than the rate of inflation, which was 10%. Assuming that percentage increase in heating is normally distributed with a standard deviation of 3% can the economist conclude at the 5% significance level that heating costs increased faster than inflation?

11.57 Xr11-57   A survey of American consumers asked respondents to report the amount of money they spend on bakery products in a typical month. If we assume that the population standard deviation is $5, can we conclude at the 10% significance level that the mean monthly expenditures on bakery products for all Americans is not equal to $30?

11.58 Xr11-58   Many Americans contributed to their 401k investment accounts. An economist wanted to determine how well these investments performed. A random sample of Americans with 401k investments were surveyed and asked to report the total amount invested. Can we infer at the 5% significance level that the mean amount for all Americans with 401k investments is greater than $125,000 assuming that investments are normally distributed with a standard deviation of $25,000?

11.59 Xr11-59   A survey of 25- to 35-year-old Americans with professional or Ph.D. degrees was asked to report their monthly incomes. Can we conclude at the 10% significance level that the mean income exceeds $12,500 assuming that the incomes are normally distributed with a standard deviation of $2,000?

11-3/CALCULATING THE PROBABILITY OF A TYPE II ERROR

To properly interpret the results of a test of hypothesis, you must be able to specify an appropriate significance level or to judge the *p*-value of a test. However, you also must understand the relationship between Type I and Type II errors. In this section, we describe how the probability of a Type II error is computed and interpreted.

Recall Example 11.1, where we conducted the test using the sample mean as the test statistic and we computed the rejection region (with $\alpha = .05$) as

$$\bar{x} > 175.34$$

A Type II error occurs when a false null hypothesis is not rejected. In Example 11.1, if $\bar{x}$ is less than 175.34, we will not reject the null hypothesis. If we do not reject the null hypothesis, we will not install the new billing system. Thus, the consequence of a Type II error in this example is that we will not install the new system when it would be cost-effective. The probability of this occurring is the probability of a Type II error. It is defined as

$$\beta = P(\bar{X} < 175.34, \text{ given that the null hypothesis is false})$$

The condition that the null hypothesis is false tells us only that the mean is not equal to 170. If we want to compute β, we need to specify a value for μ. Suppose that when the mean account is at least $180, the new billing system's savings become so attractive that the manager would hate to make the mistake of not installing the system. As a result, the manager would like to determine the probability of not installing the new system when it would produce large cost savings. Because calculating probability from an approximately normal sampling distribution requires a value of μ (as well as σ and n), we will calculate the probability of not installing the new system when μ is *equal* to 180:

$$\beta = P(\bar{X} < 175.34, \text{ given that } \mu = 180)$$

We know that $\bar{x}$ is approximately normally distributed with mean μ and standard deviation $\sigma/\sqrt{n}$. To proceed, we standardize $\bar{x}$ and use the standard normal table (Table 3 in Appendix B):

$$\beta = P\left(\frac{\bar{X} - \mu}{\sigma/\sqrt{n}} < \frac{175.34 - 180}{65/\sqrt{400}}\right) = P(Z < -1.43) = .0764$$

This tells us that when the mean account is actually $180, the probability of incorrectly not rejecting the null hypothesis is .0764. Figure 11.9 graphically depicts

FIGURE **11.9** Calculating β for $\mu = 180$, $\alpha = .05$, and $n = 400$

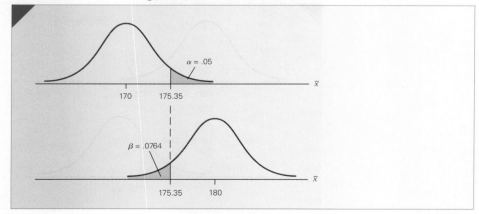

how the calculation was performed. Notice that to calculate the probability of a Type II error, we had to express the rejection region in terms of the unstandardized test statistic $\bar{x}$, and we had to specify a value for μ other than the one shown in the null hypothesis. In this illustration, the value of μ used was based on a financial analysis indicating that when μ is at least \$180 the cost savings would be very attractive.

11-3a Effect on β of Changing α

Suppose that in the previous illustration we had used a significance level of 1% instead of 5%. The rejection region expressed in terms of the standardized test statistic would be

$$z > z_{.01} = 2.33$$

or

$$\frac{\bar{x} - 170}{65/\sqrt{400}} > 2.33$$

Solving for $\bar{x}$, we find the rejection region in terms of the unstandardized test statistic:

$$\bar{x} > 177.57$$

The probability of a Type II error when $\mu = 180$ is

$$\beta = P\left(\frac{\bar{x} - \mu}{\sigma/\sqrt{n}} < \frac{177.57 - 180}{65/\sqrt{400}}\right) = P(Z < -.75) = .2266$$

Figure 11.10 depicts this calculation. Compare this figure with Figure 11.9. As you can see, by decreasing the significance level from 5% to 1%, we have shifted the critical value of the rejection region to the right and thus enlarged the area where the null hypothesis is not rejected. The probability of a Type II error increases from .0764 to .2266.

FIGURE **11.10** Calculating β for $\mu = 180$, $\alpha = .01$, and $n = 400$

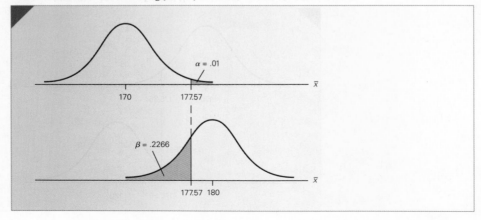

This calculation illustrates the inverse relationship between the probabilities of Type I and Type II errors alluded to in Section 11-1. It is important to understand this relationship. From a practical point of view, it tells us that if you want to decrease the probability of a Type I error (by specifying a small value of α), you increase the probability of a Type II error. In applications where the cost of a Type I error is considerably larger than the cost of a Type II error, this is appropriate. In fact, a significance level of 1% or less is probably justified. However, when the cost of a Type II error is relatively large, a significance level of 5% or more may be appropriate.

Unfortunately, there is no simple formula to determine what the significance level should be. The manager must consider the costs of both mistakes in deciding what to do. Judgment and knowledge of the factors in the decision are crucial.

11-3b Judging the Test

There is another important concept to be derived from this section. A statistical test of hypothesis is effectively defined by the significance level and the sample size, both of which are selected by the statistics practitioner. We can judge how well the test functions by calculating the probability of a Type II error at some value of the parameter. To illustrate, in Example 11.1 the manager chose a sample size of 400 and a 5% significance level on which to base the decision. With those selections, we found β to be .0764 when the actual mean is 180. If we believe that the cost of a Type II error is high and thus that the probability is too large, we have two ways to reduce the probability. We can increase the value of α; however, this would result in an increase in the chance of making a Type I error, which is very costly.

Alternatively, we can increase the sample size. Suppose that the manager chose a sample size of 1,000. We'll now recalculate β with $n = 1,000$ (and $\alpha = .05$). The rejection region is

$$z > z_{.05} = 1.645$$

or

$$\frac{\bar{x} - 170}{65/\sqrt{1,000}} > 1.645$$

which yields

$$\bar{x} > 173.38$$

The probability of a Type II error is

$$\beta = P\left(\frac{\overline{X} - \mu}{\sigma/\sqrt{n}} < \frac{173.38 - 180}{65/\sqrt{1,000}}\right) = P(Z < -3.22) = 0 \text{ (approximately)}$$

In this case, we maintained the same value of α (.05), but we reduced the probability of not installing the system when the actual mean account is $180 to virtually 0.

11-3c Developing an Understanding of Statistical Concepts: Larger Sample Size Equals More Information Equals Better Decisions

Figure 11.11 displays the previous calculation. When compared with Figure 11.9, we can see that the sampling distribution of the mean is narrower because the standard error of the mean $\sigma/\sqrt{n}$ becomes smaller as n increases. Narrower distributions represent more information. The increased information is reflected in a smaller probability of a Type II error.

FIGURE **11.11** Calculating β for $\mu = 180$, $\alpha = .05$, and $n = 1,000$

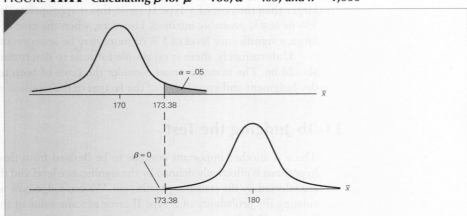

The calculation of the probability of a Type II error for $n = 400$ and for $n = 1,000$ illustrates a concept whose importance cannot be overstated. By increasing the sample size, we reduce the probability of a Type II error. By reducing the probability of a Type II error, we make this type of error less frequently. Hence, larger sample sizes allow us to make better decisions in the long run. This finding lies at the heart of applied statistical analysis and reinforces the book's first sentence: "Statistics is a way to get information from data."

Throughout this book we introduce a variety of applications in accounting, finance, marketing, operations management, human resources management, and economics. In all such applications, the statistics practitioner must make a decision, which involves converting data into information. The more information, the better the decision. Without such information, decisions must be based on guesswork, instinct, and luck. W. Edwards Deming, a famous statistician, said it best: "Without data you're just another person with an opinion."

11-3d Power of a Test

Another way of expressing how well a test performs is to report its *power*: the probability of its leading us to reject the null hypothesis when it is false. Thus, the power of a test is $1 - \beta$.

When more than one test can be performed in a given situation, we would naturally prefer to use the test that is correct more frequently. If (given the same alternative hypothesis, sample size, and significance level) one test has a higher power than a second test, the first test is said to be more powerful.

11-3e Operating Characteristic Curve

To compute the probability of a Type II error, we must specify the significance level, the sample size, and an alternative value of the population mean. One way to keep track of all these components is to draw the **operating characteristic (OC) curve**, which plots the values of β versus the values of μ. Because of the time-consuming nature of these calculations, the computer is a virtual necessity. To illustrate, we'll draw the OC curve for Example 11.1.

We used the Excel function NORMDIST to compute the probability of a Type II error in Example 11.1 for $\mu = 170, 171, \ldots, 184$, with $n = 400$.

EXCEL Function

With $\sigma = 65$ and $n = 400$, the standard error of the mean is

$$\sigma_{\bar{x}} = \frac{\sigma}{\sqrt{n}} = \frac{65}{\sqrt{400}} = 3.25$$

To calculate the probability of a Type II error in Example 11.1, we open Excel and in any empty cell type

= NORMDIST (175.35, [μ], 3.25, True)

For example, to compute β when $\mu = 180$, we type

= NORMDIST (175.35, 180, 3.25, True)

Figure 11.12 depicts this curve. Notice as the alternative value of μ increases the value of β decreases. This tells us that as the alternative value of μ moves farther from the value of μ under the null hypothesis, the probability of a Type II error decreases. In other words, it becomes easier to distinguish between $\mu = 170$ and other values of μ when μ is farther from 170. Notice that when $\mu = 170$ (the hypothesized value of μ), $\beta = 1 - \alpha$.

FIGURE **11.12** Operating Characteristic Curve for Example 11.1

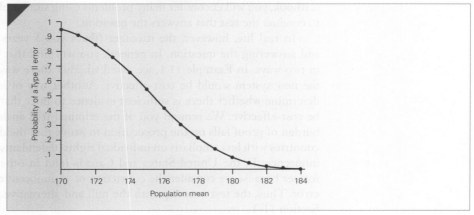

The OC curve can also be useful in selecting a sample size. Figure 11.13 shows the OC curve for Example 11.1 with $n = 100, \ 400, \ 1{,}000$, and $2{,}000$. An examination

of this chart sheds some light concerning the effect increasing the sample size has on how well the test performs at different values of μ. For example, we can see that smaller sample sizes will work well to distinguish between 170 and values of μ larger than 180. However, to distinguish between 170 and smaller values of μ requires larger sample sizes. Although the information is imprecise, it does allow us to select a sample size that is suitable for our purposes.

FIGURE **11.13**   **Operating Characteristic Curve for Example 11.1 for $n = 100$, 400, $1,000$, and $2,000$**

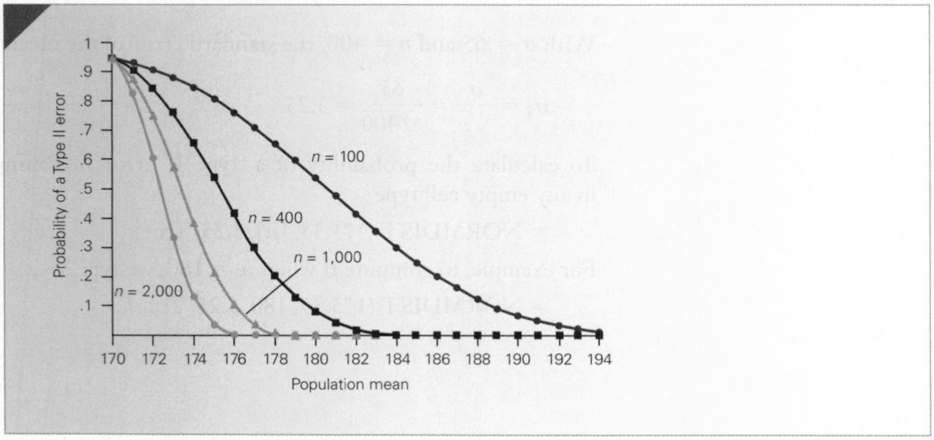

11-3f Determining the Alternative Hypothesis to Define Type I and Type II Errors

We've already discussed how the alternative hypothesis is determined. It represents the condition we're investigating. In Example 11.1, we wanted to know whether there was sufficient statistical evidence to infer that the new billing system would be cost-effective—that is, whether the mean monthly account is greater than $170. In this textbook, you will encounter many problems using similar phraseology. Your job will be to conduct the test that answers the question.

In real life, however, the manager (that's you 5 years from now) will be asking and answering the question. In general, you will find that the question can be posed in two ways. In Example 11.1, we asked whether there was evidence to conclude that the new system would be cost-effective. Another way of investigating the issue is to determine whether there is sufficient evidence to infer that the new system would *not* be cost-effective. We remind you of the criminal trial analogy. In a criminal trial, the burden of proof falls on the prosecution to prove that the defendant is guilty. In other countries with less emphasis on individual rights, defendants are required to prove their innocence. In the United States and Canada (and in other countries), we chose the former because we consider the conviction of an innocent defendant to be the greater error. Thus, the test is set up with the null and alternative hypotheses as described in Section 11-1.

In a statistical test where we are responsible for both asking and answering a question, we must ask the question so that we directly control the error that is more costly. As you have already seen, we control the probability of a Type I error by specifying its value (the significance level). Consider Example 11.1 once again. There are two possible errors: (1) conclude that the billing system is cost-effective when it isn't and (2) conclude that the system is not cost-effective when it is. If the manager concludes that the billing plan is cost-effective, the company will install the new system. If, in reality, the system is not cost-effective, the company will incur a loss. On the other hand, if the manager concludes that the billing plan is not going to be cost-effective, the company will not install the system. However, if the system is actually cost-effective, the company will lose the potential gain from installing it. Which cost is greater?

Suppose we believe that the cost of installing a system that is not cost-effective is higher than the potential loss of not installing an effective system. The error we wish to avoid is the erroneous conclusion that the system is cost-effective. We define this as a Type I error. As a result, the burden of proof is placed on the system to deliver sufficient statistical evidence that the mean account is greater than $170. The null and alternative hypotheses are as formulated previously:

$$H_0: \quad \mu = 170$$
$$H_1: \quad \mu > 170$$

However, if we believe that the potential loss of not installing the new system when it would be cost-effective is the larger cost, we would place the burden of proof on the manager to infer that the mean monthly account is less than $170. Consequently, the hypotheses would be

$$H_0: \quad \mu = 170$$
$$H_1: \quad \mu < 170$$

This discussion emphasizes the need in practice to examine the costs of making both types of error before setting up the hypotheses. However, it is important for readers to understand that the questions posed in exercises throughout this book have already taken these costs into consideration. Accordingly, your task is to set up the hypotheses to answer the questions.

EXERCISES

Developing an Understanding of Statistical Concepts

11.60 Calculate the probability of a Type II error for the following test of hypothesis, given that $\mu = 203$.

$$H_0: \quad \mu = 200$$
$$H_1: \quad \mu \neq 200$$
$$\alpha = .05, \sigma = 10, n = 100$$

11.61 Find the probability of a Type II error for the following test of hypothesis, given that $\mu = 1,050$.

$$H_0: \quad \mu = 1,000$$
$$H_1: \quad \mu > 1,000$$
$$\alpha = .01, \sigma = 50, n = 25$$

11.62 Determine β for the following test of hypothesis, given that $\mu = 48$.

$$H_0: \quad \mu = 50$$
$$H_1: \quad \mu < 50$$
$$\alpha = .05, \sigma = 10, n = 40$$

11.63 For each of Exercises 11.60 to 11.62, draw the sampling distributions similar to Figure 11.9.

11.64 A statistics practitioner wants to test the following hypotheses with $\sigma = 20$ and $n = 100$:

$$H_0: \quad \mu = 100$$
$$H_1: \quad \mu > 100$$

a. Using $\alpha = .10$ find the probability of a Type II error when $\mu = 102$.

b. Repeat part (a) with $\alpha = .02$.

c. Describe the effect on β of decreasing α.

11.65 a. Calculate the probability of a Type II error for the following hypotheses when $\mu = 37$:

$$H_0: \quad \mu = 40$$
$$H_1: \quad \mu < 40$$

The significance level is 5%, the population standard deviation is 5, and the sample size is 25.

b. Repeat part (a) with $\alpha = 15\%$.

c. Describe the effect on β of increasing α.

11.66 Draw the figures of the sampling distributions for Exercises 11.64 and 11.65.

11.67 a. Find the probability of a Type II error for the following test of hypothesis, given that $\mu = 196$:

H_0: $\mu = 200$

H_1: $\mu < 200$

The significance level is 10%, the population standard deviation is 30, and the sample size is 25.

b. Repeat part (a) with $n = 100$.

c. Describe the effect on β of increasing n.

11.68 a. Determine β for the following test of hypothesis, given that $\mu = 310$:

H_0: $\mu = 300$

H_1: $\mu > 300$

The statistics practitioner knows that the population standard deviation is 50, the significance level is 5%, and the sample size is 81.

b. Repeat part (a) with $n = 36$.

c. Describe the effect on β of decreasing n.

11.69 For Exercises 11.67 and 11.68, draw the sampling distributions similar to Figure 11.9.

11.70 For the test of hypothesis

H_0: $\mu = 1{,}000$

H_1: $\mu \neq 1{,}000$

$\alpha = .05, \sigma = 200$

draw the operating characteristic curve for $n = 25, 100,$ and 200.

11.71 Draw the operating characteristic curve for $n = 10, 50,$ and 100 for the following test:

H_0: $\mu = 400$

H_1: $\mu > 400$

$\alpha = .05, \sigma = 50$

11.72 Suppose that in Example 11.1 we wanted to determine whether there was sufficient evidence to conclude that the new system would *not* be cost-effective. Set up the null and alternative hypotheses and discuss the consequences of Type I and Type II errors. Conduct the test. Is your conclusion the same as the one reached in Example 11.1? Explain.

Applications

11.73 In Exercise 11.47, we tested to determine whether the installation of safety equipment was effective in reducing person-hours lost to industrial accidents. The null and alternative hypotheses were

H_0: $\mu = 0$

H_1: $\mu < 0$

with $\sigma = 6$, $\alpha = .10$, $n = 50$, and $\mu =$ the mean percentage change. The test failed to indicate that the new safety equipment is effective. The manager is concerned that the test was not sensitive enough to detect small but important changes. In particular, if the true reduction in time lost to accidents is actually 2% (i.e., $\mu = -2$), then the firm may miss the opportunity to install very effective equipment. Find the probability that the test with $\sigma = 6$, $\alpha = .10$, and $n = 50$ will fail to conclude that such equipment is effective. Discuss ways to decrease this probability.

11.74 The test of hypothesis in the SSA example concluded that there was not enough evidence to infer that the plan would be profitable. The company would hate to not institute the plan if the actual reduction was as little as 3 days (i.e., $\mu = 21$). Calculate the relevant probability and describe how the company should use this information.

11.75 The fast-food franchiser in Exercise 11.51 was unable to provide enough evidence that the site is acceptable and as a result the franchiser may be missing an opportunity to locate the restaurant in a profitable location. If the actual mean is 104, the restaurant is likely to be very successful. Determine the probability of a Type II error when the mean is 104. Suggest ways to improve this probability.

11.76 Refer to Exercise 11.54. A financial analyst has determined that a 2-minute reduction in the average break would increase productivity. As a result the company would hate to lose this opportunity. Calculate the probability of erroneously concluding that the renovation would not be successful when the average break is 30 minutes. If this probability is high, describe how it can be reduced.

11.77 A school-board administrator believes that the average number of days absent per year among students is less than 10 days and that the population standard deviation is 3 days. In testing to determine whether this belief is true, the administrator could use one of the following plans:

i. $n = 100$, $\alpha = .01$

ii. $n = 75$, $\alpha = .05$

iii. $n = 50$, $\alpha = .10$

Which plan has the lowest probability of a Type II error, given that the true population average is 9 days?

11.78 The feasibility of constructing a profitable electricity-producing windmill depends on the mean velocity of the wind. For a certain type of windmill, the mean would have to exceed 20 miles per hour to warrant its construction. The determination of a site's feasibility is a two-stage process. In the first stage, readings of the wind velocity are taken and the mean is calculated. The test is designed to answer the question, "Is the site feasible?" In other words, is there sufficient evidence to conclude that the mean wind velocity exceeds 20 mph? If there is enough evidence, further testing is conducted. If there is not enough evidence, the site is removed from consideration. Discuss the consequences and potential costs of Type I and Type II errors.

11.79 The number of potential sites for the first-stage test in Exercise 11.78 is quite large and the readings can be expensive. Accordingly, the test is conducted with a sample of 25 observations. Because the second-stage cost is high, the significance level is set at 1%. A financial analysis of the potential profits and costs reveals that if the mean wind velocity is as high as 25 mph, the windmill would be extremely profitable. Calculate the probability that the first-stage test will not conclude that the site is feasible when the actual mean wind velocity is 25 mph. (Assume that σ is 8.) Discuss how the process can be improved.

11-4 / THE ROAD AHEAD

We had two principal goals to accomplish in Chapters 10 and 11. First, we wanted to present the concepts of estimation and hypothesis testing. Second, we wanted to show how to produce confidence interval estimates and conduct tests of hypotheses. The importance of both goals should not be underestimated. Almost everything that follows this chapter will involve either estimating a parameter or testing a set of hypotheses. Consequently, Sections 10-2 and 11-2 set the pattern for the way in which statistical techniques are applied. It is no exaggeration to state that if you understand how to produce and use confidence interval estimates and how to conduct and interpret hypothesis tests, then you are well on your way to the ultimate goal of being competent at analyzing, interpreting, and presenting data. It is fair for you to ask what more you must accomplish to achieve this goal. The answer, simply put, is much more of the same.

In the chapters that follow, we plan to present about three dozen different statistical techniques that can be (and frequently are) employed by statistics practitioners. To calculate the value of test statistics or confidence interval estimates requires nothing more than the ability to add, subtract, multiply, divide, and compute square roots. If you intend to use the computer, all you need to know are the commands. The key, then, to applying statistics is knowing which formula to calculate or which set of commands to issue. Thus, the real challenge of the subject lies in being able to define the problem and identify which statistical method is the most appropriate one to use.

Recall that we introduced the Identify-Compute-Interpret (ICI) System in Chapter 10 (page 336). In the next section, we describe how the *Identify* stage works.

11-4a Types of Data

A number of factors determine which statistical method should be used, but two are especially important: the type of data and the purpose of the statistical inference. In Chapter 2, we pointed out that there are effectively three types of data—interval, ordinal, and nominal. Recall that nominal data represent categories such as marital status, occupation, and gender. Statistics practitioners often record nominal data by assigning numbers to the responses (e.g., 1 = Single, 2 = Married, 3 = Divorced, 4 = Widowed). Because these numbers are assigned completely arbitrarily, any calculations performed on them are meaningless. All that we can do with nominal data is count the number of times each category is observed. Ordinal data are obtained from questions whose answers represent a rating or ranking system. For example, if students are asked to rate a university professor, the responses may be excellent, good, fair, or poor. To draw inferences about such data, we convert the responses to numbers. Any numbering system is valid as long as the order of the responses is preserved. Thus "4 = Excellent, 3 = Good, 2 = Fair, 1 = Poor" is just as valid as "15 = Excellent, 8 = Good, 5 = Fair, 2 = Poor." Because of this feature, the most appropriate statistical procedures for ordinal data are ones based on a ranking process.

Interval data are real numbers, such as those representing income, age, height, weight, and volume. Computation of means and variances is permissible.

The second key factor in determining the statistical technique is the purpose of doing the work. Every statistical method has some specific objective. We address five such objectives in this book.

11-4b Problem Objectives

1. **Describe a population.** Our objective here is to describe some property of a population of interest. The decision about which property to describe is generally dictated by the type of data. For example, suppose the population of interest consists of all purchasers of computers. If we are interested in the purchasers' incomes (for which the data are interval), we may calculate the mean or the variance to describe that aspect of the population. But if we are interested in the brand of computer that has been bought (for which the data are nominal), all we can do is compute the proportion of the population that purchases each brand.

2. **Compare two populations.** In this case, our goal is to compare a property of one population with a corresponding property of a second population. For example, suppose the populations of interest are male and female purchasers of computers. We could compare the means of their incomes, or we could compare the proportion of each population that purchases a certain brand. Once again, the data type generally determines what kinds of properties we compare.

3. **Compare two or more populations.** We might want to compare the average income in each of several locations in order (for example) to decide where to build a new shopping center. Or we might want to compare the proportions of defective items in a number of production lines in order to determine which line is the best. In each case, the problem objective involves comparing two or more populations.

4. **Analyze the relationship between two variables.** There are numerous situations in which we want to know how one variable is related to another. Governments need to know what effect rising interest rates have on the unemployment rate. Companies want to investigate how the sizes of their advertising budgets influence sales volume. In most of the problems in this introductory text, the two variables to be analyzed will be of the same type; we will not attempt to cover the fairly large body of statistical techniques that has been developed to deal with two variables of different types.

5. **Analyze the relationship among two or more variables.** Our objective here is usually to forecast one variable (called the *dependent variable*) on the basis of several other variables (called *independent variables*). We will deal with this problem only in situations in which all variables are interval.

Table 11.3 lists the types of data and the five problem objectives. For each combination, the table specifies the chapter or section where the appropriate statistical technique is presented.

TABLE **11.3** **Guide to Statistical Inference Showing Where Each Technique Is Introduced**

| | DATA TYPE | | |
PROBLEM OBJECTIVE	NOMINAL	ORDINAL	INTERVAL
Describe a population	Sections 12-3, 15-1	Not covered	Sections 12-1, 12-2
Compare two populations	Sections 13-5, 15-2	Sections 19-1, 19-2	Sections 13-1, 13-3, 13-4, 19-1, 19-2
Compare two or more populations	Section 15-2	Section 19-3	Chapter 14 Section 19-3
Analyze the relationship between two variables	Section 15-2	Section 19-4	Chapter 16
Analyze the relationship among two or more variables	Not covered	Not covered	Chapters 17, 18

11-4c Other Components of the ICI System

Chapters 13, 14, 15, 16, 17, and 19 feature appendixes that list the techniques introduced up to that point, exercises that require the use of any of the previously introduced methods, and flowcharts helping to identify the correct method. The appendix to Chapter 19 is especially important in that it reviews *all* of the inferential methods introduced in this book.

11-4d Derivations

Because this book is about statistical applications, we assume that our readers have little interest in the mathematical derivations of the techniques described. However, it might be helpful for you to have some understanding about the process that produces the formulas.

As described previously, factors such as the problem objective and the type of data determine the parameter to be estimated and tested. For each parameter, statisticians have determined which statistic to use. That statistic has a sampling distribution that can usually be expressed as a formula. For example, in this chapter, the parameter of interest was the population mean μ, whose best estimator is the sample mean $\bar{x}$. Assuming that the population standard deviation σ is known, the sampling distribution of $\overline{X}$ is normal (or approximately so) with mean μ and standard deviation $\sigma/\sqrt{n}$. The sampling distribution can be described by the formula

$$Z = \frac{\overline{X} - \mu}{\sigma/\sqrt{n}}.$$

This formula also describes the test statistic for μ with σ known. With a little algebra, we were able to derive (in Section 10-2) the confidence interval estimator of μ.

In future chapters, we will repeat this process, which in several cases involves the introduction of a new sampling distribution (introduced in Chapter 8). Although its shape and formula will differ from the sampling distribution used in this chapter, the pattern will be the same. In general, the formula that expresses the sampling distribution will describe the test statistic. Then some algebraic manipulation (which we will not show) produces the interval estimator. Consequently, we will reverse the order of presentation of the two techniques. In other words, we will present the test of hypothesis first, followed by the confidence interval estimator.

CHAPTER SUMMARY

In this chapter, we introduced the concepts of hypothesis testing and applied them to testing hypotheses about a population mean. We showed how to specify the null and alternative hypotheses, set up the rejection region, compute the value of the test statistic, and, finally, to make a decision. Equally as important, we discussed how to interpret the test results. This chapter also demonstrated another way to make decisions: by calculating and using the p-value of the test. To help interpret test results, we showed how to calculate the probability of a Type II error. Finally, we provided a road map of how we plan to present statistical techniques.

IMPORTANT TERMS:

Hypothesis testing   356
Null hypothesis   356
Alternative or research hypothesis   356
Type I error   356
Type II error   356
Significance level   356
Test statistic   359
Rejection region   361
Standardized test statistic   362

Statistically significant   363
p-value of a test   364
Highly significant   366
Significant   366
Not statistically significant   366
One-tail test   370
Two-tail test   371
One-sided confidence interval estimator   373
Operating characteristic curve   383

SYMBOLS:

Symbol	Pronounced	Represents
H_0	H nought	Null hypothesis
H_1	H one	Alternative (research) hypothesis
α	alpha	Probability of a Type I error
β	beta	Probability of a Type II error
$\bar{x}_L$	X bar sub L or X bar L	Value of $\bar{x}$ large enough to reject H_0
$|z|$	Absolute z	Absolute value of z

FORMULA:

Test statistic for μ

$$Z = \frac{\bar{x} - \mu}{\sigma/\sqrt{n}}$$

EXCEL OUTPUT AND INSTRUCTIONS:

Technique	
Test of μ	367
Probability of a Type II error (and Power)	383

APPENDIX 11.A / XLSTAT Output and Instructions

Z-Test of a Mean

Example 11.1

	B	C	D	E	F	G
8	Theoretical mean: 170					
9						
10	Summary statistics:					
11						
12	Variable	Observations	Minimum	Maximum	Mean	Std. deviation
13	Accounts	400	3.19	372.73	178.00	68.37
14						
15	One-sample z-test / Upper-tailed test:					
16						
17	Difference	8.00				
18	z (Observed value)	2.46				
19	z (Critical value)	1.645				
20	p-value (one-tailed)	0.0069				
21	alpha	0.05				

Difference refers to the difference between the sample mean (178) and the hypothesized mean (170).

Instructions

1. Type or import the data into one column. (Open Xm11-01.)

2. Click **XLSTAT, Parametric tests**, and **One-sample t-test and z-test**.

3. Check **One sample** under **Data format:**. In the **Data** dialog box type the input range (A1:A401).

   Check **Column labels** if the first row of the data contains the name of the variable. Choose **Range:**, **Sheet**, or **Workbook** depending on where you wish the results to appear. Under Tests click **z-test**.

4. Click **Options** and choose **Mean > Theoretical mean** in the **Alternative hypothesis** box. Type the theoretical mean (170). Under **Variance for the z-test:**, check **User defined** and type the value of σ^2 (4225). Specify the value of α in percent (5) in the **Significance level (%)** box.

5. Click **Outputs** and check **Descriptive statistics** and **Detailed results**.

Chapter-Opening Example

	B	C	D	E	F	G
8	Theoretical mean: 22					
9						
10	Summary statistics:					
11						
12	Variable	Observations	Minimum	Maximum	Mean	Std. deviation
13	Payment	220	9	39	21.63	5.84
14						
15	One-sample z-test / Lower-tailed test:					
16						
17	Difference	-0.368				
18	z (Observed value)	-0.910				
19	z (Critical value)	-1.645				
20	p-value (one-tailed)	0.1814				
21	alpha	0.05				

Instructions

Use the same instructions as above with the following changes:

Open Xm11-00

Input range: A1:A221

Mean < Theoretical mean

Theoretical Mean 22

value of σ^2: 36

Example 11.2

	B	C	D	E	F	G
8	Theoretical mean: 6.03					
9						
10	Summary statistics:					
11						
12	Variable	Observations	Minimum	Maximum	Mean	Std. deviation
13	Costs	100	3.38	8.43	5.91	0.892
14						
15	**One-sample z-test / Two-tailed test:**					
16						
17	Difference	-0.120				
18	z (Observed value)	-1.319				
19	|z| (Critical value)	1.960				
20	p-value (Two-tailed)	0.1873				
21	alpha	0.05				

Instructions

Use the same instructions as above with the following changes:

Open Xm11-02

Input range: A1:A101

Mean ≠ Theoretical mean

Theoretical Mean 6.03

value of σ^2: .8281

APPENDIX 11.B / STATA OUTPUT AND INSTRUCTIONS

Testing a Population Mean: Standard Deviation Known

Example 11.1

```
One-sample z test
```

Variable	Obs	Mean	Std. Err.	Std. Dev.	[95% Conf. Interval]	
Accounts	400	177.9965	3.25	65	171.6266	184.3664

```
    mean = mean(Accounts)                                    z =    2.4605
Ho: mean = 170
```

Ha: mean < 170	Ha: mean != 170	Ha: mean > 170
Pr(Z < z) = 0.9931	Pr(|Z| > |z|) = 0.0139	Pr(Z > z) = 0.0069

The value of the test statistic is z = 2.4605 and the p-value = .0069.

Instructions

1. Import the data into one column.

   (Click File/Import /Excel spreadsheet (*xls,*xlsx)/Chapter11/Xm11-01.) Check **Import first row as variable names**.

2. Click **Statistics, Summaries, tables and tests, Classical tests of hypotheses**, and **z-test (mean-comparison test known variance)**.

3. Select **One-sample**, select **Accounts** in the **Variable name:** box, and type the hypothesized value of the mean in the **Hypothesized mean** box 170. Type the **Standard deviation** 65.

Chapter-Opening Example

```
One-sample z test
```

Variable	Obs	Mean	Std. Err.	Std. Dev.	[95% Conf. Interval]	
Payment	220	21.63182	.4045199	6	20.83897	22.42466

```
    mean = mean(Payment)                                     z =   -0.9102
Ho: mean = 22
```

Ha: mean < 22	Ha: mean != 22	Ha: mean > 22
Pr(Z < z) = 0.1814	Pr(|Z| > |z|) = 0.3627	Pr(Z > z) = 0.8186

The value of the test statistic is z = −.9102 and the p-value = .1814.

Instructions

Use the same instructions as above with the following changes:

Xm11-00

Hypothesized mean box 22

Standard deviation 6

Example 11.2

```
One-sample z test
```

Variable	Obs	Mean	Std. Err.	Std. Dev.	[95% Conf. Interval]
Amount~t	100	5.91	.091	.91	5.731643 6.088357

```
    mean = mean(AmountSpent)                                    z = -1.3187
Ho: mean = 6.03

    Ha: mean < 6.03              Ha: mean != 6.03              Ha: mean > 6.03
  Pr(Z < z) = 0.0936        Pr(|Z| > |z|) = 0.1873          Pr(Z > z) = 0.9064
```

The value of the test statistic is z = −1.3187 and the p-value = .1873.

Instructions

Use the same instructions as above with the following changes:

Xm11-02

Hypothesized mean box 6.03

Standard deviation .91

Yuriy Rudyy/Shutterstock.com

INFERENCE ABOUT A POPULATION

CHAPTER OUTLINE

The Number of Unemployed

DATA
GSS2018

One of the most important economic statistics is the unemployment rate. Unfortunately, it is a very poor measure because it is misleading. The United States Bureau of Labor Statistics (BLS) defines the unemployment rate as the percentage of unemployed persons who are currently in the labor force. In order to be in the labor force, a person either must have a job or have looked for work in the last 4 weeks. This leaves out a lot of people. Some are left out because they have not done anything to find work in more than 4 weeks and as a result became discouraged, and some are left out because they are not available for work at the moment. Yet to leave this group out significantly underestimates the unemployment rate.

Jupiterimages/Getty images

See page 423 for our answer.

(Continued)

The data produced by the General Social Survey may shed more light on the issue. The responses of the variable work status (WRKSTAT) are: 1. Working fulltime, 2. Working part time, 3. Temporarily not working, 4. Unemployed, laid off, 5. Retired, 6. School, 7. Keeping house, 8. Other.

There are 255,200,373 adults 18 and over in the United States. Estimate with 95% confidence the number of American adults who are either temporarily not working or unemployed, laid off.

INTRODUCTION

In the previous two chapters, we introduced the concepts of statistical inference and showed how to estimate and test a population mean. However, the illustration we chose is unrealistic because the techniques require us to use the population standard deviation σ, which, in general, is unknown. The purpose, then, of Chapters 10 and 11 was to set the pattern for the way in which we plan to present other statistical techniques. In other words, we will begin by identifying the parameter to be estimated or tested. We will then specify the parameter's estimator (each parameter has an estimator chosen because of the characteristics we discussed at the beginning of Chapter 10) and its sampling distribution. Using simple mathematics, statisticians have derived the interval estimator and the test statistic. This pattern will be used repeatedly as we introduce new techniques.

In Section 11-4, we described the five problem objectives addressed in this book, and we laid out the order of presentation of the statistical methods. In this chapter, we will present techniques employed when the problem objective is to describe a population. When the data are interval, the parameters of interest are the population mean μ and the population variance σ^2. In Section 12-1, we describe how to make inferences about the population mean under the more realistic circumstance when the population standard deviation is unknown. In Section 12-2, we continue to deal with interval data, but our parameter of interest becomes the population variance.

In Chapter 2 and Section 11-4, we pointed out that when the data are nominal, the only computation that makes sense is determining the proportion of times each value occurs. Section 12-3 discusses inference about the proportion p. In Section 12-4, we present an important application in marketing: market segmentation.

12-1 / INFERENCE ABOUT A POPULATION MEAN WHEN THE STANDARD DEVIATION IS UNKNOWN

In Sections 10-2 and 11-2, we demonstrated how to estimate and test the population mean when the population standard deviation is known. The confidence interval estimator and the test statistic were derived from the sampling distribution of the sample mean with σ known, expressed as

$$z = \frac{\bar{x} - \mu}{\sigma/\sqrt{n}}$$

In this section, we take a more realistic approach by acknowledging that if the population mean is unknown, then so is the population standard deviation. Consequently, the previous sampling distribution cannot be used. Instead, we substitute the sample standard deviation s in place of the unknown population standard deviation σ. The result is called a *t-statistic* because that is what mathematician William S. Gosset called it. In 1908, Gosset showed that the *t*-statistic defined as

$$t = \frac{\bar{x} - \mu}{s/\sqrt{n}}$$

is Student *t*-distributed when the sampled population is normal. (Gosset published his findings under the pseudonym "Student," hence the **Student *t*-distribution**.) Recall that we introduced the Student *t*-distribution in Section 8-4.

With exactly the same logic used to develop the test statistic in Section 11-2 and the confidence interval estimator in Section 10-2, we derive the following inferential methods.

Test Statistic for μ When σ Is Unknown

When the population standard deviation is unknown and the population is normal, the test statistic for testing hypotheses about μ is

$$t = \frac{\bar{x} - \mu}{s/\sqrt{n}}$$

which is Student *t*-distributed with $\nu = n - 1$ degrees of freedom.

Confidence Interval Estimator of μ When σ Is Unknown

$$\bar{x} \pm t_{\alpha/2}\frac{s}{\sqrt{n}} \qquad \nu = n - 1$$

These formulas now make obsolete the test statistic and interval estimator employed in Chapters 10 and 11 to estimate and test a population mean. Although we continue to use the concepts developed in Chapters 10 and 11 (as well as all the other chapters), we will no longer use the *z*-statistic and the *z*-estimator of μ. All future inferential problems involving a population mean will be solved using the *t*-statistic and *t*-estimator of μ shown in the preceding boxes.

EXAMPLE 12.1

DATA
Xm12-01⁺

Newspaper Recycling Plant

In the near future, nations will likely have to do more to save the environment. Possible actions include reducing energy use and recycling. Currently, most products manufactured from recycled material are considerably more expensive than those manufactured from material found in the earth. For example, it is approximately three times as expensive to produce glass bottles from recycled glass than from silica sand, soda ash, and limestone, all plentiful materials mined in numerous countries. It is more expensive to manufacture aluminum cans from recycled cans than from bauxite. Newspapers are an exception. It can be profitable to recycle newspaper. A major expense is the collection from homes. In recent years, many companies have gone into the business of collecting used newspapers from households and recycling them. A financial analyst for one such company has recently computed that the firm would make a profit if the mean weekly newspaper collection from each household exceeded 2.0 pounds. In a study to determine the feasibility of a recycling plant, a random sample of 148 households was drawn from a large community, and the weekly weight of newspapers discarded for recycling for each household was recorded and listed next. Do these data provide sufficient evidence to allow the analyst to conclude that a recycling plant would be profitable?

Weights of Discarded Newspapers

2.5	0.7	3.4	1.8	1.9	2.0	1.3	1.2	2.2	0.9	2.7	2.9	1.5	1.5	2.2
3.2	0.7	2.3	3.1	1.3	4.2	3.4	1.5	2.1	1.0	2.4	1.8	0.9	1.3	2.6
3.6	0.8	3.0	2.8	3.6	3.1	2.4	3.2	4.4	4.1	1.5	1.9	3.2	1.9	1.6
3.0	3.7	1.7	3.1	2.4	3.0	1.5	3.1	2.4	2.1	2.1	2.3	0.7	0.9	2.7
1.2	2.2	1.3	3.0	3.0	2.2	1.5	2.7	0.9	2.5	3.2	3.7	1.9	2.0	3.7
2.3	0.6	0.0	1.0	1.4	0.9	2.6	2.1	3.4	0.5	4.1	2.2	3.4	3.3	0.0
2.2	4.2	1.1	2.3	3.1	1.7	2.8	2.5	1.8	1.7	0.6	3.6	1.4	2.2	2.2
1.3	1.7	3.0	0.8	1.6	1.8	1.4	3.0	1.9	2.7	0.8	3.3	2.5	1.5	2.2
2.6	3.2	1.0	3.2	1.6	3.4	1.7	2.3	2.6	1.4	3.3	1.3	2.4	2.0	
1.3	1.8	3.3	2.2	1.4	3.2	4.3	0.0	2.0	1.8	0.0	1.7	2.6	3.1	

SOLUTION:

IDENTIFY

The problem objective is to describe the population of the amounts of newspaper discarded by each household in the population. The data are interval, indicating that the parameter to be tested is the population mean. Because the financial analyst needs to determine whether the mean is greater than 2.0 pounds, the alternative hypothesis is

H_1: $\mu > 2.0$

As usual, the null hypothesis states that the mean is equal to the value listed in the alternative hypothesis:

H_0: $\mu = 2.0$

The test statistic is

$$t = \frac{\bar{x} - \mu}{s/\sqrt{n}} \quad \nu = n - 1$$

COMPUTE

MANUALLY:

The analyst believes that the cost of a Type I error (concluding that the mean is greater than 2 when it isn't) is quite high. Consequently, the significance level is set at 1%. The rejection region is

$$t > t_{\alpha, n-1} = t_{.01,147} \approx t_{.01,150} = 2.351$$

To calculate the value of the test statistic, we need to calculate the sample mean $\bar{x}$ and the sample standard deviation s. From the data, we determine

$$\sum x_i = 322.7 \text{ and } \sum x_i^2 = 845.1$$

Thus,

$$\bar{x} = \frac{\sum x_i}{n} = \frac{322.7}{148} = 2.18$$

$$s^2 = \frac{\sum x_i^2 - \dfrac{\left(\sum x_i\right)^2}{n}}{n-1} = \frac{845.1 - \dfrac{(322.7)^2}{148}}{148-1} = .962$$

and

$$s = \sqrt{s^2} = \sqrt{.962} = .981$$

The value of μ is to be found in the null hypothesis. It is 2.0. The value of the test statistic is

$$t = \frac{\bar{x} - \mu}{s/\sqrt{n}} = \frac{2.18 - 2.0}{.981/\sqrt{148}} = 2.23$$

Because 2.23 is not greater than 2.351, we cannot reject the null hypothesis in favor of the alternative. (Students performing the calculations manually can approximate the p-value. The online appendix Approximating p-Values from the Student t Table describes how.)

EXCEL Workbook

	A	B	C	D
1	t-Test of a Mean			
2				
3	Sample mean	2.1804	t Stat	2.24
4	Sample standard deviation	0.9812	P(T<=t) one-tail	0.0134
5	Sample size	148	t Critical one-tail	2.3520
6	Hypothesized mean	2	P(T<=t) two-tail	0.0268
7	Alpha	0.01	t Critical two-tail	2.6097

INSTRUCTIONS

1. Type or import the data into one column. (Open Xm12-01.) In any empty cell, calculate the sample mean (=AVERAGE(A1:A149) and the sample standard deviation (=STDEV(A1:A149).

2. Open the **Test Statistics Workbook** and click the **t-Test_Mean** tab. Type or copy the sample mean and the sample standard deviation. Type the sample size, the value of μ under the null hypothesis and the value of α.

INTERPRET

The value of the test statistic is $t = 2.24$, and its p-value is .0134. There is not enough evidence to infer that the mean weight of discarded newspapers is greater than 2.0. Note that there is some evidence: The p-value is .0134. However, because we wanted the probability of a Type I error to be small, we insisted on a 1% significance level. Thus, we cannot conclude that the recycling plant would be profitable.

Figure 12.1 exhibits the sampling distribution for this example.

FIGURE **12.1** Sampling Distribution for Example 12.1

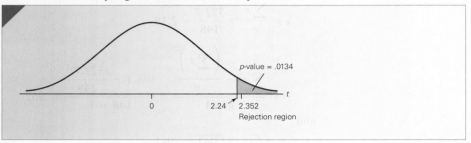

EXAMPLE **12.2**

DATA
Xm12-02

Tax Collected from Audited Returns

In 2019 (the latest year reported), 199,365,492 tax returns were filed in the United States. The Internal Revenue Service (IRS) examined 771,095, of them to determine if they were correctly done. To determine how well the auditors are performing, a random sample of these returns was drawn and the additional tax was reported, which is listed next. Estimate with 95% confidence the mean additional income tax collected from the 771,095 files audited.

Additional Income Tax

16,760.38	10,835.33	36,970.82	7,343.70	23,885.84	30,236.64
25,604.82	17,188.78	17,029.63	27,468.59	30,362.54	9,703.89
24,390.07	12,122.10	22,793.63	12,498.51	48,890.06	22,315.04
17,583.09	28,524.40	31,146.13	8,558.74	14,560.66	21,115.88
13,799.51	0.00	25,956.35	12,106.65	37,786.05	26,182.80
4,231.08	3,563.11	22,642.30	40,690.76	39,986.04	43,459.96
14,873.61	28,878.39	53,146.24	29,083.56	28,786.00	25,258.21
22,515.00	22,755.94	2,127.62	54,505.15	20,737.66	14,584.91
27,502.97	17,138.96	33,498.19	14,870.09	30,855.96	15,124.90
36,505.89	12,552.58	34,841.31	28,452.90	23,966.82	37,363.03
20,264.52	20,252.21	28,422.81	20,015.92	56,725.28	8,728.88
24,725.09	16,544.70	8,326.08	66,500.33	26,727.87	26,332.34
9,347.79	12,876.61	18,680.49	40,003.06	11,781.62	8,842.33
13,006.29	53,241.52	24,077.18	19,153.98	20,814.31	18,844.03
20,202.24	15,495.38	45,801.31	4,912.03	12,903.28	34,057.25
8,547.02	22,759.63	34,125.33	11,942.09	26,265.52	33,598.85
23,466.93	26,116.59	13,575.06	34,453.97	17,530.18	14,965.70
29,508.35	10,311.19	30,519.55	20,286.97	36,291.20	19,324.74
18,778.24	18,839.59	23,097.87	36,774.14	28,392.81	15,438.60
25,976.51	14,342.41	29,620.68	29,175.31	26,833.03	15,170.70
28,224.20	8,516.83	20,465.73	20,828.77	62,020.29	18,254.90
5,378.81	34,817.37	23,001.91	7,440.54	12,034.72	18,317.08
10,956.68	35,542.47	20,590.87	19,053.32	13,762.37	22,976.66
22,097.48	24,873.00	7,777.21	7,267.67	8,784.20	38,473.79

12,543.06	14,059.30	19,664.16	26,153.06	19,866.36	20,360.82
0.00	26,686.54	26,340.07	36,054.80	21,220.81	24,145.62
30,631.96	27,618.82	16,133.41	26,920.19	21,885.38	8,008.45
24,501.48	12,961.52	20,070.32	16,781.76	20,478.76	18,964.26
23,687.42	49,787.37	19,087.14	3,400.60	4,923.85	19,606.61
4,566.29	22,692.44	11,716.49	27,075.35	0.00	22,142.02
19,241.25	23,929.36	22,692.44	15,561.24	20,604.62	13,747.11
22,387.21	29,354.67	14,841.03	19,001.08	18,625.60	26,888.11
30,468.14	34,200.03	27,044.73	13,525.59	26,039.65	46,020.55

SOLUTION:

IDENTIFY

The problem objective is to describe the population of additional income tax. The data are interval and hence, the parameter is the population mean μ. The question asks us to estimate this parameter. The confidence interval estimator is:

$$\bar{x} \pm t_{\alpha/2}\frac{s}{\sqrt{n}}$$

COMPUTE

MANUALLY:

From the data, we determine

$$\sum x_i = 4,438,221 \quad \text{and} \quad \sum x_i^2 = 125,736,555,867$$

Thus

$$\bar{x} = \frac{\sum x_i}{n} = \frac{4,438,221}{198} = 22,415$$

$$s^2 = \frac{\sum x_i^2 - \dfrac{\left(\sum x_i\right)^2}{n}}{n-1} = \frac{125,736,555,867 - \dfrac{(4,438,221)^2}{198}}{198-1} = 133,262,368$$

And $s = \sqrt{s^2} = \sqrt{133,262,368} = 11,544$

Because we want a 95% confidence interval estimate, $1 - \alpha = .95$, $\alpha/2 = .05/2 = .025$, and $t_{\alpha/2,n-1} = t_{.025,197} \approx t_{.025,200} = 1.972$. Thus, the 95% confidence interval estimate of μ is

$$\bar{x} \pm t_{\alpha/2}\frac{s}{\sqrt{n}} = 22,415 \pm 1.972\frac{11,544}{\sqrt{198}} = 22,415 \pm 1,618$$

or

$$LCL = 20,797 \quad UCL = 24,033$$

EXCEL Workbook

	A	B	C	D	E
1	t-Estimate of a Mean				
2					
3	Sample mean	22,415	Confidence Interval Estimate		
4	Sample standard deviation	11,544	22,415	±	1618
5	Sample size	198	Lower confidence limit		20,797
6	Confidence level	0.95	Upper confidence limit		24,033

INSTRUCTIONS

1. Type or import the data into one column. (Open Xm12-02.) In any empty cell, calculate the sample mean (=AVERAGE(A1:A199)) and the sample standard deviation (=STDEV(A1:A199)).

2. Open the **Estimators Workbook** and click the *t*-**Estimate_Mean tab**. Type or copy the sample mean and the sample standard deviation. Type the sample size and the confidence level.

INTERPRET

We estimate that the mean additional tax collected lies between $20,797 and $24,033. We can use this estimate to help decide whether the IRS is auditing the individuals who should be audited.

12-1a Checking the Required Conditions

When we introduced the Student *t*-distribution, we pointed out that the *t*-statistic is Student *t*-distributed if the population from which we've sampled is normal. However, statisticians have shown that the mathematical process that derived the Student *t*-distribution is **robust**, which means that if the population is nonnormal, the results of the *t*-test and confidence interval estimate are still valid provided that the population is not *extremely* nonnormal.* To check this requirement, we draw the histogram and determine whether it is far from bell shaped. Figures 12.2 and 12.3 depict the histograms for Examples 12.1 and 12.2, respectively. Both histograms suggest that the variables are not extremely nonnormal, and in fact, may be normal.

12-1b Estimating the Totals of Finite Populations

The inferential techniques introduced thus far were derived by assuming infinitely large populations. In practice, however, most populations are finite. (Infinite populations are

---

*Statisticians have shown that when the sample size is large, the results of a *t*-test and estimator of a mean are valid even when the population is extremely nonnormal. The sample size required depends on the extent of nonnormality.

FIGURE **12.2** Histogram for Example 12.1

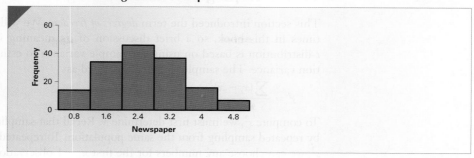

FIGURE **12.3** Histogram for Example 12.2

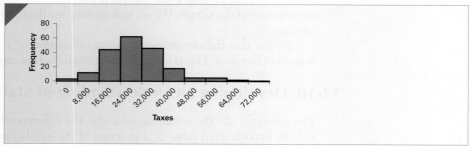

usually the result of some endlessly repeatable process, such as flipping a coin or selecting items with replacement.) When the population is small, we must adjust the test statistic and interval estimator using the finite population correction factor introduced in Chapter 9 (page 313). However, in populations that are large relative to the sample size, we can ignore the correction factor. Large populations are defined as populations that are at least 20 times the sample size.

Finite populations allow us to use the confidence interval estimator of a mean to produce a confidence interval estimator of the population total. To estimate the total, we multiply the lower and upper confidence limits of the estimate of the mean by the population size. Thus, the confidence interval estimator of the total is:

$$N\left[\bar{x} \pm t_{\alpha/2}\frac{s}{\sqrt{n}}\right]$$

For example, suppose we wish to estimate the total amount of additional income tax collected from the 771,095 returns that were audited. The 95% confidence interval estimate of the total is:

$$N\left[\bar{x} \pm t_{\alpha/2}\frac{s}{\sqrt{n}}\right] = 771,095(22,415 \pm 1,618)$$

which is

$$LCL = 16,036,462,715 \text{ and } UCL = 18,531,726,135$$

12-1c Developing an Understanding of Statistical Concepts 1

This section introduced the term *degrees of freedom*. We will encounter this term many times in this book, so a brief discussion of its meaning is warranted. The Student *t*-distribution is based on using the sample variance to estimate the unknown population variance. The sample variance is defined as

$$s^2 = \frac{\sum (x_i - \bar{x})^2}{n - 1}$$

To compute s^2, we must first determine $\bar{x}$. Recall that sampling distributions are derived by repeated sampling from the same population. To repeatedly take samples to compute s^2, we can choose any numbers for the first $n - 1$ observations in the sample. However, we have no choice on the nth value because the sample mean must be calculated first. To illustrate, suppose that $n = 3$ and we find $\bar{x} = 10$. We can have x_1 and x_2 assume any values without restriction. However, x_3 must be such that $\bar{x} = 10$. For example, if $x_1 = 6$ and $x_2 = 8$, then x_3 must equal 16. Therefore, there are only two degrees of freedom in our selection of the sample. We say that we lose one degree of freedom because we had to calculate $\bar{x}$.

Notice that the denominator in the calculation of s^2 is equal to the number of degrees of freedom. This is not a coincidence and will be repeated throughout this book.

12-1d Developing an Understanding of Statistical Concepts 2

The *t*-statistic like the *z*-statistic measures the difference between the sample mean $\bar{x}$ and the hypothesized value of μ in terms of the number of standard errors. However, when the population standard deviation σ is unknown, we estimate the standard error by $s/\sqrt{n}$.

12-1e Developing an Understanding of Statistical Concepts 3

When we introduced the Student *t*-distribution in Section 8-4, we pointed out that it is more widely spread out than the standard normal. This circumstance is logical. The only variable in the *z*-statistic is the sample mean $\bar{x}$, which will vary from sample to sample. The *t*-statistic has two variables: the sample mean $\bar{x}$ and the sample standard deviation *s*, both of which will vary from sample to sample. Because of the greater uncertainty, the *t*-statistic will display greater variability. Exercises 12.15–12.22 address this concept.

We complete this section with a review of how we identify the techniques introduced in this section.

Factors That Identify the *t*-Test and Estimator of μ

1. **Problem objective:** Describe a population.
2. **Data type:** Interval
3. **Type of descriptive measurement:** Central location

EXERCISES

Developing an Understanding of Statistical Concepts

The following exercises are "what-if" analyses designed to determine what happens to the test statistics and interval estimates when elements of the statistical inference change. These problems can be solved manually or using the Test Statistics or Estimators spreadsheets.

12.1 A statistics practitioner took a random sample of size 56. The sample mean and standard deviation are 70 and 12, respectively.
   a. Determine the 95% confidence interval estimate of the population mean.
   b. Repeat part (a) changing the sample mean to 30.
   c. Describe what happens to the width of the interval when the sample mean decreases.

12.2 The mean and standard deviation of a sample of 25 is 50 and 10, respectively.
   a. Estimate the population mean with 90% confidence.
   b. Repeat part (a) changing the sample mean to 100.
   c. Describe what happens to the width of the interval when the sample mean increases.

12.3 a. A random sample of 25 was drawn from a population. The sample mean and standard deviation are $\bar{x} = 510$ and $s = 125$. Estimate μ with 95% confidence.
   b. Repeat part (a) with $n = 50$.
   c. Repeat part (a) with $n = 100$.
   d. Describe what happens to the confidence interval estimate when the sample size increases.

12.4 a. The mean and standard deviation of a sample of 100 is $\bar{x} = 1,500$ and $s = 300$. Estimate the population mean with 95% confidence.
   b. Repeat part (a) with $s = 200$.
   c. Repeat part (a) with $s = 100$.
   d. Discuss the effect on the confidence interval estimate of decreasing the standard deviation s.

12.5 a. A statistics practitioner drew a random sample of 400 observations and found that $\bar{x} = 700$ and $s = 100$. Estimate the population mean with 90% confidence.
   b. Repeat part (a) with a 95% confidence level.
   c. Repeat part (a) with a 99% confidence level.
   d. What is the effect on the confidence interval estimate of increasing the confidence level?

12.6 a. The mean and standard deviation of a sample of 100 are
$$\bar{x} = 10 \text{ and } s = 1.$$
   Estimate the population mean with 95% confidence.
   b. Repeat part (a) with $s = 4$.
   c. Repeat part (a) with $s = 10$.
   d. Discuss the effect on the confidence interval estimate of increasing the standard deviation s.

12.7 a. A statistics practitioner calculated the mean and standard deviation from a sample of 51. They are $\bar{x} = 120$ and $s = 15$. Estimate the population mean with 95% confidence.
   b. Repeat part (a) with a 90% confidence level.
   c. Repeat part (a) with an 80% confidence level.
   d. What is the effect on the confidence interval estimate of decreasing the confidence level?

12.8 a. The sample mean and standard deviation from a sample of 81 observations are $\bar{x} = 63$ and $s = 8$. Estimate μ with 95% confidence.
   b. Repeat part (a) with $n = 64$.
   c. Repeat part (a) with $n = 36$.
   d. Describe what happens to the confidence interval estimate when the sample size decreases.

12.9 a. The sample mean and standard deviation from a random sample of 10 observations from a normal population were computed as $\bar{x} = 23$ and $s = 9$. Calculate the value of the test statistic (and for Excel users, the p-value) of the test required to determine whether there is enough evidence to infer at the 5% significance level that the population mean is greater than 20.
   b. Repeat part (a) with $n = 30$.
   c. Repeat part (a) with $n = 50$.
   d. Describe the effect on the t-statistic (and for Excel users, the p-value) of increasing the sample size.

12.10 a. A statistics practitioner is in the process of testing to determine whether there is enough evidence to infer that the population mean is different from 180. The mean and standard deviation of a sample of 200 observations are $\bar{x} = 175$ and $s = 22$. Calculate the value of the test statistic (and for Excel users, the p-value) of the test required to determine whether there is enough evidence at the 5% significance level.

b. Repeat part (a) with $s = 45$.

c. Repeat part (a) with $s = 60$.

d. Discuss what happens to the t statistic (and for Excel users, the p-value) when the standard deviation increases.

12.11 a. Calculate the test statistic (and for Excel users, the p-value) when $\bar{x} = 145$, $s = 50$, and $n = 100$. Use a 5% significance level.

$$H_0: \quad \mu = 150$$
$$H_1: \quad \mu < 150$$

b. Repeat part (a) with $\bar{x} = 140$.

c. Repeat part (a) with $\bar{x} = 135$.

d. What happens to the t-statistic (and for Excel users, the p-value) when the sample mean decreases?

12.12 a. A random sample of 25 observations was drawn from a normal population. The sample mean and sample standard deviation are $\bar{x} = 52$ and $s = 15$. Calculate the test statistic (and for Excel users, the p-value) of a test to determine if there is enough evidence at the 10% significance level to infer that the population mean is not equal to 50.

b. Repeat part (a) with $n = 15$.

c. Repeat part (a) with $n = 5$.

d. Discuss what happens to the t-statistic (and for Excel users, the p-value) when the sample size decreases.

12.13 a. A statistics practitioner wishes to test the following hypotheses:

$$H_0: \quad \mu = 600$$
$$H_1: \quad \mu < 600$$

A sample of 50 observations yielded the statistics $\bar{x} = 585$ and $s = 45$. Calculate the test statistic (and for Excel users, the p-value) of a test to determine whether there is enough evidence at the 10% significance level to infer that the alternative hypothesis is true.

b. Repeat part (a) with $\bar{x} = 590$.

c. Repeat part (a) with $\bar{x} = 595$.

d. Describe the effect of increasing the sample mean.

12.14 a. To test the following hypotheses, a statistics practitioner randomly sampled 100 observations and found $\bar{x} = 106$ and $s = 35$. Calculate the test statistic (and for Excel users, the p-value) of a test to determine whether there is enough evidence at the 1% significance level to infer that the alternative hypothesis is true.

$$H_0: \quad \mu = 100$$
$$H_1: \quad \mu > 100$$

b. Repeat part (a) with $s = 25$.

c. Repeat part (a) with $s = 15$.

d. Discuss what happens to the t-statistic (and for Excel users, the p-value) when the standard deviation decreases.

12.15 A random sample of 8 observations was drawn from a normal population. The sample mean and sample standard deviation are $\bar{x} = 40$ and $s = 10$.

a. Estimate the population mean with 95% confidence.

b. Repeat part (a) assuming that you know that the population standard deviation is $\sigma = 10$.

c. Explain why the interval estimate produced in part (b) is narrower than that in part (a).

12.16 a. Estimate the population mean with 90% confidence given the following: $\bar{x} = 175$, $s = 30$, and $n = 5$.

b. Repeat part (a) assuming that you know that the population standard deviation is $\sigma = 30$.

c. Explain why the interval estimate produced in part (b) is narrower than that in part (a).

12.17 a. After sampling 1,000 members of a normal population, you find $\bar{x} = 15,500$ and $s = 9,950$. Estimate the population mean with 90% confidence.

b. Repeat part (a) assuming that you know that the population standard deviation is $\sigma = 9,950$.

c. Explain why the interval estimates were virtually identical.

12.18 a. In a random sample of 500 observations drawn from a normal population, the sample mean and sample standard deviation were calculated as $\bar{x} = 350$ and $s = 100$. Estimate the population mean with 99% confidence.

b. Repeat part (a) assuming that you know that the population standard deviation is $\sigma = 100$.

c. Explain why the interval estimates were virtually identical.

12.19 a. A random sample of 11 observations was taken from a normal population. The sample mean and standard deviation are $\bar{x} = 74.5$ and $s = 9$. Can we infer at the 5% significance level that the population mean is greater than 70?

b. Repeat part (a) assuming that you know that the population standard deviation is $\sigma = 9$.

c. Explain why the conclusions produced in parts (a) and (b) differ.

12.20 a. A statistics practitioner randomly sampled 10 observations and found $\bar{x} = 103$ and $s = 17$. Is there sufficient evidence at the 10% significance level to conclude that the population mean is less than 110?

b. Repeat part (a) assuming that you know that the population standard deviation is $\sigma = 17$.

c. Explain why the conclusions produced in parts (a) and (b) differ.

In Section 7-4, this parameter was used to calculate probabilities based on the binomial experiment. One of the characteristics of the binomial experiment is that there are only two possible outcomes per trial. Most practical applications of inference about p involve more than two outcomes. However, in many cases we're interested in only one outcome, which we label a "success." All other outcomes are labeled as "failures." For example, in brand-preference surveys we are interested in our company's brand. In political surveys, we wish to estimate or test the proportion of voters who will vote for one particular candidate—likely the one who has paid for the survey.

12-3b Statistic and Sampling Distribution

The logical statistic used to estimate and test the population proportion is the sample proportion defined as

$$\hat{p} = \frac{x}{n}$$

where x is the number of successes in the sample and n is the sample size. In Section 9-2, we presented the approximate sampling distribution of $\hat{P}$. (The actual distribution is based on the binomial distribution, which does not lend itself to statistical inference.) The sampling distribution of $\hat{P}$ is approximately normal with mean p and standard deviation $\sqrt{p(1-p/n)}$ [provided that np and $n(1-p)$ are greater than 5]. We express this sampling distribution as

$$z = \frac{\hat{P} - p}{\sqrt{p(1-p)/n}}$$

12-3c Testing and Estimating a Proportion

As you have already seen, the formula that summarizes the sampling distribution also represents the test statistic.

> **Test Statistic for p**
>
> $$z = \frac{\hat{P} - p}{\sqrt{p(1-p)/n}}$$
>
> which is approximately normal when np and $n(1-p)$ are greater than 5.

Using the same algebra employed in Sections 10-2 and 12-1, we attempt to derive the confidence interval estimator of p from the sampling distribution. The result is

$$\hat{p} \pm z_{\alpha/2}\sqrt{p(1-p)/n}$$

This formula, although technically correct, is useless. To understand why, examine the standard error of the sampling distribution $\sqrt{p(1-p)/n}$. To produce the interval estimate, we must compute the standard error, which requires us to know the value of p, the parameter we wish to estimate. This is the first of several statistical techniques where we face the same problem: how to determine the value of the standard error. In this application, the problem is easily and logically solved: Simply estimate the value of p with $\hat{p}$.

Thus, we estimate the standard error with $\sqrt{\hat{p}(1-\hat{p})/n}$.

> **Confidence Interval Estimator of p**
>
> $$\hat{p} \pm z_{\alpha/2}\sqrt{\hat{p}(1 - \hat{p})/n}$$
>
> which is valid provided that $n\hat{p}$ and $n(1 - \hat{p})$ are greater than 5.

EXAMPLE 12.5

DATA
Xm12-05⁺

Election Day Exit Poll

When an election for political office takes place, the television networks cancel regular programming and instead provide election coverage. When the ballots are counted, the results are reported. However, for important offices such as president or senator in large states, the networks actively compete to see which will be the first to predict a winner. This is done through exit polls,* wherein a random sample of voters who exit the polling booth is asked for whom they voted. From the data, the sample proportion of voters supporting the candidates is computed. A statistical technique is applied to determine whether there is enough evidence to infer that the leading candidate will garner enough votes to win. Suppose that in the exit poll from the state of Florida during the 2000 year elections, the pollsters recorded only the votes of the two candidates who had any chance of winning, Democrat Albert Gore (code = 1) and Republican George W. Bush (code = 2). The polls close at 8:00 P.M. Can the networks conclude from these data that the Republican candidate will win the state? Should the network announce at 8:01 P.M. that the Republican candidate will win?

SOLUTION:

IDENTIFY

The problem objective is to describe the population of votes in the state. The data are nominal because the values are "Democrat" (code = 1) and "Republican" (code = 2). Thus the parameter to be tested is the proportion of votes in the entire state that are for the Republican candidate. Because we want to determine whether the network can declare the Republican to be the winner at 8:01 P.M., the alternative hypothesis is

$$H_1: \quad p > .5$$

which makes the null hypothesis

$$H_0: \quad p = .5$$

The test statistic is

$$z = \frac{\hat{p} - p}{\sqrt{p(1 - p)/n}}$$

---

*Warren Mitofsky is generally credited for creating the election day exit poll in 1967 when he worked for CBS News. Mitofsky claimed to have correctly predicted 2,500 elections and only six wrong. Exit polls are considered so accurate that when the exit poll and the actual election result differ, some newspaper and television reporters claim that the election result is wrong! In the 2004 presidential election, exit polls showed John Kerry leading. However, when the ballots were counted, George Bush won the state of Ohio. Conspiracy theorists now believe that the Ohio election was stolen by the Republicans using the exit poll as their "proof." However, Mitofsky's own analysis found that the exit poll was improperly conducted, resulting in many Republican voters refusing to participate in the poll. Blame was placed on poorly trained interviewers (*Source: Amstat News*, December 2006).

COMPUTE

MANUALLY:

It appears that this is a "standard" problem that requires a 5% significance level. Thus, the rejection region is

$$z > z_\alpha = z_{.05} = 1.645$$

From the file, we count the number of "successes," which is the number of votes cast for the Republican, and find $x = 407$. The sample size is 765. Hence, the sample proportion is

$$\hat{p} = \frac{x}{n} = \frac{407}{765} = .532$$

The value of the test statistic is

$$z = \frac{\hat{p} - p}{\sqrt{p(1 - p)/n}} = \frac{.532 - .5}{\sqrt{.5(1 - .5)/765}} = 1.77$$

Because the test statistic is (approximately) normally distributed, we can determine the p-value. It is

$$p\text{-value} = P(Z > 1.77) = 1 - p(Z < 1.77) = 1 - .9616 = .0384$$

There is enough evidence at the 5% significance level that the Republican candidate has won.

EXCEL Workbook

	A	B	C	D
1	z-Test of a Proportion			
2				
3	Sample proportion	0.532	z Stat	1.77
4	Sample size	765	P(Z<=z) one-tail	0.0384
5	Hypothesized proportion	0.5	z Critical one-tail	1.6449
6	Alpha	0.05	P(Z<=z) two-tail	0.0767
7			z Critical two-tail	1.9600

INSTRUCTIONS

1. Type or import the data into one column. (Open Xm12-05.) In any empty cell, calculate the number of "successes" (=COUNTIF A1:A766,2). Divide that number by the sample size to obtain the sample proportion.

2. Open the **Test Statistics Workbook** and click the **z-Test_Proportion** tab. Type or copy the sample proportion. Type the sample size, the value of p under the null hypothesis, and the value of α.

INTERPRET

The value of the test statistic is $z = 1.77$ and the one-tail p-value = .0382. Using a 5% significance level, we reject the null hypothesis and conclude that there is enough evidence to infer that George Bush won the presidential election in the state of Florida.

One of the key issues to consider here is the cost of Type I and Type II errors. A Type I error occurs if we conclude that the Republican will win when in fact he has lost. Such an error would mean that a network would announce at 8:01 P.M. that the Republican has won and then later in the evening would have to admit to a mistake. If a particular network were the only one that made this error, it would cast doubt on their integrity and possibly affect the number of viewers.

This is exactly what happened on the evening of the U.S. presidential elections in November 2000. Shortly after the polls closed at 8:00 P.M., all the networks declared that the Democratic candidate Albert Gore would win the state of Florida. A couple of hours later, the networks admitted that a mistake had been made and that Republican candidate George W. Bush had won. Several hours later, they again admitted a mistake and finally declared the race too close to call. Fortunately for each network, all the networks made the same mistake. However, if one network had not done this, it would have developed a better track record, which could have been used in future advertisements for news shows and would likely draw more viewers.

12-3d Missing Data

In real statistical applications, we occasionally find that the data set is incomplete. In some instances, the statistics practitioner may have failed to properly record some observations or some data may have been lost. In other cases, respondents may refuse to answer. For example, in political surveys where the statistics practitioner asks voters for whom they intend to vote in the next election, some people will answer that they haven't decided or that their vote is confidential and refuse to answer. In surveys where respondents are asked to report their income, people often refuse to divulge this information. This is a troublesome issue for statistics practitioners. We can't force people to answer our questions. However, if the number of nonresponses is high, the results of our analysis may be invalid because the sample is no longer truly random. To understand why, suppose that people who are in the top quarter of household incomes regularly refuse to answer questions about their incomes. The resulting estimate of the population household income mean will be lower than the actual value.

The issue can be complicated. There are several ways to compensate for nonresponses. The simplest method is eliminating them. To illustrate, suppose that in a political survey respondents are asked for whom they intend to vote in a two-candidate race. Surveyors record the results as 1 = Candidate A, 2 = Candidate B, 3 = "Don't know," and 4 = "Refuse to say." If we wish to infer something about the proportion of decided voters who will vote for Candidate A, we can simply omit codes 3 and 4. If we're doing the work manually, we will count the number of voters who prefer Candidate A and the number who prefer Candidate B. The sum of these two numbers is the total sample size.

In the language of statistical software, nonresponses that we wish to eliminate are collectively called *missing data*. Software packages deal with missing data in different ways. The online appendix Excel Instructions for Missing Data and Recoding Data describes how to address the problem of missing data in Excel as well as how to recode data.

We have deleted the nonresponses in the General Social Surveys (The Survey of Consumer Finances used a statistical technique to estimate the missing data.) In Excel, the nonresponses appear as blanks.

12-3e Estimating the Total Number of Successes in a Large Finite Population

As was the case with the inference about a mean, the techniques in this section assume infinitely large populations. When the populations are small, it is necessary to include the finite population correction factor. In our definition a population is small when it is less than 20 times the sample size. When the population is large and finite, we can estimate the total number of successes in the population.

To produce the confidence interval estimator of the total, we multiply the lower and upper confidence limits of the interval estimator of the proportion of successes by the population size. The confidence interval estimator of the total number of successes in a large finite population is

$$N\left(\hat{p} \pm z_{\alpha/2}\sqrt{\frac{\hat{p}(1 - \hat{p})}{n}}\right)$$

We will use this estimator in the chapter-opening example and several of this section's exercises.

The Number of Unemployed: Solution

IDENTIFY

The problem objective is to describe the population of work status of American adults. The data are nominal. The combination of problem objective and data type make the parameter to be estimated the proportion of the entire population that is unemployed. The confidence interval estimator of the population is

$$\hat{p} \pm z_{\alpha/2}\sqrt{\frac{\hat{p}(1 - \hat{p})}{n}}$$

Jupiterimages/Getty images

COMPUTE

MANUALLY:

To solve manually we count the number of 3s and 4s in the WRKSTAT column. They are 53 and 84, respectively. The sample size is 2,346. (There are two blanks representing missing data.) Thus,

$$\hat{p} = \frac{53 + 84}{2,346} = .0584$$

The confidence level is $1 - \alpha = .95$. It follows that $\alpha = .05$, $\alpha/2 = .025$, $z_{\alpha/2} = z_{.025} = 1.96$. The 95% confidence interval estimate of p is

$$\hat{p} \pm z_{\alpha/2}\sqrt{\frac{\hat{p}(1 - \hat{p})}{n}} = .0584 \pm 1.96\sqrt{\frac{.0584(1 - .0584)}{2,346}} = .0584 \pm .0095$$

$$\text{LCL} = .0489 \qquad \text{UCL} = .0679$$

(Continued)

EXCEL Workbook

	A	B	C	D	E
1	z-Estimate of a Proportion				
2					
3	Sample proportion	0.0584	Confidence Interval Estimate		
4	Sample size	2346	0.0584	±	0.0095
5	Confidence level	0.95	Lower confidence limit		0.0489
6			Upper confidence limit		0.0679

INSTRUCTIONS

1. Type or import the data into one column. (Open GSS2018.) (We copied column X into another spreadsheet.) In any empty cell, calculate the number of "successes" (=COUNTIF (A1:A2349,3) and =COUNTIF (A1:A2349,4)). Divide this number (53 + 84) by the sample size (2,346) to obtain the sample proportion.

2. Open the **Estimators Workbook** and click the **z-Estimate_Proportion** tab. Type or copy the sample proportion. Type the value of the sample size and the value of α.

INTERPRET

We estimate that the proportion of unemployed American adults lies between 4.89% and 6.79%. To determine the number of unemployed people, multiply the lower and upper limits by the population size 255,200,373. Thus,

LCL = 255,200,373(.0489) = 12,479,298

UCL = 255,200,373(.0679) = 17,328,105

12-3f Selecting the Sample Size to Estimate the Proportion

When we introduced the sample size selection method to estimate a mean in Section 10-3, we pointed out that the sample size depends on the confidence level and the bound on the error of estimation that the statistics practitioner is willing to tolerate. When the parameter to be estimated is a proportion, the bound on the error of estimation is

$$B = z_{\alpha/2} \sqrt{\frac{\hat{p}(1 - \hat{p})}{n}}$$

Solving for n, we produce the required sample size as indicated in the box.

Sample Size to Estimate a Proportion

$$n = \left(\frac{z_{\alpha/2} \sqrt{\hat{p}(1 - \hat{p})}}{B} \right)^2$$

To illustrate the use of this formula, suppose that in a brand-preference survey we want to estimate the proportion of consumers who prefer our company's brand to within .03 with 95% confidence. This means that the bound on the error of estimation is $B = .03$. Because $1 - \alpha = .95, \alpha = .05, \alpha/2 = .025$, and $z_{\alpha/2} = z_{.025} = 1.96$,

$$n = \left(\frac{1.96 \sqrt{\hat{p}(1 - \hat{p})}}{.03} \right)^2$$

To solve for n, we need to know $\hat{p}$. Unfortunately, this value is unknown, because the sample has not yet been taken. At this point, we can use either of two methods to solve for n.

Method 1 If we have no knowledge of even the approximate value of $\hat{p}$, we let $\hat{p} = .5$. We choose $\hat{p} = .5$ because the product $\hat{p}(1 - \hat{p})$ equals its maximum value at $\hat{p} = .5$. (Figure 12.6 illustrates this point.) This, in turn, results in a conservative value of n; as a result, the confidence interval will be no wider than the interval $\hat{p} \pm .03$. If, when the sample is drawn, $\hat{p}$ does not equal .5, the confidence interval estimate will be better (that is, narrower) than planned. Thus,

$$n = \left(\frac{1.96\sqrt{(.5)(.5)}}{.03} \right)^2 = (32.67)^2 = 1,068$$

If it turns out that $\hat{p} = .5$, the interval estimate is $\hat{p} \pm .03$. If not, the interval estimate will be narrower. For instance, if it turns out that $\hat{p} = .2$, then the estimate is $\hat{p} \pm .024$, which is better than we had planned.

FIGURE **12.6**   Plot of $\hat{p}$ versus $\hat{p}(1 - \hat{p})$

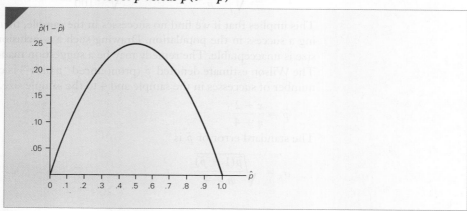

Method 2 If we have some idea about the value of $\hat{p}$, we can use that quantity to determine n. For example, if we believe that $\hat{p}$ will turn out to be approximately .2, we can solve for n as follows:

$$n = \left(\frac{1.96\sqrt{(.2)(.8)}}{.03} \right)^2 = (26.13)^2 = 683$$

Notice that this produces a smaller value of n (thus reducing sampling costs) than does method 1. If $\hat{p}$ actually lies between .2 and .8, however, the estimate will not be as good as we wanted, because the interval will be wider than desired.

Method 1 is often used to determine the sample size used in public opinion surveys reported by newspapers, magazines, television, and radio. These polls usually estimate proportions to within 3%, with 95% confidence. (The media often state the confidence level as "19 times out of 20.") If you've ever wondered why opinion polls almost always estimate proportions to within 3%, consider the sample size required to estimate a proportion to within 1%:

$$n = \left(\frac{1.96\sqrt{(.5)(.5)}}{.01} \right)^2 = (98)^2 = 9,604$$

The sample size 9,604 is 9 times the sample size needed to estimate a proportion to within 3%. Thus, to divide the width of the interval by 3 requires multiplying the sample size by 9. The cost would also increase considerably. For most applications, the increase in accuracy (created by decreasing the width of the confidence interval estimate) does not overcome the increased cost. Confidence interval estimates with 5% or 10% bounds (sample sizes 385 and 97, respectively) are generally considered too wide to be useful. Thus, the 3% bound provides a reasonable compromise between cost and accuracy.

12-3g Wilson Estimators (Optional)

When using the confidence interval estimator of a proportion when success is a relatively rare event, it is possible to find no successes, especially if the sample size is small. To illustrate, suppose that a sample of 100 produced $x = 0$, which means that $\hat{p} = 0$. The 95% confidence interval estimator of the proportion of successes in the population becomes

$$\hat{p} \pm z_{\alpha/2} \sqrt{\frac{\hat{p}(1 - \hat{p})}{n}} = 0 \pm 1.96 \sqrt{\frac{0(1 - 0)}{100}} = 0 \pm 0$$

This implies that if we find no successes in the sample, then there is no chance of finding a success in the population. Drawing such a conclusion from virtually any sample size is unacceptable. The remedy may be a suggestion made by Edwin Wilson in 1927. The Wilson estimate denoted $\tilde{p}$ (pronounced "p tilde") is computed by adding 2 to the number of successes in the sample and 4 to the sample size. Thus,

$$\tilde{p} = \frac{x + 2}{n + 4}$$

The standard error of $\tilde{p}$ is

$$\sigma_{\tilde{p}} = \sqrt{\frac{\tilde{p}(1 - \tilde{p})}{n + 4}}$$

Confidence Interval Estimator of p Using the Wilson Estimate

$$\tilde{p} \pm z_{\alpha/2} \sqrt{\frac{\tilde{p}(1 - \tilde{p})}{n + 4}}$$

Exercises 12.100 to 12.102 require the use of this technique.

We complete this section by reviewing the factors that tell us when to test and estimate a population proportion.

Factors That Identify the z-Test and Interval Estimator of p
1. **Problem objective:** Describe a population.
2. **Data type:** Nominal

EXERCISES

Developing an Understanding of Statistical Concepts

Exercises 12.82 to 12.85 are "what-if analyses" designed to determine what happens to the test statistics and interval estimates when elements of the statistical inference change. These problems can be solved manually or using an Excel spreadsheet.

12.82 a. In a random sample of 200 observations, we found the proportion of successes to be 48%. Estimate with 95% confidence the population proportion of successes.
b. Repeat part (a) with $n = 500$.
c. Repeat part (a) with $n = 1,000$.
d. Describe the effect on the confidence interval estimate of increasing the sample size.

12.83 a. The proportion of successes in a random sample of 400 was calculated as 50%. Estimate the population proportion with 95% confidence.
b. Repeat part (a) with $\hat{p} = 33\%$.
c. Repeat part (a) with $\hat{p} = 10\%$.
d. Discuss the effect on the width of the confidence interval estimate of reducing the sample proportion.

12.84 a. Calculate the p-value of the test of the following hypotheses given that $\hat{p} = .63$ and $n = 100$:
$$H_0: \quad p = .60$$
$$H_1: \quad p > .60$$
b. Repeat part (a) with $n = 200$.
c. Repeat part (a) with $n = 400$.
d. Describe the effect on the p-value of increasing the sample size.

12.85 a. A statistics practitioner wants to test the following hypotheses:
$$H_0: \quad p = .70$$
$$H_1: \quad p > .70$$
A random sample of 100 produced $\hat{p} = .73$. Calculate the p-value of the test.
b. Repeat part (a) with $\hat{p} = .72$.
c. Repeat part (a) with $\hat{p} = .71$.
d. Describe the effect on the z-statistic and its p-value of decreasing the sample proportion.

12.86 Determine the sample size necessary to estimate a population proportion to within .03 with 90% confidence assuming you have no knowledge of the approximate value of the sample proportion.

12.87 Suppose that you used the sample size calculated in Exercise 12.86 and found $\hat{p} = .5$.
a. Estimate the population proportion with 90% confidence.
b. Is this the result you expected? Explain.

12.88 Suppose that you used the sample size calculated in Exercise 12.86 and found $\hat{p} = .75$.
a. Estimate the population proportion with 90% confidence.
b. Is this the result you expected? Explain.
c. If you were hired to conduct this analysis, would the person who hired you be satisfied with the interval estimate you produced? Explain.

12.89 Re-do Exercise 12.86 assuming that you know that the sample proportion will be no less than .75.

12.90 Suppose that you used the sample size calculated in Exercise 12.89 and found $\hat{p} = .75$.
a. Estimate the population proportion with 90% confidence.
b. Is this the result you expected? Explain.

12.91 Suppose that you used the sample size calculated in Exercise 12.89 and found $\hat{p} = .92$.
a. Estimate the population proportion with 90% confidence.
b. Is this the result you expected? Explain.
c. If you were hired to conduct this analysis, would the person who hired you be satisfied with the interval estimate you produced? Explain.

12.92 Suppose that you used the sample size calculated in Exercise 12.89 and found $\hat{p} = .5$.
a. Estimate the population proportion with 90% confidence.
b. Is this the result you expected? Explain.
c. If you were hired to conduct this analysis, would the person who hired you be satisfied with the interval estimate you produced? Explain.

Applications

12.93 A statistics practitioner working for major league baseball wants to supply radio and television commentators with interesting statistics. After observing several hundred games, the statistics practitioner counted the number of times a runner on first base attempted to steal second base and found that there were 373 such attempts, of which 259 were successful. Estimate with 95% confidence the proportion of all attempted thefts of second base that are successful.

12.94 In some states, the law requires drivers to turn on their headlights when driving in the rain. A highway patrol officer believes that less than one-quarter of all drivers follow this rule. As a test, a random sample of 200 cars driving in the rain was drawn and the number whose headlights were turned on was counted and found to be 41. Does the officer have enough evidence at the 10% significance level to support the belief?

12.95 A dean of a business school wanted to know whether graduates used a statistical inference technique during their first year of employment after graduation. A random sample of 314 graduates was drawn and it was determined that 204 used a statistical technique within 1 year of graduation. Estimate with 90% confidence the proportion of all business school graduates who use their statistical education within a year of graduation.

12.96 Has the recent drop in airplane passengers resulted in better on-time performance? Before the recent downturn one airline bragged that 92% of its flights were on time. A random sample of 165 flights completed this year reveals that 153 were on time. Can we conclude at the 5% significance level that the airline's on-time performance has improved?

12.97 What type of educational background do CEOs have? In one survey, 344 CEOs of medium and large companies were asked whether they had an MBA degree. There were 97 MBAs. Estimate with 95% confidence the proportion of all CEOs of medium and large companies who have MBAs.

12.98 The GO transportation system of buses and commuter trains operates on the honor system. Train travelers are expected to buy their tickets before boarding the train. Only a small number of people will be checked on the train to see whether they bought a ticket. Suppose that a random sample of 400 train travelers was sampled and 68 of them had failed to buy a ticket. Estimate with 95% confidence the proportion of all train travelers who do not buy a ticket.

12.99 Refer to Exercise 12.98. Assuming that there are 1 million travelers per year and the fare is $3.00 estimate with 95% confidence the amount of revenue lost each year.

The following three exercises require the use of the Wilson estimator.

12.100 In Chapter 6, we discussed how an understanding of probability allows one to properly interpret the results of medical screening tests. The use of Bayes's Law requires a set of prior probabilities, which are based on historical records. Suppose that a physician wanted to estimate the probability that a woman under 35 years of age would give birth to a Down syndrome baby. A random sample of 200 births produced only one such case. Use the Wilson estimator to produce a 95% confidence interval estimate of the proportion of women under 35 who will have a Down syndrome baby.

12.101 Spam is of concern to anyone with an e-mail address. Several companies offer protection by eliminating spam e-mails as soon as they hit an inbox. To examine one such product, a manager randomly sampled the daily e-mails for 50 days after installing spam software. A total of 374 e-mails were received, of which 3 were spam. Use the Wilson estimator to estimate with 90% confidence the proportion of spam e-mails that get through.

12.102 A management professor was in the process of investigating the relationship between education and managerial level achieved. The source of the data was a survey of 385 CEOs of medium and large companies. The professor discovered that there was only one CEO who did not have at least one university degree. Estimate (using a Wilson estimator) with 99% confidence the proportion of CEOs of medium and large companies with no university degrees.

The following exercises require the use of a computer and software. The answers to Exercises 12.103 to 12.118 may be calculated manually. See Appendix A for the sample statistics.

Use a 5% significance level for all tests and a 95% confidence level for all estimates for Exercises 12.103 to 12.129.

12.103 Xr12-103 A national survey conducted by Pew Research asked a random sample of 974 American adults how they felt about doing their taxes. The responses are: 1 = Love it, 2 = Like it, 3 = Neither like nor dislike it, 4 = Dislike it, 5 = Hate it. There are 143.3 million taxpayers in the United States. Determine a confidence interval estimate of the number of American adults who hate doing their taxes.

12.104 Xr12-104 Refer to Exercise 12.103. Those who hate or dislike doing their taxes were asked the reason. The responses are: 1 = Pay too much taxes, 2 = Complicated/too much paperwork, 3 = Inconvenient/time consuming, 4 = Don't like how government uses tax money, 5 = Owe the government money, and 6 = Other. Compute a confidence interval estimate of the fraction of American adults who had indicated that they hated or disliked doing their taxes because they don't like how the government uses tax money.

12.105 Xr12-105+ There is a looming crisis in universities and colleges across North America. In most places of higher education enrollments are increasing, requiring more instructors. However, there are not enough PhDs to fill the vacancies now. Moreover, among current professors, a large proportion are nearing retirement age. On top of these problems, some universities allow professors over the age of 60 to retire early. To help devise a plan to deal with the crisis, a consultant surveyed 521 55- to 64-year-old professors and asked them whether they intended to retire before 65. The responses are: 1 = Yes or 0 = No. If the number of professors between the ages of 55 and 64 is 75,000, estimate with a confidence interval the total number of such professors who plan to retire early.

12.106 Xr12-106+ During the pandemic in 2020, governments around the world advised individuals to wear masks or other face-coverings to help slow the spread of COVID-19. In July 2020 an Abacus survey of Canadian adults (18 years and older) asked, "When you go into a public place like a retail store, do you wear a mask"? The responses are: 1 = Always or almost always, 2 = Half the time or less, 3 = Never. There are 30,706,072 Canadian adults. Compute a confidence interval estimate of the total number of Canadian adults who always or almost always wear a mask in public places.

12.107 Xr12-107+ Health care and its costs are major election issues in the United States. To gauge the mood of Americans, Gallup conducted a survey that asked, "Are you generally satisfied or dissatisfied with the total cost you pay for your health care?" The responses are 1 = Satisfied, 0 = Unsatisfied. Determine a confidence interval estimate of the proportion of Americans who are satisfied with cost of their health care.

12.108 Xr12-108+ In an election year almost everything that happens is political. Americans become more attentive to news about the upcoming election. A Gallup survey in 2020 asked American adults how closely they followed news about national politics. The responses are 1 = Very closely or 0 = Not very closely. Estimate the fraction of American adults who closely followed news about national politics in 2020.

12.109 Xr12-109 An increasing number of people are giving gift certificates as Christmas presents. To measure the extent of this practice, a random sample of people was asked (survey conducted December 26–29) whether they had received a gift certificate for Christmas: 1 = Yes or 0 = No. Compute a confidence interval estimate of the proportion of people who received a gift certificate for Christmas.

12.110 Xr12-110+ An important decision faces Christmas holiday celebrators: buy a real or artificial tree? A sample of 1,508 male and female respondents 18 years of age and over was interviewed. Respondents were asked whether they preferred a real tree (1) or an artificial tree (2). If there are 6 million Canadian households that buy Christmas trees, determine a confidence interval estimate of the total number of Canadian households that would prefer artificial Christmas trees.

12.111 Xr12-111+ Because television audiences of newscasts tend to be older (and because older people suffer from a variety of medical ailments) pharmaceutical companies' advertising often appears on national news in the three networks (ABC, CBS, and NBC). The ads concern prescription drugs such as those to treat heartburn. To determine how effective the ads are, a survey was undertaken. Adults over 50 who regularly watch network newscasts were asked whether they had contacted their physician to ask about one of the prescription drugs advertised during the newscast. The responses are: 1 = Yes or 0 = No. Determine a confidence interval estimate of the fraction of adults over 50 who have contacted their physician to inquire about a prescription drug.

12.112 Xr12-112+ In 2019 Americans' satisfaction with way things were going hit a 15-year high. In 2020, Gallup conducted a survey to determine whether the combination of the pandemic and racial unrest would change that optimism. The question was posed: "In general are you satisfied or dissatisfied with the way things are going in the United States at this time?" The responses are 1 = Satisfied or 0 = Dissatisfied. Determine a confidence interval estimate of the proportion of Americans who were satisfied with the way things were going in 2020.

12.113 Xr12-113 According to the Centers for Disease Control, vitamin D deficiency can lead to cancer and type 2 diabetes. It was also discovered that this vitamin could help ward off COVID-19. Vitamin D is found in few foods—fatty fish, mushrooms, egg yolks, and liver. It can be absorbed into the skin from the sun. Random samples of American men and women were drawn and each was tested for Vitamin D. The results are Deficient (0) and Sufficient (1). There are 255,200,373 American adults in the United States. Produce a confidence interval estimate of the total number of American adults who have vitamin D deficiency.

12.114 Xr12-114 A Gallup poll of American adults between the ages of 18 and 29 were asked whether they had a positive view of socialism. The responses are: 1 = Positive view or 0 = Not positive. The sample size of individuals between the ages of 18 and 29 was 388. Is there sufficient evidence to infer that there are more Americans in this age category who have a positive view of socialism than there are Americans who do not have a positive view of socialism?

12.115 Xr12-115 According to the American Contract Bridge League (ACBL), bridge hands that contain two 4-card suits, one 3-card suit, and one 2-card suit (4-4-3-2) occur with 21.55% probability. Suppose that a bridge-playing statistics professor with too much time and not enough to do tracked the number of hands over a 1-year period and recorded the following hands with 4-4-3-2 distribution (1) and some other distribution (0). All hands were shuffled and dealt by the players at a bridge club. Test to determine whether the proportion of

4-4-3-2 hands differs from the theoretical probability. If the answer is yes, propose a reason to explain the result.

12.116 Xr12-116+ In 2019 the economy was growing well, creating jobs and raising incomes. However, the lockdowns in reaction to the pandemic did serious damage to the economy. A Gallup survey asked a random sample of American adults this question: "Would you rate your financial situation today as excellent, good, only fair, or poor." The responses were recorded as 1 = Excellent/good, 0 = Only fair or poor. Can we infer that there are fewer American adults who rated the economy as excellent or good than Americans who rated the economy as only fair or poor?

12.117 Xr12-117 A Gallup survey asked American adults whether they were worried about their jobs. The responses are: 1 = Worried or 0 = Not worried. The responses of those aged 30 to 49 were recorded using the codes. There are 42,278,000 Americans between 30 and 49 years of age. Calculate a confidence interval estimate of the number of Americans between the ages of 30 and 49 who are worried about their jobs.

12.118 Xr12-118 When the United States imposed tariffs on Canadian steel and aluminum, Canadians were upset. A survey asked Canadians whether they would avoid cross border shopping. The responses: 1 = Will certainly, 2 = Will consider, or 3 = Will not. Can we infer that the majority of Canadians will certainly not shop across the border?

GENERAL SOCIAL SURVEY EXERCISES

GSS2018 *The following exercises are based on the General Social Survey of 2018.*

12.119 According to the census of 2010, the proportion of Americans who were never married was 26.9%. Has that figure changed? Conduct a test to answer the question (MARITAL: 5 = Never married).

12.120 In 2008 prior to the mortgage debacle, home ownership was 63.8%. Some analysts claim that the United States has not recovered. Is there enough evidence to infer that the proportion of home ownership has decreased since 2008 (DWELOWN: 1 = Own or buying, 2 = Rent, 3 = Other)?

12.121 Since 2010 the number of jobs available for people who have not completed high school has decreased. In 2010 that percentage was 12.9%. Has this resulted in a decrease in the proportion of Americans who did not complete high school? Perform a statistical test to answer the question (DEGREE: 0 = Left high school).

12.122 Has the proportion of White Americans who have divorced increased since 2010, when it was 10.4%? Conduct a statistical test to answer the question (RACE: 1 = White; MARITAL: 3 = Divorced).

12.123 An increasing number of women are attending university. Women now outnumber men in most college programs. In 2010 the fraction of women who attained a graduate degree was 10.2%. Can we infer that this proportion has increased? Conduct a statistical test to answer the question (SEX: 2 = Female; DEGREE: 4 = Graduate).

SURVEY OF CONSUMERS FINANCES SURVEY

SCF2019:\UC *The following exercises are based on the upper class, which are households whose net worth is between $3,129,610 and $16,751,000.*

12.124 It seems reasonable to assume that the heads of these households will be well educated. Conduct a test to determine whether there is sufficient evidence to infer that the proportion of heads of household in this net worth category have at least a bachelor's degree (EDCL: 4 = College degree) is more than 75%.

12.125 Is there sufficient evidence to infer that more than 80% of the heads of upper class households are married or living with partner (MARRIED: 1 = Married)?

12.126 Counting only those who are working (OCCAT1 = 1, 2), determine whether there is enough statistical evidence to conclude that more than 60% of household heads in this category are self-employed (OCCAT1: 2 = Self-employed).

12.127 In 2018 approximately 60% of Americans owned the house they lived in. We would expect that figure to be much higher in this net worth category. Determine a confidence interval estimate of the proportion of upper class households that live in their own homes (HOUSECL: 1 = Own).

12.128 Counting only those who are working (OCCAT2 = 1, 2, 3), determine whether there is enough statistical evidence to conclude that more than 80% of household heads in this category are managerial/professional (OCCAT2: 1 = Managerial/professional).

12.129 We would expect very few households to have declared bankruptcy in the years 2015 to 2019. Compute a confidence interval estimate of the proportion of upper class households that have gone bankrupt (BNKRUPLAST5: 1 = Yes) in the last 5 years.

12-4 (OPTIONAL) APPLICATIONS IN MARKETING: MARKET SEGMENTATION

Mass marketing refers to the mass production and marketing by a company of a single product for the entire market. Mass marketing is especially effective for commodity goods such as gasoline, which are very difficult to differentiate from the competition, except through price and convenience of availability. Generally speaking, however, mass marketing has given way to target marketing, which focuses on satisfying the demands of a particular segment of the entire market. For example, the Coca-Cola Company has moved from the mass marketing of a single beverage to the production of several different beverages. Among the cola products are Coca-Cola Classic, Diet Coke, and Caffeine-Free Diet Coke. Each product is aimed at a different market segment.

Because there is no single way to segment a market, managers must consider several different variables (or characteristics) that could be used to identify segments. Surveys of customers are used to gather data about various aspects of the market, and statistical techniques are applied to define the segments. Market segmentation separates consumers of a product into different groups in such a way that members of each group are similar to each other, and there are differences between groups. Market segmentation grew out of the realization that a single product can seldom satisfy the needs and wants of all consumers. Managers must then formulate a strategy to target these profitable segments, using the four elements of the marketing mix: product, pricing, promotion, and placement.

There are many ways to segment a market. Table 12.1 lists several different segmentation variables and their market segments. For example, car manufacturers can use education levels to segment the market. It is likely that high school graduates would be quite

TABLE **12.1** Market Segmentation

SEGMENTATION VARIABLE	SEGMENTS
Geographic	
Countries	Brazil, Canada, China, France, United States
Country regions	Midwest, Northeast, Southwest, Southeast
Demographic	
Age	Under 5, 5–12, 13–19, 20–29, 30–50, older than 50
Education	Some high school, high school graduate, some college, college or university graduate
Income	Under $30,000, $30,000–$49,999, $50,000–$69,999, more than $70,000
Marital status	Single, married, divorced, widowed
Social	
Religion	Catholic, Protestant, Jewish, Muslim, Buddhist
Class	Upper class, middle class, working class, lower class
Behavior	
Media usage	TV, Internet, newspaper, magazine
Payment method	Cash, check, Visa, Mastercard

similar to others in this group and that members of this group would differ from university graduates. We would expect those differences to include the types and brands of cars each group would choose to buy. However, it is likely that income level would differentiate more clearly between segments. Statistical techniques can be used to help determine the best way to segment the market. These statistical techniques are more advanced than this textbook. Consequently, we will focus our attention on other statistical applications.

It is important for marketing managers to know the size of the segment because the size (among other parameters) determines its profitability. Not all segments are worth pursuing. In some instances, the size of the segment is too small or the costs of satisfying it may be too high. The size can be determined in several ways. The census provides useful information. For example, we can determine the number of Americans in various age categories or the size of geographic residences. For other segments, we may need to survey members of a general population and use the inferential techniques introduced in the previous section, where we showed how to estimate the total number of successes.

In Section 12-3, we showed how to estimate the total number of successes in a large finite population. The confidence interval estimator is

$$N\left(\hat{p} \pm z_{\alpha/2} \sqrt{\frac{\hat{p}(1 - \hat{p})}{n}} \right)$$

The following example demonstrates the use of this estimator in market segmentation.

EXAMPLE 12.6

DATA
Xm12-06⁺

Segmenting the Breakfast Cereal Market

In segmenting the breakfast cereal market, a food manufacturer uses health and diet consciousness as the segmentation variable. Four segments are developed:

1. Concerned about eating healthy foods
2. Concerned primarily about weight
3. Concerned about health because of illness
4. Unconcerned

To distinguish between groups, surveys are conducted. On the basis of a questionnaire, people are categorized as belonging to one of these groups. A recent survey asked a random sample of 1,250 American adults (18 and older) to complete the questionnaire. The categories were recorded using the codes. The most recent census reveals that 255,200,373 Americans are 18 and older. Estimate with 95% confidence the number of American adults who are concerned about eating healthy foods.

SOLUTION:

IDENTIFY

The problem objective is to describe the population of American adults. The data are nominal. Consequently, the parameter we wish to estimate is the proportion p of

American adults who classify themselves as concerned about eating healthy. The confidence interval estimator we need to employ is

$$\hat{p} \pm z_{\alpha/2} \sqrt{\frac{\hat{p}(1 - \hat{p})}{n}}$$

from which we will produce the estimate of the size of the market segment.

COMPUTE

MANUALLY:

To solve manually, we count the number of 1s in the file. We find this value to be 269. Thus,

$$\hat{p} = \frac{x}{n} = \frac{269}{1,250} = .2152$$

The confidence level is $1 - \alpha = .95$. It follows that $\alpha = .05$, $\alpha/2 = .025$, and $z_{\alpha/2} = z_{.025} = 1.96$. The 95% confidence interval estimate of p is

$$\hat{p} \pm z_{\alpha/2} \sqrt{\frac{\hat{p}(1 - \hat{p})}{n}} = .2152 \pm 1.96 \sqrt{\frac{(.2152)(1 - .2152)}{1,250}} = .2152 \pm .0228$$

$$\text{LCL} = .1924 \qquad \text{UCL} = .2380$$

EXCEL Workbook

	A	B	C	D	E
1	z-Estimate of a Proportion				
2					
3	Sample proportion	0.2152	Confidence Interval Estimate		
4	Sample size	1250	0.2152	±	0.0228
5	Confidence level	0.95	Lower confidence limit		0.1924
6			Upper confidence limit		0.2380

INTERPRET

We estimate that the proportion of American adults who are in group 1 lies between .1924 and .2380. Because there are 255,200,373 adults in the population, we estimate that the number of adults who belong to group 1 falls between

$$\text{LCL} = N\left[\hat{p} - z_{\alpha/2} \sqrt{\frac{\hat{p}(1 - \hat{p})}{n}}\right] = 255,200,373(.1924) = 49,100,552$$

and

$$\text{UCL} = N\left[\hat{p} + z_{\alpha/2} \sqrt{\frac{\hat{p}(1 - \hat{p})}{n}}\right] = 255,200,373(.2380) = 60,737,689$$

We will return to the subject of market segmentation in other chapters where we demonstrate how statistics can be used to determine whether differences actually exist between segments.

EXERCISES

The following exercises may be solved manually. See Appendix A for the sample statistics.

12.130 <u>Xr12-130</u> A new credit card company is investigating various market segments to determine whether it is profitable to direct its advertising specifically at each one. One of the market segments is composed of Hispanic people. According to the U.S. census, there are 53,900,000 Hispanic adults (18 and over) people in the United States. A survey of 475 Hispanics asked each how they usually pay for products that they purchase. The responses are:

1. Cash
2. Check
3. Visa
4. MasterCard
5. Other credit card

Estimate with 95% confidence the number of Hispanics in the United States who usually pay by credit card.

12.131 <u>Xr12-131+</u> A California university is investigating expanding its evening programs. It wants to target people between 25 and 55 years old who have completed high school but did not complete college or university. To help determine the extent and type of offerings, the university needs to know the size of its target market. A survey of 320 California adults was drawn and all were asked to identify their highest educational attainment. The responses are:

1. Did not complete high school
2. Completed high school only
3. Some college or university
4. College or university graduate

The Public Policy Institute of California indicates that there are 10,674,896 Californians between the ages of 25 and 55. Estimate with 95% confidence the number of Californians between 25 and 55 years of age who are in the market segment the university wishes to target.

12.132 <u>Xr12-132+</u> The JC Penney department store chain segments the market for women's apparel by its identification of values. The three segments are:

1. Conservative
2. Traditional
3. Contemporary

Questionnaires about personal and family values are used to identify which segment a woman falls into. Suppose that the questionnaire was sent to a random sample of 1,836 women. Each woman was classified using the codes 1, 2, and 3. The latest census reveals that there are 125,127,519 adult women in the United States. Use a 95% confidence level.

a. Estimate the proportion of adult American women who are classified as traditional.
b. Estimate the size of the traditional market segment.

12.133 <u>Xr12-133</u> Most life insurance companies are leery about offering policies to people over 64. When they do the premiums must be high enough to overcome the predicted length of life. The president of one life insurance company was thinking about offering special discounts to Americans over 64 who held full-time jobs. The plan was based on the belief that full-time workers over 64 are likely to be in good health and would likely live well into their eighties. To help decide what to do, a random sample of the 29,983,973 Americans over the age of 64 was drawn. The sample size was 325 and respondents were asked whether they currently hold a full-time job (1 = Yes and 0 = No). Estimate with 95% confidence the size of this market segment.

Source: United States Census.

12.134 <u>Xr12-134</u> An advertising company was awarded the contract to design advertising for Rolls Royce automobiles. An executive in the firm decided to pitch the product not only to the affluent in the United States but also to those who think they are in the top 1% of income earners in the country. A survey was undertaken, which among other questions asked respondents 25 and over where their annual income ranked. The following responses were given.

1 = Top 1%
2 = Top 5% but not top 1%
3 = Top 10% but not top 5%
4 = Top 25% but not top 10%
5 = Bottom 75%

Estimate with 90% confidence the number of Americans 25 and over who believe they are in the top 1% of income earners. The number of Americans over 25 is 211,447,331.

Source: United States Census.

12.135 <u>Xr12-135</u> Suppose the survey in the previous exercise also asked those who were not in the top 1% whether they believed that within 5 years they would be in the top 1% (1 = will not be in top 1% within 5 years and 2 = will be in top 1% within 5 years). Estimate with 95% confidence the number of Americans who believe that they will be in the top 1% of income earners within 5 years.

CHAPTER SUMMARY

The inferential methods presented in this chapter address the problem of describing a single population. When the data are interval, the parameters of interest are the population mean μ and the population variance σ^2. The Student t-distribution is used to test and estimate the mean when the population standard deviation is unknown. The chi-squared distribution is used to make inferences about a population variance. When the data are nominal, the parameter to be tested and estimated is the population proportion p. The sample proportion follows an approximate normal distribution, which produces the test statistic and the interval estimator. We also discussed how to determine the sample size required to estimate a population proportion. We introduced market segmentation and described how statistical techniques presented in this chapter can be used to estimate the size of a segment.

IMPORTANT TERMS:

t-statistic   397
Student t-distribution   397

Robust   402
Chi-squared statistic   412

SYMBOLS:

Symbol	Pronounced	Represents
ν	nu	Degrees of freedom
χ^2	chi squared	Chi-squared statistic
$\hat{p}$	p hat	Sample proportion
$\tilde{p}$	p tilde	Wilson estimator

FORMULAS:

Test statistic for μ

$$t = \frac{\bar{x} - \mu}{s/\sqrt{n}}$$

Confidence interval estimator of μ

$$\bar{x} \pm t_{\alpha/2}\frac{s}{\sqrt{n}}$$

Test statistic for σ^2

$$\chi^2 = \frac{(n-1)s^2}{\sigma^2}$$

Confidence interval estimator of σ^2

$$\text{LCL} = \frac{(n-1)s^2}{\chi^2_{\alpha/2}}$$

$$\text{UCL} = \frac{(n-1)s^2}{\chi^2_{1-\alpha/2}}$$

Test statistic for p

$$z = \frac{\hat{p} - p}{\sqrt{p(1-p)/n}}$$

Confidence interval estimator of p

$$\hat{p} \pm z_{\alpha/2}\sqrt{\hat{p}(1-\hat{p})/n}$$

Sample size to estimate p

$$n = \left(\frac{z_{\alpha/2}\sqrt{\hat{p}(1-\hat{p})}}{B}\right)^2$$

Wilson estimator

$$\tilde{p} = \frac{x+2}{n+4}$$

Confidence interval estimator of p using the Wilson estimator

$$\tilde{p} \pm z_{\alpha/2}\sqrt{\tilde{p}(1-\hat{p})/(n+4)}$$

Confidence interval estimator of the total of a large finite population

$$N\left[\bar{x} \pm t_{\alpha/2}\frac{s}{\sqrt{n}}\right]$$

Confidence interval estimator of the total number of successes in a large finite population

$$N\left[\hat{p} \pm z_{\alpha/2}\sqrt{\frac{\hat{p}(1-\hat{p})}{n}}\right]$$

EXCEL OUTPUT AND INSTRUCTIONS:

Technique

t-test of μ	399
t-estimator of μ	402
Chi-squared test of σ^2	414
Chi-squared estimator of σ^2	416
z-test of p	421
z-estimator of p	424

We present the flowchart in Figure 12.7 as part of our ongoing effort to help you identify the appropriate statistical technique. This flowchart shows the techniques introduced in this chapter only. As we add new techniques in the upcoming chapters, we will expand this flowchart until it contains all the statistical inference techniques covered in this book. Use the flowchart to select the correct method in the chapter exercises that follow.

FIGURE **12.7**   **Flowchart of Techniques: Chapter 12**

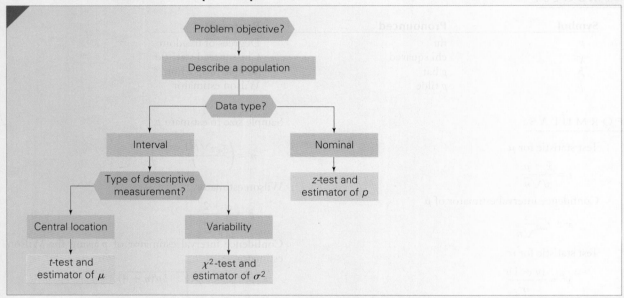

CHAPTER EXERCISES

The following exercises require the use of a computer and software. **Use a 5% significance level for all tests and a 95% confidence level for all confidence interval estimates**.

12.136 Xr12-136 The National Hockey League's Florida Panthers play in the BB&T center. The cost of parking is $20. However, Lexus occasionally pays the cost by offering free parking to drivers of Lexus cars. A statistician wanted to estimate the cost of this program. A random sample of 300 cars entering the parking lot were observed and whether the car was a Lexus (1) or not (0) was recorded. By counting the number of empty parking spots, the statistician discovered that there were 4,850 cars parked that night. Compute a confidence interval estimate of the mean amount of money Lexus had to pay the BB&T center.

12.137 <u>Xr12-137</u> Hazardous materials are constantly being shipped around the country. To help determine how dangerous these events are, an engineer recorded the distances of a random sample of trucks, trains, airplanes, and boats carrying explosives. Determine a confidence interval estimate of the mean distance.

12.138 <u>Xr12-138</u> One of the issues that came up in a recent municipal election was the high cost of housing. A candidate seeking to unseat an incumbent claimed that the average family spends more than 30% of its annual income on housing. A housing expert was asked to investigate the claim. A random sample of 125 households was drawn, and each household was asked to report the percentage of household income spent on housing costs.

a. Is there enough evidence to infer that the candidate is correct?

b. Using a confidence interval, estimate the mean percentage of household income spent on housing by all households.

c. What is the required condition for the techniques used in parts (a) and (b)? Use a graphical technique to check whether it is satisfied.

12.139 <u>Xr12-139</u> There are 604,474 bridges in the United States. A structural engineering team randomly sampled 850 bridges and categorized each as either structurally deficient (restricted to light vehicles, require immediate rehabilitation to remain open, or are closed), functionally obsolete (load carrying capacity, clearance, or approach highway alignment), or structurally sound. These three categories were recorded as 1, 2, and 3, respectively.

a. Compute a confidence interval estimate of the number of American bridges that are structurally deficient.

b. Determine a confidence interval estimate of the number of American bridges that are functionally obsolete.

12.140 <u>Xr12-140</u> Robots are being used with increasing frequency on production lines to perform monotonous tasks. To determine whether a robot welder should replace human welders in producing automobiles, an experiment was performed. The time for the robot to complete a series of welds was found to be 38 seconds. A random sample of 20 workers was taken, and the time for each worker to complete the welds was measured. The mean was calculated to be 38 seconds, the same as the robot's time. However, the robot's time did not vary, whereas there was variation among the workers' times. An analysis of the production line revealed that if the variance exceeds 17 seconds^2, there will be problems. Perform an analysis of the data, and determine whether there is enough evidence to conclude that problems using human welders are likely.

12.141 <u>Xr12-141</u> A survey of Australian adults asked, what best describes your thoughts about climate change? The responses are 1 = Human caused, 2 = Natural fluctuation, 3 = Not happening, 4 = Don't know. There are 18,802,914 Australian adults (20 and older). Determine a confidence interval estimate of the number of Australian adults who believe that climate change is caused by humans.

12.142 <u>Xr12-142</u> In a recent municipal election, the list of "eligible" voters contained 102,412 names. However, the list may contain a substantial number of names of voters who for one reason or another are ineligible. To examine the problem, an auditor was hired to delve into the matter. A random sample of 659 names was taken from the list and determined whether they were eligible (1) or ineligible (2). Produce a confidence interval estimate of the total number of ineligible voters.

12.143 <u>Xr12-143</u> An important factor in attempting to predict the demand for new cars is the age of the cars already on the road. A random sample of 650 cars was drawn and the age of each car was recorded. *Source:* R.L. Polk and Company.

a. Estimate with a confidence interval the mean age of all American cars.

b. What is the required condition for this technique to be valid? Is it satisfied?

12.144 <u>Xr12-144+</u> The profits of dairy farming depend on a number of factors. One of the most important is the amount of milk produced from each cow. The amounts typically vary from farm to farm depending on the age of the cows, how they're fed, and other factors. A survey of U.S. dairy farms asked each to report the amount of milk (in pounds) per cow per month. There are 9.34 million cows in the United States. Produce a confidence interval estimate of the total monthly production in the United States.

12.145 <u>Xr12-145</u> Opinion Research International surveyed people whose household incomes exceed $50,000 and asked each for their top money-related new year's resolutions. The responses are: 1 = Get out of credit card debt, 2 = Retire before age 65, 3 = Die broke, 4 = Make do with current finances, 5 = Look for higher paying job. Calculate a confidence interval estimate of the proportion of people whose household incomes exceed $50,000 whose top money-related resolution is to get out of credit card debt.

12.146 Xr12-146   In a large state university (with numerous campuses), the marks in an introductory statistics course are normally distributed with a mean of 68%. To determine the effect of requiring students to pass a calculus test (which at present is not a prerequisite), a random sample of 50 students who have taken calculus is given a statistics course. The marks out of 100 were recorded.

a. Calculate a confidence interval estimate of the mean statistics mark for all students who have taken calculus.

b. Do these data provide evidence to infer that students with a calculus background would perform better in statistics than students with no calculus?

12.147 Xr12-147   A random sample of complaints about U.S.-based airlines was drawn and the type of complaint was recorded: 1 = Flight problems (cancellations, delays, etc.), 2 = Customer service (unhelpful employees, inadequate means or cabin service, treatment of delayed passengers), 3 = Baggage, 4 = Ticketing/boarding, 5 = Other. Determine a confidence interval estimate of the proportion of airline complaints that are due to customer service.

12.148 Xr12-148+   The lockdowns that were a reaction to the increasing number of deaths from the pandemic in 2020 caused financial hardship to a large number of American households. A U.S. Census Bureau survey asked American adults (18 years of age and older) whether they or a member of their household experienced a loss of employment income due to a lockdown. The data were recorded as 1 = Yes, 0 = No. There are 128,451,000 households in the United States. Estimate the total number who experienced an income loss.

12.149 Xr12-149+   Despite the strong economy in 2018 and 2019, many Americans were feeling stress, worry, and anger. A Gallup survey asked a random sample of Americans 15 years old and older if they felt stress the previous day. The responses are 1 = Yes and 0 = No. Is there sufficient evidence to conclude that there are more Americans aged 15 and older who experienced stress the previous day than Americans aged 15 and older who did not experience stress the previous day?

12.150 Xr12-150+   Christmas shopping represents a major of revenue for retailers. A successful season usually means that the retailer will be profitable for the year. A Gallup survey conducted in October asked shoppers how much they expect to spend on Christmas presents. Assume that there are 25 million Christmas shoppers. Calculate a confidence interval estimate of the total amount expected to spend for presents.

12.151 Xr12-151   The routes of postal deliverers are carefully planned so that each deliverer works between 7 and 7.5 hours per shift. The planned routes assume an average walking speed of 2 miles per hour and no shortcuts across lawns. In an experiment to examine the amount of time deliverers actually spend completing their shifts, a random sample of 75 postal deliverers was secretly timed.

a. Compute a confidence interval estimate of the mean shift time for all postal deliverers.

b. Check to determine whether the required condition for this statistical inference is satisfied.

c. Is there enough evidence to conclude that postal workers are on average spending less than 7 hours per day doing their jobs?

12.152 Xr12-152   In New York City the number of taxis allowed to operate is limited by the municipal government. The number of taxis has remained constant for a number of years. That number is 13,587. Taxi records reveal that the average number of trips per day in 2010 was 27.15. The advent of Uber and Lyft has resulted in a decline in the demand for taxis. A survey of taxi drivers asked each to report the number of trips on an average day. Is there enough evidence to infer that there has been a decrease in the number of trips per day among New York City taxis?

12.153 Xr12-153   The manager of a branch of a major bank wants to improve service and is thinking about giving $1 to any customer who waits in line for a period of time that is considered excessive. (The bank ultimately decided that more than 8 minutes is excessive.) However, to get a better idea about the level of current service, the bank undertook a survey of customers. A student was hired to measure the time spent waiting in line by a random sample of 50 customers. Using a stopwatch, the student determined the amount of time between the time the customer joined the line and the time they reached the teller. The times were recorded. Construct a confidence interval estimate of the mean waiting time for the bank's customers.

12.154 Xr12-154   Obesity is defined as having a body mass index over 30, where BMI = kilograms/height^2 (where height is measured in meters). A physician took a random sample of American adults (18 and over) and classified their BMI as either: 1: Under 20, 2: 20–30, 3: Over 30. There are 255,200,373

CASE 12.2	**Pepsi's Exclusivity Agreement with a University: The Coke Side of the Equation**

DATA
C12-01

While the executives of Pepsi Cola are trying to decide what to do, the university informs them that a similar offer has gone out to the Coca-Cola Company. Furthermore, if both companies want exclusive rights, a bidding war will take

place. The executives at Pepsi would like to know how likely it is that Coke will want exclusive rights under the conditions outlined by the university.

Perform a similar analysis to the one you did in Case 12.1, but

this time from Coke's point of view. Is it likely that Coke will want to conclude an exclusivity agreement with the university? Discuss the reasons for your conclusions.

CASE 12.3	**Estimating Total Medical Costs**

DATA
C12-03

Virtually all countries have universal government-run health care systems. The United States is one notable exception. This is an issue in every election, with some politicians pushing for the United States to adopt a program similar to Canada's.

In Canada, hospitals are financed and administered by provincial governments. Physicians are paid by the government for each patient service. As a result, Canadians pay nothing for these services. The revenues that support the system are derived through income taxes, corporate taxes, and sales taxes. Despite higher taxes in Canada than those in the United States, the system is chronically underfunded,

resulting in long waiting times for, sometimes, critical procedures. For example, in some provinces, newly diagnosed cancer victims must wait several weeks before treatments can begin. Virtually everyone agrees that more money is needed. No one can agree however, on how much is needed. Unfortunately, the problem is going to worsen. Canada, like the United States, has an aging population because of the large numbers of so-called baby boomers (those born between 1946 and 1966), and because medical costs are generally higher for older people.

One of the first steps in addressing the problem is to forecast

medical costs, particularly for the 20-year period starting when the first baby boomers reached age 60 (in 2006). A statistics practitioner has been given the task of making these predictions. Accordingly, random samples of four groups of Canadians were drawn. They are

Group	Ages
1	45–64
2	65–74
3	75–84
4	85+

The medical expenses for the previous 12 months were recorded and stored in columns A to D, respectively, in C12-03.

Age Category	2028	2033	2038
45–64	9,970	10,172	10,671
65–74	4,804	4,873	4,621
75–84	2,987	3,536	4,042
85+	1,095	1,429	1,793

Source: Statistics Canada.

Projections for 2028, 2033, and 2038 of the numbers of Canadians (in thousands) in each age category are listed here.

a. Determine the 95% confidence interval estimates of the mean medical costs for each of the four age categories.

b. For each year listed, determine 95% confidence interval estimates of the total medical costs for Canadians 45 years old and older.

CASE 12.4   Estimating the Number of Alzheimer's Cases

As the U.S. population ages, the number of people needing medical care increases. Unless a cure is found in the next decade, one of the most expensive diseases requiring such care is Alzheimer's, a form of dementia.

To estimate the total number of Alzheimer's cases in the future, a survey was undertaken. The survey determined the age bracket where 1 = 65–74, 2 = 75–84, 3 = 85 and over and whether the individual had Alzheimer's (1 = no and 2 = yes).

(Adapted from the Alzheimer's Association, www.alz.org.)

Here are the projections for the number of Americans (thousands) in each of the three age categories.

DATA
C12-04

Age Category	2025	2030	2035	2040
65–74	37,093	39,227	38,162	36,644
75–84	21,345	25,750	29,162	31,067
85+	7,482	9,131	11,908	14,634

Source: United States Census.

a. Determine the 95% confidence interval estimates of the proportion of Alzheimer's patients in each of the three age categories.

b. For each year listed, determine 95% confidence interval estimates of the total number of Americans with Alzheimer's disease.

CASE 12.5   Bias in Roulette Betting

The game of roulette consists of a wheel with 38 colored and numbered slots. The numbers are 1 to 36, 0 and 00. Half of the slots numbered 1 to 36 are red and the other half are black. The two "zeros" are green. The wheel is spun and an iron ball is rolled, which eventually comes to rest in one of the slots. Gamblers can make several different kinds of bets. Most players bet on one or more numbers or on

DATA
C12-0

a color (black or red). Here is the layout of the roulette betting table:

```
 0  3  6  9 12 15 18 21 24 27 30 33 36
00  2  5  8 11 14 17 20 23 26 29 32 35
    1  4  7 10 13 16 19 22 25 28 31 34
```

Two statisticians recorded the bets on 904 spins. There were 21,731 bets.

Researchers wanted to use these data to examine *middle bias*, which is the tendency for guessers in multiple-choice exams to select the middle answers. For example, if there are five choices a, b, c, d, and e, guessers will tend to select answer c.

Most players stand on both sides of the betting table so that the middle numbers are 2, 5, 8, 11, 14, 17, 20, 23, 26, 29, 32, and 35.

a. If there is no middle bias, what proportion of the bets will be on 1 of the 12 middle numbers?

b. Conduct a test at the 5% significance level to determine whether middle bias exists.

c. The middle of the middle are the numbers 17 and 20. If there is no middle bias, what proportion of the bets will be either 17 or 20?

d. Test with a 5% significance level to determine whether middle of the middle bias exists.

Source: Maya Bar-Hillel and Ro'I Zultan, "We Sing the Praise of Good Displays: How Gamblers Bet in Casino Roulette," *Chance*, Volume 25, No. 2, 2012.

APPENDIX 12.A / XLSTAT OUTPUT AND INSTRUCTIONS

t-Test of a Mean

Example 12.1

	B	C	D	E	F	G
8	Theoretical mean: 2					
9						
10	Summary statistics:					
11						
12	Variable	Observations	Minimum	Maximum	Mean	Std. deviation
13	Newspaper	148	0.0	4.4	2.18	0.981
14						
15	One-sample t-test / Upper-tailed test:					
16						
17	Difference	0.180				
18	t (Observed value)	2.237				
19	t (Critical value)	1.655				
20	DF	147				
21	p-value (one-tailed)	0.0134				
22	alpha	0.05				

Instructions

1. Type or import the data into one column. (Open Xm12-01.)
2. Click **XLSTAT, Parametric tests**, and **One-sample t-test and z-test**.
3. Check **One sample** under **Data format:** In the **Data** dialog box type the input range (A1:A149). Check **Column labels** if the first row of the data contains the name of the variable. Choose **Range:**, **Sheet**, or **Workbook** depending on where you wish the results to appear. Under **Tests** click **Student's t test**.
4. Click **Options** and choose **Mean 1 > Theoretical mean** in the **Alternative hypothesis** box. Type the **Theoretical mean** (2). Specify the value of α in percent (5) in the **Significance level (%)** box.
5. Click **Outputs** and check **Descriptive statistics** and **Detailed results**.

t-Estimate of a Mean

Example 12.2

	B	C	D	E	F	G
9	Summary statistics:					
10						
11	Variable	Observations	Minimum	Maximum	Mean	Std. deviation
12	Additional Income Tax	198	0.000	66,500	22,415	11,544
13						
14	95% confidence interval on the mean:					
15	20,797	24,033				

Instructions

Follow the instructions above (input range: A1:A199) and at Step 4 select **Mean 1 ≠ Theoretical mean** in the **Alternative hypothesis** box. Enter the **Significance level (%)** (5). Click the **Outputs** tab and check **Descriptive statistics, Detailed results**, and **Confidence interval**.

Test of a Population Variance

Example 12.3

	B	C	D	E	F	G
8	Theoretical variance = 1					
9						
10	Summary statistics:					
11						
12	Variable	Observations	Minimum	Maximum	Mean	Std. deviation
13	Fills	25	997.8	1001.3	999.68	0.796
14						
15	**One-sample variance test / Lower-tailed test (Fills):**					
16						
17	Variance	0.633				
18	Chi-square (Observed value)	15.20				
19	Chi-square (Critical value)	13.85				
20	DF	24				
21	p-value (one-tailed)	0.0852				
22	alpha	0.05				

Instructions

1. Type or import the data into one column. (Open Xm12-03.)
2. Click **XLSTAT, Parametric tests**, and **One-sample variance test**.
3. In the **Data** dialog box type the input range (A1:A26). Check **Column labels** if the first row of the data contains the name of the variable. Choose **Range:, Sheet**, or **Workbook** depending on where you wish the results to appear.
4. Click **Options** and choose **Variance 1 < Theoretical variance** in the **Alternative hypothesis** box. Type the **Theoretical variance** (1). Specify the value of α in percent (1) in the **Significance level (%)** box.
5. Click **Outputs** and check **Descriptive statistics**, and **Detailed results**.

Estimate of a Population Variance

Example 12.4

	B	C	D	E
17	99% confidence interval on the variance:			
18	(0.334, 1.537)			

Instructions

Follow the instructions above. Specify **Variance 1 ≠ Theoretical variance** in the **Alternative hypothesis** box. Enter the **Significance level (%)** (1). Click **Outputs** and check **Descriptive statistics, Detailed results**, and **Confidence interval**.

Test of a Proportion

Example 12.5

	B	C	D
12	Frequency: 407		
13	Sample size: 765		
14	Test proportion: 0.5		
15	Hypothesized difference (D): 0		
16	Proportion:	0.532	
17			
18	z-test for one proportion / Upper-tailed test:		
19			
20	Difference	0.032	
21	z (Observed value)	1.772	
22	z (Critical value)	1.645	
23	p-value (one-tailed)	0.0382	
24	alpha	0.05	

Instructions

1. Type or import the data into one column. (Open Xm12-05.) Calculate the number of "successes" and the sample size.

2. Click **XLSTAT, Parametric tests**, and **Tests for one proportion**. (Author's note: we find XLSTAT's terminology confusing. However, these instructions will produce the correct result.)

3. Type the **Frequency** (number of successes) (407) and the **Sample size** (765). Type the **Test proportion** (.5). Select **Frequency** under **Data format:** Check the **z-test**.

4. Click the **Options** tab and select **Proportion – Test proportion > D** in the **Alternative hypothesis** box. Type the **Hypothesized difference (D)** (0).

Estimate of a Proportion

Chapter-Opening Example

	B	C	D	E	F
12	Frequency: 137				
13	Sample size: 2346				
14					
15	Proportion	0.058			
16					
17	95% confidence interval on the proportion (Wald):				
18	(0.0489,	(0.0679,			

Instructions

1. Open the GSS2018 file and count the number of 3s and 4s in Column X. There are 53 3s and 84 4s. Thus, there are 137 "successes." Determine the sample size. It is 2346.

2. Click **XLSTAT**, **Parametric tests**, and **Tests for one proportion**.

3. Enter the **Frequency** (137) and **Sample size** (2346). Select Frequency under **Data format**. Check **z-test**.

4. Click the **Options** tab and in the **Alternative hypothesis** box select **Proportion - test proportion ≠ D**. Set the **Significance level (%)** (5). Check **Variance (confidence interval): Sample** and check **Wald**.

APPENDIX 12.B / STATA OUTPUT AND INSTRUCTIONS

t-Test of a Mean

Example 12.1

```
One-sample t test

Variable      Obs       Mean    Std. Err.   Std. Dev.   [95% Conf. Interval]

Newspa~r      148    2.180405    .0806508    .9811599    2.021021    2.33979

    mean = mean(Newspaper)                                  t =   2.2369
Ho: mean = 2                                degrees of freedom =      147

    Ha: mean < 2                 Ha: mean != 2                 Ha: mean > 2
 Pr(T < t) = 0.9866       Pr(|T| > |t|) = 0.0268       Pr(T > t) = 0.0134
```

The printout shows the two-tail test and both one-tail tests. The test statistic is t = 2.2369 and the right-tail p-value is Pr(T>t) = .0134.

Instructions

1. Import the data into one column. (Click File/Import /Excel spreadsheet (*xls,*xlsx)/Chapter12/Xm12-01.) Check **Import first row as variable names**.
2. Click **Statistics, Summaries, tables and tests, Classical tests of hypotheses**, and **t-test (mean-comparison test)**.
3. Select **One-sample**, select **Newspaper** in the **Variable name:** box, and type 2 in the **Hypothesized mean:** box.

t-Estimate of a Mean

Example 12.2

```
One-sample t test

Variable      Obs       Mean    Std. Err.   Std. Dev.   [95% Conf. Interval]

Additi~x      198    22415.26    820.3915    11543.93    20797.38    24033.13

    mean = mean(AdditionalIncomeTax)                        t =  27.3226
Ho: mean = 0                                degrees of freedom =      197

    Ha: mean < 0                 Ha: mean != 0                 Ha: mean > 0
 Pr(T < t) = 1.0000       Pr(|T| > |t|) = 0.0000       Pr(T > t) = 0.0000
```

LCL = 20,797.38, UCL = 24,033.13

Instructions

1. Import the data into one column. (Click File/Import /Excel spreadsheet (*xls,*xlsx)/Chapter12/Xm12-02.) Check **Import first row as variable names**.

2. Click **Statistics, Summaries, tables and tests, Classical tests of hypotheses**, and **t-test (mean-comparison test)**.

3. Select **One-sample**, select **AdditionalIncomeTax** in the **Variable name:** box, and type any value in the **Hypothesized mean:** box since we're only interested in the confidence interval estimate. Select 95 in the **Confidence level** box.

Test and Estimate of a Population Variance

Example 12.3

```
One-sample test of variance

Variable │    Obs      Mean    Std. Err.    Std. Dev.    [95% Conf. Interval]
─────────┼──────────────────────────────────────────────────────────────────
   Fills │     25    999.68    .1591645    .7958224    999.3515     1000.008

       sd = sd(Fills)                                 c = chi2 =   15.2000
   Ho: sd = 1                              degrees of freedom =        24

       Ha: sd < 1                Ha: sd != 1                 Ha: sd > 1
   Pr(C < c) = 0.0852      2*Pr(C < c) = 0.1705        Pr(C > c) = 0.9148
```

Note: This version (Version 16) prints the confidence interval estimate of the mean, not the variance! Moreover it lists the parameter as the standard deviation (sd).

The test statistic is $\chi^2 = 15.2000$ and the one-tail (left-tail) p-value = $Pr(C < c)$ = .0852.

Instructions

1. Import or type the data into one column. (Click File/Import /Excel spreadsheet (*xls,*xlsx)/Chapter12/Xm12-03.) Check **Import first row as variable names**.

2. Click **Statistics, Summaries, tables and tests, Classical tests of hypotheses**, and **Variance-comparison test**.

3. Select **One-sample**, select **Fills** in the **Variable name:** box, and type 1 in the **Hypothesized standard deviation:** box.

Note that Stata lists the parameter as the standard deviation (sd). In future tests of the population variance, you will have to calculate the square root of the variance to input the appropriate value of the standard deviation. For example, if we want to test $\sigma^2 = 4$, type 2 in the **Hypothesized standard deviation:** box.

Test of a Proportion

Example 12.5

```
One-sample test of proportion                    Number of obs    =       765

      Variable      Mean    Std. Err.                  [95% Conf. Interval]

        Rvotes   .5320261    .0180404                   .4966676     .5673847

      p = proportion(Rvotes)                                    z =     1.7716
    Ho: p = 0.5

        Ha: p < 0.5                  Ha: p != 0.5                 Ha: p > 0.5
    Pr(Z < z) = 0.9618         Pr(|Z| > |z|) = 0.0765        Pr(Z > z) = 0.0382
```

As is the case with inference about a mean, Stata prints the confidence interval estimate:

LCL = .4966676, UCL = .5673847

The test statistic is z = 1.7716 and the right-tail p-value is Pr(Z > z) = .0382.

Instructions

Converting the data into 0-1 format

The data must be in 0-1 format where 1 represents a success. In this example, we're looking to compute the number of Republican votes where 2 = Republican and 1 = Democrat. You can convert the data in two ways.

Excel

In Xm12-05, the variable "Votes" is in column A, rows 2 to 766. In the first empty column, say column E, in cell E2 type

= if (A2 = 2,1,0)

which instructs Excel to store a 1 in cell E2 if A2 contains a 2. If not, a 0 will be stored in E2. Drag to complete the column. For Stata you will have to save the changes in Xm12-05. Thus, when you import the data, the new variable will be included.

Stata

1. In Stata, import the data as is. (Click File/Import /Excel spreadsheet (*xls,*xlsx)/ Chapter12/Xm12-05.) Check **Import first row as variable names**.
2. Click **Data, Create or change data**, and **Create new variables**. In the **Variable name** box, make up a name. We chose Rvotes. In the **Specify a value or an expression** box type Votes==2. Click **OK**. This produces a logical operation that tells Stata to convert 2s into 1s and 1s into 0s. The expression Votes==2 means that when the value of Votes is 2, the expression is true and converts the 2 in Votes

to a 1 in Rvotes. If the expression is not true, that is, the value of Votes is 1, then a 0 will be placed in Rvotes. This operation has the same result as the entry If (A2 = 2,1,0) in Excel.

Testing the Proportion

1. Click **Statistics, Summaries, tables, and tests, Classical tests of hypotheses**, and **Proportion test**.
2. Select **One-sample**. In the **Variable:** box select **Rvotes**. Type .5 in the Hypothesized proportion.

Estimate of a Proportion

Chapter-Opening Example

WRKSTAT	Freq.	Percent	Cum.
1	1,134	48.34	48.34
2	259	11.04	59.38
3	53	2.26	61.64
4	84	3.58	65.22
5	445	18.97	84.19
6	81	3.45	87.64
7	242	10.32	97.95
8	48	2.05	100.00
Total	2,346	100.00	

Instructions

The easiest way to produce a confidence interval estimate of a proportion in this example is to count the number of each value.

1. Import or type the data into one column. (Click File/Import /Excel spreadsheet (*xls,*xlsx)/GSS2018.) Check **Import first row as variable names**.
2. Click **Statistics, Summaries, tables and tests**, **Frequency tables** and **One-way table**.
3. Select **WRSTAT** in the **Categorical variable** box.
4. There are 53 3s and 84 4s. Thus, there are 137 "successes." The sample size is 2,346. The sample proportion is 137/2,346 = .0584.

One-sample test of proportion			x: Number of obs =	2346
	Mean	Std. Err.	[95% Conf. Interval]	
x	.0584	.0048415	.0489109	.0678891

LCL = .0489109, UCL = .0678891

Instructions

1. Click **Statistics, Summaries, tables and tests, Classical tests of hypotheses**, and **Proportion test calculator**.

2. Select **One-sample**. Type the **Sample size** 2346 and the **Sample proportion** .0584. Type any fraction for the **Hypothesized proportion** and select the **Confidence level** 95.

Pressmaster/Shutterstock.com

INFERENCE ABOUT COMPARING TWO POPULATIONS

General Social Survey

Comparing 2010 and 2018: Has there been a decrease in entrepreneurial drive in the United States in the last eight years?

DATA
GSS2010
GSS2018

Small businesses in the United States are extremely important to the well-being of the economy. There are about 30 million small businesses in the United States, where small business is defined as one with less than

KamiGami/Shutterstock.com

On page 514, you will find our answer.

(Continued)

455

500 employees. Businesses with less than 20 employees account for almost 90% of all businesses in the country. Small businesses create 1.5 million new jobs annually. Many of these companies start with an individual working for themselves. Thus, any decrease in Americans' plans to work for themselves will adversely affect the economy. The General Social Survey asked respondents whether they worked for themselves (WRKSLF: 1 = Yes, 2 = No). Is there enough statistical evidence to infer that the proportion of Americans working for themselves decreased between 2010 and 2018?

INTRODUCTION

We can compare learning how to use statistical techniques to learning how to drive a car. We began by describing what you are going to do in this course (Chapter 1) and then presented the essential background material (Chapters 2–9). Learning the concepts of statistical inference and applying them the way we did in Chapters 10 and 11 is akin to driving a car in an empty parking lot. You're driving, but it's not a realistic experience. Learning Chapter 12 is like driving on a quiet side street with little traffic. The experience represents real driving, but many of the difficulties have been eliminated. In this chapter, you begin to drive for real, with many of the actual problems faced by licensed drivers, and the experience prepares you to tackle the next difficulty.

In this chapter, we present a variety of techniques used to compare two populations. In Sections 13-1 and 13-3, we deal with interval variables; the parameter of interest is the difference between two means. The difference between these two sections introduces yet another factor that determines the correct statistical method—the design of the experiment used to gather the data. In Section 13-1, the samples are independently drawn, whereas in Section 13-3, the samples are taken from a matched pairs experiment. In Section 13-2, we discuss the difference between observational and experimental data, a distinction that is critical to the way in which we interpret statistical results.

Section 13-4 presents the procedures employed to infer whether two population variances differ. The parameter is the ratio σ_1^2/σ_2^2. (When comparing two variances, we use the ratio rather than the difference because of the nature of the sampling distribution.)

Section 13-5 addresses the problem of comparing two populations of nominal data. The parameter to be tested and estimated is the difference between two proportions.

13-1 / INFERENCE ABOUT THE DIFFERENCE BETWEEN TWO MEANS: INDEPENDENT SAMPLES

In order to test and estimate the difference between two population means, the statistics practitioner draws random samples from each of two populations. In this section, we discuss independent samples. In Section 13-3, where we present the matched pairs experiment, the distinction between independent samples and matched pairs will be made clear. For now, we define independent samples as samples completely unrelated to one another.

Figure 13.1 depicts the sampling process. Observe that we draw a sample of size n_1 from population 1 and a sample of size n_2 from population 2. For each sample, we compute the sample means and sample variances.

FIGURE **13.1** **Independent Samples from Two Populations**

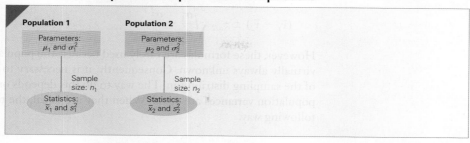

The best estimator of the difference between two population means, $\mu_1 - \mu_2$, is the difference between two sample means, $\bar{x}_1 - \bar{x}_2$. In Section 9-1, we introduced the central limit theorem, which states that in repeated sampling from a normal population whose mean is μ and whose standard deviation is σ, the sampling distribution of the sample mean is normal with mean μ and standard deviation $\sigma/\sqrt{n}$. Statisticians have shown that the difference between two independent normal random variables is also normally distributed. Thus, the difference between two sample means $\bar{x}_1 - \bar{x}_2$ is normally distributed if both populations are normal. By using the laws of expected value and variance, we derive the expected value, variance, and standard deviation (called the standard error) of the **sampling distribution** of $\bar{x}_1 - \bar{x}_2$.

Sampling Distribution of $\bar{x}_1 - \bar{x}_2$

1. $\bar{x}_1 - \bar{x}_2$ is normally distributed if the populations are normal and approximately normal if the populations are nonnormal and the sample sizes are large.

2. The expected value of $\bar{x}_1 - \bar{x}_2$ is

$$E(\bar{x}_1 - \bar{x}_2) = \mu_1 - \mu_2$$

3. The variance of $\bar{x}_1 - \bar{x}_2$ is

$$V(\bar{x}_1 - \bar{x}_2) = \frac{\sigma_1^2}{n_1} + \frac{\sigma_2^2}{n_2}$$

The standard error of $\bar{x}_1 - \bar{x}_2$ is

$$\sqrt{\frac{\sigma_1^2}{n_1} + \frac{\sigma_2^2}{n_2}}$$

Thus,

$$z = \frac{(\bar{x}_1 - \bar{x}_2) - (\mu_1 - \mu_2)}{\sqrt{\dfrac{\sigma_1^2}{n_1} + \dfrac{\sigma_2^2}{n_2}}}$$

is a standard normal (or approximately normal) random variable. It follows that the test statistic is

$$z = \frac{(\bar{x}_1 - \bar{x}_2) - (\mu_1 - \mu_2)}{\sqrt{\dfrac{\sigma_1^2}{n_1} + \dfrac{\sigma_2^2}{n_2}}}$$

The interval estimator is

$$(\bar{x}_1 - \bar{x}_2) \pm z_{\alpha/2} \sqrt{\frac{\sigma_1^2}{n_1} + \frac{\sigma_2^2}{n_2}}$$

However, these formulas are rarely used because the population variances σ_1^2 and σ_2^2 are virtually always unknown. Consequently, it is necessary to estimate the standard error of the sampling distribution. The way to do this depends on whether the two unknown population variances are equal. When they are equal, the test statistic is defined in the following way.

Test Statistic for $\mu_1 - \mu_2$ When $\sigma_1^2 = \sigma_2^2$

$$t = \frac{(\bar{x}_1 - \bar{x}_2) - (\mu_1 - \mu_2)}{\sqrt{s_p^2\left(\frac{1}{n_1} + \frac{1}{n_2}\right)}} \qquad v = n_1 + n_2 - 2$$

where

$$s_p^2 = \frac{(n_1 - 1)s_1^2 + (n_2 - 1)s_2^2}{n_1 + n_2 - 2}$$

The quantity s_p^2 is called the **pooled variance estimator**. It is the weighted average of the two sample variances with the number of degrees of freedom in each sample used as weights. The requirement that the population variances be equal makes this calculation feasible because we need only one estimate of the common value of σ_1^2 and σ_2^2. It makes sense for us to use the pooled variance estimator because, in combining both samples, we produce a better estimate.

The test statistic is Student t distributed with $n_1 + n_2 - 2$ degrees of freedom, provided that the two populations are normal. The confidence interval estimator is derived by mathematics that by now has become routine.

Confidence Interval Estimator of $\mu_1 - \mu_2$ When $\sigma_1^2 = \sigma_2^2$

$$(\bar{x}_1 - \bar{x}_2) \pm t_{\alpha/2} \sqrt{s_p^2\left(\frac{1}{n_1} + \frac{1}{n_2}\right)} \qquad v = n_1 + n_2 - 2$$

We will refer to these formulas as the **equal-variances test statistic** and **confidence interval estimator**, respectively.

When the population variances are unequal, we cannot use the pooled variance estimate. Instead, we estimate each population variance with its sample variance. Unfortunately, the sampling distribution of the resulting statistic

$$\frac{(\bar{x}_1 - \bar{x}_2) - (\mu_1 - \mu_2)}{\sqrt{\frac{s_1^2}{n_1} + \frac{s_2^2}{n_2}}}$$

is neither normally nor Student t distributed. However, it can be approximated by a Student t distribution with degrees of freedom equal to

$$\nu = \frac{(s_1^2/n_1 + s_2^2/n_2)^2}{\dfrac{(s_1^2/n_1)^2}{n_1 - 1} + \dfrac{(s_2^2/n_2)^2}{n_2 - 1}}$$

(It is usually necessary to round this number to the nearest integer.) The test statistic and confidence interval estimator are easily derived from the sampling distribution.

Test Statistic for $\mu_1 - \mu_2$ When $\sigma_1^2 \neq \sigma_2^2$

$$t = \frac{(\bar{x}_1 - \bar{x}_2) - (\mu_1 - \mu_2)}{\sqrt{\left(\dfrac{s_1^2}{n_1} + \dfrac{s_2^2}{n_2}\right)}} \qquad \nu = \frac{(s_1^2/n_1 + s_2^2/n_2)^2}{\dfrac{(s_1^2/n_1)^2}{n_1 - 1} + \dfrac{(s_2^2/n_2)^2}{n_2 - 1}}$$

Confidence Interval Estimator of $\mu_1 - \mu_2$ When $\sigma_1^2 \neq \sigma_2^2$

$$(\bar{x}_1 - \bar{x}_2) \pm t_{\alpha/2} \sqrt{\left(\dfrac{s_1^2}{n_1} + \dfrac{s_2^2}{n_2}\right)} \qquad \nu = \frac{(s_1^2/n_1 + s_2^2/n_2)^2}{\dfrac{(s_1^2/n_1)^2}{n_1 - 1} + \dfrac{(s_2^2/n_2)^2}{n_2 - 1}}$$

We will refer to these formulas as the **unequal-variances test statistic** and **confidence interval estimator**, respectively.

The question naturally arises, How do we know when the population variances are equal? The answer is that because σ_1^2 and σ_2^2 are unknown, we can't know for certain whether they're equal. However, we can perform a statistical test to determine whether there is evidence to infer that the population variances differ. We conduct the F-test of the ratio of two variances, which we briefly present here and save the details for Section 13-4.

Testing the Population Variances

The hypotheses to be tested are

$$H_0: \quad \sigma_1^2/\sigma_2^2 = 1$$

$$H_1: \quad \sigma_1^2/\sigma_2^2 \neq 1$$

The test statistic is the ratio of the sample variances s_1^2/s_2^2, which is F-distributed with degrees of freedom $v_1 = n_1 - 1$ and $v_2 = n_2 - 1$. Recall that we introduced the F distribution in Section 8-4. The required condition is the same as that for the t-test of $\mu_1 - \mu_2$, which is that both populations are normally distributed.

> This is a two-tail test so that the rejection region is
>
> $$F > F_{\alpha/2,\nu_1,\nu_2} \qquad \text{or} \qquad F < F_{1-\alpha/2,\nu_1,\nu_2}$$
>
> Put simply, we will reject the null hypothesis that states that the population variances are equal when the ratio of the sample variances is large or if it is small. Table 6 in Appendix B, which lists the critical values of the F-distribution, defines "large" and "small."

13-1a Decision Rule: Equal-Variances or Unequal-Variances t-Tests and Estimators

Recall that we can never have enough statistical evidence to conclude that the null hypothesis is true. This means that we can only determine whether there is enough evidence to infer that the population variances *differ*. Accordingly, we adopt the following rule: We will use the equal-variances test statistic and confidence interval estimator unless there is evidence (based on the F-test of the population variances) to indicate that the population variances are unequal, in which case we will apply the unequal-variances test statistic and confidence interval estimator.

EXAMPLE 13.1*

DATA
Xm13-01

Direct and Broker-Purchased Mutual Funds

Millions of investors buy mutual funds (see page 175 for a description of mutual funds), choosing from thousands of possibilities. Some funds can be purchased directly from banks or other financial institutions whereas others must be purchased through brokers, who charge a fee for this service. This raises the question, Can investors do better by buying mutual funds directly than by purchasing mutual funds through brokers? To help answer this question, a group of researchers randomly sampled the annual returns from mutual funds that can be acquired directly and mutual funds that are bought through brokers and recorded the net annual returns, which are the returns on investment after deducting all relevant fees. These are listed next.

Direct					Broker				
9.33	4.68	4.23	14.69	10.29	3.24	3.71	16.4	4.36	9.43
6.94	3.09	10.28	−2.97	4.39	−6.76	13.15	6.39	−11.07	8.31
16.17	7.26	7.1	10.37	−2.06	12.8	11.05	−1.9	9.24	−3.99
16.97	2.05	−3.09	−0.63	7.66	11.1	−3.12	9.49	−2.67	−4.44
5.94	13.07	5.6	−0.15	10.83	2.73	8.94	6.7	8.97	8.63
12.61	0.59	5.27	0.27	14.48	−0.13	2.74	0.19	1.87	7.06
3.33	13.57	8.09	4.59	4.8	18.22	4.07	12.39	−1.53	1.57
16.13	0.35	15.05	6.38	13.12	−0.8	5.6	6.54	5.23	−8.44
11.2	2.69	13.21	−0.24	−6.54	−5.75	−0.85	10.92	6.87	−5.72
1.14	18.45	1.72	10.32	−1.06	2.59	−0.28	−2.15	−1.69	6.95

Can we conclude at the 5% significance level that directly purchased mutual funds outperform mutual funds bought through brokers?

---

*Source: D. Bergstresser, J. Chalmers, and P. Tufano, "Assessing the Costs and Benefits of Brokers in the Mutual Fund Industry."

SOLUTION:

IDENTIFY

To answer the question, we need to compare the population of returns from direct and the returns from broker-bought mutual funds. The data are obviously interval (we've recorded real numbers). This problem objective–data type combination tells us that the parameter to be tested is the difference between two means, $\mu_1 - \mu_2$. The hypothesis to be tested is that the mean net annual return from directly purchased mutual funds (μ_1) is larger than the mean of broker-purchased funds (μ_2). Hence, the alternative hypothesis is

$$H_1: \quad (\mu_1 - \mu_2) > 0$$

As usual, the null hypothesis automatically follows:

$$H_0: \quad (\mu_1 - \mu_2) = 0$$

To decide which of the t-tests of $\mu_1 - \mu_2$ to apply, we conduct the F-test of σ_1^2/σ_2^2.

$$H_0: \quad \sigma_1^2/\sigma_2^2 = 1$$
$$H_1: \quad \sigma_1^2/\sigma_2^2 \neq 1$$

COMPUTE

MANUALLY:

From the data, we calculated the following statistics:

$$s_1^2 = 37.49 \quad \text{and} \quad s_2^2 = 43.34$$

Test statistic: $F = s_1^2/s_2^2 = 37.49/43.34 = 0.86$

Rejection region: $F > F_{\alpha/2, \nu_1, \nu_2} = F_{.025,49,49} \approx F_{.025,50,50} = 1.75$

or

$$F < F_{1-\alpha/2, \nu_1, \nu_2} = F_{.975,49,49} = 1/F_{.025,49,49} \approx 1/F_{.025,50,50} = 1/1.75 = .57$$

Because $F = .86$ is not greater than 1.75 or smaller than .57, we cannot reject the null hypothesis.

EXCEL Data Analysis

	A	B	C
1	F-Test: Two-Sample for Variances		
2			
3		*Direct*	*Broker*
4	Mean	6.63	3.72
5	Variance	37.49	43.34
6	Observations	50	50
7	df	49	49
8	F	0.8650	
9	P(F<=f) one-tail	0.3068	
10	F Critical one-tail	0.6222	

The value of the test statistic is $F = .8650$. Excel outputs the one-tail p-value. Because we're conducting a two-tail test, we double that value. Thus, the p-value of the test we're conducting is $2 \times .3068 = .6136$.

INSTRUCTIONS

1. Type or import the data into two columns. (Open Xm13-01.)

2. Click **Data, Data Analysis**, and **F-test Two-Sample for Variances**.

3. Specify the **Variable 1 Range** (A1:A51) and the **Variable 2 Range** (B1:B51). Type a value for α (.05).

INTERPRET

There is not enough evidence to infer that the population variances differ. It follows that we must apply the equal-variances t-test of $\mu_1 - \mu_2$.

The hypotheses are

$$H_0: \ (\mu_1 - \mu_2) = 0$$
$$H_1: \ (\mu_1 - \mu_2) > 0$$

COMPUTE

MANUALLY:

From the data, we calculated the following statistics:

$$\bar{x}_1 = 6.63$$
$$\bar{x}_2 = 3.72$$
$$s_1^2 = 37.49$$
$$s_2^2 = 43.34$$

The pooled variance estimator is

$$s_p^2 = \frac{(n_1 - 1)s_1^2 + (n_2 - 1)s_2^2}{n_1 + n_2 - 2}$$
$$= \frac{(50 - 1)37.49 + (50 - 1)43.34}{50 + 50 - 2}$$
$$= 40.42$$

The number of degrees of freedom of the test statistic is

$$\nu = n_1 + n_2 - 2 = 50 + 50 - 2 = 98$$

The rejection region is

$$t > t_{\alpha,\nu} = t_{.05,98} \approx t_{.05,100} = 1.660$$

We determine that the value of the test statistic is

$$t = \frac{(\bar{x}_1 - \bar{x}_2) - (\mu_1 - \mu_2)}{\sqrt{s_p^2\left(\frac{1}{n_1} + \frac{1}{n_2}\right)}}$$

$$= \frac{(6.63 - 3.72) - 0}{\sqrt{40.42\left(\frac{1}{50} + \frac{1}{50}\right)}}$$

$$= 2.29$$

EXCEL Data Analysis

	A	B	C
1	t-Test: Two-Sample Assuming Equal Variances		
2			
3		Direct	Broker
4	Mean	6.63	3.72
5	Variance	37.49	43.34
6	Observations	50	50
7	Pooled Variance	40.41	
8	Hypothesized Mean Difference	0	
9	df	98	
10	t Stat	2.29	
11	P(T<=t) one-tail	0.0122	
12	t Critical one-tail	1.6606	
13	P(T<=t) two-tail	0.0243	
14	t Critical two-tail	1.9845	

INSTRUCTIONS

1. Type or import the data into two columns. (Open Xm13-01.)

2. Click **Data, Data Analysis**, and **t-Test: Two-Sample Assuming Equal Variances**.

3. Specify the **Variable 1 Range** (A1:A51) and the **Variable 2 Range** (B1:B51). Type the value of the **Hypothesized Mean Difference***(0) and type a value for α(.05).

INTERPRET

The value of the test statistic is 2.29. The one-tail p-value is .0122. We observe that the p-value of the test is small (and the test statistic falls into the rejection region). As a result, we conclude that there is sufficient evidence to infer that on average directly purchased mutual funds outperform broker-purchased mutual funds.

Estimating $\mu_1 - \mu_2$: Equal-Variances

In addition to testing a value of the difference between two population means, we can also estimate the difference between means. Next we compute the 95% confidence interval estimate of the difference between the mean return for direct and broker mutual funds.

---

*This term is technically incorrect. Because we're testing $\mu_1 - \mu_2$, Excel should ask for and output the "Hypothesized Difference between Means."

COMPUTE

MANUALLY:

The confidence interval estimator of the difference between two means with equal population variances is

$$(\bar{x}_1 - \bar{x}_2) \pm t_{\alpha/2}\sqrt{s_p^2\left(\frac{1}{n_1} + \frac{1}{n_2}\right)}$$

The 95% confidence interval estimate of the difference between the return for directly purchased mutual funds and the mean return for broker-purchased mutual funds is

$$(\bar{x}_1 - \bar{x}_2) \pm t_{\alpha/2}\sqrt{s_p^2\left(\frac{1}{n_1} + \frac{1}{n_2}\right)} = (6.63 - 3.72) \pm 1.984\sqrt{40.42\left(\frac{1}{50} + \frac{1}{50}\right)}$$

$$= 2.91 \pm 2.52$$

The lower and upper limits are .39 and 5.43.

EXCEL Workbook

	A	B	C	D	E	F
1	t-Estimate of the Difference Between Two Means (Equal-Variances)					
2						
3		Sample 1	Sample 2	Confidence Interval Estimate		
4	Mean	6.63	3.72	2.91	±	2.52
5	Variance	37.49	43.34	Lower confidence limit		0.39
6	Sample size	50	50	Upper confidence limit		5.43
7	Pooled Variance	40.42				
8	Confidence level	0.95				

INSTRUCTIONS

Type or import the data into two columns (Open Xm13-01). Calculate the mean and variance for each sample. Open the **Estimators Workbook** and select the **t-Estimate_2 Means (Eq-Var)** tab. Type the means, variances, sample sizes, and the confidence level.

INTERPRET

We estimate that the return on directly purchased mutual funds is on average between .39 and 5.43 percentage points larger than broker-purchased mutual funds.

EXAMPLE 13.2†

DATA
Xm13–02

Effect of New CEO in Family-Run Businesses

What happens to the family-run business when the boss's son or daughter takes over? Does the business do better after the change if the new boss is the offspring of the owner, or does the business do better when an outsider is made chief executive officer (CEO)? In pursuit of an answer, researchers randomly selected 140 firms, 30% of which passed ownership to an offspring and 70% of which appointed an outsider as CEO. For each

†*Source:* M. Bennedsen and K. Nielsen, Copenhagen Business School and D. Wolfenzon, New York University.

company, the researchers calculated the operating income as a proportion of assets in the year before and the year after the new CEO took over. The change (operating income after − operating income before) in this variable was recorded and is listed next. Do these data allow us to infer that the effect of making an offspring CEO is different from the effect of hiring an outsider as CEO?

Offspring			Outsider						
−1.95	0.91	−3.15	0.69	−1.05	1.58	−2.46	3.33	−1.32	−0.51
0	−2.16	3.27	−0.95	−4.23	−1.98	1.59	3.2	5.93	8.68
0.56	1.22	−0.67	−2.2	−0.16	4.41	−2.03	0.55	−0.45	1.43
1.44	0.67	2.61	2.65	2.77	4.62	−1.69	−1.4	−3.2	−0.37
1.5	−0.39	1.55	5.39	−0.96	4.5	0.55	2.79	5.08	−0.49
1.41	−1.43	−2.67	4.15	1.01	2.37	0.95	5.62	0.23	−0.08
−0.32	−0.48	−1.91	4.28	0.09	2.44	3.06	−2.69	−2.69	−1.16
−1.7	0.24	1.01	2.97	6.79	1.07	4.83	−2.59	3.76	1.04
−1.66	0.79	−1.62	4.11	1.72	−1.11	5.67	2.45	1.05	1.28
−1.87	−1.19	−5.25	2.66	6.64	0.44	−0.8	3.39	0.53	1.74
−1.38	1.89	0.14	6.31	4.75	1.36	1.37	5.89	3.2	−0.14
0.57	−3.7	2.12	−3.04	2.84	0.88	0.72	−0.71	−3.07	−0.82
3.05	−0.31	2.75	−0.42	−2.1	0.33	4.14	4.22	−4.34	0
2.98	−1.37	0.3	−0.89	2.07	−5.96	3.04	0.46	−1.16	2.68

SOLUTION:

IDENTIFY

The objective is to compare two populations, and the data are interval. It follows that the parameter of interest is the difference between two population means $\mu_1 - \mu_2$, where μ_1 is the mean difference for companies where the owner's son or daughter became CEO and μ_2 is the mean difference for companies who appointed an outsider as CEO.

To determine whether to apply the equal or unequal variances t-test, we use the F-test of two variances.

$$H_0: \ \sigma_1^2/\sigma_2^2 = 1$$
$$H_1: \ \sigma_1^2/\sigma_2^2 \neq 1$$

COMPUTE

MANUALLY:

From the data, we calculated the following statistics:

$s_1^2 = 3.79$ and $s_2^2 = 8.03$

Test statistic: $F = s_1^2/s_2^2 = 3.79/8.03 = 0.47$

The degrees of freedom are $\nu_1 = n_1 - 1 = 42 - 1 = 41$ and $\nu_2 = n_2 - 1 = 98 - 1 = 97$.

Rejection region: $F > F_{\alpha/2,\nu_1,\nu_2} = F_{.025,41,97} \approx F_{.025,40,100} = 1.64$

or

$$F < F_{1-\alpha/2,\nu_1,\nu_2} = F_{.975,41,97} \approx 1/F_{.025,97,41} \approx 1/F_{.025,100,40} = 1/1.74 = .57$$

Because $F = .47$ is less than .57, we reject the null hypothesis.

EXCEL Data Analysis

	A	B	C
1	F-Test: Two-Sample for Variances		
2			
3		Offspring	Outsider
4	Mean	−0.10	1.24
5	Variance	3.79	8.03
6	Observations	42	98
7	df	41	97
8	F	0.47	
9	P(F<=f) one-tail	0.0040	
10	F Critical one-tail	0.6314	

The value of the test statistic is $F = .47$, and the p-value $= 2 \times .0040 = .0080$.

INTERPRET

There is enough evidence to infer that the population variances differ. The appropriate technique is the unequal-variances t-test of $\mu_1 - \mu_2$.

Because we want to determine whether there is a *difference* between means, the alternative hypothesis is

$$H_1: \quad (\mu_1 - \mu_2) \neq 0$$

and the null hypothesis is

$$H_0: \quad (\mu_1 - \mu_2) = 0$$

COMPUTE

MANUALLY:

From the data, we calculated the following statistics:

$$\bar{x}_1 = -.10$$
$$\bar{x}_2 = 1.24$$
$$s_1^2 = 3.79$$
$$s_2^2 = 8.03$$

The number of degrees of freedom of the test statistic is

$$\nu = \frac{(s_1^2/n_1 + s_2^2/n_2)^2}{\dfrac{(s_1^2/n_1)^2}{n_1 - 1} + \dfrac{(s_2^2/n_2)^2}{n_2 - 1}}$$

$$= \frac{(3.79/42 + 8.03/98)^2}{\dfrac{(3.79/42)^2}{42 - 1} + \dfrac{(8.03/98)^2}{98 - 1}}$$

$$= 110.69 \text{ rounded to } 111$$

The rejection region is

$$t < -t_{\alpha/2, \nu} = -t_{.025, 111} \approx -t_{.025, 110} = -1.982 \quad \text{or} \quad t > t_{\alpha/2, \nu} = t_{.025, 111} \approx 1.982$$

The value of the test statistic is computed next:

$$t = \frac{(\bar{x}_1 - \bar{x}_2) - (\mu_1 - \mu_2)}{\sqrt{\left(\dfrac{s_1^2}{n_1} + \dfrac{s_2^2}{n_2}\right)}}$$

$$= \frac{(-.10 - 1.24) - (0)}{\sqrt{\left(\dfrac{3.79}{42} + \dfrac{8.03}{98}\right)}} = -3.22$$

EXCEL Data Analysis

	A	B	C
1	t-Test: Two-Sample Assuming Unequal Variances		
2			
3		Offspring	Outsider
4	Mean	−0.10	1.24
5	Variance	3.79	8.03
6	Observations	42	98
7	Hypothesized Mean Difference	0	
8	df	111	
9	t Stat	−3.22	
10	P(T<=t) one-tail	0.0008	
11	t Critical one-tail	1.6587	
12	P(T<=t) two-tail	0.0017	
13	t Critical two-tail	1.9816	

INSTRUCTIONS

Follow the instructions for Example 13.1, except at step 2 click **Data, Data Analysis**, and **t-Test: Two-Sample Assuming Unequal Variances**.

INTERPRET

The t-statistic is -3.22, and its p-value is .0017. Accordingly, we conclude there is sufficient evidence to infer that the mean changes in operating income differ.

Estimating $\mu_1 - \mu_2$: Unequal-Variances

We can also draw inferences about the difference between the two population means by calculating the confidence interval estimator. We use the unequal-variances confidence interval estimator of $\mu_1 - \mu_2$ and a 95% confidence level.

COMPUTE

MANUALLY:

$$(\bar{x}_1 - \bar{x}_2) \pm t_{\alpha/2} \sqrt{\left(\frac{s_1^2}{n_1} + \frac{s_2^2}{n_2}\right)}$$

$$= (-.10 - 1.24) \pm 1.982 \sqrt{\left(\frac{3.79}{42} + \frac{8.03}{98}\right)}$$

$$= -1.34 \pm .82$$

$$\text{LCL} = -2.16 \quad \text{and} \quad \text{UCL} = -.52$$

EXCEL Workbook

	A	B	C	D	E	F
1	t-Estimate of the Difference Between Two Means (Unequal-Variances)					
2						
3		Sample 1	Sample 2	Confidence Interval Estimate		
4	Mean	–0.1	1.2	–1.34	±	0.82
5	Variance	3.79	8.03	Lower confidence limit		-2.16
6	Sample size	42	98	Upper confidence limit		-0.52
7	Degrees of freedom	111				
8	Confidence level	0.95				

INSTRUCTIONS

Follow the instructions for Example 13.1 except use the **t-Estimate_2 Means (Uneq-Var)** tab.

INTERPRET

We estimate that the mean change in operating incomes for outsiders exceeds the mean change in the operating income for offspring by between .52 and 2.16 percentage points.

13-1b Checking the Required Condition

Both the equal-variances and unequal-variances techniques require that the populations be normally distributed.[†] As before, we can check to see whether the requirement is satisfied by drawing the histograms of the data.

To illustrate, we used Excel to create the histograms for Example 13.1 (Figures 13.2 and 13.3) and Example 13.2 (Figures 13.4 and 13.5). Although the histograms are not perfectly bell shaped, it appears that in both examples the data are at least approximately normal. Because this technique is robust, we can be confident in the validity of the results.

FIGURE **13.2** **Histogram of Rates of Return for Directly Purchased Mutual Funds in Example 13.1**

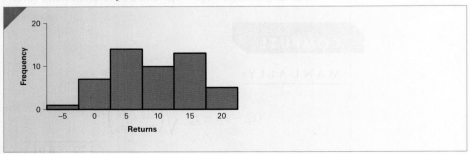

[†]As we pointed out in Chapter 12 large sample sizes can overcome the effects of extreme nonnormality.

FIGURE **13.3**   **Histogram of Rates of Return for Broker-Purchased Mutual Funds in Example 13.1**

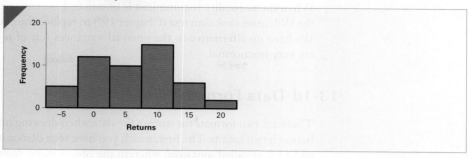

FIGURE **13.4**   **Histogram of Change in Operating Income for Offspring-Run Businesses in Example 13.2**

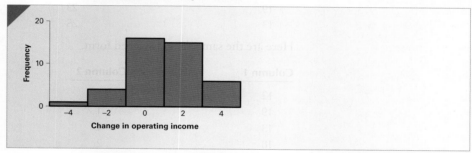

FIGURE **13.5**   **Histogram of Change in Operating Income for Outsider-Run Businesses in Example 13.2**

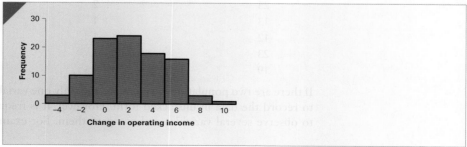

13-1c Violation of the Required Condition

When the normality requirement is unsatisfied, we can use a nonparametric technique: the Wilcoxon rank sum test (Chapter 19*) to replace the equal-variances test of $\mu_1 - \mu_2$. We have no alternative to the unequal-variances test of $\mu_1 - \mu_2$ when the populations are very nonnormal.

13-1d Data Formats

There are two formats for storing the data when drawing inferences about the difference between two means. The first, which you have seen demonstrated in both Examples 13.1 and 13.2, is called *unstacked*, wherein the observations from sample 1 are stored in one column and the observations from sample 2 are stored in a second column. We may also store the data in stacked format. In this format, all the observations are stored in one column. A second column contains the codes, usually 1 and 2, that indicate from which sample the corresponding observation was drawn. Here is an example of unstacked data.

Column 1 (Sample 1)	Column 2 (Sample 2)
12	18
19	23
13	25

Here are the same data in stacked form.

Column 1	Column 2
12	1
19	1
13	1
18	2
23	2
25	2

It should be understood that the data need not be in order. Hence, they could have been stored in this way:

Column 1	Column 2
18	2
25	2
13	1
12	1
23	2
19	1

If there are two populations to compare and only one variable, then it is probably better to record the data in unstacked form. However, it is frequently the case that we want to observe several variables and compare them. For example, suppose that we survey

---

*Instructors who wish to teach the use of nonparametric techniques for testing the difference between two means when the normality requirement is not satisfied should use the online appendixes Introduction to Nonparametric Techniques and Wilcoxon Rank Sum Test and Wilcoxon Signed Rank Sum Test.

payment spend more money on food than do families who used regular income to buy food?

13.22 Xr13-22 The cruise ship business is rapidly increasing. Although cruises have long been associated with seniors, it now appears that younger people are choosing a cruise as their vacation. To determine whether this is true, an executive for a cruise line sampled passengers 2 years ago and this year and determined their ages.

a. Do these data allow the executive to infer that cruise ships are attracting younger customers?

b. Determine a confidence interval estimate of the difference in ages between this year and 2 years ago.

13.23 Xr13-23+ Automobile insurance companies take many factors into consideration when setting rates. These factors include age, marital status, and miles driven per year. To determine the effect of gender, a random sample of young (under 25, with at least 2 years of driving experience) male and female drivers was surveyed. Each was asked how many miles they had driven in the past year. The distances (in thousands of miles) are stored in stacked format (column 1 = Driving distances and column 2 identifies the gender where 1 = Male and 2 = Female).

a. Can we conclude that male and female drivers differ in the numbers of miles driven per year?

b. Calculate a confidence interval estimate of the difference in mean distance driven by male and female drivers.

c. Check to ensure that the required condition(s) of the techniques used in parts (a) and (b) is satisfied.

13.24 Xr13-24 The president of a company that manufactures automobile air conditioners is considering switching the supplier of condensers. Supplier A, the current producer of condensers for the manufacturer, prices its product 5% higher than supplier B. The president wants to maintain the company's reputation for quality and as a result wants to be sure that supplier B's condensers last at least as long as supplier A's. After a careful analysis, the president decided to retain supplier A if there is sufficient statistical evidence that supplier A's condensers last longer on average than supplier B's. In an experiment, 30 midsize cars were equipped with air conditioners using type A condensers while another 30 midsize cars were equipped with type B condensers. The number of miles (in thousands) driven by each car before the condenser broke down was recorded. Should the president retain supplier A?

13.25 Xr13-25 In Canada there are several choices for post-secondary education. The most popular choice

is a university degree; the second most popular is a community college, which tends to emphasize vocational skills such as computer technicians. The third choice is a skilled-trade apprenticeship program such as carpentry. How well does each type of program work for its graduates? A survey was undertaken to answer the question. Random samples of individuals aged between 25 and 64 who had full-time jobs were drawn and asked to report their annual income. The file contains the responses of male apprenticeship program graduates and community college graduates. Do the data provide sufficient evidence to conclude that apprenticeship program graduates earn larger incomes than do community college graduates?

13.26 Xr13-26 Refer to Exercise 13.25. The incomes of university graduates aged between 25 and 64 who hold full-time jobs were recorded. Is there sufficient evidence to conclude that university graduates earn higher incomes than graduates of apprenticeship programs?

13.27 Xr13-27 Refer to Exercise 13.25. Are apprenticeship programs usually chosen by women as successful as the ones chosen by men? The polling company recorded the annual incomes of women who graduated from apprenticeship programs and women who went no further than high school. All were between 25 and 64 and employed full time. Is there enough evidence to conclude that female high school graduates earn more than apprenticeship program graduates?

13.28 Xr13-28 Does everyone have a cell phone? A survey asked heads of households that were born between 1965 and 1980 (Generation X) and households headed by people born after 1980 (Millennials). Each reported the annual expenditures on cellular telephone service. Can we infer from the data that Generation Xers outspend Millennials on cell phone service?

13.29 Xr13-29 We live in an era where old jobs are disappearing and new ones are being created. To judge the extent of this phenomenon, a survey was undertaken in January 2021 that asked currently employed wage and salary workers over the age of 25 how many months they have been employed in their current jobs. From the polling company's records, the data from 2011 were recorded. Is there enough evidence to infer that current wage and salary workers have shorter job tenure than those 10 years ago?

13.30 Xr13-30 A statistics professor is about to select a statistical software package for the course. One of the most important features, according to the professor, is the ease with which students learn to use the software. The selection has been narrowed down to two possibilities: software A, a menu-driven statistical package with some high-powered techniques, and software B, a spreadsheet that has the capability of performing most techniques. To help make the decision, 40 statistics students selected at random were asked to choose one of the two packages. Each student was given a statistics problem to solve by computer and the appropriate manual. The amount of time (in minutes) each student needed to complete the assignment was recorded.

a. Can the professor conclude from these data that the two software packages differ in the amount of time needed to learn how to use them?

b. Compute a confidence interval estimate of the difference in the mean amount of time needed to learn to use the two packages.

c. What are the required conditions for the techniques used in parts (a) and (b)?

d. Check to see whether the required conditions are satisfied.

13.31 Xr13-31 One factor in low productivity is the amount of time wasted by workers. Wasted time includes time spent cleaning up mistakes, waiting for more material and equipment, and performing any other activity not related to production. In a project designed to examine the problem, an operations-management consultant took a survey of 200 workers in companies that were classified as successful (on the basis of their latest annual profits) and another 200 workers from unsuccessful companies. The amount of time (in hours) wasted during a standard 40-hour workweek was recorded for each worker.

a. Do these data provide enough evidence to infer that the amount of time wasted in unsuccessful firms exceeds that of successful ones?

b. Determine a confidence interval estimate of how much more time is wasted in unsuccessful firms than in successful ones.

13.32 Xr13-32 Recent studies seem to indicate that using a cell phone while driving is dangerous. One reason for this is that drivers' reaction time may slow while they are talking on the phone. Researchers at Miami (Ohio) University measured the reaction times of a sample of drivers who owned a cell phone. Some of the sample was tested while on the phone and the rest was tested while not on the phone. Can we conclude that reaction times are slower for drivers using cell phones?

13.33 Xr13-33 Refer to Exercise 13.32. To determine whether the type of phone usage affects reaction times, another study was launched. A group of drivers was asked to participate in a discussion. Some engaged in simple chitchat, and the rest participated in a political discussion. Once again, reaction times were measured. Can we infer that the type of telephone discussion affects reaction times?

13.34 Xr13-34 Most consumers who require someone to perform various professional services undertake research before making their selection. A random sample of people who recently selected a financial planner and a random sample of individuals who chose a stockbroker were asked to report the amount of time they spent researching before deciding. Can we infer that people spend more time researching for a financial planner than they do for a stockbroker?

13.35 Xr13-35 A study by researchers at North Carolina State University found thousands of errors in 12 of the most widely used high school science texts. For example, the Statue of Liberty is left-handed; volume is equal to length multiplied by depth. The books are so bad that Philip Sadler, director of science education at the Harvard-Smithsonian Center for Astrophysics, decided to conduct a study of their effects. The physics marks of college students who had used a textbook in high school and the marks of students who did not have a high school textbook were recorded. Do these data allow us to infer that students without high school textbooks in science outperform students who used textbooks?

13.36 Xr13-36 Between Wendy's and McDonald's, which fast-food drive-through window is faster? To answer the question, a random sample of service times for each restaurant was measured. Can we infer from these data that there are differences in service times between the two chains?

Source: QSR Drive-Thru Time Study.

13.37 Xr13-37 The generation that was born before World War II (born between 1928 and 1945) is called the Silent Generation. Because many experienced the effects of the Great Depression, they tend to be frugal. Examples of behavior include among other things being careful about shutting off lights in empty rooms. A survey of two populations asked respondents to report their electricity expenditures. Can we conclude that the expenditures on electricity for the Silent Generation is lower than expenditures made by Millennials?

13.38 Xr13-38 Appliance manufacturers and retailers need to identify households that are likely customers. A random sample of households was asked to keep track of the amount of money they spend on major appliances (stoves, refrigerators, etc.). The data were recorded for Baby Boomers and Generation X. Can we conclude from the data that households headed by a Generation Xer spend more on major appliances than households headed by a Baby Boomer?

13.39 Xr13-39 Lack of sleep is a serious medical problem. It has been linked to heart attacks and automobile collisions. A Statistics Canada study asked a random sample of Canadian adults to report the amount of sleep they normally get. Can we conclude from the data that men and women differ in the amount of sleep?

13.40 Xr13-40 It is often useful for companies to know who their customers are and how they became customers. In a study of credit card use, random samples were drawn of cardholders who applied for the credit card and credit cardholders who were contacted by telemarketers or by mail. The total purchases made by each last month were recorded. Can we conclude from these data that differences exist on average between the two types of customers?

13.41 Xr13-41 Tire manufacturers are constantly researching ways to produce tires that last longer. New innovations are tested by professional drivers on racetracks. However, any promising inventions are also test-driven by ordinary drivers. The latter tests are closer to what the tire company's customers will actually experience. Suppose that to determine whether a new steel-belted radial tire lasts longer than the company's current model, two new-design tires were installed on the rear wheels of 20 randomly selected cars and two current-design tires were installed on the rear wheels of another 20 cars. All drivers were told to drive in their usual way until the tires wore out. The number of miles (thousands) driven by each driver was recorded. Can the company infer that the new tire will last longer on average than the current-design tire?

13.42 Xr13-42 It is generally believed that salespeople who are paid on a commission basis outperform salespeople who are paid a fixed salary. Some management consultants argue, however, that in certain industries the fixed-salary salesperson may sell more because the consumer will feel less sales pressure and respond to the salesperson less as an antagonist. In an experiment to study this, a random sample of 180 salespeople from a retail clothing chain was selected. Of these, 90 salespeople were paid a fixed salary, and the remaining 90 were paid a commission on each sale. The total dollar amount of 1 month's sales for each was recorded. Can we conclude that the commission salesperson outperforms the fixed salary salesperson?

13.43 Xr13-43 Credit scorecards were designed to be used to help financial institutions make decisions about loan applications. However, some insurance companies have suggested that credit scores could also be used to determine insurance premiums, particularly car insurance. The Massachusetts Public Interest Research Group has come out against this proposal. To acquire more information, a car-insurance company gathered data about a random sample of the company's customers. They recorded whether the individual was involved in an accident in the last 3 years and determined the credit score. Can we infer that there is a difference in scores between those who did and those who did not have accidents in a 3-year period?

13.44 Xr13-44+ Traditionally, wine has been sold in glass bottles with cork stoppers. The stoppers are supposed to keep air out of the bottle because oxygen is the enemy of wine, particularly red wine. Recent research appears to indicate that metal screw caps are more effective in keeping air out of the bottle. However, metal caps are perceived to be inferior and usually associated with cheaper brands of wine. To determine if this perception is wrong, a random sample of 130 people who drink at least one bottle per week on average was asked to participate in an experiment. All were given the same wine in two types of bottles. One group was given a corked bottle, and the other was given a bottle with a metal cap and asked to taste the wine and indicate what they think the retail price of the wine should be. Determine whether there is enough evidence to conclude that bottles of wine with metal caps are perceived to be cheaper.

13.45 Xr13-45 Studies have shown that tired children have trouble learning because neurons become incapable of forming new synaptic connections that are necessary to encode memory. The problem is that the school day starts too early. Awakened at dawn, teenage brains are still releasing melatonin, which makes them sleepy. Several years ago, Edina, Minnesota, changed its high school start from 7:25 A.M. to 8:30 A.M. The SAT scores for a random sample of students taken before the change and a random sample of SAT scores after the change were recorded. Can we infer from the data that SAT scores increased after the change in the school start time?

OVEREATING EXPERIMENTS

Obesity is not only a health problem but it is a financial one as well. Obesity leads to health problems such as diabetes, heart disease, and strokes. These result in increased medical costs to individuals and employers. About one-third of North Americans are obese. Why do we overeat? The reasons are complicated. However, a number of experiments have shed some light on the subject. In most of the experiments, subjects were not aware that an experiment was being conducted. Exercises 13.46 to 13.49 feature some of these experiments.

13.46 Xr13-46 **Stale Popcorn Experiment** Students were invited to watch a newly released movie shortly after lunch. Half the students were given a medium-sized bucket of popcorn and the other half a large-sized bucket. The popcorn was not fresh. In fact, it was five days old and very stale. Both sizes of containers were large enough so that none of the students could finish. At the end of the movie the buckets were weighed and the results recorded. Do these data allow researchers to conclude that the larger the bucket, the more people will eat?

Source: Adapted from Brian Wansink and SeaBum Park, "At the Movies: How External Cues and Perceived Taste Impact Consumption Volume," Food Quality and Preference 12:1 (January 2001): 69–74.

13.47 Xr13-47 **Fake Wine Experiment** Diners at a restaurant were informed on entering that they would be receiving a free glass of wine, which they were told was Cabernet Sauvignon. However, it was not. It was a cheap wine sold for $2 a bottle, popularly known as Two Buck Chuck. Half of the diners were told that the wine was from a new California winery. The other half of diners were informed that the wine they would receive was from a new North Dakota winery. (There are no wineries in North Dakota, and even if there were, the wine produced would not be considered excellent.) The restaurant featured a fixed menu so that all diners had exactly the same meal. The goal of the experiment was to determine whether the perceived quality of the wine affected their dining experience. The amount of food consumed (measured as a percentage of the amount originally served that was consumed by the diner, so that 100 represents diners who cleaned their plates) and the amount of time spent in the restaurant were recorded.

a. Is there enough statistical evidence to infer that diners who believe they are drinking a fine wine (California wine) eat more than diners who believe they are drinking an inferior wine?

b. Can we conclude that diners who believe they are drinking a fine wine (California wine) spend more time in the restaurant than diners who believe they are drinking an inferior wine?

Source: Adapted from Brian Wansink, Collin Payne, and Jill North, "Fine as North Dakota Wine: Sensory Experiences and the Intake of Companion Foods," Physiology and Behavior 90:5 (2007): 712–16.

13.48 Xr13-48 **Super Bowl Chicken Wings Experiment** A group of MBA students was invited to watch a Super Bowl game at a local sports bar. They were promised free chicken wings and free soda drinks. The students loaded up on the wings and when they were finished, could refill their plates. For half the students, waitresses cleared the plates loaded with bones. The other half did not have their bone plates picked up. After the Super Bowl was over, the number of wings consumed by each group of students was recorded. Is there sufficient statistical evidence to infer that people eat more when they are not aware of how much they have already eaten?

Source: Adapted from Brian Wansink and Collin Payne, "Counting Bones: Environmental Cues that Decrease Food Intake," Perceptual and Motor Skills 104 (2007): 273–77.

13.49 Xr13-49 **Bags of M&Ms Experiment** A researcher recruited 40 adults at a PTA meeting and asked them to view a video. To thank them for their participation, 20 adults were given a one-pound bag of M&Ms and the other half a half pound. All were told that they can snack on the M&Ms while they watched the video. The numbers of M&Ms eaten was recorded. Is there sufficient evidence to conclude that more M&Ms would be eaten by people who were given the full pound?

Source: Adapted from Brian Wansink, "Can Package Size Accelerate Usage Volume?" Journal of Marketing 60:3 (July 1996): 1–14.

13.50 Xr13-50 Is it true that an apple a day keeps the doctor away? A study designed and conducted by the National Health and Nutrition Examination Study (results published in the *Journal of the American Medical Association*) considered 8,399 American adults of whom 756 reported that they ate a small apple a day. The rest did not eat apples or ate them infrequently. The number of health care visits in the previous 36 months was recorded. Conduct a test to determine whether the adage is true.

13.51 Xr13-51 The age category 18–49 is considered a key target for retailers. To illustrate the importance of this age category, Nielsen Ratings tracks the shows that are watched by Americans between the ages of 18 and 49. There are several ways to judge the value to retailers of this age group. Suppose that random samples of Baby Boomers and those born between 1970 and 2000 were asked to report their after-tax income. Is there sufficient evidence that the 18–49 age group has a larger after-tax income that that of Baby Boomers?

13.52 **Xr13-52** Refer to Exercise 13.51. Also recorded for both groups were the housing expenditures, which include mortgage payments, rent, property tax, electricity, etc. Is there sufficient evidence to infer that the 18–49 age category spends more on housing than Baby Boomers?

13.53 **Xr13-53** In a Reason-Rupe poll, a random sample of people was asked, "Just a rough guess, what percent profit on each dollar of sales do you think the average company makes after taxes?" The results from 5 years ago and this year were recorded. Can we infer that the guesses this year are higher than they were 5 years ago?

13.54 **Xr13-54** Michigan State's Collegiate Employment Research Institute collected data from mid-August to mid-September, tapping the employment offices at 200 schools, which gathered starting salary data from 3,300 employers. The starting salaries for a random sample of electrical engineers and the starting salaries for a sample of mechanical engineers were recorded. Can we conclude that electrical engineers receive higher starting salaries than do mechanical engineers?

13.55 **Xr13-55** Does drinking hot chocolate boost the memory in older people? A random sample of people around the age of 73 was recruited. All had some form of cognitive deterioration. Half the participants drank two cups of hot chocolate a day for 30 days. Each was tested by solving puzzles that required working memory. The amount of time needed to complete the puzzles was recorded. Is there sufficient evidence to conclude that chocolate helps improve cognitive memory?

13.56 **Xr12-51+** Refer to Exercise 12.51. The researchers also recorded the number of missing teeth of a random sample of Britons. Can we infer that, in fact, Americans have more missing teeth?

13.57 **Xr13-57** Researchers at the University of California, San Diego conducted an experiment that studied the sleep of 164 American adults. The researchers used a device called a polysomnography machine to document slow-wave sleep, which is thought to be the most restorative period of sleep very important to good health. Generally, people are thought to spend 20 percent of their night in slow-wave sleep. The percentage of slow-wave sleep each individual experienced was recorded as was the race of the participants in the study. Can we infer that White American adults get more slow-wave sleep than Black American adults?

13.58 **Xr13-58** How does exercise affect memory in older adults with mild cognitive impairment? A study published in the *Journal of Aging Research* asked a random sample of women aged 70–80 with subjective memory complaints to exercise twice a week for six months. At the end of the study, all were given a test that measured verbal memory and learning. Also recorded were the results of the test for a control group that did not exercise. Can we conclude that exercise improves cognitive impairment?

13.59 **Xr13-59** Do college graduates with post-graduate degrees stay longer in their current jobs than do college graduates with no post-graduate degrees? Random samples from each population were drawn. Conduct a statistical test to answer the question.

13.60 **Xr13-60** Refer to Exercise 13.59. Are college graduates less likely to move more frequently than non-college graduates? A simple way to answer the question is to compare the amount of time (months) both groups have spent in their current home. A statistician at the Bureau of Labor Statistics took random samples of each population. Is there enough evidence that college graduates have longer tenure than non-college graduates?

13.61 **Xr13-61** A study undertaken by the Bureau of Labor Statistics wanted to determine the difference in after-tax income between college graduates and non-college graduates. Compute a confidence interval estimate of the difference.

13.62 **Xr13-62** Refer to Exercise 13.61. Is it worth pursuing a graduate degree if you already have a bachelor's degree? Determine a confidence interval estimate of the difference between the after-tax income of college graduates with a post-graduate degree and college graduates with no post-graduate degree.

13.63 **Xr13-63** Is there a tax on the poor? The tax on income is progressive in that higher-income individuals pay at a higher rate than lower-income people. For example, the top 0.1% of taxpayers earn 9.1% of the income, but pay 17.4% of all federal taxes. The top 1% of taxpayers earn 19% of the income but pay 36.9% of the taxes. The top 5% earn 33.4% but pay 57.1%, while the bottom 50% earn 13.4% but only pay 3.3% of federal taxes. However, the so-called sin taxes are regressive. To measure how taxes on tobacco and alcohol are regressive, the National Center for Policy Analysis randomly sampled low-income and high-income American adults who smoke (about one-third of low-income and one-fifth of high-income individuals smoke) and recorded their annual expenditures on tobacco. Is there sufficient statistical evidence to infer that low-income smokers spend more than high-income smokers?

13.64 Xr13-64   Refer to Exercise 13.63. The NCPA conducted another study, this one on alcohol. They randomly sampled low-income and middle-income alcohol drinkers and determined how much each spends annually on alcoholic drinks. Can we infer that low-income alcoholic drinkers spend more than middle-income?

13.65 Xr13-65   Which Canadians give the most to charity? A Statistics Canada study took random samples of men and women and recorded the amount donated to charity in the previous year. Is there sufficient evidence to infer that there are differences between the two populations?

13.66 Xr13-66   Because they have more years of education, college graduates have more disposable income than do non-college graduates. A survey asked college and non-college graduates to report the amount of money spent in the last year on vehicle purchases. Determine a confidence interval estimate of the difference between the vehicle purchases of college and non-college graduates.

13.67 Xr13-67   Refer to Exercise 13.66. Is there enough evidence to infer that vehicle purchases by college graduates with post-graduate degrees spend more on vehicle purchases than college graduates without a post-graduate degree?

13.68 Xr13-68   Because of declining health and increasing signs of dementia, seniors are often the target of fraud. A government agency took random samples of seniors in their 70s and 80s who were defrauded in the previous 12 months and recorded the amount of loss. Can we infer that seniors in their 80s suffer larger losses from fraud than seniors in their 70s?

13.69 Xr13-69   A survey of a random sample of cat owners was asked to report the amount of expenditures on veterinary services in the previous 12 months. The veterinary cost per dog was recorded from Exercise 12.172. Can we conclude that dog owners spend more money on veterinarians than cat owners?

13.70 Xr13-70   The Research College Board Organization recorded the total SAT scores for random samples of students planning to enroll in business management and students enrolling in a psychology program. Is there sufficient statistical evidence to conclude that business management students have higher total SAT scores than do psychology students?

13.71 Xr13-71   Refer to Exercise 13.70. Is there enough evidence to conclude that the SAT scores for Mathematics and Statistics students are higher than that of engineering students?

13.72 Xr13-72+   Are Canadian public servants gaming the system by taking more sick days than do private sector workers? To answer the question, Statistics Canada took a random sample of white-collar public servants and a random sample of white-collar private sector workers and recorded the number of sick days each took in the previous 12 months. Is there enough statistical evidence to infer that white-collar public servants take more sick days than do white-collar private sector workers?

13.73 Xr13-72+   Refer to Exercise 13.72. The data for public servants' sick days 5 years ago was also recorded. Is there sufficient evidence to conclude that there are more sick days this year than 5 years ago?

13.74 Xr13-74   Another advantage of working for the government is that about 80% of public sector workers have pensions, which makes it easier to retire early. To examine this issue, a financial analyst took random samples of retired public sector workers and private sector workers and asked at what age they retired. Is there sufficient evidence to infer that public sector workers retire earlier than their private sector counterparts?

GENERAL SOCIAL SURVEY EXERCISES

<u>GSS2018</u>   *The following exercises are based on the 2018 survey.*

13.75   Study after study indicates that men earn higher incomes than women (SEX: 1 = Male, 2 = Female). To determine the extent of the differential in 2018, determine a confidence interval estimate of the difference between male and female annual incomes (RINCOME).

13.76   Some economists have theorized that one of the reasons that men earn higher incomes than women (SEX: 1 = Male, 2 = Female) is that men work longer hours (HRS1). Conduct a statistical test to determine whether this contention is true.

13.77   Immigration has become an important topic in American politics. Some immigrants came to the United States to do jobs that Americans do not want to do. Many of these immigrants have little formal education. Other immigrants came to the United States with work permits. Many of these are highly educated.

a. Conduct a test to determine if American-born residents (BORN: 1 = In the United States, 2 = Elsewhere) are more educated than those born outside the United States (EDUC).

b. Are the required conditions for the statistical test satisfied? Explain.

13.78 Because many immigrants come to the United States with little money, they often are willing to take risks that can result in high incomes. However, is this enough to overcome language and culture difficulties? Is there sufficient evidence to infer that Americans born in the United States (BORN: 1 = In the United States, 2 = Elsewhere) have higher incomes than those born elsewhere (RINCOME)?

13.79 In most countries including the United States, younger people tend to be on the left side of the political spectrum. If so, we would expect Republicans to be older than Democrats.

a. Conduct a test to determine whether there is enough evidence to infer that Republicans (PARTYID2: 1 = Democrat, 3 = Republican) are older than Democrats (AGE).

b. What are the required conditions for this test? Are they satisfied?

13.80 Republicans tend to prefer smaller, less intrusive government and lower taxes. Is this because Republicans have higher incomes (PARTYID2: 1 = Democrat, 3 = Republican)?

a. Do the data allow us to conclude that Republicans earn more income (RINCOME) than Democrats?

b. Determine a confidence interval estimate of how much more Republicans earn than do Democrats.

13.81 Refer to Exercise 13.80. If it is true that Republicans (PARTYID2: 1 = Democrat, 3 = Republican) have higher incomes than Democrats, is it because they work harder? Conduct a statistical test to determine whether Republicans work longer hours (HRS1) than do Democrats.

13.82 Does education play a role to explain the results in Exercise 13.80? Test to determine whether there is enough evidence to infer that Republicans (PARTYID2: 1 = Democrat, 3 = Republican) are more educated than Democrats (EDUC).

13.83 Perhaps another way to explain the outcome of the test in Exercise 13.80 is that Republicans wait

longer to have children. Test to determine whether Republicans are older than Democrats (PARTYID2: 1 = Democrat, 3 = Republican) when their first child is born (AGEKDBRN).

13.84 As was the case with Democrats and Republicans, we would expect that Conservatives would have higher incomes (POLVIEWS2: 1 = Liberal, 3 = Conservative). Conduct a statistical test to determine whether we can conclude that conservatives' income exceeds that of liberals (RINCOME).

13.85 We can attempt to explain the results in Exercise 13.84 by determining whether Conservatives are more educated than Liberals (POLVIEWS2: 1 = Liberal, 3 = Conservative). Test to determine whether Conservatives have more education than Liberals (EDUC).

13.86 Another way to explain the results of Exercise 13.84 is to look at the differences in the number of hours of work. Is there sufficient evidence to infer that conservatives work longer hours (HRS1) than liberals (POLVIEWS2: 1 = Liberal, 3 = Conservative)?

13.87 Are government jobs more complex requiring more education than do private sector jobs? Test to determine whether there is enough evidence to conclude that government workers (WRKGOVT: 1 = Government, 2 = Private) have more education than do private sector employees (EDUC).

13.88 As a general rule, government employees (WRKGOVT: 1 = Government, 2 = Private) have more job security than do private sector employees. Do they also have higher incomes RINCOME)? Conduct a test to answer the question.

13.89 Is it true that government workers (WRKGOVT: 1 = Government, 2 = Private) work fewer hours (HRS1) than do private sector workers? Conduct a test to answer the question.

13.90 The upside to self-employment is that there is virtually no upper limit to income. If so, we would expect self-employed individuals (WRKSLF: 1 = Self-employed, 2 = Someone else) to have higher incomes (RINCOME). Conduct a test to determine whether the expectation is true.

13.91 Most jobs require employees to work 35 to 45 hours per week. There is no lower or upper limit on the amount of time for self-employed workers. Do the number of hours per week (HRS1) differ between self-employed workers (WRKSLF: 1 = Self-employed, 2 = Someone else) and other workers? Conduct a test to answer the question.

SURVEY OF CONSUMER FINANCES EXERCISES

<u>SCF2019:\UMC</u> *The following exercises deal with upper middle-class households defined as those with net worth of between $450,000 and $3,123,440.*

13.92 Incomes of people who work for themselves are likely more variable than people who work for someone else. That's because incomes for someone who is self-employed range from $0 to virtually unlimited. Is there sufficient evidence that upper middle-class heads of households who work for someone else (OCCAT1: 1 = Someone else, 2 = Self-employed/partnership) have higher incomes than heads of households who work for themselves (INCOME)?

13.93 Many jobs that required very little education have been disappearing. To measure the impact of this phenomenon, calculate a confidence interval estimate of the difference in income (INCOME) between heads of households who did finish high school and those who did not (EDCL: 1 = No high school diploma, 2 = High school diploma).

13.94 How much better do married heads of household fare against household heads who are not married? Conduct a statistical test to determine whether there is enough evidence to conclude that married (MARRIED: 1 = Married or living with partner, 2 = Neither married nor living with partner) heads of household have more assets (ASSET) than unmarried ones.

13.95 Do upper middle-class college graduates keep more cash in their checking account (CHECKING) than do people who have some college (EDCL: 3 = Some college, 4 = College degree)? Conduct a test to determine whether there is enough evidence to answer the question affirmatively.

13.96 Refer to Exercise 13.92. Test to determine whether there is enough evidence that people who work for themselves have more assets (ASSET) than people who work for someone else (OCCAT1: 1 = Someone else, 2 = Self-employed/partnership).

13.97 Do relatively educated upper middle-class heads of households find themselves more in debt? Is there sufficient evidence to infer that high school graduates (EDCL: 1 = No high school diploma, 2 = High school diploma) have more debt (DEBT) than people who did not complete high school?

13.98 Do married heads of households (MARRIED: 1 = Married or living with partner, 2 = Neither married nor living with partner) have more debt (DEBT) than unmarried ones?

13.99 Do high school graduates have larger unrealized capital gains on their primary residence (KGHOUSE) than do household heads who did not complete high school (EDCL: 1 = No high school diploma, 2 = High school diploma)? Conduct a test to answer the question.

13.100 In most countries including the United States, men have higher incomes than women. Does this hold when comparing upper middle-class heads of households (HHSEX: 1 = Male, 2 = Female)? Estimate the difference in income (INCOME) between male and female heads of upper middle-class households.

13-2 / OBSERVATIONAL AND EXPERIMENTAL DATA

As we've pointed out several times, the ability to properly interpret the results of a statistical technique is a crucial skill for students to develop. This ability is dependent on your understanding of Type I and Type II errors and the fundamental concepts that are part of statistical inference. However, there is another component that must be understood: the difference between **observational data** and **experimental data**. The difference results from the way the data are generated. The following example will demonstrate the difference between the two types.

EXAMPLE 13.3

DATA
Xm13-03

Dietary Effects of High-Fiber Breakfast Cereals

Despite some controversy, scientists generally agree that high-fiber cereals reduce the likelihood of various forms of cancer. However, one scientist claims that people who eat high-fiber cereal for breakfast will consume, on average, fewer calories for lunch than people who don't eat high-fiber cereal for breakfast. If this is true, high-fiber cereal manufacturers will be able to claim another advantage of eating their product—potential weight reduction for dieters. As a preliminary test of the claim, 150 people were randomly selected and asked what they regularly eat for breakfast and lunch. Each person was identified as either a consumer or a nonconsumer of high-fiber cereal, and the number of calories consumed at lunch was measured and recorded. These data are listed here. Can the scientist conclude at the 5% significance level that the claim is correct?

Calories Consumed at Lunch by Consumers of High-Fiber Cereal

568	646	607	555	530	714	593	647	650
498	636	529	565	566	639	551	580	629
589	739	637	568	687	693	683	532	651
681	539	617	584	694	556	667	467	
540	596	633	607	566	473	649	622	

Calories Consumed at Lunch by Nonconsumers of High-Fiber Cereal

705	754	740	569	593	637	563	421	514	536
819	741	688	547	723	553	733	812	580	833
706	628	539	710	730	620	664	547	624	644
509	537	725	679	701	679	625	643	566	594
613	748	711	674	672	599	655	693	709	596
582	663	607	505	685	566	466	624	518	750
601	526	816	527	800	484	462	549	554	582
608	541	426	679	663	739	603	726	623	788
787	462	773	830	369	717	646	645	747	
573	719	480	602	596	642	588	794	583	
428	754	632	765	758	663	476	490	573	

SOLUTION:

The appropriate technique is the unequal-variances t-test of $\mu_1 - \mu_2$, where μ_1 is the mean of the number of calories for lunch by consumers of high-fiber cereal for breakfast and μ_2 is the mean of the number of calories for lunch by nonconsumers of high-fiber cereal for breakfast. [The F-test of the ratio of two variances (not shown here) yielded $F = .3845$ and p-value $= .0008$.]

The hypotheses are

$$H_0: \ (\mu_1 - \mu_2) = 0$$
$$H_1: \ (\mu_1 - \mu_2) < 0$$

EXCEL Data Analysis

	A	B	C
1	t-Test: Two-Sample Assuming Unequal Variances		
2			
3		*Consumers*	*Nonconsumers*
4	Mean	604.02	633.23
5	Variance	4103	10670
6	Observations	43	107
7	Hypothesized Mean Difference	0	
8	df	123	
9	t Stat	−2.09	
10	P(T<=t) one-tail	0.0193	
11	t Critical one-tail	1.6573	
12	P(T<=t) two-tail	0.0386	
13	t Critical two-tail	1.9794	

INTERPRET

The value of the test statistic is −2.09. The one-tail *p*-value is .0193. We observe that the *p*-value of the test is small (and the test statistic falls into the rejection region). As a result, we conclude that there is sufficient evidence to infer that consumers of high-fiber cereal do eat fewer calories at lunch than do nonconsumers. From this result, we're inclined to believe that eating a high-fiber cereal at breakfast may be a way to reduce weight. However, other interpretations are plausible. For example, people who eat fewer calories are probably more health conscious, and such people are more likely to eat high-fiber cereal as part of a healthy breakfast. In this interpretation, high-fiber cereals do not necessarily lead to fewer calories at lunch. Instead, another factor, general health consciousness, leads to both fewer calories at lunch and high-fiber cereal for breakfast. Notice that the conclusion of the statistical procedure is unchanged. On average, people who eat high-fiber cereal consume fewer calories at lunch. However, because of the way the data were gathered, we have more difficulty interpreting this result.

Suppose that we redo Example 13.3 using the experimental approach. We randomly select 150 people to participate in the experiment. We randomly assign 75 to eat high-fiber cereal for breakfast and the other 75 to eat something else. We then record the number of calories each person consumes at lunch. Ideally, in this experiment both groups will be similar in all other dimensions, including health consciousness. (Larger sample sizes increase the likelihood that the two groups will be similar.) If the statistical result is about the same as in Example 13.3, we may have some valid reason to believe that high-fiber cereal at breakfast leads to a decrease in caloric intake at lunch.

Experimental data are usually more expensive to obtain because of the planning required to set up the experiment; observational data usually require less work to gather. Furthermore, in many situations it is impossible to conduct a controlled experiment. For example, suppose that we want to determine whether an undergraduate degree in engineering better prepares students for an MBA than does an arts degree. In a controlled experiment, we would randomly assign some students to achieve a degree in engineering and other students to obtain an arts degree. We would then make them sign up for an MBA program where we would record their grades. Unfortunately for statistical despots (and fortunately for the rest of us), we live in a democratic society, which makes the coercion necessary to perform this controlled experiment impossible.

To answer our question about the relative performance of engineering and arts students, we have no choice but to obtain our data by observational methods. We would take a random sample of engineering students and arts students who have already entered MBA programs and record their grades. If we find that engineering students do better, we may tend to conclude that an engineering background better prepares students for an MBA program. However, it may be true that better students tend to choose engineering as their undergraduate major and that better students achieve higher grades in all programs, including the MBA program.

Although we've discussed observational and experimental data in the con of the test of the difference between two means, you should be aware that the issue of how the data are obtained is relevant to the interpretation of all the techniques that follow.

EXERCISES

13.101 Refer to Exercise 13.19. If the data are observational, describe another conclusion other than the one that infers that Tastee is better for babies.

13.102 Are the data in Exercise 13.20 observational or experimental? Explain. If the data are observational, describe a method of producing experimental data.

13.103 Refer to Exercise 13.30.
a. Are the data observational or experimental?
b. If the data are observational, describe a method of answering the question with experimental data?
c. If the data are observational, produce another explanation for the statistical outcome.

13.104 Suppose that you wish to test to determine whether one method of teaching statistics is better than another.
a. Describe a data-gathering process that produces observational data.
b. Describe a data-gathering process that produces experimental data.

13.105 Put yourself in place of the director of research and development for a pharmaceutical company. When a new drug is developed it undergoes a number of tests. One of the tests is designed to determine whether the drug is safe and effective. Your company has just developed a drug that is designed to alleviate the symptoms of degenerative diseases such as multiple sclerosis. Design an experiment that tests the new drug.

13.106 You wish to determine whether MBA graduates who majored in finance attract higher starting salaries than MBA graduates who majored in marketing.
a. Describe a data-gathering process that produces observational data.
b. Describe a data-gathering process that produces experimental data.
c. If observational data indicate that finance majors attract higher salaries than do marketing majors, provide two explanations for this result.

13.107 Suppose that you are analyzing one of the hundreds of statistical studies linking smoking with lung cancer. The study analyzed thousands of randomly selected people, some of whom had lung cancer. The statistics indicate that those who have lung cancer smoked on average significantly more than those who did not have lung cancer.
a. Explain how you know that the data are observational.
b. Is there another interpretation of the statistics other than the obvious one that smoking causes lung cancer? If so, what is it? (Students who produce the best answers will be eligible for a job in the public relations department of a tobacco company.)
c. Is it possible to conduct a controlled experiment to produce data that address the question of the relationship between smoking and lung cancer? If so, describe the experiment.

13-3 / INFERENCE ABOUT THE DIFFERENCE BETWEEN TWO MEANS: MATCHED PAIRS EXPERIMENT

We continue our presentation of statistical techniques that address the problem of comparing two populations of interval data. In Section 13-1, the parameter of interest was the difference between two population means, where the data were generated from independent samples. In this section, the data are gathered from a matched pairs experiment. To illustrate why matched pairs experiments are needed and how we deal with data produced in this way, consider the following example.

EXAMPLE 13.4

DATA
Xm13-04

Comparing Salary Offers for Finance and Marketing MBA Majors, Part 1

In the last few years, a number of web-based companies that offer job placement services have been created. One such company wanted to investigate the job offers recent MBAs were obtaining. In particular, they wanted to know whether finance majors were being offered higher salaries than marketing majors. In a preliminary study, they randomly sampled 50 recently graduated MBAs, half of whom majored in finance and half in marketing. From each they obtained the highest salary offer (including benefits). These data are listed here. Can we infer that finance majors obtain higher salary offers than do marketing majors among MBAs?

Highest salary offer made to finance majors

61,228	51,836	20,620	73,356	84,186	79,782	29,523	80,645	76,125
62,531	77,073	86,705	70,286	63,196	64,358	47,915	86,792	75,155
65,948	29,392	96,382	80,644	51,389	61,955	63,573		

Highest salary offer made to marketing majors

73,361	36,956	63,627	71,069	40,203	97,097	49,442	75,188	59,854
79,816	51,943	35,272	60,631	63,567	69,423	68,421	56,276	47,510
58,925	78,704	62,553	81,931	30,867	49,091	48,843		

SOLUTION:

IDENTIFY

The objective is to compare two populations of interval data. The parameter is the difference between two means $\mu_1 - \mu_2$ (where μ_1 = mean highest salary offer to finance majors and μ_2 = mean highest salary offer to marketing majors). Because we want to determine whether finance majors are offered higher salaries, the alternative hypothesis will specify that μ_1 is greater than μ_2. The F-test for variances was conducted, and the results indicate that there is not enough evidence to infer that the population variances differ. Hence we use the equal-variances test statistic:

$$H_0: (\mu_1 - \mu_2) = 0$$
$$H_1: (\mu_1 - \mu_2) > 0$$

Test statistic: $t = \dfrac{(\bar{x}_1 - \bar{x}_2) - (\mu_1 - \mu_2)}{\sqrt{s_p^2 \left(\dfrac{1}{n_1} + \dfrac{1}{n_2}\right)}}$

from which we calculate the value of the test statistic:

$$t = \frac{\bar{x}_D - \mu_D}{s_D/\sqrt{n_D}} = \frac{5,065 - 0}{6,647/\sqrt{25}} = 3.81$$

The rejection region is

$$t > t_{\alpha,\nu} = t_{.05,24} = 1.711$$

EXCEL Data Analysis

	A	B	C
1	t-Test: Paired Two Sample for Means		
2			
3		Finance	Marketing
4	Mean	65,438	60,374
5	Variance	444,981,810	469,441,785
6	Observations	25	25
7	Pearson Correlation	0.9520	
8	Hypothesized Mean Difference	0	
9	df	24	
10	t Stat	3.81	
11	P(T<=t) one-tail	0.0004	
12	t Critical one-tail	1.7109	
13	P(T<=t) two-tail	0.0009	
14	t Critical two-tail	2.0639	

Excel prints the sample means, variances, and sample sizes for each sample (as well as the coefficient of correlation), which implies that the procedure uses these statistics. It doesn't. The technique is based on computing the paired differences from which the mean, variance, and sample size are determined. Excel should have printed these statistics.

INSTRUCTIONS

1. Type or import the data into two columns. (Open Xm13-05.)
2. Click **Data, Data Analysis**, and **t-Test: Paired Two-Sample for Means**.
3. Specify the **Variable 1 Range** (B1:B26) and the **Variable 2 Range** (C1:C26). Type the value of **the Hypothesized Mean Difference** (0) and specify a value for α (.05).

INTERPRET

The value of the test statistic is $t = 3.81$ with a p-value of .0004. There is now overwhelming evidence to infer that finance majors obtain higher salary offers than marketing majors. By redoing the experiment as matched pairs, we were able to extract this information from the data.

13-3a Estimating the Mean Difference

We derive the confidence interval estimator of μ_D using the usual form for the confidence interval.

Confidence Interval Estimator of μ_D

$$\bar{x}_D \pm t_{\alpha/2}\frac{s_D}{\sqrt{n_D}}$$

EXAMPLE 13.6

DATA
Xm13-05

Comparing Salary Offers for Finance and Marketing MBA Majors, Part 3

Compute the 95% confidence interval estimate of the mean difference in salary offers between finance and marketing majors in Example 13.5.

SOLUTION:

COMPUTE

MANUALLY:

The 95% confidence interval estimate of the mean difference is

$$\bar{x}_D \pm t_{\alpha/2}\frac{s_D}{\sqrt{n_D}} = 5,065 \pm 2.064\,\frac{6,647}{\sqrt{25}} = 5,065 \pm 2,744$$

$$\text{LCL} = 2,321 \quad \text{and} \quad \text{UCL} = 7,809$$

EXCEL Workbook

	A	B	C	D	E
1	t-Estimate of a Mean				
2					
3	Sample mean	5065	Confidence Interval Estimate		
4	Sample standard deviation	6647	5065	±	2744
5	Sample size	25	Lower confidence limit		2321
6	Confidence level	0.95	Upper confidence limit		7808

INSTRUCTIONS

1. Type or copy the data into two columns (Open Xm13-05). In each row calculate the paired differences. Calculate the mean and standard deviation of the paired differences.

2. Open the **Estimators Workbook** and click the **t-Estimate_Mean** tab. Type or copy the sample mean and the sample standard deviation. Type the sample size and the confidence level.

INTERPRET

We estimate that the mean salary offer to finance majors exceeds the mean salary offer to marketing majors by an amount that lies between $2,321 and $7,808 (using the Excel output).

13-3b Independent Samples or Matched Pairs: Which Experimental Design Is Better?

Examples 13.4 and 13.5 demonstrated that the experimental design is an important factor in statistical inference. However, these two examples raise several questions about experimental designs.

1. Why does the matched pairs experiment result in concluding that finance majors receive higher salary offers than do marketing majors, whereas the independent samples experiment could not?

2. Should we always use the matched pairs experiment? In particular, are there disadvantages to its use?

3. How do we recognize when a matched pairs experiment has been performed?

Here are our answers.

1. The matched pairs experiment worked in Example 13.5 by reducing the variation in the data. To understand this point, examine the statistics from both examples. In Example 13.4, we found $\bar{x}_1 - \bar{x}_2 = 5,201$. In Example 13.5, we computed $\bar{x}_D = 5,065$. Thus, the numerators of the two test statistics were quite similar. However, the test statistic in Example 13.5 was much larger than the test statistic in Example 13.4 because of the standard errors. In Example 13.4, we calculated

$$s_p^2 = 311,330,926 \quad \text{and} \quad \sqrt{s_p^2\left(\frac{1}{n_1} + \frac{1}{n_2}\right)} = 4,991$$

Example 13.5 produced

$$s_D = 6,647 \quad \text{and} \quad \frac{s_D}{\sqrt{n_D}} = 1,329$$

As you can see, the difference in the test statistics was caused not by the numerator, but by the denominator. This raises another question: Why was the variation in the data of Example 13.4 so much greater than the variation in the data of Example 13.5? If you examine the data and statistics from Example 13.4, you will find that there was a great deal of variation *between* the salary offers in each sample. In other words, some MBA graduates received high salary offers and others relatively low ones. This high level of variation, as expressed by s_p^2, made the difference between the sample means appear to be small. As a result, we could not conclude that finance majors attract higher salary offers.

   Looking at the data from Example 13.5, we see that there is very little variation between the observations of the paired differences. The variation caused by different GPAs has been decreased markedly. The smaller variation causes the value of the test statistic to be larger. Consequently, we conclude that finance majors obtain higher salary offers.

2. Will the matched pairs experiment always produce a larger test statistic than the independent samples experiment? The answer is, not necessarily. Suppose that in our example we found that companies did not consider GPAs when making decisions about how much to offer the MBA graduates. In such circumstances, the matched pairs experiment would result in no significant decrease in variation when compared to independent samples. It is possible that the matched pairs experiment may be less likely to reject the null hypothesis than the independent samples experiment.

The reason can be seen by calculating the degrees of freedom. In Example 13.4, the number of degrees of freedom was 48, whereas in Example 13.5, it was 24. Even though we had the same number of observations (25 in each sample), the matched pairs experiment had half the number of degrees of freedom as the equivalent independent samples experiment. For exactly the same value of the test statistic, a smaller number of degrees of freedom in a Student t distributed test statistic yields a larger p-value. What this means is that if there is little reduction in variation to be achieved by the matched pairs experiment, the statistics practitioner should choose instead to conduct the experiment with independent samples.

3. As you've seen, in this book we deal with questions arising from experiments that have already been conducted. Consequently, one of your tasks is to determine the appropriate test statistic. In the case of comparing two populations of interval data, you must decide whether the samples are independent (in which case the parameter is $\mu_1 - \mu_2$) or matched pairs (in which case the parameter is μ_D) to select the correct test statistic. To help you do so, we suggest you ask and answer the following question: Does some natural relationship exist between each pair of observations that provides a logical reason to compare the first observation of sample 1 with the first observation of sample 2, the second observation of sample 1 with the second observation of sample 2, and so on? If so, the experiment was conducted by matched pairs. If not, it was conducted using independent samples.

13-3c Observational and Experimental Data

The points we made in Section 13-2 are also valid in this section: We can design a matched pairs experiment where the data are gathered using a controlled experiment or by observation. The data in Examples 13.4 and 13.5 are observational. As a consequence, when the statistical result provided evidence that finance majors attracted higher salary offers, it did not necessarily mean that students educated in finance are more attractive to prospective employers. It may be, for example, that better students major in finance and better students achieve higher starting salaries.

13-3d Checking the Required Condition

The validity of the results of the t-test and estimator of μ_D depends on the normality of the differences (or large enough sample sizes). The histogram of the differences (Figure 13.6) is positively skewed but not enough so that the normality requirement is violated.

FIGURE **13.6** Histogram of Differences in Example 13.5

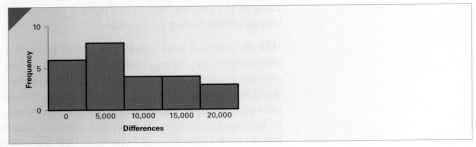

13-3e Violation of Required Condition

If the differences are very nonnormal, we cannot use the t-test of μ_D. We can, however, employ a nonparametric technique—the Wilcoxon signed rank sum test for matched pairs, which we present in Chapter 19.*

13-3f Developing an Understanding of Statistical Concepts 1

Two of the most important principles in statistics were applied in this section. The first is the concept of analyzing sources of variation. In Examples 13.4 and 13.5, we showed that by reducing the variation between salary offers in each sample we were able to detect a real difference between the two majors. This was an application of the more general procedure of analyzing data and attributing some fraction of the variation to several sources. In Example 13.5, the two sources of variation were the GPA and the MBA major. However, we were not interested in the variation between graduates with differing GPAs. Instead, we only wanted to eliminate that source of variation, making it easier to determine whether finance majors draw larger salary offers.

In Chapter 14, we will introduce a technique called the *analysis of variance* that does what its name suggests: It analyzes sources of variation in an attempt to detect real differences. In most applications of this procedure, we will be interested in each source of variation and not simply in reducing one source. We refer to the process as *explaining the variation*. The concept of explained variation is also applied in Chapters 16–18, where we introduce regression analysis.

13-3g Developing an Understanding of Statistical Concepts 2

The second principle demonstrated in this section is that statistics practitioners can design data-gathering procedures in such a way that they can analyze sources of variation. Before conducting the experiment in Example 13.5, the statistics practitioner suspected that there were large differences between graduates with different GPAs. Consequently, the experiment was organized so that the effects of those differences were mostly eliminated. It is also possible to design experiments that allow for easy detection of real differences and minimize the costs of data gathering. Unfortunately, we will not present this topic. However, you should understand that the entire subject of the design of experiments is an important one, because statistics practitioners often need to be able to analyze data to detect differences, and the cost is almost always a factor.

Here is a summary of how we determine when to use these techniques.

Factors That Identify the t-Test and Estimator of μ_D

1. **Problem objective**: Compare two populations.
2. **Data type**: Interval
3. **Descriptive measurement**: Central location
4. **Experimental design**: Matched pairs

*Instructors who wish to teach the use of nonparametric techniques for testing the mean difference when the normality requirement is not satisfied should use online appendixes Introduction to Nonparametric Techniques and Wilcoxon Signed Rank Sum Test.

EXERCISES

Applications

13.108 <u>Xr13-108</u> Many people use scanners to read documents and store them in a Word (or some other software) file. To help determine which brand of scanner to buy, a student conducts an experiment wherein eight documents are scanned by each of two scanners. The number of errors made by each was recorded. These data are listed here. Can he infer with a 10% significance level that Brand A (the more expensive scanner) is better than Brand B?

Document	1	2	3	4	5	6	7	8
Brand A	17	29	18	14	21	25	22	29
Brand B	21	38	15	19	22	30	31	37

13.109 <u>Xr13-109</u> How effective are antilock brakes, which pump very rapidly rather than lock and thus avoid skids? As a test, a car buyer organized an experiment. The buyer hit the brakes and, using a stopwatch, recorded the number of seconds it took to stop an ABS-equipped car and another identical car without ABS. The speeds when the brakes were applied and the number of seconds each took to stop on dry pavement are listed here. Can we infer using a 10% significance level that ABS is better?

Speeds	20	25	30	35	40	45	50	55
ABS	3.6	4.1	4.8	5.3	5.9	6.3	6.7	7.0
Non-ABS	3.4	4.0	5.1	5.5	6.4	6.5	6.9	7.3

13.110 <u>Xr13-110</u> In a preliminary study to determine whether the installation of a camera designed to catch cars that go through red lights affects the number of violators, the number of red-light runners was recorded for each day of the week before and after the camera was installed. These data are listed here. Can we infer at the 5% significance level that the camera reduces the number of red-light runners?

Day	Sunday	Monday	Tuesday	Wednesday
Before	7	21	27	18
After	8	18	24	19

Day	Thursday	Friday	Saturday
Before	20	24	16
After	16	19	16

13.111 <u>Xr13-111</u> In an effort to determine whether a new type of fertilizer is more effective than the type currently in use, researchers took 12 two-acre plots of land scattered throughout the county. Each plot was divided into two equal-size subplots, one of which was treated with the current fertilizer and the other of which was treated with the new fertilizer. Wheat was planted, and the crop yields were measured.

Plot	1	2	3	4	5	6	7	8	9	10	11	12
Current fertilizer	56	45	68	72	61	69	57	55	60	72	75	66
New fertilizer	60	49	66	73	59	67	61	60	58	75	72	68

a. Can we conclude at the 5% significance level that the new fertilizer is more effective than the current one?

b. Estimate with 95% confidence the difference in mean crop yields between the two fertilizers.

c. What is the required condition(s) for the validity of the results obtained in parts (a) and (b)?

d. Is the required condition(s) satisfied?

e. Are these data experimental or observational? Explain.

f. How should the experiment be conducted if the researchers believed that the land throughout the county was essentially the same?

13.112 <u>Xr13-112</u> The president of a large company is in the process of deciding whether to adopt a lunchtime exercise program. The purpose of such programs is to improve the health of workers and, in so doing, reduce medical expenses. To get more information, an exercise program for the employees in one office was instituted. It is known that during the winter months medical expenses are relatively high because of the incidence of colds and flu. Consequently, the president decides to use a matched pairs design by recording medical expenses for the 12 months before the program and for 12 months after the program. The "before" and "after" expenses (in thousands of dollars) are compared on a month-to-month basis and shown here.

a. Do the data indicate that exercise programs reduce medical expenses? (Test with $\alpha = .05$.)

b. Estimate with 95% confidence the mean savings produced by exercise programs.

c. Was it appropriate to conduct a matched pairs experiment? Explain.

Month	Jan	Feb	Mar	Apr	May	Jun
Before program	68	44	30	58	35	33
After program	59	42	20	62	25	30

Month	Jan	Feb	Mar	Apr	May	Jun
Before program	52	69	23	69	48	30
After program	56	62	25	75	40	26

The following exercises require the use of a computer and software. The answers to Exercises 13.113 to 13.127 may be calculated manually. See Appendix A for the sample statistics.

For Exercises 13.113 to 13.133 conduct all tests at the 5% significance level and produce estimates with 95% confidence.

13.113 Xr13-113   One measure of the state of the economy is the amount of money homeowners pay on their mortgage each month. To determine the extent of change between this year and 5 years ago, a random sample of 150 homeowners was drawn. The monthly mortgage payments for each homeowner for this year and for 5 years ago were recorded. (The amounts have been adjusted so that we're comparing constant dollars.) Can we infer that mortgage payments have risen over the past 5 years?

13.114 Xr13-114   Do waiters or waitresses earn larger tips? To answer this question, a restaurant consultant undertook a preliminary study. The study involved measuring the percentage of the total bill left as a tip for one randomly selected waiter and one randomly selected waitress in each of 50 restaurants during a 1-week period. What conclusions can be drawn from these data?

13.115 Xr13-115   To determine the effect of advertising in the Yellow Pages, Bell Telephone took a sample of 40 retail stores that did not advertise in the Yellow Pages last year but did so this year. The annual sales (in thousands of dollars) for each store in both years were recorded.
a. Calculate a confidence interval estimate of the improvement in sales between the two years.
b. Can we infer that advertising in the Yellow Pages improves sales?
c. Check to ensure that the required condition(s) of the techniques used in parts (a) and (b) is satisfied.
d. Would it be advantageous to perform this experiment with independent samples? Explain why or why not.

13.116 Xr13-116   Because of the high cost of energy, homeowners in northern climates need to find ways to cut their heating costs. A building contractor wanted to investigate the effect on heating costs of increasing the insulation. As an experiment, a large subdevelopment built around 1970 with minimal insulation was identified. The plan was to insulate some of the houses and compare the heating costs in the insulated homes with those that remained uninsulated. However, it was clear that the size of the house was a critical factor in determining heating costs. Consequently, the contractor found 16 pairs of identical-sized houses ranging from about 1,200 to 2,800 square feet. One house in each pair was insulated (levels of R20 in the walls and R32 in the attic) and the other house was left unchanged. The heating cost for the following winter season was recorded for each house.
a. Do these data allow the contractor to infer that the heating cost for insulated houses is less than that for the uninsulated houses?
b. Determine a confidence interval estimate of the mean savings due to insulating the house.
c. What is the required condition for the use of the techniques in parts (a) and (b)?

13.117 Xr13-117   The cost of health care is rising faster than most other items. To learn more about the problem, a survey was undertaken to determine whether differences in health care expenditures exist between men and women. The survey randomly sampled men and women aged 21, 22, ..., 65 and determined the total amount spent on health care. Do these data allow us to infer that men and women spend different amounts on health care?

13.118 Xr13-118   The fluctuations in the stock market induce some investors to sell and move their money into more stable investments. To determine the degree to which recent fluctuations affected ownership, a random sample of 170 people who confirmed that they owned some stock was surveyed. The values of the holdings were recorded at the end of last year and at the end of the year before. Can we infer that the value of the stock holdings has decreased?

13.119 Xr13-119   Are Americans more deeply in debt this year compared to last year? To help answer this question a statistics practitioner randomly sampled Americans this year and last year. The sampling was conducted so that the samples were matched by the age of the head of the household. For each, the ratio of debt payments to household income was recorded. Can we infer that the ratios are higher this year than last?

13.120 Xr13-120   Every April Americans and Canadians fill out their tax return forms. Many turn to tax preparation companies to do this tedious job. The question arises: Are there differences between companies? In an experiment, two of the largest companies were asked to prepare the tax returns of a sample of 55 taxpayers. The amounts of tax payable were recorded. Can we conclude that company 1's service results in higher tax payable?

13.121 Xr13-121   Refer to Exercise 13.41. Suppose now we redo the experiment in the following way. On 20 randomly selected cars, one of each type of tire is installed on the rear wheels and as before, the cars are driven until the tires wear out. The number of miles (thousands) until wear-out occurred was recorded. Can we conclude from these data that the new tire is superior?

13.122 Refer to Exercises 13.41 and 13.121. Explain why the matched pairs experiment produced significant results whereas the independent samples *t*-test did not.

13.123 Xr13-123   Refer to Examples 13.4 and 13.5. Suppose that another experiment is conducted. Finance and marketing MBA majors were matched according to their undergraduate GPA. As in the previous examples, the highest starting salary offers were recorded. Can we infer from these data that finance majors attract higher salary offers than marketing majors?

13.124 Discuss why the experiment in Example 13.5 produced a significant test result whereas the one in Exercise 13.123 did not.

13.125 Xr13-125   Refer to Example 13.2. The actual after and before operating incomes were recorded.

a. Test to determine whether there is enough evidence to infer that for companies where an offspring takes the helm there is a decrease in operating income.

b. Is there sufficient evidence to conclude that when an outsider becomes CEO the operating income increases?

13.126 Xr13-126   Refer to Exercise 12.162 where the IQs of first-born children were recorded. In another experiment a random sample of families with three sons was drawn. The IQs of the first-born and second-born sons were recorded. Can we infer that the IQ of first-born sons are higher than the IQs of second-born sons in families with three sons?

13.127 Xr13-127   Refer to Exercise 13.126. In yet another experiment, the IQs of the second-born and third-born sons in families with three male children were measured and recorded. Is there enough evidence to conclude that the IQ of second-born sons exceed that of third-born sons?

General Social Survey Exercises

GSS2018   *Exercises 13.128 to 13.131 are based on the 2018 survey.*

13.128 The general trend over the last century is that each generation is more educated than its predecessor. Has this trend continued? To answer this question, determine whether there is sufficient evidence that Americans are more educated than their fathers (EDUC and PAEDUC).

13.129 Is there sufficient evidence to infer that Americans are more educated than their mothers (EDUC and MAEDUC)?

13.130 The survey asks for total family income and respondents' income. The difference between them is the amount earned by the members of the respondent's family. Compute a confidence interval estimate of the mean income of the other members of the respondent's family (INCOME: Total family income; RINCOME: Respondent's income).

13.131 Do most two-income families try to have both spouses work the same number of hours? To answer the question, conduct a test to determine whether there is sufficient evidence to infer that respondents and their spouses differ in the number of hours per week of work (HRS1 and SPHRS1)?

Survey of Consumer Finances Exercises

SCF2019:\MC *The following exercises deal with middle class households defined as those with net worth of between $120,185 and $450,000.*

13.132 In terms of income, do heads of middle-class households consider this to be a better year than normal? Conduct a test to answer the question (INCOME = Household income in 2019; NORMINC = Household normal income).

13.133 Capital gains can be produced in a number of ways. Most homeowners have unrealized capital gains on their homes. Determine a confidence interval estimate of the mean amount of all capital gains except the home (KGHOUSE = Unrealized capital gains on the primary residence; KGTOTAL = Total unrealized capital gains for the household).

13-4 INFERENCE ABOUT THE RATIO OF TWO VARIANCES

In Sections 13-1 and 13-3, we dealt with statistical inference concerning the difference between two population means. The problem objective in each case was to compare two populations of interval data, and our interest was in comparing measures of central location. This section discusses the statistical technique to use when the problem objective and the data type are the same as in Sections 13-1 and 13-3, but our interest is in comparing variability. Here we will study the ratio of two population variances. We make inferences about the ratio because the sampling distribution is based on ratios rather than differences.

We have already encountered this technique when we used the F-test of two variances to determine which t-test and estimator of the difference between two means to use. In this section, we apply the technique to other problems where our interest is in comparing the variability in two populations.

In the previous chapter, we presented the procedures used to draw inferences about a single population variance. We pointed out that variance can be used to address problems where we need to judge the consistency of a production process. We also use variance to measure the risk associated with a portfolio of investments. In this section, we compare two variances, enabling us to compare the consistency of two production processes. We can also compare the relative risks of two sets of investments.

We will proceed in a manner that is probably becoming quite familiar.

13-4a Parameter

As you will see shortly, we compare two population variances by determining the ratio. Consequently, the parameter is σ_1^2/σ_2^2.

13-4b Statistic and Sampling Distribution

We have previously noted that the sample variance (defined in Chapter 4) is an unbiased and consistent estimator of the population variance. Not surprisingly, the estimator of the parameter σ_1^2/σ_2^2 is the ratio of the two sample variances drawn from their respective populations s_1^2/s_2^2.

The sampling distribution of s_1^2/s_2^2 is said to be F-distributed provided that we have independently sampled from two normal populations. (The F-distribution was introduced in Section 8-4.)

Statisticians have shown that the ratio of two independent chi-squared variables divided by their degrees of freedom is F-distributed. The degrees of freedom of the F-distribution are identical to the degrees of freedom for the two chi-squared distributions. In Section 12-2, we pointed out that $(n-1)s^2/\sigma^2$ is chi-squared distributed, provided that the sampled population is normal. If we have independent samples drawn from two normal populations, then both $(n_1-1)s_1^2/\sigma_1^2$ and $(n_2-1)s_2^2/\sigma_2^2$ are chi-squared distributed. If we divide each by their respective number of degrees of freedom and take the ratio, we produce

$$\frac{\dfrac{(n_1-1)s_1^2/\sigma_1^2}{(n_1-1)}}{\dfrac{(n_2-1)s_2^2/\sigma_2^2}{(n_2-1)}}$$

which simplifies to

$$\frac{s_1^2/\sigma_1^2}{s_2^2/\sigma_2^2}$$

This statistic is F-distributed with $\nu_1 = n_1 - 1$ and $\nu_2 = n_2 - 1$ degrees of freedom. Recall that ν_1 is called the **numerator degrees of freedom** and ν_2 is called the **denominator degrees of freedom**.

13-4c Testing and Estimating a Ratio of Two Variances

In this book, our null hypothesis will always specify that the two variances are equal. As a result, the ratio will equal 1. Thus, the null hypothesis will always be expressed as

$$H_0: \quad \sigma_1^2/\sigma_2^2 = 1$$

The alternative hypothesis can state that the ratio σ_1^2/σ_2^2 is either not equal to 1, greater than 1, or less than 1. Technically, the test statistic is

$$F = \frac{s_1^2/\sigma_1^2}{s_2^2/\sigma_2^2}$$

However, under the null hypothesis, which states that $\sigma_1^2/\sigma_2^2 = 1$, the test statistic becomes as follows.

Test Statistic for σ_1^2/σ_2^2

The test statistic employed to test that σ_1^2/σ_2^2 is equal to 1 is

$$F = \frac{s_1^2}{s_2^2}$$

which is F-distributed with $\nu_1 = n_1 - 1$ and $\nu_2 = n_2 - 1$ degrees of freedom provided that the populations are normal.

With the usual algebraic manipulation, we can derive the confidence interval estimator of the ratio of two population variances.

Confidence Interval Estimator of σ_1^2/σ_2^2

$$\text{LCL} = \left(\frac{s_1^2}{s_2^2}\right)\frac{1}{F_{\alpha/2, \nu_1, \nu_2}}$$

$$\text{UCL} = \left(\frac{s_1^2}{s_2^2}\right)F_{\alpha/2, \nu_2, \nu_1}$$

where $\nu_1 = n_1 - 1$ and $\nu_2 = n_2 - 1$

EXAMPLE 13.7

Testing the Quality of Two Bottle-Filling Machines

In Example 12.3, we applied the chi-squared test of a variance to determine whether there was sufficient evidence to conclude that the population variance was less than 1.0. Suppose that the statistics practitioner also collected data from another container-filling machine and recorded the fills of a randomly selected sample. Can we infer at the 5% significance level that the second machine is superior in its consistency?

SOLUTION:

IDENTIFY

The problem objective is to compare two populations where the data are interval. Because we want information about the consistency of the two machines, the parameter we wish to test is σ_1^2/σ_2^2, where σ_1^2 is the variance of machine 1 and σ_2^2 is the variance for machine 2. We need to conduct the F-test of σ_1^2/σ_2^2 to determine whether the variance of population 2 is less than that of population 1. Expressed differently, we wish to determine whether there is enough evidence to infer that σ_1^2 is larger than σ_2^2. Hence, the hypotheses we test are

$$H_0: \quad \sigma_1^2/\sigma_2^2 = 1$$
$$H_1: \quad \sigma_1^2/\sigma_2^2 > 1$$

COMPUTE

MANUALLY:

The sample variances are $s_1^2 = .6333$ and $s_2^2 = .4528$.
The value of the test statistic is

$$F = \frac{s_1^2}{s_2^2} = \frac{.6333}{.4528} = 1.40$$

The rejection region is

$$F > F_{\alpha, \nu_1, \nu_2} = F_{.05,24,24} = 1.98$$

Because the value of the test statistic is not greater than 1.98, we cannot reject the null hypothesis.

EXCEL Data Analysis

	A	B	C
1	F-Test Two-Sample for Variances		
2			
3		Machine 1	Machine 2
4	Mean	999.7	999.8
5	Variance	0.6333	0.4528
6	Observations	25	25
7	df	24	24
8	F	1.3988	
9	P(F<=f) one-tail	0.2085	
10	F Critical one-tail	1.9838	

The value of the test statistic is $F = 1.3988$. Excel outputs the one-tail p-value, which is .2085.

INSTRUCTIONS

1. Type or import the data into two columns. (Open Xm13-07.)
2. Click **Data, Data Analysis**, and **F-test Two-Sample for Variances**.
3. Specify the **Variable 1 Range** (A1:A26) and the **Variable 2 Range** (B1:B26). Type a value for α (.05).

INTERPRET

There is not enough evidence to infer that the variance of machine 2 is less than the variance of machine 1.

The histograms (not shown) appear to be sufficiently bell shaped to satisfy the normality requirement.

EXAMPLE 13.8

DATA
Xm13-07

Estimating the Ratio of the Variances in Example 13.7

Determine the 95% confidence interval estimate of the ratio of the two population variances in Example 13.7.

SOLUTION:

COMPUTE

MANUALLY:

We find

$$F_{\alpha/2, \nu_1, \nu_2} = F_{.025, 24, 24} = 2.27$$

Thus,

$$\text{LCL} = \left(\frac{s_1^2}{s_2^2}\right)\frac{1}{F_{\alpha/2, \nu_2, \nu_1}} = \left(\frac{.6333}{.4528}\right)\frac{1}{2.27} = .616$$

$$\text{UCL} = \left(\frac{s_1^2}{s_2^2}\right)F_{\alpha/2, \nu_2, \nu_1} = \left(\frac{.6333}{.4528}\right)2.27 = 3.17$$

We estimate that σ_1^2/σ_2^2 lies between .616 and 3.17.

EXCEL Workbook

	A	B	C	D	E
1	F-Estimate of the Ratio of Two Variances				
2					
3		Sample 1	Sample 2	Confidence Interval Estimate	
4	Sample variance	0.63	0.45	Lower confidence limit	0.6163
5	Sample size	25	25	Upper confidence limit	3.1739
6	Confidence level	0.95			

INSTRUCTIONS

1. Type or import the data into two columns (Open Xm13-07). Calculate the sample variances for each sample.
2. Open the **Estimators Workbook** and select the **F-Estimate_2 Variances** tab. Copy or type the sample variances, sample sizes, and confidence level.

As we pointed out in Chapter 11, we can often use a confidence interval estimator to test the hypotheses. In this example, the interval estimate excludes the value of 1. Consequently, we can draw the same conclusion as we did in Example 13.7.

Factors That Identify the *F*-Test and Estimator of σ_1^2/σ_2^2

1. **Problem objective**: Compare two populations.
2. **Data type**: Interval
3. **Descriptive measurement**: Variability

EXERCISES

Developing an Understanding of Statistical Concepts

Exercises 13.134 and 13.135 are "what-if analyses" designed to determine what happens to the test statistics and interval estimates when elements of the statistical inference change. These problems can be solved manually.

13.134 Random samples from two normal populations produced the following statistics:

$$s_1^2 = 350 \quad n_1 = 30 \quad s_2^2 = 700 \quad n_2 = 30$$

a. Can we infer at the 10% significance level that the two population variances differ?

b. Repeat part (a) changing the sample sizes to $n_1 = 15$ and $n_2 = 15$.

c. Describe what happens to the test statistic when the sample sizes decrease.

13.135 Random samples from two normal populations produced the following statistics:

$$s_1^2 = 28 \quad n_1 = 10 \quad s_2^2 = 19 \quad n_2 = 10$$

a. Estimate with 95% confidence the ratio of the two population variances.

b. Repeat part (a) changing the sample sizes to $n_1 = 25$ and $n_2 = 25$.

c. Describe what happens to the width of the confidence interval estimate when the sample sizes increase.

Applications

Use a 5% significance level in all tests.

13.136 Xr13-136 The manager of a dairy is in the process of deciding which of two new carton-filling machines to use. The most important attribute is the consistency of the fills. In a preliminary study the fills in the 1-liter carton were measured and listed here. Can the manager infer that the two machines differ in their consistency of fills?

Machine 1	.998	.997	1.003	1.000	.999	
	1.000	.998	1.003	1.004	1.000	
Machine 2	1.003	1.004	.997	.996	.999	1.003
	1.000	1.005	1.002	1.004	.996	

13.137 Xr13-137   An operations manager who supervises an assembly line has been experiencing problems with the sequencing of jobs. The problem is that bottlenecks are occurring because of the inconsistency of sequential operations. An experiment wherein two different methods are used to complete the same task was conducted. The times (seconds) were recorded and listed here. Can we infer that the second method is more consistent than the first method?

Method 1	8.8	9.6	8.4	9.0	8.3	9.2	9.0	8.7	8.5	9.4
Method 2	9.2	9.4	8.9	9.6	9.7	8.4	8.8	8.9	9.0	9.7

13.138 Xr13-138   A statistics professor hypothesized that not only would the means vary, but also so would the variances if the business statistics course was taught in two different ways but had the same final exam. An experiment was organized wherein one section of the course was taught using detailed PowerPoint slides whereas the other required students to read the book and answer questions in class discussions. A sample of the marks was recorded and listed next. Can we infer that the variances of the marks differ between the two sections?

Class 1	64	85	80	64	48	62	75	77	50	81	90
Class 2	73	78	66	69	79	81	74	59	83	79	84

The following exercises require the use of a computer and software. The answers to Exercises 13.139 to 13.142 may be calculated manually. See Appendix A for the sample statistics.

For Exercises 13.139 to 13.148 use a 5% significance level.

13.139 Xr13-139   A new highway has just been completed and the government must decide on speed limits. There are several possible choices. However, on advice from police who monitor traffic the objective was to reduce the variation in speeds, which it is thought to contribute to the number of collisions. It is decided to conduct an experiment to acquire more information. Signs are posted for 1 week indicating that the speed limit is 70 mph. A random sample of cars' speeds is measured. During the second week, signs are posted indicating that the maximum speed is 70 mph and that the minimum speed is 60 mph. Once again a random sample of speeds is measured. Can we infer that limiting the minimum and maximum speeds reduces the variation in speeds?

13.140 Xr13-140   In Exercise 12.80 we described the problem of whether to change all the light bulbs at Yankee Stadium or change them one by one as they burn out. There are two brands of bulbs that can be used. Because both the mean and the variance of the lengths of life are important, it was decided to test the two brands. A random sample of both brands was drawn and left on until they burned out. The times were recorded. Can the Yankee Stadium management conclude that the variances differ?

13.141 Xr13-141   In deciding where to invest a retirement fund, an investor recorded the weekly returns of two portfolios for 1 year. Can we conclude that portfolio 2 is riskier than portfolio 1?

13.142 Xr13-142   An important statistical measurement in service facilities (such as restaurants and banks) is the variability in service times. As an experiment, two bank tellers were observed, and the service times for each of 100 customers were recorded. Do these data allow us to infer that the variance in service times differs between the two tellers?

GENERAL SOCIAL SURVEY EXERCISES

<u>GSS2018</u> *Exercises 13.143 and 13.144 are based on the General Social Survey of 2018.*

13.143 There are advantages and disadvantages to working for one's self. The advantages are that the rewards can be substantial. However, it is also possible to have nothing to show for a lot of work. In theory the variation in income for self-employed individuals is greater than the variation in income for people who work for someone else (WRKSLF: 1 = Self-employed, 2 = Work for someone else). Conduct a test to determine whether there is enough evidence to support the theory (RINCOME).

13.144 Most people who work for someone else are likely to have a set number of hours that does not vary. In most cases this will be around 40 hours per week. Self-employed people do not have the luxury of having a limit on the hours they work. As a result, we would expect that the hours worked by the self-employed vary more than do the hours of employees (WRKSLF: 1 = Self-employed, 2 = Work for someone else). Is there sufficient evidence to support this theory (HRS1)?

SURVEY OF CONSUMER FINANCES EXERCISES

<u>SCF2019:\MC</u> *The following exercises deal with middle class households defined as those with net worth of between $120,185 and $450,000.*

13.145 The financial rewards for self-employment can be considerable. The downside may be that one works long hours accruing debts with little or no financial return. As a result, we theorize that the variance in compensation will be greater for the self-employed (OCCAT1: 1 = Work for someone else, 2 = Self-employed/partnership). Conduct a test to determine if the variation in income for the self-employed is greater than that of employees (INCOME).

13.146 Refer to Exercise 13.145. Is there enough evidence to conclude that the variation in net worth is greater for the self-employed than for employees (NETWORTH)?

13.147 Refer to Exercise 13.145. Is there more variation in the amount of debt of the self-employed than for employees (DEBT)?

13.148 Refer to Exercise 13.145. Do the data allow us to conclude that there is more variation in total capital gains (KGTOTAL) for self-employed individuals?

13-5 / INFERENCE ABOUT THE DIFFERENCE BETWEEN TWO POPULATION PROPORTIONS

In this section, we present the procedures for drawing inferences about the difference between populations whose data are nominal. The number of applications of these techniques is almost limitless. For example, pharmaceutical companies test new drugs by comparing the new and old or the new versus a placebo. Marketing managers compare market shares before and after advertising campaigns. Operations managers compare defective rates between two machines. Political pollsters measure the difference in popularity before and after an election.

13-5a Parameter

When data are nominal, the only meaningful computation is to count the number of occurrences of each type of outcome and calculate proportions. Consequently, the parameter to be tested and estimated in this section is the difference between two population proportions $p_1 - p_2$.

13-5b Statistic and Sampling Distribution

To draw inferences about $p_1 - p_2$, we take a sample of size n_1 from population 1 and a sample of size n_2 from population 2 (Figure 13.7 depicts the sampling process).

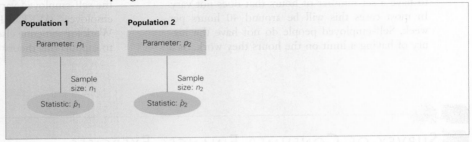

FIGURE **13.7** Sampling from Two Populations of Nominal Data

For each sample, we count the number of successes (recall that we call anything we're looking for a success), which we label x_1 and x_2, respectively. The sample proportions are then computed:

$$\hat{p}_1 = \frac{x_1}{n_1} \quad \text{and} \quad \hat{p}_2 = \frac{x_2}{n_2}$$

Statisticians have proven that the statistic $\hat{p}_1 - \hat{p}_2$ is an unbiased consistent estimator of the parameter $p_1 - p_2$. Using the same mathematics as we did in Chapter 9 to derive the sampling distribution of the sample proportion $\hat{p}$, we determine the sampling distribution of the difference between two sample proportions.

Sampling Distribution of $\hat{p}_1 - \hat{p}_2$

1. The statistic $\hat{p}_1 - \hat{p}_2$ is approximately normally distributed provided that the sample sizes are large enough so that $n_1 p_1$, $n_1(1 - p_1)$, $n_2 p_2$, and $n_2(1 - p_2)$ are all greater than or equal to 5. [Because p_1 and p_2 are unknown, we express the sample size requirement as $n_1\hat{p}_1$, $n_1(1 - \hat{p}_1)$, $n_2\hat{p}_2$, and $n_2(1 - \hat{p}_2)$ are greater than or equal to 5.]

2. The mean of $\hat{p}_1 - \hat{p}_2$ is
$$E(\hat{p}_1 - \hat{p}_2) = p_1 - p_2$$

3. The variance of $\hat{p}_1 - \hat{p}_2$ is
$$V(\hat{p}_1 - \hat{p}_2) = \frac{p_1(1 - p_1)}{n_1} + \frac{p_2(1 - p_2)}{n_2}$$

The standard error is
$$\sigma_{\hat{p}_1 - \hat{p}_2} = \sqrt{\frac{p_1(1 - p_1)}{n_1} + \frac{p_2(1 - p_2)}{n_2}}$$

Thus, the variable

$$z = \frac{(\hat{p}_1 - \hat{p}_2) - (p_1 - p_2)}{\sqrt{\dfrac{p_1(1 - p_1)}{n_1} + \dfrac{p_2(1 - p_2)}{n_2}}}$$

is approximately standard normally distributed.

13-5c Testing and Estimating the Difference between Two Proportions

We would like to use the z-statistic just described as our test statistic; however, the standard error of $\hat{p}_1 - \hat{p}_2$, which is

$$\sigma_{\hat{p}_1 - \hat{p}_2} = \sqrt{\frac{p_1(1 - p_1)}{n_1} + \frac{p_2(1 - p_2)}{n_2}}$$

is unknown because both p_1 and p_2 are unknown. As a result, the standard error of $\hat{p}_1 - \hat{p}_2$ must be estimated from the sample data. There are two different estimators of this quantity, and the determination of which one to use depends on the null hypothesis. If the null hypothesis states that $p_1 - p_2 = 0$, the hypothesized equality of the two population proportions allows us to pool the data from the two samples to produce an estimate of the common value of the two proportions p_1 and p_2. The **pooled proportion estimate** is defined as

$$\hat{p} = \frac{x_1 + x_2}{n_1 + n_2}$$

Thus, the estimated standard error of $\hat{p}_1 - \hat{p}_2$ is

$$\sqrt{\frac{\hat{p}(1 - \hat{p})}{n_1} + \frac{\hat{p}(1 - \hat{p})}{n_2}} = \sqrt{\hat{p}(1 - \hat{p})\left(\frac{1}{n_1} + \frac{1}{n_2}\right)}$$

The principle used in estimating the standard error of $\hat{p}_1 - \hat{p}_2$ is analogous to that applied in Section 13-1 to produce the pooled variance estimate s_p^2, which is used to test $\mu_1 - \mu_2$ with σ_1^2 and σ_2^2 unknown but equal. The principle roughly states that, where possible, pooling data from two samples produces a better estimate of the standard error. Here, pooling is made possible by hypothesizing (under the null hypothesis) that $p_1 = p_2$. (In Section 13-1, we used the pooled variance estimate because we assumed that $\sigma_1^2 = \sigma_2^2$.) We will call this application Case 1.

Test Statistic for $p_1 - p_2$: Case 1

If the null hypothesis specifies

$$H_0: \quad (p_1 - p_2) = 0$$

the test statistic is

$$z = \frac{(\hat{p}_1 - \hat{p}_2) - (p_1 - p_2)}{\sqrt{\hat{p}(1 - \hat{p})\left(\frac{1}{n_1} + \frac{1}{n_2}\right)}}$$

Because we hypothesize that $p_1 - p_2 = 0$, we simplify the test statistic to

$$z = \frac{(\hat{p}_1 - \hat{p}_2)}{\sqrt{\hat{p}(1 - \hat{p})\left(\frac{1}{n_1} + \frac{1}{n_2}\right)}}$$

The second case applies when, under the null hypothesis, we state that $p_1 - p_2 = D$, where D is some value other than 0. Under such circumstances, we cannot pool the sample data to estimate the standard error of $\hat{p}_1 - \hat{p}_2$. The appropriate test statistic is described next as Case 2.

Test Statistic for $p_1 - p_2$: Case 2

If the null hypothesis specifies

$$H_0: \quad (p_1 - p_2) = D \quad (D \neq 0)$$

the test statistic is

$$z = \frac{(\hat{p}_1 - \hat{p}_2) - (p_1 - p_2)}{\sqrt{\dfrac{\hat{p}_1(1 - \hat{p}_1)}{n_1} + \dfrac{\hat{p}_2(1 - \hat{p}_2)}{n_2}}}$$

which can also be expressed as

$$z = \frac{(\hat{p}_1 - \hat{p}_2) - D}{\sqrt{\dfrac{\hat{p}_1(1 - \hat{p}_1)}{n_1} + \dfrac{\hat{p}_2(1 - \hat{p}_2)}{n_2}}}$$

Notice that this test statistic is determined by simply substituting the sample statistics $\hat{p}_1$ and $\hat{p}_2$ in the standard error of $\hat{p}_1 - \hat{p}_2$.

You will find that, in most practical applications (including the exercises in this book), Case 1 applies—in most problems, we want to know whether the two population proportions differ: that is,

$$H_1: \quad (p_1 - p_2) \neq 0$$

or if one proportion exceeds the other; that is,

$$H_1: \quad (p_1 - p_2) > 0 \quad \text{or} \quad H_1: \quad (p_1 - p_2) < 0$$

In some other problems, however, the objective is to determine whether one proportion exceeds the other by a specific nonzero quantity. In such situations, Case 2 applies.

We derive the interval estimator of $p_1 - p_2$ in the same manner we have been using since Chapter 10.

Confidence Interval Estimator of $p_1 - p_2$

$$(\hat{p}_1 - \hat{p}_2) \pm z_{\alpha/2} \sqrt{\frac{\hat{p}_1(1 - \hat{p}_1)}{n_1} + \frac{\hat{p}_2(1 - \hat{p}_2)}{n_2}}$$

This formula is valid when $n_1\hat{p}_1$, $n_1(1 - \hat{p}_1)$, $n_2\hat{p}_2$, and $n_2(1 - \hat{p}_2)$ are greater than or equal to 5.

Notice that the standard error is estimated using the individual sample proportions rather than the pooled proportion. In this procedure we cannot assume that the population proportions are equal as we did in the Case 1 test statistic.

APPLICATIONS in MARKETING

Test Marketing

Marketing managers frequently make use of test marketing to assess consumer reaction to a change in a characteristic (such as price or packaging) of an existing product, or to assess consumers' preferences regarding a proposed new product. *Test marketing* involves experimenting with changes to the marketing mix in a small, limited test market and assessing consumers' reaction in the test market before undertaking costly changes in production and distribution for the entire market.

Monkey Business Images/
Shutterstock.com

EXAMPLE 13.9

DATA
Xm13-09

Test Marketing of Package Designs, Part 1

The General Products Company produces and sells a variety of household products. Because of stiff competition, one of its products, a bath soap, is not selling well. Hoping to improve sales, General Products decided to introduce more attractive packaging. The company's advertising agency developed two new designs. The first design features several bright colors to distinguish it from other brands. The second design is light green in color with just the company's logo on it. As a test to determine which design is better, the marketing manager selected two supermarkets. In one supermarket, the soap was packaged in a box using the first design; in the second supermarket, the second design was used. The product scanner at each supermarket tracked every buyer of soap over a 1-week period. The supermarkets recorded the last four digits of the scanner code for each of the five brands of soap the supermarket sold. The code for the General Products brand of soap is 9077 (the other codes are 4255, 3745, 7118, and 8855). After the trial period, the scanner data were transferred to a computer file. Because the first design is more expensive, management has decided to use this design only if there is sufficient evidence to allow it to conclude that design is better. Should management switch to the brightly colored design or the simple green one?

SOLUTION:

IDENTIFY

The problem objective is to compare two populations, soap sales in which the General Products soap is packaged in two different ways. The data are nominal because the values are "buy General Products soap" and "buy other companies' soap." These two factors tell us that the parameter to be tested is the difference between two population proportions $p_1 - p_2$, where p_1 = proportion of General Products sales in new package and p_2 = proportion of General Product's soap in old package. Because we want to know whether there is enough evidence to adopt the brightly colored design, the alternative hypothesis is

$$H_1: \quad (p_1 - p_2) > 0$$

The null hypothesis must be

$$H_0: \quad (p_1 - p_2) = 0$$

which tells us that this is an application of Case 1. Thus, the test statistic is

$$z = \frac{(\hat{p}_1 - \hat{p}_2)}{\sqrt{\hat{p}(1 - \hat{p})\left(\dfrac{1}{n_1} + \dfrac{1}{n_2}\right)}}$$

COMPUTE

MANUALLY:

To compute the test statistic manually requires the statistics practitioner to tally the number of successes in each sample, where success is represented by the code 9077. Reviewing all the sales reveals that

$$x_1 = 180 \qquad n_1 = 904 \qquad x_2 = 155 \qquad n_2 = 1{,}038$$

The sample proportions are

$$\hat{p}_1 = \frac{180}{904} = .1991$$

and

$$\hat{p}_2 = \frac{155}{1{,}038} = .1493$$

The pooled proportion is

$$\hat{p} = \frac{180 + 155}{904 + 1{,}038} = \frac{335}{1{,}942} = .1725$$

The value of the test statistic is

$$z = \frac{(\hat{p}_1 - \hat{p}_2)}{\sqrt{\hat{p}(1 - \hat{p})\left(\dfrac{1}{n_1} + \dfrac{1}{n_2}\right)}} = \frac{(.1991 - .1493)}{\sqrt{(.1725)(1 - .1725)\left(\dfrac{1}{904} + \dfrac{1}{1{,}038}\right)}} = 2.90$$

A 5% significance level seems to be appropriate. Thus, the rejection region is

$$z > z_\alpha = z_{.05} = 1.645$$

EXCEL Workbook

	A	B	C	D	E
1	z-Test of the Difference Between Two Proportions (Case 1)				
2					
3		Sample 1	Sample 2	z Stat	2.90
4	Sample proportion	0.1991	0.1493	P(Z<=z) one-tail	0.0019
5	Sample size	904	1038	z Critical one-tail	1.6449
6	Alpha	0.05		P(Z<=z) two-tail	0.0038
7				z Critical two-tail	1.9600

INSTRUCTIONS

1. Type or import the data into two columns (Open Xm13-07). Calculate the sample proportions for each sample.
2. Open the **Test Statistics Workbook** and select the **z-Test_2 Proportions (Case 1)** tab. Copy or type the sample proportions, sample sizes, and α.

INTERPRET

The value of the test statistic is $z = 2.90$; its p-value is .0019. There is enough evidence to infer that the brightly colored design is more popular than the simple design. As a result, it is recommended that management switch to the first design.

EXAMPLE 13.10

DATA
Xm13-09

Test Marketing of Package Designs, Part 2

Suppose that in Example 13.9 the additional cost of the brightly colored design requires that it outsell the simple design by more than 3%. Should management switch to the brightly colored design?

SOLUTION:

IDENTIFY

The alternative hypothesis is

$$H_1: \quad (p_1 - p_2) > .03$$

and the null hypothesis follows as

$$H_0: \quad (p_1 - p_2) = .03$$

Because the null hypothesis specifies a nonzero difference, we would apply the Case 2 test statistic.

COMPUTE

MANUALLY:

The value of the test statistic is

$$z = \frac{(\hat{p}_1 - \hat{p}_2) - (p_1 - p_2)}{\sqrt{\dfrac{\hat{p}_1(1 - \hat{p}_1)}{n_1} + \dfrac{\hat{p}_2(1 - \hat{p}_2)}{n_2}}} = \frac{(.1991 - .1493) - (.03)}{\sqrt{\dfrac{.1991(1 - .1991)}{904} + \dfrac{.1493(1 - .1493)}{1,038}}} = 1.15$$

EXCEL Workbook

	A	B	C	D	E
1	z-Test of the Difference Between Two Proportions (Case 2)				
2					
3		Sample 1	Sample 2	z Stat	1.15
4	Sample proportion	0.1991	0.1493	P(Z<=z) one-tail	0.1260
5	Sample size	904	1038	z Critical one-tail	1.6449
6	Hypothesized difference	0.03		P(Z<=z) two-tail	0.2520
7	Alpha	0.05		z Critical two-tail	1.9600

INSTRUCTIONS

1. Type or import the data into two columns (Open Xm13-07). Calculate the sample proportions for each sample.

2. Open the **Test Statistics Workbook** and select the **z-Test_2 Proportions (Case 2)** tab. Copy or type the sample proportions, sample sizes, the hypothesized difference (.03) and α.

INTERPRET

There is not enough evidence to infer that the proportion of soap customers who buy the product with the brightly colored design is more than 3% higher than the proportion of soap customers who buy the product with the simple design. In the absence of sufficient evidence, the analysis suggests that the product should be packaged using the simple design.

EXAMPLE 13.11

DATA
Xm13-09

Test Marketing of Package Designs, Part 3

To help estimate the difference in profitability, the marketing manager in Examples 13.9 and 13.10 would like to estimate the difference between the two proportions. A confidence level of 95% is suggested.

SOLUTION:

IDENTIFY

The parameter is $p_1 - p_2$, which is estimated by the following confidence interval estimator:

$$(\hat{p}_1 - \hat{p}_2) \pm z_{\alpha/2} \sqrt{\frac{\hat{p}_1(1 - \hat{p}_1)}{n_1} + \frac{\hat{p}_2(1 - \hat{p}_2)}{n_2}}$$

COMPUTE

MANUALLY:

The sample proportions have already been computed. They are

$$\hat{p}_1 = \frac{180}{904} = .1991$$

and

$$\hat{p}_2 = \frac{155}{1,038} = .1493$$

The 95% confidence interval estimate of $p_1 - p_2$ is

$$(\hat{p}_1 - \hat{p}_2) \pm z_{\alpha/2} \sqrt{\frac{\hat{p}_1(1 - \hat{p}_1)}{n_1} + \frac{\hat{p}_2(1 - \hat{p}_2)}{n_2}}$$

$$= (.1991 - .1493) \pm 1.96 \sqrt{\frac{.1991(1 - .1991)}{904} + \frac{.1493(1 - .1493)}{1,038}}$$

$$= .0498 \pm .0339$$

$$\text{LCL} = .0159 \quad \text{and} \quad \text{UCL} = .0837$$

EXCEL Workbook

	A	B	C	D	E	F
1	z-Estimate of the Difference Between Two Proportions					
2						
3		Sample 1	Sample 2	Confidence Interval Estimate		
4	Sample proportion	0.1991	0.1493	0.0498	±	0.0339
5	Sample size	904	1038	Lower confidence limit		0.0159
6	Confidence level	0.95		Upper confidence limit		0.0837

INSTRUCTIONS

1. Type or import the data into two columns (Open Xm13-07). Calculate the sample proportions for each sample.

2. Open the **Estimators Workbook** and select the **z-Estimate_2 Proportions** tab. Copy or type the sample proportions, sample sizes, and α.

General Social Survey

Comparing 2010 and 2018: Has there been a decrease in the proportion of people working for themselves?

SOLUTION:

IDENTIFY

The problem objective is to compare two populations, the 2010 and 2018 responses to the question about working for themselves (WRKSLF: 1 = Yes, 2 = No).

The hypotheses are:

$$H_0: (p_1 - p_2) = 0$$
$$H_1: (p_1 - p_2) > 0$$

where p_1 = proportion of self-employed workers in 2010 and p_2 = proportion of self-employed workers in 2018. The null hypothesis tells us that this is an application of Case 1. Thus, the test statistic is:

$$z = \frac{(\hat{p}_1 - \hat{p}_2)}{\sqrt{\hat{p}(1-\hat{p})\left(\dfrac{1}{n_1} + \dfrac{1}{n_2}\right)}}$$

COMPUTE

MANUALLY:

To calculate the test statistic, we start by counting the number of successes and sample sizes in each sample, where success is represented by WRKSLF = 1.

$x_1 = 234 \qquad n_1 = 1{,}940 \qquad x_2 = 232 \qquad n_2 = 2{,}261$

The sample proportions are

$$\hat{p}_1 = \frac{234}{1{,}940} = .1206$$

and

$$\hat{p}_2 = \frac{232}{2{,}261} = .1026$$

The pooled proportion is

$$\hat{p} = \frac{234 + 232}{1{,}940 + 2{,}261} = \frac{446}{4{,}201} = .1109$$

The value of the test statistic is

$$z = \frac{(\hat{p}_1 - \hat{p}_2)}{\sqrt{\hat{p}(1-\hat{p})\left(\frac{1}{n_1} + \frac{1}{n_2}\right)}} = \frac{(.1206 - .1026)}{\sqrt{(.1109)(1-.1109)\left(\frac{1}{1940} + \frac{1}{2261}\right)}} = 1.85$$

A 5% significance level seems to be appropriate. Thus, the rejection region is

$$z > z_\alpha = z_{.05} = 1.645$$

p-value $= P(Z > 1.85) = 1 - P(Z < 1.85) = 1 - .9678 = .0322$

EXCEL Workbook

	A	B	C	D	E
1	z-Test of the Difference Between Two Proportions (Case 1)				
2					
3		Sample 1	Sample 2	z Stat	1.85
4	Sample proportion	0.1206	0.1026	P(Z<=z) one-tail	0.0319
5	Sample size	1940	2261	z Critical one-tail	1.6449
6	Alpha	0.05		P(Z<=z) two-tail	0.0639
7				z Critical two-tail	1.9600

INSTRUCTIONS

1. Type or import the data into two columns (Open GSS2010 and GSS2018). Use the COUNTIF function to determine the frequencies for each sample.

2. Open the **Test Statistics Workbook** and select the **z-Test_2 Proportions (Case 1)** tab. Copy or type the sample proportions, sample sizes, and α.

INTERPRET

The value of the test statistic is 1.85 and using the Excel figure, the p-value is .0319. There is enough evidence to conclude that the proportion of self-employed Americans in 2018 is less than the proportion of self-employed workers in 2010.

The factors that identify the inference about the difference between two proportions are listed below.

Factors That Identify the z-Test and Estimator of $p_1 - p_2$

1. **Problem objective**: Compare two populations.
2. **Data type**: Nominal

EXERCISES

Developing an Understanding of Statistical Concepts

Exercises 13.149 to 13.151 are "what-if analyses" designed to determine what happens to the test statistics and interval estimates when elements of the statistical inference change. These problems can be solved manually or by using an Excel spreadsheet.

13.149 Random samples from two binomial populations yielded the following statistics:

$\hat{p}_1 = .45$ $n_1 = 100$ $\hat{p}_2 = .40$ $n_2 = 100$

a. Calculate the *p*-value of a test to determine whether we can infer that the population proportions differ.
b. Repeat part (a) increasing the sample sizes to 400.
c. Describe what happens to the *p*-value when the sample sizes increase.

13.150 These statistics were calculated from two random samples:

$\hat{p}_1 = .60$ $n_1 = 225$ $\hat{p}_2 = .55$ $n_2 = 225$

a. Calculate the *p*-value of a test to determine whether there is evidence to infer that the population proportions differ.
b. Repeat part (a) with $\hat{p}_1 = .95$ and $\hat{p}_2 = .90$.
c. Describe the effect on the *p*-value of increasing the sample proportions.
d. Repeat part (a) with $\hat{p}_1 = .10$ and $\hat{p}_2 = .05$.
e. Describe the effect on the *p*-value of decreasing the sample proportions.

13.151 After sampling from two binomial populations we found the following.

$\hat{p}_1 = .18$ $n_1 = 100$ $\hat{p}_2 = .22$ $n_2 = 100$

a. Estimate with 90% confidence the difference in population proportions.
b. Repeat part (a) increasing the sample proportions to .48 and .52, respectively.
c. Describe the effects of increasing the sample proportions.

Applications

For Exercises 13.152 to 13.221 conduct all tests at the 5% significance level and all estimates at the 95% confidence level.

13.152 Many stores sell extended warranties for products they sell. These are very lucrative for store owners. To learn more about who buys these warranties a random sample of a store's customers who recently purchased a product for which an extended warranty was available was drawn. Among other variables each respondent reported whether they paid the regular price or a sale price and whether they purchased an extended warranty.

	Regular Price	Sale Price
Sample size	229	178
Number who bought extended warranty	47	25

Can we conclude that those who paid the regular price are more likely to buy an extended warranty?

13.153 A firm has classified its customers in two ways: (1) according to whether the account is overdue and (2) whether the account is new (less than 12 months) or old. To acquire information about which customers are paying on time and which are overdue, a random sample of 292 customer accounts was drawn. Each was categorized as a new account (less than 12 months) and old, and whether the customer has paid or is overdue. The results are summarized next.

	New Account	Old Account
Sample size	83	209
Overdue account	12	49

Is there enough evidence to infer that new and old accounts are different with respect to overdue accounts?

Overeating Experiment (See page 478 for description.)

13.154 Chop Stick Experiment

One hundred normal-weight people and 100 over-weight people were observed at several Chinese-food buffets. Researchers recorded whether the diner used chopsticks or knife and fork. The table shown here was created.

	Normal Weight	Over-weight
Used chop sticks	26	7
Used knife and fork	74	93

Is there sufficient evidence to conclude that over-weight Chinese food eaters are less likely to use chop sticks?

Source: Brian Wansink and Collin R. Payne, "The Cues and Correlates of Overeating at the Chinese Buffet," Cornell University Food and Brand Lab working paper.

13.155 Surveys have been widely used by politicians around the world as a way of monitoring the opinions of the electorate. Six months ago, a survey was undertaken to determine the degree of support for a national party leader. Of a sample of 1,100, 56% indicated that they would vote for this politician. This month, another survey of 800 voters revealed that 46% now support the leader.

    a. Can we infer that the national leader's popularity has decreased?

    b. Can we infer that the national leader's popularity has decreased by more than 5%?

    c. Estimate the decrease in percentage support between now and 6 months ago.

13.156 The process that is used to produce a complex component used in medical instruments typically results in defective rates in the 40% range. Recently, two innovative processes have been developed to replace the existing process. Process 1 appears to be more promising, but it is considerably more expensive to purchase and operate than process 2. After a thorough analysis of the costs, management decides that it will adopt process 1 only if the proportion of defective components it produces is more than 8% smaller than that produced by process 2. In a test to guide the decision, both processes were used to produce 300 components. Of the 300 components produced by process 1, 33 were found to be defective, whereas 84 out of the 300 produced by process 2 were defective. Conduct a test to help management make a decision.

APPLICATIONS in OPERATIONS MANAGEMENT

Pharmaceutical and Medical Experiments

When new products are developed, they are tested in several ways. First, does the new product work? Second, is it better than the existing product? Third, will customers buy it at a price that is profitable? Performing a customer survey or some other experiment that yields the information needed often tests the last question. This experiment is usually the domain of the marketing manager.

The other two questions are dealt with by the developers of the new product, which usually means the research department or the operations manager. When the product is a new drug, there are particular ways in which the data are gathered. The sample is divided into two groups. One group is assigned the new drug and the other is assigned a placebo, a pill that contains no medication. The experiment is often called "double-blind" because neither the subjects who take the drug nor the physician/scientist who provides the drug knows whether any individual is taking the drug or the placebo. At the end of the experiment the data that are compiled allow statistics practitioners to do their work. Exercises 13.157–13.161 are examples of this type of statistical application. Exercise 13.162 describes a health-related problem where the use of a placebo is not possible.

13.157 Cold and allergy medicines have been available for a number of years. One serious side effect of these medications is that they cause drowsiness, which makes them dangerous for industrial workers. In recent years, a nondrowsy cold and allergy medicine has been developed. One such product, Hismanal, is claimed by its manufacturer to be the first once-a-day nondrowsy allergy medicine. The nondrowsy part of the claim is based on a clinical experiment in which 1,604 patients were given Hismanal and 1,109 patients were given a placebo. Of the first group, 7.1% reported drowsiness; of the second group, 6.4% reported drowsiness. Do these results allow us to infer that Hismanal's claim is false?

(Continued)

13.158 Plavix is a drug that is given to angioplasty patients to help prevent blood clots. A researcher at McMaster University organized a study that involved 12,562 patients in 482 hospitals in 28 countries. All the patients had acute coronary syndrome, which produces mild heart attacks or unstable angina, chest pain that may precede a heart attack. The patients were divided into two equal groups. Group 1 received daily Plavix pills, while group 2 received a placebo. After 1 year 9.3% of patients on Plavix suffered a stroke or new heart attack, or had died of cardiovascular disease, compared with 11.5% of those who took the placebo. Can we infer that Plavix is effective?

13.159 In a study that was highly publicized, doctors discovered that aspirin seems to help prevent heart attacks. The research project, which was scheduled to last for 5 years, involved 22,000 American physicians (all male). Half took an aspirin tablet three times per week, while the other half took a placebo on the same schedule. The researchers tracked each of the volunteers and updated the records regularly. Among the physicians who took aspirin, 104 suffered a heart attack; 189 physicians who took the placebo had a heart attack. Determine whether these results indicate that aspirin is effective in reducing the incidence of heart attacks.

13.160 Exercise 13.159 described the experiment that determined that taking aspirin daily reduces one's probability of suffering a heart attack. The study was conducted in 1982 and at that time the mean age of the physicians was 50. In the years following the experiment the physicians were monitored for other medical conditions. One of these was the incidence of cataracts. There were 1,084 cataracts in the aspirin group and 997 in the placebo group. Do these statistics allow researchers to conclude that aspirin leads to more cataracts?

13.161 According to the Canadian Cancer Society, more than 21,000 women will be diagnosed with breast cancer every year and more than 5,000 will die. (U.S. figures are more than 10 times those in Canada.) Surgery is generally considered the first method of treatment. However, many women suffer recurrences of cancer. For this reason many women are treated with Tamoxifen. But after 5 years, tumors develop a resistance to Tamoxifen. A new drug called Letrozole was developed by Novartis Pharmaceuticals to replace Tamoxifen. To determine its effectiveness, a study involving 5,187 breast cancer survivors from Canada, the United States, and Europe was undertaken. Half the sample received Letrozole and the other half a placebo. The study was to run for 5 years. However, after only 2.5 years it was determined that 75 women taking the drug and 132 taking the placebo had recurrences of their cancers. The study was published in the *New England Journal of Medicine*. Do these results provide sufficient evidence to infer that Letrozole works?

13.162 A study described in the *British Medical Journal* (January 2004) sought to determine whether exercise would help extend the lives of patients with heart failure. A sample of 801 patients with heart failure was recruited; 395 received exercise training and 406 did not. There were 88 deaths among the exercise group and 105 among those who did not exercise. Can researchers infer that exercise training reduces mortality?

Exercises 13.163 to 13.168 are based on the following experiment.

In an attempt to understand the frustrations of driving in large cities an experiment was conducted. At a red light in a busy intersection the lead car hesitated for 2 seconds. The researchers recorded several variables and whether the drivers in the following car honked their horn. The following tables were created from the recorded data.

Source: Traffic, Tom Vanderbilt.

13.163 Cell Phone Experiment 1

Driver in following car was female	Lead car driver using cell phone	Lead car driver not using cell phone
Honked horn	18	27
Did not honk horn	77	162

Is there enough evidence to infer that women drivers in a following car are more likely to honk when the lead car driver is using a cell phone?

13.164 Cell Phone Experiment 2

Driver in following car was male	Lead car driver used cell phone	Lead car driver did not use cell phone
Honked horn	35	34
Did not honk horn	103	170

Can we conclude that male drivers are more likely to honk when the lead car driver is using a cell phone?

13.165 Expensive Car Experiment

	Lead car was expensive (over $50,000)	Lead car was not expensive
Honked horn	33	49
Did not honk horn	122	118

Do these figures allow us to conclude that drivers behind expensive cars are less likely to honk?

13.166 Gender Experiment 1

	Lead car driver was female	Lead car driver was male
Honked horn	64	47
Did not honk horn	123	136

Is there sufficient evidence to infer that drivers behind a male driver are more likely to honk?

13.167 Gender Experiment 2

	Following car driver was female	Following car driver was male
Honked horn	68	105
Did not honk horn	143	135

Can we conclude from these statistics that women are less likely to honk?

13.168 Convertible Experiment

	Following car was a convertible	Following car was not a convertible
Honked horn	21	86
Did not honk horn	92	210

Is there enough evidence to draw the inference that drivers of convertibles are less likely to honk?

The following exercises require the use of a computer and software. The answers to Exercises 13.169–13.194 may be calculated manually. See Appendix A for the sample statistics.

13.169 Xr13-169 Automobile magazines often compare models and rate them in various ways. One question is often asked of car owners: Would you buy the same model again? Suppose that a researcher for one magazine asked a random sample of Lexus owners and a random sample of Acura owners whether they plan to buy another Lexus/Acura the next time they shop for a new car: Yes (1) or no (0). Do these data allow the researcher to infer that the two populations of car owners differ in their satisfaction levels?

13.170 Xr13-170 In July 2020, Gallup conducted a survey of Americans about policing. Gallup asked, "Which of the following best describes your view about changes that may or may not need to be made to policing in the United States?" The responses are 1 = Major changes needed, 2 = Minor changes needed, or 3 = No change needed. The survey also recorded the age category of the respondents. They are 1 = 18–34, 2 = 35–49, 3 = 50–64, 4 = 65+.

a. Is there sufficient evidence to infer that there is a difference between age categories 3 and 4 with respect to the answer that policing needs major change?

b. Do these data allow us to infer that Americans 35 to 49 years old are more likely to respond that no change is needed than Americans 18 to 34?

13.171 Xr13-171 Has the illicit use of drugs decreased over the past 10 years? Government agencies have undertaken surveys of Americans 12 years of age and older. All were asked whether they used drugs at least once in the previous month. The results of this year's survey and the results of the survey completed 10 years ago were recorded as yes (1) or no (0). Can we infer that the use of illicit drugs in the United States has increased in the past decade?

Source: Adapted from the U.S. Substance Abuse and Mental Health Services Administration, National Household Survey on Drug Abuse.

13.172 Xr13-172   It has been estimated that the oil sands in Alberta Canada contain 2 trillion barrels of oil. However, recovering the oil may damage the environment. A survey of Canadians and Americans asked, "What is more important to you with regard to the oil sands, environmental concerns (1), or the potential as a secure non-foreign supply of oil to North America (2)?" Do these data allow you to conclude that Canadians and Americans differ in their responses to this question?

Source: Flieshman-Hillard Oilsands Survey.

13.173 Xr13-173   An operations manager of a computer chip maker is in the process of selecting a new machine to replace several older ones. Although technological innovations have improved the production process, it is quite common for the machines to produce defective chips. The operations manager must choose between two machines. The cost of machine A is several thousand dollars greater than the cost of machine B. After an analysis of the costs, it was determined that machine A is warranted provided that its defective rate is more than 2% less than that of machine B. To help decide, both machines are used to produce 200 chips each. Each chip was examined: Defective (1) or nondetective (0). Should the operations manager select machine A?

13.174 Xr13-174   Throughout 2020, the entire world was anxiously looking forward to the development of a vaccine for COVID-19 that was killing people by the hundreds of thousands and crippling the economies of virtually all countries. A survey was conducted that asked American adults whether they would get the vaccine. Those who responded negatively were asked follow-up questions. What additional factors would lead you to change your mind?

Your doctor recommends the vaccine: 1 = Yes, 0 = No

The Centers for Disease Control (CDC) recommends the vaccine: 1 = Yes, 0 = No

President Trump recommends the vaccine: 1 = Yes, 0 = No

The political party was also recorded where 1 = Democrat, 2 = Republican, 3 = Independent

a. Is there enough statistical evidence to conclude that Democrats are more likely to heed the recommendation of their doctor than Independents?

b. Can we infer that the fraction of Independents and the fraction of Republicans that would heed the recommendation of the CDC differ?

c. Do the data allow us to conclude that Republicans are more likely to heed the advice of Donald Trump than Democrats?

13.175 Xr13-175   It is an unfortunate fact of university life that some entering students require a remedial course. A random sample of students that required either a remedial reading course or a remedial mathematics course 5 or more years ago was drawn. Respondents were asked whether they had graduated (1) or did not graduate (0). Is there enough statistical evidence to infer that those who required remedial mathematics had a higher graduation rate than those who required remedial reading?

13.176 Xr13-176   As a result of the lockdowns that were caused by the pandemic, many Americans lost their sources of income. The result oftentimes was that families could not afford food. A survey was conducted to determine the extent of the problem of food insecurity. Random samples of American adults were asked, "Did you or your family experience situations where sometimes or often you did not have enough food to eat?" The responses are 1 = Yes, 0 = No. Among other variables the survey reported whether the respondent completed high school or less (1) or more than a high school diploma (2). Determine a confidence interval estimate of the difference in food insecurity between those who completed high school or less and those with more than a high school diploma.

13.177 Xr13-177   One of the issues in the U.S. presidential election in 2016 was the Keystone XL pipeline, which would send Canadian oil to the refineries in Texas. The Pew Research Center conducted a survey of American adults and asked whether they were in favor (1) or opposed (0) to the pipeline. The survey identified each respondent as either male or female. Is there sufficient evidence to infer that men and women differ in their support of the pipeline?

13.178 Xr13-178+   An experiment conducted by members of the Religious Affiliation and Hiring Discrimination Organization to determine what shouldn't be on a resume should be of interest to students preparing resumes in search of summer or permanent jobs. The experiment consisted of submitting 6,400 resumes to employers that had advertised 1,600 job openings. The jobs included positions in customer service, hospitality, media, retail, real estate, shipping, and clerical duties. The postings only required an e-mailed resume. The fake job applicants were presented as young people recently graduated from college who earned a 3.7 or a higher grade-point average. Half of the resumes included mentions of religious activities and half made no reference to religion at all. For each resume the researchers recorded whether the prospective employer called the applicant back for more information or to schedule an interview (1) or no call back (0). Is there sufficient evidence to infer that including a reference to religious activity reduces the probability of a call back?

13.179 Xr13-178+ Refer to Exercise 13.178. In 2,700 of the resumes, the religion mentioned was one of the mainstream religions. However, 500 resumes made reference to a made-up religion—Wallonian. The religious designation (1 = Mainstream religion, 2 = Wallonian) was recorded. Is there sufficient evidence to infer that the Wallonians had a higher call back frequency than did the mainstream religions?

13.180 Xr13-180 To measure the cardiovascular health of Canadians, cardiologists developed the Cardiovascular Health in Ambulatory Care Research Team (CANHEART) health index. A score of 1 is assigned for each of the following cardiovascular health factors and behaviors:

1. Do not smoke
2. Physical activity equivalent to walking 30 minutes per day
3. Consumption of 5 servings of fruit and vegetables per day
4. Body mass index of less than 25
5. Not diabetic
6. Normal blood pressure (less than 140 over 90)

A score of 6 is ideal, 4 to 5 is considered to be intermediate, and a score between 0 and 3 is considered poor cardiovascular health. The scores and sex (1 = Female, 2 = Male) of a random sample of Canadian adults were recorded. Can we infer from the data that females are more likely to be in ideal cardiovascular health than males?

13.181 Xr13-181 In Exercise 9.63 we pointed out that most televised baseball games display a pitch tracker that shows whether the pitch was a ball or a strike, which in turn shows whether the umpire made the correct call. Suppose a fan kept track of a random sample of calls made by two of the more experienced umpires. In this exercise, pitches that were not in the strike zone and the batter did not swing were tracked. The fan recorded the umpire's call: Ball (1) or strike (2). Is there sufficient evidence that there is a difference in the error rate of making calls on pitches that were not in the strike zone between the two umpires?

Source: Adapted from SB Nation.

13.182 Xr13-182 Refer to Exercise 13.181. The fan also recorded the calls on pitches that were in the strike zone and the batter did not swing: The umpire's call: Ball (1) or strike (2). Can we infer from the data that there is a difference in the error rate of making calls on pitches in the strike zone between the two umpires?

13.183 Xr13-183 In June 2016 the United Kingdom voted to leave the European Union. As is the case in the United States, pollsters conducted exit polls and asked how each respondent voted: Remain (1) or leave (2) and recorded the age category: 18–24 (1), 25–49 (2), 50–64 (3), 65 and older (4).

a. Is there sufficient evidence to conclude that there is a difference in the vote between Britons aged 50 to 64 and those 65 and over?

b. Can we infer that there is a difference in the vote between 18- and 24-year-old Britons and those between 25 and 49?

13.184 Xr13-184 Surveys of workers asked a series of questions from which each was categorized as either: Thriving (1), struggling (2), or suffering (3). Each respondent was also asked whether they worked for the federal government or a private sector employer. Is there sufficient evidence to infer that government workers are more likely to be thriving when compared to other workers?

13.185 Xr13-185 A Gallup survey asks a random sample of American adults this question: "In this country, are you satisfied or dissatisfied with your freedom to choose what you do with your life?" The responses are: Satisfied (1) or dissatisfied (0). The survey results from this year and one 5 years ago were recorded. Is there enough statistical evidence to infer that American adults are less satisfied with the freedom to choose than they were 5 years ago?

13.186 Xr13-186 Waiters and waitresses expect to be tipped by their customers and most customers do tip. But what about hair stylist/barbers? A telephone survey was conducted where men and women were asked whether they tip their barbers and hair stylists: Leave tip (1) or do not leave tip (0). Is there sufficient evidence to infer that men and women differ in their providing tips to hair stylist/barber?

13.187 Xr13-187 Refer to Exercise 13.186. The survey asked men and women whether they tipped baristas (preparers and servers of coffee). The results were recorded as: Leave tip (1) or do not leave tip (0). Is there enough evidence to infer women are more likely to tip baristas than men?

13.188 Xr13-188 In September 2018 the results of a 5-year study was published in the New England Journal of Medicine. The study took random samples of American and Australian seniors (70 plus for Caucasians and 65+ for African American and Hispanic). Half took a low-dose aspirin and the other half took a placebo. After 5 years each volunteer was recorded as alive (1) or deceased (0). Is there enough evidence to infer that there is a difference in survival rates between the two groups?

13.189 Xr13-189 Refer to Exercise 13.188. The physicians conducting the experiment also recorded whether the patients suffered from a hemorrhagic stroke, which is bleeding in the brain (1) or not (0). Is there sufficient evidence to conclude that those taking aspirin suffer from a stroke more frequently than those taking the placebo?

13.190 Xr13-190   A Zogby poll asked American men and women whether they consider the major television newscasts and major newspapers trustworthy (1) or untrustworthy (0). Is there enough statistical evidence to infer that American women are more likely to believe that the major television newscasts and newspapers are trustworthy than American men?

13.191 Xr13-191   A Gallup poll asked a sample of American voters how satisfied they were with the nation's economy: Satisfied (1) or unsatisfied (0). The results of the poll 3 years ago and the one this year were recorded. Is there enough statistical evidence to infer that there was an increase in proportion satisfied between over the 3-year period?

APPLICATIONS in **MARKETING**

Stockbyte/Getty Images

Market Segmentation

In Section 12-4 we introduced market segmentation and described how the size of market segments can be estimated. Once the segments have been defined we can use statistical techniques to determine whether members of the segments differ in their purchases of a firm's products.

13.192 Xr13-192+   The market for breakfast cereals has been divided into several segments related to health. One company identified a segment as those adults who are health conscious. The marketing manager would like to know whether this segment is more likely to purchase its Special X cereal that is pitched toward the health-conscious segment. A survey of adults was undertaken. On the basis of several probing questions each was classified as either a member of the health-conscious group (code = 1) or not (code = 2). Respondents were also asked whether they buy Special X (1 = Yes and 0 = No). The data were recorded in stacked format. Can we infer from these data that health-conscious adults are more likely to buy Special X?

13.193 Xr13-193+   Quik Lube is a company that offers oil change service while the customer waits. Its market has been broken down into the following segments:
1. Working men and women too busy to wait at a dealer or service center
2. Spouses who work in the home
3. Retired persons
4. Other

A random sample of car owners was drawn. Owners classified their market segment and also reported whether they usually use the services like Quik Lube (1 = Yes, 0 = No). These data are stored in stacked format.
a. Determine whether members of segment 1 are more likely than members of segment 4 to respond that they usually use the service?
b. Can we infer that retired persons and spouses who work in the home differ in their use of services such as Quik Lube?

13.194 Xr13-194   Telemarketers obtain names and telephone numbers from several sources. To determine whether one particular source is better than a second, a random sample of names and numbers from the two different sources was obtained. For each potential customer, a statistics practitioner recorded whether that individual made a purchase (1 = Yes and 0 = No). Can we infer that differences exist between the two sources?

GENERAL SOCIAL SURVEY EXERCISES

<u>GSS2018</u>   *The following exercises are based on the 2018 survey.*

13.195 A generation ago, men were more likely to attend university and acquire a graduate degree than women. However, women now appear to be attending university in greater numbers than men. To gauge the extent of the difference, test to determine whether men and women (SEX: 1 = Male, 2 = Female) differ in completing a graduate degree (DEGREE: 4 = Graduate).

13.196 The deep recession of 2008–2010 may have changed patterns of employment. Because of the large number of layoffs, an increasing number of individuals have chosen to work for themselves. Does this apply equally to men and women (SEX: 1 = Male, 2 = Female)? Conduct a test to determine whether there is enough evidence to conclude that men and women differ in their decision to work for themselves (WRKSLF: 1 = Self-employed).

13.197 Is there sufficient evidence to conclude that foreign-born people (BORN: 1 = In the United States, 2 = Elsewhere) are more likely to have a graduate degree (DEGREE: 4 = Graduate) than people born in the United States?

13.198 Is there a difference between men and women in their preference for working for some government agency? Conduct a test to determine whether there is enough evidence to infer that women (SEX: 1 = Male, 2 = Female) are more likely to work for the government (WRKGOVT: 1 = Government) than men?

13.199 It is generally assumed that Democrats are the party of big government. If so, we would expect government workers to support the Democratic party over the Republican party. Can we infer from the data that people who work for the government (WRKGOVT: 1 = Government, 2 = Private enterprise) are more likely than private sector workers to vote for the Democrats than the Republicans (PARTYID2: 1 = Democrat, 3 = Republican)?

13.200 Most people who immigrate to the United States do so to get a job. We assume that the proportion of residents born outside the United States (BORN: 1 = In the United States, 2 = Elsewhere) to be working full time (WRKSTAT: 1 = Full time) to be no less than the proportion of native-born Americans working full time. Conduct a test of the assumption.

13.201 In theory, Republicans are more supportive of free enterprise. Do the data allow us to infer that Republicans (PARTYID2 1 = Democrat, 3 =

Republican) are more likely to work for themselves (WRKSLF: 1 = Work for themselves, 2 = Other) than Democrats?

13.202 Half a century ago men were far more likely to be the breadwinner and women were far more likely to be homemakers. There are now many households where women are the breadwinners and many households where both work outside the home. Is there a difference in the proportion of men and women (SEX: 1 = Male, 2 = Female) working full time outside the home (WRKSTAT: 1 = Working full time, 2–8 = Other)? Perform a statistical test to answer the question.

13.203 Is there enough statistical evidence to conclude that people born (BORN: 1 = In the United States, 2 = Elsewhere) in the United States are more likely to work for the government (WRKGVT: 1 = Government, 2 = Other) than people born outside the United States?

13.204 Are foreign-born people (BORN: 1 = In the United States, 2 = Elsewhere) more likely to work for themselves (WRKSLF: 1 = Work for themselves, 2 = Work for someone else) than Americans born in the United States? Conduct a test to answer the question.

Exercises 13.205 to 13.210 are knowledge-testing questions with true/false or yes/no responses recorded as 1/2. The questions were asked of approximately half the sample. We've included the responses 8 = Don't know, 9 = No answer, and 0 indicates that the question was not asked of that respondent. Determine whether men and women (SEX: 1 = Male, 2 = Female) were likely to differ in answering each quiz question correctly.

13.205 A doctor tells a couple that there is one chance in four that their child will have an inherited disease. Does this mean that if the first child has the illness, the next three will not (ODDS1: 1 = Yes, 2 = No, 8 = Don't know, 9 = No answer, 0 = Question not asked)? Correct answer: No.

13.206 A doctor tells a couple that there is one chance in four that their child will have an inherited disease. Does this mean that each of the couple's children will have the same risk of suffering the illness (ODDS2: 1 = Yes, 2 = No, 8 = Don't know, 9 = No answer, 0 = Question not asked)? Correct answer: Yes.

13.207 True or false, the center of the earth is very hot (HOTCORE: 1 = True, 2 = False, 8 = Don't know, 9 = No answer, 0 = Question not asked). Correct answer: True.

13.208 Does the Earth go around the Sun, or does the Sun go around the Earth (EARTHSUN: 1 = Earth around Sun, 2 = Sun around Earth, 8 = Don't know, 9 = No answer, 0 = Question not asked)? Correct answer: Earth around the Sun.

13.209 ELECTRONS: Electrons are smaller than atoms (ELECTRONS: 1 = True, 2 = False, 8 = Don't know, 9 = No answer, 0 = Question not asked). Correct answer: True.

13.210 Antibiotics kill viruses as well as bacteria (VIRUSES: 1 = True, 2 = False, 8 = Don't know, 9 = No answer, 0 = Question not asked). Correct answer: False.

Refer to Exercises 13.205 to 13.210. Comparing Americans who have completed junior college and Americans with a Bachelor's degree (DEGREE: 2 = Junior college, 3 = Bachelor's degree), we would expect the latter to have a higher percentage of correct answers than that of the former. For each of the following exercises, determine whether there is enough evidence to support the expectation.

13.211 ODDS1

13.212 ODDS2

13.213 HOTCORE

13.214 EARTHSUN

13.215 ELECTRON

13.216 VIRUSES.

SURVEY OF CONSUMER FINANCES EXERCISES

SCF2019:\All   *The following exercises are based on all the observations in the 2019 survey.*

13.217 Many studies show that women are more likely to have a college degree than men. However, does this apply to female and male heads (HHSEX: 1 = Male, 2 = Female) of households? Is there enough evidence to conclude that male heads of households are more likely to have a college degree than female heads of households (EDCL: 4 = College degree)?

13.218 If male heads of households (HHSEX: 1 = Male, 2 = Female) are more likely to have a college degree, does it follow that they have a higher employment rate (LF: 1 = Working in some way)? Conduct a test to answer the question.

13.219 Is there sufficient evidence to conclude that male heads of households (HHSEX: 1 = Male, 2 = Female) are more likely to own the home they live in (HOUSECL: 1 = Owns)?

13.220 Is there enough statistical evidence to infer that male heads of households (HHSEX: 1 = Male, 2 = Female) are more likely to be married (or living with partner) than female heads of households (MARRIED: 1 = Married or living with partner)?

13.221 What conclusions can you draw from the results of the four previous exercises?

CHAPTER SUMMARY

In this chapter, we presented a variety of techniques that allow statistics practitioners to compare two populations. When the data are interval and we are interested in measures of central location, we encountered two more factors that must be considered when choosing the appropriate technique. When the samples are independent, we can use either the **equal-variances** or **unequal-variances formulas**. When the samples are **matched pairs**, we have only one set of formulas. We introduced the **F-statistic**, which is used to make inferences about two population variances. When the data are nominal, the parameter of interest is the difference between two proportions. For this parameter, we had two test statistics and one interval estimator. Finally, we discussed **observational** and **experimental data**, important concepts in attempting to interpret statistical findings.

IMPORTANT TERMS:

Sampling distribution 455
Pooled variance estimator 458
Equal-variances test statistic 458
Equal-variances confidence interval estimator 458
Unequal-variances test statistic 459
Unequal-variances confidence interval estimator 459
Observational data 482
Experimental data 482
Matched pairs experiment 489
Mean of the population of differences 490
Numerator degrees of freedom 500
Denominator degrees of freedom 500
Pooled proportion estimate 507

SYMBOLS:

Symbol	Pronounced	Represents
s_p^2	s sub p squared	Pooled variance estimator
μ_D	mu sub D or mu D	Mean of the paired differences
$\bar{x}_D$	x bar sub D or x bar D	Sample mean of the paired differences
s_D	s sub D or s D	Sample standard deviation of the paired differences
n_D	n sub D or n D	Sample size of the paired differences
$\hat{p}$	p hat	Pooled proportion

FORMULAS:

Equal-variances t-test of $\mu_1 - \mu_2$

$$t = \frac{(\bar{x}_1 - \bar{x}_2) - (\mu_1 - \mu_2)}{\sqrt{s_p^2\left(\dfrac{1}{n_1} + \dfrac{1}{n_2}\right)}} \quad \nu = n_1 + n_2 - 2$$

Equal-variances interval estimator of $(\mu_1 - \mu_2)$

$$(\bar{x}_1 - \bar{x}_2) \pm t_{\alpha/2}\sqrt{s_p^2\left(\frac{1}{n_1} + \frac{1}{n_2}\right)} \quad \nu = n_1 + n_2 - 2$$

Unequal-variances t-test of $\mu_1 - \mu_2$

$$t = \frac{(\bar{x}_1 - \bar{x}_2) - (\mu_1 - \mu_2)}{\sqrt{\left(\dfrac{s_1^2}{n_1} + \dfrac{s_2^2}{n_2}\right)}} \quad \nu = \frac{(s_1^2/n_1 + s_2^2/n_2)^2}{\dfrac{(s_1^2/n_1)^2}{n_1 - 1} + \dfrac{(s_2^2/n_2)^2}{n_2 - 1}}$$

Unequal-variances interval estimator of $\mu_1 - \mu_2$

$$(\bar{x}_1 - \bar{x}_2) \pm t_{\alpha/2}\sqrt{\frac{s_1^2}{n_1} + \frac{s_2^2}{n_2}} \quad \nu = \frac{(s_1^2/n_1 + s_2^2/n_2)^2}{\dfrac{(s_1^2/n_1)^2}{n_1 - 1} + \dfrac{(s_2^2/n_2)^2}{n_2 - 1}}$$

t-test of μ_D

$$t = \frac{\bar{x}_D - \mu_D}{s_D/\sqrt{n_D}} \quad \nu = n_D - 1$$

t-estimator of μ_D

$$\bar{x}_D \pm t_{\alpha/2}\frac{s_D}{\sqrt{n_D}} \quad \nu = n_D - 1$$

F-test of σ_1^2/σ_2^2

$$F = \frac{s_1^2}{s_2^2} \quad \nu_1 = n_1 - 1 \text{ and } \nu_2 = n_2 - 1$$

F-estimator of σ_1^2/σ_2^2

$$\text{LCL} = \left(\frac{s_1^2}{s_2^2}\right)\frac{1}{F_{\alpha/2,\nu_1,\nu_2}}$$

$$\text{UCL} = \left(\frac{s_1^2}{s_2^2}\right)F_{\alpha/2,\nu_1,\nu_2}$$

z-test and estimator of $p_1 - p_2$

Case 1: $\quad z = \dfrac{(\hat{p}_1 - \hat{p}_2)}{\sqrt{\hat{p}(1 - \hat{p})\left(\dfrac{1}{n_1} + \dfrac{1}{n_2}\right)}}$

Case 2: $\quad z = \dfrac{(\hat{p}_1 - \hat{p}_2) - (p_1 - p_2)}{\sqrt{\dfrac{\hat{p}_1(1 - \hat{p}_1)}{n_1} + \dfrac{\hat{p}_2(1 - \hat{p}_2)}{n_2}}}$

z-estimator of $p_1 - p_2$

$$(\hat{p}_1 - \hat{p}_2) \pm z_{\alpha/2}\sqrt{\frac{\hat{p}_1(1 - \hat{p}_1)}{n_1} + \frac{\hat{p}_2(1 - \hat{p}_2)}{n_2}}$$

EXCEL OUTPUT AND INSTRUCTIONS:

Technique

CHAPTER EXERCISES

The following exercises require the use of a computer and software. **Use a 5% significance level for all tests and a 95% confidence level for all estimates.**

13.222 Xr13-222 Gallup conducts surveys every 2 years in the United States that ask respondents their opinions of capitalism and socialism, as well as for their political persuasions. The 2016 and 2018 surveys asked Republicans whether they had a positive view of capitalism: positive view (1) or negative view (0). Is there sufficient statistical evidence to infer that more Republicans have a positive view of capitalism in 2018 than in 2016?

13.223 Xr13-223 A restaurant located in an office building decides to adopt a new strategy for attracting customers to the restaurant. Every week it advertises in the city newspaper. To assess how well the advertising is working, the restaurant owner recorded the weekly gross sales for the 15 weeks after the campaign began and the weekly gross sales for the 24 weeks immediately prior to the campaign. Can the restaurateur conclude that the advertising campaign is successful?

13.224 Xr13-224 Every year, the Bureau of Labor Statistics administers a survey of American households called the American Time Use Survey. Respondents are asked to report their activities during an entire 24-hour day. The results are used to determine the number of hours respondents work in a typical week. The results for government and private sector workers were recorded. Is there sufficient evidence to infer that government employees work less than private sector workers?

13.225 Xr13-225 How important to your health are regular vacations? In a study, a random sample of men and women were asked how frequently they take vacations. The men and women were divided into two groups each. The members of group 1 had suffered a heart attack; the members of group 2 had not. The number of days of vacation last year was recorded for each person. Can we infer that men and women who suffer heart attacks vacation less than those who did not suffer a heart attack?

13.226 Xr13-226 Research scientists at a pharmaceutical company have recently developed a new nonprescription sleeping pill. They decide to test its effectiveness by measuring the time it takes for people to fall asleep after taking the pill. Preliminary analysis indicates that the time to fall asleep varies considerably from one person to another. Consequently, they organize the experiment in the following way. A random sample of 100 volunteers who regularly suffer from insomnia is chosen. Each person is given one pill containing the newly developed drug and one placebo. (They do not know whether the pill they are taking is the placebo or the real thing, and the order of use is random.) Each participant is fitted with a device that measures the time until sleep occurs. Can we conclude that the new drug is effective?

13.227 Xr13-227 The city of Toronto boasts four daily newspapers. Not surprisingly, competition is keen. To help learn more about newspaper readers, an advertiser selected a random sample of people who bought their newspapers from a street vendor and people who had the newspaper delivered to their homes. Each was asked how many minutes they spent reading their newspapers. Can we infer that the amount of time reading differs between the two groups?

13.228 Xr13-228 In recent years, a number of state governments have passed mandatory seat-belt laws. Although the use of seat belts is known to save lives and reduce serious injuries, compliance with seat-belt laws is not universal. In an effort to increase the use of seat belts, a government agency sponsored a 2-year study. Among its objectives was to determine whether there was enough evidence to infer that seat-belt usage increased between last year and this year. To test this belief, random samples of drivers last year and this year were asked whether they always use their seat belts (2 = Wear seat belt, 1 = Do not wear seat belt). Can we infer that seat-belt usage has increased over the last year?

13.229 Xr13-229 An important component of the cost of living is the amount of money spent on housing. Housing costs include rent (for tenants), mortgage payments and property tax (for home owners), heating, electricity, and water. An economist undertook a 5-year study to determine how housing costs have changed. Random samples of 200 households this year and 5 years ago were drawn and the percentage of total income spent on housing was recorded.
a. Conduct a test to determine whether the economist can infer that housing cost as a percentage of total income has increased over the last 5 years.
b. Use whatever statistical method you deem appropriate to check the required condition(s) of the test used in part (a).

13.230 Xr13-230 In designing advertising campaigns to sell magazines, it is important to know how much time each of a number of demographic groups spends reading magazines. In a preliminary study, 40 people were randomly selected. All were asked how much time per week they spend reading magazines; additionally, each was categorized by gender (1 = Male, 2 = Female) and by income level (1 = Low, 2 = High).
a. Is there sufficient evidence to conclude that men and women differ in the amount of time spent reading magazines?
b. Is there sufficient evidence to conclude that high-income individuals devote more time to reading magazines than low-income people?

13.231 Xr13-231 In a study to determine whether gender affects salary offers for graduating MBA students, 25 pairs of students were selected. Each pair consisted of a female and a male student who were matched according to their GPAs, courses taken, ages, and previous work experience. The highest salary offered (in thousands of dollars) to each graduate was recorded.
a. Is there enough evidence to infer that gender is a factor in salary offers?
b. Discuss why the experiment was organized in the way it was.
c. Is the required condition for the test in part (a) satisfied?

13.232 Xr13-232 Refer to Exercise 13.222. The Gallup poll also asked whether respondents had a positive view (1) or not (0) of the federal government. Do the responses for 2016 and 2018 provide sufficient evidence that Americans in 2018 viewed the federal government less positively in 2018 than in 2016?

13.233 Xr13-233 Before deciding which of two types of stamping machines should be purchased, the plant manager of an automotive parts manufacturer wants to determine the number of units that each produces. The two machines differ in cost, reliability, and productivity. The firm's accountant has calculated that machine A must produce 25 more non-defective units per hour than machine B to warrant buying machine A. To help decide, both machines were operated for 24 hours. The total number of units and the number of defective units produced by each machine per hour were recorded. These data are stored in the following way: column A = Total number of units produced by machine A; column B = Number of defectives produced by machine A; column C = Total number of units produced by machine B; column D = Number of defectives produced by machine B. Determine which machine should be purchased.

13.234 Refer to Exercise 13.233. Can we conclude that the defective rate differs between the two machines?

13.235 Xr13-235 The growing use of bicycles to commute to work has caused many cities to create exclusive bicycle lanes. These lanes are usually created by disallowing parking on streets that formerly allowed curbside parking. Merchants on such streets complain that the removal of parking will cause their businesses to suffer. To examine this problem, the mayor of a large city decided to launch an experiment on one busy street that had 1-hour parking meters. The meters were removed and a bicycle lane was created. The mayor asked the three businesses (a dry cleaner, a doughnut shop, and a convenience store) in one block to record daily sales for 2 complete weeks (Sunday to Saturday) prior to the change and 2 complete weeks after the change. The data are stored as follows: column A = Day of the week; column B = Sales before change for dry cleaner; column C = Sales after change for dry cleaner; column D = Sales before change for doughnut shop; column E = Sales after change for doughnut shop; column F = Sales before change for convenience store; and column G = Sales after change for convenience store. What conclusions can you draw from these data?

13.236 Xr12-144+   Refer to Exercise 12.144. The file contains a random sample of American and Canadian dairy farms' monthly production of milk. Is there enough statistical evidence to infer that there is a difference between the two populations?

13.237 Xr13-237   Clinical depression is linked to several other diseases. Scientists at Johns Hopkins University undertook a study to determine whether heart disease is one of these. A group of 1,190 male medical students was tracked over a 40-year period. Of these, 132 had suffered clinically diagnosed depression. For each student, the scientists recorded whether the student died of a heart attack (1) or did not (0).
a. Can we infer that men who are clinically depressed are more likely to die from a heart attack?
b. If the answer to part (a) is yes, can you interpret this to mean that depression causes heart attacks? Explain.

13.238 Xr13-238   High blood pressure (hypertension) is a leading cause of strokes. Medical researchers are constantly seeking ways to treat patients suffering from this condition. A specialist in hypertension claims that regular aerobic exercise can reduce high blood pressure just as successfully as drugs, with none of the adverse side effects. To test the claim, 50 patients who suffer from high blood pressure were chosen to participate in an experiment. For 60 days, half the sample exercised three times per week for 1 hour and did not take medication; the other half took the standard medication. The percentage reduction in blood pressure was recorded for each individual.
a. Can we conclude that exercise is more effective than medication in reducing hypertension?
b. Compute a confidence interval estimate of the difference in mean percentage reduction in blood pressure between drugs and exercise programs.
c. Check to ensure that the required condition(s) of the techniques used in parts (a) and (b) is satisfied.

13.239 Xr13-239   Most people exercise in order to lose weight. To determine better ways to lose weight, a random sample of male and female exercisers was divided into groups. The first group exercised vigorously twice a week. The second group exercised moderately four times per week. The weight loss for each individual was recorded. Can we infer that people who exercise moderately more frequently lose more weight than people who exercise vigorously?

13.240 Xr13-240   After observing the results of the test in Exercise 13.239, a statistics practitioner organized another experiment. People were matched according to gender, height, and weight. One member of each matched pair then exercised vigorously twice a week and the other member exercised moderately four times per week. The weight losses were recorded. Can we infer that people who exercise moderately lose more weight?

13.241 Xr13-241   Personal spending is usually an indicator of the health of the overall economy. An increase tends to indicate that consumers are optimistic; a decrease indicates pessimism. Gallup tracks the spending of a random sample of American adults. The results for this month and last month were recorded. Do these data allow us to conclude that these consumers are optimistic about the state of the economy?

13.242 Xr13-242   There are currently 121,678 people waiting for lifesaving organ transplants in the United States. Of these, 100,791 await kidney transplants (as of January 2016). The median wait time for an individual's first kidney transplant is 3.6 years and can vary depending on health, compatibility, and availability of organs. In 2014, 17,107 kidney transplants took place in the United States. Of these, 11,570 came from deceased donors and 5,537 came from living donors (*Source:* National Kidney Foundation). This raises the question: Are kidneys from living donors better than kidneys from deceased donors? A study conducted by the Barnes Jewish Hospital in St Louis may provide an answer. A random sample of kidney recipients was drawn and the number of years until the transplanted kidney needed replacement. Do these data provide enough evidence to infer that kidneys from living donors last longer than do kidneys from deceased donors?

13.243 Xr13-243   Most English professors complain that students don't write very well. In particular they point out that students often confuse quality and quantity. A study at the University of Texas examined this claim. In the study, undergraduate students were asked to compare the cost benefits of Japanese and American cars. All wrote their analyses on computers. Unbeknownst to the students, the computers were rigged so that some students would have to type twice as many words to fill a single page. The number of words used by each student was recorded. Can we conclude that students write in such a way as to fill the allotted space?

13.244 Xr13-244   For people in their 80s and 90s, falls can be fatal. It would be helpful if there was some way to predict who will fall. A TUG (Timed Up and GO) test is designed for that purpose. In the test the patient is timed while they rise from an arm chair, walk at a comfortable and safe pace to a line on the floor 3 meters away, turn and walk back to the chair, and sit down again. A random sample of men and women, all of whom are more than 80 years old, completed the TUG test. Each was observed for the following 12 months. Some subsequently suffered a fall. The TUG times for those who fell and those who did not were recorded. Is there enough evidence to conclude that the TUG times for those who fell were larger than those who did not fall?

13.245 Xr13-245   Many small retailers advertise in their neighborhoods by sending out flyers. People deliver these to homes and are paid according to the number of flyers delivered. Each deliverer is given several streets whose homes become their responsibility. One of the ways retailers use to check the performance of deliverers is to randomly sample some of the homes and ask homeowners whether they received the flyer. Recently, university students started a new delivery service. They have promised better service at a competitive price. A retailer wanted to know whether the new company's delivery rate is better than that of the existing firm. The retailer had both companies deliver the flyers. Random samples of homes were drawn and homeowners were asked whether they received the flyer: Yes (1) or no (0). Can we conclude that the new company is better?

13.246 Xr13-246   Medical experts advocate the use of vitamin and mineral supplements to help fight infections. A study undertaken by researchers at Memorial University recruited 96 men and women age 65 and older. One-half of them received daily supplements of vitamins and minerals, whereas the other half received placebos. The supplements contained the daily recommended amounts of 18 vitamins and minerals, including vitamins B-6, B-12, C, and D, thiamine, riboflavin, niacin, calcium, copper, iodine, iron, selenium, magnesium, and zinc. The doses of vitamins A and E were slightly less than the daily requirements. The supplements included four times the amount of beta-carotene than the average person ingests daily. The number of days of illness from infections (ranging from colds to pneumonia) was recorded for each person. Can we infer that taking vitamin and mineral supplements daily increases the body's immune system?

13.247 Xr13-247   An inspector for the Atlantic City Gaming Commission suspects that a particular blackjack dealer may be cheating (in favor of the casino) when at expensive tables. To test the belief, 500 hands each at the $100-limit table and the $3,000-limit table were observed. For each hand, whether the dealer won (1) or lost (0) was recorded. When a tie occurs, there is no winner or loser. Can the inspector conclude that the dealer is cheating at the more expensive table?

13.248 Xr13-248   In 2005 Larry Summers, then president of Harvard University, received an avalanche of criticism for his attempt to explain why in mathematics there are more male professors than female professors. He suggested that there were innate differences that might permanently thwart the search for a more perfect gender balance. In an attempt to refute Dr. Summers' hypothesis, several researchers conducted large-scale mathematics tests of male and female students. Suppose the results were recorded. Conduct whatever tests you deem necessary to draw conclusions from these data. (Note that the data are simulated but represent actual results.)

13.249 Xr13-249   Refer to Exercise 12.143. The researchers also took a random sample of 702 cars last year. Is there sufficient evidence to conclude that American cars this year are on average older than cars last year?

13.250 Xr13-250   Are Americans more generous than Canadians? Random samples of American and Canadian tax returns were examined and whether they included a charitable donation were recorded: Yes (1) or no (0). Conduct a statistical test to answer the question.

Source: Fraser Institute study.

13.251 Xr13-251   The Silent Generation is defined as people born between 1928 and 1945 and the Baby Boom Generation defined as those born between 1946 and 1964. It is assumed that the Silent Generation's housing tenure should exceed that of the housing tenure of the Baby Boomers. To help answer the question, random samples of members of both generations were asked how long they lived in their current residence. Conduct a test to determine whether the assumption is true.

13.252 Xr13-252   The Canadian General Social Survey constructed a life satisfaction index, which is a personal subjective assessment of global well-being. In the survey, respondents were asked to rate their life satisfaction on a scale of 0 to 10, where 0 means "very dissatisfied" and 10 means "very satisfied." The computed indexes were recorded for age categories 15–19, 20–29, 30–39, 40–49, 50–59, 60–69, 70–79, and 80+ as well as males and females. For this exercise we recorded the indexes for males and females in the 15–19 age category. Do these data allow us to infer in this age category, males are more satisfied than females?

13.253 Xr13-253   Refer to Exercise 13.252. Can we infer from the data that in the age category 70–79, females are more satisfied than males?

13.254 Xr13-254   Credit scores are measures of how likely the recipient of a loan will repay the loan. They can also be used as a measure of the state of the economy. A financial analyst took random samples of scores this year and compared them to random samples in 2010 when the country was still in the middle of what has been called the Great Recession. Can we infer that credit scores are higher this year than in 2010?

13.255 Xr13-255   Refer to Exercise 13.222. The 2010 and 2018 surveys asked Democrats whether they had a positive view of socialism: Positive view (1) or negative view (0). Is there sufficient statistical evidence to infer that Democrats are more likely to have a positive view of socialism in 2018 than in 2010?

13.256 Xr13-256   It seems reasonable to assume that family structure has an effect on virtually all aspects of family life. Taking random samples of families composed of married couples with no children and married couples with children, a consultant determined the estimated market value of their homes. Can we infer from the data that the values of homes occupied by married couples without children are greater than that of married couples with children?

13.257 Xr13-257   How much do customers of pizza restaurants spend and are there differences between pizza restaurants? A survey was conducted by Citi Research where random samples of customers of Pizza Hut and Papa John's reported how much they spent per person at each of the restaurants. Is there sufficient evidence to infer that there are differences in mean amount spent per person?

13.258 Xr13-258   Refer to Exercise 13.257. A similar project was conducted comparing expenditures per person at Burger King and McDonald's. Can we conclude from the data that customers at the two fast-food chains differ in their mean cost per person?

13.259 Xr13-259   A Pew survey asked Democrats whether strengthening the economy was the top priority. The responses are yes (1) and no (0). The results for this year and the one conducted in 2013 were recorded. Is there sufficient evidence to conclude that Democrats changed their priority?

13.260 Xr13-260   Refer to Exercise 13.259. The same question was posed to Republicans. Can we conclude from the responses that the Republicans changed their priority?

Overeating Experiments (See page 478.)

13.261 Xr13-261   Music Experiment

A researcher conducted a restaurant to experiment with two different kinds of music. One was faster upbeat music and the second was soft relaxing music. A random sample of diners was drawn and the type of music, the amount of time spent in the restaurant, and the amount spent on drinks were recorded. Is there sufficient evidence to conclude that when the soft relaxing music was played, diners spent more time in the restaurant and spent more money on drinks?

Source: Adapted from Ronald E. Milliman, "The Influence of Background Music on the Behavior of Restaurant Patrons," *Journal of Consumer Research* 13:1 (1986): 286–89.

13.262 Xr13-262   Cinderella Makeover Experiment

A television program in conjunction with a researcher conducted a makeover of a Hardee's Restaurant. The main room had bright lights and loud music. In a separate room, the renovation brought in plants, paintings, indirect lighting, and white tablecloths and candles on the tables. The amount of time a random sample of patrons spent in the restaurant for each room was recorded. Is there enough evidence to infer that when the restaurant features bright lights and loud music, customers spend less time in the restaurant?

13.263 Xr13-263   Refer to Exercise 13.262. Customers were also asked how likely they were to return to the restaurant: Likely (1) or unlikely (0). Is there enough evidence to infer that when the restaurant features bright lights and loud music, customers are less likely to return?

13.264 Xr13-254   Glass Size Experiment

At a camp cafeteria, teenagers were randomly given a tall skinny glass or a short wide glass. As they proceeded through the line they loaded up on the food they wanted and poured whatever drink (ounces) they chose. At the end of the line the quantity of drink they had in their glasses was recorded. Can we infer that the quantities in the short wide glasses were greater than the quantities in the tall skinny glasses?

Source: Adapted from Abby Ellin, "For Overweight Children, Are 'Fat Camps' a Solution?" *New York Times*, June 2005.

13.265 Xr12-31+   Exercise 12.31 dealt with the amount of time high school students spend per week at part-time jobs. In addition to the hours of part-time work, the school guidance counselor recorded the gender of the student surveyed (1 = Female, 2 = Male). Can we conclude that female and male high school students differ in the amount of time spent at part-time jobs?

13.266 <u>Xm12-01+</u>   The company that organized the survey to determine the amount of discarded newspaper (Example 12.1) kept track of the type of neighborhood (1 = City, 2 = Suburbs). Do these data allow the company management to infer that city households discard more newspaper than do suburban households?

13.267 <u>Xr13-267</u>   Movie studios segment their markets by age. Two segments that are particularly important to this industry are teenagers and 20- to 30-year-olds. To assess markets and guide the making of movies, a random sample of teenagers and 20- to 30-year-olds was drawn. All respondents were asked to report the number of movies they saw in theaters last year. Do these data allow us to infer that teenagers see more movies than 20- to 30-year-olds?

13.268 <u>Xr12-131+</u>   In addition to asking about educational attainment, the survey conducted in Exercise 12.131 also asked whether the respondent had plans in the next 2 years to take a course (1 = Yes, 0 = No). Can we conclude that Californians who did not complete high school are less likely to take a course in the university's evening program than Californians with at least a high school diploma?

13.269 <u>Xm12-06+</u>   The objective in the survey conducted in Example 12.6 was to estimate the size of the market segment of adults who are concerned about eating healthy foods. As part of the survey, each respondent was asked how much they spend on breakfast cereal in an average month. The marketing manager of a company that produces several breakfast cereals would like to know whether on average the market segment concerned about eating health foods outspends the other market segments. Perform a statistical test to answer the question.

13.270 <u>Xr12-35+</u>   In Exercise 12.35, we described how the office equipment chain OfficeMax offers rebates on some products. The goal in that exercise was to estimate the total amount spent by customers who bought the package of 100 CD-ROMs. In addition to tracking these amounts, an executive also determined the amounts spent in the store by another sample of customers who purchased a fax machine/copier (regular price $89.99 minus $40 manufacturer's rebate and $10 OfficeMax mail-in rebate). Can OfficeMax conclude that those who buy the fax/copier outspend those who buy the package of CD-ROMs?

13.271 <u>Xr12-105+</u>   In addition to recording whether faculty members who are between 55 and 64 plan to retire before they reach 65 in Exercise 12.105, the consultant asked faculty members to report their annual salary. Can we infer that professors aged 55 to 64 who plan to retire early have higher salaries than those who don't plan to retire early?

13.272 <u>Xr12-110+</u>   In Exercise 12.110, the statistics practitioner also recorded the gender of the respondents: Female (1) or male (2). Can we infer that men and women differ in their choices of Christmas trees?

GENERAL SOCIAL SURVEY EXERCISES

<u>GSS2010</u> <u>GSS2018</u> *Exercises 13.273 to 13.289 compare variables in the General Social Surveys of 2010 and 2018. For each, determine whether there is enough evidence to infer that the statement is true.*

13.273 America is getting older (AGE).

13.274 Families have fewer children (CHILDS).

13.275 Americans are postponing having their first child (AGEKDBRN).

13.276 Individual incomes are increasing (RINCOME).

13.277 Americans are more educated (EDUC).

13.278 The economy was considerably stronger in 2018 than in 2010. People are working longer hours (HRS1).

13.279 Because of the many alternative modes of entertainment, Americans are watching less television (TVHOURS).

13.280 The "other" category of race has increased (RACE: 3 = Other).

13.281 The divorce rate has increased (MARITAL: 3 = Divorced).

13.282 More Americans have never married (MARITAL: 5 = Never married).

13.283 Immigration has increased (BORN: 2 = Born outside the United States).

13.284 Fewer Americans are completing graduate degrees (DEGREE: 4 = Graduate degree).

13.285 The size of government as measured by the percentage of workers who are government employees is increasing (WRKGOVT: 1 = Government employee).

13.286 The number of Republicans relative to the number of Republicans and Democrats is increasing (PARTYID2: 1 = Democrat, 3 = Republican).

13.287 The number of conservatives relative to the number of conservatives and liberals is increasing (POLVIEWS2: 1 = Liberal, 3 = Conservative).

13.288 Support for capital punishment for murderers is decreasing (CAPPUN: 1 = Favor).

13.289 Support for a law requiring a police permit to buy a gun is decreasing (GUNLAW: 1 = Favor).

Refer to Exercises 13.205 to 13.210 on pages 523–524, which are knowledge-testing questions with true/false or yes/no responses recorded as 1/2. The questions were asked of approximately half the sample. We've included the responses 8 = Don't know, 9 = No answer, and 0 indicates that the question was not asked of that respondent.

For Exercises 13.290 to 13.295, test to determine whether Americans are less knowledgeable in 2018 compared to 2010.

13.290 A doctor tells a couple that there is one chance in four that their child will have an inherited disease. Does this mean that if the first child has the illness, the next three will not (ODDS1: 1 = Yes, 2 = No, 8 = Don't know, 9 = No answer, 0 = Question not asked)? Correct answer: No.

13.291 A doctor tells a couple that there is one chance in four that their child will have an inherited disease. Does this mean that each of the couple's children will have the same risk of suffering the illness (ODDS2: 1 = Yes, 2 = No, 8 = Don't know, 9 = No answer, 0 = Question not asked)? Correct answer: Yes.

13.292 True or false, the center of the earth is very hot (HOTCORE: 1 = True, 2 = False, 8 = Don't know, 9 = No answer, 0 = Question not asked). Correct answer: True.

13.293 Does the Earth go around the Sun, or does the Sun go around the Earth (EARTHSUN: 1 = Earth around Sun, 2 = Sun around Earth, 8 = Don't know, 9 = No answer, 0 = Question not asked)? Correct answer: Earth around the Sun.

13.294 ELECTRONS: Electrons are smaller than atoms (ELECTRONS: 1 = True, 2 = False, 8 = Don't know, 9 = No answer, 0 = Question not asked). Correct answer: True.

13.295 Antibiotics kill viruses as well as bacteria (VIRUSES: 1 = True, 2 = False, 8 = Don't know, 9 = No answer, 0 = Question not asked). Correct answer: False.

CASE 13.1   Testing Eli Lilly's Latest Drug Evacetrapib

DATA
C13-01

The National Center for Health Statistics provided the following list of the top 10 killers in the United States and the numbers it killed in the 2014.

Heart disease: 614,348

Cancer: 591,699

Chronic lower respiratory diseases: 147,101

Accidents (unintentional injuries): 136,053

Stroke (cerebrovascular diseases): 133,103

Alzheimer's disease: 93,541

Diabetes: 76,488

Influenza and pneumonia: 55,227

Nephritis, nephrotic syndrome, and nephrosis: 48,146

Intentional self-harm (suicide): 42,773

Source: Health United States, 2015, Table 19.

Not surprisingly, virtually every drug manufacturer is constantly looking for drugs to reduce any of the diseases on the list, with particular emphasis on the heart disease and stroke, killers 1 and 5. After spending a decade on the development of

Evacetrapib, a drug was designed to reduce bad cholesterol and increase good cholesterol. Here is a brief summary of the problem.

Cholesterol can't dissolve in the blood. It must be transported through your bloodstream by carriers called lipoproteins, which got their name because they're made of fat (lipid) and proteins.

The two types of lipoproteins that carry cholesterol to and from cells are low-density lipoprotein, or LDL, and high-density lipoprotein,

(Continued)

or HDL. LDL cholesterol and HDL cholesterol, along with one-fifth of your triglyceride level, make up your total cholesterol count, which can be determined through a blood test.

LDL cholesterol is considered the "bad" cholesterol because it contributes to plaque, a thick, hard deposit that can clog arteries and make them less flexible. This condition is known as atherosclerosis. If a clot forms and blocks a narrowed artery, heart attack or stroke can result. Another condition called peripheral artery disease can develop when plaque buildup narrows an artery supplying blood to the legs.

HDL cholesterol is considered "good" cholesterol because it helps remove LDL cholesterol from the arteries. Experts believe HDL acts as a scavenger, carrying LDL cholesterol away from the arteries and

back to the liver, where it is broken down and passed from the body. One-fourth to one-third of blood cholesterol is carried by HDL. A healthy level of HDL cholesterol may also protect against heart attack and stroke, while low levels of HDL cholesterol have been shown to increase the risk of heart disease.

When pharmaceutical companies develop a new drug it is tested extensively. The final stage of the testing protocol is actual patients.

A random sample of adult volunteers was divided so that one half took the drug and the other half took a placebo, so that neither the physician nor the volunteer knew which they were taking. The researchers tracked the results of the study and recorded the following for the drug group and the placebo group.

LDL before the study
LDL after the study
HDL before the study
HDL after the study
Heart attack occurred (0 = no heart attack, 1 = heart attack)
Stroke (0 = no stroke, 1 stroke)
Death (0 = alive, 1 = died)

Conduct statistical tests to answer the following questions.

a. Does the drug reduce LDL?
b. Does the drug increase HDL?
c. What do the data on the placebo before and after LDL and HDL tell you about the experiment?
d. Does the drug reduce heart attacks?
e. Does the drug reduce strokes?
f. Does the drug reduce the death rate?
g. What do these results tell you about the drug?

APPENDIX 13.A / XLSTAT Output and Instructions

F-Test of the Ratio of Two Variances

Example 13.1

	B	C	D	E	F	G
9	Fisher's F-test: Hypothesized ratio (R) = 1					
10						
11	Summary statistics:					
12	Variable	Observations	Minimum	Maximum	Mean	Std. deviation
13	Direct	50	-6.54	18.45	6.63	6.12
14	Broker	50	-11.07	18.22	3.72	6.58
15						
16	**Fisher's F-test / Two-tailed test:**					
17	Ratio	0.865				
18	F (Observed value)	0.865				
19	F (Critical value)	1.76				
20	DF1	49				
21	DF2	49				
22	p-value (Two-tailed)	0.6137				
23	alpha	0.05				

Instructions

1. Type or import the data into two columns. (Open Xm13-01.)

2. Click **XLSTAT, Parametric tests**, and **Two-sample comparison of variances**.

3. Check **One column per sample**. Type the input range for both samples. **Sample 1:** (A1:A51), **Sample 2:** (B1:B51). Click **Column labels** and **Fisher's F-test**.

4. Click the **Options** tab and choose **Variance 1/Variance 2 ≠ R** in the **Alternative hypothesis box**. Type the **Hypothesized ratio** (1). Type the value of α (in percent) in the **Significance level (%)** box (5).

5. Click **Outputs** and check **Descriptive statistics** and **Detailed results**.

Test of the Difference between Two Means: Independent Samples

Example 13.1

	B	C	D	E	F	G
9	Hypothesized difference (D): 0					
10	Population variances for the t-test: Assume equality					
11						
12	Summary statistics:					
13	Variable	Observations	Minimum	Maximum	Mean	Std. deviation
14	Direct	50	-6.54	18.45	6.63	6.12
15	Broker	50	-11.07	18.22	3.72	6.58
16						
17	**t-test for two independent samples / Upper-tailed test:**					
18	Difference	2.91				
19	t (Observed value)	2.29				
20	t (Critical value)	1.66				
21	DF	98				
22	p-value (one-tailed)	0.0122				
23	alpha	0.05				

Instructions

1. Type or import the data into two columns. (Open Xm13-01.)

2. Click **XLSTAT, Parametric tests,** and **Two-sample t-test and z-test.**

3. Check **One column per sample.** Type the input range for both samples. **Sample 1:** (A1:A51), **Sample 2:** (B1:B51). Click **Column labels** and **Student's t-test.**

4. Click the **Options** tab and choose **Mean 1 − Mean 2 > D** in the **Alternative hypothesis box.** Type the **Hypothesized difference (D)** (0). Click **Assume equality** under **Population variances for the t-test.** (If you click **Use an F-test,** you do not need to conduct a separate F-test of the two variances as a first step to testing the difference between two means.) Type the value of α (in percent) in the **Significance level (%)** box (5).

5. Click the **Output** tab and check **Descriptive statistics** and **Detailed results.**

Estimating the Difference between Two Means

Example 13.1

	B	C	D	E	F	G
19						
20	95% confidence interval on the difference between the means:					
21	(0.385, 5.431)					

Instructions

Follow the instructions for the t-test of the difference between two means. Specify a two-tail test. That is, choose **Mean 1 − Mean 2 ≠ D** in the **Alternative hypothesis** box. Click the **Output** tab and check **Confidence interval.**

Example 13.2

	B	C	D	E
10	Hypothesized difference (D): 0			
11	**Fisher's F-test / Two-tailed test:**			
12	Ratio	0.471		
13	F (Observed value)	0.471		
14	|F| (Critical value)	1.64		
15	DF1	41		
16	DF2	97		
17	p-value (Two-tailed)	0.0081		
18	alpha	0.05		
19				
20	**t-test for two independent samples / Two-tailed test:**			
21	Difference	-1.34		
22	t (Observed value)	-3.22		
23	|t| (Critical value)	1.98		
24	DF	110.7		
25	p-value (Two-tailed)	0.0017		
26	alpha	0.05		

Instructions

For this example, we chose to combine the F-test of two variances with the t-test of the difference between two means. To do so, click **Use an F-test** at Step 4 above.

Here is the confidence interval estimate for Example 13.2:

	B	C	D	E	F	G
34	95% confidence interval on the difference between the means:					
35	(-2.158, -0.514)					

Test of the Difference between Two Means: Matched Pairs Experiment

Example 13.5

	B	C	D	E	F	G	H
10	Summary statistics:						
11							
12	Variable	Observations	Obs. without missing data	Minimum	Maximum	Mean	Std. deviation
13	Finance	25	25	31,235	106,322	65,438	21,095
14	Marketing	25	25	29,662	99,205	60,374	21,667
15							
17	t-test for two paired samples / Upper-tailed test:						
18							
19	Difference	5065					
20	t (Observed value)	3.81					
21	t (Critical value)	1.711					
22	DF	24					
23	p-value (one-tailed)	0.0004					
24	alpha	0.05					
25	The number of degrees of freedom is approximated by the Welch-Satterthwaite formula						

There is an error in the XLSTAT output. The number of degrees of freedom is *not* approximated by the Welch-Satterthwaite formula.

Instructions

Follow the instructions for the t-test of 2 means: independent samples. Under **Data format** click **Paired samples**. Under **Options** specify the **Alternative hypothesis: Mean 1-Mean 2 > D** and specify **Hypothesized difference (D):** 0.

Here is the confidence interval estimate of the difference between two means, matched pairs experiment:

Example 13.6

	B	C	D	E	F
20	95% confidence interval on the difference between the means:				
21	2320, 7808				

Instructions

1. Follow the instructions for the t-test of 2 means: matched pairs. Under **Data format** click **Paired samples**.

2. Click **Options**. Specify the **Alternative hypothesis: Mean 1-Mean 2 ≠ D** and specify **Hypothesized difference (D):** 0.

Inference about Two Variances

Example 13.7

	B	C	D	E	F	G
9	Fisher's F-test: Hypothesized ratio (R) = 1					
10						
11	Summary statistics:					
12	Variable	Observations	Minimum	Maximum	Mean	Std. deviation
13	Machine 1	25	997.8	1001.3	999.7	0.796
14	Machine 2	25	998.5	1000.9	999.8	0.673
15						
16	**Fisher's F-test / Upper-tailed test:**					
17						
18	Ratio	1.399				
19	F (Observed value)	1.399				
20	F (Critical value)	1.984				
21	DF1	24				
22	DF2	24				
23	p-value (one-tailed)	0.2085				
24	alpha	0.05				

Instructions

1. Type or import the data into two columns. (Open Xm13-07.)

2. Click **XLSTAT, Parametric tests**, and **Two-sample comparison of variances**.

3. Check **One column per sample**. Type the input range for both samples. **Sample 1**: (A1:A26), **Sample 2**: (B1:B26). Click **Column labels** and **Fisher's F-test**.

4. Click the **Options** tab and choose **Variance 1/Variance 2 ≠ R** in the **Alternative hypothesis box**. Type the **Hypothesized ratio** (1). Type the value of α (in percent) in the **Significance level (%)** box (5).

5. Click **Outputs** and check **Descriptive statistics** and **Detailed results**.

Example 13.8

	B	C	D	E	F
19	95% confidence interval on the ratio of variances:				
20	(0.616, 3.174)				

Instructions

1. Follow the instructions for Example 13.7.

2. Click the **Options** tab and choose **Variance 1/Variance 2 ≠ R** in the **Alternative hypothesis box**. Type the **Hypothesized ratio** (1). Type the value of α (in percent) in the **Significance level (%)** box (5).

3. Click **Outputs** and check **Descriptive statistics, Confidence interval**, and **Detailed results**.

Inference about the Difference between Two Population Proportions

Example 13.9

	B	C	D
13	Sample size 1: 904		
14	Frequency 2: 155		
15	Sample size 2: 1038		
16	Hypothesized difference (D): 0		
17	Variance: pq(1/n1+1/n2)		
18			
19	z-test for two proportions / Upper-tailed test:		
20			
21	Difference	0.050	
22	z (Observed value)	2.897	
23	z (Critical value)	1.645	
24	p-value (one-tailed)	0.0019	
25	alpha	0.05	

Instructions

1. Type or import the data into two columns. (Open Xm13-09.) Count the number of "successes" and sample sizes for each sample.

2. Click **XLSTAT, Parametric tests**, and **Tests for two proportions**.

3. Enter the frequencies and sample sizes for each sample. Check **Frequencies** under **Data format:** Click **z-test**.

4. Click **Options** and choose **Proportion 1 – Proportion 2 > D** in the **Alternative hypothesis** box. Enter the **Hypothesized difference (D)** (0). Type the **Significance level (%)** (5). Check **pq(1/n1 + 1/n2)** under **Variance**.

Example 13.10

	B	C	D
13	Frequency 1: 180		
14	Sample size 1: 904		
15	Frequency 2: 155		
16	Sample size 2: 1038		
17	Hypothesized difference (D): 0.03		
18	Variance: p1q1/n1+p2q2/n2		
19	z-test for two proportions / Upper-tailed test:		
20			
21	Difference	0.050	
22	z (Observed value)	1.14	
23	z (Critical value)	1.645	
24	p-value (one-tailed)	0.1261	
25	alpha	0.05	

Instructions

Follow the instructions above with two changes. The **Hypothesized difference (D)** is (.03) and check **p1q1/n1 +p2q2/n2** under **Variance**.

Example 13.11

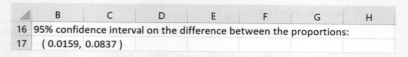

	B	C	D	E	F	G	H
16	95% confidence interval on the difference between the proportions:						
17	(0.0159, 0.0837)						

Instructions

Follow the instructions for Example 13.9 with two changes. Choose **Proportion 1 − Proportion 2 ≠ D** in the **Alternative hypothesis** box and check **p1q1/n1+p2q2/n2** under **Variance**.

APPENDIX 13.B / STATA OUTPUT AND INSTRUCTIONS

F-Test of the Ratio of Two Variances

Example 13.1

```
Variance ratio test

Variable      Obs       Mean     Std. Err.    Std. Dev.    [95% Conf. Interval]

  Direct       50      6.6312    .8658889     6.122759     4.891131    8.371269
  Broker       50      3.7232    .9310132     6.583258     1.852259    5.594141

combined       100     5.1772    .6491608     6.491608     3.889124    6.465276

      ratio = sd(Direct) / sd(Broker)                        f =      0.8650
Ho: ratio = 1                               degrees of freedom =     49, 49

      Ha: ratio < 1              Ha: ratio != 1                   Ha: ratio > 1
   Pr(F < f) = 0.3068        2*Pr(F < f) = 0.6137           Pr(F > f) = 0.6932
```

The two-tail F-test of the ratio of two variances is conducted as a first step. The test statistic is f = .8650 and the p-value is 2*Pr(F < f) = .6137, which informs us that we need to apply the equal-variance t-test of the difference between two means in Example 13.1.

Instructions

1. Import or type the data into one column. (Click File/Import /Excel spreadsheet (*xls,*xlsx)/Chapter13/Xm13-01.) Check **Import first row as variable names**.

2. Click **Statistics, Summaries, tables and tests, Classical tests of hypotheses,** and **Variance-comparison test**.

3. Select **Two-sample using variables**. In the **First variable** box select **Direct**. In the **Second variable** box select **Broker**.

Test and Estimate of the Difference between Two Means: Independent Samples

Example 13.1

```
Two-sample t test with equal variances

Variable      Obs       Mean     Std. Err.    Std. Dev.    [95% Conf. Interval]

  Direct       50      6.6312    .8658889     6.122759     4.891131    8.371269
  Broker       50      3.7232    .9310132     6.583258     1.852259    5.594141

combined       100     5.1772    .6491608     6.491608     3.889124    6.465276

    diff                2.908    1.271436                  .3848769    5.431123

     diff = mean(Direct) - mean(Broker)                     t =      2.2872
Ho: diff = 0                                degrees of freedom =          98

      Ha: diff < 0               Ha: diff != 0                    Ha: diff > 0
   Pr(T < t) = 0.9878       Pr(|T| > |t|) = 0.0243          Pr(T > t) = 0.0122
```

The test statistics is t = 2.2872 and the p-value is .0122. The 95% confidence interval estimate of the difference between the two means is

LCL = .3848769   UCL = 5.431123.

Instructions

1. Import or type the data into one column. (Click File/Import /Excel spreadsheet (*xls,*xlsx)/Chapter12/Xm13-01.) Check **Import first row as variable names**.

2. Click **Statistics, Summaries, tables and tests, Classical tests of hypotheses**, and **t-test (mean-comparison test)**.

3. Select **Two-sample using variables**. In the **First variable:** box select **Direct**. In the **Second variable:** box select **Broker**.

4. To produce the 95% confidence interval estimate, select **95** in the **Confidence level** box.

5. Do not check **Unequal variances** box.

Example 13.2

```
Variance ratio test
```

Variable	Obs	Mean	Std. Err.	Std. Dev.	[95% Conf. Interval]	
Offspr~g	42	-.1	.3002956	1.946138	-.7064593	.5064593
Outsider	98	1.235918	.2863346	2.834568	.6676234	1.804213
combined	140	.8351429	.2252244	2.664891	.3898342	1.280452

```
      ratio = sd(Offspring) / sd(Outsider)                    f =   0.4714
Ho: ratio = 1                                 degrees of freedom =   41, 97

    Ha: ratio < 1              Ha: ratio != 1               Ha: ratio > 1
 Pr(F < f) = 0.0040       2*Pr(F < f) = 0.0081          Pr(F > f) = 0.9960
```

The test statistic is F = .4714, p-value = .0081. There is enough evidence to infer that the population variances differ. Accordingly, we use the unequal-variances t-test in this example.

```
Two-sample t test with unequal variances
```

Variable	Obs	Mean	Std. Err.	Std. Dev.	[95% Conf. Interval]	
Offspr~g	42	-.1	.3002956	1.946138	-.7064593	.5064593
Outsider	98	1.235918	.2863346	2.834568	.6676234	1.804213
combined	140	.8351429	.2252244	2.664891	.3898342	1.280452
diff		-1.335918	.4149277		-2.158146	-.5136909

```
      diff = mean(Offspring) - mean(Outsider)                    t =  -3.2196
Ho: diff = 0                     Satterthwaite's degrees of freedom =  110.749

    Ha: diff < 0               Ha: diff != 0                Ha: diff > 0
 Pr(T < t) = 0.0008       Pr(|T| > |t|) = 0.0017        Pr(T > t) = 0.9992
```

The test statistic is t = −3.2196 and the two-tail p-value is .0017. The confidence interval estimate of the difference between the two means is

$$\text{LCL} = -2.158146 \qquad \text{UCL} = -.5136909$$

Instructions

Follow the instructions for Example 13.1. Check **Unequal variances**. Do not check **Welch's approximation**.

Test of the Difference between Two Means: Matched Pairs Experiment

Example 13.5

```
Paired t test
```

Variable	Obs	Mean	Std. Err.	Std. Dev.	[95% Conf. Interval]	
Finance	25	65438.2	4218.918	21094.59	56730.78	74145.62
Market~g	25	60373.68	4333.321	21666.61	51430.14	69317.22
diff	25	5064.52	1329.379	6646.895	2320.816	7808.224

```
    mean(diff) = mean(Finance - Marketing)                        t =   3.8097
Ho: mean(diff) = 0                             degrees of freedom =        24

 Ha: mean(diff) < 0          Ha: mean(diff) != 0          Ha: mean(diff) > 0
 Pr(T < t) = 0.9996       Pr(|T| > |t|) = 0.0009        Pr(T > t) = 0.0004
```

The test statistic is t = 3.8097 and the p-value = .0004. The confidence interval estimate of the mean difference is LCL = 2320.816, UCL = 7808.224.

Instructions

Follow the instructions for Example 13.1. Check **Paired**.

Inference about Two Variances

Example 13.7

```
Variance ratio test
```

Variable	Obs	Mean	Std. Err.	Std. Dev.	[95% Conf. Interval]	
Machine1	25	999.68	.1591645	.7958224	999.3515	1000.008
Machine2	25	999.812	.1345759	.6728794	999.5342	1000.09
combined	50	999.746	.1035772	.7324017	999.5379	999.9541

```
    ratio = sd(Machine1) / sd(Machine2)                          f =   1.3988
Ho: ratio = 1                                 degrees of freedom =    24, 24

    Ha: ratio < 1               Ha: ratio != 1               Ha: ratio > 1
  Pr(F < f) = 0.7915         2*Pr(F > f) = 0.4170          Pr(F > f) = 0.2085
```

Test statistic: f = 1.3988, p-value = .2085

Inference about the Difference between Two Population Proportions

Examples 13.9 and 13.11

```
Two-sample test of proportions          Supermarket1: Number of obs =      904
                                        Supermarket2: Number of obs =     1038
```

Variable	Mean	Std. Err.	z	P>|z|	[95% Conf. Interval]
Supermarket1	.199115	.0132817			.1730834 .2251467
Supermarket2	.1493256	.0110624			.1276437 .1710076
diff	.0497894	.0172853			.0159109 .0836679
	under Ho:	.0171879	2.90	0.004	

```
        diff = prop(Supermarket1) - prop(Supermarket2)         z =    2.8968
    Ho: diff = 0

  Ha: diff < 0              Ha: diff != 0               Ha: diff > 0
Pr(Z < z) = 0.9981       Pr(|Z| > |z|) = 0.0038      Pr(Z > z) = 0.0019
```

Test statistic: z = 2.8968, p-value = .0019

Confidence interval estimate: LCL = .01059109, UCL = .0836679

Instructions

1. Use Excel to convert successes (code 9077) to 1s and non-successes to 0s. (There is a flaw in Stata's **Data/Create or change variable/Create new variable** when the sample sizes differ.)

2. Click **Statistics, Summaries, tables and tests, Classical tests of hypotheses**, and **Proportion test**.

3. Select **Two-sample using variables**. In the **First variable** box select **Supermarket1**. In the **Second variable** box select **Supermarket2**.

4. To produce the 95% confidence interval estimate, select **95** in the **Confidence level** box.

An alternative method is to count the number of successes (code 9077) and sample sizes and use Proportion test calculator.

Stata does not conduct a case 2 test.

APPENDIX 13.C / REVIEW OF CHAPTERS 12 AND 13

As you may have already discovered, the ability to identify the correct statistical technique is critical; any calculation performed without it is useless. When you solved problems at the end of each section in the preceding chapters (you *have* been solving problems at the end of each section covered, haven't you?), you probably had no great difficulty identifying the correct technique to use. You used the statistical technique introduced in that section. Although those exercises provided practice in setting up hypotheses, producing computer output of tests of hypothesis and confidence interval estimators, and interpreting the results, you did not address a fundamental question faced by statistics practitioners: Which technique should I use? If you still do not appreciate the dimension of this problem, examine Table A13.1, which lists all the inferential methods covered thus far.

TABLE **A13.1** Summary of Statistical Techniques in Chapters 12 and 13

t-test of μ
Estimator of μ (including estimator of $N\mu$)
z-test of p
Estimator of p (including estimator of Np)
χ^2-test of σ^2
Estimator of σ^2
Equal-variances *t*-test of $\mu_1 - \mu_2$
Equal-variances estimator of $\mu_1 - \mu_2$
Unequal-variances *t*-test of $\mu_1 - \mu_2$
Unequal-variances estimator of $\mu_1 - \mu_2$
t-test of μ_D
Estimator of μ_D
F-test of σ_1^2/σ_2^2
Estimator of σ_1^2/σ_2^2
z-test of $p_1 - p_2$ (Case 1)
z-test of $p_1 - p_2$ (Case 2)
Estimator of $p_1 - p_2$

Counting tests and confidence interval estimators of a parameter as two different techniques, a total of 17 statistical procedures have been presented thus far, and there is much left to be done. Faced with statistical problems that require the use of some of these techniques (such as in real-world applications or on a quiz or midterm test), most students need some assistance in identifying the appropriate method. In this appendix and the appendixes of five more chapters, you will have the opportunity to practice your decision skills; we've provided exercises and cases that require all the inferential techniques introduced in Chapters 12 and 13. Solving these problems will require you to do what statistics practitioners must do: analyze the problem, identify the technique or techniques, employ statistical software and a computer to yield the required statistics, and interpret the results.

The flowchart in Figure A13.1 represents the logical process that leads to the identification of the appropriate method. Of course, it only shows the techniques covered to this point. Chapters 14, 15, 16, 17, and 19 will include appendixes that review all the techniques introduced up to that chapter. The list and the flowchart will be expanded in each appendix, and all appendixes will contain review exercises. (Some will contain cases.)

FIGURE **A13.1** **Flowchart of Techniques in Chapters 12 and 13**

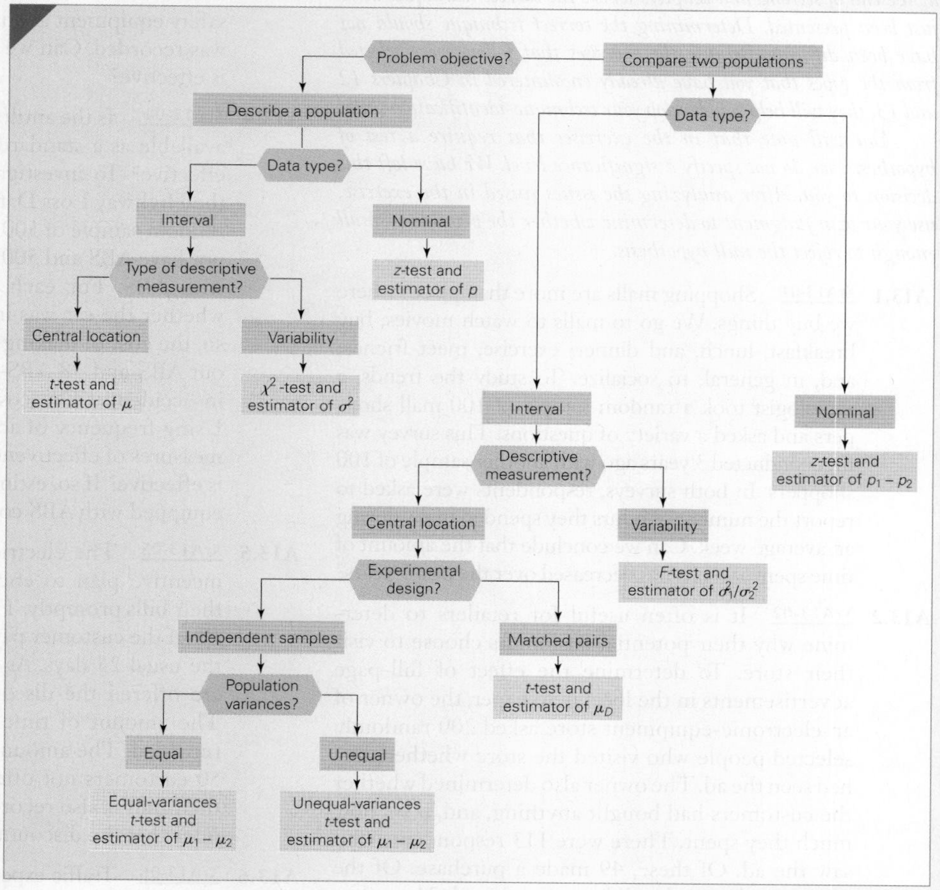

As we pointed out in Chapter 11, the two most important factors in determining the correct statistical technique are the problem objective and the data type. In some situations, once these have been recognized, the technique automatically follows. In other cases, however, several additional factors must be identified before you can proceed. For example, when the problem objective is to compare two populations and the data are interval, three other significant issues must be addressed: the descriptive measurement (central location or variability), whether the samples are independently drawn, and, if so, whether the unknown population variances are equal.

EXERCISES

The purpose of the exercises that follow is twofold. First, the exercises provide you with practice in the critical skill of identifying the correct technique. Second, they allow you to improve your ability to determine the statistics needed to answer the question and interpret the results. We believe that the first skill is underdeveloped because up to now you have had little practice. The exercises you've worked on have appeared at the end of sections and chapters where the correct techniques have just been presented. Determining the correct technique should not have been difficult. Because the exercises that follow were selected from the types that you have already encountered in Chapters 12 and 13, they will help you develop your technique-identification skills.

You will note that in the exercises that require a test of hypothesis, we do not specify a significance level. We have left this decision to you. After analyzing the issues raised in the exercise, use your own judgment to determine whether the p-value is small enough to reject the null hypothesis.

A13.1 XrA13-01   Shopping malls are more than places where we buy things. We go to malls to watch movies; buy breakfast, lunch, and dinner; exercise; meet friends; and, in general, to socialize. To study the trends, a sociologist took a random sample of 100 mall shoppers and asked a variety of questions. This survey was first conducted 3 years ago with another sample of 100 shoppers. In both surveys, respondents were asked to report the number of hours they spend in malls during an average week. Can we conclude that the amount of time spent at malls has decreased over the past 3 years?

A13.2 XrA13-02   It is often useful for retailers to determine why their potential customers choose to visit their store. To determine the effect of full-page advertisements in the local newspaper, the owner of an electronic-equipment store asked 200 randomly selected people who visited the store whether they had seen the ad. The owner also determined whether the customers had bought anything, and, if so, how much they spent. There were 113 respondents who saw the ad. Of these, 49 made a purchase. Of the 87 respondents who did not see the ad, 21 made a purchase. The amounts spent were recorded.
   a. Can we conclude that customers who see the ad are more likely to make a purchase than those who do not see the ad?
   b. Can we conclude that customers who see the ad spend more than those who do not see the ad (among those who make a purchase)?
   c. Estimate with 95% confidence the proportion of all customers who see the ad and then make a purchase.
   d. Estimate with 95% confidence the mean amount spent by customers who see the ad and make a purchase.

A13.3 XrA13-03   In an attempt to reduce the number of person-hours lost as a result of industrial accidents, a large multiplant corporation installed new safety equipment in all departments and all plants. To test the effectiveness of the equipment, a random sample of 25 plants was drawn. The number of person-hours lost in the month before installation of the safety equipment and in the month after installation was recorded. Can we conclude that the equipment is effective?

A13.4 XrA13-04   Is the antilock braking system (ABS) now available as a standard feature on many cars really effective? To investigate the effectiveness of ABS, the Highway Loss Data Institute gathered data on a random sample of 500 General Motors cars that did not have ABS and 500 GM cars that were equipped with ABS. For each year, the institute recorded whether the car was involved in an accident and, if so, the cost of making repairs. Forty-two cars without ABS and 38 ABS-equipped cars were involved in accidents. The costs of repairs were recorded. Using frequency of accidents and cost of repairs as measures of effectiveness, can we conclude that ABS is effective? If so, estimate how much better are cars equipped with ABS compared to cars without ABS.

A13.5 XrA13-05   The electric company is considering an incentive plan to encourage its customers to pay their bills promptly. The plan is to discount the bills 1% if the customer pays within 5 days as opposed to the usual 25 days. As an experiment, 50 customers are offered the discount on their September bill. The amount of time taken to pay their bills was recorded. The amount of time a random sample of 50 customers not offered the discount take to pay their bills is also recorded. Do these data allow us to infer that the discount plan works?

A13.6 XrA13-06   Traffic experts are always looking for ways to control automobile speeds. Some communities have experimented with "traffic-calming" techniques. These include speed bumps and various obstructions that force cars to slow down to drive around them. Critics point out that the techniques are counterproductive because they cause drivers to speed on other parts of these roads. In an analysis of the effectiveness of speed bumps, an expert organized a study over a 1-mile stretch of city road that had 10 stop signs. The expert then took a random sample of 100 cars and recorded their average speed (the speed limit was 30 mph) and the number of proper stops at the stop signs and repeated the observations for another sample of 100 cars after speed bumps were placed on the road. Do these data allow the statistics practitioner to conclude that the speed bumps are effective?

A13.7 XrA13-07 The proliferation of self-serve pumps at gas stations has generally resulted in poorer automobile maintenance. One feature of poor maintenance is low tire pressure, which results in shorter tire life and higher gasoline consumption. To examine this problem, an automotive expert took a random sample of cars across the country and measured the tire pressure. The difference between the recommended tire pressure and the observed tire pressure was recorded. [A recording of 8 means that the pressure of the tire is 8 pounds per square inch (psi) less than the amount recommended by the tire manufacturer.] Suppose that for each psi below recommendation, tire life decreases by 100 miles and gasoline consumption increases by 0.1 gallon per mile. Estimate with 95% confidence the effect on tire life and gasoline consumption.

A13.8 XrA1 3-08 Many North American cities encourage the use of bicycles as a way to reduce pollution and traffic congestion. So many people now regularly use bicycles to get to work and for exercise that some jurisdictions have enacted bicycle helmet laws that specify that all bicycle riders must wear helmets to protect against head injuries. Critics of these laws complain that it is a violation of individual freedom and that helmet laws tend to discourage bicycle usage. To examine this issue, a researcher randomly sampled 50 bicycle users and asked them to record the number of miles they rode weekly. Several weeks later, the helmet law was enacted. The number of miles each of the 50 bicycle riders rode weekly was recorded for the week after the law was passed. Can we infer from these data that the law discourages bicycle usage?

A13.9 XrA13-09 Cardizem CD is a prescription drug that is used to treat high blood pressure and angina. One common side effect of such drugs is the occurrence of headaches and dizziness. To determine whether its drug has the same side effects, the drug's manufacturer, Marion Merrell Dow, Inc., undertook a study. A random sample of 908 high-blood-pressure sufferers was recruited; 607 took Cardizem CD and 301 took a placebo. Each reported whether they suffered from headaches or dizziness (2 = yes, 1 = no). Can the pharmaceutical company scientist infer that Cardizem CD users are more likely to suffer headache and dizziness side effects than nonusers?

A13.10 XrA13-10 A fast-food franchiser is considering building a restaurant at a downtown location. Based on a financial analysis, a site is acceptable only if the number of pedestrians passing the location during the work day averages more than 200 per hour. To help decide whether to build on the site, a statistics

practitioner observes the number of pedestrians who pass the site each hour over a 40-hour work-week. Should the franchiser build on this site?

A13.11 XrA13-11 Most people who quit smoking cigarettes do so for health reasons. However, some quitters find that they gain weight after quitting, and scientists estimate that the health risks of smoking two packs of cigarettes per day or carrying 65 extra pounds of weight are about equivalent. In an attempt to learn more about the effects of quitting smoking, the U.S. Centers for Disease Control conducted a study. A sample of 1,885 smokers was taken. During the course of the experiment, some of the smokers quit their habit. The amount of weight gained by all the subjects was recorded. Do these data allow us to conclude that quitting smoking results in weight gains?

A3.12 XrA13-12 Golf-equipment manufacturers compete against one another by offering a bewildering array of new products and innovations. The effect of these new products on the average golfer is, however, much in doubt. One product, a perimeter-weighted iron, was designed to increase the consistency of distance and accuracy. The most important aspect of irons is consistency, which means that ideally there should be no variation in distance from shot to shot. To examine the relative merits of two brands of perimeter-weighted irons, an average golfer used the 7-iron, hitting 100 shots using each of two brands. The distance in yards was recorded. Can the golfer conclude that brand B is superior to brand A?

A13.13 XrA13-13 Managers are frequently called on to negotiate in a variety of settings. This calls for an ability to think logically, which requires an ability to concentrate and ignore distractions. In a study of the effect of distractions, a random sample of 208 students was drawn by psychologists at McMaster University. The male students were shown pictures of women of varying attractiveness. The female students were shown pictures of men of varying attractiveness. All students were then offered a choice of an immediate reward of $15 or a wait of 8 months for a reward of $75. The choices of the male and of the female students (1 = immediate reward, 2 = larger reward 8 months later) were recorded. The results are stored in the following way:

Column 1: Choices of males shown most attractive women

Column 2: Choices of males shown less attractive women

Column 3: Choices of females shown most attractive men

Column 4: Choices of females shown less attractive men

a. Can we infer that men's choices are affected by the attractiveness of women's pictures?

b. Can we infer that women's choices are affected by the attractiveness of men's pictures?

A13.14 XrA13-14   Throughout the day, many exercise shows appear on television. These usually feature attractive and fit men and women performing various exercises and urging viewers to duplicate the activity at home. Some viewers are exercisers. However, some people like to watch the shows without exercising (which explains why attractive people are used as demonstrators). Various companies sponsor the shows, and there are commercial breaks. One sponsor wanted to determine whether there are differences between exercisers and nonexercisers in terms of how well they remember the sponsor's name. A random sample of viewers was selected and called after the exercise show was over. Respondents were asked to report whether they exercised or only watched. They were also asked to name the sponsor's brand name (2 = yes, they could; 1 = no, they couldn't). Can the sponsor conclude that exercisers are more likely to remember the sponsor's brand name than those who only watch?

A13.15 XrA13-15   According to the latest census, the number of households in a large metropolitan area is 425,000. The home-delivery department of the local newspaper reports that 104,320 households receive daily home delivery. To increase home-delivery sales, the marketing department launches an expensive advertising campaign. A financial analyst tells the publisher that for the campaign to be successful, home-delivery sales must increase to more than 110,000 households. Anxious to see whether the campaign is working, the publisher authorizes a telephone survey of 400 households within 1 week of the beginning of the campaign and asks household heads whether they have the newspaper delivered. The responses were recorded where 2 = yes and 1 = no.

a. Do these data indicate that the campaign will increase home-delivery sales?

b. Do these data allow the publisher to conclude that the campaign will be successful?

A13.16 XrA13-16   The Scholastic Aptitude Test (SAT), which is organized by the Educational Testing Service (ETS), is important to high school students seeking admission to colleges and universities throughout the United States. A number of companies offer courses to prepare students for the SAT. The Stanley H. Kaplan Educational Center claims that its students gain, on average, more than 110 points by taking its course. ETS, however, insists that preparatory courses can improve a score by no more than 40 points. (The minimum and maximum scores of the SAT are 400 and 1,600, respectively.) Suppose a random sample of 40 students wrote the exam, then took the Kaplan preparatory course, and then took the exam again.

a. Do these data provide sufficient evidence to refute the ETS claim?

b. Do these data provide sufficient evidence to refute Kaplan's claim?

A13.17 XrA13-17   In assessing the value of radio advertisements, sponsors consider not only the total number of listeners but also their ages. The 18 to 34 age group is considered to spend the most money. To examine the issue, the manager of an FM station commissioned a survey. One objective was to measure the difference in listening habits between the 18 to 34 age and 35 to 50 age groups. The survey asked 250 people in each age category how much time they spent listening to FM radio per day. The results (in minutes) were recorded and stored in stacked format (column 1 = Age group and column 2 = Listening times).

a. Can we conclude that a difference exists between the two groups?

b. Estimate with a confidence interval the difference in mean time listening to FM radio between the two age groups.

c. Are the required conditions satisfied for the techniques you used in parts (a) and (b)?

GENERAL SOCIAL SURVEY EXERCISES

GSS2018 *Exercises A13.18 to A13.20 are based on the 2018 survey. In 2018 there were 244,802,964 adults in the United States (Source: U.S. Census).* **Conduct all tests at the 5% significance level. Use a 95% confidence level for estimates.**

A13.18 The survey asked, "On the whole, how satisfied are you with the work you do?" (SATJOB: 1 = Very satisfied, 2 = Moderately satisfied, 3 = A little dissatisfied, 4 = Very dissatisfied.) Is there sufficient statistical evidence to infer that the number of Americans who are very or moderately satisfied is more than the number who are a little or very dissatisfied?

A13.19 For generations, Americans believed that their children would do better than their parents. The survey asked, "When your children are at your age, will their standard of living be...?" (KIDSSOL: 1 = Much better, 2 = Somewhat better, 3 = About the same, 4 = Somewhat worse, 5 = Much worse.) Is there sufficient evidence to conclude that there are more people who say their children will do much better or somewhat better than people who will say their children will do about the same, somewhat worse, or much worse?

A13.20 In 2018 the economy was booming. The survey asked respondents, "In the next 12 months how likely is it that you will lose your job or be laid off?" (JOBLOSE: 1 = Very likely, 2 = Fairly likely, 3 = Not too likely, 4 = Not likely.) Compute a confidence interval estimate of the number of Americans who believed that it is not likely that they will be laid off.

GSS2016 GSS2018 *Exercises A13.21 to A13.23 are based on the 2016 and 2018 surveys.*

A13.21 The economy in 2018 was stronger than in 2016. Can we infer that incomes (RINCOME) were higher in 2018 than in 2016?

A13.22 Were families larger in 2018 than in 2016? Test to determine whether there is enough evidence to conclude that the average family in 2018 had more children (CHILDS) than in 2016.

A13.23 Is the average age of Americans in 2018 different from the average in 2016? Conduct a test to answer the question.

GSS2016 *Exercises A13.24 to A13.29 are based on the 2016 survey. In 2016 there were 240,834,729 adults in the United States.*

A13.24 Do government jobs require any special education? Can we infer from the data that government employees (WRKGOVT: 1 = Government, 2 =

Private) have more years of education (EDUC) than private sector workers?

A13.25 The number of private sector employees who belong to unions has been steadily decreasing in the United States for decades. However, the number of government workers who belong to unions may also be declining. To determine the number, the survey asked whether the respondent and/or spouse belong to unions (UNION: 1 = Respondent belongs, 2 = Spouse belongs, 3 = Both belong, 4 = Neither belong). Produce a confidence interval estimate of the fraction of government employees who do not belong to unions in 2016.

A13.26 The survey asked, true or false: the center of the earth is very hot (HOTCORE: 1 = True, 2 = False, 8 = Don't know, 9 = No answer, 0 = Question not asked). Is there enough evidence to conclude that in 2016 native-born Americans (BORN: 1 = USA, 2 = Somewhere else) were more likely to get the correct answer than foreign-born Americans?

A13.27 In many college disciplines, women outnumber men. Does that mean that women have more years of education than men (EDUC)? Conduct a test to answer the question (SEX: 1 = Male, 2 = Female).

A13.28 According to the U.S. Census, in 2016 women made up 51.909% of the adult population. Is there enough evidence to conclude that women are over-represented in the General Social Survey of 2016 (SEX: 1 = Male, 2 = Female)?

A13.29 Do foreign-born Americans (BORN: Born in the United States: 1 = Yes, 2 = No) work longer hours (HRS1) than Americans born in the United States? Conduct a statistical test to answer the question.

SURVEY OF CONSUMER FINANCES EXERCISES

SCF2016:\MC *The following exercises are based on the middle-class subsample of the 2016 survey.* **Conduct all tests at the 5% significance level. Use a 95% confidence level for estimates.**

A13.30 Numerous studies have shown that men make higher income (INCOME) than women (HHSEX: 1 = Male, 2 = Female). However, does this apply to male and female middle-class heads of households? Test to determine whether there is enough evidence to conclude that male heads of middle-class households have higher incomes than female heads of middle-class households.

A13.31 The middle class in the 2016 Survey of Consumer Finances had a net worth of between $89,520 and

$380,480. The average amount spent on food at home was $4,049 (*Source:* Bureau of Labor Statistics). Is there enough evidence to infer that the average middle-class household spent more than that amount in 2016 (FOODHOME)?

A13.32 Do middle-class household heads with college degrees get more heavily into debt (DEBT) than those without college degrees (EDCL: 1 = No high school diploma, 2 = High school diploma, 3 = Some college, 4 = College degree)? Conduct a test to answer the question.

Kzenon/Shutterstock.com

ANALYSIS OF VARIANCE

CHAPTER OUTLINE

General Social Survey: Liberal–Conservative Spectrum and Income

DATA
GSS2018

Are Americans' political views affected by their incomes, or perhaps vice versa? If so, we would expect that incomes would differ between groups who define themselves somewhere on the following scale (POLVIEWS). Conduct a test to determine whether there is enough evidence to infer that incomes (RINCOME) differ between the seven populations defined by their political views.

1 = Extremely liberal
2 = Liberal
3 = Slightly liberal

Maxh Herman/Shutterstock.com

See page 561 for our answer.

4 = Moderate
5 = Slightly conservative
6 = Conservative
7 = Extremely conservative

INTRODUCTION

The technique presented in this chapter allows statistics practitioners to compare two or more populations of interval data. The technique is called the **analysis of variance**, and it is an extremely powerful and commonly used procedure. The analysis of variance technique determines whether differences exist between population means. Ironically, the procedure works by analyzing the sample variance, hence the name. We will examine several different forms of the technique.

One of the first applications of the analysis of variance was conducted in the 1920s to determine whether different treatments of fertilizer produced different crop yields. The terminology of that original experiment is still used. No matter what the experiment, the procedure is designed to determine whether there are significant differences between the **treatment means**.

14-1 / ONE-WAY ANALYSIS OF VARIANCE

The analysis of variance is a procedure that tests to determine whether differences exist between two or more population means. The name of the technique derives from the way in which the calculations are performed; that is, the technique analyzes the variance of the data to determine whether we can infer that the population means differ. As in Chapter 13, the experimental design is a determinant in identifying the proper method to use. In this section, we describe the procedure to apply when the samples are independently drawn. The technique is called the **one-way analysis of variance**. Figure 14.1 depicts the sampling process for drawing independent samples. The mean and variance of population j ($j = 1, 2, \ldots, k$) are labeled μ_j and σ_j^2, respectively. Both parameters are unknown. For each population, we draw independent random samples. For each sample, we can compute the mean $\bar{x}_j$ and the variance s_j^2.

FIGURE **14.1** Sampling Scheme for Independent Samples

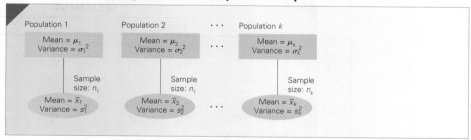

EXAMPLE 14.1

DATA
Xm14-01

Amounts Invested in Stocks and Mutual Fund Shares among Seniors

In the last decade, stockbrokers have drastically changed the way they do business. Internet trading has become quite common, and online trades can cost as little as $5. However, because of their age, older people may not be trading as much as younger people. A financial analyst wanted to see if it was worthwhile to invite older adults to invest more heavily in the stock market. But first the analyst needed to know whether there were certain age categories that differed from others. To help answer this question, a random sample of 384 older American adults was asked to report their age category and the total amount invested in the stock market ($1,000s). The age categories were 65–69, 70–74, 75 and older. Some of the data are listed next. Do these data allow the analyst to determine that there are differences in stock ownership between the three age groups? (*Source:* U.S. Census Bureau.)

Age: 65–69	Age: 70–74	Age: 75+
76.8	86.1	77.7
87.4	105.9	81.5
109.1	58.4	98
51.8	73.5	81.8
⋮	⋮	⋮

SOLUTION:

You should confirm that the data are interval (amounts invested in the stock market) and that the problem objective is to compare three populations (age categories). The parameters are the three population means: μ_1, μ_2, and μ_3. The null hypothesis will state that there are no differences between the population means. Hence,

$$H_0: \mu_1 = \mu_2 = \mu_3$$

The analysis of variance determines whether there is enough statistical evidence to show that the null hypothesis is false. Consequently, the alternative hypothesis will always specify the following:

H_1: At least two means differ

The next step is to determine the test statistic, which is somewhat more involved than the test statistics we have introduced thus far. The process of performing the analysis of variance is facilitated by the notation in Table 14.1.

TABLE **14.1** Notation for the One-Way Analysis of Variance

	TREATMENT			
	1	**2**	**j**	**k**
	x_{11}	x_{12} ···	x_{1j} ···	x_{1k}
	x_{21}	x_{22} ···	x_{2j} ···	x_{2k}
	⋮	⋮	⋮	⋮
	$x_{n_1 1}$	$x_{n_2 2}$	$x_{n_j j}$	$x_{n_k k}$
Sample size	n_1	n_2	n_j	n_k
Sample mean	$\bar{x}_1$	$\bar{x}_2$	$\bar{x}_j$	$\bar{x}_k$

x_{ij} = *i*th observation of the *j*th sample

n_j = number of observations in the sample taken from the *j*th population

$\bar{x}_j$ = mean of the *j*th sample = $\dfrac{\sum\limits_{i=1}^{n_j} x_{ij}}{n_j}$

$\bar{x}$ = grand mean of all the observations = $\dfrac{\sum\limits_{j=1}^{k}\sum\limits_{i=1}^{n_j} x_{ij}}{n}$ where $n = n_1 + n_2 + \cdots + n_k$, and *k* is the number of populations

The variable X is called the **response variable**, and its values are called **responses**. The unit that we measure is called an **experimental unit**. In this example, the response variable is the amounts invested in stocks, and the experimental units are the heads of households sampled. The criterion by which we classify the populations is called a **factor**. Each population is called a factor **level**. The factor in Example 14.1 is the age category of the head of the household and there are three levels. Later in this chapter, we'll discuss an experiment where the populations are classified using two factors. In this section, we deal with single-factor experiments only.

Test Statistic

The test statistic is computed in accordance with the following rationale. If the null hypothesis is true, the population means would all be equal. We would then expect that the sample means would be close to one another. If the alternative hypothesis is true, however, there would be large differences between some of the sample means. The statistic that measures the proximity of the sample means to each other is called the **between-treatments variation**; it is denoted **SST**, which stands for **sum of squares for treatments**.

Sum of Squares for Treatments

$$SST = \sum_{j=1}^{k} n_j (\bar{x}_j - \bar{\bar{x}})^2$$

As you can deduce from this formula, if the sample means are close to each other, all of the sample means would be close to the grand mean; as a result, SST would be small. In fact, SST achieves its smallest value (zero) when all the sample means are equal. In other words, if

$$\bar{x}_1 = \bar{x}_2 = \cdots = \bar{x}_k$$

then

$$SST = 0$$

It follows that a small value of SST supports the null hypothesis. In this example, we compute the sample means and the grand mean as

$$\bar{x}_1 = 76.21$$
$$\bar{x}_2 = 75.14$$
$$\bar{x}_3 = 82.69$$
$$\bar{\bar{x}} = 78.49$$

The sample sizes are

$$n_1 = 123$$
$$n_2 = 108$$
$$n_3 = 153$$
$$n = n_1 + n_2 + n_3 = 123 + 108 + 153 = 384$$

Then,

$$SST = \sum_{j=1}^{k} n_j(\bar{x}_j - \bar{\bar{x}})^2$$

$$= 123(76.21 - 78.49)^2 + 108(75.14 - 78.49)^2 + 153(82.69 - 78.49)^2 = 4,550$$

If large differences exist between the sample means, at least some sample means differ considerably from the grand mean, producing a large value of SST. It is then reasonable to reject the null hypothesis in favor of the alternative hypothesis. The key question to be answered in this test (as in all other statistical tests) is, How large does the statistic have to be for us to justify rejecting the null hypothesis? In our example, SST = 4,550. Is this value large enough to indicate that the population means differ? To answer this question, we need to know how much variation exists in the amounts invested which is measured by the **within-treatments variation**, which is denoted by **SSE (sum of squares for error)**. The within-treatments variation provides a measure of the amount of variation in the response variable that is not caused by the treatments. In this example, we are trying to determine whether the amounts invested in stocks vary by the age of the head of the household. However, other variables also affect the responses variable. We would expect that variables such as household income, occupation, and the size of the family would play a role in determining how much money families invest in stocks. All of these (as well as others we may not even be able to identify) are sources of variation, which we would group together and call the error. This source of variation is measured by the sum of squares for error.

Sum of Squares for Error

$$SSE = \sum_{j=1}^{k} \sum_{i=1}^{n_j} (x_{ij} - \bar{x}_j)^2$$

When SSE is partially expanded, we get

$$SSE = \sum_{i=1}^{n_1} (x_{i1} - \bar{x}_1)^2 + \sum_{i=1}^{n_2} (x_{i2} - \bar{x}_2)^2 + \cdots + \sum_{i=1}^{n_k} (x_{ik} - \bar{x}_k)^2$$

If you examine each of the k components of SSE, you'll see that each is a measure of the variability of that sample. If we divide each component by $n_j - 1$, we obtain the sample variances. We can express this by rewriting SSE as

$$SSE = (n_1 - 1)s_1^2 + (n_2 - 1)s_2^2 + \cdots + (n_k - 1)s_k^2$$

where s_j^2 is the sample variance of sample j. SSE is thus the combined or pooled variation of the k samples. This is an extension of a calculation we made in Section 13-1, where we tested and estimated the difference between two means using the pooled estimate of the common population variance (denoted s_p^2). One of the required conditions for that statistical technique is that the population variances are equal. That same condition is now necessary for us to use SSE; that is, we require that

$$\sigma_1^2 = \sigma_2^2 = \cdots = \sigma_k^2$$

Returning to our example, we calculate the sample variances as follows:

$$s_1^2 = 787.35$$

$$s_2^2 = 712.47$$

$$s_3^2 = 718.19$$

FIGURE **14.3** Histograms for Example 14.1

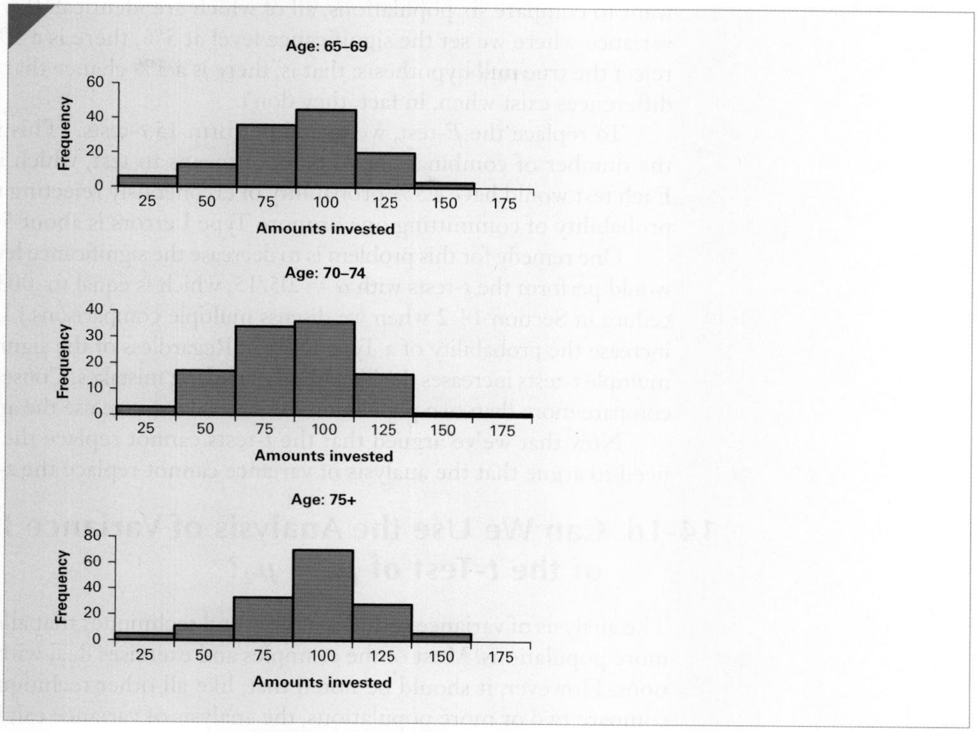

14-1b Violation of the Required Conditions

If the data are not normally distributed, we can replace the one-way analysis of variance with its nonparametric counterpart, which is the Kruskal–Wallis Test. (See Section 19-3.[*]) If the population variances are unequal, we can use several methods to correct the problem. However, these corrective measures are beyond the level of this book.

14-1c Can We Use the *t*-Test of the Difference between Two Means Instead of the Analysis of Variance?

The analysis of variance tests to determine whether there is evidence of differences between two or more population means. The *t*-test of $\mu_1 - \mu_2$ determines whether there is evidence of a difference between two population means. The question arises, Can we use *t*-tests instead of the analysis of variance? In other words, instead of testing all the means in one test as in the analysis of variance, why not test each pair of means? In Example 14.1, we would test $(\mu_1 - \mu_2)$, $(\mu_1 - \mu_3)$, and $(\mu_2 - \mu_3)$. If we find no evidence of a difference in each test, we would conclude that none of the means differ. If there was evidence of a difference in at least one test, we would conclude that some of the means differ.

There are two reasons why we don't use multiple *t*-tests instead of one *F*-test. First, we would have to perform many more calculations. Even with a computer, this extra work is tedious. Second, and more important, conducting multiple tests increases the

---

[*]Instructors who wish to teach the use of nonparametric techniques for testing the difference between two or more means when the normality requirement is not satisfied should use the online appendix Kruskal–Wallis Test and Friedman Test.

probability of making Type I errors. To understand why, consider a problem where we want to compare six populations, all of which are identical. If we conduct an analysis of variance where we set the significance level at 5%, there is a 5% chance that we would reject the true null hypothesis; that is, there is a 5% chance that we would conclude that differences exist when, in fact, they don't.

To replace the *F*-test, we would perform 15 *t*-tests. [This number is derived from the number of combinations of pairs of means to test, which is $C_2^6 = (6 \times 5)/2 = 15$.] Each test would have a 5% probability of erroneously rejecting the null hypothesis. The probability of committing one or more Type I errors is about 54%.*

One remedy for this problem is to decrease the significance level. In this illustration, we would perform the *t*-tests with $\alpha = .05/15$, which is equal to .0033. (We will use this procedure in Section 14-2 when we discuss multiple comparisons.) Unfortunately, this would increase the probability of a Type II error. Regardless of the significance level, performing multiple *t*-tests increases the likelihood of making mistakes. Consequently, when we want to compare more than two populations of interval data, we use the analysis of variance.

Now that we've argued that the *t*-tests cannot replace the analysis of variance, we need to argue that the analysis of variance cannot replace the *t*-test.

14-1d Can We Use the Analysis of Variance Instead of the *t*-Test of $\mu_1 - \mu_2$?

The analysis of variance is the first of several techniques that allow us to compare two or more populations. Most of the examples and exercises deal with more than two populations. However, it should be noted that, like all other techniques whose objective is to compare two or more populations, the analysis of variance can be used to compare only two populations. If that's the case, then why do we need techniques to compare exactly two populations? Specifically, why do we need the *t*-test of $\mu_1 - \mu_2$ when the analysis of variance can be used to test two population means?

To understand why, we still need the *t*-test to make inferences about $\mu_1 - \mu_2$. Suppose that we plan to use the analysis of variance to test two population means. The null and alternative hypotheses are

H_0: $\mu_1 = \mu_2$

H_1: At least two means differ

Of course, the alternative hypothesis specifies that $\mu_1 \neq \mu_2$. However, if we want to determine whether μ_1 is greater than μ_2 (or vice versa), we cannot use the analysis of variance because this technique allows us to test for a difference only. Thus, if we want to test to determine whether one population mean exceeds the other, we must use the *t*-test of $\mu_1 - \mu_2$ (with $\sigma_1^2 = \sigma_2^2$). Moreover, the analysis of variance requires that the population variances are equal. If they are not, we must use the unequal variances test statistic.

14-1e Relationship between the *F*-Statistic and the *t*-Statistic

It is probably useful for you to understand the relationship between the *t*-statistic and the *F*-statistic. The test statistic for testing hypotheses about $\mu_1 - \mu_2$ with equal variances is

$$t = \frac{(\bar{x}_1 - \bar{x}_2) - (\mu_1 - \mu_2)}{\sqrt{s_p^2 \left(\dfrac{1}{n_1} + \dfrac{1}{n_2} \right)}}$$

---

*The probability of committing at least one Type I error is computed from a binomial distribution with $n = 15$ and $p = .05$. Thus, $P(X \geq 1) = 1 - P(X = 0) = 1 - .463 = .537$.

If we square this quantity, the result is the F-statistic: $F = t^2$. To illustrate this point, we'll redo the calculation of the test statistic in Example 13.1 using the analysis of variance. Recall that because we were able to assume that the population variances were equal, the test statistic was as follows:

$$t = \frac{(6.63 - 3.72) - 0}{\sqrt{40.42\left(\frac{1}{50} + \frac{1}{50}\right)}} = 2.29$$

Using the analysis of variance (the Excel output is shown here), we find that the value of the test statistic is $F = 5.23$, which is $(2.29)^2$. Notice though that the analysis of variance p-value is .0243, which is twice the t-test p-value, which is .0122. The reason: The analysis of variance is conducting a test to determine whether the population means *differ*. If Example 13.1 had asked to determine whether the means differ, we would have conducted a two-tail test and the p-value would be .0243, the same as the analysis of variance p-value.

Excel Data Analysis: Analysis of Variance for Example 13.1

	A	B	C	D	E	F	G
1	Anova: Single Factor						
2							
3	SUMMARY						
4	Groups	Count	Sum	Average	Variance		
5	Direct	50	331.56	6.63	37.49		
6	Broker	50	186.16	3.72	43.34		
7							
8							
9	ANOVA						
10	Source of Variation	SS	df	MS	F	P-value	F crit
11	Between Groups	211.4	1	211.41	5.23	0.0243	3.94
12	Within Groups	3960.5	98	40.41			
13							
14	Total	4172.0	99				

14-1f Developing an Understanding of Statistical Concepts

Conceptually and mathematically, the F-test of the independent samples' single-factor analysis of variance is an extension of the t-test of $\mu_1 - \mu_2$. Moreover, if we simply want to determine whether a difference between two means exists, we can use the analysis of variance. The advantage of using the analysis of variance is that we can partition the total sum of squares, which enables us to measure how much variation is attributable to differences between populations and how much variation is attributable to differences within populations. As we pointed out in Section 13-3, explaining the variation is an extremely important topic, one that we will see again in other experimental designs of the analysis of variance and in regression analysis (Chapters 16, 17, and 18).

General Social Survey: Liberal–Conservative Spectrum and Income: Solution

IDENTIFY

The variable is income (RINCOME) of American adults, which is interval. The problem objective is to compare seven populations (the political views) and the experimental design is independent samples. Thus, we apply the one-way analysis of variance.

Maxh Herman/Shutterstock.com

(Continued)

COMPUTE

EXCEL Data Analysis

	A	B	C	D	E	F	G
1	Anova: Single Factor						
2	Groups	Count	Sum	Average	Variance		
3	E. Liberal	67	3,493,750	52,146	2,260,466,192		
4	Liberal	174	9,336,250	53,657	2,271,123,814		
5	S. Liberal	153	7,968,000	52,078	1,944,091,670		
6	Moderate	512	23,135,250	45,186	1,443,884,232		
7	S. Conservative	169	8,400,750	49,709	1,758,947,679		
8	Conservative	192	11,309,750	58,905	2,459,998,444		
9	E. Conservative	58	2,914,750	50,254	1,717,338,797		
10	ANOVA						
11	Source of Variation	SS	df	MS	F	P-value	F crit
12	Between Groups	30,332,607,575	6	5,055,434,596	2.73	0.0121	2.11
13	Within Groups	2,438,673,189,312	1318	1,850,283,148			
14	Total	2,469,005,796,887	1324				

INTERPRET

The p-value is .0121. There is enough evidence to infer that the incomes differ between the seven political views.

Factors That Identify the One-Way Analysis of Variance

1. **Problem objective**: Compare two or more populations.
2. **Data type**: Interval
3. **Experimental design**: Independent samples

EXERCISES

Developing an Understanding of Statistical Concepts

Exercises 14.1–14.3 are "what-if" analyses designed to determine what happens to the test statistic when the means, variances, and sample sizes change. These problems can be solved manually or by creating an Excel worksheet.

14.1 A statistics practitioner calculated the following statistics:

	Treatment		
Statistic	1	2	3
n	5	5	5
$\bar{x}$	10	15	20
s^2	50	50	50

a. Complete the ANOVA table.

b. Repeat part (a) changing the sample sizes to 10 each.

c. Describe what happens to the F-statistic when the sample sizes increase.

14.2 You are given the following statistics:

	Treatment		
Statistic	1	2	3
n	4	4	4
$\bar{x}$	20	22	25
s^2	10	10	10

a. Complete the ANOVA table.

b. Repeat part (a) changing the variances to 25 each.

c. Describe the effect on the F-statistic of increasing the sample variances.

14.3 The following statistics were calculated:

	Treatment			
Statistic	1	2	3	4
n	10	14	11	18
$\bar{x}$	30	35	33	40
s^2	10	10	10	10

a. Complete the ANOVA table.

b. Repeat part (a) changing the sample means to 130, 135, 133, and 140.

c. Describe the effect on the F-statistic of increasing the sample means by 100.

Applications

14.4 Xr14-04 How does an MBA major affect the number of job offers received? An MBA student randomly sampled four recent graduates, one each in finance, marketing, and management, and asked them to report the number of job offers. Can we conclude at the 5% significance level that there are differences in the number of job offers between the three MBA majors?

Finance	Marketing	Management
3	1	8
1	5	5
4	3	4
1	4	6

14.5 Xr14-05 A consumer organization was concerned about the differences between the advertised sizes of containers and the actual amount of product. In a preliminary study, six packages of three different brands of margarine that are supposed to contain 500 ml were measured. The differences from 500 ml are listed here. Do these data provide sufficient evidence to conclude that differences exist between the three brands? Use $\alpha = .10$.

Brand 1	Brand 2	Brand 3
1	2	1
3	2	2
3	4	4
0	3	2
1	0	3
0	4	4

14.6 Xr14-06 Many college and university students obtain summer jobs. A statistics professor wanted to determine whether students in different degree programs earn different amounts. A random sample of 5 students in the B.A., B.Sc., and B.B.A. programs were asked to report what they earned the previous summer. The results (in $1,000s) are listed here. Can the professor infer at the 5% significance level that students in different degree programs differ in their summer earnings?

B.A.	B.Sc.	B.B.A.
3.3	3.9	4.0
2.5	5.1	6.2
4.6	3.9	6.3
5.4	6.2	5.9
3.9	4.8	6.4

14.7 Xr14-07 Spam is the price we pay for being able to easily communicate by e-mail. Does spam affect everyone equally? In a preliminary study, university professors, administrators, and students were randomly sampled. Each person was asked to count the number of spam messages received that day. The results follow. Can we infer at the 5% significance level that the differing university communities differ in the amount of spam they receive in their e-mails?

Professors	Administrators	Students
7	5	12
4	9	4
0	12	5
3	16	18
18	10	15

14.8 Xr14-08 A management scientist believes that one way of judging whether a computer came equipped with enough memory is to determine the age of the computer. In a preliminary study, random samples of computer users were asked to identify the brand of computer and its age (in months). The categorized responses are shown here. Do these data provide sufficient evidence to conclude that there are differences in age between the computer brands? (Use $\alpha = .05$.)

IBM	Dell	HP	Other
17	8	6	24
10	4	15	12
13	21	8	15

Exercises 14.9–14.30 require the use of a computer and software. The answers may be calculated manually. See Appendix A for the sample statistics. **Use a 5% significance level for all tests.**

14.9 Xr14-09 Because there are no national or regional standards, it is difficult for university admission committees to compare graduates of different high schools. University administrators have noted that an 80% average at a high school with low standards may be equivalent to a 70% average at another school with higher standards of grading. In an effort to more equitably compare applications, a pilot study was initiated. Random samples of students who were admitted the previous year from four local high schools were drawn. All the students entered the business program with averages between 70% and 80%. Their average grades in the first year at the university were computed.

a. Can the university admissions officer conclude that there are differences in grading standards between the four high schools?

b. What are the required conditions for the test conducted in part (a)?

c. Does it appear that the required conditions of the test in part (a) are satisfied?

14.10 Xr14-10 The friendly folks at the Internal Revenue Service (IRS) in the United States and Canada Revenue Agency (CRA) are always looking for ways to improve the wording and format of its tax return forms. Three new forms have been developed recently. To determine which, if any, are superior to the current form, 120 individuals were asked to participate in an experiment. Each of the three new forms and the currently used form were filled out by 30 different people. The amount of time (in minutes) taken by each person to complete the task was recorded.

a. What conclusions can be drawn from these data?

b. What are the required conditions for the test conducted in part (a)?

c. Does it appear that the required conditions of the test in part (a) are satisfied?

114.11 Xr14-11 Are proficiency test scores affected by the education of the child's parents? (Proficiency tests are administered to a sample of students in private and public schools. Test scores can range from 0 to 500.) To answer this question, a random sample of 9-year-old children was drawn. Each child's test score and the educational level of the parent with the higher level were recorded. The education categories are less than high school, high school graduate, some college, and college graduate. Can we infer that there are differences in test scores between children whose parents have different educational levels?

14.12 Xr14-12 A manufacturer of outdoor brass lamps and mailboxes has received numerous complaints about premature corrosion. The manufacturer has identified the cause of the problem as the low-quality lacquer used to coat the brass. It has been decided to replace the current lacquer supplier with one of five possible alternatives. To judge which is best, the lacquers are each used to coat 25 brass mailboxes. For each, the number of days until the first sign of corrosion is observed has been recorded.

a. Is there sufficient evidence to allow the manufacturer to conclude that differences exist between the five lacquers?

b. What are the required conditions for the test conducted in part (a)?

c. Does it appear that the required conditions of the test in part (a) are satisfied?

14.13 Xr14-13 Large firms looking to expand their operations will often investigate regions looking at several variables including the cost of electricity, property tax, and many others. Random samples from each of the regions Northeast, Midwest, South, and West were drawn. One important variable for manufacturers is the cost of electricity. The annual cost was recorded for the sample. Do the data allow us to conclude that differences exist in the cost of electricity between the four regions?

14.14 Xr14-14 Refer to Exercise 14.13. A furniture moving company was in the process of deciding where to expand its operations. It had to decide on the four regions, Northeast, Midwest, South, and West. One vital statistic is the amount of time residents spend in their current home. The company's statistician sampled each of the regions with homeowners describing their housing tenures (in months). Is there sufficient evidence to infer that there are differences in housing tenure between the four regions?

14.15 Xr14-15 Do entering students into the programs Physical Sciences, Biological and Biomedical Sciences, and Mathematics and Statistics have similar SAT Mathematics scores? To find out, a statistics practitioner drew random samples of students from each of the three programs. Is there enough statistical evidence to conclude that there are differences in Mathematics SAT scores between the three programs?

14.16 Xr14-16 In the introduction to this chapter, we mentioned that the first use of the analysis of variance was in the 1920s. It was employed to determine whether different amounts of fertilizer yielded different amounts of crop. Suppose that a scientist at an agricultural college wanted to redo the original experiment using three different types of fertilizer. Accordingly, the scientist applied fertilizer A to 20 1-acre plots of land, fertilizer B to another 20 plots, and fertilizer C to yet another 20 plots of land. At the end of the growing season, the crop yields were recorded. Can the scientist infer that differences exist between the crop yields?

14.17 **Xr14-17** A study performed by a Columbia University professor (described in *Report on Business*, August 1991) counted the number of times per minute professors from three different departments said "uh" or "ah" during lectures to fill gaps between words. The data derived from observing 100 minutes from each of the three departments were recorded. If we assume that the more frequent use of "uh" and "ah" results in more boring lectures, can we conclude that some departments' professors are more boring than others?

14.18 **Xr14-18** Does the level of success of publicly traded companies affect the way their board members are paid? Publicly traded companies were divided into four quarters using the rate of return in their stocks to differentiate among the companies. The annual payment (in $1,000s) to their board members was recorded. Can we infer that the amount of payment differs between the four groups of companies?

14.19 **Xr14-19** Refer to Exercise 13.252, which featured the life satisfaction index created by the Canadian General Social Survey. The computed indexes were recorded for age categories $15-19$, $20-29$, $30-39$, $40-49$, $50-59$, $60-69$, $70-79$, and 80+. Do these data allow us to infer that there are differences in life satisfaction between the eight age groups?

14.20 **Xr14-20** There is a bewildering number of breakfast cereals on the market. Each company produces several different products in the belief that there are distinct markets. For example, there is a market composed primarily of children, another for diet-conscious adults, and another for health-conscious adults. Each cereal the companies produce has at least one market as its target. However, consumers make their own decisions, which may or may not match the target predicted by the cereal maker. In an attempt to distinguish between consumers, a survey of adults between the ages of 25 and 65 was undertaken. Each was asked several questions, including age, income, and years of education, as well as which brand of cereal they consumed most frequently. The cereal choices are

1. Sugar Smacks, a children's cereal
2. Special K, a cereal aimed at dieters

3. Fiber One, a cereal that is designed and advertised as healthy
4. Cheerios, a combination of healthy and tasty

The results of the survey were recorded in stacked format as follows.

Column A: Cereal choice
Column B: Age of respondent
Column C: Annual household income
Column D: Years of education

a. Determine whether there are differences between the ages of the consumers of the four cereals.
b. Determine whether there are differences between the incomes of the consumers of the four cereals.
c. Determine whether there are differences between the educational levels of the consumers of the four cereals.
d. Summarize your findings in parts (a) through (c) and prepare a report describing the differences between the four groups of cereal consumers.

APPLICATIONS in MARKETING

Test Marketing

In Chapter 13, we introduced test marketing, which allows us to determine whether changing some of the elements of the marketing mix yields different sales. In the next exercise, we apply the technique to discover the effect of different prices.

Pavel L Photo and Video/Shutterstock.com

14.21 **Xr14-21** A manufacturer of novelty items is undecided about the price to charge for a new product. The marketing manager knows that it should sell for about $10 but is unsure of whether sales will vary significantly if it is priced at either $9 or $11. To conduct a pricing experiment, the new product is distributed to a sample of 60 stores belonging to a chain of variety stores. These 60 stores are all located in similar neighborhoods. The manager randomly selects 20 stores in which to sell the item at $9, 20 stores to sell it at $10, and the remaining 20 stores to sell it at $11. Sales at the end of the trial period were recorded. What should the manager conclude?

APPLICATIONS in MARKETING

Marketing Segmentation

Section 12-4 introduced market segmentation. In Chapter 3 we demonstrated how to use statistical analyses to determine whether two segments differ in their buying behavior. The next exercise requires you to apply the analysis of variance to determine whether several segments differ.

Syda Productions/Shutterstock.com

14.22 Xr14-22   After determining in Exercise 13.267 that teenagers watch more movies than do 20–30-year-olds, teenagers were further segmented into three age groups: 12 to 14, 15 to 16, and 17 to 19. Random samples were drawn from each segment, and the number of movies each teenager saw last year was recorded. Do these data allow a marketing manager of a movie studio to conclude that differences exist between the three segments?

14.23 Xr14-23   As large cities grow larger, traffic congestion also increases. To measure how commuting time differs between California, New York, and Texas, random samples of commuters in each state were drawn. Is there sufficient evidence to infer that differences in commuting time exists between the three states?

14.24 Xr14-24   The Program for International Student Assessment (PISA) conducts tests of 15-year-olds. The tests jointly developed by the participating countries are tests for reading literary, mathematical literacy, and scientific literary. Random samples from the United States, Canada, and the United Kingdom were recorded. For each test, determine whether there are differences between the three countries.

14.25 Xr14-25   It is always important for vendors to know who their customers are. Surveys conducted by the Bureau of Labor Statistics took random samples of the four generations: Silent Generation (born 1928–1945), Baby Boom (1946–1964), Generation X (1965–1980), and Millennials (1981–1996). The management of a furniture store chain was in the process of deciding on an advertising campaign. Should they aim at all possible age categories or focus on one or two particular targets? To help decide, they conduct a survey and ask respondents to specify the generation they belong to and how much they spent last year on furniture purchases. Is there enough evidence to conclude that there are differences in furniture purchases between the four generations?

14.26 Xr14-26   Electricity is perceived as the best form of energy, because burning oil and natural gas emits carbon dioxide and because nuclear power leaves dangerous spent radioactive fuel rods. To examine the issue, random samples from the four generations (Silent, Baby Boom, Generation X, and Millennials) were drawn and each reported their annual electricity bills. Do these data allow us to conclude that differences exist in electricity bills between the four generations?

14.27 X14-27   One measure of the state of the economy is job tenure, the amount of time that employees have worked at the same job. If it is a useful measure, there should be variation between the years when the economy was strong and when it was weak. Random samples of employed wage and salary workers were taken in years 2010, 2012, 2014, 2016, 2018, and 2020. Each respondent listed the number of months that they have been with their current employer. Is there enough evidence to infer that job tenure varied over the decade?

14.28 Xr14-28   The following restaurant chains have menu prices that are quite similar: Red Lobster, Grand Lux, Outback Steakhouse, Cheesecake Factory, and Longhorn. A management consultant needed to know whether there are differences in the amount of money spent per customer. Random samples of customers of each of the restaurants were drawn. For each, the amount of money spent per customer was recorded. Can we conclude from these data that there are differences between the restaurants?

14.29 Xr14-29   A statistician conducted an informal mail survey of several countries around the world. Among other things, the statistician wanted to gauge how the citizens of each country felt about immigration. Each person was asked a series of questions that produced a scale of 0 to 100. The higher the score, the more accepting the individual was of migrants. The data from Canada, Australia, and New Zealand were recorded. Is there sufficient evidence to conclude that the three Commonwealth nations differ in their acceptance of immigrants?

14.30 Xr14-30   During the pandemic many children did not attend school. In many households, the children were expected to learn on their own using textbooks and other teaching material. A U.S. Census survey took a random sample of households with school-age children. Parents were asked to report the amount of time in minutes that their children spent in the previous 7 days learning on their own. The survey identified the education category of the head of the household. The categories are 1 = Less than high school, 2 = High school or GED, 3 = Some college/associate's degree, 4 = Bachelor's degree or higher. Is there enough statistical evidence to infer that there are differences in the amount of time children spent learning on their own between the four populations?

GENERAL SOCIAL SURVEY EXERCISES

GSS2018 *Conduct all statistical tests at the 5% significance level. The General Social Survey data are in stacked format. To apply Excel's analysis of variance techniques, the data must be unstacked. See Excel Instructions for Stacking and Unstacking Data in the Online Appendix. Because the samples are so large, these procedures will be time consuming.*

14.31 Do more educated Americans watch more television? Or is it less? The General Social Survey may help answer these questions. The survey identified five categories of DEGREE. They are 0 = Left high school, 1 = High school, 2 = Junior college, 3 = Bachelor's degree, 4 = Graduate. Conduct a test to determine whether there are differences in the amount of television (TVHOURS) between the five sub-populations.

14.32 What about class and television? The survey asked individuals to identify themselves as one of the following. CLASS: 1 = Lower class, 2 = Working class, 3 = Middle class, 4 = Upper class. Are there differences in television watching (TVHOURS) between the four classes of Americans?

The next eight exercises compare the eight categories of political parties (PARTYID: 0 = Strong Democrat, 1 = Not strong Democrat, 2 = Independent near Democrat, 3 = Independent, 4 = Independent near Republican, 5 = Not strong Republican, 6 = Strong Republican, 7 = Other party).

14.33 Which political party is more educated? Conduct a test to determine whether differences in education (EDUC) actually exist among some of the eight political categories.

14.34 Does income affect the way Americans choose which party to support? Conduct a statistical procedure to determine whether there are differences in income (RINCOME) between some or all of the eight political groups.

14.35 Refer to Exercise 14.34. If differences in income exist, is it because higher-income Americans work harder? Can we conclude from the data that there are differences in the hours worked (HRS1) between the eight political groups?

14.36 Are Democrats young and are Republicans old? Conduct a test to determine whether there are differences in ages (AGE) between the eight groups.

Exercises 14.37–14.40 examine whether differences exist between the eight political groupings with respect to the role of government.

14.37 The survey asked the question, "Should government reduce income differences between rich and poor (EQWLTH: 1 = Government should reduce differences; 2, 3, 4, 5, 6, 7 = No government action)?" Is there enough evidence to infer that there are differences among some or all of the eight political groups?

14.38 Is there enough statistical evidence to conclude that the eight political categories differ in their responses to this question: "Should government improve standard of living of poor people (HELPPOOR: 1 = Government act; 2, 3, 4, 5 = People should help themselves)?"

14.39 The question that the survey asked is, "Should government do more or less to solve country's problems (HELPNOT: 1 = Government should do more; 2, 3, 4, 5 = Government does too much)?" Can we infer from the data that there are differences among some or all of the eight political categories in their answer to the question?

14.40 With government-funded health insurance in the air, the next question may be particularly relevant. Is it government's responsibility to help pay for doctor and hospital bills (HELPSICK: 1 = Government should help; 2, 3, 4, 5 = People should help themselves)? Is there enough evidence to conclude that differences exist between the eight political categories?

Exercises 14.41–14.48 compare the seven political views (POLVIEWS: 1 = Extremely liberal, 2 = Liberal, 3 = Slightly liberal, 4 = Moderate, 5 = Slightly conservative, 6 = Conservative, 7 = Extremely conservative).

14.41 Are liberals, moderates, and conservatives all equally educated? Test to determine whether differences exist among the seven political views in the amount of education (EDUC).

14.42 What happens to Americans' political philosophies as they grow richer? If they change, we would expect differences in income (RINCOME) between the seven groups. Is there enough evidence to conclude that such differences exist?

14.43 Is it a myth that conservatives work harder than do liberals and moderates? Test to determine whether there are differences in number of hours of worked per week (HRS1) among some or all of the seven political points of view.

14.44 Is it true that younger Americans tend to be more liberal and older Americans more conservative? To help discover the truth, start by determining whether there is enough statistical evidence to conclude that there are differences in age (AGE) among the seven political viewpoints.

Exercises 14.45–14.48 examine whether differences exist between the seven political viewpoints (POLVIEWS) with respect to the role of government.

14.45 Is there enough evidence to infer that there are differences between the seven political viewpoints in their answers to the question, "Should government reduce income differences between rich and poor (EQWLTH: 1 = Government should reduce differences; 2, 3, 4, 5, 6, 7 = No government action)?"

14.46 The survey asked, "Should government improve standard of living of poor people (HELPPOOR: 1 = Government act; 2, 3, 4, 5 = People should help themselves)?" Is there enough statistical evidence to conclude that some or all of the seven groups differ in their responses to this question?

14.47 Can we infer from the data that there are differences between the seven political viewpoints in their answer to the question, "Should government do more or less to solve country's problems (HELPNOT: 1 = Government should do more; 2, 3, 4, 5 = Government does too much)?"

14.48 The survey asked, "Is it government's responsibility to help pay for doctor and hospital bills (HELPSICK: 1 = Government should help; 2, 3, 4, 5 = People should help themselves)?" Is there enough evidence to conclude that differences exist among some or all of the seven groups?

14.49 How does acquiring additional degrees contribute to higher incomes? Conduct a test to determine whether the degree holders (DEGREE: 0 = Left high school, 1 = High school, 2 = Junior college, 3 = Bachelor's degree, 4 = Graduate degree) differ in income (RINCOME).

14.50 Television networks and their advertisers are constantly surveying viewers to determine their likes and dislikes and how much time adults spend watching television per day. Do the data allow us to infer that the amount of television (TVHOURS) differs by race (RACE)?

14.51 Do educated people work longer or shorter hours than do less-educated individuals? Conduct a test to determine whether there is enough evidence to conclude that differences exist in the number of hours per week (HRS1) between the five groups of educational attainment (DEGREE: 0 = Left high school, 1 = High school, 2 = Junior college, 3 = Bachelor's degree, 4 = Graduate degree).

Exercises 14.52–14.55 test differences between the four classes (CLASS: 1 = Lower class, 2 = Working class, 3 = Middle class, 4 = Upper class) with respect to the role of government. Does the way in which respondents self-identify the class their family is in affect each one of the questions listed here?

14.52 Should government reduce income differences between rich and poor (EQWLTH: 1 = Government should reduce differences; 2, 3, 4, 5, 6, 7 = No government action)?

14.53 Should government improve standard of living of poor people (HELPPOOR: 1 = Government act; 2, 3, 4, 5 = People should help themselves)?

14.54 Should government do more or less to solve country's problems (HELPNOT: 1 = Government should do more; 2, 3, 4, 5 = Government does too much)?

14.55 Is it government's responsibility to help pay for doctor and hospital bills (HELPSICK: 1 = Government should help; 2, 3, 4, 5 = People should help themselves)?

14.56 GSS2008 GSS2010 GSS2012 GSS2014 GSS2016 GSS2018 Have educational levels kept uniform over the years 2006, 2008, 2010, 2012, 2014, 2016, and 2018? Conduct a test to determine whether the number of years of education (EDUC) differs in the 10-year period.

SURVEY OF CONSUMER FINANCES EXERCISES

SCF2019:\All *Conduct all tests at the 5% significance level. Exercises 14.57–14.62 compare the four categories of the educational attainment of the household head (EDCL: 1 = No high school diploma, 2 = High school diploma, 3 = Some college, 4 = College graduate).*

14.57 How much evidence is there that more education leads to higher incomes and more financial success? Test to determine whether differences in income (INCOME) exist between the four education categories.

14.58 Does the education category affect the net worth of households? Is so, there should be differences in net worth between the four categories of education. Conduct a test to determine whether there are such differences (NETWORTH).

14.59 Are more educated individuals likely to have more unrealized capital gains? Is there enough evidence to infer that there are differences in total unrealized capital gains (KGTOTAL)?

14.60 Is education a factor in the amount of debt carried by heads of households? Conduct a statistical test to determine whether the amount of debt (DEBT) differs between the four categories.

14.61 Do households headed by a more educated person spend their food dollars differently from households headed by less-educated people? Is there enough evidence to conclude that there are differences in the annual expenditures on food at home (FOODHOME) between the four categories of education?

14.62 Is there enough evidence to conclude that there are differences in total annual amount spent on food away (FOODAWAY) from home between the four categories?

Exercises 14.63–14.66 compare the three categories of industry classification (INDCAT: 1 = Mining + construction + manufacturing, 2 = Transportation + communications + utilities and sanitary services + wholesale trade + finance, insurance, and real estate, 4 = Agriculture + retail trade + services + public transportation). Note that there are only three categories.

14.63 Are some industries better than others in terms of financial remuneration? Conduct a test to determine whether there are differences in income (INCOME) between the three categories of industry.

14.64 Can we infer from the data that there are differences in net worth (NETWORTH) between the heads of households whose jobs are in one of the three industry classifications?

14.65 Can we infer from the data that there are differences in the amount of debt (DEBT) between the three industry classifications?

14.66 Can we infer from the data that there are differences in the total unrealized capital gains (KGTOTAL) between the three industry classifications?

14-2 / MULTIPLE COMPARISONS

When we conclude from the one-way analysis of variance that at least two treatment means differ, we often need to know which treatment means are responsible for these differences. For example, if an experiment is undertaken to determine whether different locations within a store produce different mean sales, the manager would be keenly interested in determining which locations result in significantly higher sales and which locations result in lower sales. Similarly, a stockbroker would like to know which one of several mutual funds outperforms the others, and a television executive would like to know which television commercials hold the viewers' attention and which are ignored.

Although it may appear that all we need to do is examine the sample means and identify the largest or the smallest to determine which population means are largest or smallest, this is not the case. To illustrate, suppose that in a five-treatment analysis of variance, we discover that differences exist and that the sample means are as follows:

$$\bar{x}_1 = 20 \qquad \bar{x}_2 = 19 \qquad \bar{x}_3 = 25 \qquad \bar{x}_4 = 22 \qquad \bar{x}_5 = 17$$

The statistics practitioner wants to know which of the following conclusions are valid:

1. μ_3 is larger than the other means.

2. μ_3 and μ_4 are larger than the other means.

3. μ_5 is smaller than the other means.

4. μ_5 and μ_2 are smaller than the other means.

5. μ_3 is larger than the other means, and μ_5 is smaller than the other means.

From the information we have, it is impossible to determine which, if any, of the statements are true. We need a statistical method to make this determination. The technique is called **multiple comparisons**.

EXAMPLE 14.2

DATA
Xm14-02

Comparing the Costs of Repairing Car Bumpers

Because of foreign competition, North American automobile manufacturers have become more concerned with quality. One aspect of quality is the cost of repairing damage caused by accidents. A manufacturer is considering several new types of bumpers. To test how well they react to low-speed collisions, 10 bumpers of each of four different types were installed on mid-size cars, which were then driven into a wall at 5 miles per hour. The cost of repairing the damage in each case was assessed. The data are shown below.

a. Is there sufficient evidence at the 5% significance level to infer that the bumpers differ in their reactions to low-speed collisions?

b. If differences exist, which bumpers differ?

Bumper 1	Bumper 2	Bumper 3	Bumper 4
610	404	599	272
354	663	426	405
234	521	429	197
399	518	621	363
278	499	426	297
358	374	414	538
379	562	332	181
548	505	460	318
196	375	494	412
444	438	637	499

SOLUTION:

IDENTIFY

The problem objective is to compare four populations. The data are interval, and the samples are independent. The correct statistical method is the one-way analysis of variance, which we perform using Excel.

COMPUTE

EXCEL Data Analysis

	A	B	C	D	E	F	G
1	Anova: Single Factor						
2							
3	SUMMARY						
4	*Groups*	*Count*	*Sum*	*Average*	*Variance*		
5	Bumper 1	10	3800	380.0	16,924		
6	Bumper 2	10	4859	485.9	8,197		
7	Bumper 3	10	4838	483.8	10,426		
8	Bumper 4	10	3482	348.2	14,049		
9							
10							
11	ANOVA						
12	*Source of Variation*	*SS*	*df*	*MS*	*F*	*P-value*	*F crit*
13	Between Groups	150,884	3	50,295	4.06	0.0139	2.87
14	Within Groups	446,368	36	12,399			
15							
16	Total	597,252	39				

INTERPRET

The test statistic is $F = 4.06$ and the p-value $= .0139$. There is enough statistical evidence to infer that there are differences between some of the bumpers. The question is now, Which bumpers differ?

There are several statistical inference procedures that deal with this problem. We will present three methods that allow us to determine which population means differ. All three methods apply to the one-way experiment only.

14-2a Fisher's Least Significant Difference Method

To determine which population means differ, we could perform a series of t-tests of the difference between two means on all pairs of population means to determine which are significantly different. In Chapter 13, we introduced the equal-variances t-test of the difference between two means. The test statistic and confidence interval estimator are, respectively,

$$t = \frac{(\bar{x}_1 - \bar{x}_2) - (\mu_1 - \mu_2)}{\sqrt{s_p^2\left(\frac{1}{n_1} + \frac{1}{n_2}\right)}}$$

$$(\bar{x}_1 - \bar{x}_2) \pm t_{\alpha/2} \sqrt{s_p^2\left(\frac{1}{n_1} + \frac{1}{n_2}\right)}$$

with degrees of freedom $\nu = n_1 + n_2 - 2$.

Recall that s_p^2 is the pooled variance estimate, which is an unbiased estimator of the variance of the two populations. (Recall that the use of these techniques requires that the population variances be equal.) In this section, we modify the test statistic and interval estimator.

Earlier in this chapter, we pointed out that MSE is an unbiased estimator of the common variance of the populations we're testing. Because MSE is based on all the observations in the k samples, it will be a better estimator than s_p^2 (which is based on only two samples). Thus, we could draw inferences about every pair of means by substituting MSE for s_p^2 in the formulas for test statistic and confidence interval estimator shown previously. The number of degrees of freedom would also change to $\nu = n - k$ (where n is the total sample size). The test statistic to determine whether μ_i and μ_j differ is

$$t = \frac{(\bar{x}_i - \bar{x}_j) - (\mu_i - \mu_j)}{\sqrt{\text{MSE}\left(\dfrac{1}{n_i} + \dfrac{1}{n_j}\right)}}$$

The confidence interval estimator is

$$(\bar{x}_i - \bar{x}_j) \pm t_{\alpha/2} \sqrt{\text{MSE}\left(\dfrac{1}{n_i} + \dfrac{1}{n_j}\right)}$$

with degrees of freedom $\nu = n - k$.

We define the **least significant difference (LSD)** as

$$\text{LSD} = t_{\alpha/2} \sqrt{\text{MSE}\left(\dfrac{1}{n_i} + \dfrac{1}{n_j}\right)}$$

A simple way of determining whether differences exist between each pair of population means is to compare the absolute value of the difference between their two sample means and LSD. In other words, we will conclude that μ_i and μ_j differ if

$$|\bar{x}_i - \bar{x}_j| > \text{LSD}$$

LSD will be the same for all pairs of means if all k sample sizes are equal. If some sample sizes differ, LSD must be calculated for each combination.

In Section 14-1 we argued that this method is flawed because it will increase the probability of committing a Type I error. That is, it is more likely than the analysis of variance to conclude that a difference exists in some of the population means when in fact none differ. On page 559, we calculated that if $k = 6$ and all population means are equal, the probability of erroneously inferring at the 5% significance level that at least two means differ is about 54%. The 5% figure is now referred to as the *comparisonwise Type I error rate*. The true probability of making at least one Type I error is called the *experimentwise Type I error rate*, denoted α_E. The experimentwise Type I error rate can be calculated as

$$\alpha_E = 1 - (1 - \alpha)^C$$

Here C is the number of pairwise comparisons, which can be calculated by $C = k(k - 1)/2$. Mathematicians have proven that

$$\alpha_E \leq C\alpha$$

which means that if we want the probability of making at least one Type I error to be no more than α_E, we simply specify $\alpha = \alpha_E/C$. The resulting procedure is called the **Bonferroni adjustment**.

14-2b Bonferroni Adjustment to LSD Method

The adjustment is made by dividing the specified experimentwise Type I error rate by the number of combinations of pairs of population means. For example, if $k = 6$, then

$$C = \frac{k(k - 1)}{2} = \frac{6(5)}{2} = 15$$

If we want the true probability of a Type I error to be no more than 5%, we divide this probability by C. Thus, for each test we would use a value of α equal to

$$\alpha = \frac{\alpha_E}{C} = \frac{.05}{15} = .0033$$

We use Example 14.2 to illustrate Fisher's LSD method and the Bonferroni adjustment. The four sample means are

$$\bar{x}_1 = 380.0$$
$$\bar{x}_2 = 485.9$$
$$\bar{x}_3 = 483.8$$
$$\bar{x}_4 = 348.2$$

The pairwise absolute differences are

$$|\bar{x}_1 - \bar{x}_2| = |380.0 - 485.9| = |-105.9| = 105.9$$
$$|\bar{x}_1 - \bar{x}_3| = |380.0 - 483.8| = |-103.8| = 103.8$$
$$|\bar{x}_1 - \bar{x}_4| = |380.0 - 348.2| = |31.8| = 31.8$$
$$|\bar{x}_2 - \bar{x}_3| = |485.9 - 483.8| = |2.1| = 2.1$$
$$|\bar{x}_2 - \bar{x}_4| = |485.9 - 348.2| = |137.7| = 137.7$$
$$|\bar{x}_3 - \bar{x}_4| = |483.8 - 348.2| = |135.6| = 135.6$$

From the computer output, we learn that MSE $= 12,399$ and $\nu = n - k = 40 - 4 = 36$. If we conduct the LSD procedure with $\alpha = .05$, we find $t_{\alpha/2, n-k} = t_{.025, 36} \approx t_{.025, 35} = 2.030$. Thus,

$$t_{\alpha/2} \sqrt{MSE\left(\frac{1}{n_i} + \frac{1}{n_j}\right)} = 2.030 \sqrt{12,399\left(\frac{1}{10} + \frac{1}{10}\right)} = 101.09$$

We can see that four pairs of sample means differ by more than 101.09. That is, $|\bar{x}_1 - \bar{x}_2| = 105.9$, $|\bar{x}_1 - \bar{x}_3| = 103.8$, $|\bar{x}_2 - \bar{x}_4| = 137.7$, and $|\bar{x}_3 - \bar{x}_4| = 135.6$. Hence, μ_1 and μ_2, μ_1 and μ_3, μ_2 and μ_4, and μ_3 and μ_4 differ. The other two pairs—μ_1 and μ_4, and μ_2 and μ_3—do not differ.

If we perform the LSD procedure with the Bonferroni adjustment, the number of pairwise comparisons is 6 (calculated as $C = k(k - 1)/2 = 4(3)/2$). We set $\alpha = .05/6 = .0083$. Thus $t_{\alpha/2,36} = t_{.0042,36} = 2.794$ (available from Excel and difficult to approximate manually) and

$$LSD = t_{\alpha/2} \sqrt{MSE\left(\frac{1}{n_i} + \frac{1}{n_j}\right)} = 2.794 \sqrt{12,399\left(\frac{1}{10} + \frac{1}{10}\right)} = 139.13$$

Now no pair of means differ because all the absolute values of the differences between sample means are less than 139.19.

The drawback to the LSD procedure is that we increase the probability of at least one Type I error. The Bonferroni adjustment corrects this problem. However, recall that the probabilities of Type I and Type II errors are inversely related. The Bonferroni adjustment uses a smaller value of α, which results in an increased probability of a Type II error. A Type II error occurs when a difference between population means exists, yet we cannot detect it. This may be the case in this example. The next multiple comparison method addresses this problem.

14-2c Tukey's Multiple Comparison Method

A more powerful test is **Tukey's multiple comparison method**. This technique determines a critical number similar to LSD for Fisher's test, denoted by ω (Greek letter *omega*), such that if any pair of sample means has a difference greater than ω, we conclude that the pair's two corresponding population means are different.

The test is based on the Studentized range, which is defined as the variable

$$q = \frac{\bar{x}_{max} - \bar{x}_{min}}{s/\sqrt{n}}$$

where $\bar{x}_{max}$ and $\bar{x}_{min}$ are the largest and smallest sample means, respectively, assuming that there are no differences between the population means. We define ω as follows.

Critical Number ω

$$\omega = q_\alpha(k, \nu)\sqrt{\frac{MSE}{n_g}}$$

where

k = Number of treatments

n = Number of observations ($n = n_1 + n_2 + \cdots + n_k$)

ν = Number of degrees of freedom associated with MSE ($\nu = n - k$)

n_g = Number of observations in each of k samples

α = Significance level

$q_\alpha(k, \nu)$ = Critical value of the Studentized range

Theoretically, this procedure requires that all sample sizes be equal. However, if the sample sizes are different, we can still use this technique provided that the sample sizes are at least similar. The value of n_g used previously is the *harmonic mean* of the sample sizes; that is,

$$n_g = \frac{k}{\dfrac{1}{n_1} + \dfrac{1}{n_2} + \cdots + \dfrac{1}{n_k}}$$

Table 7 in Appendix B provides values of $q_\alpha(k, \nu)$ for a variety of values of k and ν, and for $\alpha = .01$ and $.05$. Applying Tukey's method to Example 14.2, we find

$$k = 4$$
$$n_1 = n_2 = n_3 = n_4 = n_g = 10$$
$$\nu = n - k = 40 - 4 = 36$$
$$MSE = 12,399$$
$$q_{.05}(4, 36) \approx q_{.05}(4, 40) = 3.79$$

Thus,

$$\omega = q_\alpha(k, \nu)\sqrt{\frac{MSE}{n_g}} = (3.79)\sqrt{\frac{12,399}{10}} = 133.45$$

There are two absolute values larger than 133.45. Hence, we conclude that μ_2 and μ_4, and μ_3 and μ_4 differ. The other four pairs do not differ.

EXCEL Workbook

LSD Method

	A	B	C	D	E	F	G	H	I
1	LSD Method		Samples	Sample i	Sample j	Sample i	Sample j		
2	Number of treatments	4	(i,j)	Mean	Mean	Size	Size	|Difference|	LSD
3	Degrees of freedom	36	1,2	380.0	485.9	10	10	105.90	100.99
4	MSE	12,399	1,3	380.0	483.8	10	10	103.80	
5	Alpha	0.05	1,4	380.0	348.2	10	10	31.80	
6			2,3	485.9	483.8	10	10	2.10	
7			2,4	485.9	348.2	10	10	137.70	
8			3,4	483.8	348.2	10	10	135.60	

Bonferroni Adjustment to LSD Method

	A	B	C	D	E	F	G	H	I
1	LSD Method		Samples	Sample i	Sample j	Sample i	Sample j		
2	Number of treatments	4	(i,j)	Mean	Mean	Size	Size	|Difference|	LSD
3	Degrees of freedom	36	1,2	380.0	485.9	10	10	105.90	139.03
4	MSE	12,399	1,3	380.0	483.8	10	10	103.80	
5	Alpha	0.0083	1,4	380.0	348.2	10	10	31.80	
6			2,3	485.9	483.8	10	10	2.10	
7			2,4	485.9	348.2	10	10	137.70	
8			3,4	483.8	348.2	10	10	135.60	

Tukey's Method

	A	B	C	D	E	F	G
1	Tukey's Method α = 5%		Samples	Sample i	Sample j		
2	Sample size (Harmonic mean)	10	(i,j)	Mean	Mean	|Difference|	ω
3	Number of treatments	4	1,2	380.0	485.9	105.9	134.12
4	Degrees of freedom	36	1,3	380.0	483.8	103.8	
5	MSE	12,399	1,4	380.0	348.2	31.8	
6			2,3	485.9	483.8	2.1	
7			2,4	485.9	348.2	137.7	
8			3,4	483.8	348.2	135.6	

INSTRUCTIONS

1. Conduct the analysis of variance.

2. Open the **Multiple comparisons** worksheet and click the **LSD** tab.

3. Type the sample means and sample sizes of the treatments you wish to compare. Type the number of treatments in B2 (4), the degrees of freedom in B3 (36), the value of MSE in cell B4 (12,399), and the value of α in B5 (.05).

4. For the Bonferroni adjustment, divide α by the number of comparisons. In this example C = 4 × 3/2 = 6. Type into cell B5 = .05/6, which is .0083.

5. For Tukey's method, click the tab for α = 1%, 5%, or 10%. Type the sample size in B2 (10). If the sample sizes differ, calculate the harmonic mean (**=HARMEAN ([Input range])**) and type that in B2. Type the number of treatments in B3 (4), the degrees of freedom in B4 (36), and the value of MSE into B5 (12,399).

INTERPRET

Using the Bonferroni adjustment of Fisher's LSD method, we discover that none of the bumpers differ. (This is not a surprising result; since we used a very small probability of making a Type I error (.0083), the probability of making a Type II error became large.) Tukey's method tells us that bumper 4 differs from both bumpers 2 and 3. Based on this sample, bumper 4 appears to have the lowest cost of repair. Because there was not enough evidence to conclude that bumpers 1 and 4 differ, we would consider using bumper 1 if it has other advantages over bumper 4.

14-2d Which Multiple Comparison Method to Use

Unfortunately, no one procedure works best in all types of problems. Most statisticians agree with the following guidelines:

> If you have identified two or three pairwise comparisons that you wish to make before conducting the analysis of variance, use the Bonferroni method. This means that if there are 10 populations in a problem but you're particularly interested in comparing, say, populations 3 and 7 and populations 5 and 9, use Bonferroni with $C = 2$.

> If you plan to compare all possible combinations, use Tukey.

> When do we use Fisher's LSD? If the purpose of the analysis is to point to areas that should be investigated further, Fisher's LSD method is indicated.

Incidentally, to employ Fisher's LSD or the Bonferroni adjustment, you must perform the analysis of variance first. Tukey's method can be employed instead of the analysis of variance.

Exercises

Developing an Understanding of Statistical Concepts

14.67 a. Use Fisher's LSD method with $\alpha = .05$ to determine which population means differ in the following problem.

$$k = 3 \qquad n_1 = 10 \qquad n_2 = 10 \qquad n_3 = 10$$
$$\text{MSE} = 700 \ \bar{x}_1 = 128.7 \ \bar{x}_2 = 101.4 \ \bar{x}_3 = 133.7$$

  b. Repeat part (a) using the Bonferroni adjustment.
  c. Repeat part (a) using Tukey's multiple comparison method.

14.68 a. Use Fisher's LSD procedure with $\alpha = .05$ to determine which population means differ given the following statistics:

$$k = 5 \qquad n_1 = 5 \qquad n_2 = 5 \qquad n_3 = 5$$
$$\text{MSE} = 125 \quad \bar{x}_1 = 227 \quad \bar{x}_2 = 205 \quad \bar{x}_3 = 219$$
$$n_4 = 5 \qquad n_5 = 5$$
$$\bar{x}_4 = 248 \qquad \bar{x}_5 = 202$$

  b. Repeat part (a) using the Bonferroni adjustment.
  c. Repeat part (a) using Tukey's multiple comparison method

Applications

Unless specified otherwise, use a 5% significance level.

14.69 a. Apply Tukey's method to determine which brands differ in Exercise 14.5.

  b. Use the Bonferroni method to compare Brands 1 and 2 and Brands 1 and 3.

14.70 Refer to Exercise 14.6.
  a. Employ Fisher's LSD method to determine which degrees differ (use $\alpha = .10$).
  b. Repeat part (a) using the Bonferroni adjustment.

Exercises 14.71 to 14.86 require the use of a computer and software. The answers may be calculated manually. See Appendix A for the sample statistics.

14.71 <u>Xr14-09</u> a. Apply Fisher's LSD method with the Bonferroni adjustment to determine which schools differ in Exercise 14.9.
  b. Repeat part (a) applying Tukey's method instead.

14.72 <u>Xr14-10</u> a. Apply Tukey's multiple comparison method to determine which forms differ in Exercise 14.10.
  b. Repeat part (a) applying the Bonferroni adjustment.

14.73 <u>Xr14-73</u> Police cars, ambulances, and other emergency vehicles are required to carry road flares. One of the most important features of flares is their burning times. To help decide which of four brands on the market to use, a police laboratory technician measured the burning time for a random sample of 10 flares of each brand. The results were recorded to the nearest minute.

a. Can we conclude that differences exist between the burning times of the four brands of flares?

b. Apply Fisher's LSD method with the Bonferroni adjustment to determine which flares are better.

c. Repeat part (b) using Tukey's method.

14.74 Xr14-12   Refer to Exercise 14.12.

a. Apply Fisher's LSD method with the Bonferroni adjustment to determine which lacquers differ.

b. Repeat part (a) applying Tukey's method instead.

14.75 Xr14-75   An engineering student who is about to graduate decided to survey various firms in Silicon Valley to see which offered the best chance for early promotion and career advancement. The student surveyed 30 small firms (size level is based on gross revenues), 30 medium-sized firms, and 30 large firms, and determined how much time must elapse before an average engineer can receive a promotion.

a. Can the engineering student conclude that speed of promotion varies between the three sizes of engineering firms?

b. If differences exist, which of the following is true? Use Tukey's method.

  i. Small firms differ from the other two.

  ii. Medium-sized firms differ from the other two.

  iii. Large firms differ from the other two.

  iv. All three firms differ from one another.

  v. Small firms differ from large firms.

14.76 Xr14-16   a. Apply Tukey's multiple comparison method to determine which fertilizers differ in Exercise 14.16.

b. Repeat part (a) applying the Bonferroni adjustment.

14.77 Xr14-13   Refer to Exercise 14.13. Use Fisher's LSD method with the Bonferroni adjustment to determine whether there is enough evidence to infer that electricity costs differ between the South and each of the other regions.

14.78 Xr14-14   Refer to Exercise 14.14. Use Fisher's LSD method with the Bonferroni adjustment to determine whether there is enough statistical evidence to infer that the number of months that the average person stays in their residence differ between the Northeast and each of the other regions.

14.79 Xr14-11   Refer to Exercise 14.11, which analyzed proficiency test scores for each of four categories of educational attainment of their parents. Apply Fisher's LSD method with the Bonferroni adjustment to determine whether there is enough evidence to infer that the category less than high school differs from each of the others.

14.80 Xr14-80   Do younger or older people go out to eat at restaurants more frequently? The Bureau of Labor Statistics took random samples from each of the four generations (Silent, Baby Boom, Generation X, and Millennials) and asked each to describe the amount of money they spent in the previous 12 months.

a. Do these data support the belief that there are differences in the amount of money spent in restaurants between the four generations?

b. Use Tukey's multiple comparison method to determine whether there is sufficient evidence to conclude that differences in annual restaurant spending exists between each pair of the four generations.

14.81 Xr14-25   Refer to Exercise 14.25. Is there sufficient evidence to infer that the Silent Generation spend less on furniture than each of the other generations? Use Fisher's LSD method with the Bonferroni adjustment.

14.82 Xr14-26   Exercise 14.26 examined the cost of electricity for four generations. Apply Fisher's LSD method with the Bonferroni adjustment to determine whether there is sufficient evidence that Generation X differs from each of the Baby Boom generation and Millennials in terms of their electricity use.

14.83 Xr14-29   Refer to Exercise 14.29 that described the results of a survey that measured the acceptance of immigrants in Canada, Australia, and New Zealand. Apply Tukey's multiple comparison method to determine whether Canada and Australia differ, Canada and New Zealand differ, and Australia and New Zealand differ.

14.84 Xr14-30   Exercise 14.30 described a survey wherein parents of school-age children were asked to report the amount of time their children spent learning on their own as a result of the pandemic. Use the LSD method with the Bonferroni adjustment to test for differences between parents with less than a high school diploma and each of the other populations.

14.85 Xr14-85   Students who are about to start their careers are naturally curious about the incomes they may be able to earn upon graduation. A head hunter wanted to acquire information about the different occupations. A survey was conducted wherein randomly sampled wage and salary workers were asked to report the type of job and their after-tax income. The occupations are manager and professional; technical, sales, and clerical; service; and construction, operators, and laborers. Is there sufficient statistical evidence to conclude that there are differences in after-tax income between workers in the four occupational categories? Use Tukey's multiple comparison method to answer the question.

14.86 Xr14-85   Refer to Exercise 14.85. Suppose you are only interested in the three categories excluding managers and professionals. Use the LSD method with Bonferroni adjustment to determine which pairs of means differ.

GENERAL SOCIAL SURVEY EXERCISES

<u>GSS2018</u> *Use a 5% significance level for all procedures.*

14.87 Exercise 14.31 examined whether the amount of television (TVHOURS) watched differs according to the educational attainment (DEGREE). Use Fisher's LSD method with the Bonferroni adjustment to determine whether there are differences between those who left high school without graduating and each of the other four groups.

14.88 Refer to Exercise 14.32. Use Tukey's multiple comparison method to determine which pairs of means differ.

14.89 Refer to Exercise 14.33 where the analysis of variance was used to determine whether differences exist between the eight political groups with respect to years of education (EDUC). Use Fisher's LSD method with the Bonferroni adjustment to determine whether there are differences between each of the following pairs.

Strong Democrat and Strong Republican (PARTYID 0 and 6)

Not strong Democrat and Not strong Republican (PARTYID 1 and 5)

Independent near Democrat and Independent near Republican (PARTYID 2 and 4)

14.90 Refer to Exercise 14.34. Use Fisher's LSD method with the Bonferroni adjustment to determine whether there are differences in income (RINCOME) between each of the following pairs.

Independent and Independent near Democrat (PARTYID 2 and 3)

Independent and Independent near Republican (PARTYID 3 and 4)

14.91 Exercise 14.41 applied the analysis of variance to test for differences in education (EDUC) between the seven categories of political views (POLVIEWS). Use Fisher's LSD method with the Bonferroni adjustment to determine whether there are differences between each of the following pairs.

Extremely liberal and Extremely conservative (POLVIEWS 1 and 7)

Liberal and Conservative (POLVIEWS 2 and 6)

Slightly liberal and Slightly conservative (POLVIEWS 3 and 5)

14.92 Refer to Exercise 14.42. Use Fisher's LSD method with the Bonferroni adjustment to test for differences in income (RINCOME) between each of the following pairs.

Moderate and Extremely liberal (POLVIEWS 1 and 4)

Moderate and Extremely conservative (POLVIEWS 4 and 7)

14-3 / ANALYSIS OF VARIANCE EXPERIMENTAL DESIGNS

Since we introduced the matched pairs experiment in Section 13-3, the experimental design has been one of the factors that determines which technique we use. Statistics practitioners often design experiments to help extract the information they need to assist them in making decisions. The one-way analysis of variance introduced in Section 14-1 is only one of many different experimental designs of the analysis of variance. For each type of experiment, we can describe the behavior of the response variable using a mathematical expression or model. Although we will not exhibit the mathematical expressions in this chapter (we introduce models in Chapter 16), we think it is useful for you to be aware of the elements that distinguish one experimental design or model from another. In this section, we present some of these elements; in so doing, we introduce two of the experimental designs that will be presented later in this chapter.

14-3a Single-Factor and Multifactor Experimental Designs

As we pointed out in Section 14-1, the criterion by which we identify populations is called a *factor*. The experiment described in Section 14-1 is a single-factor analysis of variance because it addresses the problem of comparing two or more populations defined on the basis of only one factor. A **multifactor experiment** is one in which two or more factors define the treatments. The experiment described in Example 14.1 is a single-factor design because we had one treatment: age of the head of the household. In other words, the factor is the age, and the three age categories were the levels of this factor.

Suppose that we can also look at the gender of the household head in another study. We would then develop a two-factor analysis of variance in which the first factor, age, has three levels, and the second factor, gender, has two levels. We will discuss two-factor experiments in Section 14-5.

14-3b Independent Samples and Blocks

In Section 13-3, we introduced statistical techniques where the data were gathered from a matched pairs experiment. This type of experimental design reduces the variation within the samples, making it easier to detect differences between the two populations. When the problem objective is to compare more than two populations, the experimental design that is the counterpart of the matched pairs experiment is called the **randomized block design**. The term *block* refers to a matched group of observations from each population. Suppose that in Examples 13.4 and 13.5 we had wanted to compare the salary offers for finance, marketing, accounting, and operations management majors. To redo Example 13.5 we would conduct a randomized block experiment where the blocks are the 25 GPA groups and the treatments are the four MBA majors.

Once again, the experimental design should reduce the variation in each treatment to make it easier to detect differences.

We can also perform a blocked experiment by using the same subject (person, plant, and store) for each treatment. For example, we can determine whether sleeping pills are effective by giving three brands of pills to the same group of people to measure the effects. Such experiments are called **repeated measures** designs. Technically, this is a different design than the randomized block. However, the data are analyzed in the same way for both designs. Hence, we will treat repeated measures designs as randomized block designs.

The randomized block experiment is also called the **two-way analysis of variance**. In Section 14-4, we introduce the technique used to calculate the test statistic for this type of experiment.

14-3c Fixed and Random Effects

If our analysis includes all possible levels of a factor, the technique is called a **fixed-effects analysis of variance**. If the levels included in the study represent a random sample of all the levels that exist, the technique is called a **random-effects analysis of variance**. In Example 14.2, there were only four possible bumpers. Consequently, the study is a fixed-effects experiment. However, if there were other bumpers besides the four described in the example, and we wanted to know whether there were differences in repair costs between all bumpers, the application would be a random-effects experiment. Here's another example.

To determine whether there is a difference in the number of units produced by the machines in a large factory, 4 machines out of 50 in the plant are randomly selected for study. The number of units each produces per day for 10 days will be recorded. This experiment is a random-effects experiment because we selected a random sample of four machines and the statistical results thus allow us to determine whether there are differences between the 50 machines.

In some experimental designs, there are no differences in calculations of the test statistic between fixed and random effects. However, in others, including the two-factor experiment presented in Section 14-5, the calculations are different.

14-4 RANDOMIZED BLOCK (TWO-WAY) ANALYSIS OF VARIANCE

The purpose of designing a randomized block experiment is to reduce the within-treatments variation to more easily detect differences between the treatment means. In the one-way analysis of variance, we partitioned the total variation into the between-treatments and the within-treatments variation; that is,

$$SS(Total) = SST + SSE$$

In the randomized block design of the analysis of variance, we partition the total variation into three sources of variation,

$$SS(Total) = SST + SSB + SSE$$

where **SSB**, the **sum of squares for blocks**, measures the variation between the blocks. When the variation associated with the blocks is removed, SSE is reduced, making it easier to determine whether differences exist between the treatment means.

At this point in our presentation of statistical inference, we will deviate from our usual procedure of solving examples manually and using Excel. The calculations for this experimental design and for the experiment presented in the next section are so time consuming that solving them by hand adds little to your understanding of the technique. Consequently, although we will continue to present the concepts by discussing how the statistics are calculated, we will solve the problems only by computer.

To help you understand the formulas, we will use the following notation:

$\bar{x}[T]_j$ = Mean of the observations in the jth treatment ($j = 1, 2, \ldots, k$)

$\bar{x}[B]_i$ = Mean of the observations in the ith block ($i = 1, 2, \ldots, b$)

b = Number of blocks

Table 14.4 summarizes the notation we use in this experimental design.

TABLE 14.4 Notation for the Randomized Block Analysis of Variance

BLOCK	TREATMENTS				BLOCK MEAN
	1	**2**		**k**	
1	x_{11}	x_{12}	$\ldots$	x_{1k}	$\bar{x}[B]_1$
2	x_{21}	x_{22}	$\ldots$	x_{2k}	$\bar{x}[B]_2$
$\vdots$	$\vdots$	$\vdots$		$\vdots$	$\vdots$
b	x_{b1}	x_{b2}	$\ldots$	x_{bk}	$\bar{x}[B]_b$
Treatment mean	$\bar{x}[T]_1$	$\bar{x}[T]_2$	$\ldots$	$\bar{x}[T]_k$	

The definitions of SS(Total) and SST in the randomized block design are identical to those in the independent samples design. SSE in the independent samples design is equal to the sum of SSB and SSE in the randomized block design.

Sums of Squares in the Randomized Block Experiment

$$SS(Total) = \sum_{j=1}^{k} \sum_{i=1}^{b} (x_{ij} - \bar{\bar{x}})^2$$

$$SST = \sum_{j=1}^{k} b(\bar{x}[T]_j - \bar{\bar{x}})^2$$

$$SSB = \sum_{i=1}^{b} k(\bar{x}[B]_i - \bar{\bar{x}})^2$$

$$SSE = \sum_{j=1}^{k} \sum_{i=1}^{b} (x_{ij} - \bar{x}[T]_j - \bar{x}[B]_i + \bar{\bar{x}})^2$$

The test is conducted by determining the mean squares, which are computed by dividing the sums of squares by their respective degrees of freedom.

Mean Squares for the Randomized Block Experiment

$$MST = \frac{SST}{k-1}$$

$$MSB = \frac{SSB}{b-1}$$

$$MSE = \frac{SSE}{n-k-b+1}$$

Finally, the test statistic is the ratio of mean squares, as described in the box.

Test Statistic for the Randomized Block Experiment

$$F = \frac{MST}{MSE}$$

which is F-distributed with $\nu_1 = k - 1$ and $\nu_2 = n - k - b + 1$ degrees of freedom.

An interesting, and sometimes useful, by-product of the test of the treatment means is that we can also test to determine whether the block means differ. This will allow us to determine whether the experiment should have been conducted as a randomized block design. (If there are no differences between the blocks, the randomized block design is less likely to detect real differences between the treatment means.) Such a discovery could be useful in future similar experiments. The test of the block means is almost identical to that of the treatment means except the test statistic is

$$F = \frac{\text{MSB}}{\text{MSE}}$$

which is F-distributed with $\nu_1 = b - 1$ and $\nu_2 = n - k - b + 1$ degrees of freedom.

As with the one-way experiment, the statistics generated in the randomized block experiment are summarized in an ANOVA table, whose general form is exhibited in Table 14.5.

TABLE **14.5** ANOVA Table for the Randomized Block Analysis of Variance

SOURCE OF VARIATION	DEGREES OF FREEDOM	SUMS OF SQUARES	MEAN SQUARES	F-STATISTIC
Treatments	$k - 1$	SST	$\text{MST} = \text{SST}/(k - 1)$	$F = \text{MST}/\text{MSE}$
Blocks	$b - 1$	SSB	$\text{MSB} = \text{SSB}/(b - 1)$	$F = \text{MSB}/\text{MSE}$
Error	$n - k - b + 1$	SSE	$\text{MSE} = \text{SSE}/(n - k - b + 1)$	
Total	$n - 1$	SS(Total)		

EXAMPLE **14.3**

DATA
Xm14-03

Comparing Cholesterol-Lowering Drugs

Many North Americans suffer from high levels of cholesterol, which can lead to heart attacks. For those with very high levels (above 280), doctors prescribe drugs to reduce cholesterol levels. A pharmaceutical company has recently developed four such drugs. To determine whether any differences exist in their benefits, an experiment was organized. The company selected 25 groups of four men, each of whom had cholesterol levels in excess of 280. In each group, the men were matched according to age and weight. The drugs were administered over a 2-month period, and the reduction in cholesterol was recorded. Do these results allow the company to conclude that differences exist between the four new drugs?

Group	Drug 1	Drug 2	Drug 3	Drug 4
1	6.6	12.6	2.7	8.7
2	7.1	3.5	2.4	9.3
3	7.5	4.4	6.5	10
4	9.9	7.5	16.2	12.6
5	13.8	6.4	8.3	10.6
6	13.9	13.5	5.4	15.4
7	15.9	16.9	15.4	16.3
8	14.3	11.4	17.1	18.9
9	16	16.9	7.7	13.7
10	16.3	14.8	16.1	19.4
11	14.6	18.6	9	18.5
12	18.7	21.2	24.3	21.1
13	17.3	10	9.3	19.3
14	19.6	17	19.2	21.9
15	20.7	21	18.7	22.1
16	18.4	27.2	18.9	19.4

(Continued)

Group	Drug 1	Drug 2	Drug 3	Drug 4
17	21.5	26.8	7.9	25.4
18	20.4	28	23.8	26.5
19	21.9	31.7	8.8	22.2
20	22.5	11.9	26.7	23.5
21	21.5	28.7	25.2	19.6
22	25.2	29.5	27.3	30.1
23	23	22.2	17.6	26.6
24	23.7	19.5	25.6	24.5
25	28.4	31.2	26.1	27.4

SOLUTION:

IDENTIFY

The problem objective is to compare four populations, and the data are interval. Because the researchers recorded the cholesterol reduction for each drug for each member of the similar groups of men, we identify the experimental design as randomized block. The response variable is the cholesterol reduction, the treatments are the drugs, and the blocks are the 25 similar groups of men. The hypotheses to be tested are as follows.

H_0: $\mu_1 = \mu_2 = \mu_3 = \mu_4$

H_1: At least two means differ

COMPUTE

EXCEL Data Analysis

	A	B	C	D	E	F	G
36	ANOVA						
37	Source of Variation	SS	df	MS	F	P-value	F crit
38	Rows	3848.66	24	160.36	10.11	9.7E-15	1.67
39	Columns	195.95	3	65.32	4.12	0.0094	2.73
40	Error	1142.56	72	15.87			
41							
42	Total	5187.17	99				

The output includes block and treatment statistics (sums, averages, and variances, which are not shown here), and the ANOVA table. The F-statistic to determine whether differences exist between the four drugs (**Columns**) is 4.12. Its p-value is .0094. The other F-statistic, 10.11 (p-value $= 9.70 \times 10^{-15} =$ virtually 0), indicates that there are differences between the groups of men (**Rows**).

INSTRUCTIONS

1. Type or import the data into adjacent columns.* (Open Xm14-03 and click the **Unstacked** tab.)
2. Click **Data, Data Analysis . . .**, and **Anova: Two-Factor Without Replication**.
3. Specify the **Input Range** (A1:E26). Click **Labels** if applicable. If you do, both the treatments and blocks must be labeled (as in Xm14-03). Specify the value of α (.05).

---

*If one or more columns contain an empty cell (representing missing data), the entire row must be removed. See online appendix Excel Instructions for Deleting Rows with Blanks.

A Type I error occurs when you conclude that differences exist when, in fact, they do not. A Type II error is committed when the test reveals no difference when at least two means differ. It would appear that both errors are equally costly. Accordingly, we judge the p-value against a standard of 5%. Because the p-value $= .0094$, we conclude that there is sufficient evidence to infer that at least two of the drugs differ. An examination reveals that cholesterol reduction is greatest using drugs 2 and 4. Further testing is recommended to determine which is better.

14-4a Checking the Required Conditions

The F-test of the randomized block design of the analysis of variance has the same requirements as the independent samples design. That is, the random variable must be normally distributed and the population variances must be equal. The histograms (not shown) appear to support the validity of our results; the reductions appear to be normally distributed. The equality of variances requirement also appears to be met.

14-4b Violation of the Required Conditions

When the response is not normally distributed, we can replace the randomized block analysis of variance with the Friedman test, which is introduced in Section 19-4.

14-4c Criteria for Blocking

In Section 13-3, we listed the advantages and disadvantages of performing a matched pairs experiment. The same comments are valid when we discuss performing a blocked experiment. The purpose of blocking is to reduce the variation caused by differences between the experimental units. By grouping the experimental units into homogeneous blocks with respect to the response variable, the statistics practitioner increases the chances of detecting actual differences between the treatment means. Hence, we need to find criteria for blocking that significantly affect the response variable. For example, suppose that a statistics professor wants to determine which of four methods of teaching statistics is best. In a one-way experiment, the professor might take four samples of 10 students, teach each sample by a different method, grade the students at the end of the course, and perform an F-test to determine whether differences exist. However, it is likely that there are very large differences between the students within each class that may hide differences between classes. To reduce this variation, the statistics professor must identify variables that are linked to a student's grade in statistics. For example, overall ability of the student, completion of mathematics courses, and exposure to other statistics courses are all related to performance in a statistics course.

The experiment could be performed in the following way. The statistics professor selects four students at random whose average grade before statistics is 95–100 and then randomly assigns the students to one of the four classes. The process is repeated with students whose average is 90–95, 85–90, . . ., and 50–55. The final grades would be used to test for differences between the classes.

Any characteristics that are related to the experimental units are potential blocking criteria. For example, if the experimental units are people, we may block according to age, gender, income, work experience, intelligence, residence (country, county, or city), weight, or height. If the experimental unit is a factory and we're measuring number of units produced hourly, blocking criteria include workforce experience, age of the plant, and quality of suppliers.

14-4d Developing an Understanding of Statistical Concepts

As we explained previously, the randomized block experiment is an extension of the matched pairs experiment discussed in Section 13-3. In the matched pairs experiment, we simply remove the effect of the variation caused by differences between the experimental units. The effect of this removal is seen in the decrease in the value of the standard error (compared to the standard error in the test statistic produced from independent samples) and the increase in the value of the t-statistic. In the randomized block experiment of the analysis of variance, we actually measure the variation between the blocks by computing SSB. The sum of squares for error is reduced by SSB, making it easier to detect differences between the treatments. In addition, we can test to determine whether the blocks differ—a procedure we were unable to perform in the matched pairs experiment.

To illustrate, let's return to Examples 13.4 and 13.5, which were experiments to determine whether there was a difference in starting salaries offered to finance and marketing MBA majors. (In fact, we tested to determine whether finance majors draw higher salary offers than do marketing majors. However, the analysis of variance can test only for differences.) In Example 13.4 (independent samples), there was insufficient evidence to infer a difference between the two types of majors. In Example 13.5 (matched pairs experiment), there was enough evidence to infer a difference. As we pointed out in Section 13-3, matching by grade point average allowed the statistics practitioner to more easily discern a difference between the two types of majors. If we repeat Examples 13.4 and 13.5 using the analysis of variance, we come to the same conclusion. The Excel outputs are shown here.

EXCEL Data Analysis: Analysis of Variance for Example 13.4

	A	B	C	D	E	F	G
1	Anova: Single Factor						
2							
3	SUMMARY						
4	Groups	Count	Sum	Average	Variance		
5	Finance	25	1,640,595	65,624	360,433,294		
6	Marketing	25	1,510,570	60,423	262,228,559		
7							
8							
9	ANOVA						
10	Source of Variation	SS	df	MS	F	P-value	F crit
11	Between Groups	338,130,013	1	338,130,013	1.09	0.3026	4.04
12	Within Groups	14,943,884,470	48	311,330,926			
13							
14	Total	15,282,014,483	49				

EXCEL Data Analysis: Analysis of Variance for Example 13.5

	A	B	C	D	E	F	G
34	ANOVA						
35	Source of Variation	SS	df	MS	F	P-value	F crit
36	Rows	21,415,991,654	24	892,332,986	40.39	4.17E-14	1.98
37	Columns	320,617,035	1	320,617,035	14.51	0.0009	4.26
38	Error	530,174,605	24	22,090,609			
39							
40	Total	22,266,783,295	49				

In Example 13.4, we partition the total sum of squares [SS(Total) = 15,282,014,483] into two sources of variation: SST = 338,130,013 and SSE = 14,943,884,470. In Example 13.5, the total sum of squares is SS(Total) = 22,266,783,295, SST (sum of squares for majors) = 320,617,035, SSB (sum of squares for GPA) = 21,415,991,654, and SSE = 530,174,605. As you can see, the sums of squares for treatments are approximately equal (338,130,013 and 320,617,035). However, the two calculations differ in the sums of squares for error. SSE in Example 13.5 is much smaller than SSE in Example 13.4 because the randomized block experiment allows us to measure and remove the effect of the variation between MBA students with the same majors. The sum of squares for blocks (sum of squares for GPA groups) is 21,415,991,654, a statistic that measures how much variation exists between the salary offers within majors. As a result of removing this variation, SSE is small. Thus, we conclude in Example 13.5 that the salary offers differ between majors whereas there was not enough evidence in Example 13.4 to draw the same conclusion.

Notice that in both examples the t-statistic squared equals the F-statistic in Example 13.4, $t = 1.04$, which when squared equals 1.09, which is the F-statistic (rounded). In Example 13.5, $t = 3.81$, which when squared equals 14.51, the F-statistic for the test of the treatment means. Moreover, the p-values are also the same.

We now complete this section by listing the factors that we need to recognize to use this experiment of the analysis of variance.

Factors That Identify the Randomized Block of the Analysis of Variance

1. **Problem objective:** Compare two or more populations.

2. **Data type:** Interval

3. **Experimental design:** Blocked samples

EXERCISES

Developing an Understanding of Statistical Concepts

14.93 The following statistics were generated from a randomized block experiment with $k = 3$ and $b = 7$:

SST = 100   SSB = 50   SSE = 25

a. Test to determine whether the treatment means differ. (Use $\alpha = .05$.)
b. Test to determine whether the block means differ. (Use $\alpha = .05$.)

14.94 A randomized block experiment produced the following statistics:

$k = 5$ $b = 12$ SST = 1,500 SSB = 1,000 SS(Total) = 3,500

a. Test to determine whether the treatment means differ. (Use $\alpha = .01$.)

b. Test to determine whether the block means differ. (Use $\alpha = .01$.)

14.95 Suppose the following statistics were calculated from data gathered from a randomized block experiment with $k = 4$ and $b = 10$:

SS(Total) = 1,210   SST = 275   SSB = 625

a. Can we conclude from these statistics that the treatment means differ? (Use $\alpha = .01$.)
b. Can we conclude from these statistics that the block means differ? (Use $\alpha = .01$.)

14.96 A randomized block experiment produced the following statistics.

$k = 3$ $b = 8$ SST = 1,500   SS(Total) = 3,500

a. Test at the 5% significance level to determine whether the treatment means differ given that SSB = 500.

b. Repeat part (a) with SSB = 1,000.

c. Repeat part (a) with SSB = 1,500.

d. Describe what happens to the test statistic as SSB increases.

14.97 Xr14-97 a. Assuming that the data shown here were generated from a randomized block experiment, calculate SS(Total), SST, SSB, and SSE.

b. Assuming that the data below were generated from a one-way (independent samples) experiment, calculate SS(Total), SST, and SSE.

c. Why does SS(Total) remain the same for both experimental designs?

d. Why does SST remain the same for both experimental designs?

e. Why does SSB + SSE in part (a) equal SSE in part (b)?

Treatment		
1	2	3
7	12	8
10	8	9
12	16	13
9	13	6
12	10	11

14.98 Xr14-98 a. Calculate SS(Total), SST, SSB, and SSE, assuming that the accompanying data were generated from a randomized block experiment.

b. Calculate SS(Total), SST, and SSE, assuming that the data below were generated from a one-way (independent samples) experiment.

c. Explain why SS(Total) remains the same for both experimental designs.

d. Explain why SST remains the same for both experimental designs.

e. Explain why SSB + SSE in part (a) equals SSE in part (b).

Treatment			
1	2	3	4
6	5	4	4
8	5	5	6
7	6	5	6

Applications

14.99 Xr14-99 As an experiment to understand measurement error, a statistics professor asks four students to measure the height of the professor, a male student, and a female student. The differences (in centimeters) between the correct dimension and the ones produced by the students are listed here. Can we infer that there are differences in the errors between the subjects being measured? (Use $\alpha = .05$.)

	Errors in Measuring Heights of		
Student	Professor	Male Student	Female Student
1	1.4	1.5	1.3
2	3.1	2.6	2.4
3	2.8	2.1	1.5
4	3.4	3.6	2.9

14.100 Xr14-100 How well do diets work? In a preliminary study, 20 people who were more than 50 pounds overweight were recruited to compare four diets. The people were matched by age. The oldest four became block 1, the next oldest four became block 2, and so on. The number of pounds that each person lost is listed in the following table. Can we infer at the 1% significance level that there are differences between the four diets?

	Diet			
Block	1	2	3	4
1	5	2	6	8
2	4	7	8	10
3	6	12	9	2
4	7	11	16	7
5	9	8	15	14

The following exercises require the use of a computer and software. Use a 5% significance level.

14.101 Xr14-101 In recent years, lack of confidence in the Postal Service has led many companies to send all of their correspondence by private courier. A large company is in the process of selecting one of three possible couriers to act as its sole delivery method. To help in making the decision, an experiment was performed whereby letters were sent using each of the three couriers at 12 different times of the day to a delivery point across town. The number of minutes required for delivery was recorded.

a. Can we conclude that there are differences in delivery times between the three couriers?

b. Did the statistics practitioner choose the correct design? Explain.

14.102 Xr14-102 Refer to Exercise 14.14. Despite failing to show that differences in the three types of fertilizer exist, the scientist continued to believe that there were differences, and that the differences were masked by the variation between the plots of land. Accordingly, another experiment was conducted. In the second experiment 20 three-acre plots of land scattered across the county were divided each into three plots and the three types of fertilizer on each of the one-acre plots were applied. The crop yields were recorded.

a. Can the scientist infer that there are differences between the three types of fertilizer?

b. What do these test results reveal about the variation between the plots?

14.103 Xr14-103   A recruiter for a computer company would like to determine whether there are differences in sales ability between business, arts, and science graduates. The recruiter takes a random sample of 20 business graduates who have been working for the company for the past 2 years. Each is then matched with an arts graduate and a science graduate with similar educational and working experience. The commission earned by each (in $1,000s) in the last year was recorded.

a. Is there sufficient evidence to allow the recruiter to conclude that there are differences in sales ability between the holders of the three types of degrees?

b. Conduct a test to determine whether an independent samples design would have been a better choice.

c. What are the required conditions for the test in part (a)?

d. Are the required conditions satisfied?

14.104 Xr14-104   Exercise 14.10 described an experiment that involved comparing the completion times associated with four different income tax forms. Suppose the experiment is redone in the following way. Thirty people are asked to fill out all four forms. The completion times (in minutes) are recorded.

a. Is there sufficient evidence to infer that differences in the completion times exist between the four forms?

b. Comment on the suitability of this experimental design in this problem.

14.105 Xr14-105   Golf ball manufacturers are constantly looking for ways to improve the performance of their products. One producer came up with an idea to help high handicap golfers (i.e., they're not very good), who typically slice the ball. (For a right-handed golfer, a slice is a ball that curves to the right.) The manufacturer produced three prototypes that are designed to go straighter than conventional balls. An experiment was conducted wherein 20 high handicap golfers who slice the ball were recruited and asked to use their drivers to hit one shot with each type of ball. The distance from the green was measured.

a. Is there sufficient evidence to infer that there are differences between the three prototypes?

b. What do the data tell you about the way the experiment was conducted?

14.106 Xr14-106   Do medical specialists differ in the amount of time they devote to patient care? To answer this question a statistics practitioner organized a study. The numbers of hours of patient care per week were recorded for five specialists. The experimental design was randomized blocks. The physicians were blocked by age.

a. Can we infer that there are differences in the amount of patient care between medical specialties?

b. Can we infer that blocking by age was appropriate?

14.107 Xr14-107   Refer to Exercise 14.9. Another study was conducted in the following way. Students from each of the high schools who were admitted to the business program were matched according to their high school averages. The average grades in the first year were recorded. Can the university admissions officer conclude that there are differences in grading standards between the four high schools?

14-5 / TWO-FACTOR ANALYSIS OF VARIANCE

In Section 14-1, we addressed problems where the data were generated from single-factor experiments. In Example 14.1, the treatments were the three age categories. Thus, there were three levels of a single factor. In this section, we address the problem where the experiment features two factors. The general term for such data-gathering procedures is **factorial experiment**. In factorial experiments, we can examine the effect on the response variable of two or more factors, although in this book we address the problem of only two factors. We can use the analysis of variance to determine whether the levels of each factor are different from one another.

We will present the technique for fixed effects only. That means we will address problems where all the levels of the factors are included in the experiment. As was the case with the randomized block design, calculating the test statistic in this type of experiment is quite time consuming. As a result, we will use Excel to produce our statistics.

EXAMPLE 14.4

DATA
Xm14-04

Comparing the Lifetime Number of Jobs by Educational Level

One measure of the health of a nation's economy is how quickly it creates jobs. One aspect of this issue is the number of jobs individuals hold. As part of a study on job tenure, a survey was conducted in which Americans aged between 37 and 45 were asked how many jobs they have held in their lifetimes. Also recorded were gender and educational attainment. The categories are

Less than high school (E1)

High school (E2)

Some college/university but no degree (E3)

At least one university degree (E4)

The data are shown for each of the eight categories of gender and education. Can we infer that differences exist between genders and educational levels?

Male E1	Male E2	Male E3	Male E4	Female E1	Female E2	Female E3	Female E4
10	12	15	8	7	7	5	7
9	11	8	9	13	12	13	9
12	9	7	5	14	6	12	3
16	14	7	11	6	15	3	7
14	12	7	13	11	10	13	9
17	16	9	14	14	13	11	6
13	10	14	7	13	9	15	10
9	10	15	11	11	15	5	15
11	5	11	10	14	12	9	4
15	11	13	8	12	13	8	11

SOLUTION:

IDENTIFY

We begin by treating this example as a one-way analysis of variance. Notice that there are eight treatments. However, the treatments are defined by two different factors. One factor is gender, which has two levels. The second factor is educational attainment, which has four levels.

We can proceed to solve this problem in the same way we did in Section 14-1: We test the following hypotheses.

H_0: $\mu_1 = \mu_2 = \mu_3 = \mu_4 = \mu_5 = \mu_6 = \mu_7 = \mu_8$

H_1:   At least two means differ

COMPUTE

EXCEL Data Analysis

	A	B	C	D	E	F	G
1	Anova: Single Factor						
15	ANOVA						
16	*Source of Variation*	SS	df	MS	F	P-value	F crit
17	Between Groups	153.35	7	21.91	2.17	0.0467	2.14
18	Within Groups	726.2	72	10.09			
19							
20	Total	879.55	79				

INTERPRET

The value of the test statistic is $F = 2.17$ with a p-value of .0467. We conclude that there are differences in the number of jobs between the eight treatments.

This statistical result raises more questions—namely, can we conclude that the differences in the mean number of jobs are caused by differences between males and females? Or are they caused by differences between educational levels? Or, perhaps, are there combinations, called **interactions**, of gender and education that result in especially high or low numbers? To show how we test for each type of difference, we need to develop some terminology.

A **complete factorial experiment** is an experiment in which the data for all possible combinations of the levels of the factors are gathered. That means that in Example 14.4 we measured the number of jobs for all eight combinations. This experiment is called a complete 2×4 factorial experiment.

In general, we will refer to one of the factors as factor A (arbitrarily chosen). The number of levels of this factor will be denoted by a. The other factor is called factor B, and its number of levels is denoted by b. This terminology becomes clearer when we present the data from Example 14.4 in another format. Table 14.6 depicts the layout for a *two-way classification*, which is another name for the complete factorial experiment. The number of observations for each combination is called a **replicate**. The number of replicates is denoted by r. In this book, we address only problems in which the number of replicates is the same for each treatment. Such a design is called **balanced**.

Thus, we use a complete factorial experiment where the number of treatments is ab with r replicates per treatment. In Example 14.4, $a = 2$, $b = 4$, and $r = 10$. As a result, we have 10 observations for each of the eight treatments.

If you examine the ANOVA table, you can see that the total variation is SS(Total) = 879.55, the sum of squares for treatments is SST = 153.35, and the sum of squares for error is SSE = 726.20. The variation caused by the treatments is measured by SST. To determine whether the differences result from factor A, factor B, or some interaction between the two factors, we need to partition SST into three sources. These are SS(A), SS(B), and SS(AB).

For those whose mathematical confidence is high, we have provided an explanation of the notation as well as the definitions of the sums of squares. Learning how the sums of squares are calculated is useful but hardly essential to your ability to conduct the tests. Uninterested readers should jump to the box on page 594 where we describe the individual F-tests.

TABLE **14.6** Two-Way Classification for Example 14.4

	MALE	FEMALE
Less than high school	10	7
	9	13
	12	14
	16	6
	14	11
	17	14
	13	13
	9	11
	11	14
	15	12
High school	12	7
	11	12
	9	6
	14	15
	12	10
	16	13
	10	9
	10	15
	5	12
	11	13
Less than bachelor's degree	15	5
	8	13
	7	12
	7	3
	7	13
	9	11
	14	15
	15	5
	11	9
	13	8
At least one bachelor's degree	8	7
	9	9
	5	3
	11	7
	13	9
	8	6
	7	10
	11	15
	10	4
	8	11

14-5a How the Sums of Squares for Factors A and B and Interaction Are Computed

To help you understand the formulas, we will use the following notation:

$$x_{ijk} = k\text{th observation in the } ij\text{th treatment}$$

$$\bar{x}\,[\text{AB}]_{ij} = \text{Mean of the response variable in the } ij\text{th treatment (mean of the treatment when the factor A level is } i \text{ and the factor B level is } j)$$

$\bar{x}[A]_i$ = Mean of the observations when the factor A level is i

$\bar{x}[B]_j$ = Mean of the observations when the factor B level is j

$\bar{\bar{x}}$ = Mean of all the observations

a = Number of factor A levels

b = Number of factor B levels

r = Number of replicates

In this notation, $\bar{x}[AB]_{11}$ is the mean of the responses for factor A level 1 and factor B level 1. The mean of the responses for factor A level 1 is $\bar{x}[A]_1$. The mean of the responses for factor B level 1 is $\bar{x}[B]_1$.

Table 14.7 describes the notation for the two-factor analysis of variance.

TABLE **14.7** Notation for Two-Factor Analysis of Variance

FACTOR B	FACTOR A					
	1	2	. . .	a		
1	x_{111} x_{112} $\vdots$ x_{11r} $\quad\bar{x}[AB]_{11}$	x_{211} x_{212} $\vdots$ x_{21r} $\quad\bar{x}[AB]_{21}$		x_{a11} x_{a12} $\vdots$ x_{a1r} $\quad\bar{x}[AB]_{a1}$	$\bar{x}[B]_1$
2	x_{121} x_{122} $\vdots$ x_{12r} $\quad\bar{x}[AB]_{12}$	x_{221} x_{222} $\vdots$ x_{22r} $\quad\bar{x}[AB]_{22}$		x_{a21} x_{a22} $\vdots$ x_{a2r} $\quad\bar{x}[AB]_{a2}$	$\bar{x}[B]_2$
$\vdots$					
b	x_{1b1} x_{1b2} $\vdots$ x_{1br} $\quad\bar{x}[AB]_{1b}$	x_{2b1} x_{2b2} $\vdots$ x_{2br} $\quad\bar{x}[AB]_{2b}$		x_{ab1} x_{ab2} $\vdots$ x_{abr} $\quad\bar{x}[AB]_{ab}$	$\bar{x}[B]_b$
	$\bar{x}[A]_1$	$\bar{x}[A]_2$		$\bar{x}[A]_a$	$\bar{\bar{x}}$

The sums of squares are defined as follows.

Sums of Squares in the Two-Factor Analysis of Variance

$$\text{SS(Total)} = \sum_{i=1}^{a}\sum_{j=1}^{b}\sum_{k=1}^{r}(x_{ijk} - \bar{\bar{x}})^2$$

$$SS(A) = rb\sum_{i=1}^{a}(\bar{x}[A]_i - \bar{\bar{x}})^2$$

$$SS(B) = ra\sum_{j=1}^{b}(\bar{x}[B]_j - \bar{\bar{x}})^2$$

$$SS(AB) = r\sum_{i=1}^{a}\sum_{j=1}^{b}(\bar{x}[AB]_{ij} - \bar{x}[A]_i - \bar{x}[B]_j + \bar{\bar{x}})^2$$

$$SSE = \sum_{i=1}^{a}\sum_{j=1}^{b}\sum_{k=1}^{r}(x_{ijk} - \bar{x}[AB]_{ij})^2$$

To compute SS(A), we calculate the sum of the squared differences between the factor A level means, which are denoted $\bar{x}[A]_i$, and the grand mean, $\bar{\bar{x}}$. The sum of squares for factor B, SS(B), is defined similarly. The interaction sum of squares, SS(AB), is calculated by taking each treatment mean (a treatment consists of a combination of a level of factor A and a level of factor B), subtracting the factor A level mean, subtracting the factor B level mean, adding the grand mean, squaring this quantity, and adding. The sum of squares for error, SSE, is calculated by subtracting the treatment means from the observations, squaring, and adding.

To test for each possibility, we conduct several F-tests similar to the one performed in Section 14-1. Figure 14.4 illustrates the partitioning of the total sum of squares that leads to the F-tests. We've included in this figure the partitioning used in the one-way study. When the one-way analysis of variance allows us to infer that differences between the treatment means exist, we continue our analysis by partitioning the treatment sum of squares into three sources of variation. The first is sum of squares for factor A, which we label SS(A), which measures the variation between the levels of factor A. Its degrees of freedom are $a - 1$. The second is the sum of squares for factor B, whose degrees of freedom are $b - 1$. SS(B) is the variation between the levels of factor B. The interaction sum of squares is labeled SS(AB), which is a measure of the amount of variation between the combinations of factors A and B; its degrees of freedom are $(a - 1) \times (b - 1)$. The sum of squares for error is SSE, and its degrees of freedom are $n - ab$. (Recall that n is the total sample size, which in this experiment is $n = abr$.) Notice that SSE and its number of degrees of freedom are identical in both partitions. As in the previous experiment, SSE is the variation within the treatments.

FIGURE **14.4** Partitioning SS(Total) in Single-Factor and Two-Factor Analysis of Variance

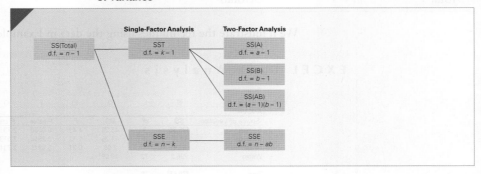

F-Tests Conducted in Two-Factor Analysis of Variance

Test for Differences between the Levels of Factor A

H_0: The means of the a levels of factor A are equal

H_1: At least two means differ

Test statistic: $F = \dfrac{\text{MS(A)}}{\text{MSE}}$

Test for Differences between the Levels of Factor B

H_0: The means of the b levels of factor B are equal

H_1: At least two means differ

Test statistic: $F = \dfrac{\text{MS(B)}}{\text{MSE}}$

Test for Interaction between Factors A and B

H_0: Factors A and B do not interact to affect the mean responses

H_1: Factors A and B do interact to affect the mean responses

Test statistic: $F = \dfrac{\text{MS(AB)}}{\text{MSE}}$

Required Conditions

1. The distribution of the response is normally distributed.
2. The variance for each treatment is identical.
3. The samples are independent.

As in the two previous experimental designs of the analysis of variance, we summarize the results in an ANOVA table. Table 14.8 depicts the general form of the table for the complete factorial experiment.

TABLE **14.8** ANOVA Table for the Two-Factor Experiment

SOURCE OF VARIATION	DEGREES OF FREEDOM	SUMS OF SQUARES	MEAN SQUARES	F-STATISTIC
Factor A	$a - 1$	SS(A)	MS(A) = SS(A)/(a − 1)	F = MS(A)/MSE
Factor B	$b - 1$	SS(B)	MS(B) = SS(B)/(b − 1)	F = MS(B)/MSE
Interaction	$(a - 1)(b - 1)$	SS(AB)	MS(AB) = SS(AB)/[(a − 1)(b − 1)]	F = MS(AB)/MSE
Error	$n - ab$	SSE	MSE = SSE/(n − ab)	
Total	$n - 1$	SS(Total)		

We'll illustrate the techniques using the data in Example 14.4.

EXCEL Data Analysis

	A	B	C	D	E	F	G
1	ANOVA						
2	Source of Variation	SS	df	MS	F	P-value	F crit
3	Sample	135.85	3	45.28	4.49	0.0060	2.7318
4	Columns	11.25	1	11.25	1.12	0.2944	3.9739
5	Interaction	6.25	3	2.08	0.21	0.8915	2.7318
6	Within	726.2	72	10.09			
7							
8	Total	879.55	79				

In the ANOVA table, **Sample** refers to factor B (educational level) and **Columns** refers to factor A (gender). Thus, MS(B) = 45.28, MS(A) = 11.25, MS(AB) = 2.08, and MSE = 10.09. The F-statistics are 4.49 (educational level), 1.12 (gender), and .21 (interaction).

INSTRUCTIONS

1. Type or import the data using the same format as Xm14-04 (tab Xm14-04 Unstacked B). (*Note:* You must label the rows and columns as we did.)
2. Click **Data, Data Analysis**, and **Anova: Two-Factor with Replication**.
3. Specify the **Input Range** (A1:C41). Type the number of replications in the **Rows per sample** box (10).
4. Specify a value for α (.05).

14-5b Test for Differences in Number of Jobs between Men and Women

H_0: The means of the two levels of factor A are equal
H_1: At least two means differ

Test statistic: $F = \dfrac{MS(A)}{MSE}$

Value of the test statistic: From the computer output, we have

MS(A) = 11.25, MSE = 10.09, and $F = 11.25/10.09 = 1.12$ (p-value = .2944)

There is no evidence at the 5% significance level to infer that differences in the number of jobs exist between men and women.

14-5c Test for Differences in Number of Jobs between Education Levels

H_0: The means of the four levels of factor B are equal
H_1: At least two means differ

Test statistic: $F = \dfrac{MS(B)}{MSE}$

Value of the test statistic: From the computer output, we find

MS(B) = 45.28 and MSE = 10.09. Thus, $F = 45.28/10.09 = 4.49$ (p-value = .0060).

There is sufficient evidence at the 5% significance level to infer that differences in the number of jobs exist between educational levels.

14-5d Test for Interaction between Factors A and B

H_0: Factors A and B do not interact to affect the mean number of jobs
H_1: Factors A and B do interact to affect the mean number of jobs

Test statistic: $F = \dfrac{MS(AB)}{MSE}$

Value of the test statistic: From the printouts,

$$\text{MS(AB)} = 2.08, \text{MSE} = 10.09, \text{and } F = 2.08/10.09 = .21 \ (\ p\text{-value} = .8915).$$

There is not enough evidence to conclude that there is an interaction between gender and education.

INTERPRET

Figure 14.5 is a graph of the mean responses for each of the eight treatments. As you can see, there are small (not significant) differences between males and females. There are significant differences between men and women with different educational backgrounds. Finally, there is no interaction.

FIGURE **14.5**   **Mean Responses for Example 14.4**

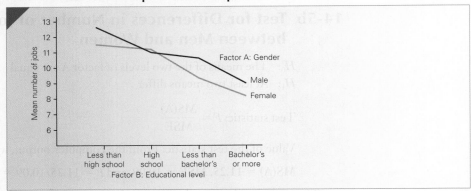

14-5e What Is Interaction?

EXAMPLE **14.5**

Comparing Lifetime Number of Jobs by Education Level

PART 2

Xm14-05

To more fully understand interaction we have changed the sample associated with men who have not finished high school (Treatment 1). We subtracted 6 from the original numbers so that the data in treatment 1 is

$$4, 3, 6, 10, 8, 11, 7, 3, 5, 9$$

(The mean is 6.6.)

SOLUTION:

EXCEL Data Analysis

	A	B	C	D	E	F	G
34	ANOVA						
35	Source of Variation	SS	df	MS	F	P-value	F crit
36	Sample	75.85	3	25.28	2.51	0.0657	2.73
37	Columns	11.25	1	11.25	1.12	0.2944	3.97
38	Interaction	120.25	3	40.08	3.97	0.0112	2.73
39	Within	726.20	72	10.09			
40							
41	Total	933.55	79				

INTERPRET

In this example there is not enough evidence (at the 5% significance level) to infer that there are differences between men and women and between the educational levels. However, there is sufficient evidence to conclude that there is interaction between gender and education.

	Male	Female
Less than high school	6.6	11.5
High school	11.0	11.2
Less than bachelor's	10.6	9.4
Bachelor's or more	9.0	8.1

Compare Figures 14.5 and 14.6. In Figure 14.5, the lines joining the response means for males and females are quite similar. In particular we see that the lines are almost parallel. However, in Figure 14.6 the lines are no longer almost parallel. It is apparent that the mean of treatment 1 is smaller; the pattern is different. For whatever reason, in this case men with less than high school have a smaller number of jobs.

FIGURE **14.6** **Mean Responses for Example 14.4a**

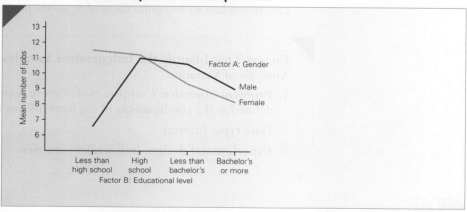

14-5f Conducting the Analysis of Variance for the Complete Factorial Experiment

In addressing the problem outlined in Example 14.4, we began by conducting a one-way analysis of variance to determine whether differences existed between the eight treatment means. This was done primarily for pedagogical reasons to enable you to see that when the treatment means differ, we need to analyze the reasons for the differences. However, in practice, we generally do not conduct this test in the complete factorial experiment (although it should be noted that some statistics practitioners prefer this "two-stage" strategy). We recommend that you proceed directly to the two-factor analysis of variance.

In the two versions of Example 14.4, we conducted the tests of each factor and then the test for interaction.

However, if there is evidence of interaction, the tests of the factors are irrelevant. There may or may not be differences between the levels of factor A and the levels of factor B. Accordingly, we change the order of conducting the F-tests.

Order of Testing in the Two-Factor Analysis of Variance

Test for interaction first. If there is enough evidence to infer that there is interaction, do not conduct the other tests.

 If there is not enough evidence to conclude that there is interaction, proceed to conduct the F-tests for factors A and B.

14-5g Developing an Understanding of Statistical Concepts

You may have noticed that there are similarities between the two-factor experiment and the randomized block experiment. In fact, when the number of replicates is one, the calculations are identical. This raises the question, What is the difference between a factor in a multifactor study and a block in a randomized block experiment? In general, the difference between the two experimental designs is that in the randomized block experiment, blocking is performed specifically to reduce variation, whereas in the two-factor model the effect of the factors on the response variable is of interest to the statistics practitioner. The criteria that define the blocks are always characteristics of the experimental units. Consequently, factors that are characteristics of the experimental units will be treated not as factors in a multifactor study, but as blocks in a randomized block experiment.

 Let's review how we recognize the need to use the procedure described in this section.

Factors That Identify the Independent Samples Two-Factor Analysis of Variance

1. **Problem objective**: Compare two or more populations (populations are defined as the combinations of the levels of two factors).

2. **Data type**: Interval

3. **Experimental design**: Independent samples

EXERCISES

14.108 A two-factor analysis of variance experiment was performed with $a = 3$, $b = 4$, and $r = 20$. The following sums of squares were computed:

$$\text{SS(Total)} = 42,450 \quad \text{SS(A)} = 1,560$$
$$\text{SS(B)} = 2,880 \quad \text{SS(AB)} = 7,605$$

Conduct whatever test you deem necessary at the 1% significance level to determine whether there are differences between the levels of factor A, the levels of factor B, or interaction between factors A and B.

14.109 A statistics practitioner conducted a two-factor analysis of variance experiment with $a = 4$, $b = 3$, and $r = 8$. The sums of squares are listed here:

$$\text{SS(Total)} = 9,420 \quad \text{SS(A)} = 203 \quad \text{SS(B)} = 859$$
$$\text{SS(AB)} = 513$$

a. Test at the 5% significance level to determine whether factors A and B interact.

b. Test at the 5% significance level to determine whether differences exist between the levels of factor A.

c. Test at the 5% significance level to determine whether differences exist between the levels of factor B.

14.110 Xr14-110 The data listed next were generated from a 2×2 factorial experiment with 3 replicates. Compute the p-value for the following tests.

replacing. If the part is under warranty, the company will incur a loss in replacing it. If the warranty has expired, customers will have to pay to replace the unit, causing some degree of displeasure that may result in them buying another company's product in the future. In either case, the company loses money. Figure 14.8 depicts the loss function. As you can see, any deviation from the target value results in some loss, with large deviations resulting in larger losses.

FIGURE **14.8** Taguchi Loss Function

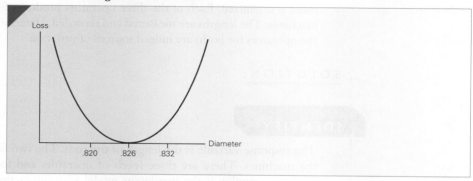

Management scientists have shown that the loss function can be expressed as a function of the production process mean and variance. In Figure 14.9 we describe a normal distribution of the diameter of the machined part with a target value of .826 mm. When the mean of the distribution is .826, any loss is caused by the variance. The statistical techniques introduced in Chapter 21 are usually employed to center the distribution on the target value. However, reducing the variance is considerably more difficult. To reduce variation, it is necessary to first find the sources of variation. We do so by conducting experiments. The principles are quite straightforward, drawing on the concepts developed in the previous section.

An important function of operations management is production design in which decisions are made about how a product is manufactured. The objective is to produce the highest quality product at a reasonable cost. This objective is achieved by choosing the machines, materials, methods, and "manpower" (personnel), the so-called 4 Ms. By altering some or all of these elements, the operations manager can alter the size, weight, or volume and, ultimately, the quality of the product.

FIGURE **14.9** Taguchi Loss Function and the Distribution of Piston Rings

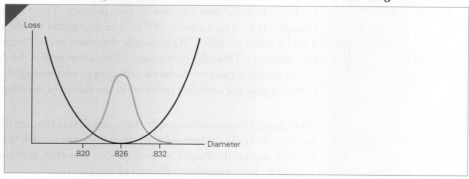

EXAMPLE 14.6

Causes of Variation

A critical component in an aircraft engine is a steel rod that must be 41.387 cm long. The operations manager has noted that there has been some variation in the lengths. In some cases, the steel rods had to be discarded or reworked because they were either too short or too long. The operations manager believes that some of the variation is caused by the way the production process has been designed. Specifically, the rods vary from machine to machine and from operator to operator. To help unravel the truth, an experiment is organized. Each of the three operators produces five rods on each of the four machines. The lengths are measured and recorded. Determine whether the machines or the operators (or both) are indeed sources of variation.

SOLUTION:

IDENTIFY

The response variable is the length of the rods. The two factors are the operators and the machines. There are three levels of operators and four levels of machines. The model we employ is the two-factor model with interaction. The computer output is shown here.

COMPUTE

EXCEL Data Analysis

	A	B	C	D	E	F	G
28	ANOVA						
29	Source of Variation	SS	df	MS	F	P-value	F crit
30	Sample	0.01513	2	0.00757	6.98	0.0022	3.19
31	Columns	0.00336	3	0.00112	1.04	0.3856	2.80
32	Interaction	0.00465	6	0.00077	0.71	0.6394	2.29
33	Within	0.05199	48	0.00108			
34							
35	Total	0.07514	59				

INTERPRET

The test for interaction yields $F = .71$ and a p-value of .6394. There is not enough evidence to infer that the two factors interact. The F-statistic for the operator factor (Sample) is 6.98 (p-value = .0022). The F-statistic for the machine factor (Columns) is 1.04 (p-value = .3856). We conclude that there are differences only between the levels of the operators. Thus, the only source of variation here is the different operators. The operations manager can now focus on reducing or eliminating this variation. For example, the manager may use only one operator in the future or investigate why the operators differ.

The causes of variation example that opened this chapter illustrate this strategy. Because we have limited our discussion to the two-factor model, the example features this experimental design. It should be understood, however, that more complicated models are needed to fully investigate sources of variation.

14-6b   Design of Experiments and Taguchi Methods

In the example just discussed, the experiment used only two factors. In practice, there are frequently many more factors. The problem is that the total number of treatments or combinations can be quite high, making any experimentation both time consuming and expensive. For example, if there are 10 factors each with 2 levels, the number of treatments is $2^{10} = 1,024$. If we measure each treatment with 10 replicates, the number of observations, 10,240, makes this experiment prohibitive. Fortunately, it is possible to reduce this number considerably. Through the use of *orthogonal arrays*, we can conduct *fractional factorial experiments* that can produce useful results at a small fraction of the cost. The experimental designs and statistical analyses are beyond the level of this book. Interested readers can find a variety of books at different levels of mathematical and statistical sophistication to learn more about this application.

EXERCISES

Applications

The following exercises require the use of a computer and software. **Use a 5% significance level.**

14.118 Xr14-118 The headrests on a car's front seats are designed to protect the driver and front-seat passenger from whiplash when the car is hit from behind. The frame of the headrest is made from metal rods. A machine is used to bend the rod into a U-shape exactly 440 millimeters wide. The width is critical; too wide or too narrow and it won't fit into the holes drilled into the car seat frame. The company has experimented with several different metal alloys in the hope of finding a material that will result in more headrest frames that fit. Another possible source of variation is the machines used. To learn more about the process the operations manager conducts an experiment. Both of the machines are used to produce 10 headrests from each of the five metal alloys now being used. Each frame is measured and the data (in millimeters) are recorded using the format shown here. Analyze the data to determine whether the alloys, machines, or both are sources of variation.

> Column B: Machine 1, rows 1 to 10 alloy A, rows 11 to 20, alloy B
> Column C: Machine 2, rows 1 to 10 alloy A, rows 11 to 20, alloy B

14.119 Xr14-119 A paint manufacturer is attempting to improve the process that fills the 1-gallon containers. The foreperson has suggested that the nozzle can be made from several different alloys. Furthermore, the way that the process "knows" when to stop the flow of paint can be accomplished in two ways: by setting a predetermined amount or by measuring the amount of paint already in the can. To determine what factors lead to variation, an experiment is conducted. For each of the four alloys that could be used to make the nozzles and the two measuring devices, five cans are filled. The amount of paint in each container is precisely measured. The data in liters were recorded in the following way:

> Column B: Device 1, rows 1 to 5 alloy A, rows 6 to 10 alloy B, etc.
> Column C: Device 2, rows 1 to 5 alloy A, rows 6 to 10 alloy B, etc.

Can we infer that the alloys, the measuring devices, or both are sources of variation?

14.120 Xr14-120 The marketing department of a firm that manufactures office furniture has ascertained that there is a growing market for a specialized desk that houses the various parts of a computer system. The operations manager is summoned to put together a plan that will produce high-quality desks at low cost. The characteristics of the desk have been dictated by the marketing department, which has specified the material that the desk will be made from and the machines used to produce the parts. However, there are three methods that can be utilized. Moreover, because of the complexity of the operation, the manager realizes that it is possible that different skill levels of the workers can yield different results. Accordingly, an experiment was conducted. Workers from each of three skill levels were chosen. These groups were further divided into two subgroups. Each subgroup assembled the desks using methods 1 and 2. The amount of time taken to assemble each of eight desks was recorded as follows. Columns B and C contain the times for methods 1 and 2; rows 1 to 8, 9 to 16, and 17 to 24 store the times for the three skill levels. What can we infer from these data?

CHAPTER SUMMARY

The analysis of variance allows us to test for differences between populations when the data are interval. The analyses of the results of three different experimental designs were presented in this chapter. The one-way analysis of variance defines the populations on the basis of one factor. The second experimental design also defines the treatments on the basis of one factor. However, the randomized block design uses data gathered by observing the results of a matched or blocked experiment (two-way analysis of variance). The third design is the two-factor experiment wherein the treatments are defined as the combinations of the levels of two factors. All the analyses of variance are based on partitioning the total sum of squares into sources of variation from which the mean squares and F-statistics are computed.

In addition, we introduced three multiple comparison methods that allow us to determine which means differ in the one-way analysis of variance.

Finally, we described an important application in operations management that employs the analysis of variance.

IMPORTANT TERMS:

Analysis of variance   551
Treatment means   551
One-way analysis of variance   551
Response variable   553
Responses   553
Experimental units   553
Factor   553
Level   553
Between-treatments variation   553
Sum of squares for treatments (SST)   553
Within-treatments variation   554
Sum of squares for error (SSE)   554
Mean squares   555
Mean squares for treatments   555
Mean squares for error   555
F-statistic   556
Analysis of variance (ANOVA) table   556
Total variation   557

SS(Total)   557
Completely randomized design   558
Multiple comparisons   570
Least significance difference (LSD)   572
Bonferroni adjustment   572
Tukey's multiple comparison method   574
Multifactor experiment   579
Randomized block design   579
Repeated measures   579
Two-way analysis of variance   579
Fixed-effects analysis of variance   579
Random-effects analysis of variance   579
Sum of squares for blocks   580
Factorial experiment   588
Interactions   590
Complete factorial experiment   590
Replicate   590
Balanced   590

SYMBOLS:

Symbol	Pronounced	Represents
$\bar{\bar{x}}$	x double bar	Overall or grand mean
q		Studentized range
ω	Omega	Critical value of Tukey's multiple comparison method
$q_\alpha(k, v)$	q sub alpha k v	Critical value of the Studentized range
n_g		Number of observations in each of k samples
$\bar{x}[T]_j$	x bar T sub j	Mean of the jth treatment
$\bar{x}[B]_i$	x bar B sub i	Mean of the ith block
$\bar{x}[AB]_{ij}$	x bar A B sub ij	Mean of the ijth treatment
$\bar{x}[A]_i$	x bar A sub i	Mean of the observations when the factor A level is i
$\bar{x}[B]_j$	x bar B sub j	Mean of the observations when the factor B level is j

FORMULAS:

One-way analysis of variance

$$SST = \sum_{j=1}^{k} n_j(\bar{x}_j - \bar{\bar{x}})^2$$

$$SSE = \sum_{j=1}^{k} \sum_{i=1}^{k} (x_{ij} - \bar{x}_j)^2$$

$$MST = \frac{SST}{k-1}$$

$$MST = \frac{SSE}{n-k}$$

$$F = \frac{MST}{MSE}$$

Least significant difference comparison method

$$LSD = t_{\alpha/2} \sqrt{MSE\left(\frac{1}{n_i} + \frac{1}{n_j}\right)}$$

Tukey's multiple comparison method

$$\omega = q_\alpha(k, v) \sqrt{\frac{MSE}{n_g}}$$

Two-way analysis of variance (randomized block design of experiment)

$$SS(Total) = \sum_{j=1}^{k} \sum_{i=1}^{b} (x_{ij} - \bar{\bar{x}})^2$$

$$SST = \sum_{j=1}^{k} b(\bar{x}[T]_j - \bar{\bar{x}})^2$$

$$SSB = \sum_{i=1}^{k} k(\bar{x}[B]_i - \bar{\bar{x}})^2$$

$$SSE = \sum_{j=1}^{k} \sum_{i=1}^{b} (x_{ij} - \bar{x}[T]_j - \bar{x}[B]_i + \bar{\bar{x}})^2$$

$$MST = \frac{SST}{k-1}$$

$$MSB = \frac{SSB}{b-1}$$

$$MSE = \frac{SSE}{n-k-b+1}$$

$$F = \frac{MST}{MSE}$$

$$F = \frac{MSB}{MSE}$$

Two-factor analysis of variance

$$SS(Total) = \sum_{i=1}^{a} \sum_{j=1}^{b} \sum_{k=1}^{r} (x_{ijk} - \bar{\bar{x}})^2$$

$$SS(A) = rb \sum_{i=1}^{a} (\bar{x}[A]_i - \bar{\bar{x}})^2$$

$$SS(B) = ra \sum_{j=1}^{b} (\bar{x}[B]_j - \bar{\bar{x}})^2$$

$$SS(AB) = r \sum_{i=1}^{a} \sum_{j=1}^{b} (\bar{x}[AB]_{ij} - \bar{x}[A]_i - \bar{x}[B]_j + \bar{\bar{x}})^2$$

$$SSE = \sum_{i=1}^{a} \sum_{j=1}^{b} \sum_{k=1}^{r} (x_{ijk} - \bar{x}[AB]_{ij})^2$$

$$MS(A) = \frac{SS(A)}{a-1}$$

$$MS(B) = \frac{SS(B)}{b-1}$$

$$MS(AB) = \frac{SS(AB)}{(a-1)(b-1)}$$

$$MSE = \frac{SSE}{n-ab}$$

$$F = \frac{MS(A)}{MSE}$$

$$F = \frac{MS(B)}{MSE}$$

$$F = \frac{MS(AB)}{MSE}$$

EXCEL OUTPUT AND INSTRUCTIONS:

CHAPTER EXERCISES

The following exercises require the use of a computer and software. **Use a 5% significance level.**

14.121 <u>Xr14-121</u> Each year billions of dollars are lost because of worker injuries on the job. Costs can be decreased if injured workers can be rehabilitated quickly. As part of an analysis of the amount of time taken for workers to return to work, a sample of male blue-collar workers aged 35 to 45 who suffered a common wrist fracture was taken. The researchers believed that the mental and physical conditions of the individual affect recovery time. Each man was given a questionnaire to complete, which measured whether he tended to be optimistic or pessimistic. Their physical condition was also evaluated and categorized as very physically fit, average, or in poor condition. The number of days until the wrist returned to full function was measured for each individual. These data were recorded in the following way:

> Column B: Time to recover for optimists ((columns 1–10) = very fit, rows 11–20 = in average condition, rows 21–30 = poor condition)
>
> Column C: Time to recover for pessimists (same format as column B)

a. What are the factors in this experiment? What are the levels of each factor?

b. Can we conclude that pessimists and optimists differ in their recovery times?

c. Can we conclude that physical condition affects recovery times?

14.122 <u>Xr14-122</u> To help high school students pick a major, a company called PayScale surveys graduates of a variety of programs. In one such survey, graduates of the following degree programs were asked what their annual salaries were after working at least 10 years in the field.

> Elementary Education
> Human Development
> Social Work
> Special Education

Can we infer that there are differences in salary between the four college degrees?

14.123 <u>Xr14-123</u> The possible imposition of a residential property tax has been a sensitive political issue in a large city that consists of five boroughs. Currently, property tax is based on an assessment system that dates back to 1950. This system has produced numerous inequities whereby newer homes tend to be assessed at higher values than older homes. A new system based on the market value of the house has been proposed. Opponents of the plan argue that residents of some boroughs would have to pay considerably more on the average, while residents of other boroughs would pay less. As part of a study examining this issue, several homes in each borough were assessed under both plans. The percentage increase (a decrease is represented by a negative increase) in each case was recorded.

a. Can we conclude that there are differences in the effect the new assessment system would have on the five boroughs?

b. If differences exist, which boroughs differ? Use Tukey's multiple comparison method.

c. What are the required conditions for your conclusions to be valid?

d. Are the required conditions satisfied?

14.124 <u>Xr14-124</u> The editor of the student newspaper was in the process of making some major changes in the newspaper's layout including changing the typeface of the print used. To help make a decision, an experiment in which 20 individuals were asked to read four newspaper pages, with each page printed in a different typeface was set up. If the reading speed differed, then the typeface that was read fastest would be used. However, if there was not enough evidence to allow the editor to conclude that such differences existed, the current typeface would be continued. The times (in seconds) to completely read one page were recorded. What should the editor do?

14.125 <u>Xr14-125</u> In marketing children's products, it is extremely important to produce television commercials that hold the attention of the children who view them. A psychologist hired by a marketing research firm wants to determine whether differences in attention span exist between children watching advertisements for different types of products. One hundred fifty children under 10 years of age were recruited for an experiment. One-third watched a 60-second commercial for a new computer game, one-third watched a commercial for a breakfast cereal, and one-third watched a commercial for children's clothes. Their attention spans (in seconds) were measured and recorded. Do these data provide enough evidence to conclude that there are differences in attention span between the three products advertised?

14.126 Xr14-126 On reconsidering the experiment in Exercise 14.125, the psychologist decides that the age of the child may influence the attention span. Consequently, the experiment is redone in the following way. Three 10-year-olds, three 9-year-olds, three 8-year-olds, three 7-year-olds, three 6-year-olds, three 5-year-olds, and three 4-year-olds are randomly assigned to watch one of the commercials, and their attention spans are measured. Do the results indicate that there are differences in the abilities of the products advertised to hold children's attention?

14.127 Xr14-127 It is important for salespeople to be knowledgeable about how people shop for certain products. Suppose that a new car salesperson believes that the age and gender of car shoppers affect the way they make an offer on a car. The initial offers made by a group of men and women shoppers on a $35,000 Ford Taurus as well as the gender and age category of the shopper were recorded. The amount of money below the asking price that each person offered initially for the car was recorded using the following format: Column B contains the data for the under 30 group; the first 25 rows store the results for female shoppers and the last 25 rows are the male shoppers. Columns C and D store the data for the 30–45 age category and over 45 category, respectively. What can we conclude from these data?

14.128 Xr14-128 Many of you reading this page probably learned how to read using the whole-language method. This strategy maintains that the natural and effective way is to be exposed to whole words in context. Students learn how to read by recognizing words they have seen before. In the past generation this has been the dominant teaching strategy throughout North America. It replaced phonics, wherein children were taught to sound out the letters to form words. The whole language method was instituted with little or no research and has been severely criticized in the past. A recent study may have resolved the question of which method should be employed. An educational psychologist at the University of Houston described the experiment at the annual meeting of the American Association for the Advancement of Science. The subjects were 375 low-achieving, poor, first-grade students in Houston schools. The students were divided into three groups. One was educated according to the whole-language philosophy, a second group was taught using a pure phonics strategy, and the third was taught employing a mixed or embedded phonics technique. At the end of the term students were asked to read words on a list of 50 words. The number of words each child could read was recorded.

a. Can we infer that differences exist between the effects of the three teaching strategies?
b. If differences exist, identify which method appears to be best.

14.129 Xr14-129 Are babies who are exposed to music before their birth smarter than those who are not? And, if so, what kind of music is best? Researchers at the University of Wisconsin conducted an experiment with rats. The researchers selected a random sample of pregnant rats and divided the sample into three groups. Mozart works were played to one group, a second group was exposed to white noise (a steady hum with no musical elements), and the third group listened to Philip Glass music (very simple compositions). The researchers then trained the young rats to run a maze in search of food. The amount of time for the rats to complete the maze was measured for all three groups.
a. Can we infer from these data that there are differences between the three groups?
b. If there are differences, determine which group is best.

14.130 Xr14-130 Increasing tuition has resulted in some students being saddled with large debts on graduation. To examine this issue, a random sample of recent graduates was asked to report whether they had student loans, and if so, how much was the debt at graduation. Each person who reported that they owed money was also asked whether their degree was a B.A., B.Sc., B.B.A., or other. Can we conclude that debt levels differ between the four types of degree?

14.131 Xr14-131 Studies indicate that single male investors tend to take the most risk, whereas married female investors tend to be conservative. This raises the question, which does best? The risk-adjusted returns for single and married men, and for single and married women were recorded. Can we infer that differences exist between the four groups of investors?

14.132 Xr14-132 Virtually all restaurants attempt to have three "seatings" on weekend nights. Three seatings means that each table gets three different sets of customers. Obviously, any group that lingers over dessert and coffee may result in the loss of one seating and profit for the restaurant. In an effort to determine which types of groups tend to linger, a random sample of 150 groups was drawn. For each group, the number of members and the length of time that the group stayed were recorded in the following way:

Column A: Length of time for 2 people
Column B: Length of time for 3 people

Column C: Length of time for 4 people
Column D: Length of time for more than 4 people

Do these data allow us to infer that the length of time in the restaurant depends on the size of the party?

14.133 Xr14-133 When the stock market has a large 1-day decline, does it bounce back the next day or does the bad news endure? To answer this question, an economist examined a random sample of daily changes to the Toronto Stock Index (TSE). He recorded the percent change. He classified declines as:

Down by less than 0.5%
Down by 0.5% to 1.5%
Down by 1.5% to 2.5%
Down by more than 2.5%

For each of these days, the percent loss the following day was recorded. Do these data allow us to infer that there are differences in changes to the TSE depending on the loss the previous day? (This exercise is based on a study undertaken by Tim Whitehead, an economist for Left Bank Economics, a consulting firm near Paris, Ontario.)

14.134 Xr14-134 Stock market investors are always seeking the "Holy Grail," a sign that tells them the market has bottomed out or achieved its highest level. There are several indicators. One is the buy signal developed by Gerald Appel, who believed that a bottom has been reached when the difference between the weekly close of the New York Stock Exchange (NYSE) index and the 10-week moving average (see Chapter 20) is −4.0 points or more. Another bottom indicator is based on identifying a certain pattern in the line chart of the stock market index. As an experiment, a financial analyst randomly selected 100 weeks. For each week it was determined whether there was an Appel buy, a chart buy, or no indication. For each type of week the percentage change over the next 4 weeks was recorded. Can we infer that the two buy indicators are not useful?

14.135 Xr14-135 Millions of North Americans spend up to several hours a day commuting to and from work. Other than the wasted time, are there other negative effects associated with fighting traffic? A study by Statistics Canada may shed light on the issue. A random sample of adults was surveyed. Among other questions respondents were asked how much time they slept and how much time was spent commuting. The categories for commuting time are 1 to 30 minutes, 31 to 60 minutes, and over 60 minutes. Is there sufficient evidence to conclude that the amount of sleep differs between commuting categories?

14.136 Xr14-136 A random sample of 500 teenagers were grouped in the following way: ages 13–14, 15–17, and 18–19. Each teenager was asked to record the number of Facebook friends each had. Is there sufficient evidence to infer that there are differences in the number of Facebook friends between the three teenage groups?

14.137 Xr14-137 How have 25- to 34-year-olds with university degrees fared financially since 1984? To answer this question, the Pew Research Center conducted surveys 20 years ago, 10 years ago, and this year recording monthly earnings for graduates with three different types of degrees. The incomes were converted into 2020 dollars.
a. Is there sufficient evidence to infer that incomes differed for 25- to 34-year-olds with professional or doctorate degrees between the three periods?
b. What are the required conditions?
c. Are they satisfied? Explain.

14.138 Xr14-138 Refer to Exercise 14.137. A similar study was conducted for Bachelor's degrees.
a. Can we infer from the data that incomes differed for 25- to 34-year-olds with Bachelor's degrees between the three periods?
b. Are the required conditions satisfied? Explain.

14.139 Xr14-139 Refer to Exercise 14.137. A similar study determined the monthly household income of households headed by 25- to 34-year-olds with only a high school diploma. The incomes were converted to 2020 dollars.
a. Is there sufficient evidence to infer that household incomes differed for 25- to 34-year-olds with high school diplomas between the three periods?
b. Are the required conditions satisfied? Explain.

14.140 Xr14-140 Does the day a house is listed for sale affect how long it takes for the sale to be completed or its selling price? A study conducted by economists attempted to answer the question. A random sample of houses that sold in a major city was studied. The number of days between the listing and the sale was recorded as well as the day of the week the listing started.
a. Is there enough evidence to conclude that differences in the number of days until the sale is made exist between the 7 days?
b. If there are differences, which days differ?

14.141 Xr14-141 Another useful measure of Americans' beliefs about the state of the economy is the age at which they believe they will retire. If nonretired people believe that they will need to work longer to be able to afford their lifestyle after retirement, it likely means that their confidence in the economy is not high. A Gallup survey conducted every 5 years starting in 2000 asked nonretired U.S. adults to predict at what age they would retire.

a. Can we infer that the predicted age of retirement has fluctuated over the years?

b. If differences exist, which years differ?

14.142 Xr14-142 Each year Michigan State University's Collegiate Employment Research Institute tracks starting salaries of graduates. The Institute recorded the starting salaries of the following engineers: chemical, civil, computer, electrical, and mechanical.

a. Is there sufficient evidence to infer that differences exist between the starting salaries?

b. If differences exist, use Tukey's method to determine which means differ.

14.143 Xr14-143 The U.S. Bureau of Labor Statistics conducts regular surveys to determine how Americans are spending their money. The annual expenditures for vehicle insurance of a random sample of American households in 2014, 2016, 2018, and 2020 were recorded. Is there sufficient evidence to infer that the expenditures differed in the four tear period?

14.144 Xr14-144 Refer to Exercise 14.143. Do Americans spend more on health care as they age? To answer the question, economists turned to the Bureau of Labor Statistics to measure how much Americans in the following age groups spend annually on health care.

(1) 55–64 (2) 65–74 (3) 75 and older

Random samples of Americans 55 and older were taken and for respondent the age category and the amount spent on health care last year were recorded.

a. Is there enough evidence to infer that differences exist between the three age groups?

b. If differences exist, which pairs differ?

14.145 Xr14-145 St Catharine's-Niagara, Kitchener-Cambridge-Waterloo, Brantford, Guelph, London, and Windsor are relatively small cities in Southwest Ontario. Because of their size the expectation is that the time it takes to get from home to work would not be large. To examine the issue a statistics practitioner took random samples of workers who commute in each city and determined their commute times. (*Source:* Adapted from Statistics Canada: Commuting to Work)

a. Is there sufficient evidence to conclude that the times differ between the six cities?

b. If differences exist, use Tukey's method to determine which means differ.

14.146 Xr14-146 Automobile insurance companies use statistics to determine their premiums. The premiums are proportional to the risks and costs of accidents. Suppose that an economist conducted a study that looked at miles driven in the previous year, ages of the drivers, and their gender. The age categories are 16–25, 26–45, 46–64, and 65+. Because of the design of the experiment there were 20 observations for each age category–gender combination.

a. Is there enough evidence to conclude that male and female drivers differ in the number of miles they drive?

b. Can we infer that there are differences between the age categories in the number of miles they drive?

14.147 Xr14-147 The National Center for Charitable Statistics estimates that individual giving in the United States in 2014 was $258.51 billion. A study to determine who gave and how much they gave was undertaken. A random sample of individuals who gave to charities was drawn. For each respondent, the study recorded the total adjusted gross income (AGI) category and the charitable giving as a percentage of AGI. The AGI categories are listed next. In this study, only individuals whose AGI was between $45,000 and $100,000 were included.

$45,000 to $49,999

$50,000 to $54,999

$55,000 to $59,999

$60,000 to $74,999

$75,000 to $100,000

a. Is there sufficient evidence to conclude that there are differences between the five AGI categories?

b. If differences exist, use Tukey's method to determine which groups differ.

14.148 Xr14-148 Refer to Exercise 14.147. The AGI categories for another study were

$100,000 to $199,999

$200,000 to $249,999

$250,000 to $499,999

$500,000 to $1,000,000

The proportion of charitable giving to AGI was recorded.

a. Is there sufficient evidence to conclude that there are differences between the four AGI categories?

b. If differences exist, use Tukey's method to determine which groups differ.

Overeating Experiments (See page 478.)

14.149 Xr14-149   Ice Cream Experiment

This experiment consisted of graduate students given either a medium-sized 17-ounce bowls or large-sized 34-ounce bowls. Students were invited to take as much of four different flavors of ice cream as they wanted. The size of the scoop also varied. One held two ounces and the other held three ounces. The students were asked to fill out a survey; while doing so, the amount of ice cream was measured and recorded. Is there sufficient evidence to conclude that either the bowl size or the scoop size or some interaction affected the amount of ice cream?

Source: Adapted from Brian Wansink, Koert van Ittersum, and James E. Painter, "Ice Cream Illusions: Bowl Size, Spoon Size, and Serving Size," *American Journal of Preventive Medicine* (September 2006).

14.150 Xr14-150   Hershey's Kisses Experiment

Deskbound secretaries were employed in this experiment. Clear-lidded candy dished filled with 30 Hershey's Kisses were placed in three different locations. The first location was the secretary's desk, the second was the top-left drawer in the secretary's desk, and the third was on the top of a file cabinet 6 feet from the secretary's desk. After 1 week, the number of Kisses consumed was counted. Do the data allow us to infer that the number of Kisses differed by location?

Source: Adapted from James E. Painter, Brian Wansink, and Julie B. Hieggelke, "How Visibility and Convenience Influence Candy Consumption," *Appetite* 38:3 (June 2002), 237–38.

14.151 Xr14-151   Brownie Experiment

A random sample of 175 people who had lunch at a company cafeteria were offered a brownie. Some were handed the brownie on a fine piece of china, others were given the brownie on a paper plate, and others were given the brownie on a paper napkin. Each person was asked how much they would be willing to pay. Is there sufficient evidence to conclude that the prices differed according to the way the brownies were offered?

The following exercises use data files associated with three exercises seen previously in this book.

14.152 Xr12-132+   In Exercise 12.132 marketing managers for the JC Penney department store chain segmented the market for women's apparel on the basis of personal and family values. The segments are Conservative, Traditional, and Contemporary. Recall that the classification was done on the basis of questionnaires. Suppose that in addition to identifying the segment the questionnaire also asked each woman to report family income (in $1,000s). Do these data allow us to infer that family incomes differ between the three market segments?

14.153 Xr13-23+   Exercise 13.23 addressed the problem of determining whether the distances young (under 25) males and females drive annually differ. Included in the data is also the number of accidents that each person was involved in the past 2 years. Responses are 0, 1, or 2 or more. Do the data allow us to infer that the distances driven differ between the drivers who have had 0, 1, or 2 or more accidents?

14.154 Xr13-193+   The objective in Exercise 13.193 was to determine whether various market segments were more likely to use the QuikLube service. Included with the data is also the age (in months) of the car. Do the data allow us to conclude that there are differences in age between the four market segments?

CASE 14.1   Baseball Umpires: If the Strike Zone Varies, Do the Scores?*

Baseball fans who watch games on television can usually see something called the pitch tracker. It allows viewers to see whether the umpire made the correct call. According to rule 2.00 of the Major League Baseball rule book, a strike zone is defined as "that area over home plate the upper limit of which is a horizontal line at the midpoint between the top of the shoulders and the top of the uniform pants, and the lower level is a line at the hollow beneath the kneecap"

and is determined by "the batter's stance as the batter is prepared to swing at a pitched ball."

For many fans, it appears that some umpires have bigger strike zones than others. That is, they call pitches strikes when the pitch was actually not in the strike zone. Umpires with large strike zones are likely to see less runs scored since the batter is at a disadvantage. We'll call this the Unequal Strike Zone Theory, which states that some umpires routinely

enlarge the strike zone resulting in lower scores. Fortunately, this theory is testable. For every game in the 2015 season, the home plate umpire, the visiting team scores, the home team scores, and the total number of runs were recorded. Test the Unequal Strike Zone Theory. Conduct an analysis that determines whether there is sufficient evidence to infer that the total number of runs per game differs between the 91 home plate umpires?

*The author wishes to thank Mr. Stacey Albom for collecting all the data in this case.

CASE 14.2   Comparing Three Methods of Treating Childhood Ear Infections*

Acute otitis media, an infection of the middle ear, is a common childhood illness. There are various ways to treat the problem. To help determine the best way, researchers conducted an experiment. One hundred and eighty children between 10 months and 2 years with recurrent acute otitis media were divided into three equal groups. Group 1 was treated by surgically removing the adenoids (adenoidectomy), the second was treated with the drug Sulfafurazole, and the third with a placebo.

Each child was tracked for 2 years, during which time all symptoms and episodes of acute otitis media were recorded. The data were recorded in the following way:

Column A: ID number
Column B: Group number
Column C: Number of episodes of the illness
Column D: Number of visits to a physician because of any infection
Column E: Number of prescriptions
Column F: Number of days with symptoms of respiratory infection

Photographee.eu/Shutterstock.com

a. Are there differences between the three groups with respect to the number of episodes, number of physician visits, number of prescriptions, and number of days with symptoms of respiratory infection?

b. Assume that you are working for the company that makes the drug Sulfafurazole. Write a report to the company's executives discussing your results.

*This case is adapted from the *British Medical Journal*, February 2004.

APPENDIX 14.A / XLSTAT Output and Instructions

Excel and XLSTAT require different formats for the techniques introduced in this chapter. The data must be unstacked for Excel. For XLSTAT the data must be stacked. See page 470 for the definition of stacked and unstacked data. For the datasets in Sections 14-1 to 14-6 we offer both formats. The tab in the Excel file displays the format. The chapter exercises have only one format—unstacked. To solve these exercises, XLSTAT users will have to stack the data.

One-Way Analysis of Variance

Example 14.1

	B	C	D	E	F	G
26	Analysis of variance (Investments):					
27						
28	Source	DF	Sum of squares	Mean squares	F	Pr > F
29	Model	2	4551.668	2275.8	3.08	**0.0471**
30	Error	381	281,455	738.7		
31	Corrected	383	286,007			

Instructions

1. Type or import the data into stacked format using two columns. (Open Xm14-01 and click the Stacked tab.)

2. Click **XLSTAT, Modeling data** and **ANOVA**.

3. Specify **Column** under **Data format:** In the **Quantitative** box type the input range (A1:A385). In the **X Exhalatory variables** check the **Qualitative** box and type the input range (B1:B385).

4. Click **Outputs** and select **Analysis of variance**.

Chapter-Opening Example

	B	C	D	E	F	G
26	Analysis of variance (RINCOM):					
27						
28	Source	DF	Sum of squares	Mean squares	F	Pr > F
29	Model	6	30,332,607,575	5,055,434,596	2.732	**0.0121**
30	Error	1318	2,438,673,189,312	1,850,283,148		
31	Corrected	1324	2,469,005,796,887			

1. Type or import the data into stacked format using two columns. (Open GSS2018.)

2. Click **XLSTAT, Modeling data** and **ANOVA**.

3. Specify **Column** under **Data format:** In the **Quantitative** box type the input range (O1:O2349). In the **X Exhalatory variables** check the **Qualitative** box and type the input range (AJ1:AJ2349).

4. Because the GSS2018 dataset contains missing data, we clicked the **Missing data** tab and checked **Remove the observations** and **Check for each Y separately**.

5. Click **Outputs** and select **Analysis of variance**.

Multiple Comparisons

Example 14.2

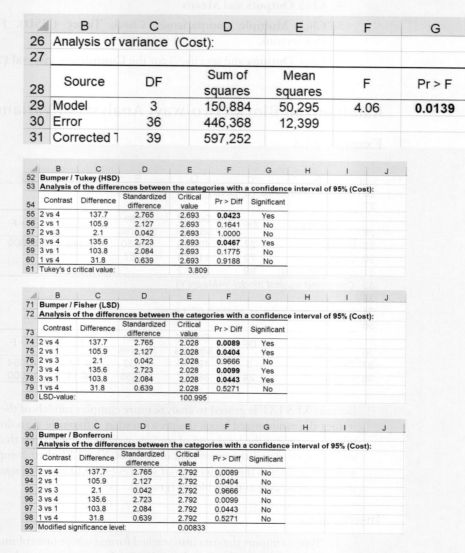

	B	C	D	E	F	G
26	Analysis of variance (Cost):					
27						
28	Source	DF	Sum of squares	Mean squares	F	Pr > F
29	Model	3	150,884	50,295	4.06	**0.0139**
30	Error	36	446,368	12,399		
31	Corrected T	39	597,252			

	B	C	D	E	F	G	H	I	J
52	Bumper / Tukey (HSD)								
53	Analysis of the differences between the categories with a confidence interval of 95% (Cost):								
54	Contrast	Difference	Standardized difference	Critical value	Pr > Diff	Significant			
55	2 vs 4	137.7	2.765	2.693	**0.0423**	Yes			
56	2 vs 1	105.9	2.127	2.693	0.1641	No			
57	2 vs 3	2.1	0.042	2.693	1.0000	No			
58	3 vs 4	135.6	2.723	2.693	**0.0467**	Yes			
59	3 vs 1	103.8	2.084	2.693	0.1775	No			
60	1 vs 4	31.8	0.639	2.693	0.9188	No			
61	Tukey's d critical value:			3.809					

	B	C	D	E	F	G	H	I	J
71	Bumper / Fisher (LSD)								
72	Analysis of the differences between the categories with a confidence interval of 95% (Cost):								
73	Contrast	Difference	Standardized difference	Critical value	Pr > Diff	Significant			
74	2 vs 4	137.7	2.765	2.028	**0.0089**	Yes			
75	2 vs 1	105.9	2.127	2.028	**0.0404**	Yes			
76	2 vs 3	2.1	0.042	2.028	0.9666	No			
77	3 vs 4	135.6	2.723	2.028	**0.0099**	Yes			
78	3 vs 1	103.8	2.084	2.028	**0.0443**	Yes			
79	1 vs 4	31.8	0.639	2.028	0.5271	No			
80	LSD-value:			100.995					

	B	C	D	E	F	G	H	I	J
90	Bumper / Bonferroni								
91	Analysis of the differences between the categories with a confidence interval of 95% (Cost):								
92	Contrast	Difference	Standardized difference	Critical value	Pr > Diff	Significant			
93	2 vs 4	137.7	2.765	2.792	0.0089	No			
94	2 vs 1	105.9	2.127	2.792	0.0404	No			
95	2 vs 3	2.1	0.042	2.792	0.9666	No			
96	3 vs 4	135.6	2.723	2.792	0.0099	No			
97	3 vs 1	103.8	2.084	2.792	0.0443	No			
98	1 vs 4	31.8	0.639	2.792	0.5271	No			
99	Modified significance level:			0.00833					

XLSTAT computes the standardized differences between the pairs. Each difference is standardized by dividing by $\sqrt{MSE\left(\dfrac{1}{n_i} + \dfrac{1}{n_j}\right)}$, which in Example 14.2 is $\sqrt{12,399\left(\dfrac{1}{10} + \dfrac{1}{10}\right)} = 49.80.$

Instructions

1. Type or import the data into stacked format using two columns. (Open Xm14-02 and click the Stacked tab.)

2. Click **XLSTAT, Modeling data** and **ANOVA**.

3. Specify **Column** under **Data format:** In the **Quantitative** box type the input range (A1:A41). In the **X Exhalatory variables** check the **Qualitative** box and type the input range (B1:B41).

4. Click **Outputs** and **Means**.

5. Click **Multiple comparisons**. Check **Tukey (HSD), Fisher (LSD),** and **Bonferroni**.

6. Click **Options** and specify 95 for the **Confidence interval (%)**.

Randomized Block (Two-way) Analysis of Variance

Example 14.3

	B	C	D	E	F	G
26	Analysis of variance (C. Level):					
27						
28	Source	DF	Sum of squares	Mean squares	F	Pr > F
29	Model	27	4044.6	149.80	9.440	0.0000
30	Error	72	1142.6	15.87		
31	Corrected Total	99	5187.2			
32	Computed against model Y=Mean(Y)					
33						
34	Type I Sum of Squares analysis (C. Level):					
35						
36	Source	DF	Sum of squares	Mean squares	F	Pr > F
37	Drug	3	195.95	65.32	4.12	0.0094
38	Group	24	3848.7	160.36	10.11	0.0000

Because XLSTAT is geared to analyze more complex models of the analysis of variance, it does the randomized block design somewhat differently than does Excel. In the first table it computes the total sum of squares as 5187.2 and divides that between the model sum of squares and the error sum of squares. XLSTAT then computes a second table, which now divides the model sum of squares (4044.6) into two sources of variation, the treatments (drugs) and the blocks (groups).

Instructions

1. Type or import the data into stacked format where one column stores the response variable, a second stores the codes for the treatments, and a third lists the blocks. (Open Xm14-03. Click the Stacked tab.)

2. Click **XLSTAT, Modeling data,** and **ANOVA**.

3. In the **Quantitative** box type the input range (A1:A101). In the **X Explanatory variables** and **Qualitative** box type the input range (B1:C101).

4. Click **Outputs** and select **Analysis of variance** and **Type I/II/III SS**. Click **OK**. Check the **Drug** box and the **Group** box.

Two-Factor Analysis of Variance

Example 14.4

	B	C	D	E	F	G
36	Type I Sum of Squares analysis (Jobs):					
37						
38	Source	DF	Sum of squares	Mean squares	F	Pr > F
39	Gender	1	11.25	11.25	1.12	0.2944
40	Education	3	135.85	45.28	4.49	0.0060
41	Gender*Education	3	6.25	2.083	0.21	0.8915

Instructions

1. Type or import the data into stacked format where one column stores the response variable, a second stores the codes for one of the factors, and a third lists the other factor. (Open Xm14-04. Click the Stacked tab.)

2. Click **XLSTAT, Modeling data**, and **ANOVA**.

3. In the **Quantitative** box type the input range (A1:A81). In the **X Explanatory variables** and **Qualitative** box type the input range (B1:C81).

4. Click **Options** and select **Interactions/level** and specify 2.

5. Click **Outputs** and choose **Analysis of variance** and **Type I/II/III SS**. Click **OK**.

6. Under **Factors and Interactions**, check all.

APPENDIX 14.B / STATA OUTPUT AND INSTRUCTIONS

One-Way Analysis of Variance

Excel and Stata require different formats for the techniques introduced in this chapter. The data must be unstacked for Excel and stacked for Stata. See page 470 for the definition of stacked and unstacked data. For the datasets in Sections 14-1 to 14-6, we offer both formats. The tab in the Excel file displays the format. The chapter exercises have only one format-unstacked. To solve these exercises, Stata users will have to stack the data.

Example 14.1

```
                    Analysis of Variance
   Source           SS         df      MS            F      Prob > F

Between groups    4551.66836     2   2275.83418     3.08    0.0471
Within groups     281455.128   381    738.72737

   Total          286006.796   383    746.754037
```

The test statistic is F = 3.08, p-value = .0471.

Instructions

1. Import or type the data into two columns. (Click File/Import /Excel spreadsheet (*xls,*xlsx)/Chapter14/Xm14-01.) In the **Worksheets** box select Xm14-01 Stacked A1:B385.

2. Click **Statistics, Linear models and related, ANOVA/MANOVA**, and **one-way ANOVA**.

3. Select **Investments** in the **Responses variable:** box and **Age Category** in the **Factor variable:** box.

Chapter-Opening Example

```
                    Analysis of Variance
   Source           SS         df      MS            F      Prob > F

Between groups    3.0333e+10     6   5.0554e+09     2.73    0.0121
Within groups     2.4387e+12   1318   1.8503e+09

   Total          2.4690e+12   1324   1.8648e+09
```

Instructions

1. Import or type the data into two columns. (Click File/Import /Excel spreadsheet (*xls,*xlsx)/GSS Files/GSS2018.)

2. Click **Statistics, Linear models and related, ANOVA/MANOVA**, and **one-way ANOVA**.

3. Select **RINCOME** in the **Responses variable:** box and **POLVIEWS** in the **Factor variable:** box.

It was not necessary to remove the rows containing blanks.

Example 14.2

```
                    Analysis of Variance
    Source          SS         df      MS            F      Prob > F

Between groups    150883.875    3    50294.625      4.06    0.0139
Within groups     446368.1     36    12399.1139

    Total         597251.975   39    15314.1532
```

Bartlett's test for equal variances: chi2(3) =   1.2996 Prob>chi2 = 0.729

```
              Comparison of Cost by Bumper
                       (Bonferroni)
Row Mean-
Col Mean          1          2          3

    2          105.9
               0.242

    3          103.8       -2.1
               0.266       1.000

    4          -31.8     -137.7     -135.6
               1.000      0.053      0.059
```

The value of the pairwise differences and p-values are shown. There is no p-value less than .05.

Instructions

Stata does not conduct Tukey's multiple comparison method.

Import Xm14-02/Stacked data and proceed through the 3 steps above. Click **Bonferroni** in the **Multiple-comparisons tests** box.

Randomized Block (Two-Way) Analysis of Variance

Example 14.3

```
         Number of obs =      100    R-squared       = 0.7797
         Root MSE      =  3.98357    Adj R-squared   = 0.6971

Source   Partial SS    df       MS          F      Prob>F

Model    4044.6113     27    149.80042     9.44    0.0000

Drug      195.9547      3     65.318233    4.12    0.0094
Group    3848.6566     24    160.36069    10.11    0.0000

Residual 1142.5578     72     15.868858

Total    5187.1691     99     52.395647
```

The test statistic to determine whether the cholesterol level differs between the four drugs is $F = 4.12$, p-value = .0094.

The test statistic to determine whether there are differences between the blocks is $F = 10.11$, p-value = 0.

Instructions

1. Import or type the data into three columns of stacked data. (Click File/Import/ Excel spreadsheet (*xls,*xlsx)/Chapter14/Xm14-03 Stacked.)

2. Click **Statistics, Linear models and related, ANOVA/MANOVA,** and **Analysis of variance and covariance.**

3. Select **Cholesterol** in the **Dependent variable:** box. In the **model** box type **Drug Group.**

Two-Factor Analysis of Variance

Example 14.4

```
              Number of obs =        80    R-squared     =  0.1744
              Root MSE      =   3.17586    Adj R-squared =  0.0941

      Source | Partial SS      df        MS        F     Prob>F

       Model | 153.35           7   21.907143    2.17    0.0467

      Gender | 11.25            1      11.25     1.12    0.2944
   Education | 135.85           3   45.283333    4.49    0.0060
Gender#Education | 6.25         3   2.0833333    0.21    0.8915

    Residual | 726.2           72   10.086111

       Total | 879.55          79   11.133544
```

The test statistics and p-values are

Gender: F = 1.12, p-value = .2944

Education: F = 4.49, p-value = .0060

Interaction: F = .21, p-value = .8915

Instructions

1. Import or type the data into three columns. (Click File/Import/Excel spreadsheet (*xls,*xlsx)/Chapter14/Xm14-04 Stacked.)

2. Follow the instructions for Example 14.3.

3. Select **Jobs** in the **Dependent variable:** box. In the **model** box type **Gender Education Gender#Education** (which represents the interaction term).

APPENDIX 14.C / REVIEW OF CHAPTERS 12 TO 14

The number of techniques introduced in Chapters 12 to 14 is up to 20. As we did in Appendix 13.C, we provide a table of the techniques, a flowchart to help you identify the correct technique, and 34 exercises to give you practice in how to choose the appropriate method. The table and the flowchart have been amended to include the three analysis of variance techniques introduced in this chapter and the three multiple comparison methods.

TABLE **A14.1** **Summary of Statistical Techniques in Chapters 12 to 14**

t-test of μ

Estimator of μ (including estimator of $N\mu$)

χ^2 test of σ^2

Estimator of σ^2

z-test of p

Estimator of p (including estimator of Np)

Equal-variances t-test of $\mu_1 - \mu_2$

Equal-variances estimator of $\mu_1 - \mu_2$

Unequal-variances t-test of $\mu_1 - \mu_2$

Unequal-variances estimator of $\mu_1 - \mu_2$

t-test of μ_D

Estimator of μ_D

F-test of σ_1^2/σ_2^2

Estimator of σ_1^2/σ_2^2

z-test of $p_1 - p_2$ (Case 1)

z-test of $p_1 - p_2$ (Case 2)

Estimator of $p_1 - p_2$

One-way analysis of variance (including multiple comparisons)

Two-way (randomized blocks) analysis of variance

Two-factor analysis of variance

FIGURE **A14.1** **Summary of Statistical Techniques in Chapters 12 to 14**

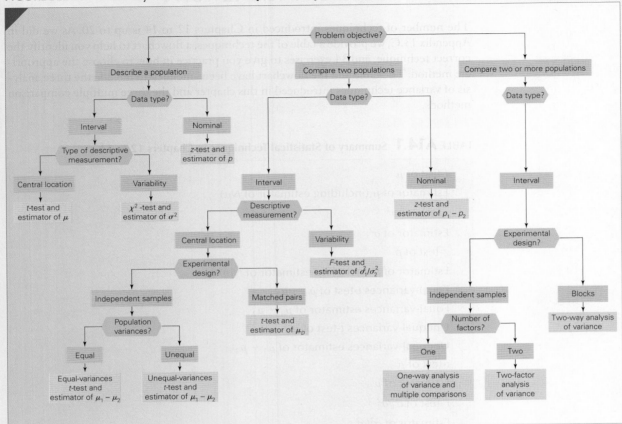

EXERCISES

Note that as we did in Appendix 13.C, we do not specify a significance level in exercises requiring a test of hypothesis. We leave this decision to you. After analyzing the issues raised in the exercise, use your own judgment to determine whether the p-value is small enough to reject the null hypothesis.

A14.1 XrA14-01 Sales of a product may depend on its placement in a store. Candy manufacturers frequently offer discounts to retailers who display their products more prominently than competing brands. To examine this phenomenon more carefully, a candy manufacturer (with the assistance of a national chain of restaurants) planned the following experiment. In 20 restaurants, the manufacturer's brand was displayed behind the cashier's counter with all the other brands (this was called position 1). In another 20 restaurants, the brand was placed separately but close to the other brands (position 2).

In a third group of 20 restaurants, the candy was placed in a special display next to the cash register (position 3). The number of packages sold during 1 week at each restaurant was recorded. Is there sufficient evidence to infer that sales of candy differ according to placement?

A14.2 XrA14-02 Advertising is critical in the residential real estate industry. Agents are always seeking ways to increase sales through improved advertising methods. A particular agent believes that by describing a house without listing the price will increase the number of inquiries. To support this belief, an experiment in which 100 houses for sale were advertised in two ways—with and without the asking price—was conducted. The number of inquiries for each house was recorded as well as whether the customer saw the ad with or without

middle-class households have higher net worth than female heads of middle-class households.

A14.32 Because credit card companies charge very high interest for carrying debts, most households attempt to pay off their credit card balances quickly. Assuming that there are 25 million middle-class households, estimate the number of people who carry a balance on credit cards (NOCCBAL: 1).

A14.33 Are male heads (HHSEX: 1 = Male, 2 = Female) of households more likely to own their homes than female heads of households (HOUSECL: 1 = Own)? Conduct a test to answer the question.

A14.34 How does the education of the head of the household (EDCL: 1 = No high school diploma, 2 = High school diploma, 3 = Some college, 4 = College degree) in middle-class homes affect assets (ASSET)? Is there enough evidence to conclude that there are differences in assets between the four categories of education?

age fotostock/SuperStock

CHI-SQUARED TESTS

CHAPTER OUTLINE

General Social Survey

Do Male and Female Americans Differ in Their Political Viewpoints?

DATA
GSS2018

Do men and women differ in their political viewpoints? One of the questions asked in the General Social Survey was, "I'm going to show you a seven-point scale on which the political views that people might hold are arranged from extremely liberal to extremely conservative. Where would you place yourself on this scale?"

1. Extremely liberal
2. Liberal
3. Slightly Liberal

iStock Photo/EyeJoy

See solution on
page 643.

4. Moderate
5. Slightly conservative
6. Conservative
7. Extremely conservative

Respondents are also identified by sex (SEX): 1 = Male and 2 = Female. Is there sufficient evidence to infer that American men and women differ in their political points of view (POLVIEWS)?

INTRODUCTION

We have seen a variety of statistical techniques that are used when the data are nominal. In Chapter 2, we introduced bar and pie charts, both graphical techniques to describe a set of nominal data. Later in Chapter 2, we showed how to describe the relationship between two sets of nominal data by producing a frequency table and a bar chart. However, these techniques simply describe the data, which may represent a sample or a population. In this chapter, we deal with similar problems, but the goal is to use statistical techniques to make inferences about populations from sample data.

This chapter develops two statistical techniques that involve nominal data. The first is a *goodness-of-fit test* applied to data produced by a *multinomial experiment*, a generalization of a binomial experiment. The second uses data arranged in a table (called a *contingency table*) to determine whether two classifications of a population of nominal data are statistically independent; this test can also be interpreted as a comparison of two or more populations. The sampling distribution of the test statistics in both tests is the chi-squared distribution introduced in Chapter 8.

15-1 / CHI-SQUARED GOODNESS-OF-FIT TEST

This section presents another test designed to describe a population of nominal data. The first such test was introduced in Section 12-3, where we discussed the statistical procedure employed to test hypotheses about a population proportion. In that case, the nominal variable could assume one of only two possible values: success or failure. Our tests dealt with hypotheses about the proportion of successes in the entire population. Recall that the experiment that produces the data is called a *binomial experiment*. In this section, we introduce the **multinomial experiment**, which is an extension of the binomial experiment, wherein there are two or more possible outcomes per trial.

Multinomial Experiment

A multinomial experiment is one that possesses the following properties.
1. The experiment consists of a fixed number n of trials.
2. The outcome of each trial can be classified into one of k categories, called *cells*.
3. The probability p_i that the outcome will fall into cell i remains constant for each trial. Moreover, $p_1 + p_2 + \cdots + p_k = 1$.
4. Each trial of the experiment is independent of the other trials.

When $k = 2$, the multinomial experiment is identical to the binomial experiment. Just as we count the number of successes (recall that we label the number of successes x) and failures in a binomial experiment, we count the number of outcomes falling into each of the k cells in a multinomial experiment. In this way, we obtain a set of observed frequencies $f_1, f_2, \ldots, f_k$, where f_i is the observed frequency of outcomes falling into cell i, for $i = 1, 2, \ldots, k$. Because the experiment consists of n trials and an outcome must fall into some cell,

$$f_1 + f_2 + \cdots + f_k = n$$

Just as we used the number of successes x (by calculating the sample proportion $\hat{p}$, which is equal to x/n) to draw inferences about p, so we use the observed frequencies to draw inferences about the cell probabilities. We'll proceed in what by now has become a standard procedure. We will set up the hypotheses and develop the test statistic and its sampling distribution. We'll demonstrate the process with the following example.

EXAMPLE 15.1

Testing Market Shares

Company A has recently conducted aggressive advertising campaigns to maintain and possibly increase its share of the market (currently 45%) for fabric softener. Its main competitor, company B, has 40% of the market, and a number of other competitors account for the remaining 15%. To determine whether the market shares changed after the advertising campaign, the marketing manager for company A solicited the preferences of a random sample of 200 customers of fabric softener. Of the 200 customers, 102 indicated a preference for company A's product, 82 preferred company B's fabric softener, and the remaining 16 preferred the products of one of the competitors. Can the analyst infer at the 5% significance level that customer preferences have changed from their levels before the advertising campaigns were launched?

SOLUTION:

The population in question is composed of the brand preferences of the fabric softener customers. The data are nominal because each respondent will choose one of three possible answers: product A, product B, or other. If there were only two categories, or if we were interested only in the proportion of one company's customers (which we would label as successes and label the others as failures), we would identify the technique as the z-test of p. However, in this problem we're interested in the proportions of all three categories. We recognize this experiment as a multinomial experiment, and we identify the technique as the **chi-squared goodness-of-fit test**.

Because we want to know whether the market shares have changed, we specify those precampaign market shares in the null hypothesis.

H_0: $p_1 = .45, p_2 = .40, p_3 = .15$

The alternative hypothesis attempts to answer our question, Have the proportions changed? Thus,

H_1:   At least one p_i is not equal to its specified value

15-1a Test Statistic

If the null hypothesis is true, we would expect the number of customers selecting brand A, brand B, and other to be 200 times the proportions specified under the null hypothesis; that is,

$$e_1 = 200(.45) = 90$$

$$e_2 = 200(.40) = 80$$

$$e_3 = 200(.15) = 30$$

In general, the **expected frequency** for each cell is given by

$$e_i = np_i$$

This expression is derived from the formula for the expected value of a binomial random variable, introduced in Section 7-4.

Figure 15.1 is a bar chart (created by Excel) showing the comparison of actual and expected frequencies.

FIGURE **15.1** Bar Chart for Example 15.1

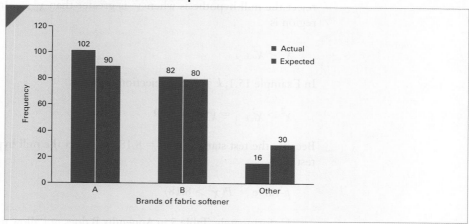

If the expected frequencies e_i and the **observed frequencies** f_i are quite different, we would conclude that the null hypothesis is false, and we would reject it. However, if the expected and observed frequencies are similar, we would not reject the null hypothesis. The test statistic defined in the box measures the similarity of the expected and observed frequencies.

Chi-Squared Goodness-of-Fit Test Statistic

$$\chi^2 = \sum_{i=1}^{k} \frac{(f_i - e_i)^2}{e_i}$$

The sampling distribution of the test statistic is approximately chi-squared distributed with $v = k - 1$ degrees of freedom, provided that the sample size is large. We will discuss this required condition later. (The chi-squared distribution was introduced in Section 8-4.)

The following table demonstrates the calculation of the test statistic. Thus, the value $x^2 = 8.18$. As usual, we judge the size of this test statistic by specifying the rejection region or by determining the p-value.

Company	Observed Frequency f_i	Expected Frequency e_i	$(f_i - e_i)$	$\dfrac{(f_i - e_i)^2}{e_i}$
A	102	90	12	1.60
B	82	80	2	0.05
Other	16	30	−14	6.53
Total	200	200		$x^2 = 8.18$

When the null hypothesis is true, the observed and expected frequencies should be similar, in which case the test statistic will be small. Thus, a small test statistic supports the null hypothesis. If the null hypothesis is untrue, some of the observed and expected frequencies will differ and the test statistic will be large. Consequently, we want to reject the null hypothesis when x^2 is greater than $x^2_{\alpha,k-1}$. In other words, the rejection region is

$$x^2 > x^2_{\alpha,k-1}$$

In Example 15.1, $k = 3$; the rejection region is

$$x^2 > x^2_{\alpha,k-1} = x^2_{.05,2} = 5.99$$

Because the test statistic is $x^2 = 8.18$, we reject the null hypothesis. The p-value of the test is

$$p\text{-value} = P(x^2 > 8.18)$$

Unfortunately, Table 5 in Appendix B does not allow us to perform this calculation (except for approximation by interpolation). The p-value must be produced by computer. Figure 15.2 depicts the sampling distribution, rejection region, and p-value.

FIGURE **15.2** **Sampling Distribution for Example 15.1**

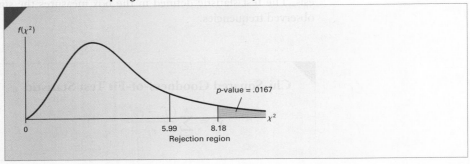

EXCEL Function

	A	B
1	Observed	Expected
2	102	90
3	82	80
4	16	30
5		0.0167

INSTRUCTIONS

1. Type the observed values into one column and the expected values into another column. (If you wish, you can type the cell probabilities specified in the null hypothesis and let Excel convert these into expected values by multiplying by the sample size.)

2. Activate an empty cell and type

$$= \text{CHITEST([Actual\_range], [Expected\_range])}$$

where the ranges are the cells containing the actual observations and the expected values. Don't include the cells containing the names of the columns. That is, type
= CHITEST(A2:A4, B2:B4),

If we have the raw data representing the nominal responses we must first determine the frequency of each category (the observed values) using the **COUNTIF** function described on page 22.

INTERPRET

There is sufficient evidence at the 5% significance level to infer that the proportions have changed since the advertising campaigns were implemented. If the sampling was conducted properly, we can be quite confident in our conclusion. This technique has only one required condition, which is satisfied. (See the next subsection.)

15-1b Required Condition

The actual sampling distribution of the test statistic defined previously is discrete, but it can be approximated by the chi-squared distribution provided that the sample size is large. This requirement is similar to the one we imposed when we used the normal approximation to the binomial in the sampling distribution of a proportion. In that approximation we needed np and $n(1 - p)$ to be 5 or more. A similar rule is imposed for the chi-squared test statistic. It is called the *rule of five*, which states that the sample size must be large enough so that the expected value for each cell must be 5 or more. Where necessary, cells should be combined to satisfy this condition. We discuss this required condition and provide more details on its application in the online appendix Rule of Five.

Factors That Identify the Chi-Squared Goodness-of-Fit Test

1. **Problem objective**: Describe a single population.
2. **Data type**: Nominal
3. **Number of categories**: 2 or more

EXERCISES

Developing an Understanding of Statistical Concepts

Exercises 15.1–15.6 are "what-if" analyses designed to determine what happens to the test statistic of the goodness-of-fit test when elements of the statistical inference change. These problems can be solved manually or using Excel's **CHITEST**.

15.1 Consider a multinomial experiment involving $n = 300$ trials and $k = 5$ cells. The observed frequencies resulting from the experiment are shown in the accompanying table, and the null hypothesis to be tested is as follows:

$$H_0: \quad p_1 = .1, p_2 = .2, p_3 = .3, p_4 = .2, p_5 = .2$$

Test the hypothesis at the 1% significance level.

Cell	1	2	3	4	5
Frequency	24	64	84	72	56

15.2 Repeat Exercise 15.1 with the following frequencies:

Cell	1	2	3	4	5
Frequency	12	32	42	36	28

15.3 Repeat Exercise 15.1 with the following frequencies:

Cell	1	2	3	4	5
Frequency	6	16	21	18	14

15.4 Review the results of Exercises 15.1–15.3. What is the effect of decreasing the sample size?

15.5 Consider a multinomial experiment involving $n = 150$ trials and $k = 4$ cells. The observed frequencies resulting from the experiment are shown in the accompanying table, and the null hypothesis to be tested is as follows:

$$H_0: \quad p_1 = .3, p_2 = .3, p_3 = .2, p_4 = .2$$

Cell	1	2	3	4
Frequency	38	50	38	24

Test the hypotheses, using $\alpha = .05$.

15.6 For Exercise 15.5, retest the hypotheses, assuming that the experiment involved twice as many trials ($n = 300$) and that the observed frequencies were twice as high as before, as shown here.

Cell	1	2	3	4
Frequency	76	100	76	48

Exercises 15.7–15.20 require the use of a computer and software. The answers may be calculated manually. See Appendix A for the sample statistics. **Use a 5% significance level.**

15.7 Xr15-07 The results of a multinomial experiment with $k = 5$ were recorded. Each outcome is identified by the numbers 1 to 5. Test to determine whether there is enough evidence to infer that the proportions of outcomes differ.

15.8 Xr15-08 A multinomial experiment was conducted with $k = 4$. Each outcome is stored as an integer from 1 to 4 and the results of a survey were recorded. Test the following hypotheses.

$$H_0: \quad p_1 = .15, p_2 = .40, p_3 = .35, p_4 = .10$$

$H_1:$ At least one p_i is not equal to its specified value

15.9 Xr15-09 To determine whether a single die is balanced, or fair, the die was rolled 600 times. Is there sufficient evidence to allow you to conclude that the die is not fair?

Applications

15.10 Xr15-10 Grades assigned by an economics instructor have historically followed a symmetrical distribution: 5% A's, 25% B's, 40% C's, 25% D's, and 5% F's. This year, a sample of 150 grades was drawn and the grades (1 = A, 2 = B, 3 = C, 4 = D, and 5 = F) were recorded. Is there sufficient evidence to infer that this year's grades are distributed differently from grades in the past?

15.11 Xr15-11 Pat Statsdud is about to write a multiple-choice exam but as usual knows absolutely nothing. Pat plans to guess one of the five choices. Pat has been given one of the professor's previous exams with the correct answers marked. The correct choices were recorded where 1 = (a), 2 = (b), 3 = (c), 4 = (d), and 5 = (e). Help Pat determine whether this professor does not randomly distribute the correct answer over the five choices? If this is true, how does it affect Pat's strategy?

15.12 Xr15-12 Financial managers are interested in the speed with which customers who make purchases on credit pay their bills. In addition to calculating the average number of days that unpaid bills (called *accounts receivable*) remain outstanding, they often prepare an aging schedule. An aging schedule classifies outstanding accounts receivable according to the time that has elapsed since billing and records the proportion of accounts receivable belonging to each classification. A large firm has determined its aging schedule for the past 5 years. These results are shown in the accompanying table. During the past few months, however, the economy has taken a downturn. The company would like to know whether the recession has affected the aging schedule. A random sample of 250 accounts receivable was drawn and each account was classified as follows:

1 = 0–14 days outstanding

2 = 15–29 days outstanding

3 = 30–59 days outstanding

4 = 60 or more days outstanding

Number of Days Outstanding	Proportion of Accounts Receivable Past 5 Years
0–14	.72
15–29	.15
30–59	.10
60 and more	.03

Determine whether the aging schedule has changed.

15.13 Xr15-13 License records in a county reveal that 15% of cars are subcompacts (1), 25% are compacts (2), 40% are midsize (3), and the rest are an assortment of other styles and models (4). A random sample of accidents involving cars licensed in the county was drawn. The type of car was recorded using the codes in parentheses. Can we infer that certain sizes of cars are involved in a higher than expected percentage of accidents?

15.14 Xr15-14 In an election held last year that was contested by three parties. Party A captured 31% of the vote, party B garnered 51%, and party C received the remaining votes. A survey of 1,200 voters asked each to identify the party that they would vote for in the next election. These results were recorded where 1 = party A, 2 = party B, and 3 = party C. Can we infer that voter support has changed since the election?

15.15 Xr15-15 Pitch trackers allow baseball fans watching televised games to see whether an umpire made the correct call. After tracking all pitches over an entire season the following probabilities were recorded.

1. Pitch was in the strike zone and the umpire called a ball — 5.28%
2. Pitch was in the strike zone and the umpire called it a strike — 34.72%
3. Pitch was outside the strike zone and the umpire called it a ball — 51.00%
4. Pitch was outside the strike zone and the umpire called it a strike — 9.00%

A new umpire has just started and the pitch tracker has recorded each outcome using these codes. Is there evidence to infer that this umpire differs in his calls?

Source: Baseballsavant.com.

15.16 Xr15-16 Refer to Exercise 15.15. After an entire season of pitches the following proportions for all pitches were observed.

1. Pitch in the strike zone — 40.0%
2. Pitch misses strike zone upper left — 14.4%
3. Pitch misses the strike zone lower left — 17.8%
4. Pitch misses strike zone upper right — 9.5%
5. Pitch misses strike zone lower right — 18.3%

A rookie pitcher starts his first game and the pitch outcome was recorded using the codes. Is there enough evidence to conclude that the rookie differs from all other pitchers?

Source: Baseballsavant.com

15.17 Xr15-17 An aging pitcher has recorded the following pitch distribution over his long career from 2005 to 2018.

1. Fast ball — 52%
2. Curve ball — 19%
3. Slider — 15%
4. Changeup — 14%

However, undergoing a surgery to repair a tendon in 2019 the pitches for the first 5 games in 2020 were recorded using the codes. Is there evidence to conclude that his pitching distribution has changed?

15.18 Xr15-18 From January 1 to December 31, 2011, there were 5,086 bank robberies in the United States. The percentage of that total for each day of the week is listed next. The number of robberies per day for the first two months of 2016 was recorded. Can we infer that the distribution of bank robberies per day has changed?

Source: FBI.

1. Monday — 17%
2. Tuesday — 18%
3. Wednesday — 17%
4. Thursday — 18%
5. Friday — 21%
6. Saturday and Sunday — 9%

15.19 Xr15-19 Using the data supplied by NOAA National Weather Service, 25,729 tornadoes struck the United States between 2000 and 2018. The percentage for each month is listed here.

January	2.7%
February	3.4%
March	6.7%

April	15.6%		October	5.1%
May	22.1%		November	5.0%
June	16.1%		December	2.9%
July	8.4%
August	6.2%
September	5.8%

The monthly number of tornadoes for 2019 was recorded. Is there enough statistical evidence to infer that the percentages have changed?

APPLICATIONS in MARKETING

Market Segmentation

Market segmentation was introduced in Section 12-4, where a statistical technique was used to estimate the size of a segment. In Chapters 13 and 14, statistical procedures were applied to determine whether market segments differ in their purchases of products and services. Exercise 15.20 requires you to apply the chi-squared goodness-of-fit test to determine whether the relative sizes of segments have changed.

15.20 Xr12-131+   Refer to Exercise 12.131 where the statistics practitioner estimated the size of market segments based on education among California adults. Suppose that census figures from 10 years ago showed the education levels and the proportions of California adults, as follows:

Level	Proportion
1. Did not complete high school	.23
2. Completed high school only	.40
3. Some college or university	.15
4. College or university graduate	.22

Determine whether there has been a change in these proportions.

GENERAL SOCIAL SURVEY EXERCISES

GSS2018   *The following exercises are based on the 2018 survey.*
Conduct all tests at the 5% significance level.

15.21 Following are the proportions of the races in the United States in 2018. Test to determine whether there is sufficient evidence that the General Social Survey in 2018 overrepresented at least one race.

	RACE Codes	2018 Proportions
Whites	1	76.6%
Blacks	2	13.4%
Other	3	10.0%

15.22 The table below lists the percentages of the categories of marital status in the United States in 2018. Can we infer that the survey overrepresented at least one category of marital status? (Combine the married and separated categories for this exercise.)

	MARITAL Codes	2018 Proportions
Married	1	50.1%
Widowed	2	5.9%
Divorced	3	11.0%
Separated	4	
Never married	5	33.0%

15.23 The table below lists the educational attainment in the United States in 2018. Can we infer that the survey overrepresented at least one education category? (Combine the bachelor's degree and graduate degrees for this exercise.)

	DEGREE Codes	2018 Proportions
Left high school	0	10.8%
High school graduate	1	28.4%
Some college, no degree	2	27.6%
Bachelor's degree	3	21.2%
Graduate degree	4	12.0%

15.24 In the United States in 2018, 63% of families lived in their own home (owned outright or paying mortgage) and 37% rented their dwelling. Is there sufficient evidence to infer that the survey overrepresented one of the categories (DWELOWN: 1 = Own or is buying, 2 = Rent, 3 = Other)? Ignore the Other category for this exercise.

15.25 In the United States in 2018, 14.5% of the population was 65 years of age and older. Is there sufficient evidence to conclude that the survey included too many older adults (AGE)?

15-2 / CHI-SQUARED TEST OF A CONTINGENCY TABLE

In Chapter 2, we developed the **cross-classification table** as a first step in graphing the relationship between two nominal variables (see page 37). Our goal was to determine whether the two variables were related. In this section we extend the technique to statistical inference. We introduce another chi-squared test, this one designed to satisfy two different problem objectives. The **chi-squared test of a contingency table** is used to determine whether there is enough evidence to infer that two nominal variables are related and to infer that differences exist between two or more populations of nominal variables. Completing both objectives entails classifying items according to two different criteria. To see how this is done, consider the following example.

EXAMPLE 15.2

DATA
Xm15-02

Relationship between Undergraduate Degree and MBA Major

The MBA program was experiencing problems scheduling its courses. The demand for the program's optional courses and majors was quite variable from one year to the next. In one year, students seem to want marketing courses; in other years, accounting or finance are the rage. In desperation, the dean of the business school turned to a statistics professor for assistance. The statistics professor believed that the problem may be the variability in the academic background of the students and that the undergraduate degree affects the choice of major. As a start, a random sample of last year's MBA students was taken and recorded the undergraduate degree and the major selected in the graduate program. The undergraduate degrees were BA, BEng, BBA, and several others. There are three possible majors for the MBA students: accounting, finance, and marketing. The results were summarized in a cross-classification table, which is shown here. Can the statistician conclude that the undergraduate degree affects the choice of major?

Undergraduate Degree	MBA Major			Total
	Accounting	Finance	Marketing	
BA	31	13	16	60
BEng	8	16	7	31
BBA	12	10	17	39
Other	10	5	7	22
Total	61	44	47	152

SOLUTION:

One way to solve the problem is to consider that there are two variables: undergraduate degree and MBA major. Both are nominal. The values of the undergraduate degree are BA, BEng, BBA, and other. The values of MBA major are accounting, finance, and marketing. The problem objective is to analyze the relationship between the two variables. Specifically, we want to know whether one variable is related to the other.

Another way of addressing the problem is to determine whether differences exist between BA's, BEng's, BBA's, and others. In other words, we treat the holders of each undergraduate degree as a separate population. Each population has three possible values represented by the MBA major. The problem objective is to compare four populations. (We can also answer the question by treating the MBA majors as populations and the undergraduate degrees as the values of the random variable.)

As you will shortly discover, both objectives lead to the same test. Consequently, we address both objectives at the same time.

The null hypothesis will specify that there is no relationship between the two variables. We state this in the following way:

H_0: The two variables are independent

The alternative hypothesis specifies one variable affects the other, expressed as

H_1: The two variables are dependent

15-2a Graphical Technique

Figure 15.3 depicts the graphical technique introduced in Chapter 2 to show the relationship (if any) between the two nominal variables.

The bar chart displays the data from the sample. It does appear that there is a relationship between the two nominal variables in the sample. However, to draw inferences about the population of MBA students we need to apply an inferential technique.

FIGURE **15.3** Bar Chart for Example 15.2

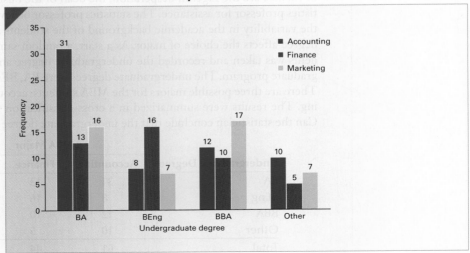

15-2b Test Statistic

The test statistic is the same as the one used to test proportions in the goodness-of-fit test; that is, the test statistic is

$$\chi^2 = \sum_{i=1}^{k} \frac{(f_i - e_i)^2}{e_i}$$

where k is the number of cells in the cross-classification table. If you examine the null hypothesis described in the goodness-of-fit test and the one described above, you will discover a major difference. In the goodness-of-fit test, the null hypothesis lists values for the probabilities p_i. The null hypothesis for the chi-squared test of a contingency table only states that the two variables are independent. However, we need the probabilities to compute the expected values e_i, which in turn are needed to calculate the value of the test statistic. (The entries in the table are the observed values f_i.) The question immediately arises, From where do we get the probabilities? The answer is that they must come from the data after we assume that the null hypothesis is true.

In Chapter 6 we introduced independent events and showed that if two events A and B are independent, the joint probability $P(A \text{ and } B)$ is equal to the product of $P(A)$ and $P(B)$. That is,

$$P(A \text{ and } B) = P(A) \times P(B)$$

The events in this example are the values each of the two nominal variables can assume. Unfortunately, we do not have the probabilities of A and B. However, these probabilities can be estimated from the data. Using relative frequencies, we calculate the estimated probabilities for the MBA major.

$$P(\text{Accounting}) = \frac{61}{152} = .401$$

$$P(\text{Finance}) = \frac{44}{152} = .289$$

$$P(\text{Marketing}) = \frac{47}{152} = .309$$

We calculate the estimated probabilities for the undergraduate degree.

$$P(\text{BA}) = \frac{60}{152} = .395$$

$$P(\text{BEng}) = \frac{31}{152} = .204$$

$$P(\text{BBA}) = \frac{39}{152} = .257$$

$$P(\text{Other}) = \frac{22}{152} = .145$$

Assuming that the null hypothesis is true, we can compute the estimated joint probabilities. To produce the expected values, we multiply the estimated joint probabilities by the sample size, $n = 152$. The results are listed in a **contingency table**, the word *contingency* derived by calculating the expected values contingent on the assumption that the null hypothesis is true (the two variables are independent).

Undergraduate Degree	MBA Major			Total
	Accounting	**Finance**	**Marketing**	
BA	$152 \times \dfrac{60}{152} \times \dfrac{61}{152} = 24.08$	$152 \times \dfrac{60}{152} \times \dfrac{44}{152} = 17.37$	$152 \times \dfrac{60}{152} \times \dfrac{47}{152} = 18.55$	60
BEng	$152 \times \dfrac{31}{152} \times \dfrac{61}{152} = 12.44$	$152 \times \dfrac{31}{152} \times \dfrac{44}{152} = 8.97$	$152 \times \dfrac{31}{152} \times \dfrac{47}{152} = 9.59$	31
BBA	$152 \times \dfrac{39}{152} \times \dfrac{61}{152} = 15.65$	$152 \times \dfrac{39}{152} \times \dfrac{44}{152} = 11.29$	$152 \times \dfrac{39}{152} \times \dfrac{47}{152} = 12.06$	39
Other	$152 \times \dfrac{22}{152} \times \dfrac{61}{152} = 8.83$	$152 \times \dfrac{22}{152} \times \dfrac{44}{152} = 6.37$	$152 \times \dfrac{22}{152} \times \dfrac{47}{152} = 6.80$	22
Total	61	44	47	152

As you can see, the expected value for each cell is computed by multiplying the row total by the column total and dividing by the sample size. For example, the BA and Accounting cell expected value is

$$152 \times \frac{60}{152} \times \frac{61}{152} = \frac{60 \times 61}{152} = 24.08$$

All the other expected values would be determined similarly.

Expected Frequencies for a Contingency Table

The expected frequency of the cell in row i and column j is

$$e_{ij} = \frac{\text{row } i \text{ total} \times \text{column } j \text{ total}}{\text{sample size}}$$

The expected cell frequencies are shown in parentheses in the following table. As in the case of the goodness-of-fit test, the expected cell frequencies should satisfy the rule of five.

	MBA Major		
Undergraduate Degree	**Accounting**	**Finance**	**Marketing**
BA	31 (24.08)	13 (17.37)	16 (18.55)
BEng	8 (12.44)	16 (8.97)	7 (9.59)
BBA	12 (15.65)	10 (11.29)	17 (12.06)
Other	10 (8.83)	5 (6.37)	7 (6.80)

We can now calculate the value of the test statistic:

$$
\begin{aligned}
\chi^2 = \sum_{i=1}^{k} \frac{(f_i - e_i)^2}{e_i} &= \frac{(31 - 24.08)^2}{24.08} + \frac{(13 - 17.37)^2}{17.37} + \frac{(16 - 18.55)^2}{18.55} \\
&+ \frac{(8 - 12.44)^2}{12.44} + \frac{(16 - 8.97)^2}{8.97} + \frac{(7 - 9.59)^2}{9.59} + \frac{(12 - 15.65)^2}{15.65} \\
&+ \frac{(10 - 11.29)^2}{11.29} + \frac{(17 - 12.06)^2}{12.06} + \frac{(10 - 8.83)^2}{8.83} \\
&+ \frac{(5 - 6.37)^2}{6.37} + \frac{(7 - 6.80)^2}{6.80} \\
&= 14.70
\end{aligned}
$$

Notice that we continue to use a single subscript in the formula of the test statistic when we should use two subscripts, one for the rows and one for the columns. We believe that it is clear, that for each cell we must calculate the squared difference between the observed and expected frequencies divided by the expected frequency. We don't believe that the satisfaction of using the mathematically correct notation overcomes the unnecessary complication.

15-2c Rejection Region and p-Value

To determine the rejection region we must know the number of degrees of freedom associated with the chi-squared statistic. The number of degrees of freedom for a contingency table with r rows and c columns is $v = (r - 1)(c - 1)$. For this example, the number of degrees of freedom is $v = (r - 1)(c - 1) = (4 - 1)(3 - 1) = 6$.

If we employ a 5% significance level, the rejection region is

$$\chi^2 > \chi^2_{\alpha,v} = \chi^2_{.05,6} = 12.6$$

Because $\chi^2 = 14.70$, we reject the null hypothesis and conclude that there is evidence of a relationship between undergraduate degree and MBA major.

The p-value of the test statistic is

$$P(\chi^2 > 14.70)$$

Unfortunately, we cannot determine the p-value manually.

Do It Yourself Excel

	A	B	C	D	E	F
1	Degree	MBA Major >	1	2	3	
2	1		31	13	16	60
3	2		8	16	7	31
4	3		12	10	17	39
5	4		10	5	7	22
6			61	44	47	152
7						
8			24.08	17.37	18.55	
9			12.44	8.97	9.59	
10			15.65	11.29	12.06	
11			8.83	6.37	6.80	
12						
13			1.99	1.10	0.35	
14			1.59	5.50	0.70	
15			0.85	0.15	2.02	
16			0.16	0.29	0.01	
17						14.70
18						0.0227

INSTRUCTIONS

For this statistical technique, you will have to create the spreadsheet yourself. We call it **Do It Yourself Excel**. We demonstrate how to create a spreadsheet to solve any exercise by providing instructions for Example 15.2.

1. Use the PivotTable to create the cross-classification table.

2. Calculate the row and column totals and the total of all the cells. For example, to determine the total of column 1 type the following in cell C6.

= SUM(C2:C5)

3. Calculate the expected values. For example to calculate the expected value for the first cell type.

= C$6*$F2/$F$6

Drag down the column and then across the rows to compute all the expected values.

4. Compute the chi-squared statistic. Start in C13 and type.

= ((C2–C8) ^ 2)/C8

Drag down the column and then across the rows.

5. Calculate the chi-squared statistic.

= SUM(C13:E16)

6. Compute the *p*-value using the CHIDIST function in which we specify the value of the chi-squared statistic (14.70) and the degrees of freedom (6).

= CHIDIST(F17,6)

File Xm15-02 contains the raw data using the following codes:

Column 1 (Undergraduate Degree)	Column 2 (MBA Major)
1 = BA	1 = Accounting
2 = BEng	2 = Finance
3 = BBA	3 = Marketing
4 = Other	

INTERPRET

There is enough evidence to infer that the undergraduate degree and MBA major are related. This suggests that the dean can predict the number of optional courses by counting the number of MBA students with each type of undergraduate degree. We can see that BA's favor accounting courses, BEng's prefer finance, BBA's are partial to marketing, and others show no particular preference.

If the null hypothesis is true, undergraduate degree and MBA major are independent of one another. This means that whether an MBA student earned a BA, BEng, BBA, or other degree does not affect the choice of major program in the MBA. Consequently, there is no difference in major choice among the graduates of the undergraduate programs. If the alternative hypothesis is true, undergraduate degree does affect the choice of MBA major. Thus, there are differences between the four undergraduate degree categories.

15-2d Rule of Five

In the previous section, we pointed out that the expected values should be at least 5 to ensure that the chi-squared distribution provides an adequate approximation of the sampling distribution. In a contingency table where one or more cells have expected values of less than 5, we need to combine rows or columns to satisfy the rule of five. This subject is discussed in the online appendix Rule of Five.

15-2e Data Formats

In Example 15.2, the data were stored in two columns, one column containing the values of one nominal variable and the second column storing the values of the second nominal variable. The data can be stored in another way. In Example 15.2, we could have recorded the data in three columns, one column for each MBA major. The columns would contain the codes representing the undergraduate degree. Alternatively, we could have stored the data in four columns, one column for each undergraduate degree. The columns would contain the codes for the MBA majors. In either case, we have to count the number of each value and construct the cross-tabulation table using the counts. We will illustrate this approach with the solution to the chapter-opening example.

General Social Survey

Do Male and Female Americans Differ in Their Political Viewpoints? Solution

IDENTIFY

The problem objective is to compare male and female political viewpoints. The variable is nominal because its values are the seven points of view ranging from Extremely liberal to Extremely conservative. Another interpretation of the problem objective is to analyze the relationship between two nominal variables, SEX and POLVIEWS. In either way, the appropriate technique is the chi-squared test of a contingency table. The hypotheses are:

H_0: The two variables are independent.

H_1: The two variables are dependent.

COMPUTE

Do It Yourself Excel

	A	B	C	D	E	F	G	H	I
1		E. Liberal	Liberal	S. Liberal	Moderate	S. Conservative	Conservative	E. Conservative	Total
2	Male	57	115	126	365	131	172	47	1013
3	Female	65	163	130	490	152	182	52	1234
4	Total	122	278	256	855	283	354	99	2247
5									
6	Expected	55.00	125.33	115.41	385.45	127.58	159.59	44.63	
7	Values	67.00	152.67	140.59	469.55	155.42	194.41	54.37	
8									
9		0.073	0.851	0.972	1.085	0.092	0.965	0.126	
10		0.060	0.699	0.798	0.891	0.075	0.792	0.103	
11									7.58
12									0.2705

INTERPRET

The p-value is .2705. There is not enough evidence to infer that the two variables are dependent. Thus, there is not enough evidence to conclude that men and women differ in their political viewpoints.

Here is a summary of the factors that tell us when to apply the chi-squared test of a contingency table. Note that there are two problem objectives satisfied by this statistical procedure.

Factors That Identify the Chi-Squared Test of a Contingency Table

1. **Problem objectives**: Analyze the relationship between two variables and compare two or more populations.
2. **Data type**: Nominal

EXERCISES

Developing an Understanding of Statistical Concepts

15.26 Conduct a test to determine whether the two classifications L and M are independent, using the data in the accompanying cross-classification table. (Use $\alpha = .05$.)

	M_1	M_2
L_1	28	68
L_2	56	36

15.27 Repeat Exercise 15.26 using the following table:

	M_1	M_2
L_1	14	34
L_2	28	18

15.28 Repeat Exercise 15.26 using the following table:

	M_1	M_2
L_1	7	17
L_2	14	9

15.29 Review the results of Exercises 15.26–15.28. What is the effect of decreasing the sample size?

15.30 Conduct a test to determine whether the two classifications R and C are independent, using the data in the accompanying cross-classification table. (Use $\alpha = .10$.)

	C_1	C_1	C_3
R_1	40	32	48
R_2	30	48	52

Applications

Use a 5% significance level.

15.31 The trustee of a company's pension plan has solicited the opinions of a sample of the company's employees about a proposed revision of the plan.

A breakdown of the responses is shown in the accompanying table. Is there enough evidence to infer that the responses differ between the three groups of employees?

Responses	Blue-Collar Workers	White-Collar Workers	Managers
For	67	32	11
Against	63	18	9

15.32 The operations manager of a company that manufactures shirts wants to determine whether there are differences in the quality of workmanship among the three daily shifts. The manager randomly selects 600 recently made shirts and carefully inspects them. Each shirt is classified as either perfect or flawed, and the shift that produced it is also recorded. The accompanying table summarizes the number of shirts that fell into each cell. Do these data provide sufficient evidence to infer that there are differences in quality between the three shifts?

Shirt Condition	Shift 1	Shift 2	Shift 3
Perfect	240	191	139
Flawed	10	9	11

15.33 One of the issues that came up in a recent national election (and is likely to arise in many future elections) is how to deal with a sluggish economy. Specifically, should governments cut spending, raise taxes, inflate the economy (by printing more money) or do none of the above and let the deficit rise? And as with most other issues, politicians need to know which parts of the electorate support these options. Suppose that a random sample of 1,000 people was asked which option they support and their political affiliations. The possible responses to the question about political affiliation were Democrat,

Republican, and Independent (which included a variety of political persuasions). The responses are summarized in the accompanying table. Do these results allow us to conclude that political affiliation affects support for the economic options?

Economic Options	Political Affiliation		
	Democrat	Republican	Independent
Cut spending	101	282	61
Raise taxes	38	67	25
Inflate the economy	131	88	31
Let deficit increase	61	90	25

15.34 Econetics Research Corporation, a well-known Montreal-based consulting firm, wants to test how it can influence the proportion of questionnaires returned from surveys. In the belief that the inclusion of an inducement to respond may be important, the firm sends out 1,000 questionnaires: Two hundred promise to send respondents a summary of the survey results, 300 indicate that 20 respondents (selected by lottery) will be awarded gifts, and 500 are accompanied by no inducements. Of these, 80 questionnaires promising a summary, 100 questionnaires offering gifts, and 120 questionnaires offering no inducements are returned. Is there sufficient evidence to infer that return rates differ between the three inducements?

Exercises 15.35–15.84 require the use of a computer and software. The answers to Exercises 15.35–15.49 may be calculated manually. See Appendix A for the sample statistics. Use a 5% significance level.

15.35 Xm02-04 (Example 2.4 revisited) A major North American city has four competing newspapers: the *Globe and Mail* (G&M), *Post*, *Sun*, and *Star*. To help design advertising campaigns, the advertising managers of the newspapers need to know which segments of the newspaper market are reading their papers. A survey was conducted to analyze the relationship between newspapers read and occupation. A sample of newspaper readers was asked to report which newspaper they read: *Globe and Mail* (1) *Post* (2), *Star* (3), *Sun* (4), and to indicate whether they were blue-collar workers (1), white-collar workers (2), or professionals (3). Can we infer that occupation and newspaper are related?

15.36 Xr15-36 To determine the actual side effects, pharmaceutical companies often conduct studies that compare the side effects of their drug versus the side effects of a placebo. One such study examined the side effects of a new cold remedy. A random sample of 250 people was given the cold remedy and another 250 were given a placebo that looked like the cold remedy. These responses were recorded as

1 = Headache, 2 = Drowsiness, 3 = Stomach upset, 4 = No side effect

Do these data provide enough evidence to infer that the reported side effects differ between the cold remedy and the placebo?

15.37 Xr15-37 A financial analyst was looking for new markets but was unsure which markets to pursue. To acquire more information, the analyst conducted a survey of Baby Boomers (born between 1946 and 1964), Generation Xers (born between 1965 and 1980), and Millennials (born between 1981 and 1996). Each was asked whether they owned stock: Yes = 1 and No = 0. Can the analyst infer that there are differences in stock ownership between the three generations?

15.38 Xr15-38 During the past decade, many cigarette smokers have attempted to quit. Unfortunately, nicotine is highly addictive. Smokers use a large number of different methods to help them quit. These include nicotine patches, hypnosis, and various forms of therapy. A researcher for the Addiction Research Council wanted to determine why some people quit while others attempted to quit but failed. The researcher surveyed 1,000 people who planned to quit smoking and determined their educational level and whether they continued to smoke 1 year later. Educational level was recorded in the following way:

1 = Did not finish high school
2 = High school graduate
3 = University or college graduate
4 = Completed a postgraduate degree

A continuing smoker was recorded as 1; a quitter was recorded as 2. Can we infer that the amount of education is a factor in determining whether a smoker will quit?

15.39 Xr15-39 Because television audiences of newscasts tend to be older (and because older people suffer from a variety of medical ailments), pharmaceutical companies' advertising often appears on national news on the three networks (ABC, CBS, and NBC). To determine how effective the ads are a survey was undertaken. Adults over 50 were asked about their primary sources of news. The responses are

1. ABC News 2. CBS News 3. NBC News
4. Newspapers 5. Radio 6. None of the above

Each person was also asked whether they suffer from heartburn, and if so, what remedy they take. The answers were recorded as follows:

1. Do not suffer from heartburn
2. Suffer from heartburn but take no remedy
3. Suffer from heartburn and take an over-the-counter remedy (e.g., Tums, Gavoscol)

4. Suffer from heartburn and take a prescription pill (e.g., Nexium)

Is there a relationship between an adult's source of news and the heartburn condition?

15.40 Xr02-64   (Exercise 2.64 revisited) The associate dean of a the WLU business school was looking for ways to improve the quality of the applicants to its MBA program. In particular, the dean wanted to know whether the undergraduate degree of applicants differed among WLU and the three nearby universities with MBA programs. A random sample of 100 applicants of the WLU program and an equal number from each of the other universities was drawn. Their undergraduate degree was recorded as BA (1), B Eng (2), BBA (3), and Other (4) as well as the university (codes 1, 2, 3, and 4). Do these data provide sufficient evidence to infer that undergraduate degree and the university to which each person applied are related?

15.41 Xr12-156+   Exercise 12.156 described a survey that asked a random sample of American households whether they owned a pet. The responses are 1 = Yes, 0 = No. The survey also recorded the household income category as 1 = Under $20,000, 2 = $20,000–$39,999, 3 = $40,000–$59,999, 4 = $60,000–$79,999, 5 = $80,000–$99,999, 6 = $100,000 or more. Do these data allow us to infer that the proportion of households that own a pet differs between the income categories?

15.42 Xr15-42   After a thorough analysis of the market, a publisher of business and economics statistics books has divided the market into three general approaches to teach applied statistics. These are (1) use of a computer and statistical software with no manual calculations, (2) traditional teaching of concepts and solution of problems by hand, and (3) mathematical approach with emphasis on derivations and proofs. The publisher wanted to know whether this market could be segmented on the basis of the educational background of the instructor. As a result, the statistics editor organized a survey that asked 195 professors of business and economics statistics to report their approach to teaching and which one of the following categories represents their highest degree:

1. Business (MBA or Ph.D. in business)
2. Economics
3. Mathematics or engineering
4. Other

Can the editor infer that there are differences in type of degree among the three teaching approaches? If so, how can the editor use this information?

15.43 Xr15-43   The general manager of a golf ball manufacturer wanted to learn more about how golfers choose the brands of balls they use. In particular the company was curious about any differences between male and female players. Random samples of 200 male and 200 female players were drawn. Each was asked which brand of golf ball they preferred. 1 = Calloway, 2 = TaylorMade, 3 = Titleist, 4 = Other. Is there sufficient evidence to conclude that the brands preferred by men and women differ?

15.44 Xr15-44   After analyzing the results of the survey described in Exercise 15.43 the manager organized another survey which took random samples of female private course members and asked them to indicate in which group does her handicap fall and what brand of clubs does she play. (Better golfers have lower handicaps.) The following variables were recorded. Handicap category: 1 = 0–9, 2 = 10–19, 3 = 20–29, 4 = 30+. The brands of clubs are 1 = Calloway, 2 = Cleveland, 3 = TaylorMade, 4 = Titleist, 5 = Other. Is there sufficient evidence to infer that golf ability and golf club choice are related?

15.45 Xr15-45   Census bureaus in many countries keep track of various aspects of the lives of their residents. One such variable is the type of household. Household types are categorized in the following way: Married couple with children (1), Married couple without children (2), Single parent (3), One person (4), Other (5). Random samples of families in the United States, Canada, and the United Kingdom were drawn and the household types recorded. Is the sufficient evidence to infer that there are differences in household types between the three countries?

15.46 Xr15-46   Obesity is a serious health concern because it is often the cause of heart disease, diabetes, and cancer. A statistics practitioner took random samples from Canada, Australia, New Zealand, and the United Kingdom and classified each person as either obese (2) or not (1). Can we conclude from these data that there are differences in obesity rates between the four Commonwealth nations?

15.47 Xr15-47   To measure the extent of cigarette smoking around the world, random samples of adults in Denmark, Finland, Norway, and Sweden were drawn. Respondents were asked whether they smoke (2 = Yes, 1 = No). Can we conclude that there are differences in smoking between the four Scandinavian countries?

15.48 Xr15-48   In 2013, the Supreme Court of the United States ruled on a California law that banned same-sex marriage. An important element of that decision was public opinion. In March, Public Policy Polling conducted a survey of Florida voters and asked each to identify themselves as either: Democrat (1), Republican (2), or Independent (3), and to choose one of the following: Gay couples should be allowed to marry legally (1), Gay couples should be allowed to form civil unions but not marry (2), There should be no legal recognition of a gay couple's relationship (3). Is there sufficient evidence to infer that there are differences in opinion about gay marriage between Democrats, Republicans, and Independents?

15.49 Xr15-49 A critical issue for service companies is how many customers cancel. Some wireless carriers lose an average of 3% of their subscribers each month. Should companies spend more effort getting new customers or trying to win back old customers who left? Researchers have argued that it is easier and cheaper to lure back customers. One telecom firm tested four win-back offers. Their offers and their costs are listed next.

1. Discount offer: $20 off for 6 months. Cost $120
2. Upgrade offer: a $35 movie channel for 3 months. Cost $105
3. Bundled offer: $20 off for 6 months, plus a $35 movie channel free for 3 months. Cost $225
4. Tailored offer: Customers who left over price get the discount; customers who left over service get the upgrade. Cost $120/$105

A random sample of customers who left was drawn and one-quarter received one type of offer. The responses were recorded where 1 = Took the offer and 2 = Did not take the offer. Can we infer that there are differences in success rates between the four win-back offers?

Source: Adapted from Winning Back Lost Customers, *Harvard Business Review,* March 2016.

The following exercises are based on the surveys of Pew Research Center, Abacus Data, and the Gallup Organization.

15.50 Xr12-106+ Exercise 12.106 described a survey of Canadians (18 and older) during the pandemic of 2020 that asked the question, "When you go into a public place like a retail store, do you wear a mask"? The responses are: 1 = Always or almost always, 2 = Half the time or less, 3 = Never. In addition to these data the survey recorded the age categories where 1 = 18–29, 2 = 30–44, 3 = 45–59, 4 = 60+. Is there enough statistical evidence to conclude that there are differences in choices about wearing masks between the age categories?

15.51 Xr12-108+ Exercise 12.108 referred to a survey that asked American adults how closely they watched news about politics where 1 = Very closely and

0 = Not very closely. The survey also recorded the ages that were categorized as 1 = 18–34, 2 = 35–54, 3 = 55+. Do the data provide enough statistical evidence to conclude that the degree to which Americans watch political news differs between the age categories?

15.52 Xr12-116+ Exercise 12.116 described a survey that asked the question, "How would you rate your financial situation today: excellent, good, only fair, or poor?" The responses were recorded as 1 = Excellent/good, 0 = Only fair or poor. The ages of the respondents were recorded as 1 = 18–29, 2 = 30–49, 3 = 50–64, 4 = 65+. Is there sufficient evidence to infer that there is a relationship between financial situation and age?

15.53 Xr15-53 A random sample of 1,002 Americans in a Gallup survey was asked how they tip at sitdown restaurants: 1 = Credit card, 2 = Debit card, 3 = Cash. They were also asked how often they tip: 1 = Always, 2 = Most of the time, 3 = Sometimes. Is there sufficient evidence to infer that there is a relationship between frequency of tipping and the method of tipping?

15.54 Xr15-54 The issue of immigration has become a high priority among voters. In the United States Immigration and Customs Enforcement (ICE) is the federal agency responsible for dealing with illegal immigrants. In July, 2018 Pew Research undertook a survey asking American men (1) and women (2) about their opinion about ICE: 1 = Very unfavorable, 2 = Mostly unfavorable, 3 = Mostly favorable, 4 = Very favorable. Can we infer that men and women differ in their opinions about ICE?

15.55 Xr15-55 Refer to Exercise 15.54. Also categorized was the age group: 1 = 18–29, 2 = 30–49, 3 = 50–64, 4 = 65+. Is there enough evidence to conclude that age and opinion about ICE are related?

15.56 Xr15-56 Pew Research has been conducting surveys of Americans asking a series of questions whose answers are converted into one of five political points of view. They are

1. Consistent conservative
2. Mostly conservative
3. Mixed
4. Mostly liberal
5. Consistent liberal

The survey identified each respondent's generation: 1 = Baby Boom, 2 = Generation X, 3 = Millennial. Can we infer that political point of view and generation are related?

15.57 Xr15-57 Refer to Exercise 15.56. The survey alluded to was a repeat of surveys conducted in 2004 and 2011. The data for Millennials is stored in the file. Is there enough statistical evidence to conclude that the opinion of Millennials has changed over the three periods?

15.58 Xr15-58 In January 2018 Pew Research conducted surveys around the world asking how the media in their country reports the news. One of the question asked respondents whether their media covered political issues fairly: Yes (1) or no (0). The responses were recorded for several countries. The ones we included are the United States, the United Kingdom, and Australia. Do the data provide enough evidence to conclude that there are differences between the three countries with respect to opinions about their media?

15.59 Xr15-59 In 2018, the Trump administration imposed tariffs on Canadian steel and aluminum. In response, the Canadian government imposed tariffs on a variety of American products. In June 2018, Abacus Data conducted a survey and asked Canadians whether they supported the action by Canada: 1 = Strongly support, 2 = Somewhat support, 3 = Oppose. The respondents stated their political party of choice: 1 = Conservative, 2 = Liberal, 3 = NDP. Is there enough statistical evidence to conclude that there are differences in support of Canada's action between the three political party supporters?

15.60 Xr15-60 An election in the province of Ontario was scheduled for June 7, 2018. An Abacus survey was conducted on June 5, which asked for which party the respondent intended to vote for: 1 = Green, 2 = Liberal, 3 = NDP, 4 = Progressive Conservative, 5 = Other. Respondents were also asked whether they had voted in an advanced poll: Yes (1) or no (0). Is there sufficient evidence to infer that there are differences in the political party between those who have already voted and those who haven't voted yet?

15.61 Xr15-61 In April 2018, Abacus Data surveyed Ontario residents and asked, "Generally speaking, do you think things in Ontario are headed in the right direction or are they off on the wrong track (1 = Right direction, 2 = Wrong direction, 3 = Unsure)?" The respondents' generations were also recorded: 1 = Baby Boom, 2 = Generation X, 3 = Millennial. Is there sufficient evidence to infer that age of Ontarians and their opinions about the direction of Ontario are related?

15.62 Xr15-62 The election of Donald Trump as president of the United States elicited joy and sadness in the United States. The overall reaction in Canada to the results of the election was negative. To gauge the mood of Canadians, Abacus Data surveyed Canadians and asked how they would have voted. The responses are 1 = Hillary Clinton, 2 = Donald Trump, 3 = Another candidate. Respondents were classified by age where 1 = 18–29, 2 = 30–44, 3 = 45–59, 4 = 60 and over. Is there sufficient evidence to conclude that the choices by Canadians differs between the different age groups?

15.63 Xr15-63 A Gallup poll asked Americans whether they are worried about their jobs. The responses are: 1 = Worried or 2 = completely satisfied. The surveys were conducted in the four regions of the United States: 1 = Northeast, 2 = Midwest, 3 = South, 4 = West. Do these data provide enough statistical evidence to conclude that there are differences in beliefs about job security between the four regions?

15.64 Xr15-64 In the private sector, union membership has been declining for decades. To see how unions are perceived, Gallup surveyed Americans and asked whether they approve or disapprove of unions: 1 = Approve, 2 = Disapprove, 3 = No opinion. Respondents were categorized by age: 1 = 18–34, 2 = 35–54, 3 = 55, and older. Is there enough evidence to infer that there are differences between the age groups with regard to support for unions?

15.65 Xr15-65 In the election of 2018, there were several newcomers who espoused the cause of socialism in the United States. To measure the relative popularity of socialism and capitalism Gallup asked Americans whether they had a positive view of capitalism: Positive (1) or not (2). Each respondent was categorized by age: 1 = 18–29, 2 = 30–49, 3 = 50–64, 4 = 65+. Is there sufficient evidence to infer that the opinion about capitalism differs between the four age categories?

15.66 Xr15-66 Refer to exercise 15.65. The survey also asked whether respondents had a positive view of socialism. Can we infer from the data that there are differences between the four age groups with respect to their opinion about socialism?

15.67 Xr12-149+ Exercise 12.149 described a Gallup survey that asked Americans 15 and older whether they felt stress the previous day. The responses are 1 = Yes and 0 = No. The survey also asked respondents to report their age category where 1 = 18–29, 2 = 30–49, 3 = 50+. Can we infer from the data that there are differences in stress between the three age groups?

15.68 Xr12-107+ Refer to Exercise 12.107. Gallup conducted a survey of Americans that asked, "Are you generally satisfied or dissatisfied with the total cost you pay for your healthcare?" The responses are 1 = Satisfied, 0 = Unsatisfied. The political party each participant favored was recorded as 1 = Republican, 2 = Independent, 3 = Democrat. Is there enough evidence to conclude that there are differences in satisfaction with their health care costs between Republicans, Independents, and Democrats?

15.69 Xr15-69 In Canada some politicians have been talking about the idea to pay for the costs of the pandemic by bringing in a new wealth tax of 1% that would be paid by people who have more than $20 million in net assets. In an Abacus survey, a random sample of Canadians was asked their opinion. The responses are: 1 = Strongly favor, 2 = Favor, 3 = Oppose, 4 = Strongly oppose. The survey also recorded the political party each respondent supports where 1 = Liberal Party, 2 = Conservative Party of Canada, 3 = New Democratic Party. Is there sufficient evidence to infer that there are differences in support of a new wealth tax between the three main Canadian parties?

15.70 Xr15-70 Refer to Exercise 15.69. Another idea is to bring in a special tax that would apply to companies whose profits have gone up because of the circumstances of the pandemic. For these companies, the corporate tax rate would be double the rate on their profits they earned in excess of their pre-pandemic profits. Do the data allow us to conclude that there are differences in support of a special tax between the three parties?

15.71 Xr15-71+ Clinical depression is a serious disorder that affects millions of people. Depression often leads to alcohol as a means of easing the pain. A Gallup survey attempted to study the relationship between depression and alcohol. A random sample of adults was drawn and after a series of question each respondent was identified as a 1 = Nondrinker, 2 = Moderate drinker, 3 = Heavy

drinker. Additionally, each respondent was asked whether they had ever been diagnosed as clinically depressed at some time in their lives (1 = Yes, 2 = No). Is there enough evidence to conclude that alcohol and depression are related?

15.72 Xr15-71+ Refer to Exercise 15.71. Each respondent was also asked whether they are currently depressed (1 = Yes, 2 = No). Is there sufficient evidence to infer that alcohol and current depression are related?

15.73 Xr15-73 Gallup asked in a recent survey conducted around the world, "In this country, are you satisfied or dissatisfied with your freedom to choose what you do with your life?" The responses are 1 = Satisfied, 2 = Dissatisfied. The results for 1 = Australia, 2 = Canada, 3 = New Zealand, and the 4 = the United States were recorded. Can we infer that there are differences between the four countries in their satisfaction with the freedom in their countries?

15.74 Xr15-74 The Patient Protection and Affordable Care Act, often shortened to the Affordable Care Act and nicknamed Obamacare, has been subject to much debate since it passed in March 2010. In November 2016, 2017, and 2018 Gallup conducted a series of surveys that asked Americans for their opinion about the act. The possible responses are: 1 = Approve, keep as is, 2 = Approve, but change significantly, 3 = Disapprove, keep, but change significantly, 4 = Disapprove, repeal and replace, 5 = No opinion. Is there sufficient statistical evidence to conclude that there have been changes over the 3-year period?

GENERAL SOCIAL SURVEY EXERCISES

Conduct a statistical test to answer each question. **Use a 5% significance level.**

GSS2018 *The following exercises refer to the following nine variables:*

SEX: *1 = Male, 2 = Female*

RACE: *1 = White, 2 = Black, 3 = Other*

WRKSLF: *1 = Self-employed, 2 = Work for someone else*

PARTYID3: *1 = Democrat, 2 = Independent, 3 = Republican*

POLVIEWS3: *1 = Liberal, 2 = Moderate, 3 = Conservative*

CAPPUN: *1 = Support capital punishment for murder, 2 = Oppose*

GUNLAW: *1 = Support a law requiring a police permit to buy a gun, 2 = Oppose*

DEGREE: *Highest degree completed of respondent: 0 = Left high school, 1 = High school, 2 = Junior college, 3 = Bachelor's degree, 4 = Graduate*

CLASS: *Which of the following four social classes would you say you belong in? 1 = Lower class, 2 = Working class, 3 = Middle class, 4 = Upper class*

15.75 An important element in the business of politics is to know who supports you and who doesn't. Is there sufficient evidence to infer that men and women differ in their support of the political parties?

15.76 Are all three categories of race equally likely to choose to work for themselves? Or does the frequency with which some choose to work for themselves differ between the three races? Conduct a test to help decide.

15.77 Do Americans who self-report which class they belong to make this decision based on their educational attainment as measured by their degree? Conduct a test to determine whether there are differences in their educational attainment between the four self-reported classes.

15.78 Is there enough statistical evidence to infer that the three races differ in their support of a law requiring a police permit to buy a gun?

15.79 Is there enough evidence to infer that American women and men are equally accomplished in terms of their educational attainment?

15.80 Do political points of view affect one's support for capital punishment for murder? Conduct a test to answer the question.

SURVEY OF CONSUMER FINANCES EXERCISES

SCF2019:\MC *Conduct all tests at the 5% significance level.*

The following exercises are based on the middle-class subsample of the 2019 survey. Exercises 15.81–15.84 examine the issue of race among middle-class households (RACE: 1 = White, non-Hispanic, 2 = Black/African American, 3 = Hispanic, 5 = Other). For each variable, test to determine whether there is sufficient evidence to conclude that differences exist between the four races.

15.81 House ownership (HOUSECL: 1 = Owns, 2 = Does not own).

15.82 Household has been turned down for credit in the previous 5 years (TURNDOWN: 0 = No, 1 = Yes).

15.83 Occupation classification for head of household: OCCAT2: 1 = Managerial/professional, 2 = Technical/sales/services, 3 = Other (including production/craft/repair workers, operators, laborers, farmers, foresters, fishers), 4 = Not working.

15.84 Household has incurred debt (HDEBT: Household has any debt: 0 = No, 1 = Yes).

15-3 / SUMMARY OF TESTS ON NOMINAL DATA

At this point in the textbook, we've described four tests that are used when the data are nominal:

z-test of p (Section 12-3)

z-test of $p_1 - p_2$ (Section 13-5)

Chi-squared goodness-of-fit test (Section 15-1)

Chi-squared test of a contingency table (Section 15-2)

In the process of presenting these techniques, it was necessary to concentrate on one technique at a time and focus on the kinds of problems each addresses. However, this approach tends to conflict somewhat with our promised goal of emphasizing the "when" of statistical inference. In this section, we summarize the statistical tests on nominal data to ensure that you are capable of selecting the correct method.

There are two critical factors in identifying the technique used when the data are nominal. The first, of course, is the problem objective. The second is the number of categories that the nominal variable can assume. Table 15.1 provides a guide to help select the correct technique.

TABLE **15.1** Statistical Techniques for Nominal Data

PROBLEM OBJECTIVE	NUMBER OF CATEGORIES	STATISTICAL TECHNIQUE
Describe a population	2	z-test of p or the chi-squared goodness-of-fit test
Describe a population	More than 2	Chi-squared goodness-of-fit test
Compare two populations	2	z-test of $p_1 - p_2$ or chi-squared test of a contingency table
Compare two populations	More than 2	Chi-squared test of a contingency table
Compare two or more populations	2 or more	Chi-squared test of a contingency table
Analyze the relationship between two variables	2 or more	Chi-squared test of a contingency table

Notice that when we describe a population of nominal data with exactly two categories, we can use either of two techniques. We can employ the z-test of p or the chi-squared goodness-of-fit test. These two tests are equivalent because if there are only two categories, the multinomial experiment is actually a binomial experiment (one of the categorical outcomes is labeled *success*, and the other is labeled *failure*). Mathematical statisticians have established that if we square the value of z, the test statistic for the test of p, we produce the χ^2-statistic; that is, $z^2 = \chi^2$. Thus, if we want to conduct a two-tail test of a population proportion, we can employ either technique. However, the chi-squared goodness-of-fit test can test only to determine whether the hypothesized values of p_1 (which we can label p) and p_2 (which we call $1 - p$) are not equal to their specified values. Consequently, to perform a one-tail test of a population proportion, we must use the z-test of p. (This issue was discussed in Chapter 14 when we pointed out that we can use either the t-test of $\mu_1 - \mu_2$ or the analysis of variance to conduct a test to determine whether two population means differ.)

When we test for differences between two populations of nominal data with two categories, we can also use either of two techniques: the z-test of $p_1 - p_2$ (Case 1) or the chi-squared test of a contingency table. Once again, we can use either technique to perform a two-tail test about $p_1 - p_2$. (Squaring the value of the z-statistic yields the value of the χ^2-statistic.) However, one-tail tests must be conducted by the z-test of $p_1 - p_2$. The rest of the table is quite straightforward. Notice that when we want to compare two populations when there are more than two categories, we use the chi-squared test of a contingency table.

Figure 15.4 offers another summary of the tests that deal with nominal data introduced in this book. There are two groups of tests: those that test hypotheses about single populations and those that test either for differences or for independence. In the first set, we have the z-test of p, which can be replaced by the chi-squared test of a multinomial experiment. The latter test is employed when there are more than two categories.

To test for differences between two proportions, we apply the z-test of $p_1 - p_2$. Instead we can use the chi-squared test of a contingency table, which can be applied to a variety of other problems.

15-3a Developing an Understanding of Statistical Concepts

Table 15.1 and Figure 15.4 summarize how we deal with nominal data. We determine the frequency of each category and use these frequencies to compute test statistics. We can then compute proportions to calculate z-statistics or use the frequencies to calculate χ^2-statistics. Because squaring a standard normal random variable produces a chi-squared variable, we can employ either statistic to test for differences. As a consequence, when you encounter nominal data in the problems described in this book (and other introductory applied statistics books), the most logical starting point in selecting the appropriate technique will be either a z-statistic or a χ^2-statistic. However, you should know that there are other statistical procedures that can be applied to nominal data, techniques that are not included in this book.

FIGURE **15.4** Tests on Nominal Data

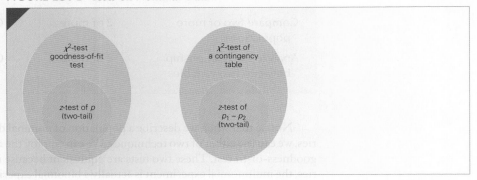

15-4 / (OPTIONAL) CHI-SQUARED TEST FOR NORMALITY

We can use the goodness-of-fit test presented in Section 15-1 in another way. We can test to determine whether data were drawn from any distribution. The most common application of this procedure is a test of normality.

In the examples and exercises shown in Section 15-1, the probabilities specified in the null hypothesis were derived from the question. In Example 15.1, the probabilities p_1, p_2, and p_3 were the market shares before the advertising campaign. To test for normality (or any other distribution), the probabilities must first be calculated using the hypothesized distribution. To illustrate, consider Example 12.1, where we tested the mean amount of discarded newspaper using the Student t distribution. The required condition for this procedure is that the data must be normally distributed. To determine whether the 148 observations in our sample were indeed taken from a normal distribution, we must calculate the theoretical probabilities assuming a normal distribution. To do so, we must first calculate the sample mean and standard deviation: $\bar{x} = 2.18$ and $s = .981$. Next, we find the probabilities of an arbitrary number of intervals. For example, we can find the probabilities of the following intervals:

Interval 1: $X \leq .709$

Interval 2: $.709 < X \leq 1.69$

Interval 3: $1.69 < X \leq 2.67$

Interval 4: $2.67 < X \leq 3.65$

Interval 5: $X > 3.65$

We will discuss the reasons for our choices of intervals later.

The probabilities are computed using the normal distribution and the values of $\bar{x}$ and s as estimators of μ and σ. We calculated the sample mean and standard deviation as $\bar{x} = 2.18$ and $s = .981$. Thus,

$$P(X \leq .709) = P\left(\frac{X - \mu}{\sigma} \leq \frac{.709 - 2.18}{.981}\right) = P(Z \leq -1.5) = .0668$$

$$P(.709 < X \leq 1.69) = P\left(\frac{.709 - 2.18}{.981} < \frac{X - \mu}{\sigma} \leq \frac{1.69 - 2.18}{.981}\right)$$

$$= P(-1.5 < Z \leq -.5) = .2417$$

$$P(1.69 < X \leq 2.67) = P\left(\frac{1.69 - 2.18}{.981} < \frac{X - \mu}{\sigma} \leq \frac{2.67 - 2.18}{.981}\right)$$

$$= P(-.5 < Z \leq .5) = .3829$$

$$P(2.67 < X \leq 3.65) = P\left(\frac{2.67 - 2.18}{.981} < \frac{X - \mu}{\sigma} \leq \frac{3.65 - 2.18}{.981}\right)$$

$$= P(.5 < Z \leq 1.5) = .2417$$

$$P(X > 3.65) = P\left(\frac{X - \mu}{\sigma} > \frac{3.65 - 2.18}{.981}\right) = P(Z > 1.5) = .0668$$

To test for normality is to test the following hypotheses:

H_0: $p_1 = .0668$, $p_2 = .2417$, $p_3 = .3829$, $p_4 = .2417$, $p_5 = .0668$

H_1:   At least two proportions differ from their specified values

We complete the test as we did in Section 15-1, except that the number of degrees of freedom associated with the chi-squared statistic is the number of intervals minus 1 minus the number of parameters estimated, which in this illustration is two. (We estimated the population mean μ and the population standard deviation σ.) Thus, in this case, the number of degrees of freedom is $k - 1 - 2 = 5 - 1 - 2 = 2$.

The expected values are

$$e_1 = np_1 = 148(.0668) = 9.89$$
$$e_2 = np_2 = 148(.2417) = 35.78$$
$$e_3 = np_3 = 148(.3829) = 56.67$$
$$e_4 = np_4 = 148(.2417) = 35.78$$
$$e_5 = np_5 = 148(.0668) = 9.89$$

The observed values are determined manually by counting the number of values in each interval. Thus,

$$f_1 = 10$$
$$f_2 = 36$$
$$f_3 = 54$$
$$f_4 = 39$$
$$f_5 = 9$$

The chi-squared statistic is

$$x^2 = \sum_{i=1}^{k} \frac{(f_i - e_i)^2}{e_i} = \frac{(10 - 9.89)^2}{9.89} + \frac{(36 - 35.78)^2}{35.78} + \frac{(54 - 56.67)^2}{56.67}$$

$$+ \frac{(39 - 35.78)^2}{35.78} + \frac{(9 - 9.89)^2}{9.89}$$

$$= .50$$

The rejection region is

$$x^2 > x_{\alpha,k-3}^2 = x_{.05,2}^2 = 5.99$$

There is not enough evidence to conclude that these data are not normally distributed.

Do It Yourself Excel

Here is the solution to Example 12.1.

	A	B	C	D
1	0.0668	9.89	10	0.001
2	0.2417	35.77	36	0.001
3	0.3829	56.67	54	0.126
4	0.2417	35.77	39	0.291
5	0.0668	9.89	9	0.079
6			SUM	0.499
7			CHIDIST	0.7791
8			P-Value	0.2209

INSTRUCTIONS

1. Compute the probabilities in Column A. Multiply the probabilities by the sample size to calculate the expected values in Column B. In Column C type or import the actual frequencies.

2. In Row 1 of Column D type

   =((C1-B1)^2)/C1

   Drag to complete the column. Compute the sum of these values. This is the test statistic.

3. Compute the probability that a chi-squared random variable with 2 (k minus 1 minus the number of parameters estimated from the data) degrees of freedom is greater than the calculated value. Excel does this with the following.

   =CHIDIST(D6,2)

   which we input in Cell D7. The p-value of the test was determined by subtracting this value from 1.

15-4a Class Intervals

In practice you can use any intervals you like. We chose the intervals we did to facilitate the calculation of the normal probabilities. The number of intervals was chosen to comply with the rule of five, which requires that all expected values be at least equal to 5. Because the number of degrees of freedom is $k - 3$, assuming that the mean and standard deviation must be estimated from the data, the minimum number of intervals is $k = 4$.

15-4b Interpreting the Results of a Chi-Squared Test for Normality

In the example above, we found that there was little evidence to conclude that the weight of discarded newspaper is not normally distributed. However, had we found evidence of nonnormality, this would not necessarily invalidate the t-test we conducted in Example 12.1. As we pointed out in Chapter 12, the t-test of a mean is a robust procedure, which means that only if the variable is extremely nonnormal and the sample size is small can we conclude that the technique is suspect. The problem here is that if the sample size is large and the variable is only slightly nonnormal, the chi-squared test for normality will, in many cases, conclude that the variable is not normally distributed. However, if the variable is even quite nonnormal and the sample size is large, the t-test will still be valid. Although there are situations in which we need to know whether a variable is nonnormal, we continue to advocate that the way to decide if the normality requirement for almost all statistical techniques applied to interval data is satisfied is to draw histograms and look for shapes that are far from bell shaped (e.g., highly skewed or bimodal). We will use this approach in Chapter 19 when we introduce nonparametric techniques that are used when interval data are nonnormal.

EXERCISES

15.85 Suppose that a random sample of 100 observations was drawn from a population. After calculating the mean and standard deviation, each observation was standardized and the number of observations in each of the following intervals was counted. Can we infer at the 5% significance level that the data were not drawn from a normal population?

Interval	Frequency
$Z \leq -1.5$	10
$-1.5 < Z \leq -0.5$	18
$-0.5 < Z \leq 0.5$	48
$0.5 < Z \leq 1.5$	16
$Z > 1.5$	8

15.86 A random sample of 50 observations yielded the following frequencies for the standardized intervals:

Interval	Frequency
$Z \leq -1$	6
$-1 < Z \leq 0$	27
$0 < Z \leq 1$	14
$Z > 1$	3

Can we infer that the data are not normal? (Use $\alpha = .10$.)

The following exercises require the use of a computer and software. **Use a 1% significance level for all tests.**

15.87 <u>Xr12-31</u>   Refer to Exercise 12.31. Test to determine whether the amount of time spent working at part-time jobs is normally distributed. If there is evidence of nonnormality, is the *t*-test invalid?

15.88 Xr12-34 Refer to Exercise 12.34. The technique that produced the confidence interval estimate of the credit card debt requires that the variable be normally distributed. Conduct a test to determine whether the required condition is unsatisfied. If there is enough evidence to conclude that the requirement is not satisfied, does this indicate that the estimate is invalid?

15.89 Xr12-37 Exercise 12.37 required you to construct a confidence interval estimate of the cost of drugs. Test to determine whether there is sufficient evidence to infer that the costs are not normally distributed.

15.90 Xr12-78 In Exercise 12.78 the question asked whether there was sufficient evidence to infer that the population variance exceeded 18 mph^2. This technique requires that the speeds be normally distributed. Conduct a test to determine whether there is enough evidence to conclude that the requirement is not satisfied.

15.91 Xr13-29 Refer to Exercise 13.29, which required a *t*-test of the difference between two means. What is the required condition, and is there enough evidence to infer that it is not satisfied?

15.92 Xr13-118 Refer to Exercise 13.118.
a. What is the required condition for the validity of the test you conducted?
b. Is there sufficient statistical evidence to conclude that the requirement is violated?

15.93 Xr13-113 Refer to Exercise 13.113 where a *t*-test was conducted.
a. What is the required condition?
b. Conduct a test to determine whether there is enough evidence to infer that the requirement is unsatisfied.

15.94 Xr13-126 Exercise 13.126 addressed the question of the difference between IQs of brothers. What is the requirement for the validity of the procedure applied in this exercise, and is there enough evidence to conclude that the required condition is unsatisfied?

15.95 Xr13-31 Refer to Exercise 13.31, where a *t*-test and estimator were employed to answer the questions.

Conduct a test to determine whether there is enough evidence to conclude that the required condition is violated.

In this section we showed how to test for normality. However, we can use the same process to test for any other distribution. Simply calculate the probabilities associated with the distribution being tested. These probabilities make up the null hypothesis and are used to calculate the expected values and the test statistic.

15.96 Xr15-96 A scientist believes that the gender of a child is a binomial random variable with probability = .5 for a boy and .5 for a girl. To help test this belief, the scientist randomly sampled 200 families with five children and recorded the number of boys. Can we infer that the number of boys in families with five children is not a binomial random variable with $p = .5$? (*Hint:* Find the probability of $X = 0$, 1, 2, 3, 4, and 5 from a binomial distribution with $n = 5$ and $p = .5$.)

15.97 The following values and frequencies were observed.

X	0	1	2	3
Frequency	208	215	65	12

A statistician believes that these data were generated from a binomial distribution, but doesn't know the value the parameter, p.
a. Find a method to estimate the parameter.
b. Conduct a test to determine whether there is enough evidence to infer that the data did not come from a binomial distribution.

15.98 Xr15-98 The Poisson distribution was introduced in Chapter 7. This distribution is used in waiting line (queuing) models. A management scientist working for a bank developed a queuing model assuming two arrivals in 10 minutes. To test this assumption, the number of arrivals in sixty 10-minute intervals was recorded. Is there enough evidence to conclude that the data are not from a Poisson distribution with a mean of 2 in 10 minutes? (Recall that all expected values should be at least 5.)

15.99 Refer to Exercise 15.98. Suppose that the management scientist believed that the arrivals are Poisson distributed, but did not know the mean. Test to determine whether there is enough evidence to conclude that arrivals are not Poisson distributed.

CHAPTER SUMMARY

This chapter introduced three statistical techniques. The first is the chi-squared goodness-of-fit test, which is applied when the problem objective is to describe a single population of nominal data with two or more categories. The second is the chi-squared test of a contingency table. This test has two objectives: to analyze the relationship between two nominal variables and to compare two or more populations of nominal data. The last procedure is designed to test for normality.

IMPORTANT TERMS:

Multinomial experiment   629
Chi-squared goodness-of-fit test   630
Expected frequency   631
Observed frequencies   631

Cross-classification table   637
Chi-squared test of a contingency table   637
Contingency table   639

SYMBOLS:

Symbol	Pronounced	Represents
f_i	f sub i	Frequency of the ith category
e_i	e sub i	Expected value of the ith category
χ^2	Chi squared	Test statistic

FORMULA:

Test statistic for all procedures

$$\chi^2 = \sum_{i=1}^{k} \frac{(f_i - e_i)^2}{e_i}$$

EXCEL OUTPUT AND INSTRUCTIONS:

Technique	
Chi-squared goodness-of-fit test	633
Chi-squared test of a contingency table	641

CHAPTER EXERCISES

Conduct all tests at the 5% significance level.

15.100 It has been estimated that employee absenteeism costs North American companies more than $100 billion per year. As a first step in addressing the rising cost of absenteeism, the personnel department of a large corporation recorded the weekdays during which individuals in a sample of 362 absentees were away over the past several months. Do these data suggest that absenteeism is higher on some days of the week than on others?

Day of the Week	Monday	Tuesday	Wednesday	Thursday	Friday
Number absent	87	62	71	68	74

15.101 Suppose that the personnel department in Exercise 15.100 continued its investigation by categorizing absentees according to the shift on which they worked, as shown in the accompanying table. Is there sufficient evidence of a relationship between the days on which employees are absent and the shift on which the employees work?

Shift	Monday	Tuesday	Wednesday	Thursday	Friday
Day	52	28	37	31	33
Evening	35	34	34	37	41

15.102 A management behavior analyst has been studying the relationship between male/female supervisory structures in the workplace and the level of employees' job satisfaction. The results of a recent survey are shown in the accompanying table. Is there sufficient evidence to infer that the level of job satisfaction depends on the boss/employee gender relationship?

Level of Satisfaction	Boss/Employee			
	Female/ Male	Female/ Female	Male/ Male	Male/ Female
Satisfied	21	25	54	71
Neutral	39	49	50	38
Dissatisfied	31	48	10	11

The following exercises require the use of a computer and software. The answers may be calculated manually. See Appendix A for the sample statistics. **Use a 5% significance level for all tests.**

15.103 Xr15-103 Do Black and White Americans differ in their choices of jobs? To answer the question random samples of wage and salary earners were drawn. Each respondent was classified as either Black (1) or White (2). Their jobs were also recorded as: 1 = Managers and professionals, 2 = Technical sales and clerical workers, 3 = Service workers, 4 = Construction worker, operators, and laborers. Is there sufficient evidence to conclude that there are differences in career choices between Black and White Americans?

Source: Adapted from Bureau of Labor Statistics.

15.104 Xr15-104 Stress is a serious medical problem that costs businesses and government billions of dollars annually. As a result, it is important to determine the causes and possible cures. It would be helpful to know whether the causes are universal or if they vary from country to country. In a survey, American (1) and Canadian (2) adults were asked to report their primary source of stress in their lives: 1 = Job, 2 = Finances, 3 = Health, 4 = Family life, 5 = Other. Do these data provide sufficient evidence to conclude that Americans and Canadians differ in their sources of stress?

15.105 Xr15-105 More than 3,000 Americans quit smoking each day. Because nicotine is one of the most addictive drugs, quitting smoking is a difficult and frustrating task. It usually takes several tries before success is achieved. There are various methods, including cold turkey, nicotine patch, hypnosis, and group therapy sessions. In an experiment to determine how these methods differ, a random sample of smokers who have decided to quit is selected. Each smoker has chosen one of the methods listed above. After 1 year, the respondents reported whether they have quit: Yes (1) or no (2), and which method they used: 1 = Cold turkey, 2 = Nicotine patch, 3 = Hypnosis, 4 = Group therapy sessions. Is there sufficient evidence to conclude that the four methods differ in their success?

15.106 Xr15-106 A newspaper publisher wondered whether the way people read a newspaper is related to the reader's educational level. A survey asked adult readers which section of the paper they read first and asked to report their highest educational level. These data were recorded (column 1 = First section read where 1 = Front page, 2 = Sports, 3 = Editorial, and 4 = Other and column 2 = Educational level where 1 = Did not complete high school, 2 = High school graduate, 3 = University or college graduate, and 4 = Postgraduate degree). Is there enough statistical evidence to conclude that the section read first is related to educational attainment?

15.107 Xr15-107 Every week, the Florida lottery draws six numbers between 1 and 49. Lottery ticket buyers are naturally interested in whether certain numbers are drawn more frequently than others. To assist players, the *Sun-Sentinel* publishes the number of times each of the 49 numbers has been drawn in the past 52 weeks. The numbers and the frequency with which each occurred were recorded.
a. If the numbers are drawn from a uniform distribution, what is the expected frequency for each number?
b. Can we infer that the data were not generated from a uniform distribution?

15.108 Xr15-108 Developers are often opposed by nearby residents in a protest known as NIMBY, which stands for Not In My Backyard. Another name is BANANA—Build Absolutely Nothing Anywhere Nor Anytime. This phenomenon occurs when a builder wants to construct houses or condominiums and the local homeowners fight to stop the development. In order to counter the protests, builders need to determine who is most likely to protest. A random sample of potential protesters was drawn and each was asked whether they will protest: Yes (1) or no (2) and their educational attainment: 1 = Less than high school, 2 = High school graduate, 3 = Some college, 4 = University graduate. Can the builder conclude that there are differences in

Instructions

1. Type or import the data into two columns. (Open Xm15-02.)

2. Click **XLSTAT, Correlation/Association tests**, and **Tests on contingency tables (Chi-square…)**.

3. Type the range of the **Row variable(s)** (A1:A153) and the range of the **Column variable(s)** (B1:B153). Select the **Data format: Qualitative variables**.

4. Click **Options** and check **Chi-square test**.

5. Click **Outputs** and check **Contingency table**.

Chapter-Opening Example

	B	C	D	E	F	G	H	I
13	Contingency table (SEX \ POLVIEWS):							
14								
15	SEX \ POLVIEWS	1	2	3	4	5	6	7
16	1	57	115	126	365	131	172	47
17	2	65	163	130	490	152	182	52
18								
19	Test of independence between the rows and the columns (SEX \ POLVIEWS):							
20								
21	Chi-square (Observed value)	7.580						
22	Chi-square (Critical value)	12.592						
23	DF	6						
24	p-value	0.2705						
25	alpha	0.05						

Instructions

The GSS2018 data set contains numerous blank cells representing missing data. To remove them click **Missing data** and choose **Remove the observations**.

APPENDIX 15.B / STATA OUTPUT AND INSTRUCTIONS

Chi-Squared Test of a Contingency Table

Example 15.2

```
                    MBA Major
   Degree        1      2      3    |  Total
   ─────────────────────────────────┼─────────
      1          31     13     16   |    60
      2           8     16      7   |    31
      3          12     10     17   |    39
      4          10      5      7   |    22
   ─────────────────────────────────┼─────────
   Total         61     44     47   |   152

        Pearson chi2(6) =  14.7019   Pr = 0.023
```

The value of the test statistic is $\chi^2 = 14.7019$, p-value $= .023$.

Instructions

1. Import or type the data into two columns. (Click File/Import /Excel spreadsheet (*xls,*xlsx)/Chapter15/Xm15-02.)

2. Click **Statistics, Summaries, tables and tests, Frequency tables**, and **Two-way with measures of association**.

3. Select **Degree** in the **Row variable:** box and **MBA Major** in the **Column variable:** box. Click **Pearson's chi-squared**.

APPENDIX 15.C / REVIEW OF CHAPTERS 12 TO 15

Here are the updated list of statistical techniques (Table A15.1) and the flowchart (Figure A15.1) for Chapters 12 to 15. Counting the two techniques of chi-squared tests introduced here (we do not include the chi-squared test for normality), we have covered 22 statistical methods.

TABLE **A15.1** Summary of Statistical Techniques in Chapters 12 to 15

t-test of μ

Estimator of μ (including estimator of $N\mu$)

χ^2-test of σ^2

Estimator of σ^2

z-test of p

Estimator of p (including estimator of Np)

Equal-variances t-test of $\mu_1 - \mu_2$

Equal-variances estimator of $\mu_1 - \mu_2$

Unequal-variances t-test of $\mu_1 - \mu_2$

Unequal-variances estimator of $\mu_1 - \mu_2$

t-test of μ_D

Estimator of μ_D

F-test of σ_1^2/σ_2^2

Estimator of σ_1^2/σ_2^2

z-test of $p_1 - p_2$ (Case 1)

z-test of $p_1 - p_2$ (Case 2)

Estimator of $p_1 - p_2$

One-way analysis of variance (including multiple comparisons)

Two-way (randomized blocks) analysis of variance

Two-factor analysis of variance

χ^2-goodness-of-fit test

χ^2-test of a contingency table

FIGURE **A15.1** **Summary of Statistical Techniques in Chapters 12 to 15**

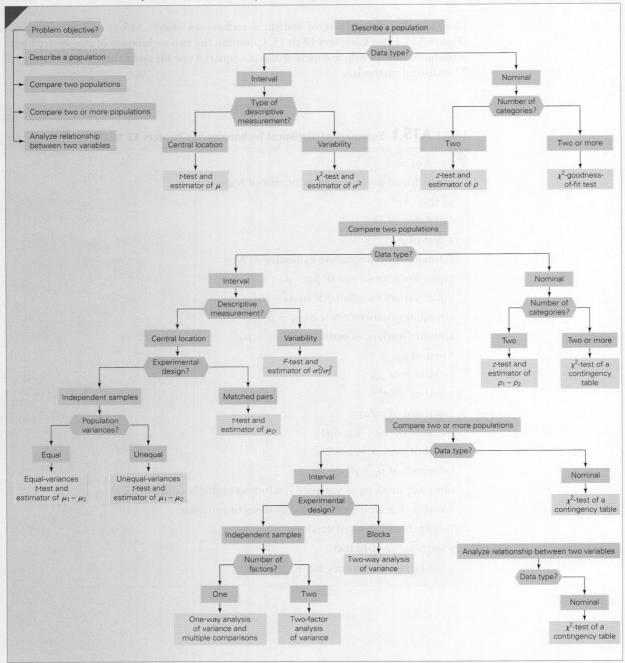

EXERCISES

We remind you that we do not specify significance levels in the exercise that follow. Choose your own.

A15.1 XrA15-01   An analysis of the applicants of all MBA programs in North America reveals that the proportions of each type of undergraduate degree are as follows:

Undergraduate Degree	Proportion (%)
BA (1)	50
BBA (2)	20
BSc (3)	15
BEng (4)	10
Other (5)	5

The director of Wilfrid Laurier University's (WLU's) MBA program recorded the undergraduate degree of the applicants for this year using the codes in parentheses. Do these data indicate that applicants to WLU's MBA program are different in terms of their undergraduate degrees from the population of MBA applicants?

A15.2 XrA15-02   The experiment to determine the effect of taking a preparatory course to improve SAT scores in Exercise A13.16 was criticized by other statisticians. They argued that the first test would provide a valuable learning experience that would produce a higher test score from the second exam even without the preparatory course. Consequently, another experiment was performed. Forty students wrote the SAT without taking any preparatory course. At the next scheduled exam (3 months later), these same students took the exam again (again with no preparatory course). The scores for both exams were recorded in columns 1 (first test scores) and 2 (second test scores). Can we infer that repeating the SAT produces higher exam scores even without the preparatory course?

A15.3 XrA15-03   How does dieting affect the brain? This question was addressed by researchers in Australia. The experiment used 40 middle-age women in Adelaide, Australia; half were on a diet and half were not. The mental arithmetic part of the experiment required the participants to add two three-digit numbers. The amount of time taken to solve the 48 problems was recorded. The participants were given another test that required them to repeat a string of five letters they had been told 10 seconds earlier. They were asked to repeat the test with five words told to them 10 seconds earlier. The data were recorded in the following way:

Column A: Identification number
Column B: 1 = dieting, 2 = not dieting
Column C: Time to solve 48 problems (seconds)
Column D: Repeat string of 5 letters (1 = no, 2 = yes)
Column E: Repeat string of 5 words (1 = no, 2 = yes)

Is there sufficient evidence to infer that dieting adversely affects the brain?

A15.4 XrA15-04   A small but important part of a university library's budget is the amount collected in fines on overdue books. Last year, a library collected $75,652.75 in fine payments; however, the head librarian suspects that some employees are not bothering to collect the fines on overdue books. In an effort to learn more about the situation, a sample of 400 students (out of a total student population of 50,000) was asked how many books they had returned late to the library in the previous 12 months. They were also asked how many days overdue the books had been. The results indicated that the total number of days overdue ranged from 0 to 55 days. The number of days overdue was recorded.
a. Estimate with 95% confidence the average number of days overdue for all 50,000 students at the university.
b. If the fine is 25 cents per day, estimate the amount that should be collected annually. Should the librarian conclude that not all the fines were collected?

A15.5 XrA15-05   An apple juice manufacturer has developed a new product—a liquid concentrate that produces 1 liter of apple juice when mixed with water. The product has several attractive features. The marketing team have to decide how to market the new product. They can create advertising that emphasizes convenience, quality, or price. To facilitate a decision, they conduct an experiment in three different small cities. In one city, they launch the product with advertising stressing the convenience of the liquid concentrate. In the second city, the advertisements emphasize the quality of the product. Advertising that highlights the relatively low cost of the liquid concentrate is used in the third city. The number of packages sold weekly is recorded for the 20 weeks following the beginning of the campaign. The marketing manager wants to know whether differences in sales exist between the three advertising strategies. (We will assume that except for the type of advertising, the three cities are identical.)

A15.6 XrA15-06   A financial analyst wanted to determine the effect income had on ownership of mutual funds and whether the relationship had changed from 4 years earlier. A random sample of adults 25 years of age and older were asked whether they owned mutual funds (No = 1 and Yes = 2) and to report the annual household income. The categories are

1. Less than $25,000
2. $25,000 to $34,999
3. $35,000 to $49,999
4. $50,000 to $74,999
5. $75,000 to $100,000
6. More than $100,000

Can we infer from the data that household income and ownership of mutual funds are related?

A15.7 XrA15-07   Refer to Exercise A15.5. Suppose that in addition to varying the marketing strategy, the manufacturer also decided to advertise in one of the two media that are available: television and newspapers. As a consequence, the experiment was repeated in the following way. Six different small cities were selected. In city 1, the marketing emphasized convenience, and all the advertising was conducted on television. In city 2, marketing also emphasized convenience, but all the advertising was conducted in the daily newspaper. Quality was emphasized in cities 3 and 4. City 3 learned about the product from television commercials, and city 4 saw newspaper advertising. Price was the marketing emphasis in cities 5 and 6. City 5 saw television commercials, and city 6 saw newspaper advertisements. In each city, the weekly sales for each of 10 weeks were recorded. What conclusions can be drawn from these data?

A15.8 XrA15-08   After a recent study, researchers reported on the effects of folic acid on the occurrence of spina bifida—a birth defect in which there is incomplete formation of the spine. A sample of 2,000 women who gave birth to children with spina bifida and who were planning another pregnancy was recruited. Before attempting to get pregnant again, half the sample was given regular doses of folic acid, and the other half was given a placebo. After 18 months, researchers recorded the result for each woman: 1 = birth to normal baby, 2 = birth to baby with spina bifida, 3 = not pregnant or no baby yet delivered. Can we infer that folic acid reduces the incidence of spina bifida in newborn babies?

A15.9 XrA15-09   Slow play of golfers is a serious problem for golf clubs. Slow play results in fewer rounds of golf and less profits for public course owners. To examine this problem, a random sample of British and American golf courses was selected. The amount of time taken (in minutes) was recorded for a random sample of British and American golfers. Can we conclude that British golfers play golf in less time than do American golfers?

A15.10 XrA15-10   The United States and Canada (among others) are countries in which a significant proportion of citizens are immigrants. Many arrive in North America with few assets but quickly adapt to a changed economic environment. The question often arises, How quickly do immigrants increase their standard of living? A study initiated by Statistics Canada surveyed three different types of families:

1. Immigrants who arrived before 1976
2. Immigrants who came to Canada after 1986
3. Canadian-born families

The survey measured family wealth, which includes houses, cars, income, and savings and recorded the results (in $1,000s). Can we infer that differences exist between the three groups? If so, what are those differences?

A15.11 XrA15-11   During the decade of the 1980s, professional baseball thrived in North America. However, in the 1990s attendance dropped, and the number of television viewers also decreased. To examine the popularity of baseball relative to other sports, surveys were performed. In 1985 and again in 1992, a Harris Poll asked a random sample of 500 people to name their favorite sport. The results, which were published in the *Wall Street Journal* (July 6, 1993), were recorded in the following way: favorite sport (1 = professional football, 2 = baseball, 3 = professional basketball, 4 = college basketball, 5 = college football, 6 = golf, 7 = auto racing, 8 = tennis, and 9 = other); year (1 = 1985, 2 = 1992). Do these results indicate that North Americans changed their favorite sport between 1985 and 1992?

A15.12 XrA15-12   In an attempt to learn more about traffic congestion in a large North American city, the number of cars passing through intersections was determined. The number of cars was counted in 5-minute samples throughout several days. The counts for one busy intersection were recorded. Estimate with 95% confidence the mean number of cars in 5 minutes. Use the result to estimate the counts for a 24-hour day.

A15.13 XrA15-13   Organizations that sponsor various leisure activities need to know the number of people who wish to participate. Bureaucrats need to know the number because many organizations apply for government grants to pay the costs. The U.S. National Endowment for the Arts conducts surveys of American adults to acquire this type of information. One part of the survey asked a random sample of adults whether they participated in exercise programs. The responses (1 = yes and 2 = no) were recorded. A recent census reveals that there are 255.2 million adults in the United States. Estimate with 95% confidence the number of American adults who participate in exercise programs.

A15.14 XrA15-14   Low back pain is a common medical problem that sometimes results in disability and absence from work. Any method of treatment that decreases absence would be welcome by individuals and insurance companies. A randomized control study was undertaken to determine whether an alternate form of treatment is effective. The study examined 134 workers who were absent from work because of low back pain. Half the sample was assigned to graded activity, a physical exercise program designed to stimulate rapid return to work. The other half was assigned to the usual care, which involves mostly rest. For each worker, the number of days absent from work because of low back pain in the following 6 months was recorded. Do these data provide sufficient evidence to infer that the graded activity is effective?

A15.15 XrA15-15   Clinical depression is a serious and sometimes debilitating disease. It is often treated by antidepressants such as Prozac and Zoloft. Recent studies may indicate another possible remedy. Researchers took a random sample of people who are clinically depressed and divided them into three groups. The first group was treated with antidepressants and light therapy, the second was treated with a placebo and light therapy, and the third group treated with a placebo. Whether the patient showed improvement (code = 1) or not (code = 2) and the group number were recorded. Can we infer that there are differences between the three groups?

A15.16 How well do airlines keep to their schedules? To help answer this question, an economist conducted a survey of 780 takeoffs in the United States and determined that 77.4% of them departed on time (defined as a departure that is within 15 minutes of its scheduled time). There were about 10 million flight departures in the United States. Estimate with 95% confidence the total number of on-time departures.

GENERAL SOCIAL SURVEY EXERCISES

Conduct all tests at the 5% significance level. Use a 95% confidence level for estimates.

GSS2016 GSS2018   *Exercises A15.17 to A15.20 are based on the 2016 and 2018 surveys.*

A15.17 Were Americans in 2018 more optimistic about their children's future than in 2016? The survey asked, "When your children are at your age, what will their standard of living be (KIDSSOL: 1 = Much better, 2 = Somewhat better, 3 = About the same, 4 = Somewhat worse, 5 = Much worse)?" Is there enough evidence to conclude that people in 2018 were more likely to believe that their children will do much better than people in 2016?

A15.18 Was the economy in 2018 better than it was in 2016? One way to judge is to ask, "In the next 12 months how likely is it that you will lose your job or be laid off (JOBLOSE: 1 = Very likely, 2 = Fairly likely, 3 = Not too likely, 4 = Not likely)?" Is there enough evidence to infer that a greater proportion of Americans in 2018 than in 2016 believed that it was not likely that they would lose their job?

A15.19 The survey asked, "On the whole, how satisfied are you with the work you do (SATJOB: 1 = Very satisfied, 2 = Moderately satisfied, 3 = A little dissatisfied, 4 = Very dissatisfied)?" Is there sufficient evidence to conclude that Americans were less likely to respond very satisfied in 2018 than in 2016?

A15.20 Were Americans more educated (EDUC) in 2016 than in 2018? Conduct a test to answer the question.

GSS2016   *The following exercises are based on the 2016 survey.*

A15.21 Are there differences in marital status (MARITAL: Marital status: 1 = Married, 2 = Widowed, 3 = Divorced, 4 = Separated, 5 = Never married) between Democrats, Independents, and Republicans (PARTYID3)? Conduct a test to answer the question.

A15.22 In the 2016 survey, men and women were asked, Does the Earth go around the Sun or does the Sun go around the Earth (EARTHSUN: 1 = Earth around Sun, 2 = Sun around Earth, 8 = Don't know, 9 = No answer, 0 = Question not asked)? Is there enough statistical evidence to conclude that men and women differ in the knowledge about the question?

A15.23 Do men and women differ in the amount of television (TVHOURS)? Conduct a test to answer this question.

A15.24 Is there sufficient evidence to infer that people who work for themselves (WRKSLF: 1 = Self-employed, 2 = Someone else) have higher incomes (RINCOME) than people who work for someone else?

A15.25 Test to determine whether incomes (RINCOME) differ between the three racial categories (RACE: 1 = White, 2 = Black, 3 = Other).

A15.26 How does education affect marital status? Conduct a test to determine whether there were differences in education (EDUC) between the five marital status categories (MARITAL: 1 = Married, 2 = Widowed, 3 = Divorced, 4 = Separated, 5 = Never married).

A15.27 Is there enough evidence to infer that there are differences between Democrats, Independents, and Republicans (PARTYID3) with respect to education (EDUC)?

A15.28 Is there a relationship between marital status (MARITAL: 1 = Married, 2 = Widowed, 3 = Divorced, 4 = Separated, 5 = Never married) and highest degree completed (DEGREE: 0 = Left high school, 1 = High school, 2 = Junior college, 3 = Bachelor's degree, 4 = Graduate degree)? Conduct a statistical test to answer the question.

A15.29 Do liberals, moderates, and conservatives (POLVIEWS3) differ in their support of a law requiring a police permit to buy a gun (GUNLAW: 1 = Favor, 2 = Oppose)? Conduct a statistical test to answer the question.

A15.30 It is assumed that Democrats are for higher taxes and Republicans are for lower taxes. Conduct a test to determine whether there is enough statistical evidence to conclude that there are differences between Democrats, Independents, and Republicans (PARTYID3) in thinking whether their own income taxes (TAX: 1 = Too high, 2 = About right, 3 = Too low)?

A15.31 Can we infer that there is a relationship between degree attained (DEGREE: 0 = Left high school, 1 = High school, 2 = Junior college, 3 = Bachelor's degree, 4 = Graduate degree) and support for a law requiring a police permit to buy a gun (GUNLAW: 1 = Favor, 2 = Oppose)?

CASE A15.1   Which Diets Work?

Every year, millions of people start new diets. There is a bewildering array of diets to choose from. The question for many people is, Which ones work? Researchers at Tufts University in Boston made an attempt to point dieters in the right direction. Four diets were used:

1. Atkins low-carbohydrate diet
2. Zone high-protein, moderate-carbohydrate diet
3. Weight Watchers diet
4. Dr. Ornish's low-fat diet

The study recruited 160 overweight people and randomly assigned 40 to each diet. The average weight before dieting was 220 pounds, and all needed to lose between 30 and 80 pounds. All volunteers agreed to follow their diets for 2 months. No exercise or regular meetings were required. The following variables were recorded for each dieter using the format shown here:

Column 1: Identification number
Column 2: Diet
Column 3: Percent weight loss
Column 4: Percent low-density lipoprotein (LDL)—"bad" cholesterol—decrease
Column 5: Percent high-density lipoprotein (HDL)—"good" cholesterol—increase
Column 6: Quit after 2 months? 1 = yes, 2 = no
Column 7: Quit after 1 year? 1 = yes, 2 = no

Is there enough evidence to conclude that there are differences between the diets with respect to

a. percent weight loss?
b. percent LDL decrease?
c. percent HDL increase?
d. proportion quitting within 2 months?
e. proportion quitting after 1 year?

AshDesign/Shutterstock.com

16

SIMPLE LINEAR REGRESSION AND CORRELATION

CHAPTER OUTLINE

Education and Income: How Are They Related?

DATA
GSS2018
You are probably a student in an undergraduate or graduate business or economics program. Your plan is to graduate, get a good job, and draw a high salary. You have probably assumed that more education equals better job equals higher income. Is this true? Fortunately, the General Social Survey recorded two variables that will help determine whether education and income are related and, if so, what the value of an additional year of education might be.

Jupiterimages/Comstock Images/
Getty Images

On page 698, we will provide our answer.

INTRODUCTION

Regression analysis is used to predict the value of one variable on the basis of other variables. This technique may be the most commonly used statistical procedure because, as you can easily appreciate, almost all companies and government institutions forecast variables such as product demand, interest rates, inflation rates, prices of raw materials, and labor costs.

The technique involves developing a mathematical equation or model that describes the relationship between the variable to be forecast, which is called the **dependent variable**, and variables that the statistics practitioner believes are related to the dependent variable. The dependent variable is denoted as Y, whereas the related variables are called **independent variables** and are denoted as $X_1, X_2, \ldots, X_k$ (where k is the number of independent variables).

If we are interested only in determining whether a relationship exists, we employ correlation analysis, a technique that we have already introduced. In Chapter 3, we presented the graphical method to describe the association between two interval variables—the scatter diagram. We introduced the coefficient of correlation and covariance in Chapter 4.

Because regression analysis involves many new techniques and concepts, we divided the presentation into three chapters. In this chapter, we present techniques that allow us to determine the relationship between only two variables. In Chapter 17, we expand our discussion to more than two variables; in Chapter 18, we discuss how to build regression models.

Here are three illustrations of the use of regression analysis.

Illustration 1   The product manager in charge of a particular brand of children's breakfast cereal would like to predict the demand for the cereal during the next year. To use regression analysis, she and her staff list the following variables as likely to affect sales:

> Price of the product
>
> Number of children 5 to 12 years of age (the target market)
>
> Price of competitors' products
>
> Effectiveness of advertising (as measured by advertising exposure)
>
> Annual sales this year
>
> Annual sales in previous years

Illustration 2   A gold speculator is considering a major purchase of gold bullion. He would like to forecast the price of gold 2 years from now (his planning horizon), using regression analysis. In preparation, he produces the following list of independent variables:

> Interest rates
>
> Inflation rate
>
> Price of oil
>
> Demand for gold jewelry
>
> Demand for industrial and commercial gold
>
> Dow Jones Industrial Average

Illustration 3   A real estate agent wants to predict the selling price of houses more accurately. She believes that the following variables affect the price of a house:

> Size of the house (number of square feet)
>
> Number of bedrooms

Frontage of the lot

Condition

Location

In each of these illustrations, the primary motive for using regression analysis is forecasting. Nonetheless, analyzing the relationship among variables can also be quite useful in managerial decision making. For instance, in the first application, the product manager may want to know how price is related to product demand so that a decision about a prospective change in pricing can be made.

Regardless of why regression analysis is performed, the next step in the technique is to develop a mathematical equation or model that accurately describes the nature of the relationship that exists between the dependent variable and the independent variables. This stage—which is only a small part of the total process—is described in the next section. In the ensuing sections of this chapter (and in Chapter 17), we will spend considerable time assessing and testing how well the model fits the actual data. Only when we're satisfied with the model do we use it to estimate and forecast.

16-1 / Model

The job of developing a mathematical equation can be quite complex, because we need to have some idea about the nature of the relationship between each of the independent variables and the dependent variable. The number of different mathematical models that could be proposed is virtually infinite. Here is an example from Chapter 4.

Profit = (Price per unit − variable cost per unit)
× Number of units sold − Fixed costs

You may encounter the next example in a finance course:

$$F = P(1 + i)^n$$

where

F = future value of an investment

P = principle or present value

i = interest rate per period

n = number of periods

These are all examples of **deterministic models**, so named because such equations allow us to determine the value of the dependent variable (on the left side of the equation) from the values of the independent variables. In many practical applications of interest to us, deterministic models are unrealistic. For example, is it reasonable to believe that we can determine the selling price of a house solely on the basis of its size? Unquestionably, the size of a house affects its price, but many other variables (some of which may not be measurable) also influence price. What must be included in most practical models is a method to represent the randomness that is part of a real-life process. Such a model is called a **probabilistic model**.

To create a probabilistic model, we start with a deterministic model that approximates the relationship we want to model. We then add a term that measures the random error of the deterministic component.

Suppose that in illustration 3, the real estate agent knows that the cost of building a new house is about \$100 per square foot and that most lots sell for about \$100,000. The approximate selling price would be

$$y = 100,000 + 100x$$

where y = selling price and x = size of the house in square feet. A house of 2,000 square feet would therefore be estimated to sell for

$$y = 100,000 + 100(2,000) = 300,000$$

We know, however, that the selling price is not likely to be exactly \$300,000. Prices may actually range from \$200,000 to \$400,000. In other words, the deterministic model is not really suitable. To represent this situation properly, we should use the probabilistic model

$$y = 100,000 + 100x + \varepsilon$$

where ε (the Greek letter epsilon) represents the **error variable**—the difference between the actual selling price and the estimated price based on the size of the house. The error thus accounts for all the variables, measurable and immeasurable, that are not part of the model. The value of ε will vary from one sale to the next, even if x remains constant. In other words, houses of exactly the same size will sell for different prices because of differences in location and number of bedrooms and bathrooms, as well as other variables.

In the three chapters devoted to regression analysis, we will present only probabilistic models. In this chapter, we describe only the straight-line model with one independent variable. This model is called the **first-order linear model**—sometimes called the **simple linear regression model**.[*]

First-Order Linear Model

$$y = \beta_0 + \beta_1 x + \varepsilon$$

where

y = dependent variable

x = independent variable

β_0 = y-intercept

β_1 = slope of the line (defined as rise/run)

ε = error variable

The problem objective addressed by the model is to analyze the relationship between two variables, x and y, both of which must be interval. To define the relationship between x and y, we need to know the value of the coefficients β_0 and β_1. However, these coefficients are population parameters, which are almost always unknown. In the next section, we discuss how these parameters are estimated.

---

[*]We use the term *linear* in two ways. The "linear" in linear regression refers to the form of the model wherein the terms form a linear combination of the coefficients β_0 and β_1. Thus, for example, the model $y = \beta_0 + \beta_1 x^2 + \varepsilon$ is a linear combination whereas $y = \beta_0 + \beta_1^2 x + \varepsilon$ is not. The simple linear regression model $y = \beta_0 + \beta_1 x + \varepsilon$ describes a straight-line or linear relationship between the dependent variable and one independent variable. In this book, we use the linear regression technique only. Hence, when we use the word *linear* we will be referring to the straight-line relationship between the variables.

SOLUTION:

IDENTIFY

Notice that the problem objective is to analyze the relationship between two interval variables. Because we believe that the odometer reading affects the selling price, we identify the former as the independent variable, which we label x, and the latter as the dependent variable, which we label y.

COMPUTE

MANUALLY:

From the data set, we find

$$\sum_{i=1}^{n} x_i = 3,601.1$$

$$\sum_{i=1}^{n} y_i = 1,484.1$$

$$\sum_{i=1}^{n} x_i y_i = 53,155.93$$

$$\sum_{i=1}^{n} x_i^2 = 133,986.59$$

Next we calculate the covariance and the variance of the independent variable x:

$$s_{xy} = \frac{1}{n-1}\left[\sum_{i=1}^{n} x_i y_i - \frac{\sum_{i=1}^{n} x_i \sum_{i=1}^{n} y_i}{n}\right]$$

$$= \frac{1}{100-1}\left[53,155.93 - \frac{(3,601.1)(1,484.1)}{100}\right] = -2.909$$

$$s_x^2 = \frac{1}{n-1}\left[\sum_{i=1}^{n} x_i^2 - \frac{\left(\sum_{i=1}^{n} x_i\right)^2}{n}\right]$$

$$= \frac{1}{100-1}\left[133,986.59 - \frac{(3,601.1)^2}{100}\right] = 43.509$$

The slope coefficient is calculated next:

$$b_1 = \frac{s_{xy}}{s_x^2} = \frac{-2.909}{43.509} = -.0669$$

The y-intercept is computed as follows:

$$\bar{x} = \frac{\sum x_i}{n} = \frac{3,601.1}{100} = 36.011$$

$$\bar{y} = \frac{\sum y_i}{n} = \frac{1,484.1}{100} = 14.841$$

$$b_0 = \bar{y} - b_1\bar{x} = 14.841 - (-.0669)(36.011) = 17.250$$

The sample regression line is

$$\hat{y} = 17.250 - 0.0669x$$

EXCEL Data Analysis

	A	B	C	D	E	F	G
1	SUMMARY OUTPUT						
2							
3	*Regression Statistics*						
4	Multiple R	0.8052					
5	R Square	0.6483					
6	Adjusted R Square	0.6447					
7	Standard Error	0.3265					
8	Observations	100					
9							
10	ANOVA						
11		*df*	*SS*	*MS*	*F*	*Significance F*	
12	Regression	1	19.26	19.26	180.64	5.75E-24	
13	Residual	98	10.45	0.11			
14	Total	99	29.70				
15							
16		*Coefficients*	*Standard Error*	*t Stat*	*P-value*	*Lower 95%*	*Upper 95%*
17	Intercept	17.25	0.182	94.73	3.57E-98	16.89	17.61
18	Odometer	−0.0669	0.0050	−13.44	5.75E-24	−0.0767	−0.0570

INSTRUCTIONS

1. Type or import data into two columns*, one storing the dependent variable and the other the independent variable. (Open Xm16-02.)
2. Click **Data, Data Analysis**, and **Regression**.
3. Specify the **Input Y Range** (A1:A101) and the **Input X Range** (B1:B101).

To draw the scatter diagram, follow the instructions provided in Chapter 3 on page 75.

The printouts include more statistics than we need right now. However, we will be discussing the rest of the printouts later.

INTERPRET

The slope coefficient b_1 is −0.0669, which means that for each additional 1,000 miles on the odometer, the price decreases by an average of $.0669 thousand. Expressed more simply, the slope tells us that for each additional mile on the odometer, the price decreases on average by $.0669 or 6.69 cents.

The intercept is $b_0 = 17.250$. Technically, the intercept is the point at which the regression line and the y-axis intersect. This means that when $x = 0$ (i.e., the car was not driven at all) the selling price is 17.250 thousand or $17,250. We might be tempted to interpret this number as the price of cars that have not been driven. However, in this case, the intercept is probably meaningless. Because our sample did not include any cars with zero miles on the odometer, we have no basis for interpreting b_0. As a general rule, we cannot determine the value of $\hat{y}$ for a value of x that is far outside the range of the sample values of x. In this example, the smallest and largest values of x are 19.1 and 49.2, respectively. Because $x = 0$ is not in this interval, we cannot safely interpret the value of $\hat{y}$ when $x = 0$.

It is important to bear in mind that the interpretation of the coefficients pertains only to the sample, which consists of 100 observations. To infer information about the population, we need statistical inference techniques, which are described subsequently.

In the sections that follow, we will return to this problem and the computer output to introduce other statistics associated with regression analysis.

---

*If one or both columns contain an empty cell (representing missing data), the row must be removed. See online appendix Excel Instructions for Deleting Rows with Blanks.

EXERCISES

16.1 The term *regression* was originally used in 1885 by Sir Francis Galton in his analysis of the relationship between the heights of children and parents. He formulated the "law of universal regression," which specifies that "each peculiarity in a man is shared by his kinsmen, but on average in a less degree." (Evidently, people spoke this way in 1885.) In 1903, two statisticians, K. Pearson and A. Lee, took a random sample of 1,078 father–son pairs to examine Galton's law ("On the Laws of Inheritance in Man, I. Inheritance of Physical Characteristics," *Biometrika* 2:457–462). Their sample regression line was

Son's height = 33.73 + .516 × Father's height

a. Interpret the coefficients.
b. What does the regression line tell you about the heights of sons of tall fathers?
c. What does the regression line tell you about the heights of sons of short fathers?

16.2 Xr16-02 Attempting to analyze the relationship between advertising and sales, the owner of a furniture store recorded the monthly advertising budget ($thousands) and the sales ($millions) for a sample of 12 months. The data are listed here.

Advertising	23	46	60	54	28	33
Sales	9.6	11.3	12.8	9.8	8.9	12.5

Advertising	25	31	36	88	90	99
Sales	12.0	11.4	12.6	13.7	14.4	15.9

a. Draw a scatter diagram. Does it appear that advertising and sales are linearly related?
b. Calculate the least squares line and interpret the coefficients.

16.3 Xr16-03 To determine how the number of housing starts is affected by mortgage rates an economist recorded the average mortgage rate and the number of housing starts in a large county for the past 10 years. These data are listed here.

Rate	8.5	7.8	7.6	7.5	8.0
Starts	115	111	185	201	206

Rate	8.4	8.8	8.9	8.5	8.0
Starts	167	155	117	133	150

a. Determine the regression line.
b. What do the coefficients of the regression line tell you about the relationship between mortgage rates and housing starts?

16.4 Xr16-04 Critics of television often refer to the detrimental effects that all the violence shown on television has on children. However, there may be another problem. It may be that watching television also reduces the amount of physical exercise, causing weight gains. A sample of 15 10-year-old children was taken. The number of pounds each child was overweight was recorded (a negative number indicates the child is underweight). In addition, the number of hours of television viewing per week was also recorded. These data are listed here.

Television	42	34	25	35	37	38	31	33
Overweight	18	6	0	−1	13	14	7	7

Television	19	29	38	28	29	36	18
Overweight	−9	8	8	5	3	14	−7

a. Draw the scatter diagram.
b. Calculate the sample regression line and describe what the coefficients tell you about the relationship between the two variables.

16.5 Xr16-05 To help determine how many beers to stock the concession manager at Yankee Stadium wanted to know how the temperature affected beer sales. Accordingly, the manager took a sample of 10 games and recorded the number of beers sold and the temperature in the middle of the game.

Temperature	80	68	78	79	87
Number of beers	20,533	1,439	13,829	21,286	30,985

Temperature	74	86	92	77	84
Number of beers	17,187	30,240	37,596	9,610	28,742

a. Compute the coefficients of the regression line.
b. Interpret the coefficients.

The exercises that follow were created to allow you to see how regression analysis is used to solve realistic problems. As a result, most feature a large number of observations. We anticipate that most students will solve these problems using a computer and statistical software. However, for students without these resources, we have computed the means, variances, and covariances that will permit them to complete the calculations manually. (See Appendix A.)

16.6 Xr16-06+ In television's early years, most commercials were 60 seconds long. Now, however, commercials can be any length. The objective of commercials remains the same—to have as many viewers as possible remember the product in a favorable way and eventually buy it. In an experiment to determine how the length of a commercial is related to people's memory of it, 60 randomly selected people were asked to watch a 1-hour television program. In the middle of the show, a commercial advertising a brand of toothpaste appeared. Some viewers watched a commercial that lasted for 20 seconds, others watched one that lasted for 24 seconds, 28 seconds, . . . , 60 seconds. The essential content of the commercials was the same. After the show, each person was given a test to measure how much they remembered about the product. The commercial times and test scores (on a 30-point test) were recorded.
   a. Draw a scatter diagram of the data to determine whether a linear model appears to be appropriate.
   b. Determine the least squares line.
   c. Interpret the coefficients.

16.7 Xr16-07 Not content with the conclusion of the chapter-opening example, an economist wanted to determine whether there is a linear relationship between education and after-tax income. A random sample of households was drawn and the years of education of the most educated person in the household and the after-tax income were recorded. Determine the least squares line and interpret the coefficients.

Source: Bureau of Labor Statistics.

16.8 Xr16-08 As a general rule the cost of land in small towns and cities is less than that of large cities. Consequently, property values and property taxes are also lower. To investigate, a realtor undertook a survey that asked a random sample of property owners to report their most recent property tax bill and the size of the city they lived in. Determine the least squares line and describe the information the coefficients provide.

Source: U.S. Census.

16.9 Xr16-09+ Florida condominiums are popular winter retreats for many North Americans. In recent years, the prices have steadily increased. A real estate agent wanted to know why prices of similar-sized apartments in the same building vary. A possible answer lies in the floor. It may be that the higher the floor, the greater the sale price of the apartment. The price of 1,200 sq. ft. condominiums in several buildings in the same location that have sold recently and the floor number of the condominium were recorded.
   a. Determine the regression line.
   b. What do the coefficients tell you about the relationship between the two variables?

16.10 Xr16-10 In 2020, the United States conducted a census of the entire country. The census is completed by mail. To help ensure that the questions are understood, a random sample of Americans take the questionnaire before it is sent out. As part of their analysis, they record the amount of time and ages of the sample. Use the least squares method to analyze the relationship between the amount of time taken to complete the questionnaire and the age of the individual answering the questions. What do the coefficients tell you about the relationship between the two variables?

16.11 Xr16-11 An economist wanted to analyze the relationship between the number of residents in a household (called consumer units) and income. A random sample of households was drawn and each reported the number of consumer units and the annual income. Compute the least squares line and briefly describe what the values of the y-intercept and slope coefficient tell you about the two variables.

16.12 Xr16-12+ According to ESPN there are 34,011 golf courses in the world. There are 15,372 in the United States, down from a peak of 16,952. Part of the problem is that golf is a time-consuming game often requiring five or more hours to complete a round. A consultant hired by the American Association of Golf Courses conducted a telephone survey of golfers. Each respondent reported the amount of time (in minutes) to complete the most recent round and the yardage of the course played. Calculate the least squares. Describe the information provided by the y-intercept and the slope coefficient.

16.13 Xr16-13 Fire damage in the United States amounts to billions of dollars, much of it insured. The time taken to arrive at the fire is critical. This raises the question, should insurance companies lower premiums if the home to be insured is close to a fire station? To help make a decision, a study was undertaken wherein a number of fires were investigated. The distance to the nearest fire station (in miles) and the percentage of fire damage were recorded. Determine the least squares line and interpret the coefficients.

16.14 Xr16-14+ A real estate agent specializing in commercial real estate wanted a more precise method of judging the likely selling price (in $1,000s) of apartment buildings. As a first effort, the price of a number of apartment buildings sold recently and the number of square feet (in 1,000s) in the building were recorded.

a. Calculate the regression line.

b. What do the coefficients tell you about the relationship between price and square footage?

16.15 Xr16-15 An economist for the federal government is attempting to produce a better measure of poverty than is currently in use. To help acquire information, the annual household income (in $1,000s) and the amount of money spent on food during one week for a random sample of households were recorded. Determine the regression line and interpret the coefficients.

16.16 Xr16-16+ An economist wanted to investigate the relationship between office rents (the dependent variable) and vacancy rates. The economist took a random sample of monthly office rents and the percentage of vacant office space in 30 different cities. Determine the regression line and interpret the coefficients.

16.17 Xr16-17+ Millions of boats are registered in the United States. As is the case with automobiles, there is an active used-boat market. Many of the boats purchased require bank financing, and, as a result, it is important for financial institutions to be capable of accurately estimating the price of boats. One variable that affects the price is the number of hours the engine has been run. To determine the effect of the hours on the price, a financial analyst recorded the price of a sample of 2015 24-foot Sea Ray cruisers (one of the most popular boats) and the number of hours they had been run. Determine the least squares line and explain what the coefficients tell you.

16.18 Xr16-18 Besides their known long-term effects, do cigarettes also cause short-term illnesses such as colds? To help answer this question, a sample of smokers was drawn. Each person was asked to report the average number of cigarettes smoked per day and the number of days absent from work due to colds last year.

a. Determine the regression line.

b. What do the coefficients tell you about the relationship between smoking cigarettes and sick days because of colds?

16.19 Xr16-19 Does living in a small town versus a large city affect incomes? To answer this question a random sample of Americans was taken and each respondent's after-tax income and the size of the city they live in were recorded. Use the least squares method to compute the coefficients of the regression line. What information to the y-intercept and slope provide?

16.20 Xr03-80 (Exercise 3.80 revisited) In an attempt to determine the factors that affect the amount of energy used, 200 households were analyzed. In each, the number of occupants and the amount of electricity used were measured. Determine the regression line and interpret the results.

16.21 Xr03-82 (Exercise 3.82 revisited) One general belief held by observers of the business world is that taller men earn more money than shorter men. In a University of Pittsburgh study, 250 MBA graduates, all about 30 years old, were polled and asked to report their height (in inches) and their annual income (to the nearest $1,000). Determine the regression line. What do the coefficients tell you?

APPLICATIONS in HUMAN RESOURCES MANAGEMENT

Retaining Workers

Human resource managers are responsible for a variety of tasks within organizations. As we pointed out in the introduction in Chapter 1, personnel or human resource managers are involved with recruiting new workers, determining which applicants are most suitable to hire, and helping with various aspects of monitoring the workforce, including absenteeism and worker turnover. For many firms, worker turnover is a costly problem. First, there is the cost of recruiting and attracting qualified workers. The firm must advertise vacant positions and make certain that applicants are judged properly. Second, the cost of

(Continued)

training hirees can be high, particularly in technical areas. Third, new employees are often not as productive and efficient as experienced employees. Consequently, it is in the interests of the firm to attract and keep the best workers. Any information that the personnel manager can obtain is likely to be useful.

16.22 Xr16-22 The human resource manager of a telemarketing firm is concerned about the rapid turnover of the firm's telemarketers. It appears that many telemarketers do not work very long before quitting. There may be a number of reasons, including relatively low pay, personal unsuitability for the work, and the low probability of advancement. Because of the high cost of hiring and training new workers, the manager decided to examine the factors that influence workers to quit. The manager reviewed the work history of a random sample of workers who have quit in the last year and recorded the number of weeks on the job before quitting and the age of each worker when originally hired.

  a. Use regression analysis to describe how the work period and age are related.
  b. Briefly discuss what the coefficients tell you.

16-3 / ERROR VARIABLE: REQUIRED CONDITIONS

In the previous section, we used the least squares method to estimate the coefficients of the linear regression model. A critical part of this model is the error variable ε. In the next section, we will present an inferential method that determines whether there is a relationship between the dependent and independent variables. Later we will show how we use the regression equation to estimate and predict. For these methods to be valid, however, four requirements involving the probability distribution of the error variable must be satisfied.

> **Required Conditions for the Error Variable**
> 1. The probability distribution of ε is normal.
> 2. The mean of the distribution is 0; that is, $E(\varepsilon) = 0$.
> 3. The standard deviation of ε is σ_ε, which is a constant regardless of the value of x.
> 4. The value of ε associated with any particular value of y is independent of ε associated with any other value of y.

Requirements 1, 2, and 3 can be interpreted in another way: For each value of x, y is a normally distributed random variable whose mean is

$$E(y) = \beta_0 + \beta_1 x$$

and whose standard deviation is σ_ε. Notice that the mean depends on x. The standard deviation, however, is not influenced by x because it is a constant over all values of x. Figure 16.3 depicts this interpretation. Notice that for each value of x, $E(y)$ changes, but the shape of the distribution of y remains the same. In other words, for each x, y is normally distributed with the same standard deviation.

FIGURE **16.3** Distribution of y Given x

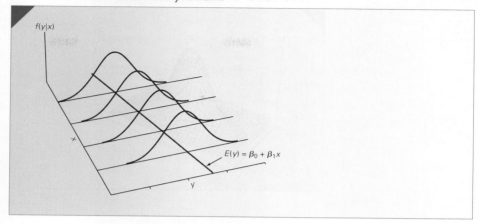

In Section 16-6, we will discuss how departures from these required conditions affect the regression analysis and how they are identified.

16-3a Observational and Experimental Data

In Chapter 5 and again in Chapter 13, we described the difference between observational and experimental data. We pointed out that statistics practitioners often design controlled experiments to enable them to interpret the results of their analyses more clearly than would be the case after conducting an observational study. Example 16.2 is an illustration of observational data. In that example, we merely observed the odometer reading and auction selling price of 100 randomly selected cars.

If you examine Exercise 16.6, you will see experimental data gathered through a controlled experiment. To determine the effect of the length of a television commercial on its viewers' memories of the product advertised, the statistics practitioner arranged for 60 television viewers to watch a commercial of differing lengths and then tested their memories of that commercial. Each viewer was randomly assigned a commercial length. The values of x ranged from 20 to 60 and were set by the statistics practitioner as part of the experiment. For each value of x, the distribution of the memory test scores is assumed to be normally distributed with a constant variance.

We can summarize the difference between the experiment described in Example 16.2 and the one described in Exercise 16.6. In Example 16.2, both the odometer reading and the auction selling price are random variables. We hypothesize that for each possible odometer reading, there is a theoretical population of auction selling prices that are normally distributed with a mean that is a linear function of the odometer reading and a variance that is constant. In Exercise 16.6, the length of the commercial is not a random variable but a series of values selected by the statistics practitioner. For each commercial length, the memory test scores are required to be normally distributed with a constant variance.

Regression analysis can be applied to data generated from either observational or controlled experiments. In both cases, our objective is to determine how the independent variable is related to the dependent variable. However, observational data can be analyzed in another way. When the data are observational, both variables are random variables. We need not specify that one variable is independent and the other is dependent. We can simply determine *whether* the two variables are related. The equivalent

FIGURE **16.4** Bivariate Normal Distribution

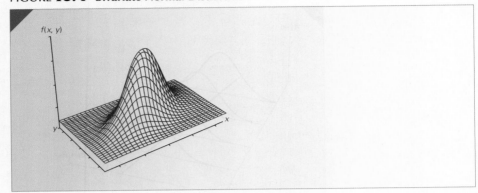

of the required conditions described in the previous box is that the two variables are bivariate normally distributed. (Recall that in Section 7-2 we introduced the bivariate distribution, which describes the joint probability of two variables.) A bivariate normal distribution is described in Figure 16.4. As you can see, it is a three-dimensional bell-shaped curve. The dimensions are the variables x, y, and the joint density function $f(x, y)$.

In Section 16-4, we will discuss the statistical technique that is used when both x and y are random variables and they are bivariate normally distributed. In Chapter 19, we will introduce a procedure applied when the normality requirement is not satisfied.

EXERCISES

16.23 Describe what the required conditions mean in Exercise 16.6. If the conditions are satisfied, what can you say about the distribution of memory test scores?

16.24 What are the required conditions for Exercise 16.10? Do these seem reasonable?

16.25 Assuming that the required conditions are satisfied in Exercise 16.17, what does this tell you about the distribution of used boat prices?

16-4 / ASSESSING THE MODEL

The least squares method produces the best straight line. However, there may, in fact, be no relationship or perhaps a nonlinear relationship between the two variables. If so, a straight-line model is likely to be impractical. Consequently, it is important for us to assess how well the linear model fits the data. If the fit is poor, we should discard the linear model and seek another one.

Several methods are used to evaluate the model. In this section, we present two statistics and one test procedure to determine whether a linear model should be employed. They are the **standard error of estimate**, the t-test of the slope, and the coefficient of determination. All these methods are based on the sum of squares for error.

16-4a Sum of Squares for Error

The least squares method determines the coefficients that minimize the sum of squared deviations between the points and the line defined by the coefficients. Recall from Section 16-2 that the minimized sum of squared deviations is called the *sum of squares for error*, denoted SSE. In that section, we demonstrated the direct method of calculating SSE. For each value of x, we compute the value of $\hat{y}$. In other words, for $i = 1$ to n, we compute

$$\hat{y}_i = b_0 + b_1 x_i$$

For each point, we then compute the difference between the actual value of y and the value calculated at the line, which is the residual. We square each residual and sum the squared values. Table 16.1 on page 678 shows these calculations for Example 16.1. To calculate SSE manually requires a great deal of arithmetic. Fortunately, there is a shortcut method available that uses the sample variances and the covariance.

Shortcut Calculation of SSE

$$\text{SSE} = \sum_{i=1}^{n} (y_i - \hat{y}_i)^2 = (n-1)\left(s_y^2 - \frac{s_{xy}^2}{s_x^2} \right)$$

where s_y^2 is the sample variance of the dependent variable.

16-4b Standard Error of Estimate

In Section 16-3, we pointed out that the error variable ε is normally distributed with mean 0 and standard deviation σ_ε. If σ_ε is large, some of the errors will be large, which implies that the model's fit is poor. If σ_ε is small, the errors tend to be close to the mean (which is 0); as a result, the model fits well. Hence, we could use σ_ε to measure the suitability of using a linear model. Unfortunately, σ_ε is a population parameter and, like most other parameters, is unknown. We can, however, estimate σ_ε from the data. The estimate is based on SSE. The unbiased estimator of the variance of the error variable σ_ε^2 is

$$s_\varepsilon^2 = \frac{\text{SSE}}{n-2}$$

The square root of s_ε^2 is called the *standard error of estimate*.

Standard Error of Estimate

$$s_\varepsilon = \sqrt{\frac{\text{SSE}}{n-2}}$$

EXAMPLE 16.3

Odometer Reading and Prices of Used Toyota Camrys—Part 2

Find the standard error of estimate for Example 16.2 and describe what it tells you about the model's fit.

SOLUTION:

COMPUTE

MANUALLY:

To compute the standard error of estimate, we must compute SSE, which is calculated from the sample variances and the covariance. We have already determined the covariance and the variance of x: -2.909 and 43.509, respectively. The sample variance of y (applying the shortcut method) is

$$s_y^2 = \frac{1}{n-1}\left[\sum_{i=1}^{n}y_i^2 - \frac{\left(\sum_{i=1}^{n}y_i\right)^2}{n}\right]$$

$$= \frac{1}{100-1}\left[22,055.23 - \frac{(1,484.1)^2}{100}\right]$$

$$= .300$$

$$\text{SSE} = (n-1)\left(s_y^2 - \frac{s_{xy}^2}{s_x^2}\right)$$

$$= (100-1)\left[.300 - \frac{(-2.909)^2}{43.509}\right]$$

$$= 10.445$$

The standard error of estimate follows:

$$s_\varepsilon = \sqrt{\frac{\text{SSE}}{n-2}} = \sqrt{\frac{10.445}{98}} = .3265$$

EXCEL Data Analysis

Standard Error	0.3265

This part of the Excel printout was copied from the complete printout on page 680.

INTERPRET

The smallest value that s_ε can assume is 0, which occurs when SSE = 0, that is, when all the points fall on the regression line. Thus, when s_ε is small, the fit is excellent, and the linear model is likely to be an effective analytical and forecasting tool. If s_ε is large, the model is a poor one, and the statistics practitioner should improve it or discard it.

We judge the value of s_ε by comparing it to the values of the dependent variable y or more specifically to the sample mean $\bar{y}$. In this example, because $s_\varepsilon = .3265$ and $\bar{y} = 14.841$, it does appear that the standard error of estimate is small. However, because there is no predefined upper limit on s_ε, it is often difficult to assess the model in this way.

In general, the standard error of estimate cannot be used as an absolute measure of the model's utility.

Nonetheless, s_ε is useful in comparing models. If the statistics practitioner has several models from which to choose, the one with the smallest value of s_ε should generally be the one used. As you'll see, s_ε is also an important statistic in other procedures associated with regression analysis.

16-4c Testing the Slope

To understand this method of assessing the linear model, consider the consequences of applying the regression technique to two variables that are not at all linearly related. If we could observe the entire population and draw the regression line, we would observe the scatter diagram shown in Figure 16.5. The line is horizontal, which means that no matter what value of x is used, we would estimate the same value for $\hat{y}$; thus, y is not linearly related to x. Recall that a horizontal straight line has a slope of 0, that is, $\beta_1 = 0$.

FIGURE **16.5** Scatter Diagram of Entire Population with $\beta_1 = 0$

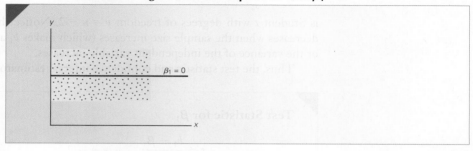

Because we rarely examine complete populations, the parameters are unknown. However, we can draw inferences about the population slope β_1 from the sample slope b_1.

The process of testing hypotheses about β_1 is identical to the process of testing any other parameter. We begin with the hypotheses. The null hypothesis specifies that there is no linear relationship, which means that the slope is 0. Thus, we specify

H_0: $\beta_1 = 0$

It must be noted that if the null hypothesis is true, it does not necessarily mean that no relationship exists. For example, a quadratic relationship described in Figure 16.6 may exist where $\beta_1 = 0$.

FIGURE **16.6** Quadratic Relationship

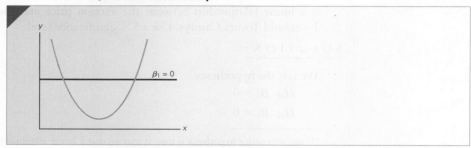

We can conduct one- or two-tail tests of β_1. Most often, we perform a two-tail test to determine whether there is sufficient evidence to infer that a linear relationship exists.* We test the alternative hypothesis

$$H_1: \quad \beta_1 \neq 0$$

16-4d Estimator and Sampling Distribution

In Section 16-2, we pointed out that b_1 is an unbiased estimator of β_1; that is,

$$E(b_1) = \beta_1$$

The estimated standard error of b_1 is

$$s_{b_1} = \frac{s_\varepsilon}{\sqrt{(n-1)s_x^2}}$$

where s_ε is the standard error of estimate and s_x^2 is the sample variance of the independent variable. If the required conditions outlined in Section 16-3 are satisfied, the sampling distribution of the t-statistic

$$t = \frac{b_1 - \beta_1}{s_{b_1}}$$

is Student t with degrees of freedom $\nu = n - 2$. Notice that the standard error of b_1 decreases when the sample size increases (which makes b_1 a consistent estimator of β_1) or the variance of the independent variable increases.

Thus, the test statistic and confidence interval estimator are as follows.

Test Statistic for β_1

$$t = \frac{b_1 - \beta_1}{s_{b_1}} \qquad \nu = n - 2$$

Confidence Interval Estimator of β_1

$$b_1 \pm t_{\alpha/2} s_{b_1} \qquad \nu = n - 2$$

EXAMPLE **16.4**

Are Odometer Reading and Price of Used Toyota Camrys Related?

Test to determine whether there is enough evidence in Example 16.2 to infer that there is a linear relationship between the auction price and the odometer reading for all 3-year-old Toyota Camrys. Use a 5% significance level.

SOLUTION:

We test the hypotheses

$$H_0: \quad \beta_1 = 0$$
$$H_1: \quad \beta_1 \neq 0$$

---

*If the alternative hypothesis is true, it may be that a linear relationship exists or that a nonlinear relationship exists but that the relationship can be approximated by a straight line.

If the null hypothesis is true, no linear relationship exists. If the alternative hypothesis is true, some linear relationship exists.

COMPUTE

MANUAL LY:

To compute the value of the test statistic, we need b_1 and s_{b_1}. In Example 16.2, we found

$$b_1 = -.0669$$

and

$$s_x^2 = 43.509$$

Thus,

$$s_{b_1} = \frac{s_\varepsilon}{\sqrt{(n-1)s_x^2}} = \frac{.3265}{\sqrt{(99)(43.509)}} = .00497$$

The value of the test statistic is

$$t = \frac{b_1 - \beta_1}{s_{b_1}} = \frac{-.0669 - 0}{.00497} = -13.46$$

The rejection region is

$$t < -t_{\alpha/2,\,\nu} = -t_{.025,98} \approx -1.984 \quad \text{or} \quad t > t_{\alpha/2,\nu} = t_{.025,98} \approx 1.984$$

EXCEL Data Analysis

	Coefficients	Standard Error	t Stat	P-value	Lower 95%	Upper 95%
Intercept	17.25	0.182	94.73	3.57E-98	16.89	17.61
Odometer	−0.0669	0.0050	−13.44	5.75E-24	−0.0767	−0.0570

INTERPRET

The value of the test statistic is $t = -13.44$, with a p-value of 0. There is overwhelming evidence to infer that a linear relationship exists. What this means is that the odometer reading may affect the auction selling price of the cars. (See the subsection on cause-and-effect relationship on page 695.)

As was the case when we interpreted the y-intercept, the conclusion we draw here is valid only over the range of the values of the independent variable. We can infer that there is a relationship between odometer reading and auction price for the 3-year-old Toyota Camrys whose odometer readings lie between 19.1 (thousand) and 49.2 (thousand) miles (the minimum and maximum values of x in the sample). Because we have no observations outside this range, we do not know how, or even whether, the two variables are related.

Notice that the printout includes a test for β_0. However, as we pointed out before, interpreting the value of the y-intercept can lead to erroneous, if not ridiculous, conclusions. Consequently, we generally ignore the test of β_0.

We can also acquire information about the relationship by estimating the slope coefficient. In this example, the 95% confidence interval estimate (approximating $t_{.025}$ with 98 degrees of freedom with $t_{.025}$ with 100 degrees of freedom) is

$$b_1 \pm t_{\alpha/2}s_{b_1} = -.0669 \pm 1.984(.00497) = -.0669 \pm .0099$$

We estimate that the slope coefficient lies between $-.0768$ and $-.0570$. Excel prints the interval estimate of the slope as well as the interval estimate of the intercept.

16-4e One-Tail Tests

If we wish to test for positive or negative linear relationships, we conduct one-tail tests. To illustrate, suppose that in Example 16.2 we wanted to know whether there is evidence of a negative linear relationship between odometer reading and auction selling price. We would specify the hypotheses as

H_0: $\beta_1 = 0$

H_1: $\beta_1 < 0$

The value of the test statistic would be exactly as computed previously (Example 16.4). However, in this case the p-value would be the two-tail p-value divided by 2; using Excel's p-value, this would be $(5.75 \times 10^{-24})/2 = 2.875 \times 10^{-24}$, which is still approximately 0.

16-4f Coefficient of Determination

The test of β_1 addresses only the question of whether there is enough evidence to infer that a linear relationship exists. In many cases, however, it is also useful to measure the strength of that linear relationship, particularly when we want to compare several different models. The statistic that performs this function is the **coefficient of determination**, which is denoted R^2. Statistics practitioners often refer to this statistic as the "R-square." Recall that we introduced the coefficient of determination in Chapter 4, where we pointed out that this statistic is a measure of the amount of variation in the dependent variable that is explained by the variation in the independent variable. However, we did not describe why we interpret the R-square in this way.

Coefficient of Determination

$$R^2 = \frac{s_{xy}^2}{s_x^2 s_y^2}$$

With a little algebra, statisticians can show that

$$R^2 = 1 - \frac{SSE}{\sum(y_i - \bar{y})^2}$$

We'll return to Example 16.1 to learn more about how to interpret the coefficient of determination. In Chapter 14, we partitioned the total sum of squares into two sources of variation. We do so here as well. We begin by adding and subtracting $\hat{y}_i$ from the deviation between y_i from the mean $\bar{y}$; that is,

$$(y_i - \bar{y}) = (y_i - \bar{y}) + \hat{y}_i - \hat{y}_i$$

We observe that by rearranging the terms, the deviation between y_i and $\bar{y}$ can be decomposed into two parts; that is,

$$(y_i - \bar{y}) = (y_i - \hat{y}_i) + (\hat{y}_i - \bar{y})$$

This equation is represented graphically (for $i = 5$) in Figure 16.7.

FIGURE **16.7** Partitioning the Deviation for $i = 5$

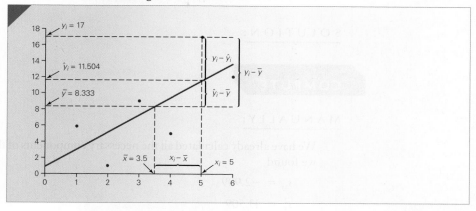

Now we ask why the values of y are different from one another. From Figure 16.7, we see that part of the difference between y_i and $\bar{y}$ is the difference between $\hat{y}_i$ and $\bar{y}$, which is accounted for by the difference between x_i and $\bar{x}$. In other words, some of the variation in y is explained by the changes to x. The other part of the difference between y_i and $\bar{y}$, however, is accounted for by the difference between y_i and $\hat{y}_i$. This difference is the residual, which represents variables not otherwise represented by the model. As a result, we say that this part of the difference is *unexplained* by the variation in x.

If we now square both sides of the equation, sum over all sample points, and perform some algebra, we produce

$$\sum (y_i - \bar{y})^2 = \sum (y_i - \hat{y}_i)^2 + \sum (\hat{y}_i - \bar{y})^2$$

The quantity on the left side of this equation is a measure of the variation in the dependent variable y. The first quantity on the right side of the equation is SSE, and the second term is denoted SSR, for sum of squares for regression. We can rewrite the equation as

Variation in y = SSE + SSR

As we did in the analysis of variance, we partition the variation of y into two parts: SSE, which measures the amount of variation in y that remains unexplained; and SSR, which measures the amount of variation in y that is explained by the variation in the independent variable x. We can incorporate this analysis into the definition of R^2.

Coefficient of Determination

$$R^2 = 1 - \frac{\text{SSE}}{\sum (y_i - \bar{y})^2} = \frac{\sum (y_i - \bar{y})^2 - \text{SSE}}{\sum (y_i - \bar{y})^2} = \frac{\text{Explained variation}}{\text{Variation in } y}$$

It follows that R^2 measures the proportion of the variation in y that can be explained by the variation in x.

EXAMPLE 16.5

Measuring the Strength of the Linear Relationship between Odometer Reading and Price of Used Toyota Camrys

Find the coefficient of determination for Example 16.2 and describe what this statistic tells you about the regression model.

SOLUTION:

COMPUTE

MANUALLY:

We have already calculated all the necessary components of this statistic. In Example 16.2 we found

$$s_{xy} = -2.909$$

$$s_x^2 = 43.509$$

and from Example 16.3

$$s_y^2 = .300$$

Thus,

$$R^2 = \frac{s_{xy}^2}{s_x^2 s_y^2} = \frac{(-2.909)^2}{(43.509)(.300)} = .6483$$

EXCEL Data Analysis

R Square	0.6483

Excel prints a second R^2 statistic called the *coefficient of determination adjusted for degrees of freedom*. We will define and describe this statistic in Chapter 17.

INTERPRET

We found that R^2 is equal to .6483. This statistic tells us that 64.83% of the variation in the auction selling prices is explained by the variation in the odometer readings. The remaining 35.17% is unexplained. Unlike the value of a test statistic, the coefficient of determination does not have a critical value that enables us to draw conclusions. In general, the higher the value of R^2, the better the model fits the data. From the t-test of β_1 we already know that there is evidence of a linear relationship. The coefficient of determination merely supplies us with a measure of the strength of that relationship. As you will discover in the next chapter, when we improve the model, the value of R^2 increases.

16-4g Other Parts of the Computer Printout

The last part of the printout shown on page 680 relates to our discussion of the interpretation of the value of R^2, when its meaning is derived from the partitioning of the variation in y. The values of SSR and SSE are shown in an analysis of variance table similar to the tables introduced in Chapter 14. The general form of the table is shown in Table 16.2. The F-test performed in the ANOVA table will be explained in Chapter 17.

TABLE **16.2** General Form of the ANOVA Table in the Simple Linear Regression Model

SOURCE	d.f.	SUMS OF SQUARES	MEAN SQUARES	F-STATISTIC
Regression	1	SSR	MSR = SSR/1	F = MSR/MSE
Error	$n - 2$	SSE	MSE = SSE/$(n - 2)$	
Total	$n - 1$	Variation in y		

Note: Excel uses the word "Residual" to refer to the second source of variation, which we called "Error."

16-4h Developing an Understanding of Statistical Concepts

Once again, we encounter the concept of explained variation. We first discussed the concept in Chapter 13 when we introduced the matched pairs experiment, where the experiment was designed to reduce the variation among experimental units. This concept was extended in the analysis of variance, where we partitioned the total variation into two or more sources (depending on the experimental design). And now in regression analysis, we use the concept to measure how the dependent variable is related to the independent variable. We partition the variation of the dependent variable into the sources: the variation explained by the variation in the independent variable and the unexplained variation. The greater the explained variation, the better the model is. We often refer to the coefficient of determination as a measure of the explanatory power of the model.

16-4i Cause-and-Effect Relationship

A common mistake is made by many students when they attempt to interpret the results of a regression analysis when there is evidence of a linear relationship. They imply that changes in the independent variable cause changes in the dependent variable. It must be emphasized that we cannot infer a causal relationship from statistics alone. Any inference about the cause of the changes in the dependent variable must be justified by a reasonable theoretical relationship. For example, statistical tests established that the more one smoked, the greater the probability of developing lung cancer. However, this analysis did not prove that smoking causes lung cancer. It only demonstrated that smoking and lung cancer were somehow related. Only when medical investigations established the connection were scientists able to confidently declare that smoking causes lung cancer.

As another illustration, consider Example 16.2 where we showed that the odometer reading is linearly related to the auction price. Although it seems reasonable to conclude that decreasing the odometer reading would cause the auction price to rise, the conclusion may not be entirely true. It is theoretically possible that the price is determined by the overall condition of the car and that the condition generally worsens when the car is driven longer. Another analysis would be needed to establish the veracity of this conclusion.

Be cautious about the use of the terms *explained variation* and *explanatory power of the model*. Do not interpret the word *explained* to mean *caused*. We say that the coefficient of determination measures the amount of variation in *y* that is explained (not caused) by the variation in *x*. Thus, regression analysis can only show that a statistical relationship exists. We cannot infer that one variable causes another.

Recall that we first pointed this out in Chapter 3 using the following sentence:

Correlation is not causation.

16-4j   Testing the Coefficient of Correlation

When we introduced the coefficient of correlation (also called the **Pearson coefficient of correlation**) in Chapter 4, we observed that it is used to measure the strength of association between two variables. However, the coefficient of correlation can be useful in another way. We can use it to test for a linear relationship between two variables.

When we are interested in determining *how* the independent variable is related to the dependent variable, we estimate and test the linear regression model. The *t*-test of the slope presented previously allows us to determine whether a linear relationship actually exists. As we pointed out in Section 16-3, the statistical test requires that for each value of *x*, there exists a population of values of *y* that are normally distributed with a constant variance. This condition is required whether the data are experimental or observational.

In many circumstances, we're interested in determining only *whether* a linear relationship exists and not the form of the relationship. When the data are observational and the two variables are bivariate normally distributed (see Section 16-3), we can calculate the coefficient of correlation and use it to test for linear association.

As we noted in Chapter 4, the population coefficient of correlation is denoted ρ (the Greek letter *rho*). Because ρ is a population parameter (which is almost always unknown), we must estimate its value from the sample data. Recall that the sample coefficient of correlation is defined as follows.

Sample Coefficient of Correlation

$$r = \frac{s_{xy}}{s_x s_y}$$

When there is no linear relationship between the two variables, $\rho = 0$. To determine whether we can infer that ρ is 0, we test the hypotheses

H_0: $\rho = 0$

H_1: $\rho \neq 0$

The test statistic is defined in the following way.

Test Statistic for Testing $\rho = 0$

$$t = r \sqrt{\frac{n-2}{1-r^2}}$$

which is Student *t* distributed with $v = n - 2$ degrees of freedom provided that the variables are bivariate normally distributed.

EXAMPLE 16.6

Are Odometer Reading and Price of Used Toyota Camrys Linearly Related? Testing the Coefficient of Correlation

Conduct the t-test of the coefficient of correlation to determine whether odometer reading and auction selling price are linearly related in Example 16.2. Assume that the two variables are bivariate normally distributed.

SOLUTION:

COMPUTE

MANUALLY:

The hypotheses to be tested are

$$H_0:\ \rho = 0$$
$$H_1:\ \rho \neq 0$$

In Example 16.2, we found $s_{xy} = -2.909$ and $s_x^2 = 43.509$. In Example 16.5, we determined that $s_y^2 = .300$. Thus,

$$s_x = \sqrt{43.509} = 6.596$$
$$s_y = \sqrt{.300} = .5477$$

The coefficient of correlation is

$$r = \frac{s_{xy}}{s_x s_y} = \frac{-2.909}{(6.596)(.5477)} = -.8052$$

The value of the test statistic is

$$t = r\sqrt{\frac{n-2}{1-r^2}} = -.8052\sqrt{\frac{100-2}{1-(-.8052)^2}} = -13.44$$

Notice that this is the same value we produced in the t-test of the slope in Example 16.4. Because both sampling distributions are Student t with 98 degrees of freedom, the p-value and conclusion are also identical.

EXCEL Workbook

	A	B	C	D
1	t-Test of Correlation Coefficient			
2				
3	Sample correlation	0.8052	t Stat	13.44
4	Sample size	100	P(T<=t) one-tail	2.85E-24
5	Alpha	0.05	t Critical one-tail	1.6604
6			P(T<=t) two-tail	5.71E-24
7			t Critical two-tail	1.9842

INSTRUCTIONS

1. Calculate the coefficient of correlation. (See page 131 for instructions.)
2. Open the **Test Statistics Workbook** and click the **t-Test_Correlation** tab.
3. Input the coefficient of correlation, the sample size, and the value of α.

Notice that the t-test of ρ and the t-test of β_1 in Example 16.4 produced identical results. This should not be surprising because both tests are conducted to determine whether there is evidence of a linear relationship. The decision about which test to use is based on the type of experiment and the information we seek from the statistical analysis. If we're interested in discovering the relationship between two variables, or if we've conducted an experiment where we controlled the values of the independent variable (as in Exercise 16.6), the t-test of β_1 should be applied. If we're interested only in determining *whether* two random variables that are bivariate normally distributed are linearly related, the t-test of ρ should be applied.

As is the case with the t-test of the slope, we can also conduct one-tail tests. We can test for a positive or a negative linear relationship.

General Social Survey: Education and Income— How Are They Related? Solution

IDENTIFY

The problem objective is to analyze the relationship between two interval variables. Because we want to know how education affects income, the independent variable is education (EDUC) and the dependent variable is income (RINCOME).

COMPUTE

EXCEL Data Analysis

	A	B	C	D	E	F	G
1	SUMMARY OUTPUT						
2	*Regression Statistics*						
3	Multiple R	0.3616					
4	R Square	0.1308					
5	Adjusted R Square	0.1301					
6	Standard Error	40,137					
7	Observations	1362					
8	ANOVA						
9		*df*	*SS*	*MS*	*F*	*Significance F*	
10	Regression	1	329,638,067,644	329,638,067,644	204.62	2.42E-43	
11	Residual	1360	2,190,944,055,383	1,610,988,276			
12	Total	1361	2,520,582,123,027				
13		*Coefficients*	*Standard Error*	*t Stat*	*P-value*	*Lower 95%*	*Upper 95%*
14	Intercept	-27,442	5,501	-4.99	6.88E-07	-38,233	-16,650
15	EDUC	5458	381.58	14.30	2.42E-43	4,710	6,207

INTERPRET

The regression equation is $\hat{y} = -27,442 + 5458x$. The slope coefficient tells us that for each additional year of education income increases on average by $5,458. The intercept is clearly meaningless. We test to determine whether there is evidence of a linear relationship.

$$H_0: \quad \beta_1 = 0$$
$$H_1: \quad \beta_1 \neq 0$$

The test statistic is $t = 14.30$ and the p-value is $2.42 \times 10{-43}$, which is virtually 0.
The coefficient of determination is $R^2 = .1308$, which means that 13.08% of the variation in income is explained by the variation in education, and the remaining 86.92% is unexplained.

16-4k Violation of the Required Condition

When the normality requirement is unsatisfied, we can use a nonparametric technique— the Spearman rank correlation coefficient (Chapter 19*) to replace the t-test of ρ.

EXERCISES

Use a 5% significance level for all tests of hypotheses and a 95% confidence level for all estimates.

16.26 You have been given the following data:

x	1	3	4	6	9	8	10
y	1	8	15	33	75	70	95

a. Draw the scatter diagram. Does it appear that x and y are related? If so, how?
b. Test to determine whether there is evidence of a linear relationship.

16.27 Suppose that you have the following data:

x	3	5	2	6	1	4
y	25	110	9	250	3	71

a. Draw the scatter diagram. Does it appear that x and y are related? If so, how?
b. Test to determine whether there is evidence of a linear relationship.

16.28 Refer to Exercise 16.2.
a. Determine the standard error of estimate.
b. Is there evidence of a linear relationship between advertising and sales?
c. Determine a confidence interval estimate of β_1.

d. Compute the coefficient of determination and interpret this value.
e. Briefly summarize what you have learned in parts (a) through (d).

16.29 Calculate the coefficient of determination and conduct a test to determine whether a linear relationship exists between housing starts and mortgage interest in Exercise 16.3.

16.30 Is there evidence of a linear relationship between the number of hours of television viewing and how overweight the child is in Exercise 16.4?

16.31 Determine whether there is evidence of a negative linear relationship between temperature and the number of beers sold at Yankee Stadium in Exercise 16.5.

The following exercises require a computer and software. The answers to 16.32–16.48 may be calculated manually. See Appendix A for the sample statistics.

16.32 Refer to Exercise 16.6.
a. Determine the value of the y-intercept b_0. What does it tell you about the linear relationship between test scores and commercial times?
b. What is the value of the slope coefficient b_1? Interpret its value.

---

*Instructors who wish to teach the use of the Spearman rank correlation coefficient here can use the online appendix Spearman Rank Correlation Coefficient and Test.

c. Determine the coefficient of correlation and the coefficient of determination. Interpret each coefficient.

d. Conduct a test to determine whether there is enough evidence to conclude that memory test scores and length of commercial are linearly related.

16.33 Refer to Exercise 16.7.

a. Is there enough statistical evidence to infer that there is a linear relationship between education and after-tax income?

b. Determine a confidence interval estimate of the marginal increase in after-tax income for each additional year of education.

c. Compute the coefficient of determination and describe what it tells you about the relationship between education and after-tax income.

16.34 Refer to Exercise 16.8.

a. Is there sufficient evidence to infer that there is a linear relationship between property tax bills and the population size of the city?

b. Determine the coefficient of determination. Describe what it informs you about the relationship between the two variables.

16.35 Refer to Exercise 16.9.

a. Do the data provide sufficient evidence to infer that there is a positive linear relationship between price and the floor of the condominium?

b. Determine the coefficient of determination and interpret its value.

16.36 Is there enough evidence to infer that age and the amount of time needed to complete the questionnaire are linearly related in Exercise 16.10?

16.37 Refer to Exercise 16.11.

a. What do the coefficients b_0 and b_1 tell you about the relationship between the two variables?

b. Is there enough evidence to infer that there is a linear relationship between the number of residents in a household and annual income?

c. Determine the coefficient of determination and describe what it tells you.

16.38 Refer to Exercise 16.12.

a. Determine the coefficient of determination and describe what it tells you.

b. Is there enough evidence to infer that there is a positive linear relationship between the length of course and the time to complete rounds?

16.39 Refer to Exercise 16.13.

a. Test to determine whether there is evidence of a linear relationship between distance to the nearest fire station and percentage of damage.

b. Compute a confidence interval estimate of the marginal increase in the percent of damage for each additional mile from the fire station.

c. Determine the coefficient of determination. What does this statistic tell you about the relationship between the two variables?

16.40 Refer to Exercise 16.14.

a. Is there enough evidence to conclude that the size and price of the apartment building are linearly related?

b. Determine the coefficient of determination and discuss what its value tells you about the two variables.

16.41 Can the economist conclude that there is sufficient statistical evidence of a linear relationship between income and food expenditures in Exercise 16.15?

16.42 Refer to Exercise 16.16.

a. Calculate a confidence interval estimate of the decrease in rent for each additional percentage point increase in the vacancy rate.

b. Determine the coefficient of correlation and the coefficient of determination and describe what each statistic tells you.

16.43 Is there enough evidence to infer that as the number of hours of engine use increases, the price decreases on average in Exercise 16.17?

16.44 Refer to Exercise 16.18.

a. Interpret the coefficients b_0 and b_1.

b. Is there enough evidence of a linear relationship between number of cigarettes smoked and number of sick days?

16.45 What do the y-intercept and slope coefficient tell you about the relationship between population size and after-tax income in Exercise 16.19?

16.46 Refer to Exercise 16.20.

a. Is there sufficient evidence to infer that electricity bills and the number of occupants are linearly related?

b. Determine the coefficients of correlation and determination. What information do these statistics provide?

16.47 Refer to Exercise 16.21.

a. Interpret the y-intercept.

b. Is there enough statistical evidence to infer that height and income are positively linearly related?

16.48 Is there enough evidence to infer that older workers have shorter job tenure in Exercise 16.22?

16.49 Xr03-89 Refer to Exercise 3.89.

 a. Conduct a regression analysis to determine whether there is enough evidence of a positive linear relationship between temperature and the distance a golf ball travels.

 b. Interpret the slope coefficient.

 c. Determine the coefficient of determination and describe the information it provides.

16.50 Xr03-88 Refer to Exercise 3.88.

 a. Is there sufficient evidence to conclude that the grade of the coin and the auction selling price are linearly related?

 b. Compute the coefficient of determination and briefly explain what it tells you.

16.51 Xr16-51 Do more educated people spend more time watching or reading news on the Internet? To help answer the question, a statistics practitioner undertook a survey that asked a random sample of people how many years of education they had and the amount of time they spend in a typical day watching or reading news on the Internet.

 a. Determine whether there is enough evidence to infer that a linear relationship exists between the two variables.

 b. If there is a linear relationship, estimate with a confidence interval the marginal increase in the time watching or reading news on the Internet for each additional year of education.

16.52 Xr16-52 In most presidential elections in the United States, the voter turnout is quite low, often in the neighborhood of 50%. Political workers would like to be able to predict who is likely to vote. Thus, it is important to know which variables are related to intention to vote. A political pollster took a random sample of registered voters 3 months before an election. Each respondent was asked the following question, "How definite is your intention to vote or not?" The results were recorded as 1 = Definitely will not vote; 2, 3, 4, 5, 6, 7, 8, 9, 10 = Definitely will vote. Also recorded was the age of the respondent. Is there sufficient evidence to infer that age and intention to vote are linearly related?

16.53 Xr16-53 National news on television features commercials describing pharmaceutical drugs that treat ailments that plague older people. Apparently, the major networks believe that older people tend to watch national newscasts. The marketing manager of a drug company conducted a survey that took a random sample of people older than 60 years of age and recorded their age and the number of days they watched national news on television in a typical week.

 a. Test to determine whether there is enough evidence to conclude that there is a linear relationship between age and number of days watching national news.

 b. Calculate the coefficient of determination and briefly describe what it tells you.

General Social Survey Exercises

GSS2018 *Excel users: You must delete rows containing empty cells. For instructions see online appendix Excel Instructions for Deleting Rows with Blanks.* **Use a 5% significance level for all tests and a 95% confidence level for all estimates.**

16.54 Does one's income (RINCOME) affect one's position on the question, Should the government reduce income differences between rich and poor (EQWLTH: 1 = Government should reduce income differences; 2, 3, 4, 5, 6, 7 = No government action)? Answer the question by testing the relationship between the two variables.

16.55 Conduct an analysis of the relationship between income (RINCOME) and age (AGE). Produce a confidence interval estimate of the average increase in income for each additional year of age.

16.56 Does television appeal to the lowest common denominator? If so, we would expect more educated people to watch less television. Is there sufficient evidence to conclude that more educated people (EDUC) watch less television (TVHOURS)?

16.57 It seems rather obvious that the longer one works, the more one earns. The question is how much more one earns annually for each additional hour of work. Conduct an analysis of annual income (RINCOME) and number of hours per week of work (HRS1).

 a. Test to determine whether there is enough evidence of a positive linear relationship.

 b. Determine a confidence interval estimate of the increase in annual income for each additional hour of work per week.

16.58 Do Americans work less as they get older? Conduct a statistical test to determine whether there is enough evidence of a negative linear relationship between age (AGE) and how many hours per week one works (HRS1).

16.59 Television advertisers always want to know who is watching their televised advertising. Do older people watch more television than do younger people? Do the data provide sufficient evidence to infer that there is a positive linear relationship between age (AGE) and television watched (TVHOURS)?

16.60 How does having more family members earning income (EARNRS) affect total family income (INCOME)? Conduct an analysis to determine whether there is a positive linear relationship between the two variables, and, if so, compute a confidence interval estimate of the average increase in total family income for each additional earner.

16.61 Are more educated (EDUC) people less likely to support government action to reduce income differences across the country differences (EQWLTH: 1 = Government should reduce income differences; 2, 3, 4, 5, 6, 7 = No government action)? Conduct a test to answer the question.

16.62 Do more educated people tend to marry individuals with similar educational experience? Test to determine whether a married person's years of education (EDUC) are positively linearly related to the spouse's level of education (SPEDUC).

16.63 An economic theory suggests that as people become richer, they tend to have more children. Analyze the relationship between household income (INCOME) and number of children (CHILDS) to test the theory.

16.64 If one spouse works longer hours, does this mean that the other spouse also works longer hours? Test the relationship between HRS1 and SPHRS1 to answer the question.

16.65 Does staying in university longer mean that people postpone having children? If so, we would expect a positive linear relationship between years of education (EDUC) and the age when people have their first child (AGEKDBRN). Test to determine whether there is sufficient statistical evidence of this relationship.

16.66 Refer to Exercise 16.65. We would expect that more educated people would have fewer children. Analyze the relationship between education (EDUC) and number of children (CHILDS).

16.67 Does the amount of education that one completes influence the amount of education their child completes? Test the relationship between years of education (EDUC) and their father's education (PAEDUC).

16.68 Refer to Exercise 16.67. Is there sufficient evidence of a positive linear relationship between the years of education (EDUC) and the years of education of one's mother (MAEDUC)?

16.69 Are harder-working Americans less likely to want government to reduce income differences? Test to determine whether there is sufficient evidence of a positive linear relationship between hours of work per week (HRS1) and position on whether government should reduce income differences (EQWLTH: 1 = Government should reduce income differences; 2, 3, 4, 5, 6, 7 = No government action).

SURVEY OF CONSUMER FINANCES EXERCISES

SCF2019:\MC *The following exercises are based on the middle class subsample. Use a 5% significance level for all tests and a 95% confidence level for all estimates.*

16.70 Children are expensive. One way to measure how expensive is to examine the relationship between debt (DEBT) and the number of children (KIDS) in the household.
   a. Is there enough evidence to conclude that more children lead to more debt?
   b. Calculate a confidence interval estimate of the marginal change in debt for each child.

16.71 Are younger middle-class people more likely to eat out at restaurants than older people? Conduct a test

to determine whether there is sufficient evidence to infer that age (AGE) and amount spent on food away from home (FOODAWAY) are negatively related.

16.72 Another way to interpret the results of Exercise 16.71 is that older people spend less on all food because their families are smaller (children have left home) or that they eat less expensive meals. If so, then we would expect that age (AGE) and amount spent on food at home (FOODHOME) are also negatively related. Conduct a test to determine whether this is true.

16.73 Does the cost of buying and leasing cars result in more debt? Determine whether there is enough evidence to conclude that more expensive vehicles (VEHIC) result in more debt (DEBT).

16.74 Is having more children an incentive to earn more income, or does having a larger income induce families to have more children? Do the data provide sufficient evidence to infer that the two variables (KIDS, INCOME) are positively linearly related?

16.75 What is the main generator of debt in middle-class households? For most households, the cost of buying a house must be at or near the top of sources of indebtedness. Conduct a test to determine whether there is a positive linear relationship between value of the house (HOUSE) and debt (DEBT).

16.76 In most middle-class households as the head of the household ages, assets accumulate and as a result, we would expect a decrease in debts.
  a. Conduct a statistical test to determine whether there is enough evidence to infer that as the age (AGE) of the head of the household increases, household debt (DEBT) decreases.

  b. Compute a confidence interval estimate of the average amount of decrease in debt for each additional year of age.

16.77 It takes many years to build up capital gains. Use a statistical analysis to determine whether there is enough evidence to conclude that as one grows older, one increases unrealized capital gains (AGE, KGTOTAL).

16.78 How much more do households have to spend on food when there are children living at home?
  a. Conduct a test to determine whether there is evidence of a positive linear relationship between total annual amount spent on food at home (FOODHOME) and number of children in the household (KIDS).
  b. Calculate a confidence interval estimate of the average increase in the amount of food consumed at home for each additional child.

16.79 Repeat Exercise 16.78 for amount spent on food away from home (FOODAWAY).

16-5 / USING THE REGRESSION EQUATION

Using the techniques in Section 16-4, we can assess how well the linear model fits the data. If the model fits satisfactorily, we can use it to forecast and estimate values of the dependent variable. To illustrate, suppose that in Example 16.2, the used-car dealer wanted to predict the selling price of a 3-year-old Toyota Camry with 40 (thousand) miles on the odometer. Using the regression equation, with $x = 40$, we get

$$\hat{y} = 17.250 - .0669x = 17.250 - 0.0669(40) = 14.574$$

We call this value the **point prediction**, and $\hat{y}$ is the point estimate or predicted value for y when $x = 40$. Thus, the dealer would predict that the car would sell for $14,574.

By itself, however, the point prediction does not provide any information about how closely the value will match the true selling price. To discover that information, we must use an interval. In fact, we can use one of two intervals: the prediction interval of a particular value of y or the confidence interval estimator of the expected value of y.

16-5a Predicting the Particular Value of y for a Given x

The first confidence interval we present is used whenever we want to predict a one-time occurrence for a particular value of the dependent variable when the independent variable is a given value x_g. This interval, often called the **prediction interval**, is calculated in the usual way (point estimator $\pm$ bound on the error of estimation). Here the point estimate for y is $\hat{y}$, and the bound on the error of estimation is shown on next page.

> **Prediction Interval**
>
> $$\hat{y} \pm t_{\alpha/2, n-2}s_\varepsilon \sqrt{1 + \frac{1}{n} + \frac{(x_g - \bar{x})^2}{(n-1)s_x^2}}$$
>
> where x_g is the given value of x and $\hat{y} = b_0 + b_1 x_g$

16-5b Estimating the Expected Value of y for a Given x

The conditions described in Section 16-3 imply that, for a given value of x, there is a population of values of y whose mean is

$$E(y) = \beta_0 + \beta_1 x$$

To estimate the mean of y or long-run average value of y, we would use the following interval referred to simply as the confidence interval. Again, the point estimator is $\hat{y}$, but the bound on the error of estimation is different from the prediction interval shown below.

> **Confidence Interval Estimator of the Expected Value of y**
>
> $$\hat{y} \pm t_{\alpha/2,\,n-2}s_\varepsilon \sqrt{\frac{1}{n} + \frac{(x_g - \bar{x})^2}{(n-1)s_x^2}}$$

Unlike the formula for the prediction interval, this formula does not include the 1 under the square-root sign. As a result, the **confidence interval estimate of the expected value of y** will be narrower than the prediction interval for the same given value of x and confidence level. This is because there is less error in estimating a mean value as opposed to predicting an individual value.

EXAMPLE 16.7

Predicting the Price and Estimating the Mean Price of Used Toyota Camrys

a. A used-car dealer is about to bid on a 3-year-old Toyota Camry equipped with all the standard features and with 40,000 ($x_g = 40$) miles on the odometer. To help decide how much to bid, the dealer needs to predict the selling price.

b. The used-car dealer mentioned in part (a) has an opportunity to bid on a lot of cars offered by a rental company. The rental company has 250 Toyota Camrys all equipped with standard features. All the cars in this lot have about 40,000 ($x_g = 40$) miles on their odometers. The dealer would like an estimate of the selling price of all the cars in the lot.

SOLUTION:

IDENTIFY

a. The dealer would like to predict the selling price of a single car. This objective requires the prediction interval

$$\hat{y} \pm t_{\alpha/2,n-2}s_\varepsilon \sqrt{1 + \frac{1}{n} + \frac{(x_g - \bar{x})^2}{(n-1)s_x^2}}$$

b. The dealer wants to determine the mean price of a large lot of cars, so this requires the confidence interval estimator of the expected value:

$$\hat{y} \pm t_{\alpha/2,n-2}s_\varepsilon \sqrt{\frac{1}{n} + \frac{(x_g - \bar{x})^2}{(n-1)s_x^2}}$$

Technically, this formula is used for infinitely large populations. However, we can interpret our problem as attempting to determine the average selling price of all Toyota Camrys equipped as described above, all with 40,000 miles on the odometer. The crucial factor in part (b) is the need to estimate the mean price of a number of cars. We arbitrarily select a 95% confidence level.

COMPUTE

MANUALLY:

From previous calculations, we have the following:

$$\hat{y} = 17.249 - .0669(40) = 14.573$$

$$s_\varepsilon = .3265$$

$$s_x^2 = 43.509$$

$$\bar{x} = 36.011$$

From Table 4 in Appendix B, we find

$$t_{\alpha/2} = t_{.025,98} \approx t_{.025,100} = 1.984$$

a. The 95% prediction interval is

$$\hat{y} \pm t_{\alpha/2,n-2}s_\varepsilon \sqrt{1 + \frac{1}{n} + \frac{(x_g - \bar{x})^2}{(n-1)s_x^2}}$$

$$= 14.573 \pm 1.984 \times .3265 \sqrt{1 + \frac{1}{100} + \frac{(40 - 36.011)^2}{(100 - 1)(43.509)}}$$

$$= 14.573 \pm .652$$

The lower and upper limits of the prediction interval are \$13,921 and \$15,225, respectively.

b. The 95% confidence interval estimator of the mean price is

$$\hat{y} \pm t_{\alpha/2,n-2}s_\varepsilon \sqrt{\frac{1}{n} + \frac{(x_g - \bar{x})^2}{(n-1)s_x^2}}$$

$$= 14.573 \pm 1.984 \times .3265 \sqrt{\frac{1}{100} + \frac{(40 - 36.011)^2}{(100 - 1)(43.509)}}$$

$$= 14.573 \pm .076$$

The lower and upper limits of the confidence interval estimate of the expected value are $14,497 and 14,649, respectively.

EXCEL Workbook

	A	B	C	D	E
1	Predict & Estimate of y				
2					
3	Sample mean of x	36.011	Confidence Interval Estimate		
4	Sample variance of x	43.509	14.573	±	0.076
5	Sample size	100	Lower confidence limit		14.497
6	Regression coefficients		Upper confidence limit		14.649
7	Intercept	17.249			
8	Slope	-0.0669	Prediction Interval		
9	SSE	10.45	14.573	±	0.652
10	Confidence level	0.95	Lower prediction limit		13.921
11	Given value of x	40	Upper prediction limit		15.225

INSTRUCTIONS

1. Calculate the mean and variance of the independent variable x.
2. Conduct a regression analysis.
3. Open the **Estimators Workbook** and click the **Prediction** tab.
4. Input the sample mean and variance of X, the sample size, the regression coefficients b_0 and b_1, SSE, the confidence level, and the given value of X.

INTERPRET

We predict that one car will sell for between $13,925 and $15,226. The average selling price of the population of 3-year-old Toyota Camrys is estimated to lie between $14,498 and $14,650. Because predicting the selling price of one car is more difficult than estimating the mean selling price of all similar cars, the prediction interval is wider than the interval estimate of the expected value.

16-5c Effect of the Given Value of x on the Intervals

Calculating the two intervals for various values of x results in the graph in Figure 16.8. Notice that both intervals are represented by curved lines. This is because the farther the given value of x is from $\bar{x}$, the greater the estimated error becomes. This part of the estimated error is measured by

$$\frac{(x_g - \bar{x})^2}{(n - 1)s_x^2}$$

which appears in both the prediction interval and the interval estimate of the expected value.

FIGURE **16.8** Interval Estimate and Prediction Interval

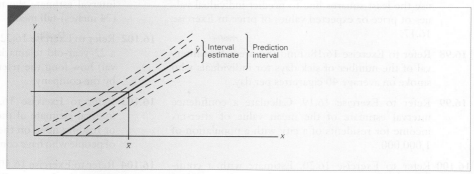

EXERCISES

16.80 Briefly describe the difference between predicting a value of y and estimating the expected value of y.

16.81 Will the prediction interval always be wider than the estimation interval for the same value of the independent variable? Briefly explain.

16.82 Use the regression equation in Exercise 16.2 to predict with 90% confidence the sales when the advertising budget is $80,000.

16.83 Estimate with 90% confidence the mean monthly number of housing starts when the mortgage interest rate is 7% in Exercise 16.3.

16.84 Refer to Exercise 16.4.
 a. Predict with 90% confidence the number of pounds overweight for a child who watches 35 hours of television per week.
 b. Estimate with 90% confidence the mean number of pounds overweight for children who watch 35 hours of television per week.

16.85 Refer to Exercise 16.5. Predict with 90% confidence the number of beers to be sold when the temperature is 75 degrees.

The following exercises require a computer and software. The answers to Exercises 16.86–16.102 may be calculated manually. See Appendix A for the sample statistics. **Use a 95% confidence level for all prediction intervals and interval estimates.**

16.86 Refer to Exercise 16.6.
 a. Calculate a prediction interval for the memory test score of a viewer who watches a 30-second commercial.
 b. Determine the confidence interval estimate of the mean memory test score of people who watch 30-second commercials.

16.87 Refer to Exercise 16.7. Compute the prediction interval of the after-tax income of an individual with 16 years of education.

16.88 Refer to Exercise 16.8. Calculate the prediction interval of the property tax of a home in a city of 500,000.

16.89 Refer to Exercise 16.9. Determine the prediction interval of the selling price of a 1,200 square foot condominium on the 15th floor.

16.90 Refer to Exercise 16.10. Compute a confidence interval estimate of the mean amount of time for 40-year-old Americans to complete the census. Discuss why this interval is so wide.

16.91 Refer to Exercise 16.11. Determine a confidence interval estimate of the mean annual income of households with four residents.

16.92 Refer to Exercise 16.12. Find the prediction interval of the amount of time to play a course that is 6,000 yards long.

16.93 Refer to Exercise 16.13. Calculate the prediction interval of the percentage loss due to fire for a house that is 8 miles away from the nearest fire station.

16.94 Refer to Exercise 16.14. Calculate a confidence interval estimate of the mean price of 60,000 square foot apartment buildings.

16.95 Refer to Exercise 16.15. Compute the prediction interval of the food budget of a family whose household income is $60,000.

16.96 Refer to Exercise 16.16. Determine the prediction interval of the monthly office rent in a city when the vacancy rate is 8%.

16.97 Explain why you should not bother attempting to use the least squares line to predict individual values of price or expected values of price in Exercise 16.17.

16.98 Refer to Exercise 16.18. Find the prediction interval of the number of sick days for individuals who smoke on average 40 cigarettes per day.

16.99 Refer to Exercise 16.19. Calculate a confidence interval estimate of the mean value of after-tax income for residents of a city with a population of 1,000,000.

16.100 Refer to Exercise 16.20. Estimate with a confidence interval the mean electricity consumption for households with four occupants.

16.101 Refer to Exercise 16.21. Compute the confidence interval estimate the mean annual income of 6'2" (74 inches)-tall men.

16.102 Refer to Exercise 16.22. The company has just hired a 22-year-old telemarketer. Predict (with an interval) how long the telemarketer will stay employed by the company.

16.103 Refer to Exercise 16.51. Calculate a confidence interval estimate of the mean time spent watching or reading news on the Internet for the population of people who have completed 12 years of education.

16.104 Refer to Exercise 16.50. Use a prediction interval to predict the auction selling price of one Canada 1925 nickel with a grade of 40.

GENERAL SOCIAL SURVEY EXERCISES

<u>GSS2018</u> *For Exercises 16.105 to 16.115, construct a prediction interval and a confidence interval estimate of the expected value of the dependent variable for the given value of the independent variable.* **Use a 95% confidence level.**

16.105 Refer to Exercise 16.55. Annual income of someone who is 45 years old.

16.106 Refer to Exercise 16.56. Number of hours of television watching per day for people with 12 years of education.

16.107 Refer to Exercise 16.57. Income of someone who works 40 hours per week.

16.108 Refer to Exercise 16.58. Number of hours of work per week for some who is 60 years old.

16.109 Refer to Exercise 16.59. Number of hours of television per day of a 65-year-old.

16.110 Refer to Exercise 16.60. Total family income of a family with four earners.

16.111 Refer to Exercise 16.61. Attitude about EQWLTH for someone with 15 years of education.

16.112 Refer to Exercise 16.62. Years of education of spouse for a person with 10 years of education.

16.113 Refer to Exercise 16.63. Number of children (CHILDS) in household with an annual income of $75,000 (INCOME).

16.114 Refer to Exercise 16.64. Number of hours of work per week of a spouse (SPHRS1) of someone who works 50 hours per week (HRS1).

16.115 Refer to Exercise 16.65. Age when first child was born for someone (AGEKDBRN) with 18 years of education (EDUC).

16.116 Pick any one (or more) of the 11 exercises above and briefly describe why the prediction interval is so wide.

16-6 REGRESSION DIAGNOSTICS—I

In Section 16-3, we described the required conditions for the validity of regression analysis. Simply put, the error variable must be normally distributed with a constant variance, and the errors must be independent of each other. In this section, we show how to diagnose violations. In addition, we discuss how to deal with observations that are unusually large or small. Such observations must be investigated to determine whether an error was made in recording them.

16-6a Residual Analysis

Most departures from required conditions can be diagnosed by examining the residuals, which we discussed in Section 16-4. Most computer packages allow you to output the values of the residuals and apply various graphical and statistical techniques to this variable.

We can also compute the standardized residuals. We standardize residuals in the same way we standardize all variables, by subtracting the mean and dividing by the standard deviation. The mean of the residuals is 0, and because the standard deviation σ_ε is unknown, we must estimate its value. The simplest estimate is the standard error of estimate s_ε. Thus,

$$\text{Standardized residuals for point } i = \frac{e_i}{s_\varepsilon}$$

EXCEL Data Analysis

Excel calculates the standardized residuals by dividing the residuals by the standard deviation of the residuals. (The difference between the standard error of estimate and the standard deviation of the residuals is that in the formula of the former the denominator is $n - 2$, whereas in the formula for the latter, the denominator is $n - 1$.)

Part of the printout (we show only the first five and last five values) for Example 16.2 follows.

	A	B	C	D
1	RESIDUAL OUTPUT			
2				
3	Observation	Predicted Price	Residuals	Standard Residuals
4	1	14.748	−0.148	−0.456
5	2	14.253	−0.153	−0.472
6	3	14.186	−0.186	−0.574
7	4	15.183	0.417	1.285
8	5	15.129	0.471	1.449
9				
10				
11				
12				
13	96	14.828	−0.028	−0.087
14	97	14.962	−0.362	−1.115
15	98	15.029	−0.529	−1.628
16	99	14.628	0.072	0.222
17	100	14.815	−0.515	−1.585

INSTRUCTIONS

Proceed with the three steps of regression analysis described on page 680. Before clicking **OK**, select **Residuals** and **Standardized Residuals**. The predicted values, residuals, and standardized residuals will be printed.

An analysis of the residuals will allow us to determine whether the error variable is nonnormal, whether the error variance is constant, and whether the errors are independent. We begin with nonnormality.

16-6b Nonnormality

As we've done throughout this book, we check for normality by drawing the histogram of the residuals. Figure 16.9 is Excel's version. As you can see, the histogram is bell shaped, leading us to believe that the error is normally distributed.

FIGURE **16.9**   **Histogram of Residuals for Example 16.2**

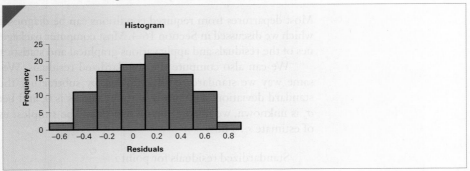

16-6c Heteroscedasticity

The variance of the error variable σ_ε^2 is required to be constant. When this requirement is violated, the condition is called **heteroscedasticity**. (You can impress friends and relatives by using this term. If you can't pronounce it, try **homoscedasticity**, which refers to the condition where the requirement is satisfied.) One method of diagnosing heteroscedasticity is to plot the residuals against the predicted values of y. We then look for a change in the spread of the plotted points.* Figure 16.10 describes such a situation. Notice that in this illustration, σ_ε^2 appears to be small when $\hat{y}$ is small and large when $\hat{y}$ is large. Of course, many other patterns could be used to depict this problem.

FIGURE **16.10**   **Plot of Residuals Depicting Heteroscedasticity**

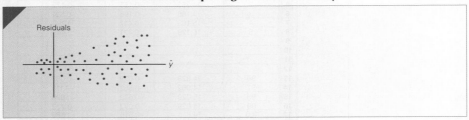

Figure 16.11 illustrates a case in which σ_ε^2 is constant. As a result, there is no apparent change in the variation of the residuals.

FIGURE **16.11**   **Plot of Residuals Depicting Homoscedasticity**

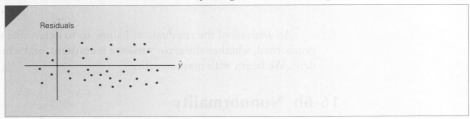

---

*The online appendix Szroeter's Test describes a test for heteroscedasticity.

Excel's plot of the residuals versus the predicted values of y for Example 16.2 is shown in Figure 16.12. There is no sign of heteroscedasticity.

FIGURE **16.12** Plot of Predicted Values versus Residuals for Example 16.2

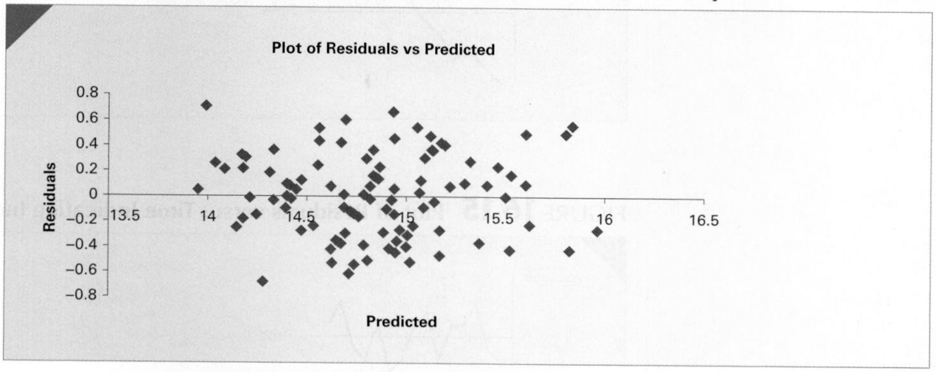

Plot of Residuals vs Predicted

(scatter plot with Residuals on the vertical axis ranging from −0.8 to 0.8 and Predicted on the horizontal axis ranging from 13.5 to 16.5)

16-6d Nonindependence of the Error Variable

In Chapter 3, we briefly described the difference between cross-sectional and time-series data. Cross-sectional data are observations made at approximately the same time, whereas a time series is a set of observations taken at successive points of time. The data in Example 16.2 are cross-sectional because all of the prices and odometer readings were taken at about the same time. If we were to observe the auction price of cars every week for, say, a year, that would constitute a time series.

Condition 4 states that the values of the error variable are independent. When the data are time series, the errors often are correlated. Error terms that are correlated over time are said to be **autocorrelated** or **serially correlated**. For example, suppose that, in an analysis of the relationship between annual gross profits and some independent variable, we observe the gross profits for the years 2001 to 2020. The observed values of y are denoted $y_1, y_2, \ldots y_{20}$, where y_1 is the gross profit for 2001, y_2 is the gross profit for 2002, and so on. If we label the residuals $e_1, e_2, \ldots, e_{20}$, then—if the independence requirement is satisfied—there should be no relationship among the residuals. However, if the residuals are related, it is likely that autocorrelation exists.

We can often detect autocorrelation by graphing the residuals against the time periods. If a pattern emerges, it is likely that the independence requirement is violated. Figures 16.13 (alternating positive and negative residuals) and 16.14 (increasing residuals) exhibit patterns indicating autocorrelation. (Notice that we joined the points to make it easier to see the patterns.) Figure 16.15 shows no pattern (the residuals appear to be randomly distributed over the time periods) and thus likely represent the occurrence of independent errors.

FIGURE **16.13** Plot of Residuals versus Time Indicating Autocorrelation (Alternating)

FIGURE **16.14** Plot of Residuals versus Time Indicating Autocorrelation (Increasing)

FIGURE **16.15** Plot of Residuals versus Time Indicating Independence

In Chapter 17, we introduce the Durbin-Watson test, which is another statistical test to determine whether one form of autocorrelation is present.

16-6e Outliers

An **outlier** is an observation that is unusually small or unusually large. To illustrate, consider Example 16.2, where the range of odometer readings was 19.1 to 49.2 thousand miles. If we had observed a value of 5,000 miles, we would identify that point as an outlier. We need to investigate several possibilities.

1. There was an error in recording the value. To detect an error, we would check the point or points in question. In Example 16.2, we could check the car's odometer to determine whether a mistake was made. If so, we would correct it before proceeding with the regression analysis.

2. The point should not have been included in the sample. Occasionally, measurements are taken from experimental units that do not belong with the sample. We can check to ensure that the car with the 5,000-mile odometer reading was actually 3 years old. We should also investigate the possibility that the odometer was rolled back. In either case, the outlier should be discarded.

3. The observation was simply an unusually large or small value that belongs to the sample and that was recorded properly. In this case, we would do nothing to the outlier. It would be judged to be valid.

Outliers can be identified from the scatter diagram. Figure 16.16 depicts a scatter diagram with one outlier. The statistics practitioner should check to determine whether the measurement was recorded accurately and whether the experimental unit should be included in the sample.

The standardized residuals also can be helpful in identifying outliers. Large absolute values of the standardized residuals should be investigated.

FIGURE **16.16** Scatter Diagram with One Outlier

16-6f Influential Observations

Occasionally, in a regression analysis, one or more observations have a large influence on the statistics. Figure 16.17 describes such an observation and the resulting least squares line. If the point had not been included, the least squares line in Figure 16.18 would have been produced. Obviously, one point has had an enormous influence on the results. Influential points can be identified by the scatter diagram. The point may be an outlier and as such must be checked.

FIGURE **16.17** Scatter Diagram with One Influential Observation

FIGURE **16.18** Scatter Diagram without the Influential Observation

16-6g Procedure for Regression Diagnostics

The order of the material presented in this chapter is dictated by pedagogical requirements. Consequently, we presented the least squares method of assessing the model's fit, predicting and estimating using the regression equation, coefficient of correlation, and finally, the regression diagnostics. In a practical application, the regression diagnostics would be conducted earlier in the process. It is appropriate to investigate violations of the required conditions when the model is assessed and before using the regression equation to predict and estimate. The following steps describe the entire process. (In Chapter 18, we will discuss model building, for which the following steps represent only a part of the entire procedure.)

1. Develop a model that has a theoretical basis; that is, for the dependent variable in question, find an independent variable that you believe is linearly related to it.

2. Gather data for the two variables. Ideally, conduct a controlled experiment. If that is not possible, collect observational data.

3. Draw the scatter diagram to determine whether a linear model appears to be appropriate. Identify possible outliers.

4. Determine the regression equation.

5. Calculate the residuals and check the required conditions:

   Is the error variable nonnormal?

   Is the variance constant?

   Are the errors independent?

   Check the outliers and influential observations.

6. Assess the model's fit.

   Compute the standard error of estimate.

   Test to determine whether there is a linear relationship. (Test β_1 or ρ.)

   Compute the coefficient of determination.

7. If the model fits the data, use the regression equation to predict a particular value of the dependent variable or estimate its mean (or both).

EXERCISES

16.117 You are given the following six points:

x	−5	−2	0	3	4	7
y	15	9	7	6	4	1

a. Determine the regression equation.
b. Use the regression equation to determine the predicted values of y.
c. Use the predicted and actual values of y to calculate the residuals.
d. Compute the standardized residuals.
e. Identify possible outliers.

16.118 Refer to Exercise 16.2. Calculate the predicted values of y and the residuals.

16.119 Compute the predicted values of y and the residuals in Exercise 16.3.

16.120 Refer to Exercise 16.4.
a. Calculate the predicted values of y.
b. Determine the residuals.
c. Plot the residuals (on the vertical axis) and the predicted values of y. What does it show?
d. Draw a histogram of the residuals. What does this graph tell you about the error term?

16.121 Calculate and plot the residuals and predicted values of y for Exercise 16.5.

The following exercises require the use of a computer and software.

16.122 Refer to Exercise 16.6.
a. Determine the residuals and the standardized residuals.
b. Draw the histogram of the residuals. Does it appear that the errors are normally distributed? Explain.
c. Identify possible outliers.
d. Plot the residuals versus the predicted values of y. Does it appear that heteroscedasticity is a problem? Explain.

16.123 Refer to Exercise 16.7.
a. Does it appear that the errors are normally distributed? Explain.
b. Does it appear that heteroscedasticity is a problem? Explain.

16.124 Is the requirement that errors are normally distributed satisfied in Exercise 16.8?

16.125 Refer to Exercise 16.9.
a. Determine the residuals and the standardized residuals.
b. Draw the histogram of the residuals. Does it appear that the errors are normally distributed? Explain.
c. Identify possible outliers.

d. Plot the residuals versus the predicted values of y. Does it appear that heteroscedasticity is a problem? Explain.

16.126 Refer to Exercise 16.10. Are the required conditions satisfied?

16.127 Refer to Exercise 16.11.
a. Determine the residuals and the standardized residuals.
b. Draw the histogram of the residuals. Does it appear that the errors are normally distributed? Explain.
c. Identify possible outliers.
d. Plot the residuals versus the predicted values of y. Does it appear that heteroscedasticity is a problem? Explain.

16.128 Check the required conditions for Exercise 16.12.

16.129 Refer to Exercise 16.13. Are the required conditions satisfied?

16.130 Refer to Exercise 16.14.
a. Determine the residuals and the standardized residuals.
b. Draw the histogram of the residuals. Does it appear that the errors are normally distributed? Explain.
c. Identify possible outliers.
d. Plot the residuals versus the predicted values of y. Does it appear that heteroscedasticity is a problem? Explain.

16.131 Are the required conditions satisfied for Exercise 16.15?

16.132 Check to ensure that the required conditions for Exercise 16.18 are satisfied.

CHAPTER SUMMARY

Simple linear regression and correlation are techniques for analyzing the relationship between two interval variables. Regression analysis assumes that the two variables are linearly related. The least squares method produces estimates of the intercept and the slope of the regression line. Considerable effort is expended in assessing how well the linear model fits the data. We calculate the standard error of estimate, which is an estimate of the standard deviation of the error variable. We test the slope to determine whether there is sufficient evidence of a linear relationship.

The strength of the linear association is measured by the coefficient of determination. When the model provides a good fit, we can use it to predict the particular value and to estimate the expected value of the dependent variable. We can also use the Pearson correlation coefficient to measure and test the relationship between two bivariate normally distributed variables. We completed this chapter with a discussion of how to diagnose violations of the required conditions.

IMPORTANT TERMS:

Regression analysis 672
Dependent variable 672
Independent variable 672
Deterministic model 673
Probabilistic model 673
Error variable 674
First-order linear model 674
Simple linear regression model 674
Least squares method 675
Residuals 677
Sum of squares for error 677
Standard error of estimate 686

Coefficient of determination 692
Pearson coefficient of correlation 696
Point prediction 703
Prediction interval 703
Confidence interval estimate of the expected value of y 704
Heteroscedasticity 710
Homoscedasticity 710
Autocorrelation 711
Serial correlation 711
Outlier 712

SYMBOLS:

Symbol	Pronounced	Represents
β_0	Beta sub zero or beta zero	y-intercept
β_1	Beta sub one or beta one	Slope coefficient
ε	Epsilon	Error variable
$\hat{y}$	y hat	Fitted or calculated value of y
b_0	b sub zero or b zero	Sample y-intercept coefficient
b_1	b sub one or b one	Sample slope coefficient
σ_ε	Sigma sub epsilon or sigma epsilon	Standard deviation of error variable
s_ε	s sub epsilon or s epsilon	Standard error of estimate
s_{b_1}	s sub b sub one or sb one	Standard error of b_1
R^2	R squared	Coefficient of determination
x_g	x sub g or xg	Given value of x
ρ	Rho	Pearson coefficient of correlation
r		Sample coefficient of correlation
e_i	e sub i or ei	Residual of ith point

FORMULAS:

Sample slope

$$b_1 = \frac{s_{xy}}{s_x^2}$$

Sample y-intercept

$$b_0 = \bar{y} - b_1\bar{x}$$

Sum of squares for error

$$SSE = \sum_{i=1}^{n} (y_i - \hat{y}_i)^2$$

Standard error of estimate

$$s_\varepsilon = \sqrt{\frac{SSE}{n-2}}$$

Test statistic for the slope

$$t = \frac{b_1 - \beta_1}{s_{b_1}}$$

Standard error of b_1

$$s_{b_1} = \frac{s_\varepsilon}{\sqrt{(n-1)s_x^2}}$$

Coefficient of determination

$$R^2 = \frac{s_{xy}^2}{s_x^2 s_y^2} = 1 - \frac{SSE}{\sum (y_i - \bar{y})^2}$$

Prediction interval

$$\hat{y} \pm t_{\alpha/2, n-2} s_\varepsilon \sqrt{1 + \frac{1}{n} + \frac{(x_g - \bar{x})^2}{(n-1)s_x^2}}$$

Confidence interval estimator of the expected value of y

$$\hat{y} \pm t_{\alpha/2, n-2} s_\varepsilon \sqrt{\frac{1}{n} + \frac{(x_g - \bar{x})^2}{(n-1)s_x^2}}$$

Sample coefficient of correlation

$$r = \frac{s_{xy}}{s_x s_y}$$

Test statistic for testing $\rho = 0$

$$t = r\sqrt{\frac{n-2}{1-r^2}}$$

EXCEL OUTPUT AND INSTRUCTIONS:

Technique

Regression	680
Correlation	697
Prediction interval	706
Regression diagnostics	709

CHAPTER EXERCISES

The following exercises require the use of a computer and software. **Conduct all tests of hypotheses at the 5% significance level.**

16.133 Xr16-133   The manager of Colonial Furniture has been reviewing weekly advertising expenditures. During the past 6 months, all advertisements for the store have appeared in the local newspaper. The number of ads per week has varied from one to seven. The store's sales staff has been tracking the number of customers who enter the store each week. The number of ads and the number of customers per week for the past 26 weeks were recorded.
   a. Determine the sample regression line.
   b. Interpret the coefficients.
   c. Can the manager infer that the larger the number of ads, the larger the number of customers?
   d. Find and interpret the coefficient of determination.
   e. In your opinion, is it a worthwhile exercise to use the regression equation to predict the number of customers who will enter the store, given that Colonial intends to advertise five times in the newspaper? If so, find a 95% prediction interval. If not, explain why not.

16.134 Xr16-134   The president of a company that manufactures car seats has been concerned about the number and cost of machine breakdowns. The problem is that the machines are old and becoming quite unreliable. However, the cost of replacing them is quite high, and the president is not certain that the cost can be made up in today's slow economy. To help make a decision about replacement, data about last month's costs for repairs and the ages (in months) of the plant's 20 welding machines were recorded.
   a. Find the sample regression line.
   b. Interpret the coefficients.
   c. Determine the coefficient of determination, and discuss what this statistic tells you.

   d. Conduct a test to determine whether the age of a machine and its monthly cost of repair are linearly related.
   e. Is the fit of the simple linear model good enough to allow the president to predict the monthly repair cost of a welding machine that is 120 months old? If so, find a 95% prediction interval. If not, explain why not.

16.135 Xr16-135   Some critics of television complain that the amount of violence shown on television contributes to violence in our society. Others point out that television also contributes to the high level of obesity among children. We may have to add financial problems to the list. A sociologist theorized that people who watch television frequently are exposed to many commercials, which in turn leads them to buy more, finally resulting in increasing debt. To test this belief, a sample of 430 families was drawn. For each, the total debt and the number of hours the television is turned on per week were recorded. Perform a statistical procedure to help test the theory.

16.136 Xr16-136   Every year, the U.S. Federal Trade Commission rates cigarette brands according to their levels of tar and nicotine, substances that are hazardous to smokers' health. Additionally, the commission includes the amount of carbon monoxide, which is a by-product of burning tobacco that seriously affects the heart. A random sample of 25 brands was taken.

   a. Are the levels of tar and nicotine linearly related?
   b. Are the levels of nicotine and carbon monoxide linearly related?

16.137 Xr16-137   Mutual funds minimize risks by diversifying the investments they make. There are mutual funds that specialize in particular types of investments. For example, the TD Precious Metal Mutual Fund buys shares in gold mining companies. The value of this mutual fund depends on a number of factors related to the companies in which the fund invests as well as on the price of gold. To investigate the relationship between the value of the fund and the price of gold, an MBA student gathered the daily fund price and the daily price of gold for a 28-day period. Can we infer from these data that there is a positive linear relationship between the value of the fund and the price of gold? (The authors are grateful to Jim Wheat for writing this exercise.)

16.138 Xr03-85 (Exercise 3.85 revisited) A very large contribution to profits for a movie theater is the sale of popcorn, soft drinks, and candy. A movie theater manager speculated that the longer the time between showings of a movie, the greater the sales of concessions. To acquire more information the manager conducted an experiment. For a month the manager varied the amount of time between movie showings and calculated the sales. Can the manager conclude that when the times between movies increase so do sales?

16.139 Xr16-139+ A computer dating service typically asks for various pieces of information such as height, weight, income, and so on. One such service requested the length of index fingers. The only plausible reason for this request is to act as a proxy on height. Women have often complained that men lie about their heights. If there is a strong relationship between heights and index fingers, the information can be used to "correct" false claims about heights. To test the relationship between the two variables researchers gathered the heights and lengths of index fingers (in centimeters) of 121 students.

a. Graph the relationship between the two variables.

b. Is there sufficient evidence to infer that height and length of index fingers are linearly related?
(The authors would like to thank Howard Waner for supplying the problem and data.)

16.140 Xr12-31+ In addition to the data recorded for Exercises 12.31 and 13.227, we recorded the grade point average of the students who held down part-time jobs. Determine whether there is evidence of a linear relationship between the hours spent at part-time jobs and the grade point averages.

GENERAL SOCIAL SURVEY EXERCISES

GSS2018 *If we interpret the responses to POLVIEWS (1 = Extremely liberal, 2 = Liberal, 3 = Slightly liberal, 4 = Moderate, 5 = Slightly conservative, 6 = Conservative, 7 = Extremely conservative) as an interval variable we can acquire useful information about where people stand on the liberal–conservative spectrum.*

16.141 Discuss what assumption(s) is necessary to make the POLVIEWS spectrum responses an interval variable.

16.142 As people grow older do they become more conservative? If so, there should be a positive linear relationship between age (AGE) and political philosophy (POLVIEWS). Use an appropriate statistical procedure to determine whether there is enough evidence to infer that as people grow older they become more conservative.

16.143 Is there sufficient evidence to conclude that as income (RINCOME) rises people grow more conservative (POLVIEWS)?

16.144 Do more educated individuals lean to the liberal end of the political philosophy spectrum? Conduct a test to determine whether there is enough evidence to conclude that as education (EDUC) increases the political philosophy score (POLVIEWS) decreases.

Exercises 16.145–16.148 address the question of what should governments do and not do. For each question determine whether there is enough evidence to infer that individuals on the liberal end of the political philosophy (POLVIEWS) would choose government action and those on the conservative end would choose no government action.

16.145 EQWLTH: Should government reduce income differences between rich and poor? (1 = Government should reduce differences; 2, 3, 4, 5, 6, 7 = No government action.)

16.146 HELPPOOR: Should government improve standard of living of poor people? (1 = Government act; 2, 3, 4, 5 = People should help themselves.)

16.147 HELPNOT: Should government do more or less to solve country's problems? (1 = Government should do more; 2, 3, 4, 5 = Government does too much.)

16.148 HELPSICK: Is it government's responsibility to help pay for doctor and hospital bills? (1 = Government should help; 2, 3, 4, 5 = People should help themselves.)

16.149 Summarize what you have discovered about the relationship between political philosophy and preference for government action in Exercises 16.146–16.149. In particular, discuss the coefficients of determination.

APPENDIX 16.B / Stata Output and Instructions

Simple Linear Regression

Example 16.2

Source	SS	df	MS		Number of obs	=	100
					F(1, 98)	=	180.64
Model	19.2556074	1	19.2556074		Prob > F	=	0.0000
Residual	10.4462926	98	.106594823		R-squared	=	0.6483
					Adj R-squared	=	0.6447
Total	29.7019	99	.300019192		Root MSE	=	.32649

Price	Coef.	Std. Err.	t	P>|t|	[95% Conf. Interval]	
Odometer	-.0668609	.0049746	-13.44	0.000	-.0767329	-.0569889
_cons	17.24873	.1820926	94.73	0.000	16.88737	17.61008

The regression equation is
$$\hat{y} = 17.24873 - .0668609x$$
The standard error of estimate (ROOT MSE) = .32649
The coefficient of determination: R^2 = .6483
Test of the slope coefficient: t = −13.44, p-value = 0
Confidence interval estimate of the slope coefficient: LCL = −.0767329, UCL = −.0569889

Instructions

1. Import or type the data into two columns. (Click File/Import /Excel spreadsheet (*xls,*xlsx)/Chapter16/Xm16-02.)

2. Click **Statistics, Linear models and related**, and **Linear regression**.

3. In the **Dependent variable:** box select **Price**. In the **Independent variables:** box select **Odometer**.

APPENDIX 16.C / REVIEW OF CHAPTERS 12 TO 16

We have now presented two dozen inferential techniques. Undoubtedly, the task of choosing the appropriate technique is growing more difficult. Table A16.1 lists all the statistical inference methods covered since Chapter 12. Figure A16.1 is a flowchart to help you choose the correct technique.

TABLE **A16.1**   **Summary of Statistical Techniques in Chapters 12 to 16**

t-test of μ

Estimator of μ (including estimator of $N\mu$)

χ^2-test of σ^2

Estimator of σ^2

z-test of p

Estimator of p (including estimator of Np)

Equal-variances t-test of $\mu_1 - \mu_2$

Equal-variances estimator of $\mu_1 - \mu_2$

Unequal-variances t-test of $\mu_1 - \mu_2$

Unequal-variances estimator of $\mu_1 - \mu_2$

t-test of μ_D

Estimator of μ_D

F-test of σ_1^2/σ_2^2

Estimator of σ_1^2/σ_2^2

z-test of $p_1 - p_2$ (Case 1)

z-test of $p_1 - p_2$ (Case 2)

Estimator of $p_1 - p_2$

One-way analysis of variance (including multiple comparisons)

Two-way (randomized blocks) analysis of variance

Two-factor analysis of variance

χ^2-goodness-of-fit test

χ^2-test of a contingency table

Simple linear regression and correlation (including t-tests of β_1 and ρ, and prediction and confidence intervals)

FIGURE **A16.1** Flowchart of Techniques in Chapters 12 to 16

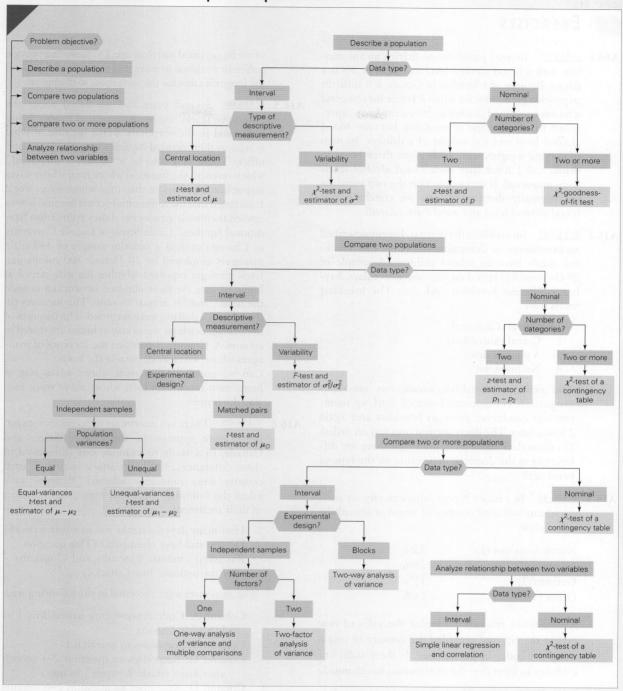

EXERCISES

A16.1 XrA16-01   In most jurisdictions, driving an automobile with a blood alcohol level in excess of .08 is a felony. Because of a number of factors, it is difficult to provide guidelines for when it is safe for someone who has consumed alcohol to drive a car. In an experiment to examine the relationship between blood alcohol level and the weight of a drinker, 50 men of varying weights were each given three beers to drink, and 1 hour later their blood alcohol levels were measured. If we assume that the two variables are normally distributed, can we conclude that blood alcohol level and weight are related?

A16.2 XrA16-02   An article in the journal *Appetite* described an experiment to determine the effect that breakfast meals have on school children. A sample of 29 children was tested on four successive days, having a different breakfast each day. The breakfast meals were

1. Cereal (Cheerios)
2. Cereal (Shreddies)
3. A glucose drink
4. No breakfast

The order of breakfast meals was randomly assigned. A computerized test of working memory was conducted prior to breakfast and again 2 hours later. The decrease in scores was recorded. Do these data allow us to infer that there are differences in the decrease depending on the type of breakfast?

A16.3 XrA16-03   In a major North American city, an analysis of cars and their country of origin produced the table below.

North American (1)	35%
Japanese (2)	25%
German (3)	15%
Other (4)	25%

A statistician randomly sampled the sales of new cars in the city and recorded the country of origin using the codes in parentheses. Is there sufficient evidence to infer that the distribution has changed?

A16.4 XrA16-04   A new antiflu vaccine designed to reduce the duration of symptoms has been developed. However, the effect of the drug varies from person to person. To examine the effect of age on the effectiveness of the drug, a sample of 140 flu sufferers was drawn. Respondents reported how long the symptoms of the flu persisted and their age. Do these data provide sufficient evidence to infer that the older the patient, the longer it takes for the symptoms to disappear?

A16.5 XrA16-05   Several years ago we heard about the "Mommy Track," the phenomenon of women being underpaid in the corporate world because of what is seen as their divided loyalties between home and office. There may also be a "Daddy Differential," which refers to the situation where men whose wives stay at home earn more than men whose wives work. It is argued that the differential occurs because bosses reward their male employees if they come from "traditional families." Linda Stroh of Loyola University of Chicago studied a random sample of 348 male managers employed by 20 *Fortune 500* companies. Each manager reported whether his wife stayed at home to care for their children or worked outside the home, and his annual income. The incomes (in thousands of dollars) were recorded. The incomes of the managers whose wives stay at home are stored in column A. Column B contains the incomes of managers whose wives work outside the home.
Can we conclude that men whose wives stay at home earn more than men whose wives work outside the home?

A16.6 XrA16-06   There are enormous differences between health care systems in the United States and Canada. In a study to examine one dimension of these differences, 300 heart attack victims in each country were randomly selected. Patients were asked the following questions regarding the effect of their treatment:

1. How many days did it take you to return to work?
2. Do you still have chest pain? (This question was asked 1 month, 6 months, and 12 months after the patients' heart attacks.)

The responses were recorded in the following way:

Column A: Code representing nationality: 1 = U.S.; 2 = Canada
Column B: Responses to question 1
Column C: Responses to question 2–1 month after heart attack: 2 = yes; 1 = no
Column D: Responses to question 2–6 months after heart attack: 2 = yes; 1 = no
Column E: Responses to question 2–12 months after heart attack: 2 = yes; 1 = no

Can we conclude that recovery is faster in the United States?

Comstock Images/Getty Images

MULTIPLE REGRESSION

CHAPTER OUTLINE

General Social Survey

Variables That Affect Income

DATA
GSS2018

In the Chapter 16 opening example, we showed using the General Social Survey that income and education are linearly related. This raises the question, What other variables affect one's income? To answer this question, we need to expand the simple linear regression technique used in the previous chapter to allow for more than one independent variable.

Here is a list of all the interval variables the General Social Survey created:

Age (AGE)

Years of education of respondent, spouse, father, and mother (EDUC, SPEDUC, PAEDUC, MAEDUC)

Mundoview/Shutterstock.com

Our answer appears on page 734.

(Continued)

731

Hours of work per week of respondent and of spouse (HRS1 and SPHRS1)

Number of family members earning money (EARNRS)

Number of children (CHILDS)

Age when first child was born (AGEKDBRN)

Number of hours of television viewing per day (TVHOURS)

Score on question, Should government reduce income differences between rich and poor? (EQWLTH)

Score on question, Should government improve standard of living of poor people? (HELPPOOR)

Score on question, Should government do more or less to solve country's problems? (HELPNOT)

Score on question, Is it government's responsibility to help pay for doctor and hospital bills? (HELPSICK)

The goal is create a regression analysis that includes all variables that you believe affect income (RINCOME).

INTRODUCTION

In the previous chapter, we employed the simple linear regression model to analyze how one variable (the dependent variable y) is related to another interval variable (the independent variable x). The restriction of using only one independent variable was motivated by the need to simplify the introduction to regression analysis. Although there are a number of applications where we purposely develop a model with only one independent variable (see Section 4-6, for example), in general we prefer to include as many independent variables as are believed to affect the dependent variable. Arbitrarily limiting the number of independent variables also limits the usefulness of the model.

In this chapter, we allow for any number of independent variables. In so doing, we expect to develop models that fit the data better than would a simple linear regression model. We begin by describing the multiple regression model and listing the required conditions. We let the computer produce the required statistics and use them to assess the model's fit and diagnose violations of the required conditions. We use the model by interpreting the coefficients, predicting the particular value of the dependent variable, and estimating its expected value.

17-1 / MODEL AND REQUIRED CONDITIONS

We now assume that k independent variables are potentially related to the dependent variable. Thus, the model is represented by the following equation:

$$y = \beta_0 + \beta_1 x_1 + \beta_2 x_2 + \cdots + \beta_k x_k + \varepsilon$$

where y is the dependent variable, $x_1, x_2, \ldots, x_k$ are the independent variables, $\beta_0, \beta_1, \ldots, \beta_k$ are the coefficients, and ε is the error variable. The independent variables may actually be functions of other variables. For example, we might define some of the independent variables as follows:

$$x_2 = x_1^2$$
$$x_5 = x_3 x_4$$
$$x_7 = \log(x_6)$$

In Chapter 18, we will discuss how and under what circumstances such functions can be used in regression analysis.

The error variable is retained because, even though we have included additional independent variables, deviations between predicted values of y and actual values of y will still occur. Incidentally, when there is more than one independent variable in the regression model, we refer to the graphical depiction of the equation as a **response surface** rather than as a straight line. Figure 17.1 depicts a scatter diagram of a response surface with $k = 2$. (When $k = 2$, the regression equation creates a plane.) Of course, whenever k is greater than 2, we can only imagine the response surface; we cannot draw it.

FIGURE 17.1 Scatter Diagram and Response Surface with $k = 2$

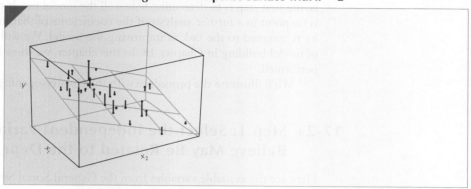

An important part of the regression analysis comprises several statistical techniques that evaluate how well the model fits the data. These techniques require the following conditions, which we introduced in the previous chapter.

Required Conditions for Error Variable

1. The probability distribution of the error variable ε is normal.
2. The mean of the error variable is 0.
3. The standard deviation of ε is σ_ε, which is a constant.
4. The errors are independent.

In Section 16-6, we discussed how to recognize when the requirements are unsatisfied. Those same procedures can be used to detect violations of required conditions in the multiple regression model.

We now proceed as we did in Chapter 16. We discuss how the model's coefficients are estimated and how we assess the model's fit. However, there is one major difference between Chapters 16 and 17. In Chapter 16, we allowed for the possibility that some students will perform the calculations manually. The multiple regression model involves so many computations that it is virtually impossible to conduct the analysis without a computer. All analyses in this chapter will be performed by Excel. Your job will be to interpret the output.

17-2 / ESTIMATING THE COEFFICIENTS AND ASSESSING THE MODEL

The multiple regression equation is expressed similarly to the simple regression equation. The general form is

$$\hat{y} = b_0 + b_1x_1 + b_2x_2 + \cdots + b_kx_k$$

where k is the number of independent variables.

The procedures introduced in Chapter 16 are extended to the multiple regression model. However, in Chapter 16, we first discussed how to interpret the coefficients and then discussed how to assess the model's fit. In practice, we reverse the process. That is, the first step is to determine how well the model fits. If the model's fit is poor, there is no point in a further analysis of the coefficients of that model. A much higher priority is assigned to the task of improving the model. We will discuss the art and science of model building in Chapter 18. In this chapter, we show how a regression analysis is performed.

We'll illustrate the procedure with the chapter-opening example.

17-2a Step 1: Select the Independent Variables That You Believe May Be Related to the Dependent Variable

Here are the available variables from the General Social Survey of 2018 and the reason why we have selected each one:

Age (AGE): For most people, income increases with age.

Years of education (EDUC): We've already shown (Chapter 16 opening example) that education is linearly related to income.

Hours of work per week (HRS1): Obviously, more hours of work should produce more income.

Spouse's hours of work (SPHRS1): It is possible that, if one's spouse works more and earns more, the other spouse may choose to work less and thus earn less.

The problem with including SPHRS1 in the regression model is that this variable has many missing values, which would reduce the sample size of the model. In fact, the decrease would be about 67%. Consequently, we have decided to exclude this variable from the model.

Number of family members earning money (EARNRS): If more family members earn income, there may be less pressure on the respondent to work harder.

Number of children (CHILDS): Children are expensive, which may encourage their parents to work harder and thus earn more.

You may be wondering why we don't simply include all the interval variables that are available to us. There are three reasons. First, the objective is to determine whether our hypothesized model is valid and whether the independent variables in the model are linearly related to the dependent variable. That is, we should screen the independent variables and include only those that in theory affect the dependent variable.

Second, by including large numbers of independent variables we increase the probability of Type I errors. For example, if we include 100 independent variables, none of which are related to the dependent variable, we're likely to conclude that five of them are linearly related to the dependent variable. This is a problem that we discussed in Chapter 14.

Third, because of a problem called multicollinearity (described in Section 17-3), we may conclude that none of the independent variables are linearly related to the dependent variable when in fact one or more are.

17-2b Step 2: Use a Computer to Compare All the Coefficients and Other Statistics

EXCEL Data Analysis

	A	B	C	D	E	F	G
1	SUMMARY OUTPUT						
2	*Regression Statistics*						
3	Multiple R	0.5269					
4	R Square	0.2776					
5	Adjusted R Square	0.2745					
6	Standard Error	36,608					
7	Observations	1171					
8	ANOVA						
9		*df*	*SS*	*MS*	*F*	*Significance F*	
10	Regression	5	599,889,787,700	119,977,957,540	89.53	8.66E-80	
11	Residual	1165	1,561,230,558,586	1,340,112,067			
12	Total	1170	2,161,120,346,285				
13							
14		*Coefficients*	*Standard Error*	*t Stat*	*P-value*	*Lower 95%*	*Upper 95%*
15	Intercept	-100,340	7633.4911	-13.14	6.70E-37	-115,317	-85,363
16	AGE	671.1	84.5	7.94	4.79E-15	505.2	836.9
17	EDUC	5604	386.7	14.49	7.00E-44	4845.1	6362.4
18	HRS1	948.7	75.1	12.64	2.13E-34	801.4	1096.0
19	EARNRS	1289	1330.3	0.969	0.3327	-1320.8	3899.2
20	CHILDS	718.8	760.7	0.945	0.3449	-773.7	2211.4

INSTRUCTIONS

1. Type or import the data (Open GSS2018). Arrange the columns so that the independent variables are in adjacent columns. Delete rows that have blanks in any of the columns (see Xm17-00).

2. Click **Data, Data Analysis**, and **Regression**.

3. Specify the **Input *Y* Range** (B1:B1172), the Input *X* **Range** (C1:G1172), and a value for α (.05).

INTERPRET

The regression equation is estimated by

$$\hat{y} \text{ (INCOME)} = -100,340 + 671.1 \text{ AGE} + 5604 \text{ EDUC} + 948.7 \text{ HRS1} + 1289 \text{ EARNRS} + 718.8 \text{ CHILDS}$$

17-2c Step 3: Assess the Model

We assess the model in three ways: the standard error of estimate, the coefficient of determination (both introduced in Chapter 16), and the *F*-test of the analysis of variance (presented subsequently).

17-2d Standard Error of Estimate

Recall that σ_ε is the standard deviation of the error variable ε and that, because σ_ε is a population parameter, it is necessary to estimate its value by using s_ε. In multiple regression, the standard error of estimate is defined as follows:

Standard Error of Estimate

$$s_\varepsilon = \sqrt{\frac{\text{SSE}}{n - k - 1}}$$

where n is the sample size and k is the number of independent variables in the model.

EXCEL Data Analysis

7	Standard Error	36,608

INTERPRET

Recall that we judge the magnitude of the standard error of estimate relative to the values of the dependent variable, and particularly to the mean of y. In this example, $\bar{y} = 51{,}913$ (not shown in printouts). It appears that the standard error of estimate is quite large.

17-2e Coefficient of Determination

Recall from Chapter 16 that the coefficient of determination is defined as:

$$R^2 = 1 - \frac{\text{SSE}}{\sum (y_i - \bar{y})^2}$$

EXCEL Data Analysis

5	R Square	0.2776

INTERPRET

This means that 27.76% of the total variation in income is explained by the variation in the five independent variables, whereas 72.24% remains unexplained.

Notice that Excel prints a second R^2 statistic, called the **coefficient of determination adjusted for degrees of freedom**, which has been adjusted to take into account the sample size and the number of independent variables. The rationale for this statistic is that, if the number of independent variables k is large relative to the sample size n, the unadjusted R^2 value may be unrealistically high. To understand this point, consider what would happen if the sample size is 2 in a simple linear regression model. The line would fit the data perfectly resulting in $R^2 = 1$ when, in fact, there may be no linear relationship. To avoid creating a false impression, the adjusted R^2 is often calculated. Its formula is as follows:

Coefficient of Determination Adjusted for Degrees of Freedom

$$R^2 = 1 - \frac{\text{SSE}/(n - k - 1)}{\sum (y_i - \bar{y})^2/(n - 1)}$$

EXCEL Data Analysis

6	Adjusted R Square	0.2745

If n is considerably larger than k, the unadjusted and adjusted R^2 values will be similar. But if SSE is quite different from 0 and k is large relative to n, the unadjusted and adjusted values of R^2 will differ substantially. If such differences exist, the analyst should be alerted to a potential problem in interpreting the coefficient of determination. In this example, the adjusted coefficient of determination is .2745, indicating that, no matter how we measure the coefficient of determination, the model's fit is not very good.

17-2f Testing the Validity of the Model

In the simple linear regression model, we tested the slope coefficient to determine whether sufficient evidence existed to allow us to conclude that there was a linear relationship between the independent variable and the dependent variable. However, because there is only one independent variable in that model, that same t-test also tested to determine whether that model is valid. When there is more than one independent variable, we need another method to test the overall validity of the model. The technique is a version of the analysis of variance, which we introduced in Chapter 14.

To test the validity of the regression model, we specify the following hypotheses:

H_0: $\beta_1 = \beta_2 = \cdots = \beta_k = 0$

H_1: At least one β_i is not equal to 0.

If the null hypothesis is true, none of the independent variables $x_1, x_2, \ldots, x_k$ is linearly related to y, and therefore the model is invalid. If at least one β_i is not equal to 0, the model does have some validity.

When we discussed the coefficient of determination in Chapter 16, we noted that the total variation in the dependent variable [measured by $\sum (y_i - \bar{y})^2$] can be decomposed into two parts: the explained variation (measured by SSR) and the unexplained variation (measured by SSE). That is:

Total variation in y = SSR + SSE

Furthermore, we established that, if SSR is large relative to SSE, the coefficient of determination will be high—signifying a good model. On the other hand, if SSE is large, most of the variation will be unexplained, which indicates that the model provides a poor fit and consequently has little validity.

The test statistic is the same one we encountered in Section 14-1, where we tested for the equivalence of two or more population means. To judge whether SSR is large enough relative to SSE to allow us to infer that at least one coefficient is not equal to 0, we compute the ratio of the two mean squares. (Recall that the mean square is the sum of squares divided by its degrees of freedom; recall, too, that the ratio of two mean squares is F distributed as long as the underlying population is normal—a required condition for this application.) The calculation of the test statistic is summarized in an analysis of variance (ANOVA) table, whose general form appears in Table 17.1. The Excel ANOVA table is shown next.

TABLE **17.1**   Analysis of Variance Table for Regression Analysis

SOURCE OF VARIATION	DEGREES OF FREEDOM	SUMS OF SQUARES	MEAN SQUARES	F-STATISTIC
Regression	k	SSR	MSR = SSR/k	F = MSR/MSE
Residual	$n - k - 1$	SSE	MSE = SSE/$(n - k - 1)$	
Total	$n - 1$	$\sum(y_i - \bar{y})^2$		

EXCEL Data Analysis

	df	SS	MS	F	Significance F
10 ANOVA					
11	df	SS	MS	F	Significance F
12 Regression	5	599,889,787,700	119,977,957,540	89.53	8.66E-80
13 Residual	1165	1,561,230,558,586	1,340,112,067		
14 Total	1170	2,161,120,346,285			

A large value of F indicates that most of the variation in y is explained by the regression equation and that the model is valid. A small value of F indicates that most of the variation in y is unexplained. The rejection region allows us to determine whether F is large enough to justify rejecting the null hypothesis. For this test, the rejection region is:

$$F > F_{\alpha,k,n-k-1}$$

In Example 17.1, the rejection region (assuming $\alpha = .05$) is:

$$F > F_{\alpha,k,n-k-1} = F_{.05,5,1165} \approx 2.21$$

As you can see from the printout, $F = 89.53$. The printout also includes the p-value of the test, which is 0. Obviously, there is a great deal of evidence to infer that the model is valid.

Although each assessment measurement offers a different perspective, all agree in their assessment of how well the model fits the data, because all are based on the sum of squares for error, SSE. The standard error of estimate is:

$$s_\varepsilon = \sqrt{\frac{SSE}{n - k - 1}}$$

and the coefficient of determination is:

$$R^2 = 1 - \frac{SSE}{\sum(y_i - \bar{y})^2}$$

When the response surface hits every single point, SSE = 0. Hence, $s_\varepsilon = 0$ and $R^2 = 1$.

If the model provides a poor fit, we know that SSE will be large [its maximum value is $\sum(y_i - \bar{y})^2$], s_ε will be large, and [since SSE is close to $\sum(y_i - \bar{y})^2$] R^2 will be close to 0.

The *F*-statistic also depends on SSE. Specifically,

$$F = \frac{MSR}{MSE} = \frac{\left(\sum(y_i - \bar{y})^2 - SSE\right)/k}{SSE/(n - k - 1)}$$

When SSE = 0:

$$F = \frac{\sum(y_i - \bar{y})^2/k}{0/(n - k - 1)}$$

which is infinitely large. When SSE is large, SSE is close to $\sum(y_i - \bar{y})^2$ and F is quite small.

The relationship among SSE, s_ε, R^2, and F is summarized in Table 17.2.

TABLE **17.2** Relationship among SSE, s_ε, R^2, and F

SSE	s_ε	R^2	F	ASSESSMENT OF MODEL
0	0	1	∞	Perfect
Small	Small	Close to 1	Large	Good
Large	Large	Close to 0	Small	Poor
$\sum(y_i - \bar{y})^2$	$\sqrt{\dfrac{\sum(y_i - \bar{y})^2}{n - k - 1}}$*	0	0	Invalid

*When n is large and k is small, this quantity is approximately equal to the standard deviation of y.

17-2g Interpreting the Coefficients

The coefficients $b_0, b_1, \ldots, b_k$ describe the relationship between each of the independent variables and the dependent variable in the sample. We need to use inferential methods (described below) to draw conclusions about the population. In our example, the sample consists of the 1,171 observations. The population is composed of all American adults.

Intercept The intercept is $b_0 = -100,340$. This is the average income when all the independent variables are zero. As we observed in Chapter 16, it is often misleading to try to interpret this value, particularly if 0 is outside the range of the values of the independent variables (as is the case here).

Age The relationship between income and age is described by $b_1 = 671.1$. From this number, we learn that in this model, for each additional year of age, income increases on average by \$671.10, assuming that the other independent variables in this model are held constant.

Education The coefficient $b_2 = 5,604$ specifies that in this sample for each additional year of education the income increases on average by \$5,604, assuming the constancy of the other independent variables.

Hours of Work The relationship between hours of work per week is expressed by $b_3 = 948.7$. We interpret this number as the average increase in annual income for each additional hour of work per week keeping the other independent variables fixed in this sample.

Number of Family Members Earning Income In this data set, the relationship between annual income and the number of family members who earn money is expressed by $b_5 = 1,289$, which tells us that for each additional family member earner, annual income increases on average by \$1,289 assuming that the other independent variables are constant.

Number of Children The relationship between annual income and number of children is expressed by $b_4 = 718.8$, which tells us that in this sample for each additional child, annual income increases on average by \$718.80 assuming that the other independent variables in this model are held constant.

17-2h Testing the Coefficients

In Chapter 16, we described how to test to determine whether there is sufficient evidence to infer that in the simple linear regression model x and y are linearly related. The null and alternative hypotheses were:

$$H_0: \ \beta_1 = 0$$
$$H_1: \ \beta_1 \neq 0$$

The test statistic was:

$$t = \frac{b_1 - \beta_1}{s_{b_1}}$$

which is Student t distributed with $\nu = n - 2$ degrees of freedom.

In the multiple regression model, we have more than one independent variable. For each such variable, we can test to determine whether there is enough evidence of a linear relationship between it and the dependent variable for the entire population when the other independent variables are included in the model.

Testing the Coefficients

$$H_0: \ \beta_i = 0$$
$$H_1: \ \beta_i \neq 0$$

(for $i = 1, 2, \ldots, k$); the test statistic is:

$$t = \frac{b_i - \beta_i}{s_{b_i}}$$

which is Student t distributed with $\nu = n - k - 1$ degrees of freedom.

To illustrate, we test each of the coefficients in the multiple regression model in the chapter-opening example. The tests that follow are performed just as all other tests in this book have been performed. We set up the null and alternative hypotheses, identify the test statistic, and use the computer to calculate the value of the test statistic and its p-value. For each independent variable, we test ($i = 1, 2, 3, 4, 5$):

$$H_0: \ \beta_i = 0$$
$$H_1: \ \beta_i \neq 0$$

Refer to page 735 and examine the computer output. The output includes the t-tests of β_i. The results of these tests pertain to the entire population of the United States in 2018. It is also important to add that these test results were determined when the other independent variables were included in the model. We add this statement because a simple linear regression will very likely result in different values of the test statistics and possibly the conclusion.

Test of β_1 (Coefficient of age)

Value of the test statistic: $t = 7.94$; p-value = 0

Test of β_2 (Coefficient of number of years of education)

Value of the test statistic: $t = 14.49$; p-value = 0

Test of β_3 (Coefficient of number of hours worked)

Value of the test statistic: $t = 12.64$; p-value = 0

Test of β_4 (Coefficient of number of earners in family)

Value of the test statistic: $t = .969$; p-value = .3327

Test of β_5 (Coefficient of number of children)

Value of the test statistic: $t = .945$; p-value = .3449

There is sufficient evidence at the 5% significance level to infer that each of the following variables is linearly related to income:

Age

Education

Number of hours of work per week

In this model, there is not enough evidence to conclude that each of the following variables is linearly related to income:

Number of earners in the family

Number of children

Note that this may mean that there is no evidence of a linear relationship between these three independent variables. However, it may also mean that there is a linear relationship between the two variables, but because of a condition called *multicollinearity*, some *t*-test of β_i revealed no linear relationship. We will discuss multicollinearity in Section 17-3.

17-2i A Cautionary Note about Interpreting the Results

Care should be taken when interpreting the results of this and other regression analyses. We might find that in one model there is enough evidence to conclude that a particular independent variable is linearly related to the dependent variable, but that in another model, no such evidence exists. Consequently, whenever a particular *t*-test is *not* significant, we state that there is not enough evidence to infer that the independent and dependent variable are linearly related *in this model*. The implication is that another model may yield different conclusions.

Furthermore, if one or more of the required conditions are violated, the results may be invalid. In Section 17-3, we introduced the procedures that allow the statistics practitioner to examine the model's requirements. We also remind you that it is dangerous to extrapolate far outside the range of the observed values of the independent variables.

17-2j *t*-Tests and the Analysis of Variance

The *t*-tests of the individual coefficients allow us to determine whether $\beta_i \neq 0$ (for $i = 1, 2, \ldots, k$), which tells us whether a linear relationship exists between x_i and y. There is a *t*-test for each independent variable. Consequently, the computer automatically performs k *t*-tests. (It actually conducts $k + 1$ *t*-tests, including the one for the intercept β_0, which we usually ignore.) The *F*-test in the analysis of variance combines these *t*-tests into a single test. That is, we test all the β_i at one time to determine whether at least one of them is not equal to 0. The question naturally arises, Why do we need the *F*-test if it is nothing more than the combination of the previously performed *t*-tests? Recall that we addressed this issue earlier. In Chapter 14, we pointed out that we can replace the analysis of variance by a series of *t*-tests of the difference between two means. However, by doing so, we increase the probability of making a Type I error. Which means that even when there is no linear relationship between each of the independent variables and the dependent variable, multiple *t*-tests will likely show some are significant. As a result, you will conclude erroneously that, since at least one β_i is not equal to 0, the model is valid. The *F*-test, on the other hand, is performed only once. Because the probability that a Type I error will occur in a single trial is equal to α, the chance of erroneously concluding that the model is valid is substantially less with the *F*-test than with multiple *t*-tests.

There is another reason that the *F*-test is superior to multiple *t*-tests. Because of a commonly occurring problem called *multicollinearity*, the *t*-tests may indicate that some independent variables are not linearly related to the dependent variable, when in fact they are. The problem of multicollinearity does not affect the *F*-test, nor does it inhibit us from developing a model that fits the data well. Multicollinearity is discussed in Section 17-3.

17-2k The *F*-Test and the *t*-Test in the Simple Linear Regression Model

It is useful for you to know that we can use the *F*-test to test the validity of the simple linear regression model. However, this test is identical to the *t*-test of β_1. The *t*-test of β_1 in the simple linear regression model tells us whether that independent variable is linearly related to the dependent variable. However, because there is only one independent variable, the *t*-test of β_1 also tells us whether the model is valid, which is the purpose of the *F*-test.

The relationship between the *t*-test of β_1 and the *F*-test can be explained mathematically. Statisticians can show that if we square a *t*-statistic with ν degrees of freedom we produce an *F*-statistic with 1 and ν degrees of freedom. (We briefly discussed this relationship in Chapter 14.) To illustrate, consider Example 16.2 on page 678. We found the *t*-test of β_1 to be -13.44, with degrees of freedom equal to 98. The *p*-value was 5.75×10^{-24}. The output included the analysis of variance table where $F = 180.64$ and the *p*-value was 5.75×10^{-24}. The *t*-statistic squared is $t^2 = (-13.44)^2 = 180.63$. (The difference is due to rounding errors.) Notice that the degrees of freedom of the *F*-statistic are 1 and 98. Thus, we can use either test to test the validity of the simple linear regression model.

EXERCISES

The following exercises require the use of a computer and statistical software. **Use a 5% significance level for all tests.**

17.1 Xr17-01 A developer who specializes in summer cottage properties is considering purchasing a large tract of land adjoining a lake. The current owner of the tract has already subdivided the land into separate building lots and has prepared the lots by removing some of the trees. The developer wants to forecast the value of each lot. From previous experience, it is known that the most important factors affecting the price of a lot are size, number of mature trees, and distance to the lake. From a nearby area, the relevant data for 60 recently sold lots were gathered.

a. Find the regression equation.
b. What is the standard error of estimate? Interpret its value.
c. What is the coefficient of determination? What does this statistic tell you?
d. What is the coefficient of determination, adjusted for degrees of freedom? Why does this value differ from the coefficient of determination? What does this tell you about the model?
e. Test the validity of the model. What does the *p*-value of the test statistic tell you?
f. Interpret each of the coefficients.
g. Test to determine whether each of the independent variables is linearly related to the price of the lot in this model.

17.2 Xr17-02 The Palm Beach County, Florida, library system has a dozen different branches. The management was in the process of deciding where to place a new library. The choices are near several "Over 55" communities (people over 55 years of age) or where young families with children are located. To understand more about their customers, a random sample of people who borrowed at least one book during the previous 12 months was drawn. The number of books borrowed, their ages, and the distance to the nearest library (in miles) were recorded. Conduct a multiple regression analysis.

a. Is there sufficient evidence that older Floridians borrow more books than younger ones?
b. Can we infer that distance to the library is a factor in determining the number of books borrowed?

17.3 Xr17-03 The president of a company that manufactures drywall wants to analyze the variables that affect demand for his product. Drywall is used to construct walls in houses and offices. Consequently, the president decides to develop a regression model in which the dependent variable is monthly sales of drywall (in hundreds of 4×8 sheets) and the independent variables are as follows:

Number of building permits issued in the county
Five-year mortgage rates (in percentage points)
Vacancy rate in apartments (in percentage points)

Vacancy rate in office buildings (in percentage points)

To estimate a multiple regression model, monthly observations from the past 2 years were recorded.

a. Analyze the data using multiple regression.
b. What is the standard error of estimate? Can you use this statistic to assess the model's fit? If so, how?
c. What is the coefficient of determination, and what does it tell you about the regression model?
d. Test the validity of the model.
e. Interpret each of the coefficients.
f. Test to determine whether each of the independent variables is linearly related to drywall demand in this model.

17.4 Xr17-04 The general manager of the Baltimore Orioles baseball team is in the process of determining which minor-league players to draft. He is aware that his team needs home-run hitters and would like to find a way to predict the number of home runs a player will hit. Being an astute statistician, he gathers a random sample of players and records the number of home runs each player hit in his first two full years as a major-league player, the number of home runs he hit in his last full year in the minor leagues, his age, and the number of years of professional baseball.

a. Develop a regression model and use a software package to produce the statistics.
b. Interpret each of the coefficients.
c. How well does the model fit?
d. Test the model's validity.
e. Do each of the independent variables belong in the model?

17.5 Xr16-17+ Refer to Exercise 16.17 that analyzed the relationship between the price of a boat and the number of hours the engine has been run. The financial analyst realized that the simple linear regression model was not useful. Each boat was examined with the results summarized in a 10-point scale where 1 is poor condition and 10 is pristine condition.

a. Conduct a multiple regression analysis.
b. Can the analyst conclude that there is enough evidence to believe that the model is valid?
c. Is there sufficient evidence to infer that a boat's condition is linearly related to its price?
d. Determine the coefficient of determination and describe the information it provides.

17.6 Xr17-06 The admissions officer of a university is trying to develop a formal system to decide which students to admit to the university. It is known that determinants of success include the standard variables—high school grades and SAT scores. However, it is also believed that students who have participated in extracurricular activities are more likely to succeed than those who have not. To investigate the issue, 100 fourth-year students were sampled and the following variables were recorded:

GPA for the first 3 years at the university (range: 0 to 12)
GPA from high school (range: 0 to 12)
SAT score (range: 400 to 1,600)
Number of hours on average spent per week in organized extracurricular activities in the last year of high school

a. Develop a model that helps the admissions officer decide which students to admit and use the computer to generate the usual statistics.
b. What is the coefficient of determination? Interpret its value.
c. Test the validity of the model.
d. Test to determine whether each of the independent variables is linearly related to the dependent variable in this model.

17.7 Xr17-07 The marketing manager for a chain of hardware stores needed more information about the effectiveness of the three types of advertising that the chain used. These are localized direct mailing (in which flyers describing sales and featured products are distributed to homes in the area surrounding a store), newspaper advertising, and local television advertisements. To determine which type is most effective, the manager collected 1 week's data from 100 randomly selected stores. For each store, the following variables were recorded:

Weekly gross sales
Weekly expenditures on direct mailing
Weekly expenditures on newspaper advertising
Weekly expenditures on television commercials

All variables were recorded in thousands of dollars.

a. Find the regression equation.
b. What are the coefficient of determination and the coefficient of determination adjusted for degrees of freedom? What do these statistics tell you about the regression equation?
c. What does the standard error of estimate tell you about the regression model?
d. Test the validity of the model.
e. Which independent variables are linearly related to weekly gross sales in this model? Explain.

17.8 Xr17-08 For many cities around the world, garbage is an increasing problem. Many North American cities have virtually run out of space to dump the garbage. A consultant for a large American city decided to gather data about the problem. The consultant took a random sample of houses and determined the following:

Y = the amount of garbage per average week (pounds)
X_1 = Size of the house (square feet)
X_2 = Number of children
X_3 = Number of adults who are usually home during the day

a. Conduct a regression analysis.
b. Is there sufficient evidence to infer that the model is valid?
c. Interpret each of the coefficients.
d. Test to determine whether each of the independent variables is linearly related to the dependent variable.

17.9 Xr17-09 A school board in a large county was analyzing the average mathematics test scores in the schools under their control. In an attempt to improve the scores of all the schools, they took a random sample of 40 schools across the county and, for each, determined the mean test score last year, the percentage of teachers in each school who have at least one university degree in mathematics, the mean age, and the mean annual income (in $1,000s) of the mathematics teachers.

a. Conduct a regression analysis to develop the equation.
b. Do the data provide enough statistical evidence to infer that the model is valid?
c. Interpret and test the coefficients.

17.10 Xr17-10+ Life insurance companies are keenly interested in predicting how long their customers will live because their premiums and profitability depend on such numbers. An actuary for one insurance company gathered data from 100 recently deceased male customers. The age at death of the customer plus the ages at death of their mother and father, the mean ages at death of grandmothers, and the mean ages at death of his grandfathers were recorded.

a. Perform a multiple regression analysis on these data.
b. Is there enough statistical evidence to conclude that the model is valid?
c. Interpret and test the coefficients.

17.11 Xr17-11 University students often complain that universities reward professors for research but not for teaching, and they argue that professors react to this situation by devoting more time and energy to the publication of their findings and less time and energy to classroom activities. Professors counter that research and teaching go hand in hand: More research makes better teachers. A student organization at one university decided to investigate the

issue. It randomly selected 50 economics professors who are employed by a multicampus university. The students recorded the salaries (in $1,000s) of the professors, their average teaching evaluations (on a 10-point scale), and the total number of journal articles published in their careers. Perform a complete analysis (produce the regression equation, assess it, and report your findings).

17.12 Xr17-12+ One critical factor that determines the success of a catalog store chain is the availability of products that consumers want to buy. If a store is sold out, future sales to that customer are less likely. Accordingly, delivery trucks operating from a central warehouse regularly resupply stores. In an analysis of a chain's operations, the general manager wanted to determine the factors that are related to how long it takes to unload delivery trucks. A random sample of 50 deliveries to one store was observed. The times (in minutes) to unload the truck, the total number of boxes, and the total weight (in hundreds of pounds) of the boxes were recorded.

a. Determine the multiple regression equation.
b. How well does the model fit the data? Explain.
c. Interpret and test the coefficients.

17.13 Xr17-13 Lotteries have become important sources of revenue for governments. Many people have criticized lotteries, however, referring to them as a tax on the poor and uneducated. In an examination of the issue, a random sample of 100 adults was asked how much they spend on lottery tickets and was interviewed about various socioeconomic variables. The purpose of this study is to test the following beliefs:

1. Relatively uneducated people spend more on lotteries than do relatively educated people.
2. Older people buy more lottery tickets than younger people.
3. People with more children spend more on lotteries than people with fewer children.
4. Relatively poor people spend a greater proportion of their income on lotteries than relatively rich people.

The following data were recorded:

Amount spent on lottery tickets as a percentage of total household income
Number of years of education
Age
Number of children
Personal income (in thousands of dollars)

a. Develop the multiple regression equation.
b. Test to determine the model's validity.
c. Test each of the beliefs. What conclusions can you draw?

17.14 Xr17-14+   The MBA program at a large university is facing a pleasant problem—too many applicants. The current admissions policy requires students to have completed at least 3 years of work experience and an undergraduate degree with a B-average or better. Until 3 years ago, the school admitted any applicant who met these requirements. However, because the program recently converted from a 2-year program (four semesters) to a 1-year program (three semesters), the number of applicants has increased substantially. The dean, who teaches statistics courses, wants to raise the admissions standards by developing a method that more accurately predicts how well an applicant will perform in the MBA program. The dean believes that the primary determinants of success are the following:

> Undergraduate grade point average (GPA)
> Graduate Management Admissions Test (GMAT) score
> Number of years of work experience

A random sample of students who completed the MBA and their MBA program GPA, as well as the three variables listed here were recorded.

a. Develop a multiple regression model.
b. Is there enough evidence to infer that the model is valid?
c. Test to determine which of the independent variables is linearly related to MBA GPA.

17.15 Xr17-15   With voter turnout during presidential elections around 50%, a vital task for politicians is to try to predict who will actually vote. A variable used to determine who is likely to vote was created and defined as follows. Definite: 1 = Definitely will not vote; 2, 3, 4, 5, 6, 7, 8, 9, 10 = Definitely will vote. A pollster conducted a survey that recorded the variable as well as age, education, and income. Develop a regression model to predict intention to vote using the following demographic independent variables:

a. Determine the regression equation.
b. Do the data provide enough statistical evidence to infer that the model is valid?
c. Test to determine whether there is sufficient evidence to infer a linear relationship between the dependent variable and each independent variable.

17.16 Xr17-16   Refer to Exercise 17.15. The pollster also recorded the following variables in addition to the variable Definite.

> Number of days in previous week watching national news on television (Days1)
> Number of days in previous week watching local television news in afternoon or early evening (Days2)

> Number of days in previous week watching local television news in late evening (Days3)
> Number of days in previous week reading a daily newspaper (Days4)
> Number of days in previous week reading a daily newspaper on the Internet (Days5)
> Number of days in previous week listening to news on radio (Days6)

The purpose of this survey is to answer this question, "Does watching news on television or reading newspapers provide indicators of who will vote?" Conduct a regression analysis with intention to vote (Definite) as the dependent variable.

a. Compute the regression equation.
b. Is there enough evidence to conclude that the model is valid?
c. Test each slope coefficient.

17.17 Xr17-17   Spring Lakes Golf Club is located in Stouffville, Ontario. It is a private course where members pay $1,000 per year and $50 per 18-hole round. To determine whether to alter the current fee structure, a random sample of 100 members was drawn. Each reported their number of rounds in the previous 30 days, their age, and their handicap.

a. Determine the regression equation.
b. Is there sufficient evidence to infer that older golfers play more rounds than younger golfers?
c. Do the data allow us to infer that better golfers (lower handicaps) play more rounds than high-handicap golfers?

17.18 Xr16-14+   Exercise 16.14 addressed the problem of determining the relationship between the price of apartment buildings and number of square feet. Hoping to improve the predictive capability of the model, the real estate agent also recorded the number of apartments, the age, and the number of floors.

a. Calculate the regression equation.
b. Test to determine whether the model is valid.
c. Determine which independent variables are related to the price of the building.

17.19 Xr16-16+   In Exercise 16.16, an economist examined the relationship between office rents and the city's office vacancy rate. The model appears to be quite poor. It was decided to add another variable that measures the state of the economy. The city's unemployment rate was chosen for this purpose.

a. Determine the regression equation.
b. Is there enough evidence to infer that the model is valid?
c. Determine which of the two independent variables is linearly related to rents.

APPLICATIONS in OPERATIONS MANAGEMENT

Location Analysis

Location analysis is one function of operations management. Deciding where to locate a plant, warehouse, or retail outlet is a critical decision for any organization. A large number of variables must be considered in this decision problem. For example, a production facility must be located close to suppliers of raw resources and supplies, skilled labor, and transportation to customers. Retail outlets must consider the type and number of potential customers. In the next example, we describe an application of regression analysis to find profitable locations for a motel chain.

17.20 Xr17-20   La Quinta Motor Inns is a moderately priced chain of motor inns located across the United States. Its market is the frequent business traveler. The chain recently launched a campaign to increase market share by building new inns. The management of the chain is aware of the difficulty in choosing locations for new motels. Moreover, making decisions without adequate information often results in poor decisions. Consequently, the chain's management acquired data on 100 randomly selected inns belonging to La Quinta. The objective was to predict which sites are likely to be profitable.

To measure profitability, La Quinta used *operating margin*, which is the ratio of the sum of profit, depreciation, and interest expenses divided by total revenue. (Although occupancy is often used as a measure of a motel's success, the company statistician concluded that occupancy was too unstable, especially during economic turbulence.) The higher the operating margin, the greater the success of the inn. La Quinta defines profitable inns as those with an operating margin in excess of 50%; unprofitable inns are those with margins of less than 30%. After a discussion with a number of experienced managers, La Quinta decided to select one or two independent variables from each of the following categories: competition, market awareness, demand generators, demographics, and physical location. To measure the degree of competition, they determined the total number of motel and hotel rooms within 3 miles of each La Quinta inn. Market awareness was measured by the number of miles to the closest competing motel. Two variables that represent sources of customers were chosen. The amount of office space and college and university enrollment in the surrounding community are demand generators. Both of these are measures of economic activity. A demographic variable that describes the community is the median household income. Finally, as a measure of the physical qualities of the location La Quinta chose the distance to the downtown core. These data are stored using the following format:

Column A: y = Operating margin, in percent

Column B: x_1 = Total number of motel and hotel rooms within 3 miles of La Quinta inn

Column C: x_2 = Number of miles to closest competition

Column D: x_3 = Office space in thousands of square feet in surrounding community

Column E: x_4 = College and university enrollment (in thousands) in nearby university or college

Column F: x_5 = Median household income (in $thousands) in surrounding community

Column G: x_6 = Distance (in miles) to the downtown core

(Continued)

a. Develop a regression analysis.
b. Test to determine whether there is enough evidence to infer that the model is valid.
c. Test each of the slope coefficients.
d. Interpret the coefficients.

GENERAL SOCIAL SURVEY EXERCISES

GSS2018   *Excel Data Analysis users: We remind you that any row that contains at least one empty cell (in dependent and independent variables column) must be removed. Conduct all tests at the 5% significance level.*

17.21 How does the amount of education of one's parents (PAEDUC, MAEDUC) affect one's education (EDUC)?
a. Develop a regression model.
b. Test the validity of the model.
c. Test the two slope coefficients.
d. Interpret the coefficients.

17.22 What determines people's opinion on the following question? Should the government reduce income differences between rich and poor (EQWLTH: 1 = Government should reduce differences; 2, 3, 4, 5, 6, 7 = No government action).
a. Develop a regression analysis using demographic variables age, (AGE), education (EDUC), income (RINCOME), and weekly hours of work (HRS1).
b. Test the model's validity.
c. Test each of the slope coefficients.
d. Interpret the coefficient of determination.

17.23 The Nielsen Ratings estimate the number of televisions tuned to various channels. However, television executives need more information. The General Social Survey may be the source of this information. Respondents were asked to report the number of hours per average day of television viewing (TVHOURS). Conduct a regression analysis using the independent variables age (AGE), education (EDUC), hours of work (HRS1), and number of children (CHILDS).
a. Test the model's validity.
b. Interpret the slope coefficients.
c. Test each slope coefficient.
d. Determine the coefficient of determination and describe what it tells you.

17.24 What determines people's opinion on the following question, Should the government improve the standard of living of poor people (HELPPOOR: 1 = Government act; 2, 3, 4, 5 = People should help themselves)?
a. Develop a regression analysis using demographic variables age (AGE), education (EDUC), income (RINCOME), and weekly hours of work (HRS1).
b. Test the model's validity.
c. Test each of the slope coefficients.
d. Interpret the coefficient of determination.

17-3 / REGRESSION DIAGNOSTICS—II

In Section 16-6, we discussed how to determine whether the required conditions are unsatisfied. The same procedures can be used to diagnose problems in the multiple regression model. Here is a brief summary of the diagnostic procedure we described in Chapter 16.

Calculate the residuals and check the following:

1. *Is the error variable nonnormal?* Draw the histogram of the residuals.

2. *Is the error variance constant?* Plot the residuals versus the predicted values of *y*.

3. *Are the errors independent (time-series data)?* Plot the residuals versus the time periods.

4. *Are there observations that are inaccurate or do not belong to the target population?* Double-check the accuracy of outliers and influential observations.

If the error is nonnormal and/or the variance is not a constant, several remedies can be attempted. These are beyond the level of this book.

Outliers and influential observations are checked by examining the data in question to ensure accuracy.

Nonindependence of a time series can sometimes be detected by graphing the residuals and the time periods and looking for evidence of autocorrelation. In Section 17-4, we introduce the Durbin–Watson test, which tests for one form of autocorrelation. We will offer a corrective measure for nonindependence.

There is another problem that is applicable to multiple regression models only. *Multicollinearity* is a condition wherein the independent variables are highly correlated. Multicollinearity distorts the t-tests of the coefficients, making it difficult to determine whether any of the independent variables are linearly related to the dependent variable. It also makes interpreting the coefficients problematic. We will discuss this condition and its remedy next.

17-3a Multicollinearity

Multicollinearity (also called *collinearity* and *intercorrelation*) is a condition that exists when the independent variables are correlated with one another. The adverse effect of multicollinearity is that the estimated regression coefficients of the independent variables that are correlated tend to have large sampling errors. There are two consequences of multicollinearity. First, because the variability of the coefficients is large, the sample coefficient may be far from the actual population parameter, including the possibility that the statistic and parameter may have opposite signs. Second, when the coefficients are tested, the t-statistics will be small, which leads to the inference that there is no linear relationship between the affected independent variables and the dependent variable. In some cases, this inference will be wrong. Fortunately, multicollinearity does not affect the F-test of the analysis of variance.

To illustrate, we'll use the General Social Survey of 2012. When we conducted a regression analysis similar to the chapter-opening example, this is the printout we produced.

	A	B	C	D	E
1		Coefficients	Standard Error	t Stat	P-value
2	Intercept	−79,060	15,407	−5.13	4.89E-07
3	AGE	484	159	3.04	0.0025
4	EDUC	5,296	579	9.15	5.76E-18
5	HRS1	888	129	6.90	2.60E-11
6	SPHRS1	-226	137	-1.65	0.0997
7	EARNRS	3,054	2,509	1.22	0.2244
8	CHILDS	-1,736	1,425	-1.22	0.2241

Notice that the number of children in the family was not statistically significant at the 5% significance level. (The p-value = .2241.) However, when we tested the coefficient of correlation between income and number of children, we found it to be statistically significant. The Excel printout of the t-test of the coefficient of correlation is shown here.

	A	B	C	D
1	t-Test of Correlation Coefficient			
2				
3	Sample correlation	−0.1425	t Stat	−2.65
4	Sample size	341	P(T<=t) one-tail	0.0042
5	Alpha	0.05	t Critical one-tail	1.6493
6			P(T<=t) two-tail	0.0084
7			t Critical two-tail	1.9670

How do we explain the apparent contradiction between the multiple regression t-test of the coefficient of the number of children and the result of the t-test of the correlation coefficient? The answer is multicollinearity.

There is a relatively high degree of correlation between number of family members who earn income and number of children. The result of the t-test of the correlation between number of earners and number of children is shown next. The result should not be surprising, as more earners in a family are very likely children.

	A	B	C	D
1	t-Test of Correlation Coefficient			
2				
3	Sample correlation	0.1539	t Stat	2.87
4	Sample size	341	P(T<=t) one-tail	0.0022
5	Alpha	0.05	t Critical one-tail	1.6493
6			P(T<=t) two-tail	0.0044
7			t Critical two-tail	1.9670

Multicollinearity affected the result of the multiple regression t-test so that it appeared that number of children is not significantly related to income, when in fact it is.

Another problem caused by multicollinearity is the interpretation of the coefficients. We interpret the coefficients as measuring the change in the dependent variable when the corresponding independent variable increases by one unit while all the other independent variables are held constant. This interpretation may be impossible when the independent variables are highly correlated, because when the independent variable increases by one unit, some or all of the other independent variables will change.

This raises two important questions for the statistics practitioner. First, how do we recognize the problem of multicollinearity when it occurs, and second, how do we avoid or correct it?

Multicollinearity exists in virtually all multiple regression models. In fact, finding two completely uncorrelated variables is rare. The problem becomes serious, however, only when two or more independent variables are highly correlated. Unfortunately, we do not have a critical value that indicates when the correlation between two independent variables is large enough to cause problems. To complicate the issue, multicollinearity also occurs when a combination of several independent variables is correlated with another independent variable or with a combination of other independent variables. Consequently, even with access to all the correlation coefficients, determining when the multicollinearity problem has reached the serious stage may be extremely difficult. A good indicator of the problem is a large F-statistic, but small t-statistics.

Minimizing the effect of multicollinearity is often easier than correcting it. The statistics practitioner must try to include independent variables that are independent of each other.

EXERCISES

The following exercises require a computer and software.

17.25 Compute the residuals and the predicted values for the regression analysis in Exercise 17.1.
  a. Is the normality requirement violated? Explain.
  b. Is the variance of the error variable constant? Explain.

17.26 Calculate the coefficients of correlation for each pair of independent variables in Exercise 17.1.

What do these statistics tell you about the independent variables and the t-tests of the coefficients?

17.27 Refer to Exercise 17.2.
  a. Determine the residuals and predicted values.
  b. Does it appear that the normality requirement is violated? Explain.
  c. Is the variance of the error variable constant? Explain.

17.28 Compute the residuals and predicted values for the regression analysis in Exercise 17.3.
   a. Does it appear that the error variable is not normally distributed?
   b. Is the variance of the error variable constant?
   c. Is multicollinearity a problem?

17.29 Refer to Exercise 17.4. Find the coefficients of correlation of the independent variables.
   a. What do these correlations tell you about the independent variables?
   b. What do they say about the *t*-tests of the coefficients?

17.30 Calculate the residuals and predicted values for the regression analysis in Exercise 17.5.
   a. Does the error variable appear to be normally distributed?
   b. Is the variance of the error variable constant?

17.31 Are the required conditions satisfied in Exercise 17.6?

17.32 Refer to Exercise 17.7.
   a. Conduct an analysis of the residuals to determine whether any of the required conditions are violated.
   b. Does it appear that multicollinearity is a problem?
   c. Identify any observations that should be checked for accuracy.

17.33 Are the required conditions satisfied for the regression analysis in Exercise 17.8?

17.34 Determine whether the required conditions are satisfied in Exercise 17.9.

17.35 Refer to Exercise 17.10. Calculate the residuals and predicted values.
   a. Is the normality requirement satisfied?
   b. Is the variance of the error variable constant?
   c. Is multicollinearity a problem?

17.36 Determine whether there are violations of the required conditions in the regression model used in Exercise 17.11.

17.37 Determine whether the required conditions are satisfied in Exercise 17.12.

17.38 Refer to Exercise 17.13.
   a. Are the required conditions satisfied?
   b. Is multicollinearity a problem? If so, explain the consequences.

17.39 Refer to Exercise 17.14. Are the required conditions satisfied?

17.40 Refer to Exercise 17.15. Check the required conditions.

17.41 Refer to Exercise 17.15. Determine whether the required conditions are satisfied.

17.42 Refer to Exercise 17.16. Are the required conditions satisfied?

GENERAL SOCIAL SURVEY EXERCISES

17.43 GSS2018 Refer to Exercise 17.24.
   a. Calculate the correlation matrix.
   b. Are there signs of the presence of multicollinearity? Explain.
   c. Test the correlation between each independent variable and the dependent variable. Which independent variables are linearly related to the dependent variable?

17.44 Refer to Exercise 17.21. Calculate the correlation between the father's and the mother's years of education. Is there any sign of multicollinearity? Explain.

17.45 Refer to Exercise 17.22.
   a. Calculate the correlation between the independent variables. Does it indicate the presence of multicollinearity? Explain.

   b. Test the correlation between each independent variable and the dependent variable. Which independent variables are linearly related to the dependent variable? Compare this conclusion with the one produced in Exercise 17.22.

17.46 Refer to Exercise 17.23.
   a. Calculate the correlation between the independent variables. Does it indicate the presence of multicollinearity? Explain.
   b. Test the correlation between each independent variable and the dependent variable. Which independent variables are linearly related to the dependent variable? Compare this conclusion with the one produced in Exercise 17.23.

17-4 / REGRESSION DIAGNOSTICS—III (TIME SERIES)

In Chapter 16, we pointed out that, in general, we check to see whether the errors are independent when the data constitute a *times series*—data gathered sequentially over a series of time periods. In Section 16-6, we described the graphical procedure for determining whether the required condition that the errors are independent is violated. We plot the residuals versus the time periods and look for patterns. In this section, we augment that procedure with the **Durbin–Watson test**.

17-4a Durbin–Watson Test

The Durbin–Watson test allows the statistics practitioner to determine whether there is evidence of **first-order autocorrelation**—a condition in which a relationship exists between consecutive residuals e_i and e_{i-1}, where i is the time period. The Durbin–Watson statistic is defined as

$$d = \frac{\sum_{i=2}^{n}(e_i - e_{i-1})^2}{\sum_{i=1}^{n}e_i^2}$$

The range of the values of d is

$$0 \leq d \leq 4$$

where small values of d ($d < 2$) indicate a positive first-order autocorrelation and large values of d ($d > 2$) imply a negative first-order autocorrelation. Positive first-order autocorrelation is a common occurrence in business and economic time series. It occurs when consecutive residuals tend to be similar. In that case, $(e_i - e_{i-1})^2$ will be small, producing a small value for d. Negative first-order autocorrelation occurs when consecutive residuals differ widely. For example, if positive and negative residuals generally alternate, $(e_i - e_{i-1})^2$ will be large; as a result, d will be greater than 2. Figures 17.2 and 17.3 depict positive first-order autocorrelation, whereas Figure 17.4 illustrates negative autocorrelation. Notice that in Figure 17.2, the first residual is a small number; the second residual, also a small number, is somewhat larger; and that trend continues. In Figure 17.3, the first residual is large and, in general, succeeding residuals decrease. In both figures, consecutive residuals are similar. In Figure 17.4, the first residual is a positive number and is followed by a negative residual. The remaining residuals follow this pattern (with some exceptions). Consecutive residuals are quite different.

FIGURE **17.2** **Positive First-Order Autocorrelation**

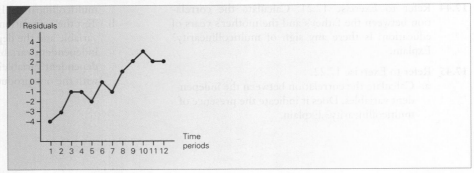

FIGURE **17.3** Positive First-Order Autocorrelation

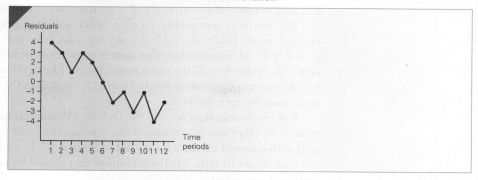

FIGURE **17.4** Negative First-Order Autocorrelation

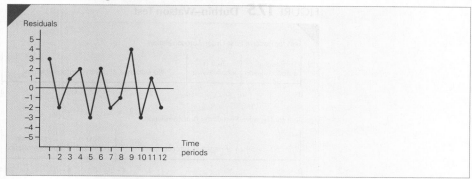

Table 8 in Appendix B is designed to test for positive first-order autocorrelation by providing values of d_L and d_U for a variety of values of n and k and for $\alpha = .01$ and .05.

The decision is made in the following way. If $d < d_L$, we conclude that there is enough evidence to show that positive first-order autocorrelation exists. If $d > d_U$, we conclude that there is not enough evidence to show that positive first-order autocorrelation exists. And if $d_L \leq d \leq d_U$, the test is inconclusive. The recommended course of action when the test is inconclusive is to continue testing with more data until a conclusive decision can be made.

For example, to test for positive first-order autocorrelation with $n = 20$, $k = 3$, and $\alpha = .05$, we test the following hypotheses:

H_0: There is no first-order autocorrelation.

H_1: There is positive first-order autocorrelation.

The decision is made as follows:

If $d < d_L = 1.00$, reject the null hypothesis in favor of the alternative hypothesis.

If $d > d_U = 1.68$, do not reject the null hypothesis.

If $1.00 \leq d \leq 1.68$, the test is inconclusive.

To test for negative first-order autocorrelation, we change the critical values. If $d > 4 - d_L$, we conclude that negative first-order autocorrelation exists. If $d < 4 - d_U$, we conclude that there is not enough evidence to show that negative first-order autocorrelation exists. If $4 - d_U \le d \le 4 - d_L$, the test is inconclusive.

We can also test simply for first-order autocorrelation by combining the two one-tail tests. If $d < d_L$ or $d > 4 - d_L$, we conclude that autocorrelation exists. If $d_U \le d \le 4 - d_U$, we conclude that there is no evidence of autocorrelation. If $d_L \le d \le d_U$ or $4 - d_U \le d \le 4 - d_L$, the test is inconclusive. The significance level will be 2α (where α is the one-tail significance level). Figure 17.5 describes the range of values of d and the conclusion for each interval.

For time-series data, we add the Durbin–Watson test to our list of regression diagnostics. In other words, we determine whether the error variable is normally distributed with constant variance (as we did in Section 17-3), we identify outliers and (if our software allows it) influential observations that should be verified, and we conduct the Durbin–Watson test.

FIGURE **17.5** **Durbin–Watson Test**

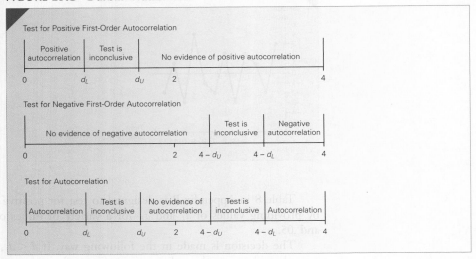

EXAMPLE **17.1**

DATA
Xm17-01

Christmas Week Ski Lift Sales

Christmas week is a critical period for most ski resorts. Because many students and adults are free from other obligations, they are able to spend several days indulging in their favorite pastime, skiing. A large proportion of gross revenue is earned during this period. A ski resort in Vermont wanted to determine the effect that weather had on its sales of lift tickets. The manager of the resort collected data on the number of lift tickets sold during Christmas week (y), the total snowfall in inches (x_1), and the average temperature in degrees Fahrenheit (x_2) for the past 20 years. Develop the multiple regression model and diagnose any violations of the required conditions.

SOLUTION:

The model is

$$y = \beta_0 + \beta_1 x_1 + \beta_2 x_2 + \varepsilon$$

EXCEL Data Analysis

	A	B	C	D	E	F
1	SUMMARY OUTPUT					
3	Regression Statistics					
4	Multiple R	0.3465				
5	R Square	0.1200				
6	Adjusted R Square	0.0165				
7	Standard Error	1712				
8	Observations	20				
10	ANOVA					
11		df	SS	MS	F	Significance F
12	Regression	2	6,793,798	3,396,899	1.16	0.3373
13	Residual	17	49,807,214	2,929,836		
14	Total	19	56,601,012			
15						
16		Coefficients	Standard Error	t Stat	P-value	
17	Intercept	8308	903.7	9.19	5.24E-08	
18	Snowfall	74.59	51.57	1.45	0.1663	
19	Temperature	-8.75	19.70	-0.44	0.6625	

INTERPRET

As you can see, the coefficient of determination is small ($R^2 = 12\%$) and the p-value of the F-test is .3373, both of which indicate that the model is poor. We used Excel to draw the histogram (Figure 17.6) of the residuals and plot the predicted values of y versus the residuals in Figure 17.7. Because the observations constitute a time series, we also used Excel to plot the time periods (years) versus the residuals (Figure 17.8).

FIGURE **17.6** Histogram of Residuals in Example 17.1

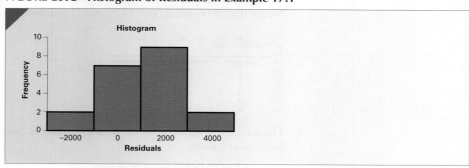

The histogram reveals that the error may be normally distributed.

FIGURE **17.7** Plot of Predicted Values versus Residuals in Example 17.1

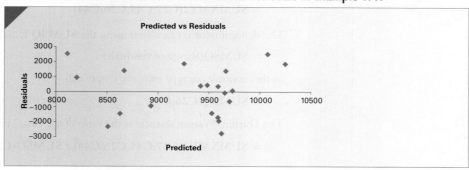

There does not appear to be any evidence of heteroscedasticity.

FIGURE **17.8** Plot of Time Periods versus Residuals in Example 17.1

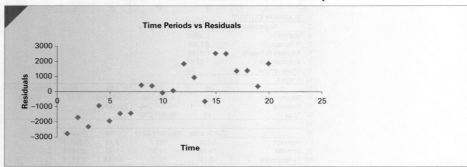

This graph reveals a serious problem. There is a strong relationship between consecutive values of the residuals, which indicates that the requirement that the errors are independent has been violated. To confirm this diagnosis, we calculated the Durbin–Watson statistic. It is .5931.

DO It Yourself Excel

INSTRUCTIONS

1. Compute the residuals by checking the **Residuals** box when you run the regression. Here are the first three and last three residuals (figures reduced to one decimal place). Notice that the residuals are in Column C and Rows 26 to 45.

	A	B	C
23	RESIDUAL OUTPUT		
24			
25	Observation	Predicted Tickets	Residuals
26	1	9629.0	-2794.0
27	2	9593.2	-1723.2
28	3	8515.0	-2342.0
43	18	8672.6	1368.4
44	19	9594.4	334.6
45	20	9259.8	1831.2

2. The numerator in the Durbin–Watson statistic is computed using the **SUMXMY2** function as follows:

    = SUMXMY2(Range1, Range2)

where Range1 is [Second residual: Last residual] and Range 2 is [First residual: Second-last residual]. In this example, the residuals are stored in C26:C45. Thus, the numerator is computed by

    = SUMXMY2(C27:C45,C26:C44)

3. The denominator is calculated using the **SUMSQ** function as follows:

    = SUMSQ(Range of residuals)

In this example we type into any empty cell

    = SUMSQ(C26:C45)

The Durbin–Watson statistic is the ratio of the two. Type into any empty cell

    = SUMXMY2(C27:C45,C26:C44) / SUMSQ(C26:C45)

The critical values are determined by noting that $n = 20$ and $k = 2$ (there are two independent variables in the model). If we wish to test for positive first-order autocorrelation with $\alpha = .05$, we find in Table 8(a) in Appendix B

$$d_L = 1.10 \quad \text{and} \quad d_U = 1.54$$

The null and alternative hypotheses are

H_0: There is no first-order autocorrelation.
H_1: There is positive first-order autocorrelation.

The rejection region is $d < d_L = 1.10$. Because $d = .5931$, we reject the null hypothesis and conclude that there is enough evidence to infer that positive first-order autocorrelation exists.

Autocorrelation usually indicates that the model needs to include an independent variable that has a time-ordered effect on the dependent variable. The simplest such independent variable represents the time periods. To illustrate, we included a third independent variable that records the number of years since the year the data were gathered. Thus, $x_3 = 1, 2, \ldots, 20$. The new model is

$$y = \beta_0 + \beta_1 x_1 + \beta_2 x_2 + \beta_3 x_3 + \varepsilon$$

EXCEL Data Analysis

	A	B	C	D	E	F
1	SUMMARY OUTPUT					
3	*Regression Statistics*					
4	Multiple R	0.8608				
5	R Square	0.7410				
6	Adjusted R Square	0.6924				
7	Standard Error	957.2				
8	Observations	20				
10	ANOVA					
11		*df*	*SS*	*MS*	*F*	*Significance F*
12	Regression	3	41,940,217	13,980,072	15.26	5.93E-05
13	Residual	16	14,660,795	916,300		
14	Total	19	56,601,012			
15						
16		Coefficients	Standard Error	t Stat	P-value	
17	Intercept	5966	631.3	9.45	6.00E-08	
18	Snowfall	70.18	28.85	2.43	0.0271	
19	Temperature	-9.23	11.02	-0.84	0.4145	
20	Time	229.97	37.13	6.19	1.29E-05	

As we did before, we calculate the residuals and conduct regression diagnostics using Excel. The results are shown in Figures 17.9–17.11.

FIGURE **17.9** Histogram of Residuals in Example 17.1 (Time Variable Included)

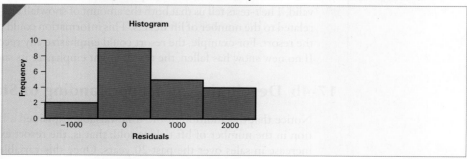

The histogram reveals that the error may be normally distributed.

FIGURE 17.10 Plot of Predicted Values versus Residuals in Example 17.1 (Time Variable Included)

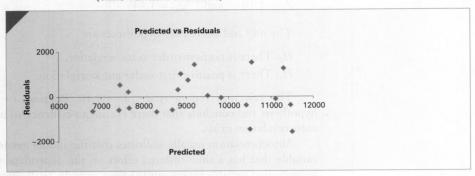

The error variable variance appears to be constant.

FIGURE 17.11 Plot of Time Periods versus Residuals in Example 17.1 (Time Variable Included)

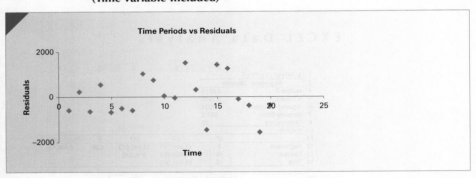

There is no sign of autocorrelation. To confirm our diagnosis, we computed the Durbin–Watson statistic and found it to be equal to 1.885.

From Table 8(a) in Appendix B, we find the critical values of the Durbin–Watson test. With $k = 3$ and $n = 20$, we find

$$d_L = 1.00 \quad \text{and} \quad d_U = 1.68$$

Because $d > 1.68$, we conclude that there is not enough evidence to infer the presence of positive first-order autocorrelation.

Notice that the model is improved dramatically. The F-test tells us that the model is valid. The t-tests tell us that both the amount of snowfall and time are significantly linearly related to the number of lift tickets. This information could prove useful in advertising for the resort. For example, the resort could emphasize any recent snowfall in its advertising. If no new snow has fallen, the resort might emphasize its snow-making facilities.

17-4b Developing an Understanding of Statistical Concepts

Notice that the addition of the time variable explained a large proportion of the variation in the number of lift tickets sold; that is, the resort experienced a relatively steady increase in sales over the past 20 years. Once this variable was included in the model,

APPENDIX 17.B / STATA OUTPUT AND INSTRUCTIONS

Multiple Regression

Chapter-Opening Example

Source	SS	df	MS			
				Number of obs	=	1,171
				F(5, 1165)	=	89.53
Model	5.9989e+11	5	1.1998e+11	Prob > F	=	0.0000
Residual	1.5612e+12	1,165	1.3401e+09	R-squared	=	0.2776
				Adj R-squared	=	0.2745
Total	2.1611e+12	1,170	1.8471e+09	Root MSE	=	36608

RINCOME	Coef.	Std. Err.	t	P>|t|	[95% Conf. Interval]	
AGE	671.0585	84.5329	7.94	0.000	505.2047	836.9122
EDUC	5603.737	386.6796	14.49	0.000	4845.07	6362.403
HRS1	948.7478	75.07715	12.64	0.000	801.4462	1096.049
EARNRS	1289.191	1330.284	0.97	0.333	-1320.83	3899.211
CHILDS	718.8115	760.7241	0.94	0.345	-773.7309	2211.354
_cons	-100339.8	7633.491	-13.14	0.000	-115316.8	-85362.9

The regression equation is

$$\hat{y} = -100339.8 + 671.0585 \text{ AGE} + 5603.737 \text{ EDUC} + 948.7478 \text{ HRS1} + 1289.191 \text{EARNRS} + 718.8115 \text{ CHILDS}$$

Test of the validity of the model: F = 89.53, p-value = 0.

Instructions

1. Import or type the data into columns. (Click File/Import/Excel spreadsheet (*xls,*xlsx)/GSS Files/GSS2018.)

2. Click **Statistics, Linear models and related**, and **Linear regression**.

3. In the **Dependent variable:** box select **RINCOME**. In the **Independent variables:** box select **AGE EDUC HRS1 EARNRS CHILDS**.

APPENDIX 17.C / REVIEW OF CHAPTERS 12 TO 17

Table A17.1 presents a list of inferential methods presented thus far, and Figure A17.1 depicts a flowchart designed to help students identify the correct statistical technique.

TABLE **A17.1** Summary of Statistical Techniques in Chapters 12 to 17

t-test of μ

Estimator of μ (including estimator of $N\mu$)

χ^2 test of σ^2

Estimator of σ^2

z-test of p

Estimator of p (including estimator of Np)

Equal-variances t-test of $\mu_1 - \mu_2$

Equal-variances estimator of $\mu_1 - \mu_2$

Unequal-variances t-test of $\mu_1 - \mu_2$

Unequal-variances estimator of $\mu_1 - \mu_2$

t-test of μ_D

Estimator of μ_D

F-test of σ_1^2/σ_2^2

Estimator of σ_1^2/σ_2^2

z-test of $p_1 - p_2$ (Case 1)

z-test of $p_1 - p_2$ (Case 2)

Estimator of $p_1 - p_2$

One-way analysis of variance (including multiple comparisons)

Two-way (randomized blocks) analysis of variance

Two-factor analysis of variance

χ^2-goodness-of-fit test

χ^2-test of a contingency table

Simple linear regression and correlation (including t-tests of β_1 and ρ, and prediction and confidence intervals)

Multiple regression (including t-tests of β_i and F-test).

FIGURE **A17.1** **Flowchart of Techniques in Chapters 12 to 17**

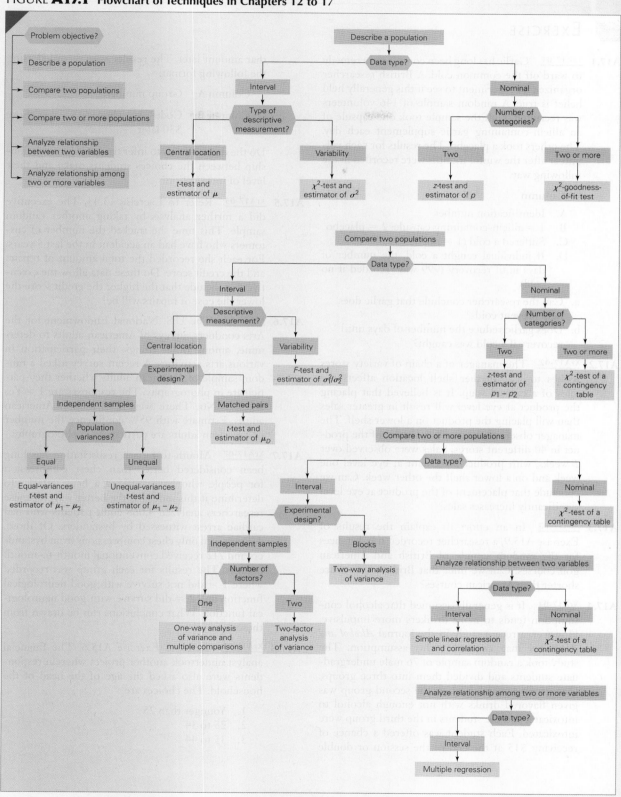

EXERCISE

A17.1 XrA17-01 Garlic has long been considered a remedy to ward off the common cold. A British researcher organized an experiment to see if this generally held belief is true. A random sample of 146 volunteers was recruited. Half the sample took one capsule of an allicin-containing garlic supplement each day. The others took a placebo. The results for each volunteer after the winter months were recorded in the following way.

Column

    A. Identification number
    B. 1 = allicin-containing capsule; 2 = placebo
    C. Suffered a cold (1 = no, 2 = yes)
    D. If individual caught a cold, the number of days until recovery (999 was recorded if no cold)

  a. Can the researcher conclude that garlic does help prevent colds?
  b. Does garlic reduce the number of days until recovery if a cold was caught?

A17.2 XrA17-02 The manager of a chain of variety stores wishes to see whether shelf location affects the sales of a canned soup. It is believed that placing the product at eye level will result in greater sales than will placing the product on a lower shelf. The manager observed the number of sales of the product in 40 different stores. Sales were observed over 2 weeks, with product placement at eye level one week and on a lower shelf the other week. Can we conclude that placement of the product at eye level significantly increases sales?

A17.3 XrA17-03 In an effort to explain the results of Exercise A15.9, a researcher recorded the distances for the random sample of British and American golf courses. Can we infer that British courses are shorter than American courses?

A17.4 XrA17-04 It is generally assumed that alcohol consumption tends to make drinkers more impulsive. However, a recent study in the journal *Alcohol and Alcoholism* may contradict this assumption. The study took a random sample of 76 male undergraduate students and divided them into three groups. One group remained sober; the second group was given flavored drinks with not enough alcohol to intoxicate; and the students in the third group were intoxicated. Each student was offered a chance of receiving $15 at the end of the session or double

that amount later. The results were recorded using the following format:

    Column A: Group number

    Column B: Code 1 = chose $15, 2 = chose $30 later

Do the data allow us to infer that there is a relationship between the choices students make and their level of intoxication?

A17.5 XrA17-05 Refer to Exercise 13.43. The executive did a further analysis by taking another random sample. This time she tracked the number of customers who have had an accident in the last 5 years. For each she recorded the total amount of repairs and the credit score. Do these data allow the executive to conclude that the higher the credit score the lower the cost of repairs will be?

A17.6 XrA17-06 The U.S. National Endowment for the Arts conducts surveys of American adults to determine, among other things, their participation in various arts activities. A recent survey asked a random sample of American adults whether they participate in photography. The responses are 1 = Yes and 2 = No. There were 255 million American adults. Estimate with 95% confidence the number of American adults are participate in photography.

A17.7 XrA17-07 Mouth-to-mouth resuscitation has long been considered better than chest compression for people who have suffered a heart attack. To determine if this indeed is the better way, Japanese researchers analyzed 4,068 adult patients who had cardiac arrest witnessed by bystanders. Of those, 439 received only chest compressions from bystanders and 712 received conventional mouth-to-mouth breaths. The results for each group was recorded where 1 = did not survive with good neurological function and 2 = did survive with good neurological function. What conclusions can be drawn from these data?

A17.8 XrA17-08 Refer to Exercise A15.6. The financial analyst undertook another project wherein respondents were also asked the age of the head of the household. The choices are

  1. Younger than 25
  2. 25 to 34
  3. 35 to 44

4. 45 to 54
5. 55 to 64
6. 65 and older

The responses to questions about ownership of mutual funds is No = 1 and Yes = 2. Do these data allow us to infer that the age of the heads of the household is related to whether they own mutual funds?

A17.9   XrA17-09   Over one decade (1995–2005), the number of hip and knee replacement surgeries increased by 87%. Because the costs of hip and knee replacements are so expensive, private health-insurance and government-operated health care plans have become more concerned. To get more information, random samples of people who had hip replacements in 1995 and in 2005 were drawn. From the files, the ages of the patients were recorded. Is there enough evidence to infer that the people who require hip replacements were getting younger?

Source: Canadian Joint Replacement Registry.

A17.10   XrA17-10   Refer to Exercise A17.9. Weight is a major factor that determines whether a person will need a hip or knee replacement and at what age. To learn more about the topic, a medical researcher randomly sampled individuals who had hip replacement (code = 1) and knee replacement (code = 2) and one of the following categories:

1. Underweight
2. Normal range
3. Overweight but not obese
4. Obese

Do the data allow the researcher to conclude that weight and the joint needing replacement are related?

A17.11   XrA17-11   Television shows with large amounts of sex or violence tend to attract more viewers. Advertisers want large audiences, but they also want viewers to remember the brand names of their products. A study was undertaken to determine the effect that shows with sex and violence have on their viewers. A random sample of 328 adults was divided into three groups. Group 1 watched violent programs, group 2 watched sexually explicit shows, and group 3 watched neutral shows. The researchers spliced nine 30-second commercials for a wide range of products. After the show, the subjects were quizzed to see if they could recall the brand name of the products. They were also asked to name the brands 24 hours later. The number of correct answers was recorded. Conduct a test to determine whether differences exist between the three groups of viewers and which type of program does best in brand recall.

A17.12   XrA17-12   In an effort to explain to customers why their electricity bills have been so high lately, and how customers could save money by reducing the thermostat settings on both space heaters and water heaters, a public utility commission has collected total kilowatt consumption figures for last year's winter months, as well as thermostat settings on space and water heaters, for 100 homes.
a. Determine the regression equation.
b. Determine the coefficient of determination and describe what it tells you.
c. Test the validity of the model.

A17.13   XrA17-13   An economist wanted to learn more about total compensation packages. A survey of 858 workers was conducted that asked respondents to report their hourly wages or salaries, their total benefits, and whether the companies they worked for produced goods or services. Determine whether differences exist between goods-producing and services-producing firms in terms of hourly wages and total benefits.

A17.14   XrA17-14   Professional athletes in North America are paid very well for their ability to play games that amateurs play for fun. To determine the factors that influence a team to pay a hockey player's salary, an MBA student randomly selected 50 hockey players who played in the 1992–1993 and 1993–1994 seasons. Their salaries at the end of the 1993–1994 season as well as a number of performance measures in the previous two seasons were recorded. The following data were recorded.

Columns A and B: Games played in 1992–1993 and 1993–1994
Columns C and D: Goals scored in 1992–1993 and 1993–1994
Columns E and F: Assists recorded in 1992–1993 and 1993–1994
Columns G and H: Plus/minus score in 1992–1993 and 1993–1994
Columns I and J: Penalty minutes served in 1992–1993 and 1993–1994
Column K: Salary in U.S. dollars

(Plus/minus is the number of goals scored by the player's team minus the number of goals scored by the opposing team while the player is on the ice.) Develop a model that analyzes the relationship between salary and the performance measures. Describe your findings.

A17.15   XrA17-15   The risks associated with smoking are well known. Virtually all physicians recommend that their patients quit. This raises the question, What are the risks for people who quit smoking compared to continuing smokers and those who have never smoked? In a study researchers took samples of each of the following groups.

Group 1: Never smokers
Group 2: Continuing smokers
Group 3: Smokers who quit

At the beginning of the 10-year research project, there were 238 people who had never smoked and 155 smokers. Over the year, 39 smokers quit. The weight gain, increase in systolic blood pressure (SBP), and increase in diastolic blood pressure (DBP) were measured and recorded. Determine whether differences exist between the three groups in terms of weight gain, increases in systolic blood pressure, and increases in diastolic blood pressure and which groups differ.

A17.16   XrA17-16   A survey was conducted among Canadian farmers, who were asked to report the number of acres in their farm. There were a total of 229,373 farms in Canada. Estimate with 95% confidence the total amount of area (in acres) that was farmed in Canada.

Source: Statistics Canada.

GENERAL SOCIAL SURVEY EXERCISES

In 2016 there were 240,834,729 adults in the United States. **Conduct all tests at the 5% significance level. Use a 95% confidence level for estimates.**

GSS2016   *The following exercises are based on the 2016 survey.*

A17.17   Repeat the chapter-opening example using the data from the 2016 survey. Interpret the coefficients and test to determine which ones are linearly related to income.

A17.18   Is there enough statistical evidence to conclude that there are differences in support of a law that requires a police permit to buy a gun (GUNLAW: 1 = Favor, 2 = Oppose) between the holders of the different degrees (DEGREE: 0 = Left high school, 1 = High school, 2 = Junior college, 3 = Bachelor's degree, 4 = Graduate degree)?

A17.19   How does one's income (RINCOME), years of education (EDUC), age (AGE), and hours of work per week (HRS1) affect how much support one has for government action to reduce income differences between rich and poor (EQWLTH: 1 = Government should reduce differences; 2, 3, 4, 5, 6, 7 = No government action)?
a. Interpret the coefficients.
b. Test to determine which variables are linearly related to EQWLTH.

A17.20   Is there enough evidence to infer that there are differences in years of education (EDUC) between the four classes (CLASS: 1 = Lower class, 2 = Working class, 3 = Middle class, 4 = Upper class)?

A17.21   How do years of education (EDUC), age (AGE), and the number of children (CHILDS) affect how much time per day is spent watching television (TVHOURS)? Determine whether there is enough evidence to infer that each independent variable is linearly related to the dependent variable.

A17.22   How are Americans doing compared to the previous generation? To answer this question the survey asked, "Compared to your parents at your age what will your standard of living be (PARSOL: 1 = Much better, 2 = Somewhat better, 3 = About the same, 4 = Somewhat worse, 5 = Much worse)?" Is there enough evidence to conclude that the majority of Americans believe that they are doing much better or somewhat better than their parents?

A17.23   The survey asked respondents, "Have you ever been unemployed in the last 10 years (UNEMP: 1 = Yes, 2 = No)?" Estimate the number of American adults who were unemployed at least once in the last 10 years.

A17.24   The survey asked this question, "Do antibiotics kill viruses as well as bacteria (VIRUSES: 1 = True, 2 = False, 8 = Don't know, 9 = No answer, 0 = Question not asked)?" Is there enough evidence to conclude that people born in the United States (BORN: 1 = Yes, 2 = No) are more likely to answer correctly than people born outside the United States?

A17.25   Can we conclude that people who work for themselves (WRKSLF: 1 = Self-employed, 2 = Someone else) work less hours (HRS1) than people who work for someone else?

A17.26   Do foreign-born and native-born Americans (BORN: 1 = Yes, 2 = No) differ in their annual incomes (RINCOME)? Is there sufficient evidence to conclude that the answer is yes?

A17.27 In 2016, the economy was growing slowly. One measure of the growth is the perception of how easy it would be for you to find a job with another employer with approximately the same income and fringe benefits you now have. This question was asked by the survey (JOBFIND: 1 = Very easy, 2 = Somewhat easy, 3 = Not easy). Can we infer from the data that there are more Americans who believe that it would be very easy or somewhat easy than Americans who believe that it would not be easy to find another job?

A17.28 Do government employees and private sector workers (WRKSLF: 1 = Self-employed, 2 = Someone else) have different degrees (DEGREE: 0 = Left high school, 1 = High school, 2 = Junior college, 3 = Bachelor's degree, 4 = Graduate degree)? Is there sufficient evidence to infer that differences exist?

A17.29 Is there enough statistical evidence to infer that there are differences in support of a law that requires a police permit to buy a gun (GUNLAW: 1 = Favor, 2 = Oppose) between the three racial groups (RACE: 1 = White, 2 = Black, 3 = Other)?

A17.30 Do liberals, moderates, and conservatives (POLVIEWS3) differ in their support of capital punishment for murderers (CAPPUN: 1 = Favor, 2 = Oppose)?

A17.31 Is there sufficient evidence to infer that Americans who work long hours (HRS1) are less supportive of government action to help poor people (HELPPOOR: 1 = Government act; 2, 3, 4, 5 = People should help themselves)?

A17.32 What effect, if any, does the education of one's mother have on one's own education? Is there enough evidence to infer that people's education (EDUC) and their mothers' education (MAEDUC) are positively linearly related?

CASE A17.1   Testing a More Effective Device to Keep Arteries Open

A stent is a metal mesh cylinder that holds a coronary artery open after a blockage has been removed. However, in many patients the stents, which are made from bare metal, become blocked as well. One cause of the reoccurrence of blockages is the body's rejection of the foreign object. In a study published in the *New England Journal of Medicine* (January 2004), a new polymer-based stent was tested. After insertion, the new stents slowly release a drug (paclitaxel) to prevent the rejection problem. A sample of 1,314 patients who were receiving a stent in a single, previously untreated coronary artery blockage, was recruited. A total of 652 were randomly assigned to receive a bare-metal stent, and 662 to receive an identical-looking polymer drug-releasing stent. The results were recorded in the following way:

Column A: Patient identification number

Column B: Stent type
(1 = bare metal,
2 = polymer based)

Column C: Reference-vessel diameter (the diameter of the artery that is blocked, in millimeters)

Column D: Lesion length (the length of the blockage, in millimeters)

Reference-vessel diameters and lesion lengths were measured before the stents were inserted.

The following data were recorded 12 months after the stents were inserted.

Column E: Blockage reoccurrence after 9 months (2 = yes, 1 = no)

Column F: Blockage that needed to be reopened (2 = yes, 1 = no)

Column G: Death from cardiac causes (2 = yes, 1 = no)

Column H: Stroke caused by stent (2 = yes, 1 = no)

a. Using the variables stored in columns C through H, determine whether there is enough evidence to infer that the polymer-based stent is superior to the bare-metal stent.

b. As a laboratory researcher in the pharmaceutical company, write a report that describes this experiment and the results.

CASE A17.2   Automobile Crashes and the Ages of Drivers*

Setting premiums for insurance is a complex task. If the premium is too high, the insurance company will lose customers; if it is too low, the company will lose money. Statistics plays a critical role in almost all aspects of the insurance business. As part of a statistical analysis, an insurance company in Florida studied the relationship between the severity of car crashes and the ages of the drivers. A random sample of crashes in 2002 in the state of Florida was drawn. For each crash, the age category of the driver was recorded as well as whether the driver was injured or killed. The data were stored as follows:

Column A: Crash number

Column B: Age category

1. 5 to 34
2. 35 to 44
3. 45 to 54
4. 55 to 64
5. 65 and over

Column C: Medical status of driver

1 = Uninjured
2 = Injured (but not killed)
3 = Killed

a. Is there enough evidence to conclude that age and medical status of the driver in car crashes are related?

b. Estimate with 95% confidence the proportion of all Florida drivers in crashes in 2002 who were uninjured.

*Adapted from Florida Department of Highway Safety and Vehicles, as reported in the *Miami Herald*, January 1, 2004, p. 2B.

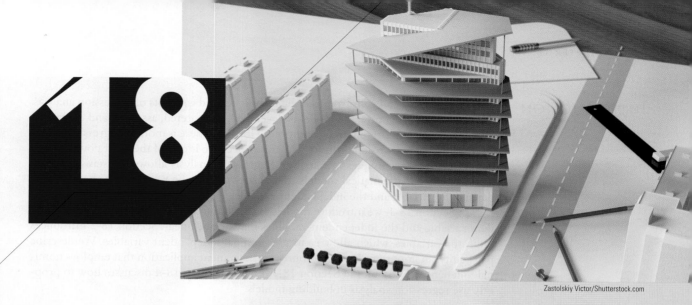

Zastolskiy Victor/Shutterstock.com

18

MODEL BUILDING

CHAPTER OUTLINE

General Social Survey: Variables That Affect Income II

**DATA
GSS2018***   In the Chapter 17 opening example, we found that one's income is
affected by age, education, and number of hours of work per week.
Determine whether income is also affected by gender and race.

Tyler Olson/Shutterstock.com

**On page 785, we will
provide our answer.**

INTRODUCTION

Chapters 16 and 17 introduced the techniques and concepts of regression analysis. We discussed how the model is developed, interpreted, assessed, and diagnosed for violations of required conditions. However, there is more to regression analysis. In this chapter, we demonstrate why this procedure is one of the most powerful and commonly used techniques in statistics. Regression analysis allows the statistics practitioner to use mathematical models to realistically describe relationships between the dependent variable and the independent variables.

In Section 18-1, we introduce models in which the relationship between the dependent variable and the independent variables may not be linear. Section 18-2 introduces indicator variables, which allow us to use nominal independent variables. We describe pay equity, an important human resources management application that employs nominal independent variables in Section 18-3. Finally, Section 18-4 discusses how to properly use regression analysis in building models.

18-1 / POLYNOMIAL MODELS

Chapter 17 introduced the multiple regression model:

$$y = \beta_0 + \beta_1 x_1 + \beta_2 x_2 + \cdots + \beta_k x_k + \varepsilon$$

We included variables $x_1, x_2, \ldots, x_k$ because we believed that these variables were each linearly related to the dependent variable. In this section, we discuss models where the independent variables may be functions of a smaller number of predictor variables. The simplest form of the **polynomial model** is described in the box.

Polynomial Model with One Predictor Variable

$$y = \beta_0 + \beta_1 x + \beta_2 x^2 + \cdots + \beta_p x^p + \varepsilon$$

Technically, this is a multiple regression model with p independent variables. However, all independent variables are based on only one variable, which we label the **predictor variable**; that is, $x_1 = x, x_2 = x^2, \ldots, x_p = x^p$. In this model, p is the **order** of the equation. For reasons that we discuss later, we rarely propose a model whose order is greater than 3. However, it is worthwhile to devote individual attention to situations where $p = 1, 2,$ and 3.

18-1a First-Order Model

When $p = 1$, we have the now-familiar simple linear regression model introduced in Chapter 16. It is also called the **first-order** polynomial model.

$$y = \beta_0 + \beta_1 x + \varepsilon$$

Obviously, this model is chosen when the statistics practitioner believes that there is a straight-line relationship between the dependent and independent variables over the range of the values of x.

18-1b Second-Order Model

With $p = 2$, the polynomial model is

$$y = \beta_0 + \beta_1 x + \beta_2 x^2 + \varepsilon$$

When we plot x versus y, the graph is shaped like a parabola, as shown in Figures 18.1 and 18.2. The coefficient β_0 represents the intercept where the response surface strikes the y-axis. The signs of β_1 and β_2 control the position of the parabola relative to the y-axis. If $\beta_1 = 0$, for example, the parabola is symmetric and centered around $x = 0$. If β_1 and β_2 have the same sign, the parabola shifts to the left. If β_1 and β_2 have opposite signs, the parabola shifts to the right. The coefficient β_2 describes the curvature. If $\beta_2 = 0$, there is no curvature. If β_2 is negative, the graph is concave (as in Figure 18.1). If β_2 is positive, the graph is convex (as in Figure 18.2). The greater the absolute value of β_2, the greater the rate of curvature, as can be seen in Figure 18.3.

FIGURE **18.1** Second-Order Model with $\beta_2 < 0$

FIGURE **18.2** Second-Order Model with $\beta_2 > 0$

FIGURE **18.3** Second-Order Model with Various Values of β_2

18-1c Third-Order Model

By setting $p = 3$, we produce the third-order model

$$y = \beta_0 + \beta_1 x + \beta_2 x^2 + \beta_3 x^3 + \varepsilon$$

Figures 18.4 and 18.5 depict this equation, whose curvature can change twice.

FIGURE **18.4** Third-Order Model with $\beta_3 < 0$

FIGURE **18.5** Third-Order Model with $\beta_3 > 0$

As you can see, when β_3 is negative, y is decreasing over the range of x, and when β_3 is positive, y increases. The other coefficients determine the position of the curvature changes and the point at which the curve intersects the y-axis.

The number of real-life applications of this model is quite small. Statistics practitioners rarely encounter problems involving more than one curvature reversal. Therefore, we will not discuss any higher-order models.

18-1d Polynomial Models with Two Predictor Variables

If we believe that two predictor variables influence the dependent variable, we can use one of the following polynomial models. The general form of this model is rather cumbersome, so we will not show it. Instead we discuss several specific examples.

18-1e First-Order Model

The first-order model is represented by

$$y = \beta_0 + \beta_1 x_1 + \beta_2 x_2 + \varepsilon$$

This model is used whenever the statistics practitioner believes that, on average, y is linearly related to each of x_1 and x_2, and the predictor variables do not interact. (Recall that we introduced interaction in Chapter 14.) This means that the effect of one predictor variable on y is independent of the value of the second predictor variable. For example, suppose that the sample regression line of the first-order model is

$$\hat{y} = 5 + 3x_1 + 4x_2$$

If we examine the relationship between y and x_1 for several values of x_2 (say, $x_2 = 1, 2$, and 3), we produce the following equations.

x_2	$\hat{y} = 5 + 3x_1 + 4x_2$
1	$\hat{y} = 9 + 3x_1$
2	$\hat{y} = 13 + 3x_1$
3	$\hat{y} = 17 + 3x_1$

The only difference in the three equations is the intercept. (See Figure 18.6.) The coefficient of x_1 remains the same, which means that the effect of x_1 on y remains the same no matter what the value of x_2. (We could also have shown that the effect of x_2 on y remains the same no matter what the value of x_1.) As you can see from Figure 18.6, the first-order model with no interaction produces parallel straight lines.

FIGURE **18.6** First-Order Model with Two Independent Variables: No Interaction

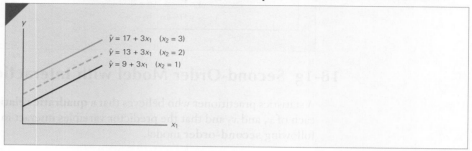

A statistics practitioner who thinks that the effect of one predictor variable on y is influenced by the other predictor variable can use the model described next.

18-1f First-Order Model with Two Predictor Variables and Interaction

Interaction means that the effect of x_1 on y is influenced by the value of x_2. (It also means that the effect of x_2 on y is influenced by x_1.)

First-Order Model with Interaction

$$y = \beta_0 + \beta_1 x_1 + \beta_2 x_2 + \beta_3 x_1 x_2 + \varepsilon$$

Suppose that the sample regression line is

$$\hat{y} = 5 + 3x_1 + 4x_2 - 2x_1 x_2$$

If we examine the relationship between y and x_1 for $x_2 = 1, 2,$ and 3, we produce the following table of equations:

x_2	$\hat{y} = 5 + 3x_1 + 4x_2 - 2x_1 x_2$
1	$\hat{y} = 9 + x_1$
2	$\hat{y} = 13 - x_1$
3	$\hat{y} = 17 - 3x_1$

As you can see, not only is the intercept different but also the coefficient of x_1 varies. Obviously, the effect of x_1 on y is influenced by the value of x_2. Figure 18.7 depicts these equations. The straight lines are clearly not parallel.

FIGURE **18.7** First-Order Model with Interaction

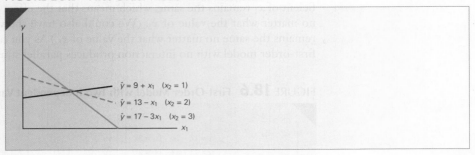

$$\hat{y} = 9 + x_1 \quad (x_2 = 1)$$
$$\hat{y} = 13 - x_1 \quad (x_2 = 2)$$
$$\hat{y} = 17 - 3x_1 \quad (x_2 = 3)$$

18-1g Second-Order Model with Interaction

A statistics practitioner who believes that a **quadratic relationship** exists between y and each of x_1 and x_2 and that the predictor variables interact in their effect on y can use the following **second-order** model.

> **Second-Order Model with Interaction**
>
> $$y = \beta_0 + \beta_1 x_1 + \beta_2 x_2 + \beta_3 x_1^2 + \beta_4 x_2^2 + \beta_5 x_1 x_2 + \varepsilon$$

Figures 18.8 and 18.9, respectively, depict this model without and with the interaction term.

FIGURE **18.8** Second-Order Model without Interaction

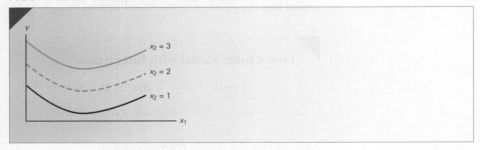

FIGURE **18.9** Second-Order Model with Interaction

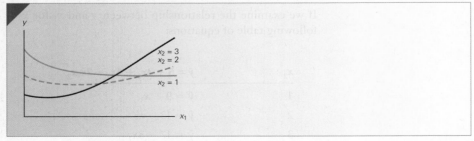

Now that we've introduced several different models, how do we know which model to use? The answer is that we employ a model based on our knowledge of the variables involved and then test that model using the statistical techniques presented in this and the preceding chapters.

EXAMPLE **18.1**

Selecting Sites for a Fast-Food Restaurant, Part 1

In trying to find new locations for their restaurants, fast-food restaurant chains like McDonald's and Wendy's usually consider a number of factors. Suppose that an analyst working for a fast-food restaurant chain has been asked to construct a regression model that will help identify new locations that are likely to be profitable. The analyst knows that this type of restaurant has, as its primary market, middle-income adults and their children, particularly those between the ages of 5 and 12. Which model should the analyst propose?

SOLUTION:

The dependent variable is gross revenue or net profit. The predictor variables will be mean annual household income and the mean age of children in the restaurant's neighborhood. The relationship between the dependent variable and each predictor variable is probably quadratic. In other words, members of relatively poor or relatively affluent households are less likely to eat at this chain's restaurants because the restaurants attract mostly middle-income customers. Figure 18.10 depicts the hypothesized relationship.

FIGURE **18.10** **Relationship between Annual Gross Revenue and Mean Household Income**

A similar relationship can be proposed for revenue and age. Neighborhoods where the mean age of children is either quite low or quite high will probably produce lower revenues than in similar areas where the mean age lies in the middle of the 5-to-12 range.

The question of whether to include the interaction term is more difficult to answer. When in doubt, it is probably best to include it. Thus, the model to be tested is

$$y = \beta_0 + \beta_1 x_1 + \beta_2 x_2 + \beta_3 x_1^2 + \beta_4 x_2^2 + \beta_5 x_1 x_2 + \varepsilon$$

where

y = Annual gross sales

x_1 = Mean annual household income in the neighborhood

x_2 = Mean age of children in the neighborhood

EXAMPLE **18.2**

Selecting Sites for a Fast-Food Restaurant, Part 2

DATA
Xm18-02

To determine whether the second-order model with interaction is appropriate, the analyst in Example 18.1 selected 25 areas at random. Each area consists of approximately 5,000 households, as well as one of the employer's restaurants and three competing fast-food restaurants. The previous year's annual gross sales, the mean annual household income, and the mean age of children (the latter two figures are available from the latest census) were recorded; some of these data are listed here (the file also contains x_1^2, x_2^2, and x_1x_2). What conclusions can be drawn from these data?

Area	Annual Gross Revenue ($Thousands) y	Mean Annual Household ($Thousands) x_1	Mean Age of Children x_2
1	$1,128	$23.5	10.5
2	1,005	17.6	7.2
3	1,212	26.3	7.6
⋮	⋮	⋮	⋮
25	950	17.8	6.1

SOLUTION:

EXCEL Data Analysis

	A	B	C	D	E	F
1	SUMMARY OUTPUT					
2						
3	*Regression Statistics*					
4	Multiple R	0.9521				
5	R Square	0.9065				
6	Adjusted R Square	0.8819				
7	Standard Error	44.70				
8	Observations	25				
9						
10	ANOVA					
11		*df*	*SS*	*MS*	*F*	*Significance F*
12	Regression	5	368,140	73,628	36.86	3.86E-09
13	Residual	19	37,956	1,998		
14	Total	24	406,096			
15						
16		*Coefficients*	*Standard Error*	*t Stat*	*P-value*	
17	Intercept	−1134.0	320.0	−3.54	0.0022	
18	Income	173.20	28.20	6.14	6.66E-06	
19	Age	23.55	32.23	0.73	0.4739	
20	Income sq	−3.726	0.542	−6.87	1.48E-06	
21	Age sq	−3.869	1.179	−3.28	0.0039	
22	(Income)(Age)	1.967	0.944	2.08	0.0509	

INTERPRET

From the computer output, we determine that the value of the coefficient of determination (R^2) is 90.65%, which tells us that the model fits the data quite well. The value of the F-statistic is 36.86, which has a p-value of approximately 0. This confirms that the model is valid.

Care must be taken when interpreting the t-tests of the coefficients in this type of model. Not surprisingly, each variable will be correlated with its square, and the interaction variable will be correlated with both of its components. As a consequence, multicollinearity distorts the t-tests of the coefficients in some cases, making it appear that some of the components should be eliminated from the model. However, in most such applications, the objective is to forecast the dependent variable and multicollinearity does not affect the model's fit or forecasting capability.

EXERCISES

18.1 Graph y versus x_1 for $x_2 = 1, 2,$ and 3 for each of the following equations.
  a. $y = 1 + 2x_1 + 4x_2$
  b. $y = 1 + 2x_1 + 4x_2 - x_1x_2$

18.2 Graph y versus x_1 for $x_2 = 2, 4,$ and 5 for each of the following equations.
  a. $y = 0.5 + 1x_1 - 0.7x_2 - 1.2x_1^2 + 1.5x_2^2$
  b. $y = 0.5 + 1x_1 - 0.7x_2 - 1.2x_1^2 + 1.5x_2^2 + 2x_1x_2$

The following exercises require the use of a computer and software.
Use a 5% significance level for all tests.

18.3 Xr18-03 The general manager of a supermarket chain believes that sales of a product are influenced by the amount of space the product is allotted on shelves. If true, this would have great significance, because the more profitable items could be given more shelf space. The manager realizes that sales volume would likely increase with more space only up to a certain point. Beyond that point, sales would likely flatten and perhaps decrease (because customers are often dismayed by very large displays). To test this belief, the manager records the number of boxes of detergent sold during 1 week in 25 stores in the chain. For each store, the shelf space (in inches) allotted to the detergent was recorded.
  a. Write the equation that represents the model.
  b. Discuss how well the model fits.

APPLICATIONS in ECONOMICS

Dustin Dennis/Shutterstock.com

Demand Curve

The law of supply and demand states that other things being equal, the higher the price of a product or service, the lower is the quantity demanded. The relationship between quantity and price is called a *demand curve*. Generally, such a curve is modeled by a quadratic equation. To estimate the demand curve, we measure the demand at several different prices and then employ regression analysis to calculate the coefficients of the model.

18.4 Xr18-04 A fast-food restaurant chain whose menu features hamburgers and chicken sandwiches is about to add a fish sandwich to its menu. There was considerable debate among the executives about the likely demand and what the appropriate price should be. A recently hired economics graduate observed that the demand curve would reveal a great deal about the relationship between price and demand. The executives decided to conduct an experiment. A random sample of 20 restaurants was drawn. The restaurants were almost identical in terms of sales and in the demographics of the surrounding area. At each restaurant, the fish sandwich was sold at a different price. The number of sandwiches sold over a 7-day period and the price were recorded. A first-order model and a second-order model were proposed.
  a. Write the equation for each model.
  b. Use regression analysis to estimate the coefficients and other statistics for each model.
  c. Which model seems to fit better? Explain.

APPLICATIONS in OPERATIONS MANAGEMENT

Learning Curve

A well-established phenomenon in operations management is the *learning curve*, which describes how quickly new workers learn to do their jobs. A number of mathematical models are used to describe the relationship between time on the job and productivity. Regression analysis allows the operations manager to select the appropriate model and use it to predict when workers achieve their highest level of productivity.

18.5 Xr18-05 A person starting a new job always takes a certain amount of time to adjust fully. In repetitive-task situations, such as on an assembly line, significant productivity gains can occur within a few days. In an experiment to study this phenomenon, the average amount of time required for a new employee to install electronic components in a computer was measured for the first 10 days. These data are shown here.

Day	1	2	3	4	5	6	7	8	9	10
Mean times (minutes)	40	41	36	38	33	32	30	32	29	30

A first-order model and a second-order model were proposed.
a. Write the equation for each model.
b. Analyze both models. Determine whether they are valid.
c. Which model fits better? Explain.

18.6 Xr17-14+ Refer to Exercise 17.14. The dean of the school of business wanted to improve the regression model, which was developed to describe the relationship between MBA program GPA and undergraduate GPA, GMAT score, and years of work experience. The dean now believes that an interaction effect may exist between undergraduate GPA and the GMAT test score.
a. Write the equation that describes the model.
b. Use a computer to generate the regression statistics. Use whatever statistics you deem necessary to assess the model's fit. Is this model valid?
c. Compare your results with those achieved in the original example.

18.7 Xr18-07 The manager of the food concession at a major league baseball stadium wanted to be able to predict the attendance of a game 24 hours in advance to prepare the correct amount of food for sale. It is believed that the two most important factors were the home team's winning percentage and the visiting team's winning percentage. In order to examine this, the manager collected the attendance figures, the home team's winning percentage, and the visiting

team's winning percentage for 40 randomly selected games from all the teams in the league.
a. Conduct a regression analysis using a first-order model with interaction.
b. Do these results indicate that your model is valid? Explain.

18.8 Xr18-08 The manager of a large hotel on the Riviera in southern France wanted to forecast the monthly vacancy rate (as a percentage) during the peak season. After considering a long list of potential variables, the two variables that were most closely related to the vacancy rate were identified: The average daily temperature and the value of the currency in American dollars. The data for 25 months were recorded.
a. Perform a regression analysis using a first-order model with interaction.
b. Perform a regression analysis using a second-order model with interaction.
c. Which model fits better? Explain.

18.9 Xr18-09 The coach and the general manager of a team in the National Hockey League are trying to decide what kinds of players to draft. To help in making their decision, they need to know which variables are most closely related to the goals differential—the difference between the number of goals their team scores and the number of goals scored by their team's opponents. (A positive differential means that their team wins, and a negative differential is a loss.) After some consideration, they decide that there are two important variables: The percentage of face-offs won and the penalty-minutes differential. The latter variable is the difference between the number of penalty minutes assessed against their team and the number of penalty minutes assessed against their team's opponents. The data from 100 games were recorded.

a. Perform a regression analysis using a first-order model with interaction.

b. Is this model valid?

c. Should the interaction term be included?

18.10 Xr18-10 The production manager of a chemical plant wants to determine the roles that temperature and pressure play in the yield of a particular chemical produced at the plant. From past experience, it is believed that when pressure is held constant, lower and higher temperatures tend to reduce the yield. When temperature is held constant, higher and lower pressures tend to increase the yield. It is not known how the yield is affected by various combinations of pressure and temperature. The manager observes 80 batches of the chemical in which the pressure and temperature were allowed to vary.

a. Which model should be used? Explain.

b. Conduct a regression analysis using the model you specified in part (a).

c. Assess how well the model fits the data.

18.11 Xr18-11 Car designers have been experimenting with ways to improve gas mileage for many years. An important element in this research is the way in which a car's speed affects how quickly fuel is burned. Competitions whose objective is to drive the farthest on the smallest amount of gas have determined that low speeds and high speeds are inefficient. Designers would like to know which speed burns gas most efficiently. As an experiment, 50 identical cars are driven at different speeds and the gas mileage measured.

a. Write the equation of the model you think is appropriate.

b. Perform a regression analysis using your model.

c. How well does it fit?

18.12 Xr18-12 The number of car accidents on a particular stretch of highway seems to be related to the number of vehicles that travel over it and the speed at which they are traveling. A city mayor has decided to ask the county sheriff to provide statistics covering the last few years, with the intention of examining these data statistically so that the city can (if possible) introduce new speed laws that will reduce traffic accidents. Using the number of accidents as the dependent variable, they obtained estimates of the number of cars passing along a stretch of road and their average speeds (in miles per hour). The observations for 60 randomly selected days were recorded.

a. Which model should the mayor use? Explain.

b. Conduct a regression analysis using a first-order model with interaction.

c. Is the model valid?

18.13 Refer to Exercise 18.12.

a. Estimate a second-order model with interaction.

b. Is there enough evidence to conclude that this model is valid in predicting the number of accidents?

18.14 Xr18-14 A growing segment of the textile industry in the United States is based on piecework, wherein workers are paid for each unit they produce, instead of receiving an hourly wage. The manager of one such company has observed that inexperienced workers perform quite poorly, but they usually improve quickly. However, very experienced workers do not perform as well as expected. Analysts attribute this phenomenon to boredom. More experienced workers grow weary of the monotonous work and become less productive. In an attempt to learn more about piecework labor, a statistics practitioner took a random sample of workers with varying years of experience and counted the number of units each produced in 8 hours.

a. Write the equation of the model that you think would fit.

b. Perform a regression analysis using your model.

c. Describe how well the model fits.

18-2 / NOMINAL INDEPENDENT VARIABLES

When we introduced regression analysis, we pointed out that all the variables must be interval. But in many real-life cases, one or more independent variables are nominal. For example, suppose that the used-car dealer in Example 16.2 believed that the color of a car is a factor in determining its auction price. Color is clearly a nominal variable.

If we assign numbers to each possible color, these numbers will be completely arbitrary, and using them in a regression model will usually be pointless. For example, suppose the dealer believes the colors that are most popular, white and silver, are likely to lead to different prices than other colors. Accordingly, a code of 1 to white cars, a code of 2 to silver cars, and a code of 3 to all other colors were assigned. If we now conduct a multiple regression analysis using odometer reading and color as independent variables, the following results would be obtained. (File Xm16-02+ contains these data. Interested readers can produce the following regression equation.)

$$\hat{y} = 17.342 - .0671x_1 - .0434x_2$$

Aside from the inclusion of the variable x_2, this equation is very similar to the one we produced in the simple regression model ($\hat{y} = 17.250 - .0669x$). The t-test of color (t-statistic $= -1.11$, and p-value $= .2694$) indicates that there is not enough evidence to infer that color is not linearly related to price. There are two possible explanations for this result. First, there is no relationship between color and price. Second, color is a factor in determining the car's price, but the way in which the dealer assigned the codes to the colors made detection of that fact impossible—that is, the dealer treated the nominal variable, color, as an interval variable. To further understand why we cannot use nominal data in regression analysis, try to interpret the coefficient of color. Such an effort is similar to attempting to interpret the mean of a sample of nominal data. It is futile. Even though this effort failed, it is possible to include nominal variables in the regression model. This is accomplished through the use of *indicator variables*.

An **indicator variable** (also called a **dummy variable**) is a variable that can assume either one of only two values (usually 0 and 1), where 1 represents the existence of a certain condition and 0 indicates that the condition does not hold. In this illustration, we would create two indicator variables to represent the color of the car:

$$I_1 = \begin{cases} 1 & \text{(if color is white)} \\ 0 & \text{(if color is not white)} \end{cases}$$

and

$$I_2 = \begin{cases} 1 & \text{(if color is silver)} \\ 0 & \text{(if color is not silver)} \end{cases}$$

Notice that we need only two indicator variables to represent the three categories. A white car is represented by $I_1 = 1$ and $I_2 = 0$. A silver car is represented by $I_1 = 0$ and $I_2 = 1$. Because cars that are painted some other color are neither white nor silver, they are represented by $I_1 = 0$ and $I_2 = 0$. It should be apparent that we cannot have $I_1 = 1$ and $I_2 = 1$, as long as we assume that no Toyota Camry is two-toned.

The effect of using these two indicator variables is to create three equations, one for each of the three colors. As you're about to discover, we can use the equations to determine how the car's color relates to its auction selling price.

In general, to represent a nominal variable with m categories, we must create $m - 1$ indicator variables. The last category represented by $I_1 = I_2 = \cdots = I_{m-1} = 0$ is called the **omitted category**.

18-2a Interpreting and Testing the Coefficients of Indicator Variables

In file Xm16-02a, we stored the values of I_1 and I_2. We then performed a multiple regression analysis using the variables odometer reading (x), I_1, and I_2.

EXCEL Data Analysis

	A	B	C	D	E	F
1	SUMMARY OUTPUT					
2						
3	*Regression Statistics*					
4	Multiple R	0.8371				
5	R Square	0.7008				
6	Adjusted R Square	0.6914				
7	Standard Error	0.3043				
8	Observations	100				
9						
10	ANOVA					
11		*df*	*SS*	*MS*	*F*	*Significance F*
12	Regression	3	20.81	6.94	74.95	4.65E-25
13	Residual	96	8.89	0.0926		
14	Total	99	29.70			
15						
16		*Coefficients*	*Standard Error*	*t Stat*	*P-value*	
17	Intercept	16.837	0.197	85.42	2.28E-92	
18	Odometer	−0.0591	0.0051	−11.67	4.04E-20	
19	I-1	0.0911	0.0729	1.25	0.2143	
20	I-2	0.3304	0.0816	4.05	0.0001	

INTERPRET

The regression equation is

$$\hat{y} = 16.837 - .0591x + .0911I_1 + .3304I_2$$

The intercept and the coefficient of odometer reading are interpreted in the usual manner. The intercept ($b_0 = 16.837$) is meaningless in the context of this problem. The coefficient of the odometer reading ($b_1 = -.0591$) tells us that for each additional mile on the odometer, the auction price decreases an average of 5.91 cents, holding the color constant. Now examine the remaining two coefficients:

$$b_2 = .0911$$
$$b_3 = .3304$$

Recall that we interpret the coefficients in a multiple regression model by holding the other variables constant. In this example, we interpret the coefficient of I_1 as follows. In this sample, a white Camry sells for .0911 thousand or $91.10 on average more than other colors (nonwhite, nonsilver) with the same odometer reading. A silver car sells for $330.40 on average more than other colors with the same odometer reading. The reason both comparisons are made with other colors is that such cars are represented by $I_1 = I_2 = 0$. Thus, for a nonwhite and nonsilver car, the equation becomes

$$\hat{y} = 16.837 - .0591x + .0911(0) + .3304(0)$$

which is

$$\hat{y} = 16.837 - .0591x$$

For a white car ($I_1 = 1$ and $I_2 = 0$), the regression equation is

$$\hat{y} = 16.837 - .0591x + .0911(1) + .3304(0)$$

which is

$$\hat{y} = 16.928 - .0591x$$

Finally, for a silver car ($I_1 = 0$ and $I_2 = 1$), the regression equation is

$$\hat{y} = 16.837 - .0591x + .0911(0) + .3304(1)$$

which simplifies to

$$\hat{y} = 17.167 - .0591x$$

Figure 18.11 depicts the graph of price versus odometer reading for the three different color categories. Notice that the three lines are parallel (with slope $= -.0591$) while the intercepts differ.

FIGURE 18.11 Price versus Odometer Reading for Three Colors

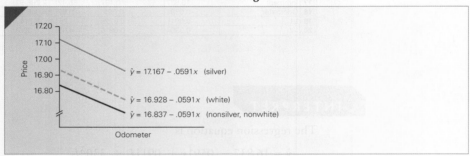

We can also perform t-tests on the coefficients of I_1 and I_2. However, because the variables I_1 and I_2 represent different groups (the three color categories), these t-tests allow us to draw inferences about the differences in auction selling prices between the groups for the entire population of similar 3-year-old Toyota Camrys.

The test of the coefficient of I_1, which is β_2, is conducted as follows:

H_0: $\beta_2 = 0$
H_1: $\beta_2 \neq 0$

Test statistic: $t = 1.25$, p-value $= .2143$

There is insufficient evidence to infer that white Camrys have a different mean selling price than do Camrys in the omitted category in the population of 3-year-old Camrys with the same odometer reading.

To determine whether silver-colored Camrys sell for a different price than Camrys in the other color category, we test

H_0: $\beta_3 = 0$
H_1: $\beta_3 \neq 0$

Test statistic: $t = 4.05$, p-value $= .0001$

We can conclude that there are differences in the mean auction selling prices between all 3-year-old, silver-colored Camrys and the omitted color category with the same odometer readings.

General Social Survey: Variables That Affect Income II

To include the nominal variables gender and race in a multiple regression model, we need to create two sets of indicator variables. The first is to represent gender.

For gender let:

$$I_1 = \begin{cases} 1 & \text{if male} \\ 0 & \text{if female} \end{cases}$$

For race let:

$$I_2 = \begin{cases} 1 & \text{if white} \\ 0 & \text{otherwise} \end{cases}$$

$$I_3 = \begin{cases} 1 & \text{if black} \\ 0 & \text{otherwise} \end{cases}$$

EXCEL Data Analysis

	A	B	C	D	E	F	G
1	SUMMARY OUTPUT						
3	*Regression Statistics*						
4	Multiple R	0.5537					
5	R Square	0.3066					
6	Adjusted R Square	0.3030					
7	Standard Error	35,880					
8	Observations	1171					
10	ANOVA						
11		*df*	*SS*	*MS*	*F*	*Significance F*	
12	Regression	6	662,592,419,138	110,432,069,856	85.78	4.59E-89	
13	Residual	1164	1,498,527,927,147	1,287,395,126			
14	Total	1170	2,161,120,346,285				
16		*Coefficients*	*Standard Error*	*t Stat*	*P-value*	*Lower 95%*	*Upper 95%*
17	Intercept	-100,260	7307	-13.72	7.92E-40	-114,596	-85924
18	I-1	14,091	2171	6.49	1.27E-10	9831	18351
19	I-2	4556	3287	1.39	0.1660	-1893	11006
20	I-3	-2286	4007	-0.571	0.5684	-10147	5575
21	AGE	646.0	77.4	8.35	1.93E-16	494.2	797.8
22	EDUC	5589	379.8	14.72	4.41E-45	4844	6334
23	HRS1	828.6	75.7	10.94	1.33E-26	680.1	977.2

INTERPRET

The model has improved slightly; the coefficient of determination has increased from .2776 to .3066 and the standard error decreased from 36,608 to 35,880.

The coefficient of variable I_1 is 14,091, which tells us that in this sample men earn an average of $14,091 more than women when the comparison is made holding the other independent variables constant. Here is how we interpret this number. Assume that this is the population coefficient (and not the sample coefficient). Imagine populations of men and women who are identical in terms of the other independent variables (race, age, education, hours of work, number of children, and number of family earners). And now when we compare incomes, the men earn on average $14,091 more than the women.

(Continued)

The t-test of the coefficient is $t = 6.49$ and with a p-value of 0. We conclude that there is enough evidence that, in the United States in 2018, average incomes of men and women were different when the other variables were held constant.

The coefficient of I_2 is 4,556. This number means that in this sample, White people earn an average of $4,556 more than the other category, which is nonwhite and nonblack, holding the other variables constant. The t-statistic is 1.39 and its p-value is .1660. There is not enough evidence to infer that the mean income of the population of White people is different from the mean income of the population of nonwhite, nonblack people.

The coefficient of I_3 is $-2,286$. In this sample, Black people earn an average of $2,286 less than the other category holding the other variables constant. The t-test value is $-.571$ and its p-value is .5684. There is not enough evidence to conclude that, in 2018, the mean income of Black people was different from the mean income of nonwhite, nonblack people.

Because only one indicator variable was statistically significant, this model is only slightly better than the model in Chapter 17.

EXERCISES

18.15 How many indicator variables must be created to represent a nominal independent variable that has five categories?

18.16 Create and identify indicator variables to represent the following nominal variables.
  a. Religious affiliation (Catholic, Protestant, and others)
  b. Working shift (8 A.M. to 4 P.M., 4 P.M. to 12 midnight, and 12 midnight to 8 A.M.)
  c. Supervisor (Jack Jones, Mary Brown, George Fosse, and Elaine Smith)

18.17 In a study of computer applications, a survey asked which microcomputer a number of companies used. The following indicator variables were created.

$$I_1 = \begin{cases} 1 & \text{(if IBM)} \\ 0 & \text{(if not)} \end{cases} \qquad I_2 = \begin{cases} 1 & \text{(if Apple)} \\ 0 & \text{(if not)} \end{cases}$$

Which computer is being referred to by each of the following pairs of values?
  a. $I_1 = 0; I_2 = 1$
  b. $I_1 = 1; I_2 = 0$
  c. $I_1 = 0; I_2 = 0$

The following exercises require the use of a computer and software.
Use 5% significance level for all tests.

18.18 Xr17-14+   Refer to Exercise 17.14. After considering the results of the initial study, the dean realized

that they may have omitted an important variable—the type of undergraduate degree. They returned to the sample of students and recorded the type of undergraduate degree using the following codes:

  1 = BA

  2 = BBA (including similar business or management degrees)

  3 = BEng or BSc

  4 = Other (including no undergraduate degree)

These data were included with the data from the original example. Can the dean conclude that the undergraduate degree is a factor in determining how well a student performs in the MBA program?

18.19 Xr16-09+   The real estate agent described in Exercise 16.9 realized that the price of Florida condominiums depends on other variables besides the floor. Accordingly, the agent went back to the list of 50 condos and determined whether they had undergone a major renovation. The categorizes are: Renovated more than 10 years ago or never (1), renovated less than 3 years ago (2), or renovated between 3 and 10 years ago (3).
  a. Conduct a multiple regression analysis with Floor and Renovated as independent variables. Describe your results.
  b. Create indicator variables to replace the Renovated variable and conduct another

There are two forms of pay equity. The first is "equal pay for equal work." This form is relatively straightforward, arguing that if two individuals do the same job with similar qualifications and experience, they should be paid the same. In many jurisdictions, it is illegal to violate equal pay for equal work. The second form is "equal pay for work of equal value." This form is controversial for several reasons, including the use of subjectively assigned measures of qualifications and working conditions.

Regression analysis is used extensively in pay-equity cases. However, the methodology used in equal-pay-for-equal-work cases differs from that used for equal-pay-for-work-of-equal-value cases. The following example illustrates how statistical analyses can be utilized for the former.

EXAMPLE 18.3

DATA
Xm18-03

Testing for Pay Equity: Equal Pay for Equal Work

A large firm employing tens of thousands of workers has been accused of discriminating against its female managers. The accusation is based on a random sample of 100 managers. The mean annual salary of the 38 female managers is $76,189, whereas the mean annual salary of the 62 male managers is $97,832. A statistical analysis reveals that the t-test of the difference between two means yields a p-value of less than 1%, which provides overwhelming evidence that male managers are paid more than female managers. In rebuttal, the president of the firm points out that the company has a strict policy of equal pay for equal work and that the difference may be the result of other variables. Accordingly, the number of years of education and the number of years of experience for each of the 100 managers in the sample were recorded. Also recorded are the salary and gender (0 = female, 1 = male). The president wanted to know whether a regression analysis would shed some light on the issue.

SOLUTION:

Using salary as the dependent variable, a multiple regression analysis was performed with the results shown here.

EXCEL Data Analysis

	A	B	C	D	E	F
1	SUMMARY OUTPUT					
2						
3	*Regression Statistics*					
4	Multiple R	0.8326				
5	R Square	0.6932				
6	Adjusted R Square	0.6836				
7	Standard Error	16,274				
8	Observations	100				
9						
10	ANOVA					
11		*df*	*SS*	*MS*	*F*	*Significance F*
12	Regression	3	57,434,095,083	19,144,698,361	72.29	1.55E-24
13	Residual	96	25,424,794,888	264,841,613		
14	Total	99	82,858,889,971			
15						
16		*Coefficients*	*Standard Error*	*t Stat*	*P-value*	
17	Intercept	−5835	16083	−0.36	0.7175	
18	Education	2119	1018	2.08	0.0401	
19	Experience	4099	317	12.92	9.89E-23	
20	Gender	1851	3703	0.50	0.6183	

INTERPRET

The model fits quite well. The coefficient of determination is .6932, which tells the president that 69.32% of the variation in salaries is explained by the model. The F-statistic is 72.29, which has a p-value of 0. There is overwhelming evidence to allow us to infer that the model is valid.

The p-values of the t-tests to determine whether there is evidence of a linear relationship between salary and each of education, experience, and gender are .0401, 0, and .6183, respectively. Both the years of education and the years of experience are linearly related to salary. However, the t-test of the slope for gender tells us that there is not enough evidence to infer that the mean salaries of all the firm's male and female managers with the same amount of education and experience differ. In other words, on average, the female managers in this firm have less education and experience than their male counterparts, which explains their lower mean salary. Before the regression analysis, we calculated the difference in sample mean salaries to be $97,832 − $76,189 = $21,643. After removing the effects of education and experience in this sample that difference was reduced to $1, 851, which is statistically insignificant.

18-3a Regression Analysis for Equal-Pay-for-Work-of-Equal-Value Cases

Cases involving the issue of equal pay for work of equal value are much more difficult. The issue generally revolves around female-dominated and male-dominated jobs. The former refers to jobs that are generally held by women (e.g., secretaries) and the latter refers to jobs generally held by men (e.g., maintenance workers). Women's groups claim that male-dominated jobs are more highly paid. Here the issue is not underpaying women who are doing exactly the same jobs performed by men. Instead, the issue is that women's jobs are undervalued. Thus, it is necessary to evaluate jobs.

Several jurisdictions have enacted laws requiring pay equity for work of equal value. One such jurisdiction is the province of Manitoba. The Manitoba Pay Equity Act is mandatory in the province's civil service, crown corporations, hospitals, and universities. The act defines gender-dominated job classes as ones with at least 10 workers where at least 70% are of the same gender. The act requires that all such jobs be evaluated to determine whether female-dominated jobs are undervalued and underpaid compared to male-dominated jobs.

Although regression analysis is employed, there are major differences between the technique described in Example 18.3 and the one used in this case. Rather than estimate a regression model that explains how several related variables affect pay, we need to develop a job evaluation system. The system is used to assign a score to each job, which is then used as an independent variable in regression where pay is again the dependent variable. The regression analysis can be conducted in several ways. The simple linear regression equation can be estimated using the male-dominated jobs only. The coefficients are then used to calculate the "correct" female-dominated job pay rates. The difference between the so-called correct and actual pay rates represents the degree of underpayment. Alternatively, a regression analysis with both male- and female-dominated jobs can be employed. An indicator variable representing gender is included. The value of the indicator variable's coefficient represents the difference between male- and female-dominated jobs and the degree of underpayment. The following example illustrates the latter type of analysis, which was adapted from the province of Manitoba Pay Equity Act manuals that describe the law and how it is to be administered.

EXAMPLE 18.4

Testing for Pay Equity: Equal Pay for Work of Equal Value

In a university, a total of eight jobs are identified as gender dominated. The female-dominated jobs are cleaner, secretary, and workers in the book store and cafeteria. The male-dominated jobs are maintenance worker, security guard, gardener, and technician. Perform a pay-equity analysis to determine whether and to what degree female-dominated jobs are undervalued and underpaid.

SOLUTION:

The hourly pay rates are as follows:

Job Categories	Pay Rate
Maintenance	13.55
Security	15.65
Gardener	13.80
Technician	19.90
Cleaner	11.85
Secretary	14.75
Bookstore	18.90
Cafeteria	13.30

After some consideration, the following factors were selected as part of the job evaluation system:

Knowledge and training

Responsibility

Mental effort

Physical effort

Working conditions

Each factor is assigned a weight that reflects its importance. The weights (which must sum to 1) are 25%, 23%, 22%, 15%, and 15%, respectively.

A score for each job is determined by assigning a value between 1 and 10 for each of the five factors and then multiplying by the weight. Smaller values represent less-demanding requirements or better conditions.

The male-dominated jobs are evaluated as follows:

Factors	Weight	Maintenance	Security	Gardener	Technician
Knowledge and training	.25	1	2	3	9
Responsibility	.23	2	7	1	7
Mental effort	.22	2	3	1	8
Physical effort	.15	7	1	6	4
Working conditions	.15	7	4	8	1
Total score		3.25	3.52	3.30	6.37

As you can see, the scores assigned to the maintenance workers and gardeners reflect relatively small demands on knowledge, training, and mental effort but high demands on physical effort and poor working conditions. The technician, on the other hand, has excellent working conditions but requires a high level of knowledge and training.

The evaluations of the female-dominated jobs are as follows:

Factors	Weight	Cleaner	Secretary	Bookstore	Cafeteria
Knowledge and training	.25	1	6	4	2
Responsibility	.23	2	7	7	2
Mental effort	.22	2	6	7	2
Physical effort	.15	7	3	2	5
Working conditions	.15	5	1	1	6
Total score		2.95	5.03	4.60	3.05

As was the case with the male-dominated jobs, the scores for the female-dominated jobs are based on a subjective assessment of the requirements and work that the jobs entail.

The score and an indicator variable are used as independent variables in a regression analysis with pay as the dependent variable. The following data are used in the regression analysis:

Job Categories	Pay Rate	Score	Gender
Maintenance	13.55	3.25	1
Security	15.65	3.52	1
Gardener	13.80	3.30	1
Technician	19.90	6.37	1
Cleaner	11.85	2.95	0
Secretary	14.75	5.03	0
Bookstore	18.90	4.60	0
Cafeteria	13.30	3.05	0

where

$$\text{Gender} = \begin{cases} 1 & \text{if male-dominated job} \\ 0 & \text{if female-dominated job} \end{cases}$$

The results of the regression are shown below.

EXCEL Data Analysis

	A	B	C	D	E	F
1	SUMMARY OUTPUT					
2						
3	Regression Statistics					
4	Multiple R	0.8515				
5	R Square	0.7251				
6	Adjusted R Square	0.6152				
7	Standard Error	1.75				
8	Observations	8				
9						
10	ANOVA					
11		df	SS	MS	F	Significance F
12	Regression	2	40.39	20.19	6.59	0.0396
13	Residual	5	15.31	3.06		
14	Total	7	55.70			
15						
16		Coefficients	Standard Error	t Stat	P-value	
17	Intercept	7.15	2.31	3.10	0.0270	
18	Score	1.93	0.547	3.54	0.0166	
19	Gender	0.633	1.242	0.51	0.6318	

> ### INTERPRET
>
> We cannot apply the usual statistical inference because the eight observations represent the entire population under consideration. Instead we simply use the coefficients of interest. In this case we discover that male-dominated jobs are paid an average of .63 more than female-dominated jobs after adjusting for the value of each job. If we accept the validity of this analysis (see Exercises 18.29 and 18.30), we conclude that the holders of female-dominated jobs need to have their pay rates increased by 63 cents per hour.

EXERCISES

The following exercises require a computer and software.

18.41  Pay equity for men and women has been an ongoing source of conflict for a number of years in North America. Suppose that a statistics practitioner is investigating the factors that affect salary differences between male and female university professors. It is believed that the following variables have some impact on a professor's salary:

Number of years since first degree

$$\text{Highest degree} = \begin{cases} 1 \text{ if Highest degree is a Ph.D.} \\ 0 \text{ if Highest degree is not a Ph.D.} \end{cases}$$

Average score on teaching evaluations
Number of articles published in refereed journals

$$\text{Gender} = \begin{cases} 1 & \text{if Professor is male} \\ 0 & \text{if Professor is female} \end{cases}$$

A random sample of 100 university professors was taken and the following data were recorded:

Column 1: Annual salary
Column 2: Number of years since first degree
Column 3: Highest degree
Column 4: Mean score on teaching evaluation
Column 5: Number of articles published
Column 6: Gender

a. Can the statistics practitioner conclude that the model is valid?

b. Can the statistics practitioner conclude at the 5% significance level that there is gender discrimination?

An Excel spreadsheet, **Pay Equity** *(stored in the* **Excel Workbooks** *folder), was created to perform the analysis described in Example 18.4. The jobs, pay rates, job scores, and the values of the indicator variable are shown at the bottom of the sheet. These data were used as inputs in the regression analysis. The worksheet is set up so that any change in the factor scores and/or weights automatically changes the job scores at the bottom of the page.*

18.42 Re-do Example 18.4. Change the weights for knowledge and training to 15% and for working conditions to 25%. What effect does this have on the conclusion? Briefly explain why the result was predictable.

18.43 Re-do Example 18.4 by assigning your own values to each factor and to the weights. What conclusion did you reach?

18.44 Discuss how the factor values and weights affect the final result. Explain the strengths and weaknesses of the statistical analysis.

18-4 / MODEL BUILDING

At this point, we have described several different regression models. You now have the use of nominal predictor variables and the tools to describe a variety of nonlinear relationships. In this section, we describe how the statistics practitioner builds a model.

Regression analysis is used either to determine how one or more predictor variables are related to a dependent variable or to predict the value of the dependent variable and estimate its expected value. Although the process differs between the two objectives, there are many similarities in the approach.

Here is the procedure that is employed in the building of a model.

18-4a Procedure for Building a Model

1. *Identify the dependent variable.* Clearly define the variable that you wish to analyze or predict. For example, if you want to forecast sales, decide whether it is to be the number of units sold, gross revenue, or perhaps net profits. In addition, decide whether to forecast weekly, monthly, or annual figures.

2. *List potential predictors.* Using your knowledge of the dependent variable, produce a list of predictors that may be related to the dependent variable. Although we cannot establish a causal relationship, we should attempt to include predictor variables that cause changes in the dependent variable. Bear in mind the problems caused by multicollinearity and the cost of gathering, storing, and processing data. Be selective in your choices. It is best to use the fewest independent variables that produce a satisfactory model.

3. *Gather the required observations for the potential models.* A general rule is that there should be at least six observations for each independent variable used in the equation.

4. *Identify several possible models.* Once again, use your knowledge of the dependent variable and predictor variables to formulate a model. For example, if you believe that a predictor variable affects the dependent variable, but you are uncertain about the form of the relationship, then formulate first- and second-order models with and without interaction. It may be helpful to draw a scatter diagram of the dependent variable and each predictor variable to discover the nature of the relationship.

5. *Use statistical software to estimate the models.* Use one or more of the variable selection methods described in the previous section to determine which variables to include in the model. If the objective is to determine which predictor variables are related to the dependent variable, you will need to ensure that multicollinearity is not a problem. If it is, attempt to reduce the number of independent variables.

6. *Determine whether the required conditions are satisfied.* If not, attempt to correct the problem. At this point, you may have several "equal" models from which to choose.

7. *Use your judgment and the statistical output to select the best model.* This may be the most difficult part of the process. There may be a model that fits best, but another one may be a better predictor, and yet another may feature fewer variables and, thus, be easier to work with. Experience with regression helps. Taking another statistics course is likely your best strategy.

CHAPTER SUMMARY

This chapter completes our discussion of the regression technique, which began in Chapter 16. We presented several additional models for predicting the value of one variable on the basis of other variables. Polynomial models with one and two independent variables were presented. We discussed how indicator variables allow us to use nominal variables and we described how indicator variables are used in pay equity discussions. We completed the chapter by providing some advice on how statisticians build models.

IMPORTANT TERMS:

Polynomial model   772
Predictor variable   772
Order   772
First-order   772
Interaction   775

Quadratic relationship   776
Second-order   776
Indicator variable   782
Dummy variable   782
Omitted category   782

SYMBOLS:

Symbol	Pronounced	Represents
I_i	I sub i or $I\,i$	Indicator variable

iStockphoto.com/clu

NONPARAMETRIC STATISTICS

CHAPTER OUTLINE

General Social Survey

Do Democrats, Independents, and Republicans Differ in the Number of Times per Week They Read Newspapers?

DATA
GSS2018

Because of the way politics have evolved, it appears that campaigns for president start at least 2 years before the actual election. And of course there are elections for representatives every 2 years. This means that politics is part of the regular news that appears in newspapers across the country. In the business of politics, it is important to know where voters are getting their information. Historically, newspapers have been critical to political campaigns because almost all newspapers make recommendations about whom to vote for. This raises the question,

Kiyoshi Ota/Getty Images

(See Solution on page 832.)

Do supporters of the three political affiliations (PARTYID3: 1 = Democrat, 2 = Independent, 3 = Republican) read newspapers with the same frequency? One of the questions asked in the 2018 General Social Survey was, How often do you read the newspaper (NEWS: 1 = Every day, 2 = A few times a week, 3 = Once a week, 4 = Less than once a week, 5 = Never)? After we introduce the appropriate statistical technique, we will provide our answer (see page 832).

INTRODUCTION

Throughout this book, we have presented statistical techniques that are used when the data are either interval or nominal. In this chapter, we introduce statistical techniques that deal with ordinal data. We will introduce three methods that compare two populations, two procedures used to compare two or more populations, and a technique to analyze the relationship between two variables. As you've seen when we compare two or more populations of interval data, we measure the difference between means. However, as we discussed in Chapter 2, when the data are ordinal, the mean is not an appropriate measure of location. As a result, the methods in this chapter do not enable us to test the difference in population means; instead, we will test characteristics of populations without referring to specific parameters. For this reason, these techniques are called **nonparametric techniques**. Rather than testing to determine whether the population means differ, we will test to determine whether the *population locations* differ.

Although nonparametric methods are designed to test ordinal data, they have another area of application. The statistical tests described in Sections 13-1 and 13-3 and in Chapter 14 require that the populations be normally distributed. If the data are extremely nonnormal, the *t*-tests and *F*-test are invalid. Fortunately, nonparametric techniques can be used instead. For this reason, nonparametric procedures are often (perhaps more accurately) called **distribution-free statistics**. The techniques presented here can be used when the data are interval and the required condition of normality is unsatisfied. In such circumstances, we will treat the interval data as if they were ordinal. For this reason, even when the data are interval and the mean is the appropriate measure of location, we will choose instead to test population locations.

Figure 19.1 depicts the distributions of two populations when their locations are the same. Notice that because we don't know (or care) anything about the shape of the distributions, we represent them as nonnormal. Figure 19.2 describes a circumstance when the location of population 1 is to the right of the location of population 2. The location of population 1 is to the left of the location of population 2 in Figure 19.3.

FIGURE **19.1** **Population Locations Are the Same**

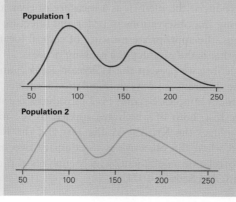

Population 1

Population 2

FIGURE **19.2** Location of Population 1 Is to the Right of the Location of Population 2

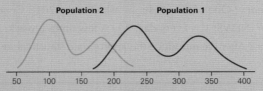

FIGURE **19.3** Location of Population 1 Is to the Left of the Location of Population 2

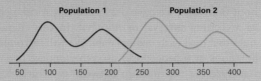

When the problem objective is to compare two populations, the null hypothesis will state

H_0:   The two population locations are the same

The alternative hypothesis can take on any one of the following three forms.

1. If we want to know whether there is sufficient evidence to infer that there is a difference between the two populations, the alternative hypothesis is

    H_1:   The location of population 1 is different from the location of population 2

2. If we want to know whether we can conclude that the random variable in population 1 is larger in general than the random variable in population 2 (see Figure 19.2), the alternative hypothesis is

    H_1:   The location of population 1 is to the right of the location of population 2

3. If we want to know whether we can conclude that the random variable in population 1 is smaller in general than the random variable in population 2 (see Figure 19.3), the alternative hypothesis is

    H_1:   The location of population 1 is to the left of the location of population 2

As you will see, nonparametric tests utilize a ranking procedure as an integral part of the calculations. You've actually dealt with such a process already in this book. In Chapter 4, we introduced the median as a measure of central location. The median is computed by placing the observations in order and selecting the observation that falls in the middle. Thus, the appropriate measure of central location of ordinal data is the median, a statistic that is the product of a ranking process.

In the next section, we present the Wilcoxon Rank Sum Test employed when we wish to test for the differences between population locations when the data are generated from independent samples. Section 19-2 introduces the sign test and the Wilcoxon signed Rank Sum Test, both of which are applied to the matched pairs experiment. Section 19-3 introduces the Kruskal–Wallis Test and the Friedman Test, procedures that are employed when the objective is to compare two or more populations. The Spearman rank correlation coefficient, which analyzes the relationship between two variables, is presented in Section 19-4.

19-1/WILCOXON RANK SUM TEST

The test we introduce in this section deals with problems with the following characteristics:

1. The problem objective is to compare two populations.

2. The data are either ordinal or interval where the normality requirement necessary to perform the equal-variances t-test of $\mu_1 - \mu_2$ is unsatisfied.

3. The samples are independent.

To illustrate how to compute the test statistic for the **Wilcoxon Rank Sum Test** for independent samples, we offer the following example.

EXAMPLE 19.1

Wilcoxon Rank Sum Test

Suppose that we want to determine whether the following observations drawn from two populations allow us to conclude at the 5% significance level that the location of population 1 is to the left of the location of population 2.

Sample 1:	22	23	20
Sample 2:	18	27	26

We want to test the following hypotheses:

H_0: The two population locations are the same.

H_1: The location of population 1 is to the left of the location of population 2.

Test Statistic

The first step is to rank all six observations, with rank 1 assigned to the smallest observation and rank 6 to the largest.

Sample 1	Rank	Sample 2	Rank
22	3	18	1
23	4	27	6
20	2	26	5
	$T_1 = 9$		$T_2 = 12$

Observe that 18 is the smallest number, so it receives a rank of 1; 20 is the second-smallest number, and it receives a rank of 2. We continue until rank 6 is assigned to 27, which is the largest of the observations. In case of ties, we average the ranks of the tied observations. The second step is to calculate the sum of the ranks of each sample. The rank sum of sample 1, denoted as T_1, is 9. The rank sum of sample 2, denoted as T_2, is 12.

(Note that T_1 plus T_2 must equal the sum of the integers from 1 to 6, which is 21.) We can use either rank sum as the test statistic. We arbitrarily select T_1 as the test statistic and label it T. The value of the test statistic in this example is $T = T_1 = 9$.

Sampling Distribution of the Test Statistic

A small value of T indicates that most of the smaller observations are in sample 1 and that most of the larger observations are in sample 2. This would imply that the location of population 1 is to the left of the location of population 2. Therefore, in order for us to conclude statistically that this is the case, we need to show that T is small. The definition of "small" comes from the sampling distribution of T. As we did in Section 9-1 when we derived the sampling distribution of the sample mean, we can derive the sampling distribution of T by listing all possible values of T. In Table 19.1, we show all possible rankings of two samples of size 3.

TABLE **19.1** All Possible Ranks and Rank Sums of Two Samples of Size 3

RANKS OF SAMPLE 1	RANK SUM	RANKS OF SAMPLE 2	RANK SUM
1, 2, 3	6	4, 5, 6	15
1, 2, 4	7	3, 5, 6	14
1, 2, 5	8	3, 4, 6	13
1, 2, 6	9	3, 4, 5	12
1, 3, 4	8	2, 5, 6	13
1, 3, 5	9	2, 4, 6	12
1, 3, 6	10	2, 4, 5	11
1, 4, 5	10	2, 3, 6	11
1, 4, 6	11	2, 3, 5	10
1, 5, 6	12	2, 3, 4	9
2, 3, 4	9	1, 5, 6	12
2, 3, 5	10	1, 4, 6	11
2, 3, 6	11	1, 4, 5	10
2, 4, 5	11	1, 3, 6	10
2, 4, 6	12	1, 3, 5	9
2, 5, 6	13	1, 3, 4	8
3, 4, 5	12	1, 2, 6	9
3, 4, 6	13	1, 2, 5	8
3, 5, 6	14	1, 2, 4	7
4, 5, 6	15	1, 2, 3	6

If the null hypothesis is true and the two population locations are identical, then it follows that each possible ranking is equally likely. Because there are 20 different possibilities, each value of T has the same probability, namely, 1/20. Notice that there is one value of 6, one value of 7, two values of 8, and so on. Table 19.2 summarizes the values of T and their probabilities, and Figure 19.4 depicts this sampling distribution.

TABLE **19.2** Sampling Distribution of *T* with Two Samples of Size 3

T	P(T)
6	1/20
7	1/20
8	2/20
9	3/20
10	3/20
11	3/20
12	3/20
13	2/20
14	1/20
15	1/20
Total	1

FIGURE **19.4** Sampling Distribution of *T* with Two Samples of Size 3

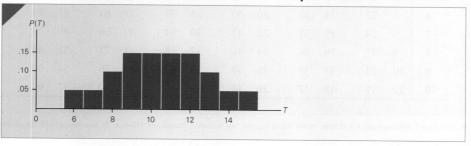

From this sampling distribution we can see that $P(T \le 6) = P(T = 6) = 1/20 = .05$. Because we're trying to determine whether the value of the test statistic is small enough for us to reject the null hypothesis at the 5% significance level, we specify the rejection region as $T \le 6$. Because $T = 9$, we cannot reject the null hypothesis.

Statisticians have generated the sampling distribution of T for various combinations of sample sizes. The critical values are provided in Table 9 in Appendix B and reproduced here as Table 19.3. Table 19.3 provides values of T_L and T_U for sample sizes between 3 and 10 (n_1 is the size of sample 1, and n_2 is the size of sample 2). The values of T_L and T_U in part (a) of the table are such that

$$P(T \le T_L) = P(T \ge T_U) = .025$$

The values of T_L and T_U in part (b) of the table are such that

$$P(T \le T_L) = P(T \ge T_U) = .05$$

Part (a) is used either in a two-tail test with $\alpha = .05$ or in a one-tail test with $\alpha = .025$. Part (b) is employed either in a two-tail test with $\alpha = .10$ or in a one-tail test with $\alpha = .05$. Because no other values are provided, we are restricted to those values of α.

TABLE **19.3** **Critical Values of the Wilcoxon Rank Sum Test**

(a) $\alpha = .025$ one-tail; $\alpha = .05$ two-tail

n_2 \ n_1	3		4		5		6		7		8		9		10	
	T_L	T_U	T_L	T_U	T_L	T_U	T_L	T_U	T_L	T_U	T_L	T_U	T_L	T_U	T_L	T_U
4	6	18	11	25	17	33	23	43	31	53	40	64	50	76	61	89
5	6	21	12	28	18	37	25	47	33	58	42	70	52	83	64	96
6	7	23	12	32	19	41	26	52	35	63	44	76	55	89	66	104
7	7	26	13	35	20	45	28	56	37	68	47	81	58	95	70	110
8	8	28	14	38	21	49	29	61	39	73	49	87	60	102	73	117
9	8	31	15	41	22	53	31	65	41	78	51	93	63	108	76	124
10	9	33	16	44	24	56	32	70	43	83	54	98	66	114	79	131

(b) $\alpha = .05$ one-tail; $\alpha = .10$ two-tail

n_2 \ n_1	3		4		5		6		7		8		9		10	
	T_L	T_U	T_L	T_U	T_L	T_U	T_L	T_U	T_L	T_U	T_L	T_U	T_L	T_U	T_L	T_U
3	6	15	11	21	16	29	23	37	31	46	39	57	49	68	60	80
4	7	17	12	24	18	32	25	41	33	51	42	62	52	74	63	87
5	7	20	13	27	19	36	26	46	35	56	45	67	55	80	66	94
6	8	22	14	30	20	40	28	50	37	61	47	73	57	87	69	101
7	9	24	15	33	22	43	30	54	39	66	49	79	60	93	73	107
8	9	27	16	36	24	46	32	58	41	71	52	84	63	99	76	114
9	10	29	17	39	25	50	33	63	43	76	54	90	66	105	79	121
10	22	31	18	42	26	54	35	67	46	80	57	95	69	111	83	127

Source: From F. Wilcoxon and R.A. Wilcox, "Some Rapid Approximate Statistical Procedures" (1964), p. 28. Reproduced with the permission of American Cyanamid Company.

Although it is possible to derive the sampling distribution of the test statistic for any other sample sizes, the process can be quite tedious. Fortunately it is also unnecessary. Statisticians have shown that when the sample sizes are larger than 10, the test statistic is approximately normally distributed with mean $E(T)$ and standard deviation σ_T where

$$E(T) = \frac{n_1(n_1 + n_2 + 1)}{2}$$

and

$$\sigma_T = \sqrt{\frac{n_1 n_2 (n_1 + n_2 + 1)}{12}}$$

Thus, the standardized test statistic is

$$z = \frac{T - E(T)}{\sigma_T}$$

EXAMPLE 19.2

Comparing Pharmaceutical Painkillers

A pharmaceutical company is planning to introduce a new painkiller. In a preliminary experiment to determine its effectiveness, 30 people were randomly selected, of whom 15 were given the new painkiller and 15 were given aspirin. All 30 were told to use the drug when headaches or other minor pains occurred and to indicate which of the following statements most accurately represented the effectiveness of the drug they took:

    5 = The drug was extremely effective.

    4 = The drug was quite effective.

    3 = The drug was somewhat effective.

    2 = The drug was slightly effective.

    1 = The drug was not at all effective.

The responses are listed here using the codes. Can we conclude at the 5% significance level that the new painkiller is perceived to be more effective?

    New painkiller: 3, 5, 4, 3, 2, 5, 1, 4, 5, 3, 3, 5, 5, 5, 4

    Aspirin: 4, 1, 3, 2, 4, 1, 3, 4, 2, 2, 2, 4, 3, 4, 5

SOLUTION:

IDENTIFY

The objective is to compare two populations: the perceived effectiveness of the new painkiller and of aspirin. We recognize that the data are ordinal; except for the order of the codes, the numbers used to record the results are arbitrary. Finally, the samples are independent. These factors tell us that the appropriate technique is the Wilcoxon Rank Sum Test. We denote the effectiveness scores of the new painkiller as sample 1 and the effectiveness scores of aspirin as sample 2. Because we want to know whether the new painkiller is better than aspirin, the alternative hypothesis is

H_1:   The location of population 1 is to the right of the location of population 2.

We specify the null hypothesis as

H_0:   The two population locations are the same.

COMPUTE

MANUALLY:

If the alternative hypothesis is true, the location of population 1 will be located to the right of the location of population 2. It follows that T and z would be large. Our job is to determine whether z is large enough to reject the null hypothesis in favor of the alternative hypothesis. Thus, the rejection region is

$$z > z_\alpha = z_{.05} = 1.645$$

We compute the test statistic by ranking all the observations.

New Painkiller	Rank	Aspirin	Rank
3	12	4	19.5
5	27	1	2
4	19.5	3	12
3	12	2	6
2	6	4	19.5
5	27	1	2
1	2	3	12
4	19.5	4	19.5
5	27	2	6
3	12	2	6
3	12	2	6
5	27	4	19.5
5	27	3	12
5	27	4	19.5
4	19.5	5	27
	$T_1 = 276.5$		$T_2 = 188.5$

Notice that three "ones" occupy ranks 1, 2, and 3. The average is 2. Thus, each "one" is assigned a rank of 2. There are five "twos" whose ranks are 4, 5, 6, 7, and 8, the average of which is 6. We continue until all the observations have been similarly ranked. The rank sums are computed with $T_1 = 276.5$ and $T_2 = 188.5$. The unstandardized test statistic is $T = T_1 = 276.5$. To standardize, we determine $E(T)$ and σ_T as follows.

$$E(T) = \frac{n_1(n_1 + n_2 + 1)}{2} = \frac{15(31)}{2} = 232.5$$

$$\sigma_T = \sqrt{\frac{n_1 n_2(n_1 + n_2 + 1)}{12}} = \sqrt{\frac{(15)(15)(31)}{12}} = 24.1$$

The standardized test statistic is calculated next:

$$z = \frac{T - E(T)}{\sigma_T} = \frac{276.5 - 232.5}{24.1} = 1.83$$

The p-value of the test is

$$p\text{-value} = P(Z > 1.83) = 1 - .9664 = .0336$$

Do It Yourself Excel

	A	B	C	D
1	New Painkiller	Aspirin	Rank: New Painkiller	Rank: Aspririn
2	3	4	12	19.5
3	5	1	27	2
4	4	3	19.5	12
5	3	2	12	6
6	2	4	6	19.5
7	5	1	27	2
8	1	3	2	12
9	4	4	19.5	19.5
10	5	2	27	6
11	3	2	12	6
12	3	2	12	6
13	5	4	27	19.5
14	5	3	27	12
15	5	4	27	19.5
16	4	5	19.5	27
17			276.5	188.5

Excel Workbook

	A	B	C	D
1	Wilcoxon Rank Sum Test			
2	Sample 1 Size	15	z Stat	1.83
3	Sample 2 Size	15	P(Z<=z) one-tail	0.0340
4	Test Statistic T	276.5	z Critical one-tail	1.6449
5	Expected Value	232.50	P(Z<=z) two-tail	0.0680
6	Standard Deviation	24.11	z Critical two-tail	1.9600
7	Alpha	0.05		

INSTRUCTIONS

1. Type or import the observations into two columns. (Open Xm19-02.)

2. Compute the ranks for each observation using the Excel function **RANK.AVG**. Specify the number whose rank you are computing, the range of the data, and the order of the ranking. In this example type into cell C2

    =RANK.AVG(A2, $A$2:$B$16,1)

    which calculates the rank of the number in cell A2; the range is $A$2:$B$16 and "1" specifies the order is smallest to largest. If more than one value has the same rank, the average rank is returned. After determining the rank of each value, calculate the rank sums. The T statistic is the sum of the ranks of sample 1, which in this example is $T_1 = 276.5$.

3. To compute the z statistic and p-value, open the **Nonparametric Techniques** workbook and select the **Wilcoxon Rank Sum Test**. Type the sample sizes, test statistic T, and a value for α.

INTERPRET

The test statistic is $z = 1.83$. The p-value is .0340. There is enough evidence to infer that the new painkiller is perceived to be more effective than aspirin.

Excel Instructions for Stacked Data

Stacked data is the format wherein the observations of the variable are in one column and the codes that identify from which sample the corresponding observation was drawn are in a second column. For example, suppose that the observations are in A1:A30 and the codes (say, 1 and 2) are in B1:B30. Type into cell C1

=RANK.AVG(A1,A$1:A$30,1)

and drag to complete column C. To calculate the rank sums, type into any empty cell

=SUMIF(B1:B30,"1",C1:C30)

This function computes the sum of the values in column C where the corresponding value in column B is the code 1. Repeat for code 2.

As we pointed out in the introduction to this chapter, the Wilcoxon Rank Sum Test is used to compare two populations when the data are either ordinal or interval. Example 19.2 illustrated the use of the Wilcoxon Rank Sum Test when the data are ordinal. In the next example we demonstrate its use when the data are interval.

EXAMPLE 19.3

DATA
Xm19-03

Retaining Workers

Because of the high cost of hiring and training new employees, employers would like to ensure that they retain highly qualified workers. To help develop a hiring program, the human resources manager of a large company wanted to compare how long business and nonbusiness university graduates worked for the company before quitting to accept a position elsewhere. The manager selected a random sample of 25 business and 20 nonbusiness graduates who had been hired 5 years ago. The number of months each had worked for the company was recorded. (Those who had not quit were recorded as having worked for 60 months.) The data are listed below. Can the human resources manager conclude at the 5% significance level that a difference in duration of employment exists between business and nonbusiness graduates?

Duration of Employment (Months)

Business Graduates	Nonbusiness Graduates
60 11 18 19 5 25 60 7 8 17 37 4 8	25 60 22 24 23 36 39 15 35 16 28
28 27 11 60 25 5 13 22 11 17 9 4	9 60 29 16 22 60 17 60 32

SOLUTION:

IDENTIFY

The problem objective is to compare two populations whose data are interval. The samples are independent. Thus, the appropriate parametric technique is the t-test of $\mu_1 - \mu_2$, which requires that the populations be normally distributed. However, when the histograms are drawn (see Figures 19.5 and 19.6), it becomes clear that this requirement is unsatisfied. It follows that the correct statistical procedure is the Wilcoxon Rank Sum Test. The null and alternative hypotheses are

H_0: The two population locations are the same.

H_1: The location of population 1 (business graduates) is different from the location of population 2 (nonbusiness graduates).

FIGURE **19.5**   Histogram of Length of Employment of Business Graduates
in Retaining Workers Example

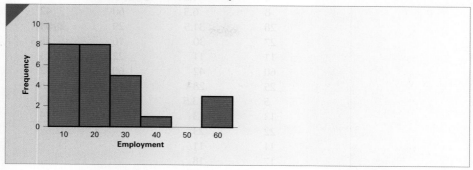

FIGURE **19.6**   Histogram of Length of Employment of Nonbusiness Graduates
in Retaining Workers Example

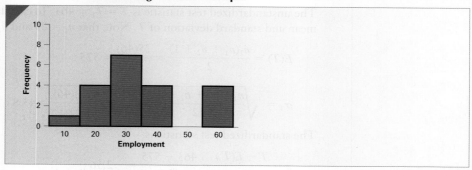

COMPUTE

MANUALLY:

The rejection region is

$$z < -z_{\alpha/2} = -z_{.025} = -1.96 \quad \text{or} \quad z > z_{\alpha/2} = z_{.025} = 1.96$$

We calculate the value of the test statistic in the following way.

Business	Rank	Nonbusiness	Rank
60	42	25	28
11	11	60	42
18	20	22	23
19	21	24	26
5	3.5	23	25
25	28	36	36
60	42	39	38
7	5	15	14
8	6.5	35	35
17	18	16	15.5
37	37	28	31.5

(Continued)

Business	Rank	Nonbusiness	Rank
4	1.5	9	8.5
8	6.5	60	42
28	31.5	29	33
27	30	16	15.5
11	11	22	23
60	42	60	42
25	28	17	18
5	3.5	60	42
13	13	32	34
22	23		$T_2 = 572$
11	11		
17	18		
9	8.5		
4	1.5		
	$T_1 = 463$		

The unstandardized test statistic is $T = T_1 = 463$. To calculate z, we first determine the mean and standard deviation of T. Note that $n_1 = 25$ and $n_2 = 20$.

$$E(T) = \frac{n_1(n_1 + n_2 + 1)}{2} = \frac{25(46)}{2} = 575$$

$$\sigma_T = \sqrt{\frac{n_1 n_2(n_1 + n_2 + 1)}{12}} = \sqrt{\frac{(25)(20)(46)}{12}} = 43.8$$

The standardized test statistic is

$$z = \frac{T - E(T)}{\sigma_T} = \frac{463 - 575}{43.8} = -2.56$$

$$p\text{-value} = 2P(Z < -2.56) = 2(1 - .9948) = .0104$$

Do It Yourself Excel

We used the RANK.AVG function to compute $T_1 = 463$. The **Wilcoxon Rank Sum Test** in the **Nonparametric Techniques** workbook produced this output.

Excel Workbook

	A	B	C	D
1	Wilcoxon Rank Sum Test			
2	Sample 1 Size	25	z Stat	-2.56
3	Sample 2 Size	20	P(Z<=z) one-tail	0.0053
4	Test Statistic T	463	z Critical one-tail	1.6449
5	Expected Value	575.00	P(Z<=z) two-tail	0.0105
6	Standard Deviation	43.78	z Critical two-tail	1.9600
7	Alpha	0.05		

INTERPRET

$z = -2.56$, p-value $= .0105$. There is sufficient evidence to conclude that the duration of employment is different for business and nonbusiness graduates.

19-1a Required Conditions

The Wilcoxon Rank Sum Test (like the other nonparametric tests presented in this chapter) actually tests to determine whether the population *distributions* are identical. This means that it tests not only for identical locations but also for identical spreads (variances) and shapes (distributions). Unfortunately, this means that the rejection of the null hypothesis may not necessarily signify a difference in population locations. The rejection of the null hypothesis may result instead from a difference in distribution shapes or spreads. To avoid this problem, we will require that the two probability distributions be identical except with respect to location, which then becomes the sole focus of the test. This requirement is made for the tests introduced in the next two sections (sign test, Wilcoxon Signed Rank Sum Test, Kruskal–Wallis Test, and Friedman Test).

Both histograms (Figures 19.5 and 19.6) are approximately bimodal. Although there are differences between them, it would appear that the required condition for the use of the Wilcoxon Rank Sum Test is roughly satisfied in the example about retaining workers.

19-1b Developing an Understanding of Statistical Concepts

When applying nonparametric techniques, we do not perform any calculations using the original data. Instead, we perform computations only on the ranks. (We determine the rank sums and use them to make our decision.) As a result, we do not care about the actual distribution of the data (hence the name *distribution-free techniques*), and we do not specify parameters in the hypotheses (hence the name *nonparametric techniques*). Although there are other techniques that do not specify parameters in the hypotheses, we use the term *nonparametric* for procedures that feature these concepts.

Here is a summary of how to identify the Wilcoxon Rank Sum Test.

Factors That Identify the Wilcoxon Rank Sum

1. **Problem objective**: Compare two populations.
2. **Data type**: Ordinal or interval but nonnormal
3. **Experimental design**: Independent samples

EXERCISES

Developing an Understanding of Statistical Concepts

Exercises 19.1 and 19.2 are "what-if" analyses designed to determine what happens to the test statistics and p-values when elements of the statistical inference change. These problems can be solved manually or by creating an Excel spreadsheet.

19.1 a. Given the following statistics calculate the value of the test statistic to determine whether the population locations differ.

$$T_1 = 250 \qquad n_1 = 15$$
$$T_2 = 215 \qquad n_2 = 15$$

b. Repeat part (a) with $T_1 = 275$ and $T_2 = 190$.

c. Describe the effect on the test statistic of increasing T_1 to 275.

19.2 a. From the following statistics, test (with $\alpha = .05$) to determine whether the location of population 1 is to the right of the location of population 2.

$$T_1 = 1,205 \qquad n_1 = 30$$
$$T_2 = 1,280 \qquad n_2 = 40$$

b. Repeat part (a) with $T_1 = 1,065$.

c. Discuss the effect on the test statistic and p-value of decreasing T_1 to 1,065.

19.3 Xr19-03 Use the Wilcoxon Rank Sum Test on the following data to determine whether the location of population 1 is to the left of the location of population 2. (Use $\alpha = .05$.)

Sample 1:   75   60   73   66   81
Sample 2:   90   72   103   82   78

19.4 Xr19-04 Use the Wilcoxon Rank Sum Test on the following data to determine whether the two population locations differ. (Use a 10% significance level.)

Sample 1:   15   7   22   20   32   18   26   17   23   30
Sample 2:   8   27   17   25   20   16   21   17   10   18

Exercises 19.5 to 19.34 require the use of a computer and software.
Conduct tests of hypotheses at the 5% significance level.

19.5 a. Xr19-05a In a taste test of a new beer, 25 people rated the new beer and another 25 rated the leading brand on the market. The possible ratings were Poor, Fair, Good, Very Good, and Excellent. The responses for the new beer and the leading beer were stored using a 1-2-3-4-5 coding system. Can we infer that the new beer is less highly rated than the leading brand?

b. Xr19-05b The responses were recoded so that 3 = Poor, 8 = Fair, 22 = Good, 37 = Very Good, and 55 = Excellent. Can we infer that the new beer is less highly rated than the leading brand?

c. What does this exercise tell you about ordinal data?

19.6 a. Xr19-06a To determine whether the satisfaction rating of an airline differs between business class and economy class, a survey was performed. Random samples of both groups were asked to rate their satisfaction with the quality of service using the following responses:

Very satisfied
Quite satisfied
Somewhat satisfied
Neither satisfied nor dissatisfied
Somewhat dissatisfied
Quite dissatisfied
Very dissatisfied

Using a 7-6-5-4-3-2-1 coding system, the results were recorded. Can we infer that business and economy class differ in their degree of satisfaction with the service?

b. Xr19-06b The responses were recoded using the values 88-67-39-36-25-21-18. Can we infer that business and economy class differ in their degree of satisfaction with the service?

c. What is the effect of changing the codes? Why was this expected?

19.7 a. Xr19-07 Refer to Example 19.2. Suppose that the responses were coded as follows:

100 = The drug was extremely effective.
60 = The drug was quite effective.
40 = The drug was somewhat effective.
35 = The drug was slightly effective.
10 = The drug was not at all effective.

Determine whether we can infer that the new painkiller is more effective than aspirin.

b. Why are the results of Example 19.2 and part (a) identical?

Applications

19.8 Xr19-08 A survey of statistics professors asked them to rate the importance of teaching nonparametric techniques. The possible responses are

Very important
Quite important
Somewhat important
Not too important
Not important at all

The professors were classified as either a member of the Mathematics Department or a member of some other department. The responses were coded (codes 5, 4, 3, 2, and 1, respectively) and recorded. Can we infer that members of the Mathematics Department rate nonparametric techniques as more important than do members of other departments?

19.9 Xr19-09 In recent years, insurance companies offering medical coverage have given discounts to companies that are committed to improving the health of their employees. To help determine whether this policy is reasonable, the general manager of one large insurance company organized a study of a random sample of 30 workers who regularly participate in their company's lunchtime exercise program and 30 workers who do not. Over a 2-year period he observed the total dollar amount of medical expenses for each individual. Can the manager conclude that companies that provide exercise programs should be given discounts?

19.10 Xr19-10 Feminist organizations often use the issue of who does the housework in two-career families as a gauge of equality. Suppose that a study was undertaken and a random sample of 125 two-career families was taken. The wives were asked to report the number of hours of housework they performed the previous week. The results, together with the responses from a survey performed last year (with a different sample of two-career families), were recorded. Can we conclude that women are doing less housework today than last year?

19.11 <u>Xr19-11</u> The American public's support for the space program is important for the program's continuation and for the financial health of the aerospace industry. In a poll conducted by the Gallup organization last year, a random sample of 100 Americans was asked, "Should the amount of money being spent on the space program be increased or kept at current levels (3), decreased (2), or ended altogether (1)?" The survey was conducted again this year. The results were recorded using the codes in parentheses. Can we conclude that public support decreased between this year and last year?

19.12 <u>Xr19-12</u> Certain drugs differ in their side effects depending on the gender of the patient. In a study to determine whether men or women suffer more serious side effects when taking a powerful penicillin substitute, 50 men and 50 women were given the drug. Each was asked to evaluate the level of stomach upset on a 4-point scale, where 4 = extremely upset, 3 = somewhat upset, 2 = not too upset, and 1 = not upset at all. Can we conclude that men and women experience different levels of stomach upset from the drug?

19.13 <u>Xr19-13</u> The president of Tastee Inc., a baby-food producer, claims that Tastee is superior to that of the leading competitor because babies gain weight faster with her product. As an experiment, 40 healthy newborn infants are randomly selected. For two months, 15 of the babies are fed Tastee baby food and the other 25 are fed the competitor's product. Each baby's weight gain (in ounces) was recorded. If we use weight gain as our criterion, can we conclude that Tastee baby food is indeed superior? (This exercise is identical to Exercise 13.17 except for the data.)

19.14 <u>Xr19-14</u> Do the ways that women dress influence the ways that other women judge them? This question was addressed by a researcher at Ohio State University. The experiment consisted of asking women to rate how professional two women looked. One woman wore a size 6 dress and the other wore a size 14. Suppose that the researcher asked 20 women to rate the woman wearing the size 6 dress and another 20 to rate the woman wearing the size 14 dress. The ratings were as follows:

4 = Highly professional
3 = Somewhat professional
2 = Not very professional
1 = Not at all professional

Do these data provide sufficient evidence to infer that women perceive another woman wearing a size 6 dress as more professional than one wearing a size 14 dress?

19.15 <u>Xr19-15</u> The image of the lowly prune is not very good. It is perceived as a product used by seniors to help avoid constipation. However, in reality it is a nutritious and (for many) a tasty treat. To help improve the image of the prune, a company that produces the product decided to see the effect of changing its name to dried plums (which is what a prune is). To gauge the effect, a random sample of shoppers was asked how likely it was that they would purchase the product. Half the sample was shown a package that identified its contents as prunes. The other half was shown packages labeled dried plums. The responses are

Highly unlikely (1)
Somewhat unlikely (2)
Somewhat likely (3)
Highly likely (4)

Can we infer from these data that changing the name of prunes to dried plums increases the likelihood that shoppers will buy the product?

19.16 <u>Xr13-44+</u> Refer to Exercise 13.44 where respondents were asked to taste the same wine in two different bottles. The first bottle was capped using a cork, and the second had a metal screw cap. Respondents were also asked to taste the wine and rate it using the following categories.

1 = Poor
2 = Fair
3 = Good
4 = Very good
5 = Excellent

Do these data provide sufficient evidence to infer that wine bottled with a screw cap is perceived to be inferior?

GENERAL SOCIAL SURVEY EXERCISES

<u>GSS2018</u> *Exercises 19.17 to 19.27 are based on the 2018 survey.*

In Exercises 19.17 to 19.19, test to determine whether men and women differ with respect to the indicated variable.

19.17 Thinking about the next 12 months, how likely do you think it is that you will lose your job or be laid off (JOBLOSE: 1 = Very likely, 2 = Fairly likely, 3 = Not too likely, 4 = Not likely)?

19.18 About how easy would it be for you to find a job with another employer with approximately the same income and fringe benefits you now have

(JOBFIND: 1 = Very easy, 2 = Somewhat easy, 3 = Not easy)?

19.19 On the whole, how satisfied are you with the work you do (SATJOB: 1 = Very satisfied, 2 = Moderately satisfied, 3 = A little dissatisfied, 4 = Very dissatisfied)?

In Exercises 19.20 to 19.22, test to determine whether there is enough evidence to infer that there are differences in perception between people born in the United States and foreign-born Americans (BORN: 1 = U.S., 2 = Elsewhere).

19.20 Thinking about the next 12 months, how likely do you think it is that you will lose your job or be laid off (JOBLOSE: 1 = Very likely, 2 = Fairly likely, 3 = Not too likely, 4 = Not likely)?

19.21 About how easy would it be for you to find a job with another employer with approximately the same income and fringe benefits you now have (JOBFIND: 1 = Very easy, 2 = Somewhat easy, 3 = Not easy)?

19.22 On the whole, how satisfied are you with the work you do (SATJOB: 1 = Very satisfied, 2 = Moderately satisfied, 3 = A little dissatisfied, 4 = Very dissatisfied)?

19.23 Do public sector workers (WRKGOVT: 1 = Government, 2 = Private) believe that they are less likely to lose their jobs in the next 12 months than private sector employees (JOBLOSE: 1 = Very likely, 2 = Fairly likely, 3 = Not too likely, 4 = Not likely)?

19.24 Almost everyone dreams of being rich enough to quit working. Respondents were asked, "If you were to get enough money to live as comfortably as you would like for the rest of your life, would you continue to work, or would you stop working (RICHWORK: 1 = Continue working, 2 = Stop working)?" Is there enough evidence to conclude that those who would continue working have greater job satisfaction than those who would stop working (SATJOB: 1 = Very satisfied, 2 = Moderately satisfied, 3 = A little dissatisfied, 4 = Very dissatisfied)?

19.25 Do Democrats and Republicans (PARTYID3: 1 = Democrat, 3 = Republican) differ in their views about the federal income tax that they have to pay (TAX: Do you consider the amount of federal income tax which you have to pay as too high, about right, or too low: 1 = Too high, 2 = About right, 3 = Too low)?

19.26 Refer to Exercise 19.25. Is there sufficient evidence to infer that people who work for themselves (WRKSLF: 1 = Self-employed, 2 = Work for someone else) differ from those who work for someone else with respect to how they describe the federal income tax they have to pay?

19.27 It is well known that on average women live about 4 years longer than men. However, are they healthier? Conduct a test to determine if women (SEX: 1 = Male, 2 = Female) consider themselves to be healthier than men (HEALTH: 1 = Excellent, 2 = Good, 3 = Fair, 4 = Poor).

GSS2016 GSS2018 *Exercises 19.28 to 19.32 compare various aspects of 2016 and 2018.*

19.28 Is there sufficient evidence to infer that Americans were healthier (HEALTH: 1 = Excellent, 2 = Good, 3 = Fair, 4 = Poor) in 2018 than in 2016?

19.29 Were Americans more worried about their chances of losing their jobs (JOBLOSE: 1 = Very likely, 2 = Fairly likely, 3 = Not too likely, 4 = Not likely) in 2016 than in 2018?

19.30 Were Americans more optimistic about their children's standard of living (KIDSSOL: When your children are at the age you are now, do you think their standard of living will be 1 = Much better, 2 = Somewhat better, 3 = About the same, 4 = Somewhat worse, or 5 = Much worse than your standard of living is now) in 2018 than they were in 2016?

19.31 Studies indicate that Americans are becoming less trusting of the media. Does this mean that they read newspapers less frequently in 2018 than in 2016 (NEWS: Do you read newspapers... 1 = Every day, 2 = Few times per week, 3 = Once per week, 4 = Less than once per week, 5 = Never)? Conduct a test to answer the question.

19.32 The economy was booming in 2018. Did this make people happier? Conduct a test to determine whether there is enough evidence to infer that Americans were happier in 2018 than in 2016 (HAPPY: Taken altogether, how would you say things are these days would you say you are ... 1 = Very happy, 2 = Pretty happy, 3 = Not too happy).

Survey of Consumer Finances Exercises

19.33 The education (EDUC) variable in the General Social Survey is the number of years of education. In the Survey of Consumer Finances, the education (EDUC) variable is defined as follows:

EDUC: -1 = Less than first grade, 1 = 1–4 grades, 2 = 5 or 6 grades, 3 = 7 or 8 grades, 4 = 9th grade, 5 = 10th grade, 6 = 11th grade, 7 = 12th grade but no diploma, 8 = High school graduate or equivalent, 9 = Some college but no degree, 10 = Associate degree or occupation/vocation program, 11 = Associate degree-academic program, 12 = Bachelor's

degree, 13 = Master's degree, 14 = Doctorate or professional school degree.

Is this variable interval (as in the General Social Survey) or ordinal? Explain.

SCF2019:\MC *The following exercise is based on the middle-class subsample of the 2019 survey.*

19.34 Is there sufficient evidence to infer that in middle-class households, female heads of household have more education than male heads of households?

19-2 / Sign Test and Wilcoxon Signed Rank Sum Test

In the preceding section, we discussed the nonparametric technique for comparing two populations of data that are either ordinal or interval (nonnormal) and where the data are independently drawn. In this section, the problem objective and data type remain as they were in Section 19-1, but we will be working with data generated from a matched pairs experiment. We have dealt with this type of experiment before. In Section 13-3, we dealt with the mean of the paired differences represented by the parameter μ_D. In this section, we introduce two nonparametric techniques that test hypotheses in problems with the following characteristics:

1. The problem objective is to compare two populations.

2. The data are either ordinal or interval (where the normality requirement necessary to perform the parametric test is unsatisfied).

3. The samples are matched pairs.

To extract all the potential information from a matched pairs experiment, we must create the matched pair differences. Recall that we did so when conducting the t-test and estimate of μ_D. We then calculated the mean and standard deviation of these differences and determined the test statistic and confidence interval estimator. The first step in both nonparametric methods presented here is the same: Compute the differences for each pair of observations. However, if the data are ordinal, we cannot perform any calculations on those differences because differences between ordinal values have no meaning.

To understand this point, consider comparing two populations of responses of people rating a product or service. The responses are "excellent," "good," "fair," and "poor." Recall that we can assign any numbering system as long as the order is maintained. The simplest system is 4-3-2-1. However, any other system such as 66-38-25-11 (or another set of numbers of decreasing order) is equally valid. Now suppose that in one matched pair the sample 1 response was "excellent" and the sample 2 response was "good." Calculating the matched pairs difference under the 4-3-2-1 system gives a difference of $4 - 3 = 1$. Using the 66-38-25-11 system gives a difference of $66 - 38 = 28$. If we treat this and other differences as real numbers, we are likely to produce different results depending on which numbering system we used. Thus, we cannot use any method that uses the actual differences. However, we can use the sign of the differences. In fact, when the data are ordinal that is the only method that is valid. In other words, no matter what numbering system is used we know that "excellent" is better than "good." In the 4-3-2-1 system the difference between "excellent" and "good" is +1. In the 66-38-25-11 system the difference is +28. If we ignore the magnitude of the number and record only the sign, the two numbering systems (and all other systems where the rank order is maintained) will produce exactly the same result.

As you will shortly discover, the sign test uses only the sign of the differences. That's why it's called the *sign test*.

When the data are interval, however, differences have real meaning. Although we can use the sign test when the data are interval, doing so results in a loss of potentially useful information. For example, knowing that the difference in sales between two matched used-car salespeople is 25 cars is much more informative than simply knowing that the first salesperson sold more cars than the second salesperson. As a result, when the data are interval, but not normal, we will use the *Wilcoxon Signed Rank Sum Test*, which incorporates not only the sign of the difference (hence the name) but also the magnitude.

19-2a Sign Test

The **sign test** is employed in the following situations:

1. The problem objective is to compare two populations.

2. The data are ordinal.

3. The experimental design is matched pairs.

19-2b Test Statistic and Sampling Distribution

The sign test is quite simple. For each matched pair, we calculate the difference between the observation in sample 1 and the related observation in sample 2. We then count the number of positive differences and the number of negative differences. If the null hypothesis is true, we expect the number of positive differences to be approximately equal to the number of negative differences. Expressed another way, we expect the number of positive differences and the number of negative differences each to be approximately equal to half the total sample size. If either number is too large or too small, we reject the null hypothesis. By now you know that the determination of what is too large or too small comes from the sampling distribution of the test statistic. We will arbitrarily choose the test statistic to be the number of positive differences, which we denote x. The test statistic x is a binomial random variable, and under the null hypothesis, the binomial proportion is $p = .5$. Thus, the sign test is none other than the z-test of p introduced in Section 12-3.

Recall from Sections 7-4 and 9-2 that x is binomially distributed and that, for sufficiently large n, x is approximately normally distributed with mean $\mu = np$ and standard deviation $\sqrt{np(1 - p)}$. Thus, the standardized test statistic is

$$z = \frac{x - np}{\sqrt{np(1 - p)}}$$

The null hypothesis

H_0:   The two population locations are the same

is equivalent to testing

H_0: $p = .5$

Therefore, the test statistic, assuming that the null hypothesis is true, becomes

$$z = \frac{x - np}{\sqrt{np(1 - p)}} = \frac{x - .5n}{\sqrt{n(.5)(.5)}} = \frac{x - .5n}{.5\sqrt{n}}$$

The normal approximation of the binomial distribution is valid when $np \geq 5$ and $n(1 - p) \geq 5$. When $p = .5$,

$$np = n(.5) \geq 5$$

and

$$n(1 - p) = n(1 - .5) = n(.5) \geq 5$$

implies that n must be greater than or equal to 10. Thus, this is one of the required conditions of the sign test. However, the quality of the inference with very small sample size is poor. Larger sample sizes are recommended and will be used in the examples and exercises that follow.

It is common practice in this type of test to eliminate the matched pairs of observations when the differences equal 0. Consequently, n equals the number of nonzero differences in the sample.

EXAMPLE 19.4

DATA
Xm19-04

Comparing the Comfort of Two Midsize Cars

In an experiment to determine which of two cars is perceived to have the more comfortable ride, 25 people rode (separately) in the back seat of an expensive European model and also in the back seat of a North American midsize car. Each of the 25 people was asked to rate the ride on the following 5-point scale:

1 = Ride is very uncomfortable.
2 = Ride is quite uncomfortable.
3 = Ride is neither uncomfortable nor comfortable.
4 = Ride is quite comfortable.
5 = Ride is very comfortable.

The results are shown here. Do these data allow us to conclude at the 5% significance level that the European car is perceived to be more comfortable than the North American car?

	Comfort Ratings	
Respondent	European Car	North American Car
1	3	4
2	2	1
3	5	4
4	3	2

| | Comfort Ratings | |
Respondent	European Car	North American Car
5	2	1
6	5	3
7	2	3
8	4	2
9	4	2
10	2	2
11	2	1
12	3	4
13	2	1
14	3	4
15	2	1
16	4	3
17	5	4
18	2	3
19	5	4
20	3	1
21	4	2
22	3	3
23	3	4
24	5	2
25	5	3

SOLUTION:

IDENTIFY

The problem objective is to compare two populations of ordinal data. Because the same 25 people rated both cars, we recognize the experimental design as matched pairs. The sign test is applied, with the following hypotheses:

H_0:   The two population locations are the same.

H_1:   The location of population 1 (European car rating) is to the right of the location of population 2 (North American car rating).

COMPUTE

MANUALLY:

The rejection region is

$$z > z_\alpha = z_{.05} = 1.645$$

To calculate the value of the test statistic, we calculate the paired differences and count the number of positive, negative, and zero differences. The matched pairs differences are

−1   1   1   1   1   2   −1   2   2   0   1   −1   1

−1   1   1   1   −1   1   2   2   0   −1   3   2

There are 17 positive, 6 negative, and 2 zero differences. Thus, $x = 17$ and $n = 23$. The value of the test statistic is

$$z = \frac{x - .5n}{.5\sqrt{n}} = \frac{17 - .5(23)}{.5\sqrt{23}} = 2.29$$

Because the test statistic is normally distributed, we can calculate the p-value of the test:

$$p\text{-value} = P(Z > 2.29) = 1 - .9890 = .0110.$$

Do It Yourself Excel

Excel Workbook

	A	B	C	D	E	F
1	Sign Test					
2			Binomial Probability		Normal Approximation	
3	Positive Differences	17	Test Statistic X	17	z Stat	2.29
4	Negative Differences	6	P(X>= x) one-tail	0.0173	P(Z<=z) one-tail	0.0109
5	Total	23	P(X>= x) two-tail	0.0347	z Critical one-tail	1.6449
6	Alpha	0.05			P(Z<=z) two-tail	0.0218
7					z Critical two-tail	1.9600

INSTRUCTIONS

1. Type or import the data into two columns. (Open Xm19-04.)

2. Calculate the paired differences.

3. Determine the number of positive differences and negative differences using the **IF** function.

   Assuming that the paired differences are in column D, type into cell E2

   =IF(D2>0,1,0)

   and in cell F2

   =IF(D2<0,1,0)

   Drag to complete columns E and F. Column E lists 1s when the paired differences are positive and 0 when the differences are not positive. Column F lists 1s when the paired differences are negative and 0 when the differences are not negative.

4. Sum columns E and F. The results are the number of positive differences and negative differences.

5. To compute the test statistic and p-value open the **Nonparametric Techniques** workbook and select the **Sign Test**. Type the number of positive differences and negative differences sample sizes, and a value for α.

   For computer users, we recommend that you use the exact binomial distribution to determine the p-value. Because this is a one-tail (right-tail) test, the p-value is

   $$P(X \geq 17)$$

   where X is binomial with $n = 23$ and $p = .5$. Using the BINOMDIST function we calculate the p-value as

   $$p\text{-value} = P(X \geq 17) = 1 - P(X \leq 16) = 1 - .9827 = .0173$$

INTERPRET

The *p*-value of the manually calculated test statistic is .0110. The *p*-value of the Excel-computed test statistic is .0173. There is enough evidence to infer that people perceive the European car as providing a more comfortable ride than the North American car.

19-2c Checking the Required Conditions

As we noted in Section 19-1, the sign test requires that the populations be identical in shape and spread. The histogram of the ratings for the European car (Figure 19.7) suggests that the ratings may be uniformly distributed between 2 and 5. The histogram of the ratings for the North American car (Figure 19.8) seems to indicate that the ratings are uniformly distributed between 1 and 4. Thus, both sets of ratings have the same shape and spread but their locations differ. The other condition is that the sample size exceeds 10.

FIGURE **19.7** Histogram of Ratings of European Car in Example 19.4

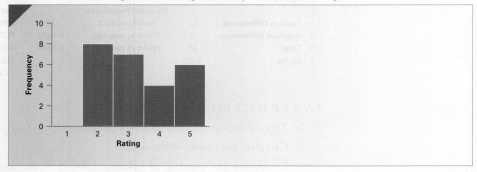

FIGURE **19.8** Histogram of Ratings of North American Car in Example 19.4

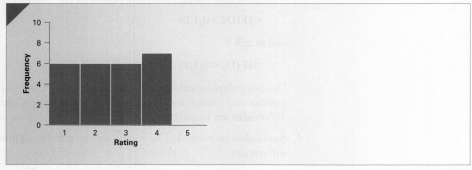

19-2d Wilcoxon Signed Rank Sum Test

The **Wilcoxon Signed Rank Sum Test** is used under the following circumstances:

1. The problem objective is to compare two populations.

2. The data (matched pairs differences) are interval, but not normally distributed.

3. The samples are matched pairs.

The Wilcoxon Signed Rank Sum Test is the nonparametric counterpart of the t-test of μ_D. Because the data are interval, we can refer to the Wilcoxon Signed Rank Sum Test as a test of μ_D. However, to be consistent with the other nonparametric techniques and to avoid confusion, we will express the hypotheses to be tested in the same way as we did in Section 19-1.

19-2e Test Statistic and Sampling Distribution

We begin by computing the paired differences. As we did in the sign test, we eliminate all differences that are equal to 0. Next, we rank the absolute values of the nonzero differences where 1 = smallest value and n = largest value, with n = number of nonzero differences. (We average the ranks of tied observations.) The sum of the ranks of the positive differences (denoted T^+) and the sum of the ranks of the negative differences (denoted T^-) are then calculated. We arbitrarily select T^+, which we label T, as our test statistic.

For relatively small samples, which we define as $n \leq 30$, the critical values of T can be determined from Table 10 in Appendix B (reproduced here as Table 19.4). This table lists values of T_L and T_U for sample sizes between 6 and 30. The values of T_L and T_U in part (a) of the table are such that

$$P(T \leq T_L) = P(T \geq T_U) = .025$$

The values of T_L and T_U in part (b) of the table are such that

$$P(T \leq T_L) = P(T \geq T_U) = .05$$

Part (a) is used either in a two-tail test with $\alpha = .05$ or in a one-tail test with $\alpha = .025$. Part (b) is employed either in a two-tail test with $\alpha = .10$ or in a one-tail test with $\alpha = .05$.

For relatively large sample sizes (we will define this to mean $n > 30$), T is approximately normally distributed with mean

$$E(T) = \frac{n(n + 1)}{4}$$

and standard deviation

$$\sigma_T = \sqrt{\frac{n(n + 1)(2n + 1)}{24}}$$

Thus, the standardized test statistic is

$$z = \frac{T - E(T)}{\sigma_T}$$

TABLE **19.4** **Critical Values of the Wilcoxon Signed Rank Sum Test**

	(a) $\alpha = .025$ One-Tail $\alpha = .05$ Two-Tail		(b) $\alpha = .05$ One-Tail $\alpha = .10$ Two-Tail	
n	T_L	T_U	T_L	T_U
6	1	20	2	19
7	2	26	4	24
8	4	32	6	30
9	6	39	8	37

(*Continued*)

TABLE **19.4** (Continued)

n	(a) $\alpha = .025$ One-Tail $\alpha = .05$ Two-Tail		(b) $\alpha = .05$ One-Tail $\alpha = .10$ Two-Tail	
	T_L	T_U	T_L	T_U
10	8	47	11	44
11	11	55	14	52
12	14	64	17	61
13	17	74	21	70
14	21	84	26	79
15	25	95	30	90
16	30	106	36	100
17	35	118	41	112
18	40	131	47	124
19	46	144	54	136
20	52	158	60	150
21	59	172	68	163
22	66	187	75	178
23	73	203	83	193
24	81	219	92	208
25	90	235	101	224
26	98	253	110	241
27	107	271	120	258
28	117	289	130	276
29	127	308	141	294
30	137	328	152	313

EXAMPLE 19.5

DATA
Xm19-05

Comparing Flextime and Fixed Time Schedules

Traffic congestion on roads and highways costs industry billions of dollars annually as workers struggle to get to and from work. Several suggestions have been made about how to improve this situation, one of which is called *flextime*—workers are allowed to determine their own schedules (provided they work a full shift). Such workers will likely choose an arrival and departure time to avoid rush-hour traffic. In a preliminary experiment designed to investigate such a program, the general manager of a large company wanted to compare the times it took workers to travel from their homes to work at 8 A.M. with travel time under the flextime program. A random sample of 32 workers was selected. The employees recorded the time (in minutes) it took to arrive at work at 8 A.M. on Wednesday of one week. The following week, the same employees arrived at work at times of their own choosing. The travel time on Wednesday of that week was recorded. These results are listed in the following table. Can we conclude at the 5% significance level that travel times under the flextime program are different from travel times to arrive at work at 8 A.M.?

| Worker | Travel Time | |
	Arrival at 8:00 A.M.	Flextime Program
1	34	31
2	35	31
3	43	44
4	46	44
5	16	15
6	26	28
7	68	63
8	38	39
9	61	63
10	52	54
11	68	65
12	13	12
13	69	71
14	18	13
15	53	55
16	18	19
17	41	38
18	25	23
19	17	14
20	26	21
21	44	40
22	30	33
23	19	18
24	48	51
25	29	33
26	24	21
27	51	50
28	40	38
29	26	22
30	20	19
31	19	21
32	42	38

SOLUTION:

IDENTIFY

The objective is to compare two populations; the data are interval and were produced from a matched pairs experiment. If matched pairs differences are normally distributed, we should apply the t-test of μ_D. To judge whether the data are normal, we computed the paired differences and drew the histogram (actually Excel did). Figure 19.9 depicts this histogram. Apparently, the normality requirement is not satisfied, indicating that we should employ the Wilcoxon Signed Rank Sum Test.

FIGURE **19.9**   Histogram of the Differences for Example 19.5

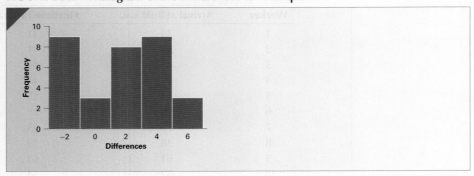

Because we want to know whether the two groups of times differ, we perform a two-tail test whose hypotheses are

H_0:   The two population locations are the same.

H_1:   The location of population 1 (travel times for current work schedule) is different from the location of population 2 (travel times for flextime program).

COMPUTE

MANUALLY:

For each worker, we compute the difference between travel time with arrival at 8 A.M. and travel time under flextime.

| Worker | Travel Time | | Difference | \|Difference\| | Rank | \|Rank\| |
	Arrival at 8:00 A.M.	Flextime Program				
1	34	31	3	3	21.0	
2	35	31	4	4	27.0	
3	43	44	−1	1		4.5
4	46	44	2	2	13.0	
5	16	15	1	1		4.5
6	26	28	−2	2		13.0
7	68	63	5	5	31.0	
8	38	39	−1	1		4.5
9	61	63	−2	2		13.0
10	52	54	−2	2		13.0
11	68	65	3	3	21.0	
12	13	12	1	1		4.5
13	69	71	−2	2		13.0
14	18	13	5	5	31.0	
15	53	55	−2	2		13.0
16	18	19	−1	1		4.5
17	41	38	3	3	21.0	
18	25	23	2	2	13.0	

Worker	Arrival at 8:00 A.M.	Flextime Program	Difference	|Difference|	Rank	|Rank|
		Travel Time				
19	17	14	3	3	21.0	
20	26	21	5	5	31.0	
21	44	40	4	4	27.0	
22	30	33	−3	3		21.0
23	19	18	1	1	4.5	
24	48	51	−3	3		21.0
25	29	33	−4	4		27.0
26	24	21	3	3	21.0	
27	51	50	1	1	4.5	
28	40	38	2	2	13.0	
29	26	22	4	4	27.0	
30	20	19	1	1	4.5	
31	19	21	−2	2		13.0
32	42	38	4	4	27.0	

$$T^+ = 367.5 \quad T^- = 160.5$$

The differences and the absolute values of the differences are calculated. We rank the absolute differences. (If there were any zero differences, we would eliminate them before ranking the absolute differences.) Ties are resolved by calculating the averages. The ranks of the negative differences are offset to facilitate the summing of the ranks. The rank sums of the positive and negative differences are

$$T^+ = 367.5 \quad \text{and} \quad T^- = 160.5$$

The test statistic is

$$z = \frac{T - E(T)}{\sigma_T}$$

where

$$T = T^+ = 367.5$$

$$E(T) = \frac{n(n + 1)}{4} = \frac{32(33)}{4} = 264$$

$$\sigma_T = \sqrt{\frac{n(n + 1)(2n + 1)}{24}} = \sqrt{\frac{32(33)(65)}{24}} = 53.48$$

Thus,

$$z = \frac{T - E(T)}{\sigma_T} = \frac{367.5 - 264}{53.48} = 1.94$$

The rejection region is

$$z < -z_{\alpha/2} = -z_{.025} = -1.96 \quad \text{or} \quad z > z_{\alpha/2} = z_{.025} = 1.96$$

The p-value is $2P(Z > 1.94) = 2(1 - .9738) = .0524$

Do It Yourself Excel

Excel Workbook

	A	B	C	D
1	Wilcoxon Signed Rank Sum Test			
2				
3	Sample Size	32	Z Stat	1.94
4	Test Statistic T	367.5	P(Z<=z) one-tail	0.0265
5	Expected Value	264.00	z Critical one-tail	1.6449
6	Standard Deviation	53.48	P(Z<=z) two-tail	0.0529
7	Alpha	0.05	z Critical two-tail	1.9600

INSTRUCTIONS

1. Type or import the data into two columns. (Open Xm19-05.)

2. Calculate the paired differences. Delete all rows where the paired difference is equal to 0. In a second column, compute the absolute value of the paired differences.

3. Assuming that the absolute values of the paired differences are stored in Column D, type into Column E

   =RANK.AVG(D2, D$2:D$33,1)

   and drag to complete the column.

4. In any empty cell type

   =SUMIF(C2:C33,"<0",E2:E33)

   which will compute the sum of the ranks in column E where the corresponding value in Column C is negative. Repeat for positive paired differences.

   =SUMIF(C2:C33,">0",E2:E33)

5. To compute the test statistic and *p*-value, open the **Nonparametric Techniques** workbook and select the **Wilcoxon Signed Rank Sum Test**. Type the sample size (number of nonzero paired differences) and the test statistic $T = T^+$.

INTERPRET

The value of the test statistic is $z = 1.94$. The *p*-value $= .0529$. There is not enough evidence to infer that flextime commutes are different from the commuting times under the current schedule.

Here is how we recognize when to use the two techniques introduced in this section.

Factors That Identify the Sign Test

1. **Problem objective**: Compare two populations.
2. **Data type**: Ordinal
3. **Experimental design**: Matched pairs

> **Factors That Identify the Wilcoxon Signed Rank Sum Test**
>
> 1. **Problem objective**: Compare two populations.
> 2. **Data type**: Interval
> 3. **Distribution of differences**: Nonnormal
> 4. **Experimental design**: Matched pairs

EXERCISES

19.35 In a matched pairs experiment, if we find 30 negative, 5 zero, and 15 positive differences, perform the sign test to determine whether the two population locations differ. (Use a 5% significance level.)

19.36 Suppose that in a matched pairs experiment we find 28 positive differences, 7 zero differences, and 41 negative differences. Can we infer at the 10% significance level that the location of population 1 is to the left of the location of population 2?

19.37 A matched pairs experiment yielded the following results:

Positive differences: 18

Zero differences: 0

Negative differences: 12

Can we infer at the 5% significance level that the location of population 1 is to the right of the location of population 2?

19.38 Xr19-38   Use the sign test on the following data to determine whether the location of population 1 is to the right of the location of population 2. (Use $\alpha = .05$.)

Pair	1	2	3	4	5	6	7	8	9	10	11	12	13	14	15	16
Sample 1	5	3	4	2	3	4	3	5	4	3	4	5	4	5	3	2
Sample 2	3	2	4	3	3	1	3	4	2	5	1	2	2	3	1	2

19.39 Given the following statistics from a matched pairs experiment, perform the Wilcoxon Signed Rank Sum Test to determine whether we can infer at the 5% significance level that the two population locations differ.

$$T^+ = 660 \quad T^- = 880 \quad n = 55$$

19.40 A matched pairs experiment produced the following statistics. Conduct a Wilcoxon Signed Rank Sum Test to determine whether the location of population 1 is to the right of the location of population 2. (Use $\alpha = .01$.)

$$T^+ = 3,457 \quad T^- = 2,429 \quad n = 108$$

19.41 Perform the Wilcoxon Signed Rank Sum Test for the following matched pairs to determine whether the two population locations differ. (Use $\alpha = .10$.)

Pair	1	2	3	4	5	6
Sample 1	9	12	13	8	7	10
Sample 2	5	10	11	9	3	9

19.42 Xr19-42   Perform the Wilcoxon Signed Rank Sum Test to determine whether the location of population 1 differs from the location of population 2 given the data shown here. (Use $\alpha = .05$.)

Pair	1	2	3	4	5	6	7	8	9	10	11	12
Sample 1	18.2	14.1	24.5	11.9	9.5	12.1	10.9	16.7	19.6	8.4	21.7	23.4
Sample 2	18.2	14.1	23.6	12.1	9.5	11.3	9.7	17.6	19.4	8.1	21.9	21.6

Exercises 19.43 to 19.59 require the use of a computer and software. **Use a 5% significance level, unless specified otherwise.**

Developing an Understanding of Statistical Concepts

19.43 a. Xr19-43a   In a taste test of a new beer 100 people rated the new beer and the leading brand on the market. The possible ratings were Poor, Fair, Good, Very good, and Excellent. The responses for the new beer and the leading beer were recorded using a 1-2-3-4-5 coding system. Can we infer that the new beer is more highly rated than the leading brand?

b. Xr19-43b   The responses were recoded so that 3 = Poor, 8 = Fair, 22 = Good, 37 = Very good, and 55 = Excellent. Can we infer that the new beer is more highly rated than the leading brand?

c. Why are the answers to parts (a) and (b) identical?

19.44 a. Xr19-44a   A random sample of 50 people was asked to rate two brands of ice cream using the following responses:

Delicious

OK

Not bad

Terrible

The responses were converted to codes 4, 3, 2, and 1, respectively. Can we infer that Brand A is preferred?

b. Xr19-44b   The responses were recoded using the values 28-25-16-3. Can we infer that Brand A is preferred?

c. Compare your answers for parts (a) and (b). Are they identical? Explain why.

19.45   Xr19-45   Refer to Example 19.4. Suppose that the responses have been recorded in the following way:

   6 = Ride is very uncomfortable.
 24 = Ride is quite uncomfortable.
 28 = Ride is neither uncomfortable nor comfortable.
 53 = Ride is quite comfortable.
 95 = Ride is very comfortable.

a. Do these data allow us to conclude that the European car is perceived to be more comfortable than the North American car?

b. Compare your answer with that obtained in Example 19.4. Explain why the results are identical.

19.46   a. Xr19-46   Data from a matched pairs experiment were recorded. Use the sign test to determine whether the population locations differ.

b. Repeat part (a) using the Wilcoxon Signed Rank Sum Test.

c. Why do the answers to parts (a) and (b) differ?

19.47   a. Xr19-47   Data from a matched pairs experiment were recorded. Use the sign test to determine whether the population locations differ.

b. Repeat part (a) using the Wilcoxon Signed Rank Sum Test.

c. Why do the results of parts (a) and (b) differ?

Applications

19.48   Xr19-48   Research scientists at a pharmaceutical company have recently developed a new nonprescription sleeping pill. They decide to test its effectiveness by measuring the time it takes for people to fall asleep after taking the pill. Preliminary analysis indicates that the time to fall asleep varies considerably from one person to another. Consequently, they organize the experiment in the following way. A random sample of 100 volunteers who regularly suffer from insomnia is chosen. Each person is given one pill containing the newly developed drug and one placebo. (A placebo is a pill that contains absolutely no medication.) Participants are told to take one pill one night and the second pill one night a week later. (They do not know whether the pill they are taking is the placebo or the new drug, and the order of use is random.) Each participant

is fitted with a device that measures the time until sleep occurs. Can we conclude that the new drug is effective? (This exercise is identical to Exercise 13.198, except for the data.)

19.49   Xr19-49   Suppose that the housework study referred to in Exercise 19.10 was repeated with some changes. In the revised experiment, 60 women were asked last year and again this year how many hours of housework they perform weekly. Can we conclude at the 1% significance level that women as a group are doing less housework now than last year?

19.50   Xr19-50   At the height of the energy shortage during the 1970s, governments were actively seeking ways to persuade consumers to reduce their energy consumption. Among other efforts undertaken, several advertising campaigns were launched. To provide input on how to design effective advertising messages, a poll was taken in which people were asked how concerned they were about shortages of gasoline and electricity. There were four possible responses to the questions:

   Not concerned at all (1)
   Not too concerned (2)
   Somewhat concerned (3)
   Very concerned (4)

A poll of 150 individuals was undertaken. Do these data provide enough evidence to allow us to infer that concern about a gasoline shortage exceeded concern about an electricity shortage?

19.51   Xr19-51   A locksmith is in the process of selecting a new key-cutting machine. If there is a difference in key-cutting speed between the two machines under consideration, the locksmith will purchase the faster one. If there is no difference, he will purchase the cheaper machine. The times (in seconds) required to cut each of the 35 most common types of keys were recorded. What should he do?

19.52   Xr19-52   A large sporting-goods store located in Florida is planning a renovation that will result in an increase in the floor space for one department. The manager of the store has narrowed the choice about which department's floor space to increase to two possibilities: the tennis-equipment department or the swimming-accessories department. The manager would like to enlarge the tennis-equipment department because it is believed that this department improves the overall image of the store. It is decided, however, that if the swimming-accessories department can be shown to have higher gross sales, the manager will choose that department. Each of the two departments' weekly gross sales data for the past 32 weeks were collected. Which department should be enlarged?

19.53 Xr19-53 Does the brand name of an ice cream affect consumers' perceptions of it? The marketing manager of a major dairy pondered this question. It was decided to ask 60 randomly selected people to taste the same flavor of ice cream in two different dishes. The dishes contained exactly the same ice cream but were labeled differently. One was given a name that suggested that its maker was European and sophisticated; the other was given a name that implied that the product was domestic and inexpensive. The tasters were asked to rate each ice cream on a 5-point scale, where $1 =$ Poor, $2 =$ Fair, $3 =$ Good, $4 =$ Very good, and $5 =$ Excellent. Do the results allow the manager to conclude at the 10% significance level that the European brand is preferred?

19.54 Xr19-54 Do children feel less pain than adults? That question was addressed by nursing professors at the University of Alberta and the University of Saskatchewan. Suppose that in a preliminary study, 50 8-year-old children and their mothers were subjected to moderately painful pressure on their hands. Each was asked to rate the level of pain as Very severe (4), Severe (3), Moderate (2), or Weak (1). The data were recorded using the codes in parentheses. Can we conclude at the 1% significance level that children feel less pain than adults?

19.55 Xr19-55 In a study to determine whether gender affects salary offers for graduating MBA students, 45 pairs of students were selected. Each pair consisted of a male and a female student who had almost identical grade-point averages, courses taken, ages, and previous work experience. The highest salary offered to each student upon graduation was recorded. Is there sufficient evidence to allow us to conclude that the salary offers differ between men and women? (This exercise is identical to Exercise 13.203, except for the data.)

19.56 Xr19-56 Admissions officers at universities and colleges face the problem of comparing grades achieved at different high schools. As a step toward developing a more informed interpretation of such grades, an admissions officer at a large state university conducts the following experiment. The records of 100 students from the same local high school (high school 1) who just completed their first year at the university were selected. Each of these students was paired (according to average grade in the last year of high school) with a student from another local high school (high school 2) who also just completed the first year at the university. For each matched pair, the average letter grades ($4 =$ A, $3 =$ B, $2 =$ C, $1 =$ D, or $0 =$ F) in the first year of university study were recorded. Do these results allow us to conclude that, in comparing two students with the same high-school average (one from high school 1 and the other from high school 2), preference in admissions should be given to the student from high school 1?

19.57 Xr19-57 Some movie studios believe that by adding sexually explicit scenes to the home video version of a movie, they can increase the movie's appeal and profitability. A studio decided to test this belief. They organized a study that involved 40 movies that were rated PG-13. Versions of each movie were created by adding scenes that changed the rating to R. The two versions of the movies were then made available to rental shops. For each of the 40 pairs of movies, the total number of rentals in one major city during a 1-week period was recorded.
a. Do these data provide enough evidence to support the belief?
b. As an analyst for a movie studio write a report detailing the statistical analysis.

GENERAL SOCIAL SURVEY EXERCISES

19.58 The survey asked these two questions.
1. Compared to your parents at your age is your standard of living ... (PARSOL: 1 = Much better, 2 = Somewhat better, 3 = About the same, 4 = Somewhat worse, 5 = Much worse)?
2. When your children are at your age will their standard of living be... (KIDSSOL 1 = Much better, 2 = Somewhat better, 3 = About the same, 4 = Somewhat worse, 5 = Much worse)?

Is there enough evidence to infer that Americans are more optimistic about their children than themselves?

19.59 Do married couples typically have the same completed degrees? Conduct a test to determine whether there is enough evidence to conclude that married couples do not have the same degrees (DEGREE, SPDEG, Highest degree completed of respondent and spouse: 0 = Left high school, 1 = High school, 2 = Junior college, 3 = Bachelor's degree, 4 = Graduate).

19-3 / KRUSKAL–WALLIS TEST AND FRIEDMAN TEST

In this section we introduce two statistical procedures designed to compare two or more populations. The first test is the **Kruskal–Wallis Test**, which is applied to problems with the following characteristics:

1. The problem objective is to compare two or more populations.

2. The data are either ordinal or interval, but nonnormal.

3. The samples are independent.

When the data are interval and normal, we use the one-way analysis of variance F-test presented in Section 14-1 to determine whether differences exist. When the data are not normal, we will treat the data as if they were ordinal and employ the Kruskal–Wallis Test.

The second procedure is the **Friedman Test**, which is applied to problems with the following characteristics:

1. The problem objective is to compare two or more populations.

2. The data are either ordinal or interval, but not normal.

3. The data are generated from a randomized block experiment.

The parametric counterpart is the two-way analysis of variance, which we use when the data are interval and normal.

19-3a Hypotheses

The null and alternative hypotheses for both tests are similar to those we specified in the analysis of variance. Because the data are ordinal or are treated as ordinal, we test population locations instead of population means. In all applications of the Kruskal–Wallis Test and the Friedman Test, the null and alternative hypotheses are

H_0: The locations of all k populations are the same.
H_1: At least two population locations differ.

Here, k represents the number of populations to be compared.

19-3b Kruskal–Wallis Test

Test Statistic The test statistic is calculated in a way that closely resembles the way in which the Wilcoxon Rank Sum Test was calculated. The first step is to rank all the observations. As before, 1 = smallest observation and n = largest observation, where $n = n_1 + n_2 + \cdots + n_k$. In case of ties, average the ranks.

If the null hypothesis is true, the ranks should be evenly distributed among the k samples. The degree to which this is true is judged by calculating the rank sums (labeled $T_1, T_2, \ldots, T_k$). The last step is to calculate the test statistic, which is denoted H.

Test Statistic for Kruskal–Wallis Test

$$H = \left[\frac{12}{n(n+1)} \sum_{j=1}^{k} \frac{T_j^2}{n_j} \right] - 3(n+1)$$

Although it is impossible to see from this formula, if the rank sums are similar, the test statistic will be small. As a result, a small value of H supports the null hypothesis. Conversely, if considerable differences exist between the rank sums, the test statistic will be large. To judge the value of H, we need to know its sampling distribution.

Sampling Distribution The distribution of the test statistic can be derived in the same way we derived the sampling distribution of the test statistic in the Wilcoxon Rank Sum Test. In other words, we can list all possible combinations of ranks and their probabilities to yield the sampling distribution. A table of critical values can then be determined. However, this is necessary only for small sample sizes. For sample sizes greater than or equal to 5, the test statistic H is approximately chi-squared distributed with $k - 1$ degrees of freedom. Recall that we introduced the chi-squared distribution in Section 8-4.

Rejection Region and p-Value As we noted previously, large values of H are associated with different population locations. Consequently, we want to reject the null hypothesis if H is sufficiently large. Thus, the rejection region is

$$H > \chi_{\alpha, k-1}^2$$

and the p-value is

$$P(\chi^2 > H)$$

Figure 19.10 describes this sampling distribution and the p-value.

FIGURE **19.10** Sampling Distribution of H

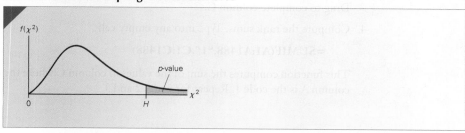

General Social Survey

Do Democrats, Independents, and Republicans Differ in the Number of Times per Week That They Read Newspapers?

SOLUTION:

IDENTIFY

The problem objective is to compare three populations (Democrats, Independents, and Republicans). The data are ordinal and the samples are independent. These factors are sufficient to justify the use of the Kruskal–Wallis test. The null and alternative hypotheses are:

H_0:   The locations of all three populations are the same.

H_1:   At least two population locations differ.

COMPUTE

Do It Yourself Excel

Excel Workbook

	A	B	C	D	E	F	G
1	Kruskal - Wallis Test						
2			Rank Sum	Rank Sum Squared	Rank Sum Squared/sample size		
3	Sample	n_j	T_j	T_j^2	T_j^2/n_j	H	p-value
4	1	484	319,323.5	101,967,497,652.3	210,676,648.0	31.86	0.00000
5	2	652	524,959.5	275,582,476,640.3	422,672,510.2		
6	3	351	262,045.0	68,667,582,025.0	195,634,136.8		
13	Total	1487			828,983,295.0		

INSTRUCTIONS

Stacked Data

1. Type or import the data into two columns, one for the variable (NEWS) and the other identifying the political party (PARTYID3).

2. Delete all rows containing blanks representing missing data. (See the online appendix.)

3. Use the **RANK.AVG** to calculate the ranks. If the data for PARTYID3 are in column A and the data for NEWS are in column B, type into cell C2:

    =RANK.AVG(B2, $B$2:$B$1488, 1)

    Drag to complete column C.

4. Compute the rank sums. Type into any empty cell

    =SUMIF(A1:A1488,"1",C1:C1488)

    This function computes the sum of the values in column C where the corresponding value in column A is the code 1. Repeat for codes 2 and 3.

5. Determine the sample sizes.

For this example, the following statistics were computed. (Output not shown.)

Sample	Sample Size	Rank Sum
1	484	319,323.5
2	652	524,959.5
3	351	262,045

6. To complete the calculations, open the **Nonparametric Techniques** workbook and select the **Kruskal-Wallis Test**. Type the values of the sample sizes and rank sums.

INTERPRET

There is more than enough evidence to infer that the frequency of newspaper reading differs between Democrats, Independents, and Republicans.

Excel Instructions for Unstacked Data

1. If the data are unstacked, type or import the data into adjacent columns.

2. Use the **RANK.AVG** function to compute the ranks. For example, suppose the dataset consists of three columns stored in columns A, B, and C containing 15, 20, and 12 observations, respectively. In cell D1 type

   =RANK.AVG(A1, $A$1:$C$20,1)

   Drag to complete the columns and rows. The ranks of the observations in columns A, B, and C will be in columns D, E, and F, respectively. Compute the rank sums and use the **Nonparametric Techniques** workbook.

19-3c Kruskal–Wallis Test and the Wilcoxon Rank Sum Test

When the Kruskal–Wallis Test is used to test for a difference between two populations, it will produce the same outcome as the two-tail Wilcoxon Rank Sum Test. However, the Kruskal–Wallis Test can determine only whether a difference exists. To determine, for example, if one population is located to the right of another, we must apply the Wilcoxon Rank Sum Test.

19-3d Friedman Test

Test Statistic To calculate the test statistic, we first rank each observation within each block, where 1 = smallest observation and k = largest observation, averaging the ranks of ties. Then we compute the rank sums, which we label $T_1, T_2, \ldots, T_k$. The test statistic is defined as follows. (Recall that b = number of blocks.)

Test Statistic for the Friedman Test

$$F_r = \left[\frac{12}{b(k)(k+1)} \sum_{j=1}^{k} T_j^2 \right] - 3b(k+1)$$

Sampling Distribution of the Test Statistic The test statistic is approximately chi-squared distributed with $k - 1$ degrees of freedom, provided that either k or b is greater than or equal to 5. As was the case with the Kruskal–Wallis Test, we reject the null hypothesis when the test statistic is large. Hence, the rejection region is

$$F_r > \chi^2_{\alpha, k-1}$$

and the p-value is

$$P(\chi^2 > F_r)$$

Figure 19.11 depicts the sampling distribution and p-value.

FIGURE **19.11** Sampling Distribution of F_r

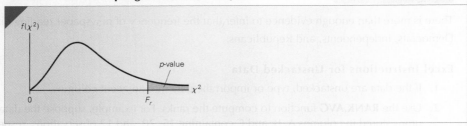

This test, like all the other nonparametric tests, requires that the populations being compared be identical in shape and spread.

EXAMPLE **19.6**

DATA
Xm19-06

Comparing Managers' Evaluations of Job Applicants

The personnel manager of a national accounting firm has been receiving complaints from senior managers about the quality of recent hirings. All new accountants are hired through a process in which four managers interview candidates and rate them on several dimensions, including academic credentials, previous work experience, and personal suitability. Each manager then summarizes the results and produces an evaluation of the candidate. There are five possibilities:

1. The candidate is in the top 5% of applicants.
2. The candidate is in the top 10% of applicants, but not in the top 5%.
3. The candidate is in the top 25% of applicants, but not in the top 10%.
4. The candidate is in the top 50% of applicants, but not in the top 25%.
5. The candidate is in the bottom 50% of applicants.

The evaluations are then combined in making the final decision. The personnel manager believes that the quality problem is caused by the evaluation system. However, they need to know whether there is general agreement or disagreement between the interviewing managers in their evaluations. To test for differences between the managers, a random sample of the evaluations of eight applicants was taken. The results are shown below. What conclusions can the personnel manager draw from these data? Employ a 5% significance level.

Applicant	Manager			
	1	**2**	**3**	**4**
1	2	1	2	2
2	4	2	3	2
3	2	2	2	3
4	3	1	3	2
5	3	2	3	5
6	2	2	3	4
7	4	1	5	5
8	3	2	5	3

SOLUTION:

IDENTIFY

The problem objective is to compare the four populations of managers' evaluations, which we can see are ordinal data. This experiment is identified as a randomized block design because the eight applicants were evaluated by all four managers. (The treatments are the managers, and the blocks are the applicants.) The appropriate statistical technique is the Friedman Test. The null and alternative hypotheses are as follows:

H_0: The locations of all four populations are the same.

H_1: At least two population locations differ.

COMPUTE

MANUALLY:

The rejection region is

$$F_r > \chi^2_{\alpha,k-1} = \chi^2_{.05,3} = 7.81$$

The following table demonstrates how the ranks are assigned and the rank sums calculated. Notice how the ranks are assigned by moving across the rows (blocks) and the rank sums computed by adding down the columns (treatments).

Applicant	Manager			
	1 (Rank)	**2 (Rank)**	**3 (Rank)**	**4 (Rank)**
1	2(3)	1(1)	2(3)	2(3)
2	4(4)	2(1.5)	3(3)	2(1.5)
3	2(2)	2(2)	2(2)	3(4)
4	3(3.5)	1(1)	3(3.5)	2(2)
5	3(2.5)	2(1)	3(2.5)	5(4)
6	2(1.5)	2(1.5)	3(3)	4(4)
7	4(2)	1(1)	5(3.5)	5(3.5)
8	3(2.5)	2(1)	5(4)	3(2.5)
	$T_1 = 21$	$T_2 = 10$	$T_3 = 24.5$	$T_4 = 24.5$

The value of the test statistic is

$$F_r = \left[\frac{12}{b(k)(k+1)} \sum_{j=1}^{k} T_j^2 \right] - 3b(k+1)$$

$$= \left[\frac{12}{(8)(4)(5)} (21^2 + 10^2 + 24.5^2 + 24.5^2) \right] - 3(8)(5)$$

$$= 10.61$$

Do It Yourself Excel

	A	B	C	D	E	F	G	H
1	Manager 1	Manager 2	Manager 3	Manager 4	Manager 1	Manager 2	Manager 3	Manager 4
2	2	1	2	2	3	1	3	3
3	4	2	3	2	4	1.5	3	1.5
4	2	2	2	3	2	2	2	4
5	3	1	3	2	3.5	1	3.5	2
6	3	2	3	5	2.5	1	2.5	4
7	2	2	3	4	1.5	1.5	3	4
8	4	1	5	5	2	1	3.5	3.5
9	3	2	5	3	2.5	1	4	2.5
10				Rank Sums	21	10	24.5	24.5

Excel Workbook

	A	B	C	D	E	F	G
1	Friedman Test						
2				Rank Sums	Rank Sum Squared		
3			Samples	T_j	T_j^2	Fr	p-value
4	Number of samples	4	1	21	441	10.61	0.0140
5	Number of blocks	8	2	10	100		
6			3	24.5	600.25		
7			4	24.5	600.25		
13		Total			1741.5		

INSTRUCTIONS

1. Type or import the data into adjacent columns. (Open Xm19-06.)

2. Delete all rows where any entries are blank (missing data).

3. Use the **RANK.AVG** to calculate the ranks of each row. In cell F2 type

    =RANK.AVG (B2,$B2:$E2,1)

    Drag to complete row 2. Repeat for the remaining rows.

4. Compute the column totals (rank sums) for each sample.

5. To complete the calculations, open the **Nonparametric Techniques** workbook and select the **Friedman Test**. Type the number of samples, k, the number of blocks, b, and the rank sums.

INTERPRET

The p-value of the test is .0140. There appears to be sufficient evidence to infer that the managers' evaluations differ.

19-3e The Friedman Test and the Sign Test

The relationship between the Friedman and sign tests is the same as the relationship between the Kruskal–Wallis and Wilcoxon Rank Sum Tests; that is, we can use the Friedman Test to determine whether two populations differ. The conclusion will be the same as that produced from the sign test. However, we can use the Friedman Test to determine only whether a difference exists. If we want to determine whether one population is, for example, to the left of another population, we must use the sign test.

Here is a list of the factors that tell us when to use the Kruskal–Wallis Test and the Friedman Test.

Factors That Identify the Kruskal–Wallis Test

1. **Problem objective**: Compare two or more populations.
2. **Data type**: Ordinal or interval but not normal
3. **Experimental design**: Independent samples

Factors That Identify the Friedman Test

1. **Problem objective**: Compare two or more populations.
2. **Data type**: Ordinal or interval but not normal
3. **Experimental design**: Randomized blocks

EXERCISES

19.60 Conduct the Kruskal–Wallis Test on the following statistics. Use a 5% significance level.

$T_1 = 984$ $n_1 = 23$
$T_2 = 1,502$ $n_2 = 36$
$T_3 = 1,430$ $n_3 = 29$

19.61 From the following statistics, use the Kruskal–Wallis Test (with $\alpha = .01$) to determine whether the population locations differ.

$T_1 = 1,207$ $n_1 = 25$
$T_2 = 1,088$ $n_2 = 25$
$T_3 = 1,310$ $n_3 = 25$
$T_4 = 1,445$ $n_4 = 25$

19.62 Apply the Kruskal–Wallis Test and the following statistics to determine whether there is enough statistical evidence at the 10% significance level to infer that the population locations differ.

$T_1 = 3,741$ $n_1 = 47$
$T_2 = 1,610$ $n_2 = 29$
$T_3 = 4,945$ $n_3 = 67$

19.63 Xr19-63 Use the Kruskal–Wallis Test on the following data to determine whether the population locations differ. (Use $\alpha = .05$.)

Sample 1:	27	33	18	29	41	52	75
Sample 2:	37	12	17	22	30		
Sample 3:	19	12	33	41	28	18	

19.64 Xr19-64 Using the Kruskal–Wallis Test, determine whether there is enough evidence provided by the accompanying data to enable us to infer that at least two population locations differ. (Use $\alpha = .05$.)

Sample 1:	25	15	20	22	23
Sample 2:	19	21	23	22	28
Sample 3:	27	25	22	29	28

Developing an Understanding of Statistical Concepts

Exercise 19.65 requires the use of a computer and software.

19.65 a. <u>Xr19-65a</u>   Four random samples of 50 people each were asked to rate four different computer printers in terms of their ease of use. The responses are:

> Very easy to use
> Easy to use
> Difficult to use
> Very difficult to use

The responses were coded using a 4-3-2-1 system. Do these data yield enough evidence at the 5% significance level to infer that differences in ratings exist among the four printers?

b. <u>Xr19-65b</u>   The responses were recoded using a 25-22-5-2 system. Do these data yield enough evidence to infer that differences in ratings exist between the four printers?

c. Why are the results of parts (a) and (b) identical?

19.66 <u>Xr19-66</u>   Apply the Friedman Test to the accompanying table of data to determine whether we can conclude that at least two population locations differ. (Use $\alpha = .10$.)

Block	Treatment			
	1	**2**	**3**	**4**
1	10	12	15	9
2	8	10	11	6
3	13	14	16	11
4	9	9	12	13
5	7	8	14	10

19.67 <u>Xr19-67</u>   The following data were generated from a blocked experiment. Conduct a Friedman Test to determine whether at least two population locations differ. (Use $\alpha = .05$.)

Block	Treatment		
	1	**2**	**3**
1	7.3	6.9	8.4
2	8.2	7.0	7.3
3	5.7	6.0	8.1
4	6.1	6.5	9.1
5	5.9	6.1	8.0

Developing an Understanding of Statistical Concepts

Exercises 19.68 to 19.93 require the use of a computer and software. Use a 5% significance level.

19.68 a. <u>Xr19-68a</u>   A random sample of 30 people was asked to rate each of four different premium brands of coffee. The ratings are:

> Excellent
> Good
> Fair
> Poor

The responses were assigned numbers 1 through 4, respectively. Can we infer that differences exist between the ratings of the four brands of coffee?

b. <u>Xr19-68b</u>   Suppose that the codes were 12, 31, 66, and 72, respectively. Can we infer that differences exist between the ratings of the four brands of coffee?

c. Compare your answers in parts (a) and (b). Why are they identical?

19.69 a. <u>Xr19-69</u>   Refer to Example 19.6. Suppose that the responses were recoded so that the numbers equaled the midpoint of the range of percentiles. That is:

> 97.5 = The candidate is in the top 5% of applicants
> 92.5 = The candidate is in the top 10% of applicants, but not in the top 5%
> 82.5 = The candidate is in the top 25% of applicants, but not in the top 10%
> 62.5 = The candidate is in the top 50% of applicants, but not in the top 25%
> 25 = The candidate is in the bottom 50% of applicants

Can we conclude that differences exist between the ratings assigned by the four professors?

b. Compare your answer in part (a) with the one obtained in Example 19.6. Are they the same? Explain why.

Applications *Use a 5% significance level.*

19.70 <u>Xr19-70</u>   In an effort to determine whether differences exist between three methods of teaching statistics, a professor of business taught the course differently in each of three large sections. Lecturing in the first section, case method in the second section and extensive use of the computer in the third section. At the end of the semester, each student was asked to evaluate the course on a 7-point scale, where 1 = Atrocious, 2 = Poor, 3 = Fair, 4 = Average, 5 = Good, 6 = Very good, and 7 = Excellent. From each section, the professor chose 25 evaluations at random. Is there evidence that differences in student satisfaction exist with respect to at least two of the three teaching methods?

19.71 <u>Xr19-71</u>   Applicants to MBA programs must take the Graduate Management Admission Test (GMAT). There are several companies that offer assistance in preparing for the test. To determine whether they work, and if so, which one is best, an experiment was conducted. Several hundred MBA applicants were surveyed and asked to report their GMAT score and which, if any, GMAT preparation course they took. The responses are course A, course B, course C, or no preparatory course. Do these data allow us to infer that there are differences between the four groups of GMAT scores?

19.72 Xr19-72 Ten judges were asked to test the quality of four different brands of orange juice. The judges assigned scores using a 5-point scale where 1 = Bad, 2 = Poor, 3 = Average, 4 = Good, and 5 = Excellent. The results are shown here. Can we conclude that there are differences in sensory quality between the four brands of orange juice?

Judge	Orange Juice Brand			
	1	2	3	4
1	3	5	4	3
2	2	3	5	4
3	4	4	3	4
4	3	4	5	2
5	2	4	4	3
6	4	5	5	3
7	3	3	4	4
8	2	3	3	3
9	4	3	5	4
10	2	4	5	3

19.73 Xr19-73 The manager of a chain of electronic-products retailers is trying to decide on a location for its newest store. After a thorough analysis, the choice has been narrowed to three possibilities. An important factor in the decision is the number of people passing each location. The number of people passing each location per day was counted during 30 days.

a. Which techniques should be considered to determine whether the locations differ? What are the required conditions? How do you select a technique?

b. Can management conclude that there are differences in the numbers of people passing the three locations if the number of people passing each location is not normally distributed?

19.74 Xr19-74 In recent years, lack of confidence in the U.S. Postal Service has led many companies to send all of their correspondence by private courier. A large company is in the process of selecting one of three possible couriers to act as its sole delivery method. To help make the decision, an experiment was performed whereby letters were sent using each of the three couriers at 12 different times of the day to a delivery point across town. The number of minutes required for delivery was recorded. Can we conclude that there are differences in delivery times between the three couriers? (This exercise is identical to Exercise 14.101, except for the data.)

19.75 Xr19-75 The manager of a personnel company is in the process of examining the company's advertising programs. Currently, the company advertises in each of the three local newspapers for a wide variety of positions, including computer programmers, secretaries, and receptionists. The manager has decided that only one newspaper will be used if it can be determined that there are differences between the newspapers in the number of inquiries. The following experiment was performed. For 1 week (6 days), six different jobs were advertised in each of the three newspapers. The number of inquiries was counted, and the results appear in the accompanying table.

Job Advertised	Newspaper		
	1	2	3
Receptionist	14	17	12
Systems analyst	8	9	6
Junior secretary	25	20	23
Computer programmer	12	15	10
Legal secretary	7	10	5
Office manager	5	9	4

a. What techniques should be considered to apply in reaching a decision? What are the required conditions? How do we determine whether the conditions are satisfied?

b. Assuming that the data are not normally distributed, can we conclude that differences exist between the newspapers' abilities to attract potential employees?

19.76 Xr19-76 Because there are no national or regional standards, it is difficult for university admission committees to compare graduates of different high schools. University administrators have noted that an 80% average at a high school with low standards may be equivalent to a 70% average at another school with higher standards of grading. In an effort to more equitably compare applications, a pilot study was initiated. Random samples of students who were admitted the previous year from four local high schools were drawn. All the students entered the business program with averages between 70% and 80%. Their average grades in the first year at the university were computed. Can the university admissions officer conclude that there are differences in grading standards between the four high schools? (This exercise is identical to Exercise 14.9, except for the data.)

19.77 Xr19-77 Many North Americans suffer from high levels of cholesterol, which can lead to heart attacks. For those with very high levels (over 280), doctors prescribe drugs to reduce cholesterol levels. A pharmaceutical company has recently developed three such drugs. To determine whether any differences exist in their benefits, an experiment was organized. The company selected 25 groups of four men, each of whom had cholesterol levels in excess of 280. In each group, the men were matched according to age and weight. The drugs were administered over a 2-month period, and the reduction in cholesterol was recorded. Do these results allow the company to conclude differences exist between the four new drugs? (This exercise is identical to Example 14.3, except for the data.)

19.78 Xr19-78 A well-known soft-drink manufacturer has used the same secret recipe for its product since its introduction over 100 years ago. In response to a decreasing market share, however, the company is contemplating changing the recipe. They have developed two alternative recipes. In a preliminary study, they asked 20 people to taste the original recipe and the two new recipes. He asked each to evaluate the taste of the product on a 5-point scale, where 1 = Awful, 2 = Poor, 3 = Fair, 4 = Good, and 5 = Wonderful. They decided that unless significant differences exist between evaluations of the products, he will not make any changes. Can we conclude that there are differences in the ratings of the three recipes?

19.79 Xr19-79 The management of fast-food restaurants is extremely interested in knowing how their customers rate the quality of food and service and the cleanliness of the restaurants. Customers are given the opportunity to fill out customer comment cards. Suppose that one franchise wanted to compare how customers rate the three shifts (4:00 P.M. to midnight, midnight to 8:00 A.M., and 8:00 A.M. to 4:00 P.M.). In a preliminary study, 100 customer cards were randomly selected from each shift. The responses to the question concerning speed of service were recorded, where 4 = Excellent, 3 = Good, 2 = Fair, and 1 = Poor, and are listed here. Do these data provide sufficient evidence to indicate whether customers perceive the speed of service to be different between the three shifts?

19.80 Xr19-80 A consumer testing service compared the effectiveness of four different brands of drain cleaner. The experiment consisted of using each product on 50 different clogged sinks and measuring the amount of time that elapsed until each drain became unclogged. The recorded times were measured in minutes.
   a. Which techniques should be considered as possible procedures to apply to determine whether differences exist? What are the required conditions? How do you decide?
   b. If a statistical analysis has shown that the times are not normally distributed, can the service conclude that differences exist between the speeds at which the four brands perform?

19.81 Xr19-81 During the last presidential campaign, the Gallup organization surveyed a random sample of

30 registered Democrats in January, another 30 in February, and yet another 30 in March. All 90 Democrats were asked to "rate the chances of the Democrats winning the presidential race in your state." The responses and their numerical codes were Excellent (4), Good (3), Fair (2), and Poor (1). Do these data allow us to infer that Democrats' ratings of their chances of winning the presidency changed over the 3-month period?

19.82 Xr19-82 It is common practice in the advertising business to create several different advertisements and then ask a random sample of potential customers to rate the ads on several different dimensions. Suppose that an advertising firm developed four different ads for a new breakfast cereal and asked a sample of 400 shoppers to rate the believability of the advertisements. One hundred people viewed ad 1, another 100 viewed ad 2, another 100 saw ad 3, and another 100 saw ad 4. The ratings were Very believable (4), Quite believable (3), Somewhat believable (2), and Not believable at all (1). Can the firm's management conclude that differences exist in believability between the four ads?

19.83 Xr19-83 Do university students become more supportive of their varsity teams as they progress through their 4-year stint? To help answer this question, a sample of students was drawn. Each was asked their class standing (freshman, sophomore, junior, or senior) and to what extent they supported the university's football team, the Hawks. The responses to the latter question are:

Wildly fanatic
Support the Hawks wholeheartedly
Support the Hawks, but not that enthusiastically
Who are the Hawks?

The responses were coded using a 4-3-2-1 numbering system. Can we conclude that the four levels of students differ in their support for the Hawks?

19.84 Xr19-84 In anticipation of buying a new scanner, a student turned to a website that reported the results of surveys of users of the different scanners. A sample of 133 responses was listed showing the ease of use of five different brands. The survey responses were:

Very easy
Easy
Not easy
Difficult
Very difficult

The responses were assigned numbers from 1 to 5. Can we infer that there are differences in perceived ease of use between the five brands of scanners?

GENERAL SOCIAL SURVEY EXERCISES

Conduct all tests at the 5% significance level.

19.85 Do more educated people derive more satisfaction from their jobs? Test to determine whether there are differences in job satisfaction (SATJOB: 1 = Very satisfied, 2 = Moderately satisfied, 3 = A little dissatisfied, 4 = Very dissatisfied) between the degree holders (DEGREE: 0 = Left high school, 1 = Finished high school, 2 = Junior college, 3 = Bachelor's degree, 4 = Graduate degree).

19.86 Respondents were asked the following question, Compared to your parents at your age is your standard of living (PARSOL: 1 = Much better, 2 = Somewhat better, 3 = About the same, 4 = Somewhat worse, 5 = Much worse)? Test to determine whether we can infer that differences in perception exist between the three races (RACE).

19.87 Are there differences between the five categories of marital status (MARITAL) with respect to health (HEALTH: 1 = Excellent, 2 = Good, 3 = Fair, 4 = Poor)? Conduct a statistical test to answer the question.

19.88 Do less-educated people believe that they have a higher probability of losing their job? Test to determine whether there is enough evidence to conclude that there are differences in perceived likelihood of losing their jobs (JOBLOSE: 1 = Very likely, 2 = Fairly likely, 3 = Not too likely, 4 = Not likely) between the degree holders (DEGREE: 0 = Left high school, 1 = Finished high school, 2 = Junior college, 3 = Bachelor's degree, 4 Graduate degree).

19.89 Is there enough statistical evidence to infer that there are differences between the three race categories (RACE) with respect to how likely they are to lose their jobs (JOBLOSE: 1 = Very likely, 2 = Fairly likely, 3 = Not too likely, 4 = Not likely)?

19.90 Is there enough statistical evidence to conclude that Democrats, Republicans, and Independents (PARTYID3: 1 = Democrat, 2 = Independent, 3 = Republican) differ in their views about the federal income tax that they have to pay (TAX: Do you consider the amount of federal income tax that you have to pay as too high, about right, or too low: 1 = Too high, 2 = About right, 3 = Too low)?

19.91 Can we infer from the data that liberals, moderates, and conservatives (POLVIEWS3: 1 = Liberal, 2 = Moderate, 3 = Conservative) differ in their views about the federal income tax that they have to pay (TAX: Do you consider the amount of federal income tax that you have to pay as too high, about right, or too low: 1 = Too high, 2 = About right, 3 = Too low)?

19.92 Are there differences between the races with respect to their perceptions of their health (HEALTH: Would you say your own health, in general, is . . . 1. Excellent, 2. Good, 3. Fair, 4. Poor)? Use an appropriate statistical technique to determine whether there is enough evidence to infer that there are differences between the races (RACE: 1. White, 2. Black, 3. Other).

19.93 How does educational attainment affect newspaper readership? Is there enough evidence to conclude that there are differences between the five educational attainment groups (DEGREE: Highest degree completed of respondent, spouse, father, mother: 0 = Left high school, 1 = High school, 2 = Junior college, 3 = Bachelor's degree, 4 = Graduate) with respect to how frequently they read newspapers (NEWS: 1 = Every day, 2 = Few times per week, 3 = Once per week, 4 = Less than once per week, 5 = Never)?

19-4 / SPEARMAN RANK CORRELATION COEFFICIENT

In Section 17-4, we introduced the test of the coefficient of correlation, which allows us to determine whether there is evidence of a linear relationship between two interval variables. Recall that the required condition for the t-test of ρ is that the variables are bivariate normally distributed. In many situations, however, one or both variables may be ordinal; or if both variables are interval, the normality requirement may not be satisfied. In such cases, we measure and test to determine whether a relationship exists by employing a nonparametric technique, the **Spearman rank correlation coefficient**.

The Spearman rank correlation coefficient is calculated like all of the other previously introduced nonparametric methods by first ranking the data. We then calculate the *Pearson correlation coefficient* of the ranks.

The population Spearman correlation coefficient is labeled ρ_s, and the sample statistic used to estimate its value is labeled r_s.

Sample Spearman Rank Correlation Coefficient

$$r_s = \frac{s_{ab}}{s_a s_b}$$

where a and b are the ranks of x and y, respectively, s_{ab} is the covariance of the values of a and b, s_a is the standard deviation of the values of a, and s_b is the standard deviation of the values of b.

We can test to determine whether a relationship exists between the two variables. The hypotheses to be tested are

H_0: $\rho_s = 0$

H_1: $\rho_s \neq 0$

(We also can conduct one-tail tests.) The test statistic is the absolute value of r_s. To determine whether the value of r_s is large enough to reject the null hypothesis, we refer to Table 11 in Appendix B, reproduced here as Table 19.5, which lists the critical values of the test statistic for one-tail tests. To conduct a two-tail test, the value of α must be doubled. The table lists critical values for $\alpha = .01$, $.025$, and $.05$ and for $n = 5$ to 30. When n is greater than 30, r_s is approximately normally distributed with mean 0 and standard deviation $1/\sqrt{n-1}$. Thus, for $n > 30$, the test statistic is as shown in the box.

Test Statistic for Testing $\rho_s = 0$ When $n > 30$

$$z = \frac{r_s - 0}{1/\sqrt{n-1}} = r_s \sqrt{n-1}$$

which is standard normally distributed

TABLE **19.5** Critical Values for the Spearman Rank Correlation Coefficient

The α values correspond to a one-tail test of H_0: $\rho_s = 0$. The value should be doubled for two-tail tests.

n	$\alpha = .05$	$\alpha = .025$	$\alpha = .01$
5	.900	—	—
6	.829	.886	.943
7	.714	.786	.893
8	.643	.738	.833
9	.600	.683	.783

TABLE **19.5** (*Continued*)

n	$\alpha = .05$	$\alpha = .025$	$\alpha = .01$
10	.564	.648	.745
11	.523	.623	.736
12	.497	.591	.703
13	.475	.566	.673
14	.457	.545	.646
15	.441	.525	.623
16	.425	.507	.601
17	.412	.490	.582
18	.399	.476	.564
19	.388	.462	.549
20	.377	.450	.534
21	.368	.438	.521
22	.359	.428	.508
23	.351	.418	.496
24	.343	.409	.485
25	.336	.400	.475
26	.329	.392	.465
27	.323	.385	.456
28	.317	.377	.448
29	.311	.370	.440
30	.305	.364	.432

EXAMPLE 19.7

DATA
Xm19-07

Testing the Relationship between Aptitude Tests and Performance

The production manager of a firm wants to examine the relationship between aptitude test scores given before hiring production-line workers and performance ratings received by the employees 3 months after starting work. The results of the study would allow the firm to decide how much weight to give to these aptitude tests relative to other work-history information obtained, including references. The aptitude test results range from 0 to 100. The performance ratings are as follows:

1 = Employee has performed well below average.
2 = Employee has performed somewhat below average.
3 = Employee has performed at the average level.
4 = Employee has performed somewhat above average.
5 = Employee has performed well above average.

A random sample of 40 workers was drawn. The results of the first three and last three are listed next. Can the firm's manager infer at the 5% significance level that aptitude test scores are correlated with performance rating?

Employee	Aptitude	Performance
1	59	3
2	47	2
3	58	4
38	53	1
39	63	5
40	85	3

SOLUTION:

IDENTIFY

The problem objective is to analyze the relationship between two variables. The aptitude test score is interval, but the performance rating is ordinal. We will treat the aptitude test score as if it were ordinal and calculate the Spearman rank correlation coefficient. To answer the question, we specify the hypotheses as

$$H_0: \quad \rho_s = 0$$
$$H_1: \quad \rho_s \neq 0$$

COMPUTE

MANUALLY:

We rank each of the variables separately, averaging any ties that we encounter.

Employee	Aptitude	Rank a	Performance	Rank b
1	59	20	3	20.5
2	47	4	2	9
3	58	17	4	31.5
38	53	9.5	1	2.5
39	63	27	5	38
40	85	40	3	20.5

The next step is to calculate the following sums:

$$\sum a_i b_i = 18,319$$

$$\sum a_i = 820 \quad \sum b_i = 820$$

$$\sum a_i^2 = 22,131.5$$

$$\sum b_i^2 = 21,795.5$$

Using the shortcut calculation on page 122, we determine that the covariance of the ranks is

$$s_{ab} = \frac{1}{n-1}\left(\sum a_i b_i - \frac{\sum a_i \sum b_i}{n}\right) = \frac{1}{40-1}\left[18,319 - \frac{(820)(820)}{40}\right] = 38.69$$

The sample variances of the ranks (using the short-cut formula on page 110) are

$$s_a^2 = \frac{1}{n-1}\left[\sum a_i^2 - \frac{\left(\sum a_i\right)^2}{n}\right] = \frac{1}{40-1}\left[22,131.5 - \frac{(820)^2}{40}\right] = 136.45$$

$$s_b^2 = \frac{1}{n-1}\left[\sum b_i^2 - \frac{\left(\sum ab_i\right)^2}{n}\right] = \frac{1}{40-1}\left[21,795.5 - \frac{(820)^2}{40}\right] = 127.83$$

The standard deviations are

$$s_a = \sqrt{s_a^2} = \sqrt{136.45} = 11.68$$
$$s_b = \sqrt{s_b^2} = \sqrt{127.83} = 11.31$$

Thus,

$$r_s = \frac{s_{ab}}{s_a s_b} = \frac{38.69}{(11.68)(11.31)} = .2929$$

The value of the test statistic is

$$z = r_s\sqrt{n-1} = .2929\sqrt{40-1} = 1.83$$
$$p\text{-value} = 2P(Z > 1.83) = 2(1 - .9664) = .0672$$

Do It Yourself Excel

Excel Workbook

	A	B	C	D
1	Spearman Rank Correlation Test			
2				
3	Spearman Rank Correlation Coefficient	0.2930	Z Stat	1.83
4	Sample Size	40	P(Z<=z) one-tail	0.0336
5	Alpha	0.05	z Critical one-tail	1.6449
6			P(Z<=z) two-tail	0.0673
7			z Critical two-tail	1.9600

INSTRUCTIONS

1. Type or Import the data into two columns. (Open Xm19-07.)

2. Use the **RANK.AVG** function to convert the data into ranks. In this example assuming that the data are in columns B and C. In column D row 2 type

   =RANK.AVG(B2, B$2:B$41,1)

   Drag to complete column D. Repeat to store the ranks of the data in column C in column E.

3. Calculate the coefficient of correlation for the ranks. In any empty cell, type

   =CORREL (D2:D41, E2:E41)

4. Open the **Nonparametric Techniques** workbook and click **Spearman Rank Correlation Test**.

5. Type the correlation, sample size, and α.

INTERPRET

The test statistic is $z = 1.83$ and the p-value $= .0673$. There is not enough evidence to believe that the aptitude test scores and performance ratings are related.

EXERCISES

19.94 Test the following hypotheses:

$$H_0 \quad \rho_s = 0$$
$$H_1: \quad \rho_s \neq 0$$
$$n = 50 \quad r_s = .23 \quad \alpha = .05$$

19.95 Is there sufficient evidence at the 5% significance level to infer that there is a positive relationship between two ordinal variables given that $r_s = .15$ and $n = 12$?

19.96 Xr19-96 A statistics student asked seven first-year economics students to report their grades in the required mathematics and economics courses. The results (where 1 = F, 2 = D, 3 = C, 4 = B, 5 = A) are as follows:

Mathematics	4	2	5	4	2	2	1
Economics	5	2	3	5	3	3	2

Calculate the Spearman rank correlation coefficient, and test to determine whether we can infer that a relationship exists between the grades in the two courses. (Use $\alpha = .05$.)

19.97 Xr19-97 Does the number of commercials shown during a half-hour television program affect how viewers rate the show? In a preliminary study eight people were asked to watch a pilot for a situation comedy and rate the show (1 = Terrible, 2 = Bad, 3 = OK, 4 = Good, 5 = Very good). Each person was shown a different number of 30-second commercials. The data are shown here. Calculate the Spearman rank correlation coefficient and test with a 10% significance level to determine whether there is a relationship between the two variables.

Number of commercials	1	2	3	4	5	6	7	8
Rating	4	5	3	3	3	2	3	1

19.98 Xr19-98 The weekly returns of two stocks for a 13-week period were recorded and are listed here. Assuming that the returns are not normally distributed, can we infer at the 5% significance level that the stock returns are correlated?

Stock 1	−7	−4	−7	−3	2	−10	−10
Stock 2	6	6	−4	9	3	−3	7
Stock 1	5	1	−4	2	6	−13	
Stock 2	−3	4	7	9	5	−7	

19.99 Xr19-99 The general manager of an engineering firm wants to know whether a draftsman's experience influences the quality of their work. The manager selects 24 draftsmen at random and records their years of work experience and their quality rating (as assessed by their supervisors, where 5 = Excellent, 4 = Very good, 3 = Average, 2 = Fair, and 1 = Poor). The data are listed here. Can we infer from these data that years of work experience is a factor in determining the quality of work performed? (Use $\alpha = .05$.)

Draftsman	Experience	Rating	Draftsman	Experience	Rating
1	1	1	13	8	2
2	17	4	14	20	5
3	20	4	15	21	3
4	9	5	16	19	2
5	2	2	17	1	1
6	13	4	18	22	3
7	9	3	19	20	4
8	23	5	20	11	3
9	7	2	21	18	5
10	10	5	22	14	4
11	12	5	23	21	3
12	24	2	24	21	1

The following exercises require the use of a computer and software.
Use a 5% significance level.

19.100 <u>Xm16-02</u> Refer to Example 16.2. If the required condition is not satisfied conduct another more appropriate test to determine whether odometer reading and price are related.

19.101 <u>Xr19-101</u> At the completion of most courses in universities and colleges, a course evaluation is undertaken. Some professors believe that the way in which students fill out the evaluations is based on how well the student is doing in the course. To test this theory, a random sample of course evaluations was selected. Two answers were recorded. The questions and answers are:

a. How would you rate the course?

    1. Poor   2. Fair   3. Good   4. Very good   5. Excellent

b. What grade do you expect in this course?

    1. F   2. D   3. C   4. B   5. A

Is there enough evidence to conclude that the theory is correct?

19.102 <u>Xr19-102</u> Many people suffer from heartburn. It appears, however, that the problem may increase with age. A researcher for a pharmaceutical company wanted to determine whether age and the incidence and extent of heartburn are related. A random sample of 325 adults was drawn. They were asked to give their age and to rate the severity of heartburn (1 = Low, 2 = Moderate, 3 = High, 4 = Very high). Do these data provide sufficient evidence to indicate that older people suffer more severe heartburn?

19.103 <u>Xr16-06</u> Assume that the conditions for the test conducted in Exercise 16.6 are not met. Do the data allow us to conclude that the longer the commercial, the higher the memory test score will be?

19.104 <u>Xr16-07</u> Assume that the normality requirement in Exercise 16.9 is not met. Test to determine whether the price of a condominium and floor number are positively related.

19.105 <u>Xr19-105</u> Many people who quit smoking gain weight. Many explain that after they quit smoking food tastes better. To examine the relationship between smoking and taste, a researcher randomly sampled 280 smokers. Each was asked how many cigarettes they smoked on an average day. In addition, each person was asked to taste and rate some vanilla ice cream. The responses are 5 = Excellent, 4 = Very good, 3 = Good, 2 = Fair, and 1 = Poor. Can the researcher infer that the more a person smokes the less taste sensation they have?

19.106 <u>Xr19-106</u> Gambling on sports is big business in the United States and Canada. A television executive wants to know whether the amount of money wagered on a professional football game affects the enjoyment of viewers. A random sample of 200 men who regularly watch football Sunday afternoons and wager on the outcomes was drawn. Each was asked to report the amount wagered on the game they watched and to rate the enjoyment (where 1 = Not enjoyable, 2 = Somewhat enjoyable, 3 = Moderately, enjoyable, and 4 = Very enjoyable). Do these data provide enough evidence to conclude that the greater the wager the more enjoyable the game is for the viewer?

GENERAL SOCIAL SURVEY EXERCISES

<u>GSS2018</u> **Conduct all tests with a 5% significance level.**

19.107 Do older Americans have a greater fear of losing their jobs? Test to determine whether there is enough evidence to conclude that as one gets older (AGE) the probability of losing one's job (JOBLOSE: 1 = Very likely, 2 = Fairly likely, 3 = Not too likely, 4 = Not likely) decreases.

19.108 Is there sufficient evidence to infer that more educated (EDUC) people read newspapers more often (NEWS: 1 = Every day, 2 = A few times per week, 3 = Once a week, 4 = Less than once a week, 5 = Never)?

19.109 Do the most satisfying jobs also produce the highest income? Test to determine whether there is enough evidence to infer that more satisfying jobs (SATJOB: 1 = Very satisfied, 2 = Moderately satisfied, 3 = A little dissatisfied, 4 = Very dissatisfied) have higher incomes (RINCOME).

19.110 Can we infer from the data that jobs that are most secure (JOBLOSE: 1 = Very likely, 2 = Fairly likely, 3 = Not too likely, 4 = Not likely) are also the most satisfying (SATJOB: 1 = Very satisfied, 2 = Moderately satisfied, 3 = A little dissatisfied, 4 = Very dissatisfied)?

19.111 Can we conclude from the data that more educated (EDUC) people are more likely to perceive themselves as healthier (HEALTH: 1 = Excellent, 2 = Good, 3 = Fair, 4 = Poor)?

19.112 Are more educated people (EDUC) more likely to believe that compared to their parents at their age their standard of living is better (PARSOL: 1 = Much better, 2 = Somewhat better, 3 = About the same, 4 = Somewhat worse, 5 = Much worse)? Perform an appropriate test to answer the question.

19.113 Is it a myth that younger Americans do not read newspapers, choosing instead to get their news from the Internet or television (or not at all)? Conduct a test to determine whether there is sufficient statistical evidence to conclude that younger people (AGE) read newspapers (NEWS: 1 = Every day, 2 = A few times per week, 3 = Once a week, 4 = Less than once a week, 5 = Never) less frequently than older people.

19.114 If one works longer hours (HRS1), does the chances of losing one's job (JOBLOSE: 1 = Very likely, 2 = Fairly likely, 3 = Not too likely, 4 = Not likely) become less likely? Conduct a test to answer the question.

19.115 Does age (AGE) affect one's belief concerning the federal income tax that one has to pay (TAX: Do you consider the amount of federal income tax that you have to pay as too high, about right, or too low: 1 = Too high, 2 = About right, 3 = Too low)?

19.116 Are richer people healthier? Conduct a test to determine whether there is enough evidence to infer that higher income (RINCOME) individuals are healthier (HEALTH: Would you say your own health, in general, is . . . 1. Excellent, 2. Good, 3. Fair, 4. Poor)?

19.117 Are richer (RINCOME) Americans pessimistic about their children's chances of having a higher standard of living (KIDSSOL: When your children are at your age will their standard of living be. . . 1. Much better, 2. Somewhat better, 3. About the same, 4. Somewhat worse, 5. Much worse)? Conduct a statistical test to answer the question.

CHAPTER SUMMARY

Nonparametric statistical tests are applied to problems where the data are either ordinal or interval but not normal. The Wilcoxon Rank Sum Test is used to compare two populations of ordinal or interval data when the data are generated from independent samples. The sign test is used to compare two populations of ordinal data drawn from a matched pairs experiment. The Wilcoxon Signed Rank Sum Test is employed to compare two populations of nonnormal interval data taken from a matched pairs experiment. When the objective is to compare two or more populations of independently sampled ordinal or interval nonnormal data the Kruskal–Wallis Test is employed. The Friedman Test is used instead of the Kruskal–Wallis Test when the samples are blocked. To determine whether two variables are related, we employ the test of the Spearman rank correlation coefficient.

IMPORTANT TERMS:

Nonparametric techniques   799
Distribution-free statistics   799
Wilcoxon Rank Sum Test   801
Sign test   816

Wilcoxon Signed Rank Sum Test   820
Kruskal–Wallis Test   830
Friedman Test   830
Spearman rank correlation coefficient   841

SYMBOLS:

Symbol	Pronounced	Represents
T_i	T sub i or $T i$	Rank sum of sample i ($i = 1, 2, \ldots, k$)
T^+	T plus	Rank sum of positive differences
T^-	T minus	Rank sum of negative differences
σ_T	Sigma sub T or sigma T	Standard deviation of the sampling distribution of T
ρ_s	Rho sub s or rho s	Spearman rank correlation coefficient

FORMULAS:

Wilcoxon Rank Sum Test

$$T = T_1$$

$$E(T) = \frac{n_1(n_1 + n_2 + 1)}{2}$$

$$\sigma_T = \sqrt{\frac{n_1 n_2 (n_1 + n_2 + 1)}{12}}$$

$$z = \frac{T - E(T)}{\sigma_T}$$

Sign test

$$x = \text{number of positive differences}$$

$$z = \frac{x - .5n}{.5\sqrt{n}}$$

Wilcoxon Signed Rank Sum Test

$$T = T^+$$

$$E(T) = \frac{n(n + 1)}{4}$$

$$\sigma_T = \sqrt{\frac{n(n + 1)(2n + 1)}{24}}$$

$$z = \frac{T - E(T)}{\sigma_T}$$

Kruskal–Wallis Test

$$H = \left[\frac{12}{n(n + 1)} \sum_{j=1}^{k} \frac{T_j^2}{n_j} \right] - 3(n + 1)$$

Friedman Test

$$F_r = \left[\frac{12}{b(k)(k + 1)} \sum_{j=1}^{k} T_j^2 \right] - 3b(k + 1)$$

Spearman rank correlation coefficient

$$r_s = \frac{s_{ab}}{s_a s_b}$$

Spearman test statistic for $n > 30$

$$z = r_s \sqrt{n - 1}$$

EXCEL OUTPUT AND INSTRUCTIONS:

Technique	
Wilcoxon Rank Sum Test	807
Sign test	819
Wilcoxon Signed Rank Sum Test	826
Kruskal–Wallis Test	832
Friedman Test	836
Spearman rank correlation coefficient	845

CHAPTER EXERCISES

The following exercises require the use of a computer and software. Use a 5% significance level.

19.118 <u>Xr19-118</u> Are education and income related? To answer this question, a random sample of people was selected and each was asked to indicate into which of the following categories of education they belonged:

1. Less than high school
2. High school graduate
3. Some college or university but no degree
4. University degree
5. Postgraduate degree

Additionally, respondents were asked for their annual income group from the following choices:

1. Under $25,000
2. $25,000 up to but not including $40,000
3. $40,000 up to but not including $60,000
4. $60,000 up to $100,000
5. Greater than $100,000

Conduct a test to determine whether more education and higher incomes are linked.

19.119 <u>Xr19-119</u> In a study to determine which of two teaching methods is perceived to be better, two sections of an introductory marketing course were taught in different ways by the same professor. At the course's completion, each student rated the course on a boring/stimulating spectrum, with 1 = Very boring, 2 = Somewhat boring, 3 = A little boring, 4 = Neither boring nor stimulating, 5 = A little stimulating, 6 = Somewhat stimulating, and 7 = Very stimulating. Can we conclude that the ratings of the two teaching methods differ?

19.120 Xr19-120   The researchers at a large carpet manufacturer have been experimenting with a new dyeing process in hopes of reducing the streakiness that frequently occurs with the current process. As an experiment, 15 carpets are dyed using the new process, and another 15 are dyed using the existing method. Each carpet is rated on a 5-point scale of streakiness, where 5 is Extremely streaky, 4 is Quite streaky, 3 is Somewhat streaky, 2 is A little streaky, and 1 is Not streaky at all. Is there enough evidence to infer that the new method is better?

19.121 Xr19-121   The student newspaper was in the process of making some major changes in the newspaper's layout. They were also contemplating changing the typeface of the print used. To help make a decision, they set up an experiment in which 20 individuals were asked to read four newspaper pages, with each page printed in a different typeface. If the reading speed differed, the typeface that was read fastest would be used. However, if there was not enough evidence to allow the editor to conclude that such differences exist, the current typeface would be continued. The times (in seconds) to completely read one page were recorded. We have determined that the times are not normally distributed. Determine the course of action the newspaper should follow. (This exercise is identical to Exercise 14.124, except in this exercise, the data are not normally distributed.)

19.122 Xr19-122   Large potential profits for pharmaceutical companies exist in the area of hair growth drugs. The head chemist for a large pharmaceutical company is conducting experiments to determine which of two new drugs is more effective in growing hair among balding men. One experiment was conducted as follows. A total of 30 pairs of men—each pair of which was matched according to their degree of baldness—was selected. One man used drug A, and the other used drug B. After 10 weeks, the men's new hair growth was examined, and the new growth was judged using the following ratings:

0 = No growth
1 = Some growth
2 = Moderate growth

Do these data provide sufficient evidence that drug B is more effective?

19.123 Xr19-123   Suppose that a precise measuring device for new hair growth has been developed and is used in the experiment described in Exercise 19.122. The percentages of new hair growth for the 30 pairs of men involved in the experiment were recorded. Do these data allow the chemist to conclude that drug B is more effective?

19.124 Xr19-124   The printing department of a publishing company wants to determine whether there are differences in durability between three types of book bindings. Twenty-five books with each type of binding were selected and placed in machines that continually opened and closed them. The numbers of openings and closings until the pages separated from the binding were recorded.
a. What techniques should be considered to determine whether differences exist between the types of bindings? What are the required conditions? How do you decide which technique to use?
b. If we know that the number of openings and closings is not normally distributed, test to determine whether differences exist between the types of bindings.

19.125 Xr19-125   In recent years, consumers have become more safety conscious, particularly about children's products. A manufacturer of children's pajamas is looking for material that is as nonflammable as possible. In an experiment to compare a new fabric with the kind now being used, 50 pieces of each kind were exposed to an open flame, and the number of seconds until the fabric burst into flames was recorded. Because the new material is much more expensive than the current material, the manufacturer will switch only if the new material can be shown to be better. On the basis of these data, what should the manufacturer do?

19.126 Xr19-126   Samuel's is a chain of family restaurants. Like many other service companies, Samuel's surveys its customers on a regular basis to monitor their opinions. Two questions (among others) asked in the survey are as follows:
a. While you were at Samuel's, did you find the service Slow (1), Moderate (2), or Fast (3)?
b. What day was your visit to Samuel's?

The responses of a random sample of 269 customers were recorded. Can the manager infer that there are differences in customer perceptions of the speed of service between the days of the week?

19.127 Xr19-127   An advertising firm wants to determine the relative effectiveness of two recently produced commercials for a car dealership. An important attribute of such commercials is their believability. To judge this aspect of the commercials, 60 people were randomly selected. Each watched both commercials and then rated them on a 5-point scale (where 1 = Not believable, 2 = Somewhat believable, 3 = Moderately believable, 4 = Quite believable, and 5 = Very believable). Do these data provide sufficient evidence to indicate that there are differences in believability between the two commercials?

19.128 Xr19-128   Researchers at the U.S. National Institute of Aging in Bethesda, Maryland, have been studying hearing loss. They have hypothesized that as men age they will lose their hearing faster than comparably aged women because many more men than women have worked at jobs where noise levels have been excessive. To test their beliefs, the researchers randomly selected one man and one woman aged 45, 46, 47, . . . , 78, 79, 80 and measured the percentage hearing loss for each person. What conclusions can be drawn from these data?

19.129 Xr19-129   In a Gallup poll this year, 200 people were asked, "Do you feel that the newspaper you read most does a good job of presenting the news?" The same question was asked of another 200 people 10 years ago. The possible responses were as follows:

    3 = Good job
    2 = Fair job
    1 = Not a good job

Do these data provide enough evidence to infer that people perceive newspapers as doing a better job 10 years ago than today?

19.130 Xr10-130   It is common practice in many MBA programs to require applicants to arrange for a letter of reference. Some universities have their own forms in which referees assess the applicant using the following categories:

    5: The candidate is in the top 5% of applicants.
    4: The candidate is in the top 10% of applicants, but not in the top 5%.
    3: The candidate is in the top 25% of applicants, but not in the top 10%.
    2: The candidate is in the top 50% of applicants, but not in the top 25%.
    1: The candidate is in the bottom 50% of applicants.

However, the question arises, Are the referees' ratings related to how well the applicant performs in the MBA program? To answer the question, a random sample of recently graduated MBAs was drawn. For each, the rating of the referee and the MBA grade-point average (GPA) were recorded. Do these data present sufficient evidence to infer that the letter of reference and the MBA GPA are related?

19.131 Xr19-131   The increasing number of traveling businesswomen represents a large potential clientele for the hotel industry. Many hotel chains have made changes designed to attract more women. To help direct these changes, a hotel chain commissioned a study to determine whether major differences exist between male and female business travelers. A total of 100 male and 100 female executives were questioned on a variety of topics, one of which was the number of trips they had taken in the previous 12 months. We would like to know whether these data provide enough evidence to allow us to conclude that businesswomen and businessmen differ in the number of business trips taken per year.

19.132 Xr19-132   To examine the effect that a tough midterm test has on student evaluations of professors, a statistics professor had the class evaluate the teaching effectiveness before the midterm test. The questionnaire asked for opinions on a number of dimensions, but the last question is considered the most important. It is, "How would you rate the overall performance of the instructor?" The possible responses are 1 = poor, 2 = fair, 3 = good, and 4 = excellent. After a difficult test, the evaluation was redone. The evaluation scores before and after the test for each of the 40 students in the class were recorded. Do the data allow the professor to conclude that the results of the midterm negatively influence student opinion?

19.133 Xr19-133   The town of Stratford, Ontario, is very much dependent on the Shakespearean Festival it holds every summer for its financial well-being. Thousands of people visit Stratford to attend one or more Shakespearean plays and spend money in hotels, restaurants, and gift shops. As a consequence, any sign that the number of visitors will decrease in the future is cause for concern. Two years ago, a survey of 100 visitors asked how likely it was that they would return within the next 2 years. This year the survey was repeated with another 100 visitors. The likelihood of returning within 2 years was measured as:

    4 = Very likely
    3 = Somewhat likely
    2 = Somewhat unlikely
    1 = Very unlikely

Conduct whichever statistical procedures you deem necessary to determine whether the citizens of Stratford should be concerned about the results of the two surveys.

19.134 Xr19-134   Scientists have been studying the effects of lead in children's blood, bones, and tissue for a number of years. It is known that lead reduces intelligence and can cause a variety of other problems.

A study directed by Dr. Herman Needleman, a psychiatrist at the University of Pittsburgh Medical Center, examined some of these problems. Two hundred boys attending public schools in Pittsburgh were recruited. Each boy was categorized as having low or high levels of lead in their bones. Each boy was then assessed by his teachers on a 4-point scale (where 1 = low, 2 = moderate, 3 = high, and 4 = extreme) on degrees of aggression. Is there evidence to infer that boys with high levels of lead are more aggressive than boys with low levels of lead?

19.135 Xr19-135　How does gender affect teaching evaluations? Several researchers addressed this question during the past decade. In one study several female and male professors in the same department with similar backgrounds were selected. A random sample of 100 female students was drawn. Each student evaluated a female professor and a male professor. A sample of 100 male students was drawn and each also evaluated a female professor and a male professor. The ratings were based on a 4-point scale (where 1 = Poor, 2 = Fair, 3 = Good, and 4 = Excellent). The evaluations were recorded in the following way:

Column 1 = Female student
Column 2 = Female professor rating
Column 3 = Male professor rating
Column 4 = Male student
Column 5 = Female professor rating
Column 6 = Male professor rating

a. Can we infer that female students rate female professors higher than they rate male professors?
b. Can we infer that male students rate male professors higher than they rate female professors?

19.136 Xr19-136　It is an unfortunate fact of life that the characteristics that one is born with play a critical role in later life. For example, race is a critical factor in almost all aspects of North American life. Height and weight also determine how friends, teachers, employers, and customers will treat you. And now we may add physical attractiveness to this list. A recent study followed the careers of students from a prestigious U.S. law school. A panel of independent raters examined the graduation yearbook photos of the students and rated their appearance as unattractive, neither attractive nor unattractive, or attractive. The annual incomes in thousands of dollars 5 years after graduation were recorded. Assuming that incomes are not normally distributed, can we infer that incomes of lawyers are affected by physical attractiveness?

19.137 Xr19-137　According to a CNN news report, 9% of full-time workers telecommute. This means that they do not work in their employers' offices but instead perform their work at home using a computer and modem. To ascertain whether such workers are more satisfied than their nontelecommuting counterparts, a study was undertaken. A random sample of telecommuters and regular office workers was taken. Each was asked how satisfied they were with their current employment. The responses are 1 = Very unsatisfied, 2 = Somewhat unsatisfied, 3 = Somewhat satisfied, and 4 = Very satisfied. What conclusions can we draw from these data?

19.138 Xr19-138　How does alcohol affect judgment? To provide some insight, an experiment was conducted. A random sample of customers of an Ohio club was selected. Each respondent was asked to assess the attractiveness of members of the opposite sex who were in the club at the time. The assessment was to be made on a 5-point scale (where 1 = Very unattractive, 2 = Unattractive, 3 = Neither attractive nor unattractive, 4 = Attractive, and 5 = Very attractive). The survey was conducted 3 hours before closing and again just before closing using another group of respondents. Can we conclude that the assessments made just before closing are higher than those made 3 hours earlier? If so, what does this imply about the effects of alcohol on judgment?

19.139 Xr19-139　Can you become addicted to exercise? In a study conducted at the University of Wisconsin at Madison, a random sample of dedicated exercisers who usually work out every day was drawn. Each completed a questionnaire that gauged their mood on a 5-point scale (where 5 = Very relaxed and happy, 4 = Somewhat relaxed and happy, 3 = Neutral feeling, 2 = Tense and anxious, and 1 = Very tense and anxious). The group was then instructed to abstain from all workouts for the next 3 days. Moreover, they were told to be as physically inactive as possible. Each day their mood was measured using the same questionnaire. Column 1 stores the code identifying the respondent and columns 2 through 5 store the measures of mood for the day before the experiment began and for the 3 days of the experiment, respectively.

a. Can we infer that for each day the exercisers abstained from physical activity they were less happy than when they were exercising?
b. Do the data indicate that by the third day moods were improving?
c. Draw two possible conclusions from your findings.

CASE 19.1

Customer Ratings of an Automobile Service Center

A number of retailers regularly survey their customers to determine among other things, whether they were happy with their purchase or service and whether they intended to return. A chain of hardware stores/automobile service centers is one such company. At the completion of repair work customers are asked to fill out the following form:

A random sample of 134 responses was drawn. The responses to questions 1 through 4 (1 = poor, 2 = fair, 3 = good, 4 = very good) are stored in columns A through D, respectively. Responses to question 5 (2 = yes, 1 = no) are stored in column E. Column F stores a 1 if a positive comment was made, 2 if a

negative comment was made, and 3 if no comment was made.

a. Can we infer that those who say they will return assess each category higher than those who will not return?

b. Is there sufficient evidence to infer that those who make positive comments, negative

comments, and no comments differ in their assessment of each category?

c. Prepare a presentation for the company's executives describing your analysis.

Tell us what you think.				
Are You Satisfied?	**Very Good**	**Good**	**Fair**	**Poor**
1. Quality of work performed				
2. Fairness of price				
3. Explanation of work and guarantee				
4. Checkout process				
5. Will return in future				
Comments? YES NO				

APPENDIX 19.A / XLSTAT OUTPUT AND INSTRUCTIONS

Note: Because of the way XLSTAT deals with tied values, the test statistic and p-value will differ from the test statistic and p-value calculated manually or by Do-It-Yourself Excel.

XLSTAT can perform all the nonparametric tests (except for the Spearman rank correlation test) on stacked or unstacked data.

Wilcoxon Rank Sum Test

Example 19.2

XLSTAT performs the Mann–Whitney Test, which produces the same result as the Wilcoxon Rank Sum Test.

$$U = T_1 - \frac{n_1(n_1 + 1)}{2}$$

For large samples, we use the normal approximation

$$Z = \frac{U - E(U)}{\sigma_U}$$

where

$$E(U) = \frac{n_1 n_2}{2}$$

and

$$\sigma_U = \sqrt{\frac{n_1 n_2 (n_1 + n_2 + 1)}{12}}$$

	B	C	D	E	F	G	H
19	Mann-Whitney test / Upper-tailed test:						
20							
21	U	156.50					
22	U (standardized)	1.871					
23	Expected value	112.5					
24	Variance (U)	552.8					
25	p-value (one-tailed)	0.0306					
26	alpha	0.05					
27	An approximation has been used to compute the p-value.						
28	Ties have been detected in the data and the appropriate corrections have been applied.						

The value of the test statistic is 1.871 and the p-value = .0306.

Instructions

1. Type or import the data into two columns. (Open Xm19-02. Click the Unstacked tab.)

2. Click **XLSTAT, Nonparametric tests**, and **Comparison of two samples (Wilcoxon, Mann-Whitney,...)**.

3. Check **One column per sample**. Enter the ranges of the two samples (A1:A16) (B1:B16).

4. Click the **Options** tab and choose **Alternative Hypothesis Sample 1 − Sample 2 > D** and specify the **Hypothesized difference D** (0). Check **Asymptotic p-value**. Do not check **Continuity correction**.

Example 19.3

	B	C	D	E	F	G	H
19	Mann-Whitney test / Two-tailed test:						
20							
21	U	138					
22	U (standardized)	-2.565					
23	Expected value	250.0					
24	Variance (U)	1907					
25	p-value (Two-tailed)	0.0103					
26	alpha	0.05					
27	An approximation has been used to compute the p-value.						
28	Ties have been detected in the data and the appropriate corrections have been applied.						

Instructions

1. Follow the instructions for Example 19.2.

2. Click Options and select **Sample 1 − Sample 2 ≠ D** in the **Alternative Hypothesis** box.

Sign Test

Example 19.4

	B	C	D	E	F	G	H
18	Sign test / Upper-tailed test:						
19							
20	N+	17					
21	Expected value	11.500					
22	Variance (N+)	5.750					
23	p-value (one-tailed)	0.0173					
24	alpha	0.05					
25	The p-value is computed using an exact method.						
26	Ties have been detected in the data and the appropriate corrections have been applied.						

XLSTAT calculates the *p*-value using the binomial distribution (exact distribution). In this example X is binomial with $n = 23$ and $p = .5$. Hence (using Excel)

$$p\text{-value} = P(X \geq 17) = .0173$$

Instructions

1. Type or import the data into two columns. (Open Xm19-04. Click the Unstacked tab.)

2. Click **XLSTAT, Nonparametric tests**, and **Comparison of two samples (Wilcoxon, Mann-Whitney,...)**.

3. Check **Paired samples** and **Sign test**. Enter the ranges of the two samples (B1:B26) (C1:C26).

4. Click the **Options** tab and choose **Alternative Hypothesis Sample 1 − Sample 2 > D** and specify the **Hypothesized difference D** (0).

Wilcoxon Signed Rank Sum Test

Example 19.5

	B	C	D	E	F	G	H	I
19	Wilcoxon signed-rank test / Two-tailed test:							
20								
21	V	367.5						
22	V (standardized)	1.947						
23	Expected value	264.0						
24	Variance (V)	2824.5						
25	p-value (Two-tailed)	0.0515						
26	alpha	0.05						
27	The exact p-value could not be computed. An approximation has been used to compute the p-value.							
28	Ties have been detected in the data and the appropriate corrections have been applied.							

The value of the tests statistic $= 1.947$ and p-value $= .0515$.

Instructions

Use the same instructions for the Wilcoxon, Mann–Whitney Test except choose **Paired samples** and **Wilcoxon signed rank sum**. Choose **Sample 1 − Sample 2 ≠ D**.

Kruskal–Wallis Test

Chapter-Opening Example

	B	C	D	E	F	G	H
33	Kruskal-Wallis test / Two-tailed test (NEWS):						
34							
35	K (Observed value)	35.23					
36	K (Critical value)	5.991					
37	DF	2					
38	p-value (one-tailed)	< 0.0001					
39	alpha	0.05					
40	An approximation has been used to compute the p-value.						
41	Ties have been detected in the data and the appropriate corrections have been applied.						

The test statistic is $K = 35.23$ and p-value is approximately 0.

Instructions

XLSTAT can conduct this test with stacked data. However, it cannot do so with missing data. Delete rows with blanks in either column. See online appendix Excel Instructions for Deleting Rows with Blanks. Alternatively, unstack the data and click the **Missing data** tab.

1. Type or import the data into adjacent columns. (Open GSS2018.) Copy columns AH and BG into a new spreadsheet (Columns A and B, respectively).

2. Click **XLSTAT, Nonparametric tests**, and **Comparison of k samples (Kruskal-Wallis, Friedman…)**.

3. Choose **One column per variable** under **Data format**. Specify the **Data: B1:B1488** and **Sample identifiers: A1:A1488**. Select **Kruskal-Wallis test**.

4. Click the **Options** tab and check **Asymptotic p-value**.

5. Click the **Outputs** tab and check **Summary table**.

Friedman Test

Example 19.6

	A	B	C	D	E	F	G
19	Friedman's test:						
20							
21	Q (Observed value)	12.86					
22	Q (Critical value)	7.815					
23	DF	3					
24	p-value (one-tailed)	0.0049					
25	alpha	0.05					
26	An approximation has been used to compute the p-value.						
27	Ties have been detected in the data and the appropriate corrections have been applied.						

Test statistic $= 12.86$, p-value $= .0049$.

Instructions

1. Type or import the data into adjacent columns. (Open Xm19-06. Click the Unstacked tab.)

2. Click **XLSTAT, Nonparametric tests**, and **Comparison of k samples (Kruskal-Wallis, Friedman...)**.

3. Check **Paired samples** and **Friedman test**. In the **Samples** box type the range of the observations (B1:E9).

4. Click the **Options** tab and check **Asymptotic p-value**. Click **outputs** and check **Summary table**.

Spearman Rank Correlation Coefficient

Example 19.7

	B	C	D	E	F	G
8	Correlation matrix (Spearman):					
9						
10	Variables	Aptitude	Performance			
11	Aptitude	**1**	0.2930			
12	Performance	0.2930	**1**			
13	Values in bold are different from 0 with a significance level alpha=0.05					
14						
15	p-values (Spearman):					
16						
17	Variables	Aptitude	Performance			
18	Aptitude	**0**	0.0669			
19	Performance	0.0669	**0**			

The Spearman correlation coefficient $= .2930$ and the p-value $= .0669$.

Instructions

1. Type or import the data into adjacent columns. (Open Xm19-07.)

2. Click **XLSTAT, Correlation/Association test**, and **Correlation tests**.

3. Enter the input range (B1:C41) and choose **Spearman**.

4. Click the **Outputs tab** and check **Correlations** and **p-values**.

APPENDIX 19.B / Stata Output and Instructions

The Wilcoxon Rank Sum Test (Section 19-1) and the Kruskal–Wallis Test (Section 19-3) require stacked data whereas Excel uses unstacked data. For the exercises in these sections, we offer both formats. The chapter exercises have only one format—unstacked. To solve exercises using the Wilcoxon Rank Sum Test and the Kruskal–Wallis Test, Stata users will have to stack the data.

Wilcoxon Rank Sum Test

Example 19.2

Two-sample Wilcoxon rank-sum (Mann-Whitney) test

TypeofDrug	obs	rank sum	expected
1	15	276.5	232.5
2	15	188.5	232.5
combined	30	465	465

```
unadjusted variance      581.25
adjustment for ties      -28.45
                        _____
adjusted variance        552.80
```

Ho: DrugEf~s(Typeof~g==1) = DrugEf~s(Typeof~g==2)

$$z = 1.871$$
$$\text{Prob} > |z| = 0.0613$$
$$\text{Exact Prob} = 0.0673$$

When there are tied values, Stata adjusts the variance so that the test statistic and p-value are slightly different from the Excel calculations. Stata conducts a two-tail test only. It does so by computing the area in the tail of the sampling distribution and then multiplying by 2 to produce the p-value. In this example we determine the one-tail p-value by dividing Stata's value by 2. The test statistic is $z = 1.871$ and the p-value = $.0613/2 = .0307$.

Instructions

1. Import or type the data into columns. (Click File/Import /Excel spreadsheet (*xls,*xlsx)/Chapter 19/Xm19-02 Stacked A1:B31.) Click **Import first row as variable names**.

2. Click **Statistics, Summaries, tables, and tests, Nonparametric tests of hypotheses**, and **Wilcoxon rank-sum test**.

3. In the **Variable:** box select **Drug Effectiveness**. In the **Grouping variable:** box select **Type of Drug.**

Example 19.3

```
Two-sample Wilcoxon rank-sum (Mann-Whitney) test
```

Degree	obs	rank sum	expected
1	25	463	575
2	20	572	460
combined	45	1035	1035

```
unadjusted variance      1916.67
adjustment for ties        -9.85
                         _____
adjusted variance        1906.82

Ho: Durati~t(Degree==1) = Durati~t(Degree==2)
         z =  -2.565
  Prob > |z| =   0.0103
  Exact Prob =   0.0095
```

The test statistic is $z = -2.565$ and the p-value $= .0103$.

Sign Test

Example 19.4

```
Sign test
```

sign	observed	expected
positive	17	11.5
negative	6	11.5
zero	2	2
all	25	25

```
One-sided tests:
  Ho: median of European - American = 0 vs.
  Ha: median of European - American > 0
      Pr(#positive >= 17) =
         Binomial(n = 23, x >= 17, p = 0.5) =  0.0173

  Ho: median of European - American = 0 vs.
  Ha: median of European - American < 0
      Pr(#negative >= 6) =
         Binomial(n = 23, x >= 6, p = 0.5) =  0.9947

Two-sided test:
  Ho: median of European - American = 0 vs.
  Ha: median of European - American != 0
      Pr(#positive >= 17 or #negative >= 17) =
         min(1, 2*Binomial(n = 23, x >= 17, p = 0.5)) =  0.0347
```

Stata conducts the two-tail and both one-tail tests and computes the p-value using the exact (binomial distribution), which is .0173.

Instructions

1. Import the data in unstacked format. (Click File/Import /Excel spreadsheet (*xls,*xlsx)/Chapter 19/Xm19-04 Unstacked **A1:C26**.) Click **Import first row as variable names**.

2. Click **Statistics, Summaries, tables, and tests, Nonparametric tests of hypotheses**, and **Test equality of matched pairs**.

3. In the **Variable:** box select **European**. In the **Expression:** box select **American**.

Wilcoxon Signed Rank Sum Test

Example 19.5

```
Wilcoxon signed-rank test

         sign |   obs   sum ranks    expected
     ---------+-------------------------------
     positive |    20       367.5         264
     negative |    12       160.5         264
         zero |     0           0           0
     ---------+-------------------------------
          all |    32         528         528

unadjusted variance      2860.00
adjustment for ties       -35.50
adjustment for zeros        0.00
                         --------
adjusted variance        2824.50

Ho: Arrival800 = Flextime
            z =    1.947
   Prob > |z| =   0.0515
   Exact Prob =   0.0509
```

Stata conducts a two-tail test, which is what is required in this example. Test statistic: $z = 1.947$ and p-value $= .0515$.

Instructions

1. Import the data in unstacked format. (Click File/Import /Excel spreadsheet (*xls,*xlsx)/Chapter 19/Xm19-05 Unstacked **A1:C33**.) Click **Import first row as variable names**.

2. Click **Statistics, Summaries, tables, and tests Nonparametric tests of hypotheses**, and **Wilcoxon matched-pairs signed-rank test**.

3. In the **Variable:** box select **Arrival800**. In the **Expression:** box select **Flextime**.

Kruskal–Wallis Test

Chapter-Opening Example

```
Kruskal-Wallis equality-of-populations rank test
```

PARTYID3	Obs	Rank Sum
1	484	319323.50
2	652	524959.50
3	351	262045.00

```
chi-squared =      31.864 with 2 d.f.
probability =       0.0001

chi-squared with ties =   35.234 with 2 d.f.
probability =       0.0001
```

The unadjusted test statistic is $\chi^2 = 31.864$ and its p-value $= .0001$.

Instructions

1. Import the data in stacked data format. (Click File/Import /Excel spreadsheet (*xls,*xlsx)/GSS Files/GSS2018.) Click **Import first row as variable names**.

2. Click **Statistics, Summaries, tables, and tests Nonparametric tests of hypotheses**, and **Kruskal-Wallis rank test**.

3. Select **NEWS** in the **Outcome variable:** box and select **PARTYID3** in the **Variable defining groups:** box.

Stata does not perform the Friedman Test.

Spearman Rank Correlation Coefficient Test

Example 19.7

```
Number of obs =        40
Spearman's rho =       0.2930

Test of Ho: Aptitude and Performance are independent
    Prob > |t| =       0.0665
```

The Spearman correlation coefficient is .2930. The *p*-value of the test is .0665.

Instructions

1. Import the data in unstacked format. (Click File/Import /Excel spreadsheet (*xls,*xlsx)/Chapter 19/Xm19-07.) Click **Import first row as variable names**.

2. Click **Statistics, Summaries, tables, and tests, Nonparametric tests of hypotheses**, and **Spearman's rank correlation**.

3. Select **Aptitude Performance** in the **Variables (leave empty for all):** box.

APPENDIX 19.C / REVIEW OF STATISTICAL INFERENCE (CHAPTERS 12 TO 19)

Although there are four more chapters to go in this book, we have completed our presentation of statistical inference. (The remaining techniques—times-series analysis and forecasting, statistical process control, and decision analysis—address different kinds of problems, which tend to be easy to identify.) The list of statistical techniques in Table A19.1 and the flowchart in Figure A19.1 now contain all the statistical inference methods presented in this book. Use them to determine how each of the exercises is to be addressed. Because these exercises were drawn from a wide variety of applications and collectively require the use of all the techniques introduced in this book, they provide the same kind of challenge faced by real statistics practitioners. By attempting to solve these problems, you will be getting realistic exposure to statistical applications. Incidentally, this also provides practice in the approach required to succeed in a statistics course examination.

TABLE **A19.1** **Summary of Statistical Techniques in Chapters 12 to 19**

Problem objective: Describe a population.

Data type: Interval

Descriptive measurement: Central location

Parameter: μ

Test statistic: $t = \dfrac{\bar{x} - \mu}{s/\sqrt{n}}$

Interval estimator: $\bar{x} \pm t_{\alpha/2}\dfrac{s}{\sqrt{n}}$

Required condition: Population is normal.

Descriptive measurement: Variability

Parameter: σ^2

Test statistic: $\chi^2 = \dfrac{(n-1)s^2}{\sigma^2}$

Interval estimator: LCL $= \dfrac{(n-1)s^2}{\chi^2_{\alpha/2}}$ UCL $= \dfrac{(n-1)s^2}{\chi^2_{1-\alpha/2}}$

Required condition: Population is normal.

Data type: Nominal

Number of categories: Two

Parameter: p

Test statistic: $z = \dfrac{\hat{p} - p}{\sqrt{p(1-p)/n}}$

Interval estimator: $\hat{p} \pm z_{\alpha/2}\sqrt{\hat{p}(1-\hat{p})/n}$

Required condition: $np \geq 5$ and $n(1-p) \geq 5$ (for test)

$n\hat{p} \geq 5$ and $n(1-\hat{p}) \geq 5$ (for estimate)

TABLE A19.1 (*Continued*)

Number of categories: Two or more

Parameters: $p_1, p_2, \ldots, p_k$

Statistical technique: Chi-squared goodness-of-fit

Test statistic: $\chi^2 = \sum \dfrac{(f_i - e_i)^2}{e_i}$

Required condition: $e_i \geq 5$

Problem objective: Compare two populations.

Data type: Interval

Descriptive measurement: Central location

Experimental design: Independent samples

Population variances: $\sigma_1^2 = \sigma_2^2$

Parameter: $\mu_1 - \mu_2$

Test statistic: $t = \dfrac{(\overline{x}_1 - \overline{x}_2) - (\mu_1 - \mu_2)}{\sqrt{s_p^2\left(\dfrac{1}{n_1} + \dfrac{1}{n_2}\right)}}$

Interval estimator: $(\overline{x}_1 - \overline{x}_2) \pm t_{\alpha/2}\sqrt{s_p^2\left(\dfrac{1}{n_1} + \dfrac{1}{n_2}\right)}$

Required condition: Populations are normal.
If populations are nonnormal, apply the Wilcoxon Rank Sum Test.

Population variances: $\sigma_1^2 \neq \sigma_2^2$

Parameter: $\mu_1 - \mu_2$

Test statistic: $t = \dfrac{(\overline{x}_1 - \overline{x}_2) - (\mu_1 - \mu_2)}{\sqrt{\left(\dfrac{s_1^2}{n_1} + \dfrac{s_2^2}{n_2}\right)}}$

Interval estimator: $(\overline{x}_1 - \overline{x}_2) \pm t_{\alpha/2}\sqrt{\left(\dfrac{s_1^2}{n_1} + \dfrac{s_2^2}{n_2}\right)}$

Required condition: Populations are normal.

Experimental design: Matched pairs

Parameter: μ_D

Test statistic: $t = \dfrac{\overline{x}_D - \mu_D}{s_D/\sqrt{n_D}}$

Interval estimator: $\overline{x}_D \pm t_{\alpha/2}\dfrac{s_D}{\sqrt{n_D}}$

Required condition: Differences are normal.
If differences are nonnormal, apply Wilcoxon Signed Rank Sum Test.
Nonparametric technique: Wilcoxon Signed Rank Sum Test

Test statistic: $z = \dfrac{T - E(T)}{\sigma_T}$

Required condition: Populations are identical in shape and spread.

(*Continued*)

TABLE A19.1 (*Continued*)

Descriptive measurement: Variability

Parameter: σ_1^2/σ_2^2

Test statistic: $F = \dfrac{s_1^2}{s_2^2}$

Interval estimator: $\text{LCL} = \left(\dfrac{s_1^2}{s_2^2}\right)\dfrac{1}{F_{\alpha/2,\nu_1,\nu_2}}$ $\text{UCL} = \left(\dfrac{s_1^2}{s_2^2}\right)F_{\alpha/2,\nu_2,\nu_1}$

Required condition: Populations are normal.

Data type: Ordinal

Experimental design: Independent samples

Nonparametric technique: Wilcoxon Rank Sum Test

Test statistic: $z = \dfrac{T - E(T)}{\sigma_T}$

Required condition: Populations are identical in shape and spread.

Experimental design: Matched pairs

Nonparametric technique: Sign test

Test statistic: $z = \dfrac{x - .5n}{.5\sqrt{n}}$

Required condition: Populations are identical in shape and spread.

Data type: Nominal

Number of categories: Two

Parameter: $p_1 - p_2$

Test statistic:

Case 1: H_0: $p_1 - p_2 = 0$ $z = \dfrac{(\hat{p}_1 - \hat{p}_2)}{\sqrt{\hat{p}(1 - \hat{p})\left(\dfrac{1}{n_1} + \dfrac{1}{n_2}\right)}}$

Case 2: H_0: $p_1 - p_2 = D$ $(D \neq 0)$ $z = \dfrac{(\hat{p}_1 - \hat{p}_2) - (p_1 - p_2)}{\sqrt{\dfrac{\hat{p}_1(1 - \hat{p}_1)}{n_1} + \dfrac{\hat{p}_2(1 - \hat{p}_2)}{n_2}}}$

Interval estimator: $(\hat{p}_1 - \hat{p}_2) \pm z_{\alpha/2}\sqrt{\dfrac{\hat{p}_1(1 - \hat{p}_1)}{n_1} + \dfrac{\hat{p}_2(1 - \hat{p}_2)}{n_2}}$

Required condition: $n_1\hat{p}_1$, $n_1(1 - \hat{p}_1)$, $n_2\hat{p}_2$, and $n_2(1 - \hat{p}_2) \geq 5$

Number of categories: Two or more

Statistical technique: Chi-squared test of a contingency table

Test statistic: $\chi^2 = \sum \dfrac{(f_i - e_i)^2}{e_i}$

Required condition: $e_i \geq 5$

Problem objective: Compare two or more populations.

Data type: Interval

Experimental design: Independent samples

TABLE **A19.1** (*Continued*)

Number of factors: One

Parameters: $\mu_1, \mu_2, \ldots, \mu_k$

Statistical technique: (One-way analysis of variance)

Test statistic: $F = \dfrac{MST}{MSE}$

Statistical technique: Multiple comparisons:

Fisher and Bonferroni adjustment: $LSD = t_{\alpha/2} \sqrt{MSE\left(\dfrac{1}{n_i} + \dfrac{1}{n_j}\right)}$

Tukey: $\omega = q_\alpha(k, \nu) \sqrt{\dfrac{MSE}{n_g}}$

Required conditions: Populations are normal with equal variances. If populations are nonnormal, apply the Kruskal–Wallis Test.

Number of factors: Two

Parameters: $\mu_1, \mu_2, \ldots, \mu_k$

Statistical technique: (Two-factor analysis of variance)

Test statistics: $F = \dfrac{MS(AB)}{MSE} \quad F = \dfrac{MS(A)}{MSE} \quad F = \dfrac{MS(B)}{MSE}$

Required conditions: Populations are normal with equal variances.

Experimental design: Randomized blocks

Parameters: $\mu_1, \mu_2, \ldots, \mu_k$

Statistical technique: (Two-way analysis of variance)

Test statistics: $F = \dfrac{MST}{MSE} \quad F = \dfrac{MSB}{MSE}$

Required conditions: Populations are normal with equal variances. If populations are nonnormal, apply the Friedman Test.

Data type: Ordinal

Experimental design: Independent samples

Nonparametric technique: Kruskal–Wallis Test

Test statistic: $H = \left[\dfrac{12}{n(n + 1)} \sum_{j=1}^{k} \dfrac{T_j^2}{n_j}\right] - 3(n + 1)$

Required condition: Populations are identical in shape and spread and $n_j \geq 5$.

Experimental design: Randomized blocks

Nonparametric technique: Friedman Test

Test statistic: $F_r = \left[\dfrac{12}{b(k)(k + 1)} \sum_{j=1}^{k} T_j^2\right] - 3b(k + 1)$

Required condition: Populations are identical in shape and spread and $n_j \geq 5$.

Data type: Nominal

Number of categories: Two or more

Statistical technique: Chi-squared test of a contingency table

Test statistic: $\chi^2 = \sum \dfrac{(f_i - e_i)^2}{e_i}$

Required condition: $e_i \geq 5$

(*Continued*)

TABLE **A19.1** (*Continued*)

Problem objective: Analyze the relationship between two variables.

Data type: Interval

Parameters: β_0, β_1, ρ

Statistical technique: Simple linear regression and correlation

Test statistic: $t = \dfrac{b_1 - \beta_1}{s_{b_1}}; \ t = r\sqrt{\dfrac{n-2}{1-r^2}}$

Prediction interval: $\hat{y} \pm t_{\alpha/2, n-2}s_\varepsilon \sqrt{1 + \dfrac{1}{n} + \dfrac{(x_g - \bar{x})^2}{(n-1)s_x^2}}$

Interval estimator of expected value: $\hat{y} \pm t_{\alpha/2, n-2}s_\varepsilon \sqrt{\dfrac{1}{n} + \dfrac{(x_g - \bar{x})^2}{(n-1)s_x^2}}$

Required conditions: ε is normally distributed with mean 0 and standard deviation σ_ε; ε values are independent.

To test whether two bivariate normally distributed variables are linearly related:

Parameter: ρ

Test statistic: $t = r\sqrt{\dfrac{n-2}{1-r^2}}$

If x and y are not bivariate normally distributed, apply the Spearman rank correlation coefficient test.

Data type: Ordinal

Statistical technique: Spearman rank correlation coefficient test

Parameter: ρ_s

Test statistic: $z = r_s\sqrt{n-1}$

Required condition: none

Data type: Nominal

Statistical technique: Chi-squared test of a contingency table

Test statistic: $\chi^2 = \sum \dfrac{(f_i - e_i)^2}{e_i}$

Required condition: $e_i \geq 5$

Problem objective: Analyze the relationship among two or more variables.

Data type: Interval

Parameters: $\beta_0, \beta_1, \beta_2, \ldots, \beta_k$

Statistical technique: multiple regression

Test statistics: $t = \dfrac{b_i - \beta_i}{s_{b_i}} (i = 1, 2, \ldots, k); \quad F = \dfrac{\text{MSR}}{\text{MSE}}$

Required conditions: ε is normally distributed with mean 0 and standard deviation σ_ε; ε values are independent.

FIGURE **A19.1** Flowchart of All Statistical Inference Techniques

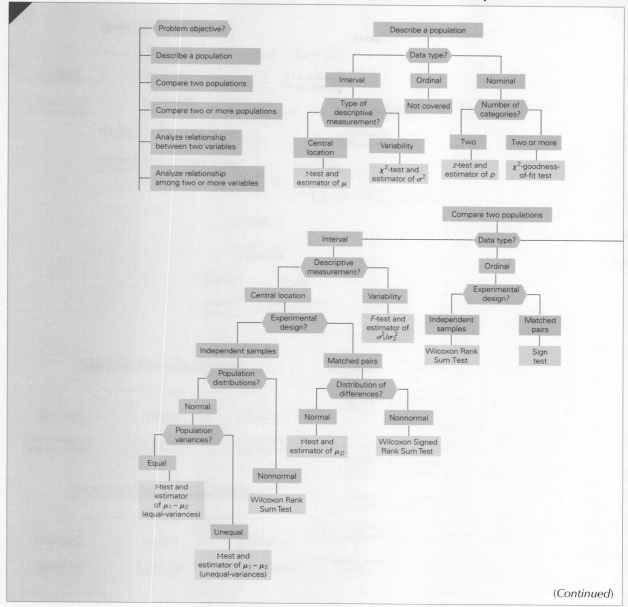

(Continued)

FIGURE **A19.1** (*Continued*)

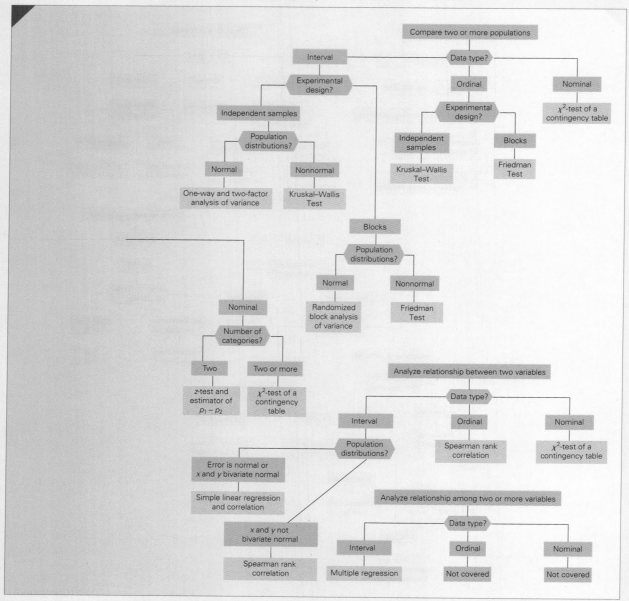

EXERCISES

Use a 5% significance level for all tests and a 95% confidence level for all estimates.

A19.1 XrA19-01 Most supermarkets load groceries into plastic bags. However, plastic bags take many years to decompose in garbage dumps. To determine how big the problem might be, a random sample of American households was each asked to determine the number of plastic bags they use and discard in a week. The last census revealed that there are about 130 million households in the United States. Estimate with 95% confidence the total number of plastic bags discarded per week.

A19.2 XrA19-02 Some customers spend a great deal of time doing research before choosing a particular brand of a product, particularly an expensive product. Does this result in a more satisfied customer? To shed light on this question, a random sample of people who purchased a new car within the last 2 years was drawn. Respondents were asked to report the amount of time spent researching (reading newspaper reports and brochures, as well as looking on the Internet) in hours and their level of satisfaction measured in the following way:

1. Extremely dissatisfied
2. Somewhat dissatisfied
3. Neither satisfied or dissatisfied
4. Somewhat satisfied
5. Extremely satisfied

Do the data allow us to infer that those who do more research are more satisfied with their choice?

A19.3 XrA19-03 Burger King Restaurants regularly survey customers to determine how well they are doing. Suppose that a survey asked customers to rate (among other things) the speed of service. The responses are

1 = Poor
2 = Good
3 = Very good
4 = Excellent

The responses for the day shift and night shift were recorded. Can we infer that night shift customers rate the service differently than the day shift?

A19.4 XrA19-04 In an effort to analyze the results of Exercise A15.9, the researcher recorded the total travel length of the course. This variable measures the total distance golfers must walk to play a round of golf. It is the sum of the golf-course playing distance plus the distance golfers must walk from the

green to the next tee. What can you conclude from these data?

A19.5 XrA19-05+ In city after city, downtown cores have become less and less populated and poorer because shoppers have taken their money to the suburbs and to shopping malls. One reason often given for the decline in downtown shops is the difficulty in parking. To shed more light on the issue, a random sample of 197 adults was asked to rate the difficulty in parking using the following responses:

Poor (1), Acceptable (2), Good (3), Very good (4), Excellent (5)

These adults were also asked how often they shopped at a downtown store in a typical month. Do these data allow us to infer that the problem of parking is one reason for the decline in downtown shopping?

A19.6 XrA19-05+ Refer to A19.5. To acquire information about who is shopping downtown, the statistics practitioner also recorded the annual household income (in $1,000s) of the respondents. Is there enough evidence to infer that affluent people shop downtown more frequently than poorer people?

A19.7 XrA19-07 Why do some students do well in university while others struggle? To help answer this question, a random sample of first-year students at four universities was selected. Those who had a grade point average of more than 3.0 (group 1) and those who had a grade point average of less than 2.0 (group 2) were surveyed. For each student, researchers recorded the results of tests (scored 0 to 10) that measure the following.

Interpersonal skills (strong social skills, ability to interact effectively)
Stress management (being able to work well under pressure or resist and delay an impulse)

Do these data provide sufficient evidence to infer that students whose GPA is more than 3.0 score higher in interpersonal skills and stress management than students whose GPA is less than 2.0?

A19.8 XrA19-08 The issue of immigration, legal and illegal, has political and economic ramifications. An important component of the issue is how well immigrants integrate into the American economy. A University of Florida study attempted to answer this question. Researchers randomly surveyed U.S.-born Americans, immigrants who arrived in the United States before 1980, and immigrants who arrived after 1980 in Miami-Dade County, the state of Florida, and the United States. Each respondent was employed full-time and was asked to report annual earnings. Conduct tests to determine whether differences exist between the three groups in each of the three geographic regions.

A19.9 XrA19-09   During the pandemic year of 2020, lockdowns resulted in many people staying at home and with nothing to do except to eat. A survey asked American households how much they spent on food at home in 2020. According to a U.S. government study, the average food expenditure at home was $4,643 in 2019. Is there sufficient evidence to infer that there was an increase in 2020?

A19.10 XrA19-10   An online investment company undertook a study to examine how well investors who administered their own portfolios did. They recorded the annual return on investment, the number of years that they have been doing investing, whether they had taken at least one university finance course (1 = Yes, 0 = No), and whether they had taken at least one university statistics course (1 = Yes, 0 = No). Conduct a multiple regression analysis.
   a. Is there enough evidence that more experience produces higher rates of return?
   b. Is there sufficient evidence that taking a finance course yields lower returns on investment?
   c. Is there sufficient evidence that taking a statistics course improves return on investment?

A19.11 XrA19-11   An important measure of the health of a nation's economy is total debt. A Canadian survey asked a random sample of households how much money (in $1,000s) they owed. This includes mortgages, loans, and credit card debt. Assuming that there are 10 million households in Canada, estimate with 95% confidence the total debt in Canada.

A19.12 XrA19-12   In Chapter 7, we showed that diversification reduces the risk associated with a portfolio of investments. (Most experts advise their clients that the portfolios should contain between 20 and 30 stocks scattered in different industries.) Do investors understand this concept? To help answer this question, a random sample of investors' portfolios was sampled. This survey was a duplicate of the one done 5 years earlier. The number of stocks in each sampled portfolio was recorded. Do these data allow us to infer that investors' portfolios are becoming more diverse?

A19.13 XrA19-13   The cost of taking an extra year to earn an MBA is quite high. To determine whether it is worthwhile, a BBA graduate surveyed 200 people who had either a BBA or an MBA and recorded their annual salary (in $1,000s) after 5 years of work. The student determined that the added cost of the MBA is warranted only if the mean income of MBAs is more than $5,000 greater than that of BBAs. Can we conclude that acquiring an MBA is worthwhile?

A19.14 XrA19-14   Flonase is a nasal allergy treatment; like all drugs, it has side effects. Before approving it, the company (GlaxoSmithKline) performed a number of experiments to determine the drug's side effects. In one such experiment, a random sample of 1,707 volunteers was drawn. Of these, 167 were given a 100-mcg dose once a day (1), 782 were given 200 mcg daily (2), and the remaining 758 were given a placebo spray once a day (3). Volunteers reported whether they had any side effects and, if so, which was the most serious. The following data were recorded.

   1. Headache
   2. Pharyngitis (sore throat)
   3. Epistaxis (nosebleed)
   4. Other side effect
   5. No side effect

Do these data allow us to infer that there are differences in side effects between the three groups of volunteers?

A19.15 XrA19-15   A statistician took random samples of teenagers 13 to 18 years old and asked each how many friends they had on Facebook. Also recorded were the age category, where 1 = 13–14, 2 = 15–16, and 3 = 17–18. Is there sufficient evidence to infer that there are differences in the number of friends between the three age categories?

A19.16 XrA19-16   Obesity among children in North America is said to be at near-epidemic proportions. Some experts blame television for the problem, citing the statistic that children watch an average of 26 hours per week. During this time, children are not engaged in any physical activity, which results in weight gains. However, the problem may be compounded by a reduction in metabolic rate. In an experiment to address this issue scientists took a random sample of 223 children aged 8 to 12; 41 of them were obese. Each child's metabolic rate (the amount of calories burned per hour) was measured while at rest and also measured while the child watched a television program. The differences between the two rates were recorded; column 1 contains the numbers representing the decrease in metabolic rate, and column 2 codes the children as 1 = obese and 2 = nonobese.
   a. Do these data allow us to conclude that there is a decrease in metabolism when children watch television?
   b. Can we conclude that the decrease in metabolism while watching television is greater among obese children?

A19.17 XrA19-17   Scrabble is one of the oldest and most popular board games. It is played all over the world, and there is even an annual world championship competition. The game is played by forming words and placing them on the board to obtain the maximum number of points. It is generally believed that a large vocabulary is the only skill required to be successful. However, there is a strategic element to the game that suggests that mathematical skills are just as necessary. To determine which skills are most in demand, a statistician recruited a random sample of fourth-year university English and mathematics majors and asked them to play the game. A total of 500 games was played by different pairs of English and mathematics majors. The scores in each game were recorded.

a. Can we conclude that mathematics majors win more frequently than do English majors?

b. Do these data allow us to infer that the average score obtained by English majors is greater than that for mathematics majors?

c. Why are the results of parts (a) and (b) not the same?

A19.18 XrA19-18   Ever since the discovery of germs, parents have been telling their children to wash their hands. Common sense tells us that this should help minimize the spread of infectious diseases and lead to better health. A study in Michigan tracked a random sample of children, some of whom washed their hands four or more times during the school day. The number of sick days from colds and flu and the number of sick days from stomach illness were recorded for the past year. Column 1 contains a code representing whether the child washed their hands four or more times per school day (1) or not (2). Column 2 stores the number of sick days from cold and flu and column 3 contains the number of sick days from stomach illness.

a. Do these data allow us to infer that children who washed their hands four or more times during the school day will have fewer sick days from cold and flu than other children?

b. Repeat part (a) for sick days from stomach illness.

A19.19 XrA19-19   Under the rules of Canada's Employment Insurance (EI) plan, some workers can use EI repeatedly after working only a short time. The amount of time needed to qualify for EI varies by region and by occupation. In a study undertaken by researchers, regular users of EI were surveyed and asked, among other questions, how frequently they used EI and how satisfied they were with their employment situation. The responses are

1. Very unsatisfied
2. Somewhat unsatisfied

3. Neither unsatisfied or satisfied
4. Somewhat satisfied
5. Very satisfied

Do the data allow us to conclude that workers who use EI more often are more satisfied with their employment situation?

A19.20 XrA19-20   Winter is the influenza season in North America. It has generally been accepted that young healthy North Americans need not receive flu shots because, although many contract the disease, few die from it. However, there are economic consequences. Sick days cost both employees and employers. A study published in the *New England Journal of Medicine* reported the results of an experiment to determine whether it is useful for young healthy people to take flu shots. A random sample of working adults was selected. Half received a flu shot in November; the other half received a placebo. The numbers of sick days over the next 6-month period were recorded in columns 1 (flu shot) and 2 (placebo). Columns 3 (flu shot) and 4 (placebo) contain the number of visits to the doctor.

a. Can we conclude that those who take flu shots have fewer sick days?

b. Can we conclude that those who take flu shots visit their doctors less frequently?

A19.21 XrA19-21   The high cost of medical care makes it imperative that hospitals operate efficiently and effectively. As part of a larger study, patients leaving a hospital were surveyed. They were asked how satisfied they were with the treatment they received. The responses were recorded with a measure of the degree of severity of their illness (as determined by the admitting physician) and the length of stay. These data are recorded in the following way:

Column 1: Satisfaction level (1 = very unsatisfied; 2 = somewhat unsatisfied; 3 = neither satisfied nor dissatisfied; 4 = somewhat satisfied; 5 = very satisfied)

Column 2: Severity of illness (1 = least severe and 10 = most severe)

Column 3: Number of days in hospital

a. Is the satisfaction level affected by the severity of illness?

b. Is the satisfaction level higher for patients who stay for shorter periods of time?

A19.22 XrA19-22   What should be the priority of paramedics who respond to accidents? Should they treat the patients with their limited facilities or should they rush the victims to the nearest hospital (an approach known as "scoop and run")? A research project may provide the answer. Researchers looked at the care of 1,846 trauma patients—those with life-threatening injuries—in Montreal (1), Toronto (2), and Quebec City (3). Montreal uses physicians to provide advanced life support (ALS) at the scene of the accident. Toronto uses paramedics to provide ALS, and Quebec City uses emergency medical services who apply only basic life support. The outcomes (survived = 1, died = 2) and city were recorded. Determine whether there are differences in the death rate between the three cities. What recommendation would you make?

A19.23 XrA19-23   How many golfers are there in the United States? A survey of American adults (age 18 and above) asked whether they had played golf at least once a month during the summer. The responses are 2 = yes and 1 = no. The survey also asked respondents to indicate which of the following household income categories they fell into.

1. Less than $15,000
2. $15,000 to $24,999
3. $25,000 to $34,999
4. $35,000 to $49,999
5. $50,000 to $75, 000
6. More than $75,000

Test to determine whether income is a determinant in who plays golf.

A19.24 XrA19-24   One of the arguments put forth by advocates of lower university tuition fees is that children

of low or moderate income families will not be able to pay for a child's university education. To examine this issue, a random sample of families whose children were at least 20 years old was drawn. Each family was asked to specify which of the following household income categories they fell into and whether at least one child had attended university (2 = yes and 1 = no).

1. Less than $25,000
2. $50,000 to $75,000
3. More than $100,000

Do these data allow researchers to conclude that family income affects whether children attend university?

A19.25 XrA19-25   Because of the high cost of hospital stays, anything that can reduce their length and the costs of medication would be appreciated by insurance companies, hospitals, and patients. A physician researcher was searching for ways to reduce costs and decided to investigate the effect of the room the patient stayed in. The researcher gathered data on the length of stay and the amount of pain medication (measured in morphine equivalents). Also recorded was whether the room was sunny or dim. Do these data allow the researcher to conclude that the length of stay and the amount of pain medication is lower in bright rooms than in dim ones?

GENERAL SOCIAL SURVEY EXERCISES

GSS2016   Exercises A19.26 to A19.39 are based on the 2016 survey. In 2016 there were 240,834,729 adults in the United States (*Source:* U.S. Census). ***Conduct all tests at the 5% significance level. Use a 95% confidence level for estimates.***

A19.26 Develop a regression model with income (RINCOME) as the dependent variable and years of education (EDUC), age (AGE), number of hours of work per week (HRS1), and whether the respondent worked for the government (WRKGOVT: 1 = Government, 2 = Private).
a. Test to determine whether the model is valid.
b. Interpret the coefficient for WRKGOVT.

A19.27 The survey asked whether antibiotics kill viruses as well as bacteria (VIRUSES: 1 = True, 2 = False, 8 = Don't know, 9 = No answer, 0 = Question not asked). Can we infer that women are more knowledgeable than men on this subject?

A19.28 Is there enough evidence to infer that there are differences in income (RINCOME) between people who

work for the government and people who work in the private sector (WRKGOVT: 1 = Government, 2 = Private)?

A19.29 Does one's educational attainment affect how hard one needs to work? Test to determine whether there is sufficient evidence to conclude that differences exist in the hours of work per week (HRS1) between the five educational attainments (DEGREE Highest degree completed: 0 = Left high school, 1 = High school, 2 = Junior college, 3 = Bachelor's degree, 4 = Graduate degree).

A19.30 How knowledgeable were Americans in 2016? A knowledge-based question asked, Does the Earth go around the Sun or does the Sun go around the Earth (EARTHSUN: 1 = Earth around Sun, 2 = Sun around Earth, 8 = Don't know, 9 = No answer, 0 = Question not asked)? Can we infer from the data that Americans born in the United States are less knowledgeable than Americans born outside the United States (BORN in the United States: 1 = Yes, 2 = No)?

A19.31 When Americans turn 65, Medicare pays many of their medical bills. As people age (AGE) do they become more supportive of government action to help sick people (HELPSICK: Is it government's responsibility to help pay for doctor and hospital bills? 1 = Government should help; 2, 3, 4, 5 = People should help themselves)?

A19.32 A greater proportion of the population attends some post-secondary school, college, or university. Is there sufficient evidence to infer that Americans in 2016 are more educated (EDUC) than their fathers (PAEDUC)?

A19.33 Does the amount of education (EDUC) affect respondents' beliefs about the role of government in the following question: "Should government do more or less to solve the country's problems?" The responses are HELPNOT: 1 = Government should do more; 2, 3, 4, 5 = Government does too much.

A19.34 The survey asked respondents if electrons are smaller than atoms (ELECTRON: 1 = True, 2 = False, 8 = Don't know, 9 = No answer, 0 = Question not asked). Estimate the number of American adults who did not know that electrons are smaller than atoms.

A19.35 Optimistic parents believe that their children will do well in the future. On this subject the survey asked, "When your children are at your age will their standard of living be... (KIDSSOL: 1 = Much better, 2 = Somewhat better, 3 = About the same, 4 = Somewhat worse, 5 = Much worse)?" Is there enough evidence to infer that women are more optimistic about their children's future than men?

A19.36 Is there enough evidence to infer that native-born Americans (BORN: Born in the United States: 1 = Yes, 2 = No) watch more television (TVHOURS) than foreign-born Americans?

A19.37 Are people born in the United States (BORN in the United States: 1 = Yes, 2 = No) less healthy (HEALTH: Would you say your own health, in general, is ... 1 = Excellent, 2 = Good, 3 = Fair, 4 = Poor) than people born in another country? Conduct a statistical procedure to answer the question.

A19.38 Can we infer that there is a relationship between degree attained (DEGREE: 0 = Left high school, 1 = High school, 2 = Junior college, 3 = Bachelor's degree, 4 = Graduate degree) and support for capital punishment for murderers (CAPPUN: 1 = Favor, 2 = Oppose)?

A19.39 Is there sufficient evidence to infer that there are differences in health (HEALTH: Would you say your own health, in general, is ... 1 = Excellent, 2 = Good, 3 = Fair, 4 = Poor) between the three racial groups (RACE: 1 = White, 2 = Black, 3 = Other)?

GSS2016 GSS2018   *Exercises A19.40 to A19.43 are based on the 2016 and 2018 surveys.*

A19.40 Did Americans in 2018 think that they were more successful than their parents compared to 2016? The survey asked, "Compared to your parents at your age is your standard of living... (PARSOL: 1 = Much better, 2 = Somewhat better, 3 = About the same, 4 = Somewhat worse, 5 = Much worse)?" Is there enough evidence to conclude that in 2018 Americans were more likely to think that they would do much better than their parents compared to 2016?

A19.41 How much stronger was the economy in 2018 compared to 2016? One way to gauge the difference is the unemployment rate. The GSS asked, "Have you ever been unemployed in the last 10 years (UNEMP: 1 = Yes, 2 = No)?" Is there enough evidence to infer that in 2018 Americans were less likely than in 2016 to have been unemployed in the previous 10 years?

A19.42 Are Americans postponing having children? Conduct a test to determine whether there is enough evidence to infer that the age at which Americans have their first child (AGEKDBRN) is greater in 2018 than in 2016.

A19.43 The survey asked, "How easy would it be for you to find a job with another employer with approximately the same income and fringe benefits you now have (JOBFIND: 1 = Very easy, 2 = Somewhat easy, 3 = Not easy)?" Is there enough evidence to conclude that in 2018 Americans believed that it would be easier to find another job than in 2016?

20

Nuno Andre/Shutterstock.com

TIME-SERIES ANALYSIS AND FORECASTING

CHAPTER OUTLINE

Housing Starts

DATA
Xm20-00

At the end of 2017, a major builder of residential houses in the Northeast United States wanted to predict the number of housing units that would be started in 2018. This information would be extremely useful in determining a variety of variables, including housing demand, availability of labor, and the price of building materials. To help develop an accurate forecasting model, an economist collected data on the number of housing starts (in thousands) for the previous 28 quarters (2011–2017). Forecast the number of housing starts for the four quarters of 2018. (*Source*: Federal Reserve Bank of St. Louis.)

See solution on page 896.

iStockPhoto/stockroll

INTRODUCTION

Any variable that is measured over time in sequential order is called a **time series**. We introduced time series in Chapter 3 and demonstrated how we use a line chart to graphically display the data. Our objective in this chapter is to analyze time series in order to detect patterns that will enable us to forecast future values of the time series. There is an almost unlimited number of such applications in management and economics. Some examples follow.

1. Governments want to know future values of interest rates, unemployment rates, and percentage increases in the cost of living.

2. Housing industry economists must forecast mortgage interest rates, demand for housing, and the cost of building materials.

3. Many companies attempt to predict the demand for their products and their share of the market.

4. Universities and colleges often try to forecast the number of students who will be applying for acceptance at postsecondary-school institutions.

Forecasting is a common practice among managers and government decision makers. This chapter focuses on time-series forecasting, which uses historical time-series data to predict future values of variables such as sales or unemployment rates. This entire chapter is an application tool for both economists and managers in all functional areas of business because forecasting is such a vital factor in decision making in these areas.

For example, the starting point for aggregate production planning by operations managers is to forecast the demand for the company's products. These forecasts will make use of economists' forecasts of macroeconomic variables (such as gross domestic product, disposable income, and housing starts) as well as the marketing managers' internal forecasts of their customers' future needs. Not only are these sales forecasts critical to production planning but also they are the key to accurate pro forma (i.e., forecasted) financial statements, which are produced by the accounting and financial managers to assist in their planning for future financial needs such as borrowing. Likewise, the human resources department will find such forecasts of a company's growth prospects to be invaluable in their planning for future worker requirements.

There are many different forecasting techniques. Some are based on developing a model that attempts to analyze the relationship between a dependent variable and one or more independent variables. We presented some of these methods in the chapters on regression analysis (Chapters 16, 17, and 18). The forecasting methods to be discussed in this chapter are all based on time series, which we discuss in the next section. In Sections 20-2 and 20-3, we deal with methods for detecting and measuring which time-series components exist. After we uncover this information, we can develop forecasting tools. We will only scratch the surface of this topic. Our objective is to expose you to the concepts of forecasting and to introduce some of the simpler techniques. The level of this text precludes the investigation of more complicated methods.

20-1/ TIME-SERIES COMPONENTS

A time series can consist of four different components as described in the box.

> **Time-Series Components**
>
> 1. Long-term trend
> 2. Cyclical variation
> 3. Seasonal variation
> 4. Random variation

A **trend** (also known as a **secular trend**) is a long-term, relatively smooth pattern or direction exhibited by a series. Its duration is more than 1 year. For example, the population of the United States exhibited a trend of relatively steady growth from 156 million in 1952 to 330 million in 2020. (The data are stored in Ch20:\Fig20-01.) Figure 20.1 exhibits the line chart.

FIGURE **20.1** U.S. Population (millions), 1952–2020

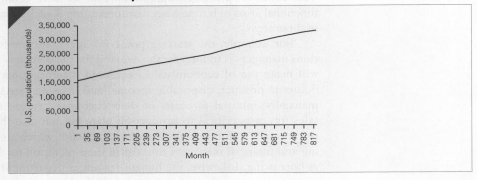

The trend of a time series is not always linear. For example, Figure 20.2 describes U.S. annual retail book sales in $billions. As you can see, sales increased from 1992 to 2008 and have decreased since then (data are stored in Ch20:\Fig20-02).

FIGURE **20.2** U.S. Annual Book Sales ($billions), 1992–2017

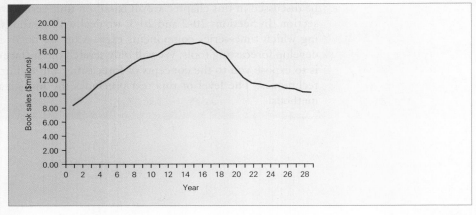

Cyclical variation is a wavelike pattern describing a long-term trend that is generally apparent over a number of years, resulting in a cyclical effect. By definition, it has duration of more than 1 year. Examples include business cycles that record periods of economic recession and inflation, long-term product-demand cycles, and cycles in monetary and financial sectors. However, cyclical patterns that are consistent and predictable are quite rare. For practical purposes, we will ignore this type of variation.

Seasonal variation refers to cycles that occur over short, repetitive calendar periods and, by definition, have a duration of less than 1 year. The term *seasonal variation* may refer to the four traditional seasons or to systematic patterns that occur during a month, a week, or even one day. Demand for restaurants features "seasonal" variation throughout the day. An illustration of seasonal variation is provided in Figure 20.3, which graphs monthly U.S. traffic volume (in millions of miles and where period 1 is January). (Data are in Ch20:\Fig20-03.) It is obvious from the graph that Americans drive more during the summer months than during the winter months.

FIGURE **20.3** U.S. Traffic Volume (Millions of Miles), 2014–2019

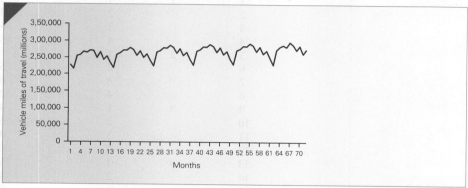

Random variation is caused by irregular and unpredictable changes in a time series that are not caused by any other components. It tends to mask the existence of the other more predictable components. Because random variation exists in almost all time series, one of the objectives of this chapter is to introduce ways to reduce the random variation, which will enable statistics practitioners to describe and measure the other components. By doing so, we hope to be able to make accurate predictions of the time series.

20-2 SMOOTHING TECHNIQUES

If we can determine which components actually exist in a time series, we can develop better forecasts. Unfortunately, the existence of random variation often makes the task of identifying components difficult. One of the simplest ways to reduce random variation is to smooth the time series. In this section, we introduce two methods: *moving averages* and *exponential smoothing*.

20-2a Moving Averages

A **moving average** for a time period is the arithmetic mean of the values in that time period and those close to it. For example, to compute the three-period moving average for any time period, we would average the time-series values in that time period, the previous period, and the following period. We compute the three-period moving averages for all time periods except the first and the last. To calculate the five-period moving average, we average the value in that time period, the values in the two preceding periods, and the values in the two following time periods. We can choose any number of periods with which to calculate the moving averages.

Gasoline Sales, Part 1

As part of an effort to forecast future sales, an operator of five independent gas stations recorded the quarterly gasoline sales (in thousands of gallons) for the past 4 years. These data are shown below. Calculate the three-quarter and five-quarter moving averages. Draw graphs of the time series and the moving averages.

Time Period	Year	Quarter	Gasoline Sales (Thousands of Gallons)
1	1	1	39
2		2	37
3		3	61
4		4	58
5	2	1	18
6		2	56
7		3	82
8		4	27
9	3	1	41
10		2	69
11		3	49
12		4	66
13	4	1	54
14		2	42
15		3	90
16		4	66

SOLUTION:

COMPUTE

MANUALLY:

To compute the first three-quarter moving average, we group the gasoline sales in periods 1, 2, and 3, and then average them. Thus, the first moving average is

$$\frac{39 + 37 + 61}{3} = \frac{137}{3} = 45.7$$

The second moving average is calculated by dropping the first period's sales (39), adding the fourth period's sales (58), and then computing the new average. Thus, the second moving average is

$$\frac{37 + 61 + 58}{3} = \frac{156}{3} = 52.0$$

The process continues as shown in the following table. Similar calculations are made to produce the five-quarter moving averages (also shown in the table).

Time Period	Gasoline Sales	Three-Quarter Moving Average	Five-Quarter Moving Average
1	39	–	–
2	37	45.7	–
3	61	52.0	42.6
4	58	45.7	46.0
5	18	44.0	55.0
6	56	52.0	48.2
7	82	55.0	44.8
8	27	50.0	55.0
9	41	45.7	53.6
10	69	53.0	50.4
11	49	61.3	55.8
12	66	56.3	56.0
13	54	54.0	60.2
14	42	62.0	63.6
15	90	66.0	–
16	66	–	–

Notice that we place the moving averages in the center of the group of values being averaged. It is for this reason that we prefer to use an odd number of periods in the moving averages. Later in this section, we discuss how to deal with an even number of periods.

Figure 20.4 displays the line chart for gasoline sales, and Figure 20.5 shows the three-period and five-period moving averages.

FIGURE **20.4** Quarterly Gasoline Sales

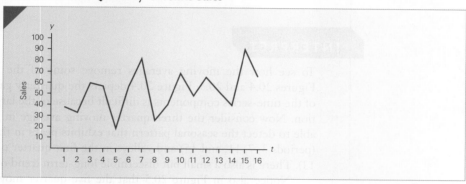

FIGURE **20.5** Quarterly Gasoline Sales and Three-Quarter and Five-Quarter Moving Averages

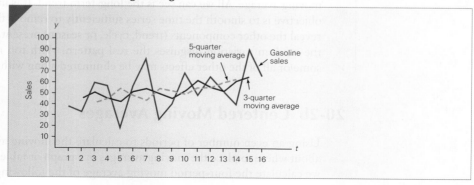

EXCEL Data Analysis

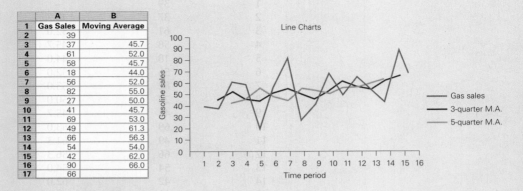

	A	B
1	Gas Sales	Moving Average
2	39	
3	37	45.7
4	61	52.0
5	58	45.7
6	18	44.0
7	56	52.0
8	82	55.0
9	27	50.0
10	41	45.7
11	69	53.0
12	49	61.3
13	66	56.3
14	54	54.0
15	42	62.0
16	90	66.0
17	66	

INSTRUCTIONS

1. Type or import the data into one column. (Open Xm20-01.)
2. Click **Data, Data Analysis**, and **Moving Average**.
3. Specify the **Input Range** (A1:A17). Specify the number of periods (3), and the **Output Range** (B1).
4. Delete the cells containing N/A.
5. To draw the line charts, follow the instructions on page 69.

INTERPRET

To see how the moving averages remove some of the random variation, examine Figures 20.4 and 20.5. Figure 20.4 depicts the quarterly gasoline sales. Discerning any of the time-series components is difficult because of the large amount of random variation. Now consider the three-quarter moving average in Figure 20.5. You should be able to detect the seasonal pattern that exhibits peaks in the third quarter of each year (periods 3, 7, 11, and 15) and valleys in the first quarter of the year (periods 5, 9, and 13). There is also a small but discernible long-term trend of increasing sales.

Notice also in Figure 20.5 that the five-quarter moving average produces more smoothing than the three-quarter moving average. In general, the longer the time period over which we average, the smoother the series becomes. Unfortunately, in this case we've smoothed too much—the seasonal pattern is no longer apparent in the five-quarter moving average. All we can see is the long-term trend. It is important to realize that our objective is to smooth the time series sufficiently to remove the random variation and to reveal the other components (trend, cycle, or season) present. With too little smoothing, the random variation disguises the real pattern. With too much smoothing, however, some or all of the other effects may be eliminated along with the random variation.

20-2b Centered Moving Averages

Using an even number of periods to calculate the moving averages presents a problem about where to place the moving averages in a graph or table. For example, suppose that we calculate the four-period moving average of the following time series:

Period	Time Series
1	15
2	27
3	20
4	14
5	25
6	11

The first moving average is

$$\frac{15 + 27 + 20 + 14}{4} = 19.0$$

However, because this value represents time periods 1, 2, 3, and 4, we must place it between periods 2 and 3. The next moving average is

$$\frac{27 + 20 + 14 + 25}{4} = 21.5$$

and it must be placed between periods 3 and 4. The moving average that falls between periods 4 and 5 is

$$\frac{20 + 14 + 25 + 11}{4} = 17.5$$

There are several problems that result from placing the moving averages between time periods, including graphing difficulties. Centering the moving average corrects the problem. We do this by computing the two-period moving average of the four-period moving average. Thus, the centered moving average for period 3 is

$$\frac{19.0 + 21.5}{2} = 20.25$$

The centered moving average for period 4 is

$$\frac{21.5 + 17.5}{2} = 19.50$$

The following table summarizes these results.

Period	Time Series	Four-Period Moving Average	Four-Period Centered Moving Average
1	15	—	—
2	27	19.0	—
3	20	21.5	20.25
4	14	17.5	19.50
5	25	—	—
6	11	—	—

20-2c Exponential Smoothing

Two drawbacks are associated with the moving average method of smoothing time series. First, we do not have moving averages for the first and last sets of time periods. If the time series has few observations, the missing values can represent an important loss of information. Second, the moving average "forgets" most of the previous time-series values. For example, in the five-quarter moving average described in Example 20.1, the average for quarter 4 reflects quarters 2, 3, 4, 5, and 6 but is not affected by quarter 1. Similarly, the moving average for quarter 5 forgets quarters 1 and 2. Both of these problems are addressed by **exponential smoothing**.

Exponentially Smoothed Time Series

$$S_t = wy_t + (1 - w)S_{t-1} \text{ for } t \geq 2$$

where

S_t = Exponentially smoothed time series at time period t

y_t = Time series at time period t

S_{t-1} = Exponentially smoothed time series at time period $t - 1$

w = Smoothing constant, where $0 \leq w \leq 1$

We begin by setting

$$S_1 = y_1$$

Then

$$
\begin{aligned}
S_2 &= wy_2 + (1 - w)S_1 \\
&= wy_2 + (1 - w)y_1 \\
S_3 &= wy_3 + (1 - w)S_2 \\
&= wy_3 + (1 - w)[wy_2 + (1 - w)y_1] \\
&= wy_3 + w(1 - w)y_2 + (1 - w)^2 y_1
\end{aligned}
$$

and so on. In general, we have

$$S_t = wy_t + w(1 - w)y_{t-1} + w(1 - w)^2 y_{t-2} + \cdots + (1 - w)^{t-1} y_1$$

This formula states that the smoothed time series in period t depends on all the previous observations of the time series.

The smoothing constant w is chosen on the basis of how much smoothing is required. A small value of w produces a great deal of smoothing. A large value of w results in very little smoothing. Figure 20.6 depicts a time series and two exponentially smoothed series with $w = .1$ and $w = .5$.

FIGURE **20.6** **Time Series and Two Exponentially Smoothed Series**

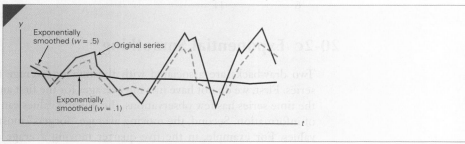

EXAMPLE 20.2

Gasoline Sales, Part 2

Apply the exponential smoothing technique with $w = .2$ and $w = .7$ to the data in Example 20.1, and graph the results.

SOLUTION:

COMPUTE

MANUALLY:

The exponentially smoothed values are calculated from the formula

$$S_t = wy_t + (1 - w)S_{t-1}$$

The results with $w = .2$ and $w = .7$ are shown in the following table.

Time Period	Gasoline Sales	Exponentially Smoothed with $w = .2$	Exponentially Smoothed with $w = .7$
1	39	39.0	39.0
2	37	38.6	37.6
3	61	43.1	54.0
4	58	46.1	56.8
5	18	40.5	29.6
6	56	43.6	48.1
7	82	51.2	71.8
8	27	46.4	40.4
9	41	45.3	40.8
10	69	50.1	60.6
11	49	49.8	52.5
12	66	53.1	61.9
13	54	53.3	56.4
14	42	51.0	46.3
15	90	58.8	76.9
16	66	60.2	69.3

Figure 20.7 shows the exponentially smoothed time series.

FIGURE **20.7** Quarterly Gasoline Sales and Exponentially Smoothed Sales with $w = .2$ and $w = .7$

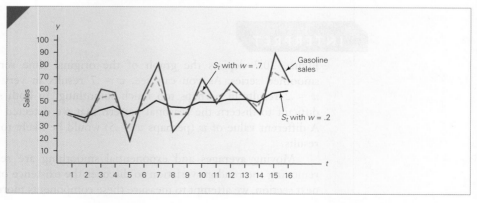

EXCEL Data Analysis

	A	B	C
1	Gas Sales	Damping factor = .8	Damping factor = .3
2	39	39.0	39.0
3	37	38.6	37.6
4	61	43.1	54.0
5	58	46.1	56.8
6	18	40.5	29.6
7	56	43.6	48.1
8	82	51.2	71.8
9	27	46.4	40.4
10	41	45.3	40.8
11	69	50.1	60.6
12	49	49.8	52.5
13	66	53.1	61.9
14	54	53.3	56.4
15	42	51.0	46.3
16	90	58.8	76.9
17	66	60.2	69.3

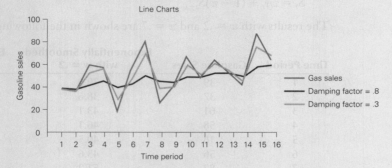

INSTRUCTIONS

1. Type or import the data into one column (Open Xm20-01.)

2. Click **Data, Data Analysis**, and **Exponential Smoothing**.

3. Specify the **Input Range** (A1:A17). Type the **Damping factor**, which is $1 - w$ (.8). Specify the **Output Range** (B1). To calculate the second exponentially smoothed time series specify $1 - w$ (.3) **Output Range** (C1).

To modify the table so that the smoothed values appear the way we calculated, manually click the cell containing the last smoothed value displayed here (58.8) and drag it to the cell below to reveal the final smoothed value (60.2 and 69.3).

INTERPRET

Figure 20.7 depicts the graph of the original time series and the exponentially smoothed series. As you can see, $w = .7$ results in very little smoothing, whereas $w = .2$ results in perhaps too much smoothing. In both smoothed time series, it is difficult to discern the seasonal pattern that we detected by using moving averages. A different value of w (perhaps $w = .5$) would be likely to produce more satisfactory results.

Moving averages and exponential smoothing are relatively crude methods of removing the random variation to discover the existence of other components. In the next section, we attempt to measure these components more precisely.

EXERCISES

20.1 Xr20-01 For the following time series, compute the three-period moving averages.

Period	Time Series	Period	Time Series
1	48	7	43
2	41	8	52
3	37	9	60
4	32	10	48
5	36	11	41
6	31	12	30

20.2 Compute the five-period moving averages for the time series in Exercise 20.1.

20.3 For Exercises 20.1 and 20.2, graph the time series and the two moving averages.

20.4 Xr20-04 For the following time series, compute the three-period moving averages.

Period	Time Series	Period	Time Series
1	16	7	24
2	22	8	29
3	19	9	21
4	24	10	23
5	30	11	19
6	26	12	15

20.5 For Exercise 20.4, compute the five-period moving averages.

20.6 For Exercises 20.4 and 20.5, graph the time series and the two moving averages.

20.7 Xr20-07 Apply exponential smoothing with $w = .1$ to help detect the components of the following time series.

Period	1	2	3	4	5
Time Series	12	18	16	24	17

Period	6	7	8	9	10
Time Series	16	25	21	23	14

20.8 Repeat Exercise 20.7 with $w = .8$.

20.9 For Exercises 20.7 and 20.8, draw the time series and the two sets of exponentially smoothed values. Does there appear to be a trend component in the time series?

20.10 Xr20-10 Apply exponential smoothing with $w = .1$ to help detect the components of the following time series.

Period	1	2	3	4	5
Time Series	38	43	42	45	46

Period	6	7	8	9	10
Time Series	48	50	49	46	45

20.11 Repeat Exercise 20.10 with $w = .8$.

20.12 For Exercises 20.10 and 20.11, draw the time series and the two sets of exponentially smoothed values. Does there appear to be a trend component in the time series?

20.13 Xr20-13 The following daily sales figures have been recorded in a medium-size merchandising firm.

Day	Week 1	2	3	4
Monday	43	51	40	64
Tuesday	45	41	57	58
Wednesday	22	37	30	33
Thursday	25	22	33	38
Friday	31	25	37	25

a. Compute the 3-day moving averages.
b. Plot the time series and the moving averages on a graph.
c. Does there appear to be a seasonal (weekly) pattern?

20.14 For Exercise 20.13, compute the 5-day moving averages, and superimpose these on the same graph. Does this help you answer part (c) of Exercise 20.13?

20.15 Xr20-15 The following quarterly sales of a department store chain were recorded for the years 2017–2020.

Quarter	Year 2017	2018	2019	2020
1	18	33	25	41
2	22	20	36	33
3	27	38	44	52
4	31	26	29	45

a. Calculate the four-quarter centered moving averages.
b. Graph the time series and the moving averages.
c. What can you conclude from your time-series smoothing?

20.16 Repeat Exercise 20.15, using exponential smoothing with $w = .4$.

20.17 Repeat Exercise 20.15, using exponential smoothing with $w = .8$.

20-3 / TREND AND SEASONAL EFFECTS

In the previous section, we described how smoothing a time series can give us a clearer picture of which components are present. In order to forecast, however, we often need more precise measurements of the time-series components.

20-3a Trend Analysis

A trend can be linear or nonlinear and, indeed, can take on a whole host of functional forms. The easiest way of measuring the long-term trend is by regression analysis, where the independent variable is time. If we believe that the long-term trend is approximately linear, we will use the linear model introduced in Chapter 16:

$$y = \beta_0 + \beta_1 t + \varepsilon$$

If we believe that the trend is nonlinear, we can use one of the polynomial models described in Chapter 18. For example, the quadratic model is

$$y = \beta_0 + \beta_1 t + \beta_2 t^2 + \varepsilon$$

In most realistic applications, the linear model is used. We will demonstrate how the long-term trend is measured and applied later in this section.

20-3b Seasonal Analysis

Seasonal variation may occur within a year or within shorter intervals, such as a month, week, or day. To measure the seasonal effect, we compute seasonal indexes, which gauge the degree to which the seasons differ from one another. One requirement necessary to calculate seasonal indexes is a time series sufficiently long enough to allow us to observe the variable over several seasons. For example, if the seasons are defined as the quarters of a year, we need to observe the time series for at least 4 years. The **seasonal indexes** are computed in the following way.

20-3c Procedure for Computing Seasonal Indexes

1. Remove the effect of seasonal and random variation by regression analysis; that is, compute the sample regression line

   $$\hat{y}_t = b_0 + b_1 t$$

2. For each time period compute the ratio

   $$\frac{y_t}{\hat{y}_t}$$

   This ratio removes most of the trend variation.

3. For each type of season, compute the average of the ratios in step 2. This procedure removes most (but seldom all) of the random variation, leaving a measure of seasonality.

4. Adjust the averages in step 3 so that the average of all the seasons is 1 (if necessary).

EXAMPLE 20.3

Hotel Quarterly Occupancy Rates

The tourist industry is subject to seasonal variation. In most resorts, the spring and summer seasons are considered the "high" seasons. Fall and winter (except for Christmas and New Year's) are "low" seasons. A hotel in Bermuda has recorded the occupancy rate for each quarter for the past 5 years. These data are shown here. Measure the seasonal variation by computing the seasonal indexes.

Year	Quarter	Occupancy Rate
2016	1	.561
	2	.702
	3	.800
	4	.568
2017	1	.575
	2	.738
	3	.868
	4	.605
2018	1	.594
	2	.738
	3	.729
	4	.600
2019	1	.622
	2	.708
	3	.806
	4	.632
2020	1	.665
	2	.835
	3	.873
	4	.670

SOLUTION:

COMPUTE

MANUALLY:

We performed a regression analysis with y = occupancy rate and t = time period $1, 2, \ldots, 20$. The regression equation is

$$\hat{y} = .639368 + .005246t$$

For each time period, we computed the ratio

$$\frac{y_t}{\hat{y}_t}$$

In the next step, we collected the ratios associated with each quarter and computed the average. We then computed the seasonal indexes by adjusting the average ratios so that they summed to 4.0, if necessary. In this example, it was not necessary.

Year	Quarter	t	y_t	$\hat{y} = .639368 + .005246t$	Ratio $\dfrac{y_t}{\hat{y}_t}$
2016	1	1	.561	.645	.870
	2	2	.702	.650	1.080
	3	3	.800	.655	1.221
	4	4	.568	.660	.860
2017	1	5	.575	.666	.864
	2	6	.738	.671	1.100
	3	7	.868	.676	1.284
	4	8	.605	.681	.888
2018	1	9	.594	.687	.865
	2	10	.738	.692	1.067
	3	11	.729	.697	1.046
	4	12	.600	.702	.854
2019	1	13	.622	.708	.879
	2	14	.708	.713	.993
	3	15	.806	.718	1.122
	4	16	.632	.723	.874
2020	1	17	.665	.729	.913
	2	18	.835	.734	1.138
	3	19	.873	.739	1.181
	4	20	.670	.744	.900

		Quarter		
Year	1	2	3	4
2016	.870	1.080	1.221	.860
2017	.864	1.100	1.284	.888
2018	.865	1.067	1.046	.854
2019	.879	.993	1.122	.874
2020	.913	1.138	1.181	.900
Average	.878	1.076	1.171	.875
Index	.878	1.076	1.171	.875

INTERPRET

The seasonal indexes tell us that, on average, the occupancy rates in the first and fourth quarters are below the annual average, and the occupancy rates in the second and third quarters are above the annual average. We expect the occupancy rate in the first quarter to be 12.2% (100% − 87.8%) below the annual rate. The second and third quarters' rates are expected to be 7.6% and 17.1%, respectively, above the annual rate. The fourth quarter's rate is 12.5% below the annual rate.

Figure 20.8 depicts the time series and the regression trend line.

FIGURE **20.8** **Time Series and Trend for Example 20.3**

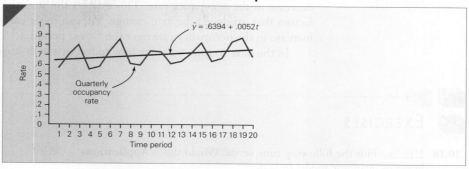

20-3d Deseasonalizing a Time Series

One application of seasonal indexes is to remove the seasonal variation in a time series. The process is called **deseasonalizing**, and the result is called a **seasonally adjusted time series**. Often this allows the statistics practitioner to more easily compare the time series across seasons. For example, the unemployment rate varies according to the season. During the winter months, unemployment usually rises; it falls in the spring and summer. The seasonally adjusted unemployment rate allows economists to determine whether unemployment has increased or decreased over the previous months. The process is easy: Simply divide the time series by the seasonal indexes. To illustrate, we have deseasonalized the occupancy rates in Example 20.3. The results are shown next.

Year	Quarter	Occupancy Rate y_t	Seasonal Index	Seasonally Adjusted Occupancy Rate
2016	1	.561	.878	.639
	2	.702	1.076	.652
	3	.800	1.171	.683
	4	.568	.875	.649
2017	1	.575	.878	.655
	2	.738	1.076	.686
	3	.868	1.171	.741
	4	.605	.875	.691
2018	1	.594	.878	.677
	2	.738	1.076	.686
	3	.729	1.171	.623
	4	.600	.875	.686
2019	1	.622	.878	.708
	2	.708	1.076	.658
	3	.806	1.171	.688
	4	.632	.875	.722
2020	1	.665	.878	.757
	2	.835	1.076	.776
	3	.873	1.171	.746
	4	.670	.875	.766

By removing the seasonality, we can see when there has been a "real" increase or decrease in the occupancy rate. This enables the statistics practitioner to examine the factors that produced the rate change. We can more easily see that there has been an increase in the occupancy rate over the 5-year period.

In the next section, we show how to forecast with seasonal indexes.

EXERCISES

20.18 Xr20-18   Plot the following time series. Would the linear or quadratic model fit better?

Period	1	2	3	4	5	6	7	8
Time Series	.5	.6	1.3	2.7	4.1	6.9	10.8	19.2

20.19 Xr20-19   Plot the following time series to determine which of the trend models appears to fit better.

Period	1	2	3	4	5
Time Series	55	57	53	49	47

Period	6	7	8	9	10
Time Series	39	41	33	28	20

20.20   Refer to Exercise 20.18. Use regression analysis to calculate the linear and quadratic trends. Which line fits better?

20.21   Refer to Exercise 20.19. Use regression analysis to calculate the linear and quadratic trends. Which line fits better?

20.22 Xr20-22   For the following time series, compute the seasonal (daily) indexes.

The regression line is

$$\hat{y} = 16.8 + .366t \quad (t = 1, 2, \ldots, 20)$$

		Week		
Day	1	2	3	4
Monday	12	11	14	17
Tuesday	18	17	16	21
Wednesday	16	19	16	20
Thursday	25	24	28	24
Friday	31	27	25	32

20.23 Xr20-23   Given the following time series, compute the seasonal indexes.

The regression equation is

$$\hat{y} = 47.7 - 1.06t \quad (t = 1, 2, \ldots, 20)$$

		Year			
Quarter	1	2	3	4	5
1	55	41	43	36	50
2	44	38	39	32	25
3	46	37	39	30	24
4	39	30	35	25	22

Applications

20.24 Xr20-24   The quarterly earnings (in $millions) of a large soft-drink manufacturer have been recorded for the years 2017–2020. These data are listed here. Compute the seasonal indexes given the regression line

$$\hat{y} = 61.75 + 1.18t \quad (t = 1, 2, \ldots, 16)$$

		Year		
Quarter	2017	2018	2019	2020
1	52	57	60	66
2	67	75	77	82
3	85	90	94	98
4	54	61	63	67

The following exercises require a computer and software.

20.25 Xr20-25   The United States does extremely well in summer Olympic games. But does it do as well in winter Olympic games? Here are the total number of medals won by the United States in each winter Olympic games, which started in 1924.

Year	1924	1928	1932	1936	1948	1952	1956
Medals	4	6	12	4	9	11	7

Year	1960	1964	1968	1972	1976	1980	1984
Medals	10	7	7	8	10	12	8

Year	1988	1992	1994	1998	2002	2006	2010
Medals	6	11	13	13	34	25	37

Year	2014	2018
Medals	28	23

a. Plot the time series.
b. Use regression analysis to determine the trend.

20.26 Xr20-26   There has been a downward trend in property crime since 1993. To measure the extent of the trend, we have recorded the annual number of property crimes.
a. Plot the numbers.
b. Use regression analysis to measure the trend.

20.27 Xr20-27   The number of cable television subscribers has increased over the past 5 years. The marketing

manager for a cable company has recorded the numbers of subscribers for the past 24 quarters.
a. Plot the numbers.
b. Compute the seasonal (quarterly) indexes.

20.28 Xr20-28 The owner of a pizzeria wants to forecast the number of pizzas that will sell each day. The numbers sold daily for the past 4 weeks were recorded. Calculate the seasonal (daily) indexes.

20.29 Xr20-29 A manufacturer of ski equipment is in the process of reviewing the accounts receivable. There appears to be a seasonal pattern with the accounts receivable increasing in the winter months and decreasing during the summer. The quarterly accounts receivable (in $millions) were recorded. Compute the seasonal (quarterly) indexes.

20-4 / INTRODUCTION TO FORECASTING

Many different forecasting methods are available for the statistics practitioner. One factor to be considered in choosing among them is the type of component that makes up the time series. Even then, however, we have several different methods from which to choose. One way of deciding which method to apply is to select the technique that achieves the greatest forecast accuracy. The most commonly used measures of forecast accuracy are **mean absolute deviation (MAD)** and the **sum of squares for forecast errors (SSE)**.

Mean Absolute Deviation

$$MAD = \frac{\sum_{i=1}^{n} |y_t - F_t|}{n}$$

where

y_t = Actual value of the time series at time period t

F_t = Forecasted value of the time series at time period t

n = Number of time periods

Sum of Squares for Forecast Error

$$SSE = \sum_{i=1}^{n} (y_t - F_t)^2$$

MAD averages the absolute differences between the actual and forecast values; SSE is the sum of the squared differences. Which measure to use in judging forecast accuracy depends on the circumstances. If avoiding large errors is important, SSE should be used because it penalizes large deviations more heavily than does MAD. Otherwise, use MAD.

It is probably best to use some of the observations of the time series to develop several competing forecasting models and then forecast for the remaining time periods. Afterward, compute MAD or SSE for the forecasts. For example, if we have 5 years of monthly observations, use the first 4 years to develop the forecasting models and then use them to forecast the fifth year. Because we know the actual values in the fifth year, we can choose the technique that results in the most accurate forecast using either MAD or SSE.

EXAMPLE 20.4

Comparing Forecasting Models

Annual data from 1976 to 2016 were used to develop three different forecasting models. Each model was used to forecast the time series for 2017, 2018, 2019, and 2020. The forecasted and actual values for these years are shown here. Use MAD and SSE to determine which model performed best.

Year	Actual Time Series	1	2	3
2017	129	136	118	130
2018	142	148	141	146
2019	156	150	158	170
2020	183	175	163	180

SOLUTION:

For model 1, we have

$$\text{MAD} = \frac{|129 - 136| + |142 - 148| + |156 - 150| + |183 - 175|}{4}$$

$$= \frac{7 + 6 + 6 + 8}{4} = 6.75$$

$$\text{SSE} = (129 - 136)^2 + (142 - 148)^2 + (156 - 150)^2 + (183 - 175)^2$$

$$= 49 + 36 + 36 + 64 = 185$$

For model 2, we compute

$$\text{MAD} = \frac{|129 - 118| + |142 - 141| + |156 - 158| + |183 - 163|}{4}$$

$$= \frac{11 + 1 + 2 + 20}{4} = 8.5$$

$$\text{SSE} = (129 - 118)^2 + (142 - 141)^2 + (156 - 158)^2 + (183 - 163)^2$$

$$= 121 + 1 + 4 + 400 = 526$$

The measures of forecast accuracy for model 3 are

$$\text{MAD} = \frac{|129 - 130| + |142 - 146| + |156 - 170| + |183 - 180|}{4}$$

$$= \frac{1 + 4 + 14 + 3}{4} = 5.5$$

$$\text{SSE} = (129 - 130)^2 + (142 - 146)^2 + (156 - 170)^2 + (183 - 180)^2$$

$$= 1 + 16 + 196 + 9 = 222$$

Model 2 is inferior to both models 1 and 3, no matter how we measure forecast accuracy. Using MAD, model 3 is best—but using SSE, model 1 is most accurate. The choice between model 1 and model 3 should be made on the basis of whether we prefer a model that consistently produces moderately accurate forecasts (model 1) or one whose forecasts come quite close to most actual values but miss badly in a small number of time periods (model 3).

EXERCISES

20.30 For the actual and forecast values of a time series shown here, calculate MAD and SSE.

Period	1	2	3	4	5
Forecast	173	186	192	211	223
Actual Value	166	179	195	214	220

20.31 Two forecasting models were used to predict the future values of a time series. These are shown here together with the actual values. Compute MAD and SSE for each model to determine which was more accurate.

Period	1	2	3	4
Forecast (Model 1)	7.5	6.3	5.4	8.2
Forecast (Model 2)	6.3	6.7	7.1	7.5
Actual	6.0	6.6	7.3	9.4

20.32 Calculate MAD and SSE for the forecasts that follow.

Period	1	2	3	4	5
Forecast	63	72	86	71	60
Actual	57	60	70	75	70

20.33 Three forecasting techniques were used to predict the values of a time series. These values are given in the following table. Compute MAD and SSE for each technique to determine which was most accurate.

Period	1	2	3	4	5
Forecast (Model 1)	21	27	29	31	35
Forecast (Model 2)	22	24	26	28	30
Forecast (Model 3)	17	20	25	31	39
Actual	19	24	28	32	38

20-5 / FORECASTING MODELS

There is a large number of different forecasting techniques available to statistics practitioners. However, many are beyond the level of this book. In this section, we present three models. Similar to the method of choosing the correct statistical inference technique in Chapters 12 to 19, the choice of model depends on the time-series components.

20-5a Forecasting with Exponential Smoothing

If the time series displays a gradual trend or no trend and no evidence of seasonal variation, exponential smoothing can be effective as a forecasting method. Suppose that t represents the most recent time period and we've computed the exponentially smoothed value S_t. This value is then the forecasted value at time $t + 1$; that is,

$$F_{t+1} = S_t$$

If we wish, we can forecast two or three or any number of periods into the future:

$$F_{t+2} = S_t \qquad \text{or} \qquad F_{t+3} = S_t$$

It must be understood that the accuracy of the forecast decreases rapidly for predictions more than one time period into the future. However, as long as we're dealing with time series with no cyclical or seasonal variation, we can produce reasonably accurate predictions for the next time period.

20-5b Forecasting with Seasonal Indexes

If the time series is composed of seasonal variation and long-term trend, we can use seasonal indexes and the regression equation to forecast.

> **Forecast of Trend and Seasonality**
>
> The forecast for time period t is
>
> $$F_t = [b_0 + b_1 t] \times SI_t$$
>
> where
>
> $$F_t = \text{Forecast for period } t$$
> $$b_0 + b_1 t = \text{Regression equation}$$
> $$SI_t = \text{Seasonal index for period } t$$

EXAMPLE 20.5

Forecasting Hotel Occupancy Rates

Forecast hotel occupancy rates for next year in Example 20.3.

SOLUTION:

In the process of computing the seasonal indexes, we computed the trend line. It is

$$\hat{y} = .639 + .00525t$$

For $t = 21, 22, 23,$ and 24, we calculate the forecasted trend values.

Quarter	t	$\hat{y} = .639 + .00525t$
1	21	$.639 + .00525(21) = .749$
2	22	$.639 + .00525(22) = .755$
3	23	$.639 + .00525(23) = .760$
4	24	$.639 + .00525(24) = .765$

We now multiply the forecasted trend values by the seasonal indexes calculated in Example 20.3. The seasonalized forecasts are as follows:

Quarter	t	Trend Value $\hat{y}_t$	Seasonal Index	Forecast $F_t = \hat{y}_t \times SI_t$
1	21	.749	.878	$.749 \times .878 = .658$
2	22	.755	1.076	$.755 \times 1.076 = .812$
3	23	.760	1.171	$.760 \times 1.171 = .890$
4	24	.765	.875	$.765 \times .875 = .670$

INTERPRET

We forecast that the quarterly occupancy rates during the next year will be .658, .812, .890, and .670.

20-5c Autoregressive Model

In Chapter 17, we discussed autocorrelation wherein the errors are not independent of one another. The existence of strong autocorrelation indicates that the model has been misspecified, which usually means that until we improve the regression model, it will not provide an adequate fit. However, autocorrelation also provides us with an opportunity to develop another forecasting technique. If there is no obvious trend or seasonality and we believe that there is a correlation between consecutive residuals, the **autoregressive model** may be most effective.

Autoregressive Forecasting Model

$$y_t = \beta_0 + \beta_1 y_{t-1} + \varepsilon$$

The model specifies that consecutive values of the time series are correlated. We estimate the coefficient in the usual way. The estimated regression line is defined as

$$\hat{y}_t = b_0 + b_1 y_{t-1}$$

EXAMPLE 20.6

DATA
Xm20-06

Forecasting Scotiabank Stock

A relatively simplistic way to forecast the price of a stock is to use an autoregressive model. We recorded the monthly adjusted (for dividends and splits) closing price on the first of the month of Scotiabank (Toronto Stock Exchange) from 2017 to 2019. The table below lists the first three and the last three monthly closing prices.

Year	Month	Adjusted Closing Price
2017	January	64.02
	February	63.43
	March	64.05
2019	October	70.14
	November	69.58
	December	68.11

SOLUTION:

We will use the monthly closing prices in December 2016 to November 2019 as the independent variable and the prices from January 2017 to December 2019 as the dependent variable. File Xm20-06 stores the data in the format necessary to determine the autoregressive model.

EXCEL Data Analysis

	A	B	C	D	E
16			Coefficients	Standard Error	t Stat	P-value
17	Intercept	28.83	8.78	3.29	0.0024
18	Scotiabank	0.565	0.133	4.23	0.0002

INTERPRET

The regression equation is

$$\hat{y}_t = 28.83 + .565y_{t-1}$$

Because the last price of Scotiabank (December 2019) is 68.11, our forecast for January 2020

$$\hat{y}_{37} = 28.83 + .565y_{36}$$
$$= 28.83 + .565(68.11) = 67.31$$

The actual January 2020 closing price was 67.11. Obviously, this is a quite accurate forecast.

20-5d When to Use the Autoregressive Model

The autoregressive model works best when the variable is stable. We chose a Canadian bank because Canadian banks are very conservative. We also chose a stable period of time (2017–2019).

To compare, we used an autoregressive model to forecast the January 2021 adjusted closing price of Amazon stock. The forecast we produced was 3,289.03 and the actual price was 3,120.83—a poor prediction. Amazon stock was very volatile, and the period we chose included 2020, the year of the pandemic when all economic indicators registered large changes.

Housing Starts: Solution

A preliminary examination of the data reveals that there is a small upward trend over the 7-year period. Moreover, the number of housing starts varies by quarter, which is not surprising since there is decreased building activity during the fall and winter in the northeast United States. The presence of these components suggests that we determine the linear trend and seasonal (quarterly) indexes. With housing starts as the dependent variable and the quarter as the independent variable, Excel yielded the following regression line:

$$\hat{y} = 10.1 + .217t \qquad t = 1, 2, \ldots, 28$$

The seasonal indexes were computed as follows.

Quarter	Index
1	.7345
2	1.1493
3	1.1213
4	.9961

The regression equation was used again to predict the number of housing starts based on the linear trend:

$$\hat{y} = 10.1 + .217t \qquad t = 29, 30, 31, 32$$

These figures were multiplied by the seasonal indexes, which resulted in the following forecasts.

Period	Quarter	$\hat{y} = 10.1 + .217t$	Seasonal Index	Forecasts
29	1	16.39	.7345	12.0
30	2	16.61	1.1493	19.1
31	3	16.83	1.1213	18.9
32	4	17.04	.9961	17.0

This table displays the forecasted and actual housing starts for 2018.

Period	Quarter	Forecasts	Actual
29	1	12.0	11.6
30	2	19.1	18.7
31	3	18.9	18.1
32	4	17.0	16.1

The size of the error was measured by MAD and SSE. They are

$$MAD = .619$$
$$SSE = 1.707$$

Figure 20.9 depicts the actual time series (quarters 1 to 28) and forecasts (quarters 29 to 32).

FIGURE **20.9** Time Series, Trend, and Forecasts of Housing Starts

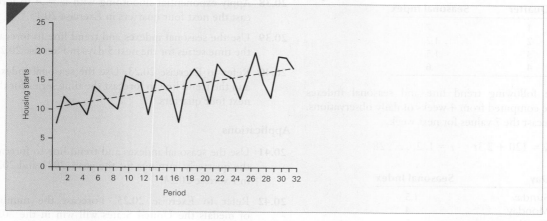

Forecasters Beware!

This forecasting model depends on the future values of the variable to reflect to some extent the history of the variable. Sudden shocks to the system generally produce large forecasting errors. To see the effect of the pandemic of 2020, we included the data from 2020 in Figure 20.3. Figure 20.10 displays the monthly traffic volume from 2014 to 2020.

(Continued)

FIGURE **20.10** U.S. Traffic Volume (Millions of Miles), 2014–2020

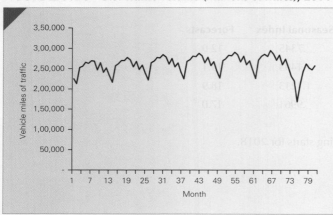

EXERCISES

20.34 The following trend line and seasonal indexes were computed from 10 years of quarterly observations. Forecast the next year's time series.

$$\hat{y} = 150 + 3t \qquad t = 1, 2, \ldots, 40$$

Quarter	Seasonal Index
1	.7
2	1.2
3	1.5
4	.6

20.35 The following trend line and seasonal indexes were computed from 4 weeks of daily observations. Forecast the 7 values for next week.

$$\hat{y} = 120 + 2.3t \qquad t = 1, 2, \ldots, 28$$

Day	Seasonal Index
Sunday	1.5
Monday	.4
Tuesday	.5
Wednesday	.6
Thursday	.7
Friday	1.4
Saturday	1.9

20.36 Use the following autoregressive equation to forecast the next value of the time series if the last observed value is 65.

$$\hat{y} = 625 - 1.3y_{t-1}$$

20.37 The following autoregressive equation was developed. Forecast the next value if the last observed value was 11.

$$\hat{y} = 155 + 21y_{t-1}$$

20.38 Apply exponential smoothing with $w = .4$ to forecast the next four quarters in Exercise 20.15.

20.39 Use the seasonal indexes and trend line to forecast the time series for the next 5 days in Exercise 20.22.

20.40 Refer to Exercise 20.23. Use the seasonal indexes and the trend line to forecast the time series for the next four quarters.

Applications

20.41 Use the seasonal indexes and trend line to forecast the quarterly earnings for the years 2021 and 2022 in Exercise 20.24.

20.42 Refer to Exercise 20.25. Forecast the number of medals the United States will win in the 2022 Winter Olympics using the following methods.
 a. Autoregressive forecasting model.
 b. Exponential smoothing method with $w = .5$.

20.43 Refer to Exercise 20.26. Forecast the number of property crimes in the United States in 2018 using an autoregressive model.

20.44 Use the seasonal indexes and trend line from Exercise 20.27 to forecast the number of cable subscribers for the next four quarters.

20.45 Refer to Exercise 20.28. Use the seasonal indexes and trend line to forecast the number of pizzas to be sold for each of the next 7 days.

20.46 Apply the trend line and seasonal indexes from Exercise 20.29 to forecast accounts receivable for the next four quarters.

Exercises 20.47–20.51 are based on the following problem.

Xr20-47 The revenues (in $millions) of a chain of ice cream stores are listed for each quarter during the previous 5 years.

	Year				
Quarter	**2016**	**2017**	**2018**	**2019**	**2020**
1	16	14	17	18	21
2	25	27	31	29	30
3	31	32	40	45	52
4	24	23	27	24	32

20.47 Plot the time series.

20.48 Discuss why exponential smoothing is not recommended as a forecasting tool in this problem.

20.49 Use regression analysis to determine the trend line.

20.50 Determine the seasonal indexes.

20.51 Using the seasonal indexes and trend line, forecast revenues for the next four quarters.

20.52 **Xr20-52** The number of housing starts (in 1,000s) in the northeast United States for the years 2004 to 2009 were recorded.
  a. Use the 2004–2008 data to calculate the seasonal indexes.
  b. Use the indexes and regression analysis to forecast the number of housing starts in 2009.
  c. Calculate SSE and MAD to measure how well (or poorly) the forecasts fared.

CHAPTER SUMMARY

In this chapter, we discussed the classical time series and its decomposition into trend, seasonal, and random variation. Moving averages and exponential smoothing were used to remove some of the random variation, making it easier to detect trend and seasonality. The long-term trend was measured by regression analysis. Seasonal variation was measured by computing the seasonal indexes. Three forecasting techniques were described in this chapter: exponential smoothing, forecasting with seasonal indexes, and the autoregressive model.

IMPORTANT TERMS:

Time series   875
Forecasting   875
Trend   876
Secular trend   876
Cyclical variation   877
Seasonal variation   877
Random variation   877
Moving average   877

Exponential smoothing   882
Seasonal indexes   886
Deseasonalizing   889
Seasonally adjusted time series   889
Mean absolute deviation (MAD)   891
Sum of squares for forecast error (SSE)   891
Autoregressive model   895

SYMBOLS:

Symbol	Represents
y_t	Time series
S_t	Exponentially smoothed time series
w	Smoothing constant
F_t	Forecasted time series

FORMULAS:

Exponential smoothing

$$S_t = wy_t + (1 - w)S_{t-1}$$

Mean absolute deviation

$$MAD = \frac{\sum_{i=1}^{n} |y_t - F_t|}{n}$$

Sum of squares for error

$$SSE = \sum_{i=1}^{n} (y_t - F_t)^2$$

Forecast of trend and seasonality

$$F_t = [b_0 + b_1 t] \times SI_t$$

Autoregressive model

$$y_t = \beta_0 + \beta_1 y_{t-1} + \varepsilon$$

EXCEL INSTRUCTIONS:

Technique

Moving averages	880
Exponential smoothing	884

Konstantin Chagin/Shutterstock.com

21

STATISTICAL PROCESS CONTROL

CHAPTER OUTLINE

21-1   Process Variation

21-2   Control Charts

21-3   Control Charts for Variables: $\bar{x}$ and S Charts

21-4   Control Charts for Attributes: p Chart

Detecting the Source of Defective Discs

Data
Xm21-00

A company that produces compact discs (CDs) has been receiving complaints from its customers about the large number of discs that will not store data properly. Company management has decided to institute statistical process control to remedy the problem. Every hour, a random sample of 200 discs is taken, and each disc is tested to determine whether it is defective. The number of defective discs in the samples of size 200 for the first 40 hours is shown here (in chronological order). Using these data, draw a p chart to monitor the production process. Was the process out of control when the sample results were generated?

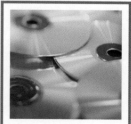

Comstock Images/Getty Images

See solution on page 923.

| 19 | 5 | 16 | 20 | 6 | 12 | 18 | 6 | 13 | 15 | 10 | 6 | 7 | 10 | 18 | 20 | 13 | 6 | 8 | 3 |
| 8 | 7 | 4 | 19 | 3 | 19 | 9 | 10 | 10 | 18 | 15 | 16 | 5 | 14 | 3 | 10 | 19 | 13 | 19 | 9 |

901

INTRODUCTION

Operations managers are responsible for developing and maintaining the production processes that deliver quality products and services. In Section 14-6, we demonstrated an important application of the analysis of variance that is used to investigate sources of variation and determine ways to reduce that variation. The goal is to select the methods, materials, machines, and personnel (workers) that combine to yield the production process that features the smallest amount of variation at a reasonable cost. Once the production process is operating, it is necessary to constantly monitor the process to ensure that it functions the way it was designed. The statistical methods we are about to introduce are the most common applications of statistics. At any point in time, there are literally thousands of firms applying these methods. This chapter deals with the subject of **statistical process control or SPC** (formerly called **quality control**).

There are two general approaches to the management of quality. The first approach is to produce the product and, at the completion of the production process, inspect the unit to determine whether it conforms to specifications; if it doesn't, the unit is either discarded or repaired. This approach has several drawbacks. Foremost among them is producing substandard products that are later discarded or fixed is costly. In recent years, this approach has been employed by a decreasing number of companies. Instead, many firms have adopted the **prevention approach**. Using the concepts of hypothesis testing, statistics practitioners concentrate on the production process. Rather than inspect the product, they inspect the process to determine when the process starts producing units that do not conform to specifications. This allows them to correct the production process before it creates a large number of defective products.

In Section 21-1, we discuss the problem of process variation and why it is often the key to the management of quality. In Section 21-2, we also introduce the concept and logic of control charts and show why they work. In the rest of the chapter, we introduce three specific control charts.

21-1 / PROCESS VARIATION

All production processes result in variation; that is, no product is exactly the same as another. You can see for yourself that this is true by weighing, for example, two boxes of breakfast cereal that are supposed to weigh 16 ounces each. They not only will not weigh exactly 16 ounces but also will not even have equal weights. All products exhibit some degree of variation. There are two sources of variation: *chance* and *assignable variation*. **Chance or common variation** is caused by a number of randomly occurring events that are part of the production process and, in general, cannot be eliminated without changing the process. In effect, chance variation was built into the product when the production process was first set up, perhaps as a result of a statistical analysis that attempted to minimize but not necessarily eliminate such variation. In Section 14-6, we discuss statistical techniques that allow firms to experiment to search for sources of variation and, in so doing, reduce the variation.

Assignable or special variation is caused by specific events or factors that are frequently temporary and that can usually be identified and eliminated. To illustrate, consider a paint company that produces and sells paint in 1-gallon cans. The cans are filled by an automatic valve that regulates the amount of paint in each can. The designers of the valve acknowledge that there will be some variation in the amount of paint even when the valve is working as it was designed to work. This is chance variation.

Occasionally the valve will malfunction, causing the variation in the amount delivered to each can to increase. This increase is the assignable variation.

Perhaps the best way to understand what is happening is to consider the volume of paint in each can as a random variable. If the only sources of variation are caused by chance, then each can's volume is drawn from identical distributions; that is, each distribution has the same shape, mean, and standard deviation. Under such circumstances, the production process is said to be **under control**. In recognition of the fact that variation in output will occur even when the process is under control and operating properly, most processes are designed so that their products will fall within designated **specification limits** or "specs." For example, the process that fills the paint cans may be designed so that the cans contain between .99 and 1.01 gallons. Inevitably, some event or combination of factors in a production process will cause the process distribution to change. When it does, the process is said to be **out of control**. There are several possible ways for the process to go out of control. Here is a list of the most commonly occurring possibilities and their likely assignable causes.

1. **Level shift**. This is a change in the mean of the process distribution. Assignable causes include machine breakdown, new machine or operator, or a change in the environment. In the paint-can illustration, a temperature or humidity change may affect the density of the paint, resulting in less paint in each can.

2. **Instability**. This is the name we apply to the process when the standard deviation increases. (As we discuss later, a decrease in the standard deviation is desirable.) This may be caused by a machine in need of repair, defective materials, worn tools, or a poorly trained operator. Suppose, for example, that a part in the valve that controls the amount of paint wears down, causing greater variation than normal.

3. **Trend**. When there is a slow steady shift (either up or down) in the process distribution mean, the result is a trend. This is frequently the result of less-than-regular maintenance, operator fatigue, residue or dirt buildup, or gradual loss of lubricant. If the paint-control valve becomes increasingly clogged, we would expect to see a steady decrease in the amount of paint delivered.

4. **Cycle**. This is a repeated series of small observations followed by large observations. Likely assignable causes include environmental changes, worn parts, or operator fatigue. If there are changes in the voltage in the electricity that runs the machines in the paint-can example, we might see series of overfilled cans and series of underfilled cans.

The key to quality is to detect when the process goes out of control so that we can correct the malfunction and restore control. The control chart is the statistical method that we use to detect problems.

EXERCISES

21.1 What is meant by *chance variation*?

21.2 Provide two examples of production processes and their associated chance variation.

21.3 What is meant by *special variation*?

21.4 Your education as a statistics practitioner can be considered a production process overseen by the course instructor. The variable we measure is the grade achieved by each student.

a. Discuss chance variation—that is, describe the sources of variation that the instructor has no control over.

b. Discuss special variation.

21-2 / CONTROL CHARTS

A **control chart** is a plot of statistics over time. For example, an $\bar{x}$ **chart** plots a series of sample means taken over a period of time. Each control chart contains a **centerline** and *control limits*. The control limit above the centerline is called the **upper control limit** and that below the centerline is called the **lower control limit**. If, when the sample statistics are plotted, all points are randomly distributed between the control limits, we conclude that the process is under control. If the points are not randomly distributed between the control limits, we conclude that the process is out of control.

To illustrate the logic of control charts, let us suppose that in the paint-can example described previously we want to determine whether the central location of the distribution has changed from one period to another. We will draw our conclusion from an $\bar{x}$ chart. For the moment, let us assume that we know the mean μ and standard deviation σ of the process when it is under control. We can construct the $\bar{x}$ chart as shown in Figure 21.1. The chart is drawn so that the vertical axis plots the values of $\bar{x}$ that will be calculated and the horizontal axis tracks the samples in the order in which they are drawn. The centerline is the value of μ. The control limits are set at three standard errors from the centerline. Recall that the standard error of $\bar{x}$ is $\sigma/\sqrt{n}$. Hence, we define the control limits as follows:

$$\text{Lower control limit} = \mu - 3\frac{\sigma}{\sqrt{n}}$$

$$\text{Upper control limit} = \mu + 3\frac{\sigma}{\sqrt{n}}$$

FIGURE **21.1** $\bar{x}$ Chart: μ and σ Known

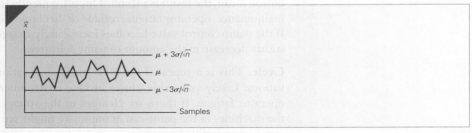

After we've constructed the chart by drawing the centerline and control limits, we use it to plot the sample means, which are joined to make it easier to interpret. The principles underlying control charts are identical to the principles of hypothesis testing. The null and alternative hypotheses are

H_0: The process is under control.

H_1: The process is out of control.

For an $\bar{x}$ chart, the test statistic is the sample mean $\bar{x}$. However, because we're dealing with a dynamic process rather than a fixed population, we test a series of sample means: We compute the mean for each of a continuing series of samples taken over time. For each series of samples, we want to determine whether there is sufficient evidence to infer that the process mean has changed. We reject the null hypothesis if at any time the sample mean falls outside the control limits. It is logical to ask why we use 3 standard errors and not 2 or 1.96 or 1.645 as we did when we tested hypotheses about a population mean in Chapter 11. The answer lies in the way in which all tests are conducted. Because test conclusions are based on sample data, there are two possible errors. In statistical process control, a Type I error occurs if we conclude that the process is out of control when, in fact, it is not. This error can be quite expensive because the production process must be stopped and the causes of the variation found and repaired. Consequently, we want the probability of a Type I error to be small. With control limits set at 3 standard errors from the mean, the probability of a Type I error for each sample is

$$\alpha = P(|z| > 3) = .0026$$

Recall that a small value of α results in a relatively large value of the probability of a Type II error. A Type II error occurs when at any sample we do not reject a false null hypothesis. This means that, for each sample, we are less likely to recognize when the process goes out of control. However, because we will be performing a series of tests (one for each sample), we will eventually discover that the process is out of control and take steps to rectify the problem.

Suppose that in order to test the production process that fills 1-gallon paint cans, we choose to take a sample of size 4 every hour. Let us also assume that we know the mean and standard deviation of the process distribution of the amount of paint when the process is under control, say, $\mu = 1.001$ and $\sigma = .006$. (This means that when the valve is working the way it was designed, the amount of paint put into each can is a random variable whose mean is 1.001 gallons and whose standard deviation is .006 gallon.) Thus,

$$\text{Centerline} = \mu = 1.001$$

$$\text{Lower control limit} = \mu - 3\frac{\sigma}{\sqrt{n}} = 1.001 - 3\frac{.006}{\sqrt{4}} = 1.001 - .009 = .992$$

$$\text{Upper control limit} = \mu + 3\frac{\sigma}{\sqrt{n}} = 1.001 + 3\frac{.006}{\sqrt{4}} = 1.001 + .009 = 1.010$$

Figure 21.2 depicts a situation in which the first 15 samples were taken when the process was under control. However, after the 15th sample was drawn, the process went out of control and produced sample means outside the control limits. We conclude that the process distribution has changed because the data display variability beyond that predicted for a process with the specified mean and standard deviation. This means that the variation is assignable and that the cause must be identified and corrected.

As we stated previously, SPC is a slightly different form of hypothesis testing. The concept is the same, but there are differences that you should be aware of. The most important difference is that when we tested means and proportions in Chapters 11 and 12, we were dealing with fixed but unknown parameters of populations. For instance, in Example 11.1 the population we dealt with was the account balances of the department store customers.

FIGURE 21.2 $\bar{x}$ **Chart: Process Out of Control**

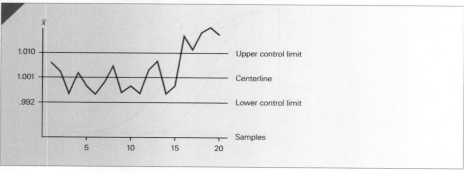

The population mean balance was a constant value that we simply did not know. The purpose of the test was to determine whether there was enough statistical evidence to allow us to infer that the mean balance was greater than $170. So we took one sample and based the decision on the sample mean. When dealing with a production process, it's important to realize that the process distribution itself is variable; that is, at any time, the process distribution of the amount of paint fill may change if the valve malfunctions. Consequently, we do not simply take one sample and make the decision. Instead, we plot a number of statistics over time in the control chart. Simply put, in Chapters 11 through 18, we assumed static population distributions with fixed but unknown parameters, whereas in this chapter we assume a dynamic process distribution with parameters subject to possible shifts.

21-2a Sample Size and Sampling Frequency

In designing a control chart, the statistics practitioner must select a sample size and a sampling frequency. These decisions are based on several factors, including the costs of making Type I and Type II errors, the length of the production run, and the typical change in the process distribution when the process goes out of control. A useful aid in making the decision is the operating characteristic (OC) curve.

Operating Characteristic Curve Recall that in Chapter 11 we drew the **operating characteristic (OC) curve** that plotted the probabilities of Type II errors and population means. Here is how the OC curve for the $\bar{x}$ chart is drawn.

Suppose that when the production process is under control the mean and standard deviation of the process variable are μ_0 and σ, respectively. For specific values of α and n, we can compute the probability of a Type II error when the process mean changes to $\mu_1 = \mu_0 + k\sigma$. A Type II error occurs when a sample mean falls between the control limits when the process is out of control. In other words, the probability of a Type II error is the probability that the $\bar{x}$ chart will be unable to detect a shift of $k\sigma$ in the process mean on the first sample after the shift has occurred. Figure 21.3 depicts the OC curve for $n = 2, 3, 4,$ and 5. Figure 21.4 is the OC curve for $n = 10, 15, 20,$ and 25. (We drew two sets of curves because one alone would not provide the precision we need.) We can use the OC curves to help determine the sample size we should use.

Figure 21.3 tells us that for small shifts in the mean of 1 standard deviation or less, samples of size 2 to 5 produce probabilities of not detecting shifts that range between .8 and .95 (approximately). To appreciate the effect of large probabilities of Type II errors, consider the paint-can illustration. Suppose that when the process goes out of

FIGURE **21.3** Operating Characteristic Curve for n = 2, 3, 4, and 5

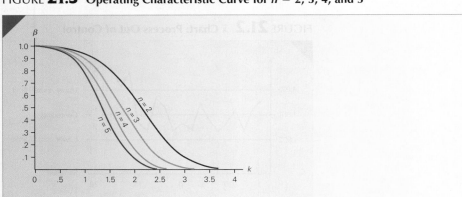

FIGURE **21.4** Operating Characteristic Curve for n = 10, 15, 20, and 25

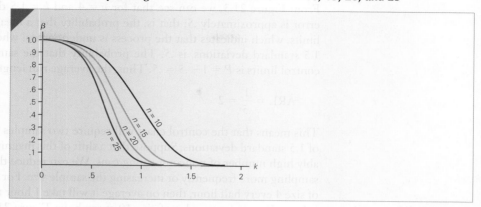

control it shifts the mean by about 1 standard deviation. The probability that the first sample after the shift will not detect this shift is approximately .85. The probability that it will not detect the shift for the first m samples after the shift is $.85^m$. Thus, for m = 5 the probability of not detecting the shift for the first five samples after the shift is .44. If the process fills 1,000 cans per hour, a large proportion of the 5,000 cans filled will be overfilled or underfilled (depending on the direction of the shift). Figure 21.4 suggests that when the shift moves the process mean by 1 standard deviation, samples of size 15 or 20 are recommended. For n = 15, the probability that a shift of 1 standard deviation will not be detected by the first sample is approximately .2.

If the typical shift is 2 or more standard deviations, samples of size 4 or 5 will likely suffice. For n = 5, the probability of a Type II error is about .07.

21-2b Average Run Length

The **average run length (ARL)** is the expected number of samples that must be taken before the chart indicates that the process has gone out of control. The ARL is determined by

$$ARL = \frac{1}{P}$$

where P is the probability that a sample mean falls outside the control limits. Assuming that the control limits are defined as 3 standard errors above and below the centerline, the probability that a sample mean falls outside the control limits when the process is under control is

$$P = P(|z| > 3) = .0026$$

Thus,

$$ARL = \frac{1}{.0026} = 385$$

This means that when the process is under control, the $\bar{x}$ chart will erroneously conclude that it is out of control once every 385 samples on average. If the sampling plan calls for samples to be taken every hour, on average there will be a *false alarm* once every 385 hours.

We can use the OC curve to determine the average run length until the $\bar{x}$ chart detects a process that is out of control. Suppose that when the process goes out of control, it typically shifts the process mean 1.5 standard deviations to the right or left. From Figure 21.3, we can see that for $n = 4$ and $k = 1.5$ the probability of a Type II error is approximately .5; that is, the probability that a mean falls between the control limits, which indicates that the process is under control when there has been a shift of 1.5 standard deviations, is .5. The probability that the sample mean falls outside the control limits is $P = 1 - .5 = .5$. Thus, the average run length is

$$\text{ARL} = \frac{1}{.5} = 2$$

This means that the control chart will require two samples on average to detect a shift of 1.5 standard deviations. Suppose that a shift of this magnitude results in an unacceptably high number of nonconforming cans. We can reduce that number in two ways: by sampling more frequently or increasing the sample size. For example, if we take samples of size 4 every half hour, then on average it will take 1 hour to detect the shift and make repairs. If we take samples of size 10 every hour, Figure 21.4 indicates that the probability of a Type II error when the shift is 1.5 standard deviations is about .05. Thus, $P = 1 - .05 = .95$ and

$$\text{ARL} = \frac{1}{.95} = 1.05$$

This tells us that a sample size of 10 will allow the statistics practitioner to detect a shift of 1.5 standard deviations about twice as quickly as a sample of size 4.

21-2c Changing the Control Limits

Another way to decrease the probability of a Type II error is to increase the probability of making a Type I error. Thus, we may define the control limits so that they are two standard errors above and below the centerline. To judge whether this is advisable, it is necessary to draw the OC curve for this plan.

In our demonstration of the logic of control charts, we resorted to traditional methods of presenting inferential methods; we assumed that the process parameters were known. When the parameters are unknown, we estimate their values from the sample data. In the next two sections, we discuss how to construct and use control charts in more realistic situations. In Section 21-3, we present control charts when the data are interval. In the context of statistical process control, we call these **control charts for variables**. Section 21-4 demonstrates the use of control charts that record whether a unit is defective or nondefective. These are called **control charts for attributes**.

EXERCISES

21.5 If the control limits of an $\bar{x}$ chart are set at 2.5 standard errors from the centerline, what is the probability that on any sample the control chart will indicate that the process is out of control when it is under control?

21.6 Refer to Exercise 21.5. What is the average run length until the $\bar{x}$ chart signals that the process is out of control when it is under control?

21.7 The control limits of an $\bar{x}$ chart are set at two standard errors from the centerline. Calculate the probability that on any sample the control chart will indicate that the process is out of control when it is under control.

21.8 Refer to Exercise 21.7. Determine the ARL until the $\bar{x}$ chart signals that the process is out of control when it is under control.

Exercises 21.9 to 21.15 are based on the following scenario.

A production facility produces 100 units per hour and uses an $\bar{x}$ chart to monitor its quality. The control limits are set at 3 standard errors from the mean. When the process goes out of control, it usually shifts the mean by 1.5 standard deviations. Sampling is conducted once per hour with a sample size of 3.

21.9 On average, how many units will be produced until the control chart signals that the process is out of control when it is under control?

21.10 Refer to Exercise 21.9.
    a. Find the probability that the $\bar{x}$ chart does not detect a shift of 1.5 standard deviations on the first sample after the shift occurs.
    b. Compute the probability that the $\bar{x}$ chart will not detect the shift for the first eight samples after the shift.

21.11 Refer to Exercise 21.10. Find the average run length to detect the shift.

21.12 The operations manager is unsatisfied with the current sampling plan. He changes it to samples of size 2 every half hour. What is the average number of units produced until the chart indicates that the process is out of control when it is not?

21.13 Refer to Exercise 21.12.
    a. Find the probability that the $\bar{x}$ chart does not detect a shift of 1.5 standard deviations on the first sample after the shift occurs.
    b. Compute the probability that the $\bar{x}$ chart will not detect the shift for the first eight samples after the shift.

21.14 Refer to Exercise 21.13. What is the average run length to detect the shift?

21.15 Write a brief report comparing the sampling plans described in Exercises 21.9 and 21.12. Discuss the relative costs of the two plans and the frequency of Type I and Type II errors.

Exercises 21.16 to 21.22 are based on the following scenario.

A firm that manufactures computers uses statistical process control to monitor all its production processes. For one component, the company draws samples of size 10 every 30 minutes. The company makes 4,000 of these components per hour. The control limits of the $\bar{x}$ chart are set at 3 standard errors from the mean. When the process goes out of control, it usually shifts the mean by .75 standard deviation.

21.16 On average how many units will be produced until the control chart signals that the process is out of control when it is under control?

21.17 Refer to Exercise 21.16.
    a. Find the probability that the $\bar{x}$ chart does not detect a shift of .75 standard deviation on the first sample after the shift occurs.
    b. Compute the probability that the $\bar{x}$ chart will not detect the shift for the first four samples after the shift.

21.18 Refer to Exercise 21.17. Find the average run length to detect the shift.

21.19 The company is considering changing the sampling plan so that 20 components are sampled every hour. What is the average number of units produced until the chart indicates that the process is out of control when it is not?

21.20 Refer to Exercise 21.19.
    a. Find the probability that the $\bar{x}$ chart does not detect a shift of .75 standard deviation on the first sample after the shift occurs.
    b. Compute the probability that the $\bar{x}$ chart will not detect the shift for the first four samples after the shift.

21.21 Refer to Exercise 21.20. What is the average run length to detect the shift?

21.22 Write a brief report comparing the sampling plans described in Exercises 21.16 and 21.19. Discuss the relative costs of the two plans and the frequency of Type I and Type II errors.

21-3 CONTROL CHARTS FOR VARIABLES: $\overline{X}$ AND S CHARTS

There are several ways to judge whether a change in the process distribution has occurred when the data are interval. To determine whether the distribution means have changed, we employ the $\bar{x}$ chart. To determine whether the process distribution standard deviation has changed, we can use the S (which stands for *standard deviation*) chart or the R (which stands for *range*) chart.

Throughout this textbook, we have used the sample standard deviation to estimate the population standard deviation. However, for a variety of reasons, SPC frequently employs the range instead of the standard deviation. This is primarily because computing the range is simpler than computing the standard deviation. Because many practitioners conducting SPC perform calculations by hand (with the assistance of a calculator), they select the computationally simple range as the method to estimate the process standard deviation. In this section, we will introduce control charts that feature the sample standard deviation. In the online appendix Control Charts for Variables $\bar{x}$ and R, we employ the sample range to construct our charts.

21-3a $\bar{x}$ Chart

In Section 21-2, we determined the centerline and control limits of an $\bar{x}$ chart using the mean and standard deviation of the process distribution. However, it is unrealistic to believe that the mean and standard deviation of the process distribution are known. Thus, to construct the $\bar{x}$ chart, we need to estimate the relevant parameters from the data.

We begin by drawing samples when we have determined that the process is under control. The sample size must lie between 2 and 25. We discuss later how to determine that the process is under control. For each sample, we compute the mean and the standard deviation. The estimator of the mean of the distribution is the mean of the sample means (denoted $\bar{\bar{x}}$):

$$\bar{\bar{x}} = \frac{\sum_{j=1}^{k} \bar{x}_j}{k}$$

where $\bar{x}_j$ is the mean of the jth sample and there are k samples. (Note that $\bar{\bar{x}}$ is simply the average of all nk observations.)

To estimate the standard deviation of the process distribution, we calculate the sample variance s_j^2 for each sample. We then compute the pooled standard deviation,[*] which we denote S and define as

$$S = \sqrt{\frac{\sum_{j=1}^{k} s_j^2}{k}}$$

In the previous section, where we assumed that the process distribution mean and variance were known, the centerline and control limits were defined as

Centerline $= \mu$

Lower control limit $= \mu - 3\dfrac{\sigma}{\sqrt{n}}$

Upper control limit $= \mu + 3\dfrac{\sigma}{\sqrt{n}}$

Because the values of μ and σ are unknown, we must use the sample data to estimate them. The estimator of μ is $\bar{\bar{x}}$, and the estimator of μ is S. Therefore, the centerline and control limits are as shown in the box.

---

[*]This formula requires that the sample size be the same for all samples, a condition that is imposed throughout this chapter.

Centerline and Control Limits for $\bar{x}$ Chart

$$\text{Centerline} = \bar{\bar{x}}$$

$$\text{Lower control limit} = \bar{\bar{x}} - 3\frac{S}{\sqrt{n}}$$

$$\text{Upper control limit} = \bar{\bar{x}} + 3\frac{S}{\sqrt{n}}$$

EXAMPLE **21.1**

Data
Xm21-01

Statistical Process Control at Lear Seating, Part 1

Lear Seating of Kitchener, Ontario, manufactures seats for Chrysler, Ford, and General Motors cars. Several years ago, Lear instituted statistical process control, which has resulted in improved quality and lower costs. One of the components of a front-seat cushion is a wire spring produced from 4-mm (millimeter) steel wire. A machine is used to bend the wire so that the spring's length is 500 mm. If the springs are longer than 500 mm, they will loosen and eventually fall out. If they are too short, they won't easily fit into position. (In fact, in the past, when there were a relatively large number of short springs, workers incurred arm and hand injuries when attempting to install the springs.) To determine whether the process is under control, random samples of four springs are taken every hour. The last 25 samples are shown here. Construct an $\bar{x}$ chart from these data.

SAMPLE

1	501.02	501.65	504.34	501.10
2	499.80	498.89	499.47	497.90
3	497.12	498.35	500.34	499.33
4	500.68	501.39	499.74	500.41
5	495.87	500.92	498.00	499.44
6	497.89	499.22	502.10	500.03
7	497.24	501.04	498.74	503.51
8	501.22	504.53	499.06	505.37
9	499.15	501.11	497.96	502.39
10	498.90	505.99	500.05	499.33
11	497.38	497.80	497.57	500.72
12	499.70	500.99	501.35	496.48
13	501.44	500.46	502.07	500.50
14	498.26	495.54	495.21	501.27
15	497.57	497.00	500.32	501.22
16	500.95	502.07	500.60	500.44
17	499.70	500.56	501.18	502.36
18	501.57	502.09	501.18	504.98
19	504.20	500.92	500.02	501.71
20	498.61	499.63	498.68	501.84
21	499.05	501.82	500.67	497.36
22	497.85	494.08	501.79	501.95
23	501.08	503.12	503.06	503.56
24	500.75	501.18	501.09	502.88
25	502.03	501.44	498.76	499.39

SOLUTION:

COMPUTE

MANUALLY:

The means and variances for each sample were computed and are listed in Table 21.1. We then calculated the mean of the means (which is also the mean of all 100 numbers) and the pooled standard deviation:

$$\bar{\bar{x}} = 500.296$$

$$S = 1.971$$

Thus, the centerline and control limits are

Centerline $= \bar{\bar{x}} = 500.296$

Lower control limit $= \bar{\bar{x}} - 3\dfrac{S}{\sqrt{n}} = 500.296 - 3\dfrac{1.971}{\sqrt{4}} = 497.340$

Upper control limit $= \bar{\bar{x}} + 3\dfrac{S}{\sqrt{n}} = 500.296 + 3\dfrac{1.971}{\sqrt{4}} = 503.253$

The centerline and control limits are drawn and the sample means plotted in the order in which they occurred.

TABLE **21.1** Means and Variances of Samples in Example 21.1

SAMPLE					$\bar{x}_j$	S_j^2
1	501.02	501.65	504.34	501.10	502.03	2.46
2	499.80	498.89	499.47	497.90	499.02	0.69
3	497.12	498.35	500.34	499.33	498.79	1.89
4	500.68	501.39	499.74	500.41	500.56	0.47
5	495.87	500.92	498.00	499.44	498.56	4.63
6	497.89	499.22	502.10	500.03	499.81	3.11
7	497.24	501.04	498.74	503.51	500.13	7.51
8	501.22	504.53	499.06	505.37	502.55	8.61
9	499.15	501.11	497.96	502.39	500.15	3.91
10	498.90	505.99	500.05	499.33	501.07	10.99
11	497.38	497.80	497.57	500.72	498.37	2.49
12	499.70	500.99	501.35	496.48	499.63	4.91
13	501.44	500.46	502.07	500.50	501.12	0.61
14	498.26	495.54	495.21	501.27	497.57	7.95
15	497.57	497.00	500.32	501.22	499.03	4.24
16	500.95	502.07	500.60	500.44	501.02	0.54
17	499.70	500.56	501.18	502.36	500.95	1.25
18	501.57	502.09	501.18	504.98	502.46	2.97
19	504.20	500.92	500.02	501.71	501.71	3.23
20	498.61	499.63	498.68	501.84	499.69	2.27
21	499.05	501.82	500.67	497.36	499.73	3.78
22	497.85	494.08	501.79	501.95	498.92	14.00
23	501.08	503.12	503.06	503.56	502.71	1.22
24	500.75	501.18	501.09	502.88	501.48	0.91
25	502.03	501.44	498.76	499.39	500.41	2.48

Do It Yourself Excel

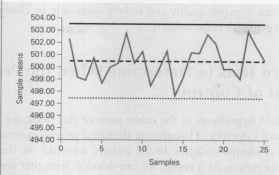

INSTRUCTIONS

1. Type or import the data into rows and columns where each row stores the observations for each sample. (Open Xm21-01.)

2. For each row, compute the sample means. In this example type into cell F1

   = **AVERAGE(B1:E1)**

   Drag to complete the column F.

3. For each row calculate the sample variances. In cell G1 type

   = **VAR(B1:E1)**

   Drag to complete the column G.

4. Compute the average of the sample means. In cell F26 type

   = **AVERAGE(F1:F25)**

5. Compute the pooled standard deviation. In cell G26 type

   = **SQRT(SUM(G1:G25)/25)**

6. Compute the control limits

   = **F$26 – 3*G$26/SQRT(4)**
   = **F$26 + 3*G$26/SQRT(4)**

7. To draw the $\bar{x}$ chart with centerline and control limits, store the sample means in one column. Type the value of the centerline and drag to complete the column. Do the same for the upper and lower control limits. Highlight all four columns and draw the line chart.

INTERPRET

As you can see, no point lies outside the control limits. We conclude that the variation in the lengths of the springs is caused by chance—that is, there is not enough evidence to infer that the process is out of control. No remedial action by the operator is called for.

We stress that statistical process control allows us to detect assignable variation only. In Example 21.1, we determined that the process is under control, which means that there are no detectable sources of assignable variation. However, this does not mean that the process is a good one. It may well be that the production process yields a large proportion of defective units because the amount of chance variation is large.

Recall that in Section 14-6 we noted that chance variation decreases product quality and increases costs. If the costs of producing defective units are high because of large chance variation, we can improve quality and reduce costs only by changing the process itself, which is management's responsibility.

21-3b Pattern Tests to Determine When the Process Is Out of Control

When we tested hypotheses in the other parts of this book, we used only one sample statistic to make a decision. However, in statistical process control, the decision is made from a series of sample statistics. In the $\bar{x}$ chart, we make the decision after plotting at least 25 sample means. As a result, we can develop tests that are based on the pattern the sample means make when plotted. To describe them, we need to divide the $\bar{x}$ chart between the control limits into six zones, as shown in Figure 21.5. The C zones represent the area within one standard error of the centerline. The B zones are the regions between one and two standard errors from the centerline. The spaces between two and three standard errors from the centerline are defined as A zones.

FIGURE **21.5** Zones of $\bar{x}$ Chart

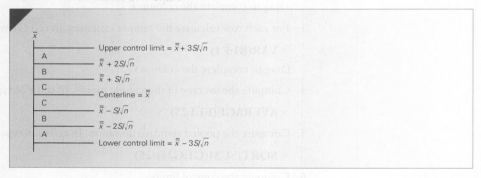

The width of the zones is one standard error of $\bar{x}$ ($S/\sqrt{n}$). If the calculations were performed manually, the value of S will be known. However, if a computer was used, the centerline and control limits are the only statistics printed. We can calculate $S/\sqrt{n}$ by finding the difference between the upper and lower control limits and dividing the difference by 6; that is,

$$S/\sqrt{n} = \frac{(\bar{\bar{x}} + 3S/\sqrt{n}) - (\bar{\bar{x}} - 3S/\sqrt{n})}{6} = \frac{503.253 - 497.340}{6} = .9855$$

Figure 21.6 describes the centerline, control limits, and zones for Example 21.1.

Several pattern tests can be applied.

Test 1: One point beyond zone A. This is the method discussed previously, where we conclude that the process is out of control if any point is outside the control limits.

Test 2: Nine points in a row in zone C or beyond (on the same side of the centerline).

Test 3: Six increasing or six decreasing points in a row.

Test 4: Fourteen points in a row alternating up and down.

Test 5: Two out of three points in a row in zone A or beyond (on the same side of the centerline).

FIGURE **21.6**   Zones of $\bar{x}$ Chart: Example 21.1

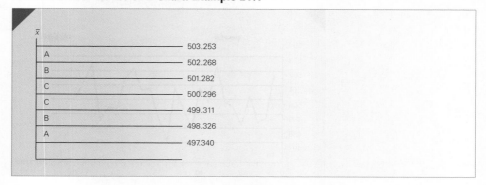

Test 6: Four out of five points in a row in zone B or beyond (on the same side of the centerline).

Test 7: Fifteen points in a row in zone C (on both sides of the centerline).

Test 8: Eight points in a row beyond zone C (on both sides of the centerline).

In the examples shown in Figure 21.7, each of the eight tests indicates a process out of control.

FIGURE **21.7**   Examples of Patterns Indicating Process Out of Control

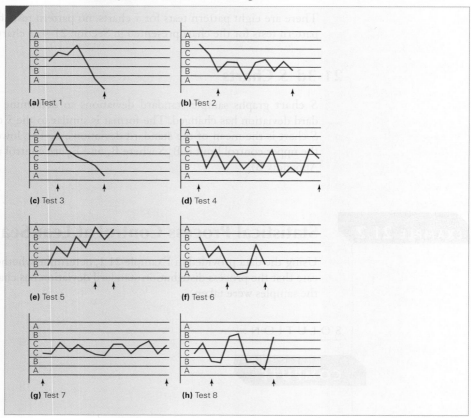

FIGURE **21.8** $\bar{x}$ **Chart with Zones: Example 21.1**

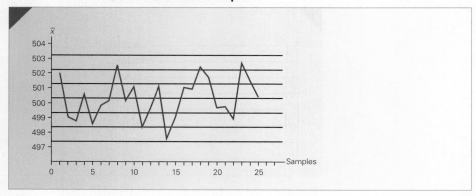

All eight tests are based on the same concepts used to test hypotheses throughout this book. In other words, each pattern is a rare event that is unlikely to occur when a process is under control. Thus, when any one of these patterns is recognized, the statistics practitioner has reason to believe that the process is out of control. In fact, it is often possible to identify the cause of the problem from the pattern in the control chart.

Figure 21.8 depicts the zones and the means for Example 21.1. After checking each of the eight pattern tests, we conclude that the process is under control.

21-3c Pattern Tests in Practice

There are eight pattern tests for $\bar{x}$ charts, no pattern tests for S and R charts, and four pattern tests for the chart presented in Section 21-4 (p charts).

21-3d S Charts

S chart graphs sample standard deviations to determine whether the process standard deviation has changed. The format is similar to the $\bar{x}$ chart. The centerline of the S chart is the mean of the standard deviations, $\overline{S}$. The lower control limit is $B_3\overline{S}$ and the upper control limit is $B_4\overline{S}$ where B_3 and B_4 are control chart constants (Table 12 in Appendix B).

EXAMPLE 21.2

Statistical Process Control at Lear Seating, Part 2

Using the data provided in Example 21.1, determine whether there is evidence to indicate that the process distribution standard deviation has changed over the period when the samples were taken.

SOLUTION:

COMPUTE

Do It Yourself Excel

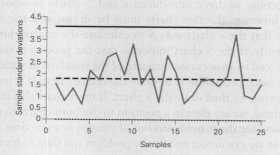

INSTRUCTIONS

1. Type or import the data into one column. (Open Xm21-1.)

2. For each sample, calculate the sample standard deviation. Compute the mean sample standard deviation $\bar{S}$.

3. Calculate the lower and upper control limits.

   Lower control limit = $B_3\bar{S} = 0$

   Upper control limit = $B_4\bar{S} = 2.266(1.80) = 4.08$

4. Draw a line chart with the centerline and control limits as in Example 21.1.

INTERPRET

There are no points outside the control limits. Because we do not apply any of the pattern tests, we conclude that there is no evidence to believe that the standard deviation has changed over this period.

21-3e Good News and Bad News about S Charts

In analyzing S charts, we would conclude that the process distribution has changed if we observe points outside the control limits. Obviously, points above the upper control limit indicate that the process standard deviation has increased—an undesirable situation. Points below the lower control limit also indicate that the process standard deviation has changed. However, cases in which the standard deviation has decreased are welcome occurrences because reducing the variation generally leads to improvements in quality. The operations manager should investigate cases where the sample standard deviations or ranges are small to determine the factors that produced such results. The objective is to determine whether permanent improvements in the production process can be made. Care must be exercised in cases in which the S chart reveals a decrease in the standard deviation because this is often caused by improper sampling.

21-3f Using the x̄ and S Charts

In this section, we have introduced x̄ and S charts as separate procedures. In actual practice, however, the two charts must be drawn and assessed together. The reason for this is that the x̄ chart uses S to calculate the control limits and zone boundaries. Consequently, if the S chart indicates that the process is out of control, the value of S will not lead to an accurate estimate of the standard deviation of the process distribution. The usual procedure is to draw the S chart first. If it indicates that the process is under control, we then draw the x̄ chart. If the x̄ chart also indicates that the process is under control, we are then in a position to use both charts to maintain control. If either chart shows that the process was out of control at some time during the creation of the charts, then we can detect and fix the problem and then redraw the charts with new data.

21-3g Monitoring the Production Process

When the process is under control, we can use the control chart limits and centerline to monitor the process in the future. We do so by plotting all future statistics on the control chart.

EXAMPLE **21.3**

Statistical Process Control at Lear Seating, Part 3

After determining that the process is under control, the company in Example 21.1 began using the statistics generated in the creation of the x̄ and S charts to monitor the production process. The sampling plan calls for samples of size 4 every hour. The following table lists the lengths of the springs taken during the first 6 hours.

Sample				
1	502.653	498.354	502.209	500.080
2	501.212	494.454	500.918	501.855
3	500.086	500.826	496.426	503.591
4	502.994	500.481	502.996	503.113
5	500.549	498.780	502.480	499.836
6	500.441	502.666	502.569	503.248

SOLUTION:

After each sample is taken, the mean and standard deviation are computed. The standard deviations are plotted on the S chart using the previously determined control limits when the process variation was deemed to be in control. The sample means are plotted on the x̄ chart, again using the zone limits determined when the process was deemed to be in control, and the pattern tests are checked after each point is plotted. The first six samples are shown in Figure 21.9. After the standard deviation and mean of the sixth sample are plotted, the technician would stop the production process. Although the process variation still appears to be in control, the fourth and sixth means on the x̄ chart combine to indicate that test 5 has failed; there are two out of three points in a row that are in zone A or beyond. Thus, it appears that the process mean has shifted upward. Technicians need to find the source of the problem and make repairs. After repairs are completed, production resumes and new control charts and their centerlines and control limits are recalculated.

FIGURE **21.9** S and $\bar{x}$ Charts for Example 21.3

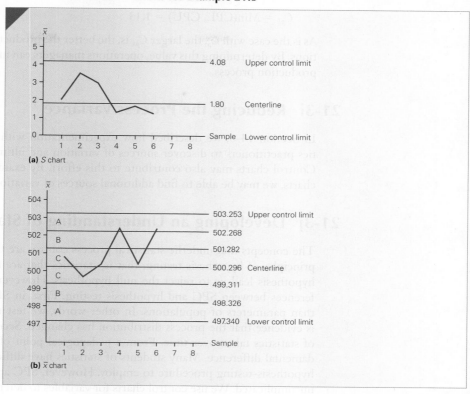

(a) S chart

(b) $\bar{x}$ chart

21-3h Process Capability Index

In Section 14-6, we discussed the **process capability index**, which measures the capability of the process to produce units whose dimensions fall within the specifications. We defined the index as

$$C_p = \frac{\text{USL} - \text{LSL}}{6\sigma}$$

where USL and LSL are the upper and lower specification limits, respectively. To compute the process capability index, we need to know these limits and the process standard deviation. The standard deviation is a population parameter that is generally unknown. Thus, C_p measures the theoretical or potential process capability. To produce a measure of the process's actual capability, we must use statistics computed in the construction of the control chart. Suppose that in Example 21.1 the operations manager determined that the springs will fit, provided that their lengths fall between the lower specification limit LSL = 493 and the upper specification limit USL = 507. In Example 21.1, we found $\bar{\bar{x}} = 500.296$ and $S = 1.971$.

We define the following:

$$\text{CPL} = \frac{\bar{\bar{x}} - \text{LSL}}{3S} = \frac{500.296 - 493}{3(1.971)} = 1.23$$

$$\text{CPU} = \frac{\text{USL} - \bar{\bar{x}}}{3S} = \frac{507 - 500.296}{3(1.971)} = 1.13$$

We define the process capability index as the smaller of these two indexes; that is,

$$C_{pk} = \text{Min}(\text{CPL}, \text{CPU}) = 1.13$$

As is the case with C_p, the larger C_{pk} is, the better the production process meets specifications. By determining this value, operations managers can measure improvements in the production process.

21-3i Reducing the Process Variance

In Section 14-6, we described how experimentation with the four M's allows statistics practitioners to discover sources of variation and ultimately reduce that variation. Control charts may also contribute to this effort. By examining the results of control charts, we may be able to find additional sources of variation.

21-3j Developing an Understanding of Statistical Concepts

The concepts that underlie statistical process control are the same as the fundamental principles of hypothesis testing; that is, statistics that are not consistent with the null hypothesis lead us to reject the null hypothesis. However, there are two critical differences between SPC and hypothesis testing. First, in SPC we test processes rather than parameters of populations. In other words, we test to determine whether there is evidence that the process distribution has changed. Second, in SPC we test a series of statistics taken over time. From a pedagogical point of view, there is another fundamental difference. Many students of statistics have difficulty identifying the correct hypothesis-testing procedure to employ. However, SPC applications tend to be rather uncomplicated. We use control charts for variables to determine whether the process is under control when the product produced must be measured quantitatively. Identifying the correct technique is seldom difficult and thus does not require the technique-identification skills developed throughout this book.

EXERCISES

21.23 Given the following statistics drawn from 30 samples of size 4, calculate the centerline and control limits for the $\bar{x}$ chart.

$$\bar{\bar{x}} = 453.6 \qquad S = 12.5$$

21.24 The mean of the sample means and the pooled standard deviation of 40 samples of size 9 taken from a production process under control are shown here. Compute the centerline, control limits, and zone boundaries for the $\bar{x}$ chart.

$$\bar{\bar{x}} = 181.1 \qquad S = 11.0$$

21.25 Twenty-five samples of size 4 were taken from a production process. The sample means are listed in chronological order below. The mean of the sample means and the pooled standard deviation are $\bar{\bar{x}} = 13.3$ and $S = 3.8$, respectively.

14.5	10.3	17.0	9.4	13.2	9.3	17.1
5.5	5.3	16.3	10.5	11.5	8.8	12.6
10.5	16.3	8.7	9.4	11.4	17.6	20.5
21.1	16.3	18.5	20.9			

a. Find the centerline and control limits for the $\bar{x}$ chart.
b. Plot the sample means on the $\bar{x}$ chart.
c. Is the process under control? Explain.

The following exercises require a computer and statistical software.

21.26 Xr21-26 Thirty samples of size 4 were drawn from a production process.
a. Construct an S chart.
b. Construct an $\bar{x}$ chart.
c. Do the charts allow you to conclude that the process is under control?

d. If the process went out of control, which of the following is the likely cause: level shift, instability, trend, or cycle?

21.27 Xr21-27 The fence of a saw is set so that it automatically cuts 2-by-4 boards into 96-inch lengths needed to produce prefabricated homes. To ensure that the lumber is cut properly, three pieces of wood are measured after each 100 cuts are made. The measurements in inches for the last 40 samples were recorded.

a. Do these data indicate that the process is out of control?

b. If so, when did it go out of control? What is the likely cause: level shift, instability, trend, or cycle?

c. Speculate on how the problem could be corrected.

21.28 Xr21-28 An arc extinguishing unit (AEU) is used in the high-voltage electrical industry to eliminate the occurrence of electrical flash from one live 25,000-volt switch contact to another. A small but important component of an AEU is a nonconductive sliding bearing called a (ST-90811) pin guide. The dimensional accuracy of this pin guide is critical to the overall operation of the AEU. If any one of its dimensions is "out of spec" (specification), the part will bind within the AEU, causing failure. This would cause the complete destruction of both the AEU and the 25,000 volt-switch contacts, resulting in a power blackout. A pin guide has a square shape with a circular hole in the center, as shown below with its specified dimensions. The specification limits are LSL = .4335 and USL = .4435.

Because of the critical nature of the dimensions of the pin guide, statistical process control is used during long production runs to check that the production process is under control. Suppose that samples of five pin guides are drawn every hour. The results of the last 25 samples were recorded. Do these data allow the technician to conclude that the process is out of control?

21.29 Refer to Exercise 21.28. Find the process capability index C_{pk}.

21.30 Xr21-30 KW Paints is a company that manufactures various kinds of paints and sells them in 1- and 4-liter cans. The cans are filled on an assembly line with an automatic valve regulating the amount of paint. If the cans are overfilled, paint and money will be wasted. If the cans are underfilled, customers will complain. To ensure that the proper amount of paint goes into each can, statistical process control is used. Every hour, five cans are opened, and the volume of paint is measured. The results from the last 30 hours from the 1-liter production line were recorded. To avoid rounding errors, we recorded the volumes in cubic centimeters (cc) after subtracting 1,000. Thus, the file contains the amounts of overfill and underfill. Draw the $\bar{x}$ and S charts to determine whether the process is under control.

21.31 Refer to Exercise 21.30. If the lower and upper specification limits are 995 cc and 1005 cc, respectively, what is C_{pk}?

21.32 Xr21-32 Lear Seating of Kitchener, Ontario, produces seats for Cadillacs and other GM cars and trucks. The Cadillac seat includes a part called the EK headrest. The frame of the headrest is made from steel rods. A machine is used to bend the rod into a U-shape described as shown. The width is critical; if it is too wide or too narrow, it will not fit into the holes drilled into the seat frame. The process is checked by drawing samples of size 3 every 2 hours. The last 20 samples were recorded.

a. What do these data tell you about the process?

b. If it went out of control, at what sample did this occur?

c. What is the likely assignable cause?

21.33 Xr21-33 The degree to which nuts and bolts are tightened in numerous places on a car is often important. For example, in Toyota cars, a nut holds the rear signal light. If the nut is not tightened sufficiently, it will loosen and fall off; if it is too tight, the light may break. The nut is tightened with a torque wrench with a set clutch. The target torque is 8 kgf/cm (kilogram-force per centimeter) with specification limits LSL = 7 kgf/cm and USL = 9 kgf/cm. Statistical process control is employed to constantly check the process. Random samples of size 4 are drawn after every 200 nuts are tightened. The data from the last 25 samples were recorded.

a. Determine whether the process is under control.

b. If it is out of control, identify when this occurred and the likely cause.

21.34 Xr21-34 The seats for the *F*-150 series Ford trucks are manufactured by Lear Seating. The frames must be 1,496 mm wide with specification limits LSL = 1,486 mm and USL = 1,506 mm. Frames that are wider than 1,506 mm or narrower than 1,486 mm result in assembly problems because seat cushions and/or other parts won't fit. The process is tested by drawing random samples of five frames every 2 hours. The last 25 samples were recorded. What can we conclude from these data?

21.35 Xr21-35 Long Manufacturing produces heat exchangers, primarily for the automotive industry. One such product, a transmission oil cooler, is used in the cooling of bus transmissions. It is composed of a series of copper tubes that are soldered into a header. The header must have a diameter of 4.984 inches with specification limits LSL = 4.978 inches and USL = 4.990 inches. Oversized headers result in fluid mixing and possible failure of the device. For every 100 headers produced, the operations manager draws a sample of size 4. The data from the last 25 samples were recorded. What can we conclude from these data?

21.36 Find the process capability index for Exercise 21.35.

21.37 Xr21-37 Refer to Exercise 21.35. Nuts and bolts are used in the assembly of the transmission oil coolers. They are supposed to be tightened by a torque wrench to 7 foot-pounds with specification limits LSL = 6 foot-pounds and USL = 8 foot-pounds. To test the process, three nuts are tested every 3 hours. The results for the last 75 hours were recorded. Does it appear that the process is under control?

21.38 Xr21-38 Motor oil is packaged and sold in plastic bottles. The bottles are often handled quite roughly in delivery to the stores (bottles are packed in boxes, which are stacked to conserve truck space), in the stores themselves, and by consumers. The bottles must be hardy enough to withstand this treatment without leaking. Before leaving the plant, the bottles undergo statistical process control procedures. Five out of every 10,000 bottles are sampled. The burst strength (the pressure required to burst the bottle) is measured in pounds per square inch (psi). The process is designed to produce bottles that can withstand as much as 800 psi. The burst strengths of the last 30 samples were recorded.

a. Draw the appropriate control chart(s).
b. Does it appear that the process went out of control? If so, when did this happen, and what are the likely causes and remedies?

21.39 Xr21-39 Almost all computer hardware and software producers offer a toll-free telephone number to solve problems associated with their products. The ability to work quickly to resolve difficulties is critical. One software maker's policy is that all calls must be answered by a software consultant within 120 seconds. (All calls are initially answered by computer and the caller is put on hold until a consultant attends to the caller.) To help maintain the quality of the service, four calls per day are monitored. The amount of time before the consultant responds to the calls was recorded for the last 30 days.

a. Draw the appropriate control chart(s).
b. Does it appear that the process went out of control? If so, when did this happen, and what are the likely causes and remedies?

21.40 Xr21-40 Plastic pipe is used for plumbing in almost all new homes. If the pipes are too narrow or too wide, they will not connect properly with other parts of the plumbing system. A manufacturer of 3-inch-diameter pipes uses statistical process control to maintain the quality of its products. The sampling plan is to draw samples of three 10-foot-long pipes every hour and measure the diameters. Twenty hours ago, the production process was shut down for repairs. The results of the first 20 samples taken since were recorded. Does it appear that the production process is under control?

21.41 If the specification limits for the plastic pipes in Exercise 21.40 are LSL = 2.9 inches and USL = 3.1 inches, determine the process capability index C_{pk}.

21.42 Calculate the process capability index for Exercise 21.34. Does the value of this index indicate that the production process is poor? Explain.

21-4 / CONTROL CHARTS FOR ATTRIBUTES: p CHART

In this section, we introduce a control chart that is used to monitor a process whose results are categorized as either defective or nondefective. We construct a **p chart** to track the proportion of defective units in a series of samples.

21-4a p Chart

We draw the p chart in a way similar to the construction of the $\bar{x}$ chart. We draw samples of size n from the process at a minimum of 25 time periods. For each sample, we calculate the sample proportion of defective units, which we label $\hat{p}_j$. We then compute the mean of the sample proportions, which is labeled $\bar{p}$; that is,

$$\bar{p} = \frac{\sum_{j=1}^{k} \hat{p}_j}{k}$$

The centerline and control limits are as follows.

Centerline and Control Limits for the p Chart

$$\text{Centerline} = \bar{p}$$

$$\text{Lower control limit} = \bar{p} - 3\sqrt{\frac{\bar{p}(1-\bar{p})}{n}}$$

$$\text{Upper control limit} = \bar{p} + 3\sqrt{\frac{\bar{p}(1-\bar{p})}{n}}$$

If the lower limit is negative, set it equal to 0.

21-4b Pattern Tests

Test 1: One point beyond zone A.

Test 2: Nine points in a row in zone C or beyond (on the same side of the centerline).

Test 3: Six increasing or six decreasing points in a row.

Test 4: Fourteen points in a row alternating up and down.

We'll demonstrate this technique using the chapter-opening example.

Detecting the Source of Defective Discs: Solution

For each sample, we compute the proportion of defective discs and calculate the mean sample proportion, which is $\bar{p} = .05762$. Thus,

$$\text{Centerline} = \bar{p} = .05762$$

$$\text{Lower control limit} = \bar{p} - 3\sqrt{\frac{\bar{p}(1-\bar{p})}{n}}$$

$$= .05762 - 3\sqrt{\frac{(.05762)(1-.05762)}{200}}$$

$$= .008188$$

$$\text{Upper control limit} = \bar{p} + 3\sqrt{\frac{p(1-\bar{p})}{n}}$$

$$= .05762 + 3\sqrt{\frac{(.05762)(1-.05762)}{200}}$$

$$= .1071$$

Because

$$\sqrt{\frac{\bar{p}(1-\bar{p})}{n}} = \sqrt{\frac{(.05762)(1-.05762)}{200}} = .01648$$

The boundaries of the zones are as follows:

Zone C: $.05762 \pm .01648 = (.04114, .0741)$

Zone B: $.05762 \pm 2(.01648) = (.02467, .09057)$

Zone A: $.05762 \pm 3(.01648) = (.008188, .1071)$

The following output exhibits this p chart.

Do It Yourself Excel

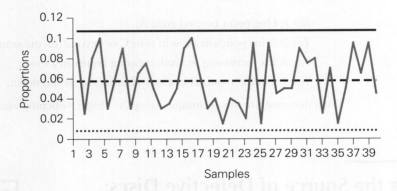

INSTRUCTIONS

1. Compute the mean proportion defective.

2. Calculate the control limits.

3. Draw the line chart of the proportion defectives, centerline, and control limits.

INTERPRET

None of the points lies outside the control limits (test 1), and the other test results are negative. There is no evidence to infer that the process is out of control. However, this does not mean that 5.76% is an acceptable proportion of defects. Management should continually improve the process to reduce the defective rate and improve the process.

The comment we made about S charts is also valid for p charts: Sample proportions that are less than the lower control limit indicate a change in the process that we would like to make permanent. We need to investigate the reasons for such a change just as vigorously as we investigate the causes of large proportions of defects.

EXERCISES

21.43 To ensure that a manufacturing process is under control, 40 samples of size 1,000 were drawn, and the number of defectives in each sample was counted. The mean sample proportion was .035. Compute the centerline and control limits for the p chart.

21.44 Xr21-44 Random samples of 200 copier machines were taken on an assembly line every hour for the past 25 hours. The number of defective machines is shown here. Are there any points beyond the control limits? If so, what do they tell you about the production process?

> 3   5   3   2   2   11   12   6   7   5   0   7   8
> 2   10   6   4   2   10   5   4   11   10   13   14

21.45 Xr21-45 Raytheon of Canada Limited produces printed circuit boards (PCBs), which involve a number of soldering operations. At the end of the process, the PCBs are tested to determine whether they work properly. There are several causes of PCB failure, including bad flux, improper heating, and impurities. A reject rate of less than .80% is considered acceptable. Statistical process control is used by Raytheon to constantly check quality. Every hour, 500 PCBs are tested. The number of defective PCBs for the past 25 hours is shown here. Draw a p chart and apply the pattern tests to determine whether the process is under control.

> 3   1   2   2   1   2   3   3   3   2   3   0   0
> 0   2   0   0   2   4   1   1   1   4   1   3

21.46 Xr21-46 A plant produces 1,000 cordless telephones daily. A random sample of 100 telephones is inspected each day. After 30 days, the following number of defectives were found. Construct a p chart to determine whether the process is out of control.

> 5   0   4   3   0   3   1   1   5   0   2   1   6   0   3
> 0   5   5   8   5   0   1   9   6   11   6   6   4   5   10

21.47 Xr21-47 The Woodsworth Publishing Company produces millions of books containing hundreds of millions of pages each year. To ensure the quality of the printed page, Woodsworth uses statistical process control. In each production run, 1,000 pages

are randomly inspected. The examiners look for print clarity and whether the material is centered on the page properly. The numbers of defective pages in the last 40 production runs are listed here. Draw the p chart. Using the pattern tests, can we conclude that the production process is under control?

> 11   9   17   19   15   15   18   21   18   6   27   14   7   18
> 18   19   17   15   7   16   17   22   12   12   12   16   12
> 9   21   17   20   17   17   18   23   29   24   27   23   21

The following exercises require the use of a computer and statistical software.

21.48 Xr21-48 A company that manufactures batteries employs statistical process control to ensure that its product functions properly. The sampling plan for the D-cell batteries calls for samples of 500 batteries to be taken and tested. The numbers of defective batteries in the last 30 samples were recorded. Determine whether the process is under control.

21.49 Xr21-49 A courier delivery company advertises that it guarantees delivery by noon the following day. The statistical process control plan calls for sampling 2,000 deliveries each day to ensure that the advertisement is reasonable. The number of late deliveries for the last 30 days were recorded. What can we conclude from these data?

21.50 Xr21-50 Optical scanners are used in all supermarkets to speed the checkout process. Whenever the scanner fails to read the bar code on the product, the cashier is required to manually punch the code into the register. Obviously, unreadable bar codes slow the checkout process. Statistical process control is used to determine whether the scanner is working properly. Once a day at each checkout counter, a sample of 500 scans is taken, and the number of times the scanner is unable to read the bar code is determined. (The sampling process is performed automatically by the cash register.) The results for one checkout counter for the past 25 days were recorded.

a. Draw the appropriate control chart(s).
b. Does it appear that the process went out of control? If so, identify when this happened and suggest several possible explanations for the cause.

CHAPTER SUMMARY

In this chapter, we introduced **statistical process control** and explained how it contributes to the maintenance of quality. We discussed how **control charts** detect changes in the process distribution and introduced the $\bar{x}$ **chart**, S **chart**, and p **chart**.

IMPORTANT TERMS:

Statistical process control (SPC)   902
Quality control   902
Prevention approach   902
Chance or common variation   902
Assignable or special variation   902
Under control   903
Specification limits   903
Out of control   903
Control chart   904
$\bar{x}$ chart   904

Centerline   904
Upper control limit   904
Lower control limit   904
Operating characteristic (OC) curve   906
Average run length (ARL)   907
Control charts for variables   908
Control charts for attributes   908
S chart   916
Process capability index   919
p chart   922

SYMBOLS:

Symbol	Pronounced	Represents
S		Pooled standard deviation
s_j	s-sub-j	Standard deviation of the jth sample
$\hat{p}_j$	p-hat-sub-j	Proportion of defectives in jth sample
$\bar{p}$	p-bar	Mean proportion of defectives

FORMULAS:

Centerline and control limits for $\bar{x}$ chart using S

$$\text{Centerline} = \bar{x}$$

$$\text{Lower control limit} = \bar{x} - 3\frac{S}{\sqrt{n}}$$

$$\text{Upper control limit} = \bar{x} + 3\frac{S}{\sqrt{n}}$$

Centerline and control limits for the p chart

$$\text{Centerline} = \bar{p}$$

$$\text{Lower control limit} = \bar{p} - 3\sqrt{\frac{\bar{p}(1-\bar{p})}{n}}$$

$$\text{Upper control limit} = \bar{p} + 3\sqrt{\frac{\bar{p}(1-\bar{p})}{n}}$$

EXCEL OUTPUT AND INSTRUCTIONS:

Technique	
$\bar{x}$ chart using S	913
S chart	917
p chart	924

Mike Kemp/Rubberball/Getty Images

DECISION ANALYSIS

CHAPTER OUTLINE

Acceptance Sampling

A factory produces a small but important component used in computers. The factory manufactures the component in 1,000-unit lots. Because of the relatively advanced technology, the manufacturing process results in a large proportion of defective units. In fact, the operations manager has observed that the percentage of defective units per lot has been either 15% or 35%. In the past year, 60% of the lots have had 15% defectives, and 40% have had 35% defectives. The current policy of the company is to send the lot to the customer, replace all defectives, and pay any additional costs. The total cost of replacing a defective unit that has been sent to the customer is $10/unit.

Image Source/Getty Images

On page 939 we provide answers to our questions.

(Continued)

927

Because of the high costs, the company management is considering inspecting all units and replacing the defective units before shipment. The sampling cost is $2/unit, and the replacement cost is $.50/unit. Each unit sells for $5.

a. Based on the history of the past year, should the company adopt the 100% inspection plan?

b. Is it worthwhile to take a sample of size 2 from the lot before deciding whether to inspect 100%?

INTRODUCTION

In previous chapters, we dealt with techniques for summarizing data in order to make decisions about population parameters and population characteristics. Our focus in this chapter is also on decision making, but the types of problems we deal with here differ in several ways. First, the technique for hypothesis testing concludes with either rejecting or not rejecting some hypothesis concerning a dimension of a population. In decision analysis, we deal with the problem of selecting one alternative from a list of several possible decisions. Second, in hypothesis testing, the decision is based on the statistical evidence available. In decision analysis, there may be no statistical data, or if there are data, the decision may depend only partly on them. Third, costs (and profits) are only indirectly considered (in the selection of a significance level or in interpreting the *p*-value) in the formulation of a hypothesis test. Decision analysis directly involves profits and losses. Because of these major differences, the only topics covered previously in the text that are required for an understanding of decision analysis are probability (including Bayes's Law) and expected value.

22-1 / DECISION PROBLEM

You would think that, by this point in the text, we would already have introduced all the necessary concepts and terminology. Unfortunately, because decision analysis is so radically different from statistical inference, several more terms must be defined. They will be introduced in the following example.

EXAMPLE 22.1

An Investment Decision

An investor wants to invest $1 million for 1 year. After analyzing and eliminating numerous possibilities, the choice has been narrowed to one of three alternatives. These alternatives are referred to as **acts** and are denoted a_i.

a_1: Invest in a guaranteed income certificate paying 3%.
a_2: Invest in a bond with a coupon value of 2%
a_3: Invest in a well-diversified portfolio of stocks.

The payoffs associated with the last two acts depend on a number of factors, foremost among which is interest rates. There are three possible **states of nature**, denoted s_j.

s_1: Interest rates increase.
s_2: Interest rates stay the same.
s_3: Interest rates decrease.

After further analysis, the amount of profit for each possible combination of an act and a state of nature has been determined. Of course, the payoff for the guaranteed income certificate will be $30,000 no matter which state of nature occurs. The profits from each alternative investment are summarized in Table 22.1, in what is called a **payoff table**. Notice that for example, when the decision is a_2 and the state of nature is s_1, the investor would suffer a $15,000 loss, which is represented by a $-$15,000 payoff.

TABLE **22.1** Payoff Table for Example 22.1

STATES OF NATURE	a_1 (GIC)	a_2 (BOND)	a_3 (STOCKS)
s_1 (interest rates increase)	$30,000	$-$15,000	$40,000
s_2 (interest rates stay the same)	30,000	20,000	27,500
s_3 (interest rates decrease)	30,000	60,000	15,000

Another way of expressing the consequence of an act involves measuring the opportunity loss associated with each combination of an act and a state of nature. An **opportunity loss** is the difference between what the decision maker's profit for an act is and what the profit could have been had the best decision been made. For example, consider the first row of Table 22.1. If s_1 is the state of nature that occurs and the investor chooses act a_1, the profit is equal to $30,000. However, had act a_3 been chosen the profit would be $40,000. The difference between what could have been made ($40,000) and what was actually made ($30,000) is the opportunity loss. Thus, given that s_1 is the state of nature, the opportunity loss of act a_1 is $10,000. The opportunity loss of act a_2 is $55,000, which is the difference between $40,000 and $-$15,000. The opportunity loss of act a_3 is 0, because there is no opportunity loss when the best alternative is chosen. In a similar manner, we can compute the remaining opportunity losses for this example (see Table 22.2). Notice that we can never experience a negative opportunity loss.

TABLE **22.2** Opportunity Loss Table for Example 22.1

STATES OF NATURE	a_1 (GIC)	a_2 (BOND)	a_3 (STOCKS)
s_1 (interest rates increase)	$10,000	$55,000	0
s_2 (interest rates stay the same)	0	10,000	2,500
s_3 (interest rates decrease)	30,000	0	45,000

Decision Trees

Most problems involving a simple choice of alternatives can readily be resolved by using the payoff table (or the opportunity loss table). In other situations, however, the decision maker must choose between sequences of acts. In Section 22-2, we introduce one form of such situations. In these cases, a payoff table will not suffice to determine the best alternative; instead, we require a **decision tree**.

In Chapter 6, we suggested the probability tree as a useful device for computing probabilities. In this type of tree, all the branches represent stages of events. In a decision tree, however, the branches represent both acts and events (states of nature).

FIGURE **22.1** Decision Tree for Example 22.1

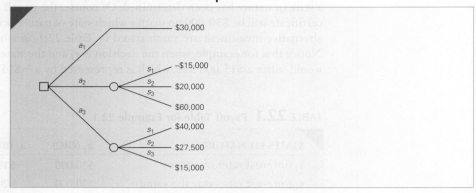

We distinguish between them in the following way: A square node represents a point where a decision is to be made; a point where a state of nature occurs is represented by a round node. Figure 22.1 depicts the decision tree for Example 22.1.

The tree begins with a square node; that is, we begin by making a choice among a_1, a_2, and a_3. The branches emanating from the square node represent these alternatives. At the ends of branches a_2 and a_3, we reach round nodes representing the occurrence of some state of nature. These are depicted as branches representing s_1, s_2, and s_3. At the end of branch a_1, we don't really have a state of nature, because the payoff is fixed at $30,000 no matter what happens to interest rates.

At the ends of the branches, the payoffs are shown (alternatively, we could have worked with opportunity losses instead of with payoffs). These are, of course, the same values that appear in Table 22.1.

Up to this point, all we have done is set up the problem; we have not made any attempt to determine the decision. It should be noted that in many real-life problems, determining the payoff table or decision tree can be a formidable task in itself. Many managers, however, have observed that this task is often extremely helpful in decision making.

Expected Monetary Value Decision

In many decision problems, it is possible to assign probabilities to the states of nature. For example, if the decision involves trying to decide whether to draw to an inside straight in the game of poker, the probability of succeeding can easily be determined by the use of simple rules of probability. If we must decide whether to replace a machine that has broken down frequently in the past, we can assign probabilities on the basis of the relative frequency of the breakdowns. In many other instances, however, formal rules and techniques of probability cannot be applied. In Example 22.1, the historical relative frequencies of the ups and downs of interest rates will supply scant useful information to help the investor assign probabilities to the behavior of interest rates during the coming year. In such cases, probabilities must be assigned subjectively. In other words, the determination of the probabilities must be based on the experience, knowledge, and (perhaps) guesswork of the decision maker.

If, in Example 22.1, the investor has some knowledge about a number of economic variables, a reasonable guess about what will happen to interest rates in the next year might be made. Suppose, for example, that our investor believes that future interest rates are most likely to remain essentially the same as they are today and that (of the remaining two states of nature) rates are more likely to decrease than to increase. The investor might then guess the following probabilities:

$$P(s_1) = .2, P(s_2) = .5, P(s_3) = .3$$

Because the probabilities are subjective, we would expect another decision maker to produce a completely different set of probabilities. In fact, if this were not true, we would rarely have buyers and sellers of stocks (or any other investment), because everyone would be a buyer (and there would be no sellers) or everyone would be a seller (with no buyers).

After determining the probabilities of the states of nature, we can address the *expected monetary value decision*. We now calculate what we expect will happen for each decision. Because we generally measure the consequences of each decision in monetary terms, we compute the **expected monetary value (EMV)** of each act. Recall from Section 7-1 that we calculate expected values by multiplying the values of the random variables by their respective probabilities and then summing the products. Thus, in our example, the expected monetary value of alternative a_1 is:

$$EMV(a_1) = .2(30,000) + .5(30,000) + .3(30,000) = \$30,000$$

The expected values of the other decisions are found in the same way:

$$EMV(a_2) = .2(-15,000) + .5(20,000) + .3(60.000) = \$25,000$$
$$EMV(a_3) = .2(40,000) + .5(27,500) + .3(15,000) = \$26,250$$

We choose the decision with the largest expected monetary value, which is a_1, and label its expected value EMV*. Hence, EMV* = \$30,000.

In general, the expected monetary values do not represent possible payoffs. For example, the expected monetary value of act a_2 is \$25,000, yet the payoff table indicates that the only possible payoffs from choosing a_2 are $-\$15,000$, \$20,000, and \$60,000. Of course, the expected monetary value of act a_1 (\$30,000) is possible, because that is the only payoff of the act.

What, then, does the expected monetary value represent? If the investment is made a large number of times, with exactly the same payoffs and probabilities, the expected monetary value is the average payoff per investment. That is, if the investment is repeated an infinite number of times with act a_2, 20% of the investments will result in a \$15,000 loss, 50% will result in a \$20,000 profit, and 30% will result in a \$60,000 profit. The average of all these investments is the expected monetary value, \$25,000. If act a_3 is chosen, the average payoff in the long run will be \$26,250.

An important point is raised by the question of how many investments are going to be made. The answer is one. Even if the investor intends to make the same type of investment annually, the payoffs and the probabilities of the states of nature will undoubtedly change from year to year. Hence, we are faced with having determined the expected monetary value decision on the basis of an infinite number of investments, when there will be only one investment. We can rationalize this apparent contradiction in two ways. First, the expected value decision is the only method that allows us to combine the two most important factors in the decision process—the payoffs and their probabilities. It seems inconceivable that, where both factors are known, the investor would want to ignore either one. (There are processes that make decisions on the basis of the payoffs alone; however, these processes assume no knowledge of the probabilities, which is not the case with our example.) Second, typical decision makers make a large number of decisions over their lifetimes. By using the expected value decision, the decision maker should perform at least as well as anyone else. Thus, despite the problem of interpretation, we advocate the expected monetary value decision.

Expected Opportunity Loss Decision

We can also calculate the **expected opportunity loss (EOL)** of each act. From the opportunity loss table (Table 22.2), we get the following values:

$$EOL(a_1) = .2(10,000) + .5(0) + .3(30,000) = \$11,000$$
$$EOL(a_2) = .2(55,000) + .5(10,000) + .3(0) = \$16,000$$
$$EOL(a_3) = .2(0) + .5(2,500) + .3(45,000) = \$14,750$$

Because we want to minimize losses, we choose the act that produces the smallest expected opportunity loss, which is a_1. We label its expected value EOL*. Observe that the EMV decision is the same as the EOL decision. This is not a coincidence—the opportunity loss table was produced directly from the payoff table.

Rollback Technique for Decision Trees

Figure 22.2 presents the decision tree for Example 22.1, with the probabilities of the states of nature included. The process of determining the EMV decision is called the **rollback technique**; it operates as follows. Beginning at the end of the tree (right-hand side), we calculate the expected monetary value at each round node. The numbers above the round nodes in Figure 22.2 specify these expected monetary values.

At each square node, we make a decision by choosing the branch with the largest EMV. In our example, there is only one square node. Our optimal decision is, of course, a_1.

FIGURE **22.2** Rollback Technique for Example 22.1

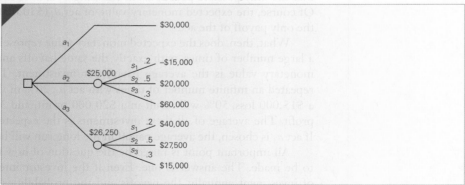

EXERCISES

22.1 Set up the opportunity loss table from the following payoff table:

	a_1	a_2
s_1	55	26
s_2	43	38
s_3	29	43
s_4	15	51

22.2 Draw the decision tree for Exercise 22.1.

22.3 If we assign the following probabilities to the states of nature in Exercise 22.1, determine the EMV decision:

$$P(s_1) = .4 \quad P(s_2) = .1 \quad P(s_3) = .3 \quad P(s_4) = .2$$

22.4 Given the following payoff table, draw the decision tree:

	a_1	a_2	a_3
s_1	20	5	−1
s_2	8	5	4
s_3	−10	5	10

22.5 Refer to Exercise 22.4. Set up the opportunity loss table.

22.6 If we assign the following probabilities to the states of nature in Exercise 22.5, determine the EOL decision:

$$P(s_1) = .2 \quad P(s_2) = .6 \quad P(s_3) = .2$$

Applications

22.7 A baker must decide how many specialty cakes to bake each morning. The daily demand for cakes ranges from 0 to 3. Each cake costs $3.00 to produce and sells for $8.00, and any unsold cakes are thrown into the garbage at the end of the day.
  a. Set up a payoff table to help the baker decide how many cakes to bake.
  b. Set up the opportunity loss table.
  c. Draw the decision tree.

22.8 Refer to Exercise 22.7. Assume that the probability of each value of demand is the same for all possible demands.
  a. Determine the EMV decision.
  b. Determine the EOL decision.

22.9 The manager of a large shopping center in Buffalo is in the process of deciding on the type of snow-clearing service to hire for the parking lot. Two services are available. The White Christmas Company will clear all snowfalls for a flat fee of $40,000 for the entire winter season. The Weplowem Company charges $18,000 for each snowfall it clears. Set up the payoff table to help the manager decide, assuming that the number of snowfalls per winter season ranges from 0 to 4.

22.10 Refer to Exercise 22.9. Using subjective assessments the manager has assigned the following probabilities to the number of snowfalls. Determine the optimal decision.

$$P(0) = .05 \quad P(1) = .15 \quad P(2) = .30 \quad P(3) = .40$$
$$P(4) = .10$$

22.11 The owner of a clothing store must decide how many men's shirts to order for the new season. For a particular type of shirt, she must order in quantities of 100 shirts. If she orders 100 shirts, her cost is $10 per shirt; if she orders 200 shirts, her cost is $9 per shirt; and if she orders 300 or more shirts, her cost is $8.50 per shirt. Her selling price

for the shirt is $12, but any shirts that remain unsold at the end of the season are sold at her famous "half-price, end-of-season sale." For the sake of simplicity, she is willing to assume that the demand for this type of shirt will be 100, 150, 200, or 250 shirts. Of course, she cannot sell more shirts than she stocks. She is also willing to assume that she will suffer no loss of goodwill among her customers if she understocks and the customers cannot buy all the shirts they want. Furthermore, she must place her order today for the entire season; she cannot wait to see how the demand is running for this type of shirt.
  a. Construct the payoff table to help the owner decide how many shirts to order.
  b. Set up the opportunity loss table.
  c. Draw the decision tree.

22.12 Refer to Exercise 22.11. The owner has assigned the following probabilities:

$$P(\text{Demand} = 100) = .2, \quad P(\text{Demand} = 150) = .25,$$
$$P(\text{Demand} = 200) = .40, \quad P(\text{Demand} = 250) = .15$$

Find the EMV decision.

22.13 A building contractor must decide how many mountain cabins to build in the ski resort area of Chick-oh-pee. The cost to build each cabin is $26,000 and sells each for $33,000. All cabins unsold after 10 months will be sold to a local investor for $20,000. The contractor believes that the demand for cabins follows a Poisson distribution, with a mean of .5. Any probability less than .01 can be treated as 0. Construct the payoff table and the opportunity loss table for this decision problem.

22.14 The electric company is in the process of building a new power plant. There is some uncertainty regarding the size of the plant to be built. If the community that the plant will service attracts a large number of industries, the demand for electricity will be high. If commercial establishments (offices and retail stores) are attracted, demand will be moderate. If neither industries nor commercial stores locate in the community, the electricity demand will be low. The company can build a small, medium, or large plant, but if the plant is too small, the company will incur extra costs. The total costs (in $millions) of all options are shown in the accompanying table.

	Size of Plant		
Electricity Demand	**Small**	**Medium**	**Large**
Low	220	300	350
Moderate	330	320	350
High	440	390	350

The following probabilities are assigned to the electricity demand:

Demand	P(Demand)
Low	.15
Moderate	.55
High	.30

a. Determine the act with the largest expected monetary value. (*Caution*: All the values in the table are costs.)
b. Draw up an opportunity loss table.
c. Calculate the expected opportunity loss for each decision, and determine the optimal decision.

22.15 A retailer buys bushels of mushrooms for $2 each and sells them for $5 each. The quality of the mushrooms begins to decline after the first day they are offered for sale; therefore, to sell the mushrooms for $5/bushel, they must be sold on first day. Bushels not sold on the first day can be sold to a wholesaler who buys day-old mushrooms at the following rates.

Amount purchased (bushels)	1	2	3	4 or more
Price per bushel	$2.00	$1.75	$1.50	$1.25

A 90-day observation of past demand yields the following information:

Daily demand (bushels)	10	11	12	13
Number of days	9	18	36	27

a. Set up a payoff table that could be used by the retailer to decide how many bushels to buy.
b. Find the optimal number of bushels the retailer should buy to maximize profit.

22.16 An international manufacturer of electronic products is contemplating introducing a new type of compact disk player. After some analysis of the market, the president of the company concludes that, within 2 years, the new product will have a market share of 5%, 10%, or 15%. The subjective probabilities of these events are .15, .45, and .40, respectively. If the product captures only a 5% market share, the company will lose $28 million. A 10% market share will produce a $2 million profit, and a 15% market share will produce an $8 million profit. If the company decides not to begin production of the new compact disk player, there will be no profit or loss. Based on the expected value decision, what should the company do?

22-2 ACQUIRING, USING, AND EVALUATING ADDITIONAL INFORMATION

In this section, we discuss methods of introducing and incorporating additional information into the decision process. Such information generally has value, but it also has attendant costs; that is, we can acquire useful information from consultants, surveys, or other experiments, but we usually must pay for this information. We can calculate the maximum price that a decision maker should be willing to pay for any information by determining the value of perfect information. We begin by calculating the **expected payoff with perfect information (EPPI)**.

If we knew in advance which state of nature would occur, we would certainly make our decisions accordingly. For instance, if the investor in Example 22.1 knew before investing the money what interest rates would do, the best act to suit that case would be chosen. Referring to Table 22.1, if s_1 was going to occur, act a_3 would be chosen; if s_2 were certain to occur, act a_1 would be chosen, and if s_3 were certain, act a_2 would be chosen. Thus, in the long run, the expected payoff from perfect information would be:

$$\text{EPPI} = .2(40,000) + .5(30,000) + .3(60,000) = \$41,000$$

Notice that we compute EPPI by multiplying the probability of each state of nature by the largest payoff associated with that state of nature and then summing the products.

This figure, however, does not represent the maximum amount to pay for perfect information. Because the investor could make an expected profit of EMV* = $30,000 without perfect information, we subtract EMV* from EPPI to determine the **expected value of perfect information (EVPI)**. That is:

$$EVPI = EPPI - EMV^* = \$41,000 - \$30,000 = \$11,000$$

This means that, if perfect information were available, the investor should be willing to pay up to $11,000 to acquire it.

You may have noticed that the expected value of perfect information (EVPI) equals the smallest expected opportunity loss (EOL*). Again, this is not a coincidence—it will always be the case. In future questions, if the opportunity loss table has been determined, you need only calculate EOL* in order to know EVPI.

22-2a Decision Making with Additional Information

Suppose the investor in our continuing example wants to improve the decision-making capabilities. There is a company, Investment Management Consultants (IMC), who, for a fee of $5,000, will analyze the economic conditions and forecast the behavior of interest rates over the next 12 months. The investor, who is quite shrewd, asks for some measure of IMC's past successes. IMC has been forecasting interest rates for many years and so displays various conditional probabilities (referred to as **likelihood probabilities**), as shown in Table 22.3. Table 22.3 uses the following notation:

I_1: IMC predicts that interest rates will increase.
I_2: IMC predicts that interest rates will stay the same.
I_3: IMC predicts that interest rates will decrease.

TABLE **22.3** Likelihood Probabilities $P(I_i \mid s_j)$

	I_1 (PREDICT s_1)	I_2 (PREDICT s_2)	I_3 (PREDICT s_3)
s_1	$P(I_1 \mid s_1) = .60$	$P(I_2 \mid s_1) = .30$	$P(I_3 \mid s_1) = .10$
s_2	$P(I_1 \mid s_2) = .10$	$P(I_2 \mid s_2) = .80$	$P(I_3 \mid s_2) = .10$
s_3	$P(I_1 \mid s_3) = .10$	$P(I_2 \mid s_3) = .20$	$P(I_3 \mid s_3) = .70$

The I_i terms are referred to as **experimental outcomes**, and the process by which we gather additional information is called the **experiment**.

Examine the first line of Table 22.3. When s_1 actually did occur in the past, IMC correctly predicted s_1 60% of the time; 30% of the time, it predicted s_2; and 10% of the time, it predicted s_3. The second row gives the conditional probabilities of $I_1, I_2,$ and I_3 when s_2 actually occurred. The third row shows the conditional probabilities of $I_1, I_2,$ and I_3 when s_3 actually occurred.

The following question now arises: How is the investor going to use the forecast that IMC produces? One approach is simply to assume that whatever IMC forecasts will actually take place and to choose the act accordingly. There are several drawbacks to this approach. Foremost among them is that it puts the investor in the position of ignoring whatever knowledge (in the form of subjective probabilities) the investor had concerning the issue. Instead the decision maker should use this information to modify the initial assessment of the probabilities of the states of nature. To incorporate the investor's subjective probabilities with the consultant's forecast requires the use of Bayes's Law, which we introduced in Section 6-4. We'll review Bayes's Law in the context of our example.

Suppose that the investor pays IMC the $5,000 fee and IMC forecasts that s_1 will occur. We want to revise our estimates for the probabilities of the states of nature, given that I_1 is the outcome of the experiment. That is, we want $P(s_1|I_1)$, $P(s_2|I_1)$, and $P(s_3|I_1)$. Before proceeding, let's develop some terminology.

Recall from Section 6-4 that the original probabilities, $P(s_1)$, $P(s_2)$, and $P(s_3)$, are called **prior probabilities**, because they were determined prior to the acquisition of any additional information. In this example, they were based on the investor's experience. The set of probabilities we want to compute—$P(s_1|I_1)$, $P(s_2|I_1)$, and $P(s_3|I_1)$—are called **posterior or revised probabilities**.

Now we will calculate the posterior probabilities, first by using a probability tree and then by applying a less time-consuming method. Figure 22.3 depicts the probability tree. We begin with the branches of the prior probabilities, which are followed by the likelihood probabilities.

FIGURE **22.3** Probability Tree to Compute Posterior Probabilities

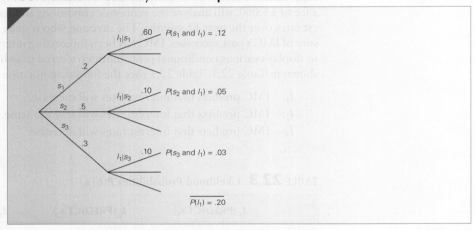

Notice that we label only $P(I_1|s_1)$, $P(I_1|s_2)$, and $P(I_1|s_3)$ because (at this point) we are assuming that I_1 is the experimental outcome. Now recall that conditional probability is defined as:

$$P(A|B) = \frac{P(A \text{ and } B)}{P(B)}$$

At the end of each branch, we have the joint probability $P(s_j \text{ and } I_1)$. By summing the joint probabilities $P(s_j \text{ and } I_1)$ for $j = 1$, 2, and 3, we calculate $P(I_1)$. Finally:

$$P(s_j|I_1) = \frac{P(s_j \text{ and } I_1)}{P(I_1)}$$

Table 22.4 performs exactly the same calculations as the probability tree except without the tree. So, for example, our revised probability for s_3, which was initially .3, is now .15.

TABLE **22.4** Posterior Probabilities for I_1

s_j	$P(s_j)$	$P(I_1|s_j)$	$P(s_j \text{ and } I_1)$	$P(s_j|I_1)$
s_1	.2	.60	(.2)(.60) = .12	.12/.20 = .60
s_2	.5	.10	(.5)(.10) = .05	.05/.20 = .25
s_3	.3	.10	(.3)(.10) = .03	.03/.20 = .15
			$P(I_1) = .20$	

After the probabilities have been revised, we can use them in exactly the same way we used the prior probabilities. That is, we can calculate the expected monetary value of each act:

$$\text{EMV}(a_1) = .60(30,000) + .25(30,000) + .15(30,000) = \$30,000$$
$$\text{EMV}(a_2) = .60(-15,000) + .25(20,000) + .15(60,000) = \$5,000$$
$$\text{EMV}(a_3) = .60(40,000) + .25(27,500) + .15(15,000) = \$33,125$$

Thus, if IMC forecasts s_1, the optimal act is a_3, and the expected monetary value of the decision is $33,125.

As a further illustration, we now repeat the process for I_2 and I_3 in Tables 22.5 and 22.6, respectively.

TABLE **22.5** Posterior Probabilities for I_2

s_j	$P(s_j)$	$P(I_2|s_j)$	$P(s_j \text{ and } I_2)$	$P(s_j|I_1)$
s_1	.2	.30	(.2)(.30) = .06	.06/.52 = .115
s_2	.5	.80	(.5)(.80) = .40	.40/.52 = .770
s_3	.3	.20	(.3)(.20) = .06	.06/.52 = .115
			$P(I_2) = .52$	

Applying the posterior probabilities for I_2 from Table 22.5 to the payoff table, we find the following:

$$\text{EMV}(a_1) = .115(30,000) + .770(30,000) + .115(30,000) = \$30,000$$
$$\text{EMV}(a_2) = .115(-15,000) + .770(20,000) + .115(60,000) = \$20,575$$
$$\text{EMV}(a_3) = .115(40,000) + .770(27,500) + .115(15,000) = \$27,500$$

As you can see, if IMC predicts that s_2 will occur, the optimal act is a_1, with an expected monetary value of $30,000.

TABLE **22.6** Posterior Probabilities for I_3

s_j	$P(s_j)$	$P(I_3|s_j)$	$P(s_j \text{ and } I_3)$	$P(s_j|I_1)$
s_1	.2	.10	(.2)(.10) = .02	.02/.28 = .071
s_2	.5	.10	(.5)(.10) = .05	.05/.28 = .179
s_3	.3	.70	(.3)(.70) = .21	.21/.28 = .750
			$P(I_3) = .28$	

With the set of posterior probabilities for I_3 from Table 22.6, the expected monetary values are as follows:

$$\text{EMV}(a_1) = .071(30,000) + .179(30,000) + .750(30,000) = \$30,000$$
$$\text{EMV}(a_2) = .071(-15,000) + .179(20,000) + .750(60,000) = \$47,515$$
$$\text{EMV}(a_3) = .071(40,000) + .179(27,500) + .750(15,000) = \$19,013$$

If IMC predicts that s_3 will occur, the optimal act is a_2, with an expected monetary value of $47,515.

At this point, we know the following:

If IMC predicts s_1, then the optimal act is a_3.
If IMC predicts s_2, then the optimal act is a_1.
If IMC predicts s_3, then the optimal act is a_2.

Thus, even before IMC makes its forecast, the investor knows which act is optimal for each of the three possible IMC forecasts. Of course, all these calculations can be performed before paying IMC its $5,000 fee. This leads to an extremely important calculation. By performing the computations just described, the investor can determine *whether* IMC should be hired, that is, we can determine whether the value of IMC's forecast exceeds the cost of its information. Such a determination is called a **preposterior analysis**.

22-2b Preposterior Analysis

The objective of a preposterior analysis is to determine whether the value of the prediction is greater or less than the cost of the information. *Posterior* refers to the revision of the probabilities, and the *pre* indicates that this calculation is performed before paying the fee.

We begin by finding the expected monetary value of using the additional information. This value is denoted EMV′, which for our example is determined on the basis of the following analysis:

If IMC predicts s_1, then the optimal act is a_3, and the expected payoff is $33,125.
If IMC predicts s_2, then the optimal act is a_1, and the expected payoff is $30,000.
If IMC predicts s_3, then the optimal act is a_2, and the expected payoff is $47,515.

A useful by-product of calculating the posterior probabilities is the set of probabilities of I_1, I_2, and I_3:

$$P(I_1) = .20, \qquad P(I_2) = .52, \qquad P(I_3) = .28$$

(Notice that these probabilities sum to 1.) Now imagine that the investor seeks the advice of IMC an infinite number of times. (This is the basis for the expected value decision.) The set of probabilities of I_1, I_2, and I_3 indicates the following outcome distribution: 20% of the time, IMC will predict s_1 and the expected monetary value will be $33,125; 52% of the time, IMC will predict s_2 and the expected monetary value will be $30,000; and 28% of the time, IMC will predict s_3 and the expected monetary value will be $47,515.

The expected monetary value with additional information is the weighted average of the expected monetary values, where the weights are $P(I_1)$, $P(I_2)$, and $P(I_3)$. Hence:

$$\text{EMV}' = .20(33,125) + .52(30,000) + .28(47,515) = \$35,529$$

The value of IMC's forecast is the difference between the expected monetary value with additional information (EMV′) and the expected monetary value without additional information (EMV*). This difference is called the **expected value of sample information** and is denoted EVSI. Thus:

$$\text{EVSI} = \text{EMV}' - \text{EMV}^* = \$35,529 - \$30,000 = \$5,529$$

By using IMC's forecast, the investor can make an average additional profit of $5,529 in the long run. Because the cost of the forecast is only $5,000, the investor is advised to hire IMC.

If you review this problem, you'll see that the investor had to make two decisions. The first (chronologically) was whether to hire IMC, and the second was which type of investment to make. A decision tree is quite helpful in describing the acts and states of nature in this question. Figure 22.4 provides the complete tree diagram.

FIGURE **22.4** Complete Decision Tree for Example 22.1

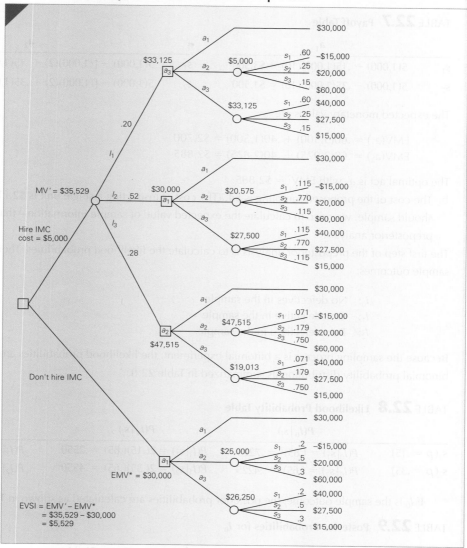

Acceptance Sampling: Solution

a. The two alternatives are

a_1: No inspection (the current policy)

a_2: 100% inspection

The two states of nature are

s_1: The lot contains 15% defectives

s_2: The lot contains 35% defectives

(Continued)

Based on the past year's historical record,

$$P(s_1) = .60 \text{ and } P(s_2) = .40$$

The payoff table is constructed as shown in Table 22.7.

TABLE **22.7** **Payoff Table**

	a_1		a_2
s_1	$5(1,000) - .15(1,000)(10) = \$3,500$	s_1	$5(1,000) - [(1,000)(2) + .15(1,000)(.50)] = \$2,925$
s_2	$5(1,000) - .35(1,000)(10) = \$1,500$	s_2	$5(1,000) - [(1,000)(2) + .35(1,000)(.50)] = \$2,825$

The expected monetary values are

$$EMV(a_1) = .60(3,500) + .40(1,500) = \$2,700$$
$$EMV(a_2) = .60(2,925) + .40(2,825) = \$2,885$$

The optimal act is a_2 with $EMV^* = \$2,885$.

b. The cost of the proposed sampling is $4. (The cost of inspecting a single unit is $2.) To determine whether we should sample, we need to calculate the expected value of sample information—that is, we need to perform a preposterior analysis.

The first step of the preposterior analysis is to calculate the likelihood probabilities. There are three possible sample outcomes:

I_0: No defectives in the sample
I_1: One defective in the sample
I_2: Two defectives in the sample

Because the sampling process is a binomial experiment, the likelihood probabilities are calculated by using the binomial probability distribution as summarized in Table 22.8.

TABLE **22.8** **Likelihood Probability Table**

	$P(I_0 \mid s_j)$	$P(I_1 \mid s_j)$	$P(I_2 \mid s_j)$
$s_1(p = .15)$	$P(I_0\mid s_1) = (.85)^2 = .7225$	$P(I_1\mid s_1) = 2(.15)(.85) = .2550$	$P(I_2\mid s_1) = (.15)^2 = .0225$
$s_2(p = .35)$	$P(I_0\mid s_2) = (.65)^2 = .4225$	$P(I_1\mid s_2) = 2(.35)(.65) = .4550$	$P(I_2\mid s_2) = (.35)^2 = .1225$

If I_0 is the sample outcome, the posterior probabilities are calculated as shown in Table 22.9.

TABLE **22.9** **Posterior Probabilities for I_0**

s_j	$P(s_j)$	$P(I_0 \mid s_j)$	$P(s_j \text{ and } I_0)$	$P(s_j \mid I_0)$
s_1	.60	.7225	$(.60)(.7225) = .4335$	$.4335/.6025 = .720$
s_2	.40	.4225	$(.40)(.4225) = .1690$	$.1690/.6025 = .280$
			$P(I_0) = .6025$	

The expected monetary values if the sample outcome is I_0 are

$$EMV(a_1) = .720(3,500) + .280(1,500) = \$2,940$$
$$EMV(a_2) = .720(2,925) + .280(2,825) = \$2,897$$

Therefore, the optimal act is a_1.

If I_1 is the sample outcome, the posterior probabilities are calculated as shown in Table 22.10.

TABLE 22.10 Posterior Probabilities for I_1

s_j	$P(s_j)$	$P(I_1 \mid s_j)$	$P(s_j \text{ and } I_1)$	$P(s_j \mid I_1)$
s_1	.60	.2550	$(.60)(.2550) = .1530$	$.1530/.3350 = .457$
s_2	.40	.4550	$(.40)(.4550) = .1820$	$.1820/.3350 = .543$
			$P(I_1) = .3350$	

The expected monetary values if the sample outcome is I_1 are

$$EMV(a_1) = .457(3,500) + .543(1,500) = \$2,414$$
$$EMV(a_2) = .457(2,925) + .543(2,825) = \$2,871$$

Therefore, the optimal act is a_2.

If I_2 is the sample outcome, the posterior probabilities are calculated as shown in Table 22.11.

TABLE 22.11 Posterior Probabilities for I_2

s_j	$P(s_j)$	$P(I_2 \mid s_j)$	$P(s_j \text{ and } I_2)$	$P(s_j \mid I_2)$
s_1	.60	.0225	$(.60)(.0225) = .0135$	$.0135/.0625 = .216$
s_2	.40	.1225	$(.40)(.1225) = .0490$	$.0490/.0625 = .784$
			$P(I_2) = .0625$	

The expected monetary values if the sample outcome is I_2 are

$$EMV(a_1) = .216(3,500) + .784(1,500) = \$1,932$$
$$EMV(a_2) = .216(2,925) + .784(2,825) = \$2,847$$

Therefore, the optimal act is a_2.

We can now summarize these results, as shown in Table 22.12.

TABLE 22.12 Summary of Optimal Acts

Sample Outcome	Probability	Optimal Act	Expected Monetary Value ($)
I_0	.6025	a_1	2,940
I_1	.3350	a_2	2,871
I_2	.0625	a_2	2,847

The expected monetary value with additional information is

$$EMV' = .6025(2,940) + .3350(2,871) + .0625(2,847) = \$2,911$$

The expected value of sample information is

$$EVSI = EMV' - EMV^* = 2,911 - 2,885 = \$26$$

Because the expected value of sample information is $26 and the sampling cost is $4, the company should take a sample of 2 units before deciding whether to inspect 100%. The optimal sequence is as follows:

1. Take a sample of 2 units.
2. If there are no defective units in the sample, continue the current policy of no inspection. If either one or two of the sample units are defective, perform a complete inspection of the lot.

22-2c Bayesian Statistics

In Chapters 10–18, we dealt with inference about unknown parameters. In Chapter 10, we pointed out that when interpreting the confidence interval estimate, we cannot make probability statements about parameters because they are not variables. However, Bayesian statistics specifies that parameters are variables, and we can assume various probability distributions. The acceptance sampling example illustrates this concept. The parameter was the proportion p of defective units in the 1,000-unit batch. The example was unrealistic because we allowed the parameter to assume one of only two values, 15% and 35%. We assigned prior probabilities using the relative frequency approach; that is, based on historic records we had

$$P(p = 15\%) = .60 \quad \text{and} \quad P(p = 35\%) = .40$$

To make the problem more realistic, we let p be a continuous random variable rather than a discrete one. In other words, p can take on any value between 0 and 100%. We assign a density function also based on historical records. We can express the payoffs as a linear function of p. Then, using calculus, we can determine the optimum decision. We can also revise the prior probabilities based on the outcome of the sampling of two units. The technique requires some calculus, but the concept is the same as the one developed in this chapter. It should be noted that there is a parallel universe of Bayesian statistics that more or less matches the material in the inference part of this book. Interested readers can learn more about Bayesian statistics from additional courses dedicated to the subject.

EXERCISES

22.17 Find EPPI, EMV*, and EVPI for the accompanying payoff table and probabilities.

	a_1	a_2	a_3
s_1	60	110	75
s_2	40	110	150
s_3	220	120	85
s_4	250	120	130

$P(s_1) = .10 \quad P(s_2) = .25 \quad P(s_3) = .50 \quad P(s_4) = .15$

22.18 For Exercise 22.17, determine the opportunity loss table and compute EOL*. Confirm that EOL* = EVPI.

22.19 Given the following payoff table and probabilities, determine EVPI.

	a_1	a_2	a_3	a_4
s_1	65	20	45	30
s_2	70	110	80	95

$P(s_1) = .5 \quad P(s_2) = .5$

22.20 Redo Exercise 22.19, changing the probabilities to the following values.
a. $P(s_1) = .75 \quad P(s_2) = .25$
b. $P(s_1) = .95 \quad P(s_2) = .05$

22.21 What conclusion can you draw about the effect of the probabilities on EVPI from Exercises 22.19 and 22.20?

22.22 Determine the posterior probabilities, given the following prior and likelihood probabilities.

Prior Probabilities

$P(s_1) = .25 \quad P(s_2) = .40 \quad P(s_3) = .35$

Likelihood Probabilities

	I_1	I_2	I_3	I_4
s_1	.40	.30	.20	.10
s_2	.25	.25	.25	.25
s_3	0	.30	.40	.30

22.23 Calculate the posterior probabilities from the prior and likelihood probabilities that follow.

Prior Probabilities

$P(s_1) = .5 \quad P(s_2) = .5$

Likelihood Probabilities

	I_1	I_2
s_1	.98	.02
s_2	.05	.95

22.24 With the accompanying payoff table and the prior and posterior probabilities computed in Exercise 22.23, calculate the following.
a. The optimal act for each experimental outcome
b. The expected value of sample information

Payoff Table

	a_1	a_2	a_3
s_1	10	18	23
s_2	22	19	15

22.25 Given the following payoff table, prior probabilities, and likelihood probabilities, find the expected value of sample information.

Payoff Table

	a_1	a_2
s_1	60	90
s_2	90	90
s_3	150	90

Prior Probabilities

$$P(s_1) = \frac{1}{3} \quad P(s_2) = \frac{1}{3} \quad P(s_3) = \frac{1}{3}$$

Likelihood Probabilities

	I_1	I_2
s_1	.7	.3
s_2	.5	.5
s_3	.2	.8

22.26 Repeat Exercise 22.25 with the following prior probabilities.

$$P(s_1) = .5 \quad P(s_2) = .4 \quad P(s_3) = .1$$

22.27 Repeat Exercise 22.25 with the following prior probabilities.

$$P(s_1) = .90 \quad P(s_2) = .05 \quad P(s_3) = .05$$

22.28 What conclusions can you draw about the effect of the prior probabilities on EVSI from Exercises 22.25 to 22.27?

Applications

22.29 A sporting-goods storeowner has the opportunity to purchase a lot of 50,000 footballs for $100,000. The storeowner can sell some or all by taking out mail-order advertisements in a magazine. Each football will be sold for $6. The advertising cost is $25,000, and the mailing cost per football is $1. The subjective demand distribution is as follows.

Demand	P(Demand)
10,000	.2
30,000	.5
50,000	.3

What is the maximum price the owner should pay for additional information about demand?

22.30 What is the maximum price the electronics product manufacturer should be willing to pay for perfect information regarding the market share in Exercise 22.16?

22.31 To improve decision-making capability, the electronics products manufacturer in Exercise 22.16 performs a survey of potential buyers of compact disc players. The product is described to 25 individuals, 3 of whom say they would buy it. Using this additional information together with the prior probabilities, determine whether the new product should be produced.

22.32 A radio station that currently directs its programming toward middle-age listeners is contemplating switching to rock-and-roll music. After analyzing advertising revenues and operating costs, the owner concludes that, for each percentage point of market share, revenues increase by $100,000 per year. Fixed annual operating costs are $700,000. The owner believes that, with the change, the station will get a 5%, 10%, or 20% market share, with probabilities .4, .4, and .2, respectively. The current annual profit is $285,000.
a. Set up the payoff table.
b. Determine the optimal act.
c. What is the most the owner should be willing to pay to acquire additional information about the market share?

22.33 There is a garbage crisis in North America—too much garbage and no place to put it. As a consequence, the idea of recycling has become quite popular. A waste-management company in a large city is willing to begin recycling newspapers, aluminum cans, and plastic containers. However, it is profitable to do so only if a sufficiently large proportion of households is willing to participate. In this city, 1 million households are potential recyclers. After some analysis, it was determined that, for every 1,000 households that participate in the program, the contribution to profit is $500. It was also discovered that fixed costs are $55,000 per year. It is believed that 50,000, 100,000, 200,000, or 300,000 households will participate, with probabilities .5, .3, .1, and .1, respectively. A preliminary survey was performed wherein 25 households were asked whether they would be willing to be part of this recycling program. Suppose only 3 of the 25 respond affirmatively, incorporate this information into the decision-making process to decide whether the waste-management company should proceed with the recycling venture.

22.34 Repeat Exercise 22.33, given that 12 out of 100 households respond affirmatively.

22.35 Suppose that in Exercise 22.14 a consultant offers to analyze the problem and predict the amount of electricity required by the new community. The consultant provides the set of likelihood probabilities given here. Perform a preposterior analysis to determine the expected value of the consultant's sample information.

	I_1 (predict low demand)	I_2 (predict moderate demand)	I_3 (predict high demand)
s_1	.5	.3	.2
s_2	.3	.6	.1
s_3	.2	.2	.6

22.36 In Exercise 22.32, suppose that it is possible to survey radio listeners to determine whether they would tune in to the station if the format changed to rock and roll. What would a survey of size 2 be worth?

22.37 Suppose that in Exercise 22.32 a random sample of 25 radio listeners revealed that 2 people would be regular listeners of the station. What is the optimal decision now?

22.38 The president of an automobile battery company must decide which one of three new types of batteries to produce. The fixed and variable costs of each battery are shown in the accompanying table.

Battery	Fixed Cost ($)	Variable Cost (per Unit) ($)
1	900,000	20
2	1,150,000	17
3	1,400,000	15

The president believes that demand will be 50,000, 100,000, or 150,000 batteries, with probabilities .3, .3, and .4, respectively. The selling price of the battery will be $40.
a. Determine the payoff table.
b. Determine the opportunity loss table.
c. Find the expected monetary value for each act, and select the optimal one.
d. What is the most the president should be willing to pay for additional information about demand?

22.39 Credibility is often the most effective feature of an advertising campaign. Suppose that, for a particular advertisement, 32% of people surveyed currently believe what the ad claims. A marketing manager believes that for each 1-point increase in

that percentage, annual sales will increase by $1 million. For each 1-point decrease, annual sales will decrease by $1 million. The manager believes that a change in the advertising approach can influence the ad's credibility. The probability distribution of the potential percentage changes is listed here.

Percentage Change	Probability
−2	.1
−1	.1
0	.2
+1	.3
+2	.3

If for each dollar of sales the profit contribution is 10 cents and the overall cost of changing the ad is $58,000, should the ad be changed?

22.40 Suppose that in Exercise 22.39 it is possible to perform a survey to determine the percentage of people who believe the ad. What would a sample of size 1 be worth?

22.41 Suppose that in Exercise 22.39 a sample of size 5 showed that only one person believes the new ad. In light of this additional information, what should the manager do?

22.42 Max the Bookie is trying to decide how many telephones to install in his new bookmaking operation. Because of heavy police activity, he cannot increase or decrease the number of telephones once he sets up his operation. He has narrowed the possible choices to three. He can install 25, 50, or 100 telephones. His profit for 1 year (the usual length of time he can remain in business before the police close him down) depends on the average number of calls he receives. The number of calls is Poisson distributed. After some deliberation, he concludes that the average number of calls per minute can be .5, 1.0, or 1.5, with probabilities of .50, .25, and .25, respectively. Max then produces the payoffs given in the accompanying table.

Payoff Table

	25 Telephones ($)	50 Telephones ($)	100 Telephones ($)
$s_1(\mu = .5)$	50,000	30,000	20,000
$s_2(\mu = 1.0)$	50,000	60,000	40,000
$s_3(\mu = 1.5)$	50,000	60,000	80,000

Max's assistant, Lefty (who attended a business school for 2 years), points out that Max may be able to get more information by observing a competitor's similar operation. However, he will be able to watch for only 10 minutes, and doing so will cost him $4,000. Max determines that if he counts fewer than 8 calls, that would be a low number; at least 8 but fewer than 17 would be a medium number; and at least 17 would be a large number of calls. Max also decides that, if the experiment is run, he will record only whether there is a small, medium, or large number of calls. Help Max by performing a preposterior analysis to determine whether the sample should be taken. Conclude by specifying clearly what the optimal strategy is.

22.43 The Megabuck Computer Company is thinking of introducing two new products. The first, Model 101, is a small computer designed specifically for children between ages 8 and 16. The second, Model 202, is a medium-size computer suitable for managers. Because of limited production capacity, Megabuck has decided to produce only one of the products.

The profitability of each model depends on the proportion of the potential market that would actually buy the computer. For Model 101, the size of the market is estimated at 10 million, whereas for Model 202, the estimate is 3 million.

After careful analysis, the management of Megabuck has concluded that the percentage of buyers of Model 101 is 5%, 10%, or 15%. The respective profits are given here.

Percent Who Buy Model 101	Net Profits ($Millions)
5	20
10	100
15	210

An expert in probability from the local university estimated the probability of the percentages as $P(5\%) = .2$, $P(10\%) = .4$, and $P(15\%) = .4$.

A similar analysis for Model 202 produced the following table.

Percent Who Buy Model 202	Net Profits ($Millions)
30	70
40	100
50	150

For this model, the expert estimated the probabilities as $P(30\%) = .1$, $P(40\%) = .4$, and $P(50\%) = .5$.

a. Based on this information, and with the objective of maximizing expected profit, which model should Megabuck produce?
b. To make a better decision, Megabuck sampled 10 potential buyers of Model 101 and 20 potential buyers of Model 202. Only 1 of the 10 wished to purchase the Model 101, whereas 9 of the 20 indicated that they would buy Model 202. Given this information, revise the prior probabilities and determine which model should be produced.

22.44 A major movie studio has just completed its latest epic, a musical comedy about the life of Attila the Hun. Because the movie is different (no sex or violence), the studio is uncertain about how to distribute it. The studio executives must decide whether to release the movie to North American audiences or to sell it to a European distributor and realize a profit of $12 million. If the movie is shown in North America, the studio profit depends on its level of success, which can be classified as excellent, good, or fair. The payoffs and the prior subjective probabilities of the success levels are shown in the accompanying table.

Success Level	Payoff ($Million)	Probability
Excellent	33	.5
Good	12	.3
Fair	−15	.2

Another possibility is to have the movie shown to a random sample of North Americans and use their collective judgment to help the studio make a decision. These judgments are categorized as "rave review," "lukewarm response," and "poor response." The cost of the sample is $100,000. The sampling process has been used several times in the past. The likelihood probabilities describing the audience judgments and the movie's success level are shown next. Perform a preposterior analysis to determine what the studio executives should do.

	Judgment		
Success Level	Rave Review	Lukewarm Response	Poor Response
Excellent	.8	.1	.1
Good	.5	.3	.2
Fair	.4	.3	.3

CHAPTER SUMMARY

The objective of decision analysis is to select the optimal act from a list of alternative acts. We define as optimal the act with the largest expected monetary value or smallest expected opportunity loss. The expected values are calculated after assigning prior probabilities to the states of nature. The acts, states of nature, and their consequences may be presented in a payoff table, an opportunity loss table, or a decision tree. We also discussed a method by which additional information in the form of an experiment can be incorporated in the analysis. This method involves combining prior and likelihood probabilities to produce posterior probabilities. The preposterior analysis allows us to decide whether to pay for and acquire the experimental outcome. That decision is based on the expected value of sample information and on the sampling cost.

IMPORTANT TERMS:

Acts   928
States of nature   928
Payoff table   929
Opportunity loss   929
Decision tree   929
Expected monetary value (EMV)   931
Expected opportunity loss (EOL)   932
Rollback technique   932
Expected payoff with perfect information (EPPI)   934

Expected value of perfect information (EVPI)   935
Likelihood probabilities   935
Experimental outcomes   935
Experiment   935
Prior probabilities   936
Posterior or revised probabilities   936
Preposterior analysis   938
Expected value of sample information   938

SYMBOLS:

Symbol	Represents
a_i	Acts
s_j	States of nature
I_i	Experimental outcomes
$P(s_j)$	Prior probability
$P(I_i \mid s_j)$	Likelihood probability
$P(s_j \text{ and } I_i)$	Joint probability
$P(s_j \mid I_i)$	Posterior probability

Cosma/Shutterstock.com

23

CONCLUSION

We have come to the end of the journey that began with the words "Statistics is a way to get information from data." You will shortly write the final examination in your statistics course. (We assume that readers of this book are taking a statistics course and not just reading it for fun.) If you believe that this event will be the point where you and statistics part company, you could not be more wrong. In the world into which you are about to graduate, the potential applications of statistical techniques are virtually limitless.

This raises the question, What statistical concepts and techniques will you need for your life after the final exam? We don't expect students to remember the formulas (or computer commands) that calculate the confidence interval estimates or test statistics. (Statistics reference books are available for that purpose.) However, you must know what you can and cannot do with statistical techniques. You must remember a number of important principles that were covered in this book. To assist you, we have selected the 12 most important concepts and list them here. They are drawn from the "Developing an Understanding of Statistical Concepts" subsections that are scattered throughout the book. We hope that they prove useful to you.

23-1 / TWELVE STATISTICAL CONCEPTS YOU NEED FOR LIFE AFTER THE STATISTICS FINAL EXAM

1. Statistical techniques are processes that convert data into information. Descriptive techniques describe and summarize; inferential techniques allow us to make estimates and draw conclusions about populations from samples.

2. We need a large number of techniques because there are numerous objectives and types of data. There are three types of data: interval (real numbers), nominal (categories), and ordinal (ratings). Each combination of data type and objective requires specific techniques.

3. We gather data by various sampling plans. However, the validity of any statistical outcome is dependent on the validity of the sampling. "Garbage in, garbage out" very much applies in statistics.

4. The sampling distribution is the source of statistical inference. The confidence interval estimator and the test statistic are derived directly from the sampling distribution. All inferences are actually probability statements based on the sampling distribution.

5. All tests of hypotheses are conducted similarly. We assume that the null hypothesis is true. We then compute the value of the test statistic. If the difference between what we have observed (and calculated) and what we expect to observe is too large, we reject the null hypothesis. The standard that decides what is "too large" is determined by the probability of a Type I error.

6. In any test of hypothesis (and in most decisions) there are two possible errors: Type I and Type II. The relationship between the probabilities of these errors helps us decide where to set the standard. If we set the standard so high that the probability of a Type I error is very small, we increase the probability of a Type II error. A procedure designed to decrease the probability of a Type II error must have a relatively large probability of a Type I error.

7. We can improve the exactitude of a confidence interval estimator or decrease the probability of a Type II error by increasing the sample size. More data mean more information, which results in narrower intervals or lower probabilities of making mistakes, which in turn leads to better decisions.

8. The sampling distributions that are used for interval data are the Student t and the F. These distributions are related so that the various techniques for interval data are themselves related. We can use the analysis of variance in place of the t-test of two means. We can use regression analysis with indicator variables in place of the analysis of variance. We often build a model to represent relationships among interval variables, including indicator variables.

9. In analyzing interval data, we attempt to explain as much of the variation as possible. By doing so, we can learn a great deal about whether populations differ and what variables affect the response (dependent) variable.

10. The techniques used on nominal data require that we count the number of times each category occurs. The counts are then used to compute statistics. The sampling distributions we use for nominal data are the standard normal and the chi-squared. These distributions are related, as are the techniques.

11. The techniques used on ordinal data are based on a ranking procedure. We call these techniques *nonparametric*. Because the requirements for the use of non-parametric techniques are less stringent than those for a parametric procedure, we often use nonparametric techniques in place of parametric ones when the required conditions for the parametric test are not satisfied. To ensure the validity of a statistical technique, we must check the required conditions.

12. We can obtain data through experimentation or by observation. Observational data lend themselves to several conflicting interpretations. Data gathered by an experiment are more likely to lead to a definitive interpretation. In addition to designing experiments, statistics practitioners can also select particular sample sizes to produce the accuracy and confidence they desire.

APPENDIX A

DATA FILE SAMPLE STATISTICS

Chapter 10

10.34 $\bar{x} = 252.38$
10.35 $\bar{x} = 1,810.16$
10.36 $\bar{x} = 12.10$
10.37 $\bar{x} = 10.21$
10.38 $\bar{x} = .510$
10.39 $\bar{x} = 26.81$
10.40 $\bar{x} = 19.28$
10.41 $\bar{x} = 15.00$
10.42 $\bar{x} = 585,063$
10.43 $\bar{x} = 109.6, n = 200$
10.44 $\bar{x} = 227.48, n = 300$
10.45 $\bar{x} = 314,245, n = 150$
10.46 $\bar{x} = 27.19$

Chapter 11

11.43 $\bar{x} = 5,065$
11.44 $\bar{x} = 48,415$
11.45 $\bar{x} = 569$
11.46 $\bar{x} = 32.02, n = 50$
11.47 $\bar{x} = -1.20$
11.48 $\bar{x} = 55.8$
11.49 $\bar{x} = 5.04$
11.50 $\bar{x} = 19.39$
11.51 $\bar{x} = 105.7$
11.52 $\bar{x} = 4.84$
11.53 $\bar{x} = 5.64$
11.54 $\bar{x} = 29.92$
11.55 $\bar{x} = 231.56$
11.56 $\bar{x} = 10.44, n = 174$
11.57 $\bar{x} = 29.51, n = 277$
11.58 $\bar{x} = 126,837, n = 410$
11.59 $\bar{x} = 12,770, n = 105$

Chapter 12

12.31 $\bar{x} = 7.15, s = 1.65, n = 200$
12.32 $\bar{x} = 4.66, s = 2.37, n_1 = 240$
12.33 $\bar{x} = 20.53, s = 6.00, n = 250$
12.34 $\bar{x} = 15,137, s = 5,263, n = 306$
12.35 $\bar{x} = 59.04, s = 20.63, n = 122$
12.36 $\bar{x} = 15.77, s = 4.26, n = 94$
12.37 $\bar{x} = 44.14, s = 7.88, n = 475$
12.38 $\bar{x} = 2,828, s = 739, n = 315$
12.39 $\bar{x} = 13.94, s = 2.16, n = 212$
12.40 $\bar{x} = 15.27, s = 5.72, n = 116$
12.41 $\bar{x} = 997.3, s = 9.98, n = 50$
12.42 $\bar{x} = 89.27, s = 17.30, n = 85$
12.43 $\bar{x} = 15.02, s = 8.31, n = 83$
12.44 $\bar{x} = 96,100, s = 34,468, n = 473$
12.45 $\bar{x} = 1,125, s = 317.7, n = 364$
12.46 $\bar{x} = 27,852, s = 9,252, n = 347$
12.47 $\bar{x} = 354.6, s = 90.32, n = 681$
12.48 $\bar{x} = 25,228, s = 5,544, n = 184$
12.49 $\bar{x} = 366,203, s = 122,277, n = 452$
12.50 $\bar{x} = 46,699, s = 9,032, n = 608$
12.51 $\bar{x} = 7.309, s = 5.583, n = 178$
12.52 $\bar{x} = 1,158, s = 396.5, n = 325$
12.53 $\bar{x} = 530.7, s = 97.17, n = 485$
12.77 $s^2 = 270.58, n = 25$
12.78 $s^2 = 22.56, n = 245$
12.79 $s^2 = 4.725, n = 90$
12.80 $s^2 = 174.47, n = 100$
12.81 $s^2 = 19.68, n = 25$
12.103 $n(1) = 51, n(2) = 291,$
$n(3) = 70, n(4) = 301,$
$n(5) = 261$
12.104 $n(1) = 28, n(2) = 174,$
$n(3) = 135, n(4) = 67,$
$n(5) = 51, n(6) = 107$
12.105 $n(0) = 466, n(1) = 55$
12.106 $n(1) = 479, n(2) = 187,$
$n(3) = 201$
12.107 $n(0) = 299, n(1) = 456$
12.108 $n(0) = 475, n(1) = 347$
12.109 $n(0) = 92, n(1) = 28$
12.110 $n(1) = 603, n(2) = 905$
12.111 $n(0) = 92, n(1) = 334$
12.112 $n(0) = 512, n(1) = 127$
12.113 $n(0) = 205, n(1) = 369$
12.114 $n(0) = 751, n(1) = 817$
12.115 $n(0) = 786, n(1) = 254$
12.116 $n(0) = 761, n(1) = 716$
12.117 $n(0) = 365, n(1) = 116$
12.118 $n(1) = 371, n(2) = 206,$
$n(3) = 132$
12.130 $n(1) = 81, n(2) = 47,$
$n(3) = 167, n(4) = 146,$
$n(5) = 34$
12.131 $n(1) = 63, n(2) = 125,$
$n(3) = 45, n(4) = 87$
12.132 $n(1) = 418, n(2) = 536,$
$n(3) = 882$
12.133 $n(0) = 290, n(1) = 35$
12.134 $n(1) = 72, n(2) = 77,$
$n(3) = 37, n(4) = 50,$
$n(5) = 176$
12.135 $n(1) = 289, n(2) = 51$

Chapter 13

13.17 Baby boom: $\bar{x}_1 = 4,557, s_1 = 760,$
$n_1 = 429;$
Gen X: $\bar{x}_2 = 5,179, s_2 = 802,$
$n_2 = 464$
13.18 October: $\bar{x}_1 = 941.9, s_1 = 310.5,$
$n_1 = 319;$
November: $\bar{x}_2 = 846.9, s_2 = 339.3,$
$n_2 = 341$
13.19 Tastee: $\bar{x}_1 = 36.93, s_1 = 4.23,$
$n_1 = 15;$
Competitor: $\bar{x}_2 = 31.36,$
$s_2 = 3.35, n_2 = 25$
13.20 Oat bran: $\bar{x}_1 = 10.01, s_1 = 4.43,$
$n_1 = 120;$
Other: $\bar{x}_2 = 9.12, s_2 = 4.45,$
$n_2 = 120$
13.21 Regular income: $\bar{x}_1 = 208.5,$
$s_1 = 30.86, n_1 = 177;$
Stimulus: $\bar{x}_2 = 217.5, s_2 = 37.17,$
$n_2 = 93$
13.22 Two years ago: $\bar{x}_1 = 59.81,$
$s_1 = 7.02, n_1 = 125;$
This year: $\bar{x}_2 = 57.40, s_2 = 6.99,$
$n_2 = 159$
13.23 Male: $\bar{x}_1 = 10.23, s_1 = 2.87,$
$n_1 = 100;$
Female: $\bar{x}_2 = 9.66, s_2 = 2.90,$
$n_2 = 100$
13.24 A: $\bar{x}_1 = 115.50, s_1 = 21.69,$
$n_1 = 30;$
B: $\bar{x}_2 = 110.20, s_2 = 21.93,$
$n_2 = 30$
13.25 Apprentice: $\bar{x}_1 = 72,955,$
$s_1 = 15,389, n_1 = 288;$
College: $\bar{x}_2 = 67,964, s_2 = 13,679,$
$n_2 = 311$
13.26 University: $\bar{x}_1 = 82,082,$
$s_1 = 16,036, n_1 = 258;$
Apprentice: $\bar{x}_2 = 72,955,$
$s_2 = 15,389, n_2 = 288$
13.27 High school: $\bar{x}_1 = 43,366,$
$s_1 = 14,247, n_1 = 199;$
Apprentice: $\bar{x}_2 = 38,197,$
$s_2 = 10,041, n_2 = 218$
13.28 Gen X: $\bar{x}_1 = 1491, s_1 = 515,$
$n_1 = 223;$
Millennial: $\bar{x}_2 = 1064, s_2 = 184,$
$n_2 = 241$
13.29 Job tenure: 2011: $\bar{x}_1 = 60.97,$
$s_1 = 19.70, n_1 = 97;$
Job tenure 2021 $\bar{x}_2 = 60.48,$
$s_2 = 19.13, n_2 = 101$
13.30 A: $\bar{x}_1 = 70.42, s_1 = 20.54, n_1 = 24;$
B: $\bar{x}_2 = 56.44, s_2 = 9.03, n_2 = 16$
13.31 Successful: $\bar{x}_1 = 5.02, s_1 = 1.39,$
$n_1 = 200;$
Unsuccessful: $\bar{x}_2 = 7.80,$
$s_2 = 3.09, n_2 = 200$
13.32 Phone: $\bar{x}_1 = .646, s_1 = .045,$
$n_1 = 125;$
Not: $\bar{x}_2 = .601, s_2 = .053,$
$n_2 = 145$
13.33 Chitchat: $\bar{x}_1 = .654, s_1 = .048,$
$n_1 = 95;$
Politics: $\bar{x}_2 = .662, s_2 = .045,$
$n_2 = 90$

13.34 Planner: $\bar{x}_1 = 6.18$, $s_1 = 1.59$, $n_1 = 64$;
Broker: $\bar{x}_2 = 5.94$, $s_2 = 1.61$, $n_2 = 81$

13.35 With book: $\bar{x}_1 = 63.71$, $s_1 = 5.90$, $n_1 = 173$;
W/O book: $\bar{x}_2 = 66.80$, $s_2 = 6.85$, $n_2 = 202$

13.36 Wendy's: $\bar{x}_1 = 149.85$, $s_1 = 21.82$, $n_1 = 213$;
McDonalds: $\bar{x}_2 = 154.43$, $s_2 = 23.64$, $n_2 = 202$

13.37 Silent generation: $\bar{x}_1 = 1,016$, $s_1 = 190.6$, $n_1 = 183$;
Millennial: $\bar{x}_2 = 1,137$, $s_2 = 351.9$, $n_2 = 241$

13.38 Baby boom: $\bar{x}_1 = 296.7$, $s_1 = 107.6$, $n_1 = 173$;
Gen X: $\bar{x}_2 = 334.1$, $s_2 = 91.50$, $n_2 = 201$

13.39 Men: $\bar{x}_1 = 488.4$, $s_1 = 19.62$, $n_1 = 124$;
Women: $\bar{x}_2 = 498.1$, $s_2 = 21.93$, $n_2 = 187$

13.40 Applied: $\bar{x}_1 = 130.9$, $s_1 = 31.99$, $n_1 = 100$;
Contacted: $\bar{x}_2 = 126.1$, $s_2 = 26.00$, $n_2 = 100$

13.41 New: $\bar{x}_1 = 73.6$, $s_1 = 15.60$, $n_1 = 20$;
Current: $\bar{x}_2 = 69.2$, $s_2 = 15.06$, $n_2 = 20$

13.42 Fixed: $\bar{x}_1 = 60,245$, $s_1 = 10,506$, $n_1 = 90$;
Commission: $\bar{x}_2 = 63,563$, $s_2 = 10,755$, $n_2 = 90$

13.43 Accident: $\bar{x}_1 = 634.0$, $s_1 = 49.45$, $n_1 = 93$;
No accident: $\bar{x}_2 = 661.9$, $s_2 = 52.69$, $n_2 = 338$

13.44 Cork: $\bar{x}_1 = 14.20$, $s_1 = 2.84$, $n_1 = 130$;
Metal: $\bar{x}_2 = 11.27$, $s_2 = 4.42$, $n_2 = 130$

13.45 Before: $\bar{x}_1 = 496.9$, $s_1 = 73.78$, $n_1 = 335$;
After: $\bar{x}_2 = 511.3$, $s_2 = 69.06$, $n_2 = 288$

13.46 Big: $\bar{x}_1 = 93.81$, $s_1 = 15.89$, $n_1 = 48$;
Medium: $\bar{x}_2 = 61.25$, $s_2 = 8.96$, $n_2 = 48$

13.47 Wine consumed: Cal: $\bar{x}_1 = 97.7$, $s_1 = 5.10$, $n_1 = 24$;
ND: $\bar{x}_2 = 94.6$, $s_2 = 7.36$, $n_2 = 24$
Time: Cal: $\bar{x}_1 = 64.0$, $s_1 = 9.44$, $n_1 = 24$;
ND: $\bar{x}_2 = 57.3$, $s_2 = 9.14$, $n_2 = 24$

13.48 Cleaned: $\bar{x}_1 = 10.04$, $s_1 = 2.32$, $n_1 = 28$;
Dirty: $\bar{x}_2 = 8.64$, $s_2 = 1.85$, $n_2 = 28$

13.49 One: $\bar{x}_1 = 136.8$, $s_1 = 24.16$, $n_1 = 20$;
Half: $\bar{x}_2 = 72.8$, $s_2 = 9.87$, $n_2 = 20$

13.50 Apple: $\bar{x}_1 = 4.69$, $s_1 = 2.93$, $n_1 = 756$;
No apple: $\bar{x}_2 = 4.86$, $s_2 = 3.05$, $n_2 = 7643$

13.51 Baby boom: $\bar{x}_1 = 66,697$, $s_1 = 15,504$, $n_1 = 222$;
18–49: $\bar{x}_2 = 67,980$, $s_2 = 10,725$, $n_2 = 188$

13.52 Baby boom: $\bar{x}_1 = 19,856$, $s_1 = 3,969$, $n_1 = 222$;
18–49: $\bar{x}_2 = 21,015$, $s_2 = 6,668$, $n_2 = 188$

13.53 This year: $\bar{x}_1 = 34.97$, $s_1 = 9.85$, $n_1 = 521$;
5 years ago: $\bar{x}_2 = 31.63$, $s_2 = 6.77$, $n_2 = 483$

13.54 Electrical: $\bar{x}_1 = 57,030$, $s_1 = 4,990$, $n_1 = 129$;
Mechanical: $\bar{x}_2 = 56,055$, $s_2 = 4,421$, $n_2 = 97$

13.55 No chocolate: $\bar{x}_1 = 166.8$, $s_1 = 22.86$, $n_1 = 30$;
Chocolate $\bar{x}_2 = 116.7$, $s_2 = 14.79$, $n_2 = 30$

13.56 U.S.: $\bar{x}_1 = 7.31$, $s_1 = 5.58$, $n_1 = 178$;
U.K.: $\bar{x}_2 = 6.97$, $s_2 = 6.82$, $n_2 = 177$

13.57 White: $\bar{x}_1 = 20.15$, $s_1 = 3.83$, $n_1 = 134$;
Black: $\bar{x}_2 = 14.82$, $s_2 = 3.75$, $n_2 = 30$

13.58 Exercise: $\bar{x}_1 = 74.85$, $s_1 = 10.67$, $n_1 = 86$;
No exercise: $\bar{x}_2 = 67.81$, $s_2 = 10.57$, $n_2 = 98$

13.59 Post-grad: $\bar{x}_1 = 73.03$, $s_1 = 20.29$, $n_1 = 152$;
Not: $\bar{x}_2 = 55.80$, $s_2 = 9.55$, $n_2 = 177$

13.60 College: $\bar{x}_1 = 77.38$, $s_1 = 20.33$, $n_1 = 134$;
Not college: $\bar{x}_2 = 69.95$, $s_2 = 20.84$, $n_2 = 177$

13.61 College: $\bar{x}_1 = 89,987$, $s_1 = 29,222$, $n_1 = 241$;
Non-college: $\bar{x}_2 = 44,113$, $s_2 = 14,274$, $n_2 = 257$

13.62 College: $\bar{x}_1 = 106,661$, $s_1 = 33,135$, $n_1 = 225$;
Non-college: $\bar{x}_2 = 78,738$, $s_2 = 19,057$, $n_2 = 234$

13.63 Low: $\bar{x}_1 = 1,453$, $s_1 = 361.4$, $n_1 = 438$;
High: $\bar{x}_2 = 1,247$, $s_2 = 367.8$, $n_2 = 571$

13.64 Low: $\bar{x}_1 = 1,158$, $s_1 = 396.5$, $n_1 = 325$;
Middle: $\bar{x}_2 = 1,092$, $s_2 = 241.5$, $n_2 = 441$

13.65 Male: $\bar{x}_1 = 448.3$, $s_1 = 98.99$, $n_1 = 552$;
Female: $\bar{x}_2 = 443.0$, $s_2 = 99.18$, $n_2 = 577$

13.66 College: $\bar{x}_1 = 5,076$, $s_1 = 1,570$, $n_1 = 257$;
Non-college: $\bar{x}_2 = 3,299$, $s_2 = 1,047$, $n_2 = 283$

13.67 Post-graduate: $\bar{x}_1 = 5,497$, $s_1 = 1,565$, $n_1 = 173$;
College: $\bar{x}_2 = 4,791$, $s_2 = 886$, $n_2 = 202$

13.68 80s: $\bar{x}_1 = 1,029$, $s_1 = 305.5$, $n_1 = 166$; 70s: $\bar{x}_2 = 621.1$, $s_2 = 190.7$, $n_2 = 183$

13.69 Dog: $\bar{x}_1 = 227.1$, $s_1 = 69.2$, $n_1 = 84$;
Cat: $\bar{x}_2 = 90.0$, $s_2 = 27.2$, $n_2 = 85$

13.70 Business: $\bar{x}_1 = 1,501$, $s_1 = 205.4$, $n_1 = 215$;
Psychology: $\bar{x}_2 = 1,484$, $s_2 = 173.7$, $n_2 = 162$

13.71 Math/stats: $\bar{x}_1 = 1,681$, $s_1 = 207.3$, $n_1 = 176$;
Engineering: $\bar{x}_2 = 1,620$, $s_2 = 201.2$, $n_2 = 241$

13.72 Private: $\bar{x}_1 = 6.44$, $s_1 = 3.89$, $n_1 = 524$;
Government: $\bar{x}_2 = 10.53$, $s_2 = 4.09$, $n_2 = 409$

13.73 This year: $\bar{x}_1 = 10.53$, $s_1 = 4.09$, $n_1 = 409$;
5 years ago: $\bar{x}_2 = 10.32$, $s_2 = 4.24$, $n_2 = 397$

13.74 Public: $\bar{x}_1 = 61.30$, $s_1 = 3.02$, $n_1 = 46$;
Private: $\bar{x}_2 = 62.74$, $s_2 = 3.02$, $n_2 = 57$

13.113 D = X [This year] − X [5 years ago]: $\bar{x}_D = 12.40$, $s_D = 99.14$, $n_D = 150$

13.114 D = X [Waiter] − X [Waitress]: $\bar{x}_D = -1.16$, $s_D = 2.22$, $n_D = 50$

13.115 D = X [This year] − X [Last year]: $\bar{x}_D = 19.75$, $s_D = 30.63$, $n_D = 40$

13.116 D = X [Insulated] − X [Uninsulated]: $\bar{x}_D = -57.4$, $s_D = 13.14$, $n_D = 15$

13.117 D = X [Men] − X [Women]: $\bar{x}_D = -42.94$, $s_D = 317.2$, $n_D = 45$

13.118 D = X [Last year] − X [Year before]: $\bar{x}_D = -183.3$, $s_D = 1,569$, $n_D = 170$

13.119 D = X [This year] − X [Last year]: $\bar{x}_D = .0422$, $s_D = .1633$, $n_D = 38$

13.120 D = X [Company 1] − X [Company 2]: $\bar{x}_D = 520.9$, $s_D = 1,855$ $n_D = 55$

13.121 D = X [New] − X [Current]: $\bar{x}_D = 4.55$, $s_D = 7.22$, $n_D = 20$

13.123 D = X [Finance] − X [Marketing]: $\bar{x}_D = 4,587$, $s_D = 22,851$, $n_D = 25$

13.125 a. Offspring D = X [After] − X [Before]: $\bar{x}_D = -.100$, $s_D = 1.946$, $n_D = 42$

13.125 b. Outsider D = X [After] − X [Before]: $\bar{x}_D = 1.236$, $s_D = 2.835$, $n_D = 98$

13.126 D = X [First-born IQ] − X [Second-born IQ]: $\bar{x}_D = 2.84$, $s_D = 12.09$, $n_D = 100$

13.127 D = X [Second-born IQ] − X [Third-born IQ]: $\bar{x}_D = 1.00$, $s_D = 9.01$, $n_D = 80$

13.139 Week 1: $s_1^2 = 19.38$, $n_1 = 100$; Week 2: $s_2^2 = 12.70$, $n_2 = 100$

13.140 Brand A 1: $s_1^2 = 41,309$, $n_1 = 100$; Brand B 2: $s_2^2 = 19,850$, $n_2 = 100$

13.141 Portfolio 1: $s_1^2 = .0261$, $n_1 = 52$; Portfolio 2: $s_2^2 = .0875$, $n_2 = 52$

13.142 Teller 1: $s_1^2 = 3.35$, $n_1 = 100$;
Teller 2: $s_2^2 = 10.95$, $n_2 = 100$

13.169 Lexus: $n_1(0) = 33$, $n_1(1) = 317$;
Acura: $n_2(0) = 33$, $n_2(1) = 261$

13.170 18–34: $n_1(1) = 185$,
$n_1(2) = 36$, $n_1(3) = 7$;
35–49: $n_2(1) = 113$,
$n_2(2) = 61$, $n_2(3) = 12$;
50–64: $n_3(1) = 81$,
$n_3(2) = 95$, $n_3(3) = 13$;
65+: $n_4(1) = 75$,
$n_4(2) = 76$, $n_4(3) = 11$

13.171 This year: $n_1(0) = 306$,
$n_1(1) = 171$;
10 years ago: $n_2(0) = 304$,
$n_2(1) = 158$

13.172 Canada: $n_1(1) = 230$,
$n_1(2) = 215$;
U.S.: $n_2(1) = 165$, $n_2(2) = 275$

13.173 Machine A: $n_1(0) = 189$,
$n_1(1) = 11$;
Machine B: $n_2(0) = 178$,
$n_2(1) = 22$

13.174 Doctor: Democrat: $n_1(0) = 251$,
$n_1(1) = 75$;
Republican: $n_2(0) = 201$,
$n_2(1) = 44$;
Independent: $n_3(0) = 382$,
$n_3(1) = 67$.
CDC: Democrat: $n_1(0) = 248$,
$n_1(1) = 78$; Republican:
$n_2(0) = 213$, $n_2(1) = 32$;
Independent: $n_3(0) = 373$,
$n_3(1) = 76$.
Trump: Democrat: $n_1(0) = 293$,
$n_1(1) = 33$; Republican:
$n_2(0) = 216$, $n_2(1) = 29$;
Independent: $n_3(0) = 409$,
$n_3(1) = 40$.

13.175 Math: $n_1(0) = 331$, $n_1(1) = 123$;
Reading: $n_2(0) = 331$,
$n_2(1) = 68$

13.176 HS or less: $n_1(0) = 108$,
$n_1(1) = 13$;
More than HS: $n_2(0) = 786$,
$n_2(1) = 22$

13.177 Men: $n_1(0) = 155$, $n_1(1) = 501$;
Women: $n_2(0) = 183$,
$n_2(1) = 486$

13.178 No religion: $n_1(0) = 2,928$,
$n_1(1) = 272$;
Religion: $n_2(0) = 2,960$,
$n_2(1) = 240$

13.179 Mainstream: $n_1(0) = 2,501$,
$n_1(1) = 199$;
Wallonian: $n_2(0) = 459$,
$n_2(1) = 41$

13.180 Female: $n_1(0) = 40$, $n_1(1) = 60$,
$n_1(2) = 188$, $n_1(3) = 203$,
$n_1(4) = 454$, $n_1(5) = 409$,
$n_1(6) = 199$;
Male: $n_1(0) = 73$, $n_1(1) = 161$,
$n_1(2) = 175$, $n_1(3) = 199$,
$n_1(4) = 392$, $n_1(5) = 316$,
$n_1(6) = 85$

13.181 Umpire A: $n_1(1) = 849$,
$n_1(2) = 119$;
Umpire B: $n_2(1) = 718$,
$n_2(2) = 168$

13.182 Umpire A: $n_1(1) = 44$,
$n_1(2) = 278$;
Umpire B: $n_2(1) = 46$,
$n_2(2) = 272$

13.183 18–24: $n_1(1) = 191$, $n_1(2) = 74$;
25–49: $n_2(1) = 230$, $n_2(2) = 196$;
50–64: $n_3(1) = 176$, $n_3(2) = 243$;
65+: $n_4(1) = 195$, $n_4(2) = 347$

13.184 Federal: $n_1(1) = 214$,
$n_1(2) = 191$, $n_1(3) = 81$;
Other: $n_1(1) = 689$, $n_1(2) = 832$,
$n_1(3) = 466$

13.185 This year: $n_1(0) = 205$,
$n_1(1) = 773$;
5 years ago: $n_2(0) = 125$,
$n_2(1) = 851$

13.186 Women: $n_1(0) = 109$,
$n_1(1) = 413$;
Men: $n_2(0) = 130$, $n_2(1) = 371$

13.187 Women: $n_1(0) = 282$,
$n_1(1) = 240$;
Men: $n_2(0) = 308$, $n_2(1) = 214$

13.188 Aspirin: $n_1(0) = 96$, $n_1(1) = 891$;
Placebo: $n_2(0) = 94$, $n_2(1) = 893$

13.189 Aspirin: $n_1(0) = 936$, $n_1(1) = 37$;
Placebo: $n_2(0) = 955$, $n_2(1) = 26$

13.190 Men: $n_1(0) = 530$, $n_1(1) = 491$;
Women: $n_2(0) = 542$, $n_2(1) = 594$

13.191 Three years ago: $n_1(0) = 445$,
$n_1(1) = 378$;
This year: $n_2(0) = 360$,
$n_2(1) = 496$

13.192 Health: $n_1(0) = 199$, $n_1(1) = 32$;
Not: $n_2(0) = 563$, $n_2(1) = 56$

13.193 Segment 1: $n_1(0) = 95$,
$n_1(1) = 68$;
Segment 2: $n_2(0) = 34$,
$n_2(1) = 20$;
Segment 3: $n_3(0) = 13$,
$n_3(1) = 10$;
Segment 4: $n_4(0) = 79$,
$n_4(1) = 29$

13.194 Source 1: $n_1(0) = 344$,
$n_1(1) = 38$;
Source 2: $n_2(0) = 275$,
$n_2(1) = 41$

Chapter 14

14.9

Sample	$\bar{x}_j$	s_j^2	n_j
1	68.83	52.28	20
2	65.08	37.38	26
3	62.01	63.46	16
4	64.64	56.88	19

14.10

Sample	$\bar{x}_j$	s_j^2	n_j
1	90.17	991.5	30
2	95.77	900.9	30
3	106.83	928.7	30
4	111.17	1,023	30

14.11

Sample	$\bar{x}_j$	s_j^2	n_j
1	196.8	914.0	41
2	207.8	861.1	73
3	223.4	1,195	86
4	232.7	1,080	79

14.12

Sample	$\bar{x}_j$	s_j^2	n_j
1	164.6	1,164	25
2	185.6	1,720	25
3	154.8	1,114	25
4	182.6	1,658	25
5	178.9	841.8	25

14.13

Sample	$\bar{x}_j$	s_j^2	n_j
1	1,328	367,419	36
2	1,254	375,354	43
3	1,633	506,689	77
4	1,286	421,996	44

14.14

Sample	$\bar{x}_j$	s_j^2	n_j
1	587.3	90,379	36
2	550.6	34,031	43
3	470.1	42,649	77
4	501.0	39,138	44

14.15

Sample	$\bar{x}_j$	s_j^2	n_j
1	584.7	5,521	47
2	551.2	8,178	42
3	613.3	4,899	50

14.16

Sample	$\bar{x}_j$	s_j^2	n_j
1	551.5	2,742	20
2	576.8	2,641	20
3	559.5	3,129	20

14.17

Sample	$\bar{x}_j$	s_j^2	n_j
1	5.81	6.22	100
2	5.30	4.05	100
3	5.33	3.90	100

14.18

Sample	$\bar{x}_j$	s_j^2	n_j
1	74.1	250.0	30
2	75.7	184.2	30
3	78.5	233.4	30
4	81.3	242.9	30

14.19

Sample	$\bar{x}_j$	s_j^2	n_j
1	8.25	2.19	175
2	7.48	4.78	377
3	7.81	2.08	399
4	7.70	2.68	400
5	7.68	3.29	453
6	8.00	2.64	375
7	8.20	3.08	201
8	81.8	3.38	126

14.20 a.

Sample	$\bar{x}_j$	s_j^2	n_j
1	31.30	28.34	63
2	34.42	23.20	81
3	37.38	31.16	40
4	39.93	72.03	111

b.

Sample	$\bar{x}_j$	s_j^2	n_j
1	37.22	39.82	63
2	38.91	40.85	81
3	41.48	61.38	40
4	41.75	46.59	111

c.

Sample	$\bar{x}_j$	s_j^2	n_j
1	11.75	3.93	63
2	12.41	3.39	81
3	11.73	4.26	40
4	11.89	4.30	111

14.21

Sample	$\bar{x}_j$	s_j^2	n_j
1	153.6	654.3	20
2	151.5	924.1	20
3	133.3	626.8	20

14.22

Sample	$\bar{x}_j$	s_j^2	n_j
1	18.54	178.0	61
2	19.34	171.4	83
3	20.29	297.5	91

14.23

Sample	$\bar{x}_j$	s_j^2	n_j
1	26.59	97.26	315
2	31.36	159.6	404
3	24.56	113.9	352

14.24

Reading

Sample	$\bar{x}_j$	s_j^2	n_j
1	500.3	611.8	624
2	524.4	686.3	409
3	493.8	608.3	498

Mathematics

Sample	$\bar{x}_j$	s_j^2	n_j
1	486.6	619.5	624
2	527.5	654.0	409
3	492.0	648.3	498

Science

Sample	$\bar{x}_j$	s_j^2	n_j
1	502.0	659.3	624
2	528.9	882.2	409
3	513.9	716.0	498

14.25

Sample	$\bar{x}_j$	s_j^2	n_j
1	353.2	8,683	26
2	514.2	16,459	73
3	621.2	9,705	57
4	515.3	11,486	53

14.26

Sample	$\bar{x}_j$	s_j^2	n_j
1	1,352	162,470	26
2	1,548	190,747	73
3	1,570	176,064	57
4	1,136	146,810	53

14.27

Sample	$\bar{x}_j$	s_j^2	n_j
1	5.10	3.24	105
2	5.20	3.86	112
3	5.40	3.58	115
4	5.50	3.74	117
5	5.10	2.70	121
6	5.00	3.60	125

14.28

Sample	$\bar{x}_j$	s_j^2	n_j
1	20.50	2.04	100
2	20.10	2.16	100
3	20.00	2.42	100
4	19.70	2.47	100
5	18.75	1.95	100

14.29

Sample	$\bar{x}_j$	s_j^2	n_j
1	80.22	44.57	82
2	76.12	70.81	75
3	75.98	60.33	53

14.30

Sample	$\bar{x}_j$	s_j^2	n_j
1	281.4	3,080	53
2	231.6	2,476	142
3	239.8	3,611	147
4	249.3	4,128	131

14.73

Sample	$\bar{x}_j$	s_j^2	n_j
1	61.60	80.49	10
2	57.30	70.46	10
3	61.80	22.18	10
4	51.80	75.29	10

14.75

Sample	$\bar{x}_j$	s_j^2	n_j
1	53.17	194.6	30
2	49.37	152.6	30
3	44.33	129.9	30

14.80

Sample	$\bar{x}_j$	s_j^2	n_j
1	2,299	624,133	26
2	3,245	1,079,157	73
3	4,229	1,865,492	57
4	3,223	1,008,041	53

14.85

Sample	$\bar{x}_j$	s_j^2	n_j
1	118,119	687,858,213	169
2	72,318	562,808,937	102
3	60,966	272,952,317	91
4	65,350	331,355,956	55

Chapter 15

15.7

Cell	1	2	3	4	5
Frequency	28	17	19	17	19

15.8

Cell	1	2	3	4
Frequency	41	107	66	19

15.9

Cell	1	2	3	4	5	6
Frequency	114	92	84	101	107	102

15.10

Cell	1	2	3	4	5
Frequency	11	32	62	29	16

15.11

Cell	1	2	3	4	5
Frequency	8	4	3	8	2

15.12

Cell	1	2	3	4
Frequency	159	28	47	16

15.13

Cell	1	2	3	4
Frequency	36	58	74	29

15.14

Cell	1	2	3
Frequency	408	571	221

15.15

Cell	1	2	3	4
Frequency	9	123	149	39

15.16

Cell	1	2	3	4	5
Frequency	36	26	24	14	15

15.17

Cell	1	2	3	4
Frequency	248	108	47	109

15.18

Cell	1	2	3	4	5	6
Frequency	137	133	143	136	171	99

15.19

Cell	1	2	3	4	5	6	7	8	9	10	11	12
Freq.	21	26	107	272	506	172	99	73	87	66	19	72

15.20

Cell	1	2	3	4
Frequency	63	125	45	87

15.35

Occupation/Newspaper	1	2	3	4
1	27	18	38	37
2	29	43	21	15
3	33	51	22	20

15.36

Side effect/Drug	1	2
1	19	17
2	23	18
3	14	16
4	194	199

15.37

Own/Generation	1	2	3
0	147	106	90
1	20	24	32

15.38

Smoker/Education	1	2	3	4
1	34	251	159	16
2	23	212	248	57

15.39

Heartburn/Source	1	2	3	4	5	6
1	60	65	73	67	57	47
2	23	19	26	11	16	21
3	13	14	9	10	9	10
4	25	28	24	7	14	10

15.40

University/Degree	1	2	3	4
1	44	11	34	11
2	52	14	27	7
3	31	27	18	24
4	40	12	42	6

15.41

Own pet/Income	1	2	3	4	5	6
0	52	56	49	34	25	87
1	30	44	46	42	35	126

15.42

Approach/Degree	1	2	3	4
1	51	8	5	11
2	24	14	12	8
3	26	9	19	8

15.43

Golf ball/Gender	1	2
1	53	74
2	42	36
3	67	38
4	38	52

15.44

Handicap/Golf club	1	2	3	4	5
1	10	7	5	6	5
2	5	7	12	20	8
3	13	10	20	13	17
4	17	3	19	24	33

15.45   Household/

Country	1	2	3
1	65	94	63
2	85	78	105
3	27	31	21
4	83	80	90
5	40	17	21

15.46   Obese/

Country	1	2	3	4
1	152	151	147	151
2	48	49	53	49

15.47   Smoker/

Country	1	2	3	4
1	420	398	395	430
2	80	102	105	70

15.48   Party/Marry

	1	2	3
1	48	21	43
2	24	53	37
3	23	25	21

15.49   Took offer/

Offer	1	2	3	4
1	521	436	567	538
2	637	627	639	658

Chapter 16

16.6 Lengths: $\bar{x} = 38.00$, $s_x^2 = 193.90$, Test: $\bar{y} = 13.80$, $s_y^2 = 47.96$, $s_{xy} = 51.86$, $n = 60$

16.7 Education: $\bar{x} = 13.52$, $s_x^2 = 15.13$, After-tax income: $\bar{y} = 64,293$, $s_y^2 = 406,827,073$, $s_{xy} = 40,245$, $n = 511$

16.8 Population: $\bar{x} = 2,339,626$, $s_x^2 = 5,994,336,071,650$, Property tax: $\bar{y} = 3,058$, $s_y^2 = 1,186,973$, $s_{xy} = 880,267,351$, $n = 582$

16.9 Floors: $\bar{x} = 15.54$, $s_x^2 = 60.50$, Price: $\bar{y} = 255,308$, $s_y^2 = 920,281,250$, $s_{xy} = 98,842$, $n = 50$

16.10 Age: $\bar{x} = 45.49$, $s_x^2 = 107.51$, Time: $\bar{y} = 11.55$, $s_y^2 = 42.54$, $s_{xy} = 9.67$, $n = 229$

16.11 Consumer units: $\bar{x} = 2.54$, $s_x^2 = 2.22$, Income: $\bar{y} = 82,976$, $s_y^2 = 961,444,307$, $s_{xy} = 29,282$, $n = 204$

16.12 Yardage: $\bar{x} = 5,982$, $s_x^2 = 265,811$, Time: $\bar{y} = 253.5$, $s_y^2 = 1,313$, $s_{xy} = 4,314$, $n = 404$

16.13 Distance: $\bar{x} = 4.88$, $s_x^2 = 4.27$, Percent: $\bar{y} = 49.22$, $s_y^2 = 243.94$, $s_{xy} = 22.83$, $n = 85$

16.14 Size: $\bar{x} = 53.93$, $s_x^2 = 688.2$, Price: $\bar{y} = 6,465$, $s_y^2 = 11,918,489$, $s_{xy} = 30,945$, $n = 40$

16.15 Income: $\bar{x} = 59.42$, $s_x^2 = 115.2$, Food: $\bar{y} = 270.3$, $s_y^2 = 1,797$, $s_{xy} = 225.7$, $n = 150$

16.16 Vacancy: $\bar{x} = 11.33$, $s_x^2 = 35.47$, Rent: $\bar{y} = 17.20$, $s_y^2 = 11.24$, $s_{xy} = -10.78$, $n = 30$

16.17 Hours: $\bar{x} = 1,199$, $s_x^2 = 59,153$, Price: $\bar{y} = 28,168$, $s_y^2 = 3,532,606$, $s_{xy} = -67,788$, $n = 60$

16.18 Cigarettes: $\bar{x} = 37.64$, $s_x^2 = 108.3$, Days: $\bar{y} = 14.43$, $s_y^2 = 19.80$, $s_{xy} = 20.55$, $n = 231$

16.19 Population size: $\bar{x} = 1,945,695$, $s_x^2 = 4,855,243,217,430$, After-tax Income: $\bar{y} = 46,630$, $s_y^2 = 128,400,520$, $s_{xy} = 5,034,634,039$, $n = 292$

16.20 Occupants: $\bar{x} = 4.75$, $s_x^2 = 4.84$, Electricity: $\bar{y} = 762.6$, $s_y^2 = 56,725$, $s_{xy} = 310.0$, $n = 200$

16.21 Height: $\bar{x} = 68.95$, $s_x^2 = 9.97$, Income: $\bar{y} = 59.59$, $s_y^2 = 71.95$, $s_{xy} = 6.020$, $n = 250$

16.22 Age: $\bar{x} = 37.28$, $s_x^2 = 55.11$, Employment: $\bar{y} = 26.28$, $s_y^2 = 4.00$, $s_{xy} = -6.44$, $n = 80$

APPENDIX B

TABLES

TABLE 1 Binomial Probabilities

Tabulated values are $P(X \le k) = \sum_{x=0}^{k} p(x_i)$. (Values are rounded to four decimal places.)

n = 5

k	p														
	0.01	0.05	0.10	0.20	0.25	0.30	0.40	0.50	0.60	0.70	0.75	0.80	0.90	0.95	0.99
0	0.9510	0.7738	0.5905	0.3277	0.2373	0.1681	0.0778	0.0313	0.0102	0.0024	0.0010	0.0003	0.0000	0.0000	0.0000
1	0.9990	0.9774	0.9185	0.7373	0.6328	0.5282	0.3370	0.1875	0.0870	0.0308	0.0156	0.0067	0.0005	0.0000	0.0000
2	1.0000	0.9988	0.9914	0.9421	0.8965	0.8369	0.6826	0.5000	0.3174	0.1631	0.1035	0.0579	0.0086	0.0012	0.0000
3	1.0000	1.0000	0.9995	0.9933	0.9844	0.9692	0.9130	0.8125	0.6630	0.4718	0.3672	0.2627	0.0815	0.0226	0.0010
4	1.0000	1.0000	1.0000	0.9997	0.9990	0.9976	0.9898	0.9688	0.9222	0.8319	0.7627	0.6723	0.4095	0.2262	0.0490

n = 6

k	p														
	0.01	0.05	0.10	0.20	0.25	0.30	0.40	0.50	0.60	0.70	0.75	0.80	0.90	0.95	0.99
0	0.9415	0.7351	0.5314	0.2621	0.1780	0.1176	0.0467	0.0156	0.0041	0.0007	0.0002	0.0001	0.0000	0.0000	0.0000
1	0.9985	0.9672	0.8857	0.6554	0.5339	0.4202	0.2333	0.1094	0.0410	0.0109	0.0046	0.0016	0.0001	0.0000	0.0000
2	1.0000	0.9978	0.9842	0.9011	0.8306	0.7443	0.5443	0.3438	0.1792	0.0705	0.0376	0.0170	0.0013	0.0001	0.0000
3	1.0000	0.9999	0.9987	0.9830	0.9624	0.9295	0.8208	0.6563	0.4557	0.2557	0.1694	0.0989	0.0159	0.0022	0.0000
4	1.0000	1.0000	0.9999	0.9984	0.9954	0.9891	0.9590	0.8906	0.7667	0.5798	0.4661	0.3446	0.1143	0.0328	0.0015
5	1.0000	1.0000	1.0000	0.9999	0.9998	0.9993	0.9959	0.9844	0.9533	0.8824	0.8220	0.7379	0.4686	0.2649	0.0585

n = 7

k	p														
	0.01	0.05	0.10	0.20	0.25	0.30	0.40	0.50	0.60	0.70	0.75	0.80	0.90	0.95	0.99
0	0.9321	0.6983	0.4783	0.2097	0.1335	0.0824	0.0280	0.0078	0.0016	0.0002	0.0001	0.0000	0.0000	0.0000	0.0000
1	0.9980	0.9556	0.8503	0.5767	0.4449	0.3294	0.1586	0.0625	0.0188	0.0038	0.0013	0.0004	0.0000	0.0000	0.0000
2	1.0000	0.9962	0.9743	0.8520	0.7564	0.6471	0.4199	0.2266	0.0963	0.0288	0.0129	0.0047	0.0002	0.0000	0.0000
3	1.0000	0.9998	0.9973	0.9667	0.9294	0.8740	0.7102	0.5000	0.2898	0.1260	0.0706	0.0333	0.0027	0.0002	0.0000
4	1.0000	1.0000	0.9998	0.9953	0.9871	0.9712	0.9037	0.7734	0.5801	0.3529	0.2436	0.1480	0.0257	0.0038	0.0000
5	1.0000	1.0000	1.0000	0.9996	0.9987	0.9962	0.9812	0.9375	0.8414	0.6706	0.5551	0.4233	0.1497	0.0444	0.0020
6	1.0000	1.0000	1.0000	1.0000	0.9999	0.9998	0.9984	0.9922	0.9720	0.9176	0.8665	0.7903	0.5217	0.3017	0.0679

(Continued)

TABLE 1 (*Continued*)

n = 8

k	0.01	0.05	0.10	0.20	0.25	0.30	0.40	0.50	0.60	0.70	0.75	0.80	0.90	0.95	0.99
								p							
0	0.9227	0.6634	0.4305	0.1678	0.1001	0.0576	0.0168	0.0039	0.0007	0.0001	0.0000	0.0000	0.0000	0.0000	0.0000
1	0.9973	0.9428	0.8131	0.5033	0.3671	0.2553	0.1064	0.0352	0.0085	0.0013	0.0004	0.0001	0.0000	0.0000	0.0000
2	0.9999	0.9942	0.9619	0.7969	0.6785	0.5518	0.3154	0.1445	0.0498	0.0113	0.0042	0.0012	0.0000	0.0000	0.0000
3	1.0000	0.9996	0.9950	0.9437	0.8862	0.8059	0.5941	0.3633	0.1737	0.0580	0.0273	0.0104	0.0004	0.0000	0.0000
4	1.0000	1.0000	0.9996	0.9896	0.9727	0.9420	0.8263	0.6367	0.4059	0.1941	0.1138	0.0563	0.0050	0.0004	0.0000
5	1.0000	1.0000	1.0000	0.9988	0.9958	0.9887	0.9502	0.8555	0.6846	0.4482	0.3215	0.2031	0.0381	0.0058	0.0001
6	1.0000	1.0000	1.0000	0.9999	0.9996	0.9987	0.9915	0.9648	0.8936	0.7447	0.6329	0.4967	0.1869	0.0572	0.0027
7	1.0000	1.0000	1.0000	1.0000	1.0000	0.9999	0.9993	0.9961	0.9832	0.9424	0.8999	0.8322	0.5695	0.3366	0.0773

n = 9

k	0.01	0.05	0.10	0.20	0.25	0.30	0.40	0.50	0.60	0.70	0.75	0.80	0.90	0.95	0.99
								p							
0	0.9135	0.6302	0.3874	0.1342	0.0751	0.0404	0.0101	0.0020	0.0003	0.0000	0.0000	0.0000	0.0000	0.0000	0.0000
1	0.9966	0.9288	0.7748	0.4362	0.3003	0.1960	0.0705	0.0195	0.0038	0.0004	0.0001	0.0000	0.0000	0.0000	0.0000
2	0.9999	0.9916	0.9470	0.7382	0.6007	0.4628	0.2318	0.0898	0.0250	0.0043	0.0013	0.0003	0.0000	0.0000	0.0000
3	1.0000	0.9994	0.9917	0.9144	0.8343	0.7297	0.4826	0.2539	0.0994	0.0253	0.0100	0.0031	0.0001	0.0000	0.0000
4	1.0000	1.0000	0.9991	0.9804	0.9511	0.9012	0.7334	0.5000	0.2666	0.0988	0.0489	0.0196	0.0009	0.0000	0.0000
5	1.0000	1.0000	0.9999	0.9969	0.9900	0.9747	0.9006	0.7461	0.5174	0.2703	0.1657	0.0856	0.0083	0.0006	0.0000
6	1.0000	1.0000	1.0000	0.9997	0.9987	0.9957	0.9750	0.9102	0.7682	0.5372	0.3993	0.2618	0.0530	0.0084	0.0001
7	1.0000	1.0000	1.0000	1.0000	0.9999	0.9996	0.9962	0.9805	0.9295	0.8040	0.6997	0.5638	0.2252	0.0712	0.0034
8	1.0000	1.0000	1.0000	1.0000	1.0000	1.0000	0.9997	0.9980	0.9899	0.9596	0.9249	0.8658	0.6126	0.3698	0.0865

TABLE **1** (*Continued*)

n = 10

k	|	0.01	0.05	0.10	0.20	0.25	0.30	0.40	0.50	0.60	0.70	0.75	0.80	0.90	0.95	0.99
0	|	0.9044	0.5987	0.3487	0.1074	0.0563	0.0282	0.0060	0.0010	0.0001	0.0000	0.0000	0.0000	0.0000	0.0000	0.0000
1	|	0.9957	0.9139	0.7361	0.3758	0.2440	0.1493	0.0464	0.0107	0.0017	0.0001	0.0000	0.0000	0.0000	0.0000	0.0000
2	|	0.9999	0.9885	0.9298	0.6778	0.5256	0.3828	0.1673	0.0547	0.0123	0.0016	0.0004	0.0001	0.0000	0.0000	0.0000
3	|	1.0000	0.9990	0.9872	0.8791	0.7759	0.6496	0.3823	0.1719	0.0548	0.0106	0.0035	0.0009	0.0000	0.0000	0.0000
4	|	1.0000	0.9999	0.9984	0.9672	0.9219	0.8497	0.6331	0.3770	0.1662	0.0473	0.0197	0.0064	0.0001	0.0000	0.0000
5	|	1.0000	1.0000	0.9999	0.9936	0.9803	0.9527	0.8338	0.6230	0.3669	0.1503	0.0781	0.0328	0.0016	0.0001	0.0000
6	|	1.0000	1.0000	1.0000	0.9991	0.9965	0.9894	0.9452	0.8281	0.6177	0.3504	0.2241	0.1209	0.0128	0.0010	0.0000
7	|	1.0000	1.0000	1.0000	0.9999	0.9996	0.9984	0.9877	0.9453	0.8327	0.6172	0.4744	0.3222	0.0702	0.0115	0.0001
8	|	1.0000	1.0000	1.0000	1.0000	1.0000	0.9999	0.9983	0.9893	0.9536	0.8507	0.7560	0.6242	0.2639	0.0861	0.0043
9	|	1.0000	1.0000	1.0000	1.0000	1.0000	1.0000	0.9999	0.9990	0.9940	0.9718	0.9437	0.8926	0.6513	0.4013	0.0956

n = 15

k	|	0.01	0.05	0.10	0.20	0.25	0.30	0.40	0.50	0.60	0.70	0.75	0.80	0.90	0.95	0.99
0	|	0.8601	0.4633	0.2059	0.0352	0.0134	0.0047	0.0005	0.0000	0.0000	0.0000	0.0000	0.0000	0.0000	0.0000	0.0000
1	|	0.9904	0.8290	0.5490	0.1671	0.0802	0.0353	0.0052	0.0005	0.0000	0.0000	0.0000	0.0000	0.0000	0.0000	0.0000
2	|	0.9996	0.9638	0.8159	0.3980	0.2361	0.1268	0.0271	0.0037	0.0003	0.0000	0.0000	0.0000	0.0000	0.0000	0.0000
3	|	1.0000	0.9945	0.9444	0.6482	0.4613	0.2969	0.0905	0.0176	0.0019	0.0001	0.0000	0.0000	0.0000	0.0000	0.0000
4	|	1.0000	0.9994	0.9873	0.8358	0.6865	0.5155	0.2173	0.0592	0.0093	0.0007	0.0001	0.0000	0.0000	0.0000	0.0000
5	|	1.0000	0.9999	0.9978	0.9389	0.8516	0.7216	0.4032	0.1509	0.0338	0.0037	0.0008	0.0001	0.0000	0.0000	0.0000
6	|	1.0000	1.0000	0.9997	0.9819	0.9434	0.8689	0.6098	0.3036	0.0950	0.0152	0.0042	0.0008	0.0000	0.0000	0.0000
7	|	1.0000	1.0000	1.0000	0.9958	0.9827	0.9500	0.7869	0.5000	0.2131	0.0500	0.0173	0.0042	0.0000	0.0000	0.0000
8	|	1.0000	1.0000	1.0000	0.9992	0.9958	0.9848	0.9050	0.6964	0.3902	0.1311	0.0566	0.0181	0.0003	0.0000	0.0000
9	|	1.0000	1.0000	1.0000	0.9999	0.9992	0.9963	0.9662	0.8491	0.5968	0.2784	0.1484	0.0611	0.0022	0.0001	0.0000
10	|	1.0000	1.0000	1.0000	1.0000	0.9999	0.9993	0.9907	0.9408	0.7827	0.4845	0.3135	0.1642	0.0127	0.0006	0.0000
11	|	1.0000	1.0000	1.0000	1.0000	1.0000	0.9999	0.9981	0.9824	0.9095	0.7031	0.5387	0.3518	0.0556	0.0055	0.0000
12	|	1.0000	1.0000	1.0000	1.0000	1.0000	1.0000	0.9997	0.9963	0.9729	0.8732	0.7639	0.6020	0.1841	0.0362	0.0004
13	|	1.0000	1.0000	1.0000	1.0000	1.0000	1.0000	1.0000	0.9995	0.9948	0.9647	0.9198	0.8329	0.4510	0.1710	0.0096
14	|	1.0000	1.0000	1.0000	1.0000	1.0000	1.0000	1.0000	1.0000	0.9995	0.9953	0.9866	0.9648	0.7941	0.5367	0.1399

(*Continued*)

TABLE **1** (*Continued*)

n = 20

k	0.01	0.05	0.10	0.20	0.25	0.30	0.40	0.50	0.60	0.70	0.75	0.80	0.90	0.95	0.99
0	0.8179	0.3585	0.1216	0.0115	0.0032	0.0008	0.0000	0.0000	0.0000	0.0000	0.0000	0.0000	0.0000	0.0000	0.0000
1	0.9831	0.7358	0.3917	0.0692	0.0243	0.0076	0.0005	0.0000	0.0000	0.0000	0.0000	0.0000	0.0000	0.0000	0.0000
2	0.9990	0.9245	0.6769	0.2061	0.0913	0.0355	0.0036	0.0002	0.0000	0.0000	0.0000	0.0000	0.0000	0.0000	0.0000
3	1.0000	0.9841	0.8670	0.4114	0.2252	0.1071	0.0160	0.0013	0.0000	0.0000	0.0000	0.0000	0.0000	0.0000	0.0000
4	1.0000	0.9974	0.9568	0.6296	0.4148	0.2375	0.0510	0.0059	0.0003	0.0000	0.0000	0.0000	0.0000	0.0000	0.0000
5	1.0000	0.9997	0.9887	0.8042	0.6172	0.4164	0.1256	0.0207	0.0016	0.0000	0.0000	0.0000	0.0000	0.0000	0.0000
6	1.0000	1.0000	0.9976	0.9133	0.7858	0.6080	0.2500	0.0577	0.0065	0.0003	0.0000	0.0000	0.0000	0.0000	0.0000
7	1.0000	1.0000	0.9996	0.9679	0.8982	0.7723	0.4159	0.1316	0.0210	0.0013	0.0002	0.0000	0.0000	0.0000	0.0000
8	1.0000	1.0000	0.9999	0.9900	0.9591	0.8867	0.5956	0.2517	0.0565	0.0051	0.0009	0.0001	0.0000	0.0000	0.0000
9	1.0000	1.0000	1.0000	0.9974	0.9861	0.9520	0.7553	0.4119	0.1275	0.0171	0.0039	0.0006	0.0000	0.0000	0.0000
10	1.0000	1.0000	1.0000	0.9994	0.9961	0.9829	0.8725	0.5881	0.2447	0.0480	0.0139	0.0026	0.0000	0.0000	0.0000
11	1.0000	1.0000	1.0000	0.9999	0.9991	0.9949	0.9435	0.7483	0.4044	0.1133	0.0409	0.0100	0.0001	0.0000	0.0000
12	1.0000	1.0000	1.0000	1.0000	0.9998	0.9987	0.9790	0.8684	0.5841	0.2277	0.1018	0.0321	0.0004	0.0000	0.0000
13	1.0000	1.0000	1.0000	1.0000	1.0000	0.9997	0.9935	0.9423	0.7500	0.3920	0.2142	0.0867	0.0024	0.0000	0.0000
14	1.0000	1.0000	1.0000	1.0000	1.0000	1.0000	0.9984	0.9793	0.8744	0.5836	0.3828	0.1958	0.0113	0.0003	0.0000
15	1.0000	1.0000	1.0000	1.0000	1.0000	1.0000	0.9997	0.9941	0.9490	0.7625	0.5852	0.3704	0.0432	0.0026	0.0000
16	1.0000	1.0000	1.0000	1.0000	1.0000	1.0000	1.0000	0.9987	0.9840	0.8929	0.7748	0.5886	0.1330	0.0159	0.0000
17	1.0000	1.0000	1.0000	1.0000	1.0000	1.0000	1.0000	0.9998	0.9964	0.9645	0.9087	0.7939	0.3231	0.0755	0.0010
18	1.0000	1.0000	1.0000	1.0000	1.0000	1.0000	1.0000	1.0000	0.9995	0.9924	0.9757	0.9308	0.6083	0.2642	0.0169
19	1.0000	1.0000	1.0000	1.0000	1.0000	1.0000	1.0000	1.0000	1.0000	0.9992	0.9968	0.9885	0.8784	0.6415	0.1821

TABLE **1** (*Continued*)

n = 25

k	0.01	0.05	0.10	0.20	0.25	0.30	0.40	0.50	0.60	0.70	0.75	0.80	0.90	0.95	0.99
0	0.7778	0.2774	0.0718	0.0038	0.0008	0.0001	0.0000	0.0000	0.0000	0.0000	0.0000	0.0000	0.0000	0.0000	0.0000
1	0.9742	0.6424	0.2712	0.0274	0.0070	0.0016	0.0001	0.0000	0.0000	0.0000	0.0000	0.0000	0.0000	0.0000	0.0000
2	0.9980	0.8729	0.5371	0.0982	0.0321	0.0090	0.0004	0.0000	0.0000	0.0000	0.0000	0.0000	0.0000	0.0000	0.0000
3	0.9999	0.9659	0.7636	0.2340	0.0962	0.0332	0.0024	0.0001	0.0000	0.0000	0.0000	0.0000	0.0000	0.0000	0.0000
4	1.0000	0.9928	0.9020	0.4207	0.2137	0.0905	0.0095	0.0005	0.0000	0.0000	0.0000	0.0000	0.0000	0.0000	0.0000
5	1.0000	0.9988	0.9666	0.6167	0.3783	0.1935	0.0294	0.0020	0.0001	0.0000	0.0000	0.0000	0.0000	0.0000	0.0000
6	1.0000	0.9998	0.9905	0.7800	0.5611	0.3407	0.0736	0.0073	0.0003	0.0000	0.0000	0.0000	0.0000	0.0000	0.0000
7	1.0000	1.0000	0.9977	0.8909	0.7265	0.5118	0.1536	0.0216	0.0012	0.0000	0.0000	0.0000	0.0000	0.0000	0.0000
8	1.0000	1.0000	0.9995	0.9532	0.8506	0.6769	0.2735	0.0539	0.0043	0.0001	0.0000	0.0000	0.0000	0.0000	0.0000
9	1.0000	1.0000	0.9999	0.9827	0.9287	0.8106	0.4246	0.1148	0.0132	0.0005	0.0000	0.0000	0.0000	0.0000	0.0000
10	1.0000	1.0000	1.0000	0.9944	0.9703	0.9022	0.5858	0.2122	0.0344	0.0018	0.0002	0.0000	0.0000	0.0000	0.0000
11	1.0000	1.0000	1.0000	0.9985	0.9893	0.9558	0.7323	0.3450	0.0778	0.0060	0.0009	0.0001	0.0000	0.0000	0.0000
12	1.0000	1.0000	1.0000	0.9996	0.9966	0.9825	0.8462	0.5000	0.1538	0.0175	0.0034	0.0004	0.0000	0.0000	0.0000
13	1.0000	1.0000	1.0000	0.9999	0.9991	0.9940	0.9222	0.6550	0.2677	0.0442	0.0107	0.0015	0.0000	0.0000	0.0000
14	1.0000	1.0000	1.0000	1.0000	0.9998	0.9982	0.9656	0.7878	0.4142	0.0978	0.0297	0.0056	0.0000	0.0000	0.0000
15	1.0000	1.0000	1.0000	1.0000	1.0000	0.9995	0.9868	0.8852	0.5754	0.1894	0.0713	0.0173	0.0001	0.0000	0.0000
16	1.0000	1.0000	1.0000	1.0000	1.0000	0.9999	0.9957	0.9461	0.7265	0.3231	0.1494	0.0468	0.0005	0.0000	0.0000
17	1.0000	1.0000	1.0000	1.0000	1.0000	1.0000	0.9988	0.9784	0.8464	0.4882	0.2735	0.1091	0.0023	0.0000	0.0000
18	1.0000	1.0000	1.0000	1.0000	1.0000	1.0000	0.9997	0.9927	0.9264	0.6593	0.4389	0.2200	0.0095	0.0002	0.0000
19	1.0000	1.0000	1.0000	1.0000	1.0000	1.0000	0.9999	0.9980	0.9706	0.8065	0.6217	0.3833	0.0334	0.0012	0.0000
20	1.0000	1.0000	1.0000	1.0000	1.0000	1.0000	1.0000	0.9995	0.9905	0.9095	0.7863	0.5793	0.0980	0.0072	0.0000
21	1.0000	1.0000	1.0000	1.0000	1.0000	1.0000	1.0000	0.9999	0.9976	0.9668	0.9038	0.7660	0.2364	0.0341	0.0001
22	1.0000	1.0000	1.0000	1.0000	1.0000	1.0000	1.0000	1.0000	0.9996	0.9910	0.9679	0.9018	0.4629	0.1271	0.0020
23	1.0000	1.0000	1.0000	1.0000	1.0000	1.0000	1.0000	1.0000	0.9999	0.9984	0.9930	0.9726	0.7288	0.3576	0.0258
24	1.0000	1.0000	1.0000	1.0000	1.0000	1.0000	1.0000	1.0000	1.0000	0.9999	0.9992	0.9962	0.9282	0.7226	0.2222

TABLE 2 Poisson Probabilities

Tabulated values are $P(X \leq k) = \sum_{x=0}^{k} p(x_i)$. (Values are rounded to four decimal places.)

k	0.10	0.20	0.30	0.40	0.50	1.0	1.5	2.0	2.5	3.0	3.5	4.0	4.5	5.0	5.5	6.0
0	0.9048	0.8187	0.7408	0.6703	0.6065	0.3679	0.2231	0.1353	0.0821	0.0498	0.0302	0.0183	0.0111	0.0067	0.0041	0.0025
1	0.9953	0.9825	0.9631	0.9384	0.9098	0.7358	0.5578	0.4060	0.2873	0.1991	0.1359	0.0916	0.0611	0.0404	0.0266	0.0174
2	0.9998	0.9989	0.9964	0.9921	0.9856	0.9197	0.8088	0.6767	0.5438	0.4232	0.3208	0.2381	0.1736	0.1247	0.0884	0.0620
3	1.0000	0.9999	0.9997	0.9992	0.9982	0.9810	0.9344	0.8571	0.7576	0.6472	0.5366	0.4335	0.3423	0.2650	0.2017	0.1512
4		1.0000	1.0000	0.9999	0.9998	0.9963	0.9814	0.9473	0.8912	0.8153	0.7254	0.6288	0.5321	0.4405	0.3575	0.2851
5				1.0000	1.0000	0.9994	0.9955	0.9834	0.9580	0.9161	0.8576	0.7851	0.7029	0.6160	0.5289	0.4457
6						0.9999	0.9991	0.9955	0.9858	0.9665	0.9347	0.8893	0.8311	0.7622	0.6860	0.6063
7						1.0000	0.9998	0.9989	0.9958	0.9881	0.9733	0.9489	0.9134	0.8666	0.8095	0.7440
8							1.0000	0.9998	0.9989	0.9962	0.9901	0.9786	0.9597	0.9319	0.8944	0.8472
9								1.0000	0.9997	0.9989	0.9967	0.9919	0.9829	0.9682	0.9462	0.9161
10									0.9999	0.9997	0.9990	0.9972	0.9933	0.9863	0.9747	0.9574
11									1.0000	0.9999	0.9997	0.9991	0.9976	0.9945	0.9890	0.9799
12										1.0000	0.9999	0.9997	0.9992	0.9980	0.9955	0.9912
13											1.0000	0.9999	0.9997	0.9993	0.9983	0.9964
14												1.0000	0.9999	0.9998	0.9994	0.9986
15													1.0000	0.9999	0.9998	0.9995
16														1.0000	0.9999	0.9998
17															1.0000	0.9999
18																1.0000
19																
20																

TABLE **2** (*Continued*)

k	6.50	7.00	7.50	8.00	8.50	9.00	9.50	10	11	12	13	14	15
							μ						
0	0.0015	0.0009	0.0006	0.0003	0.0002	0.0001	0.0001	0.0000	0.0000	0.0000	0.0000	0.0000	0.0000
1	0.0113	0.0073	0.0047	0.0030	0.0019	0.0012	0.0008	0.0005	0.0002	0.0001	0.0000	0.0000	0.0000
2	0.0430	0.0296	0.0203	0.0138	0.0093	0.0062	0.0042	0.0028	0.0012	0.0005	0.0002	0.0001	0.0000
3	0.1118	0.0818	0.0591	0.0424	0.0301	0.0212	0.0149	0.0103	0.0049	0.0023	0.0011	0.0005	0.0002
4	0.2237	0.1730	0.1321	0.0996	0.0744	0.0550	0.0403	0.0293	0.0151	0.0076	0.0037	0.0018	0.0009
5	0.3690	0.3007	0.2414	0.1912	0.1496	0.1157	0.0885	0.0671	0.0375	0.0203	0.0107	0.0055	0.0028
6	0.5265	0.4497	0.3782	0.3134	0.2562	0.2068	0.1649	0.1301	0.0786	0.0458	0.0259	0.0142	0.0076
7	0.6728	0.5987	0.5246	0.4530	0.3856	0.3239	0.2687	0.2202	0.1432	0.0895	0.0540	0.0316	0.0180
8	0.7916	0.7291	0.6620	0.5925	0.5231	0.4557	0.3918	0.3328	0.2320	0.1550	0.0998	0.0621	0.0374
9	0.8774	0.8305	0.7764	0.7166	0.6530	0.5874	0.5218	0.4579	0.3405	0.2424	0.1658	0.1094	0.0699
10	0.9332	0.9015	0.8622	0.8159	0.7634	0.7060	0.6453	0.5830	0.4599	0.3472	0.2517	0.1757	0.1185
11	0.9661	0.9467	0.9208	0.8881	0.8487	0.8030	0.7520	0.6968	0.5793	0.4616	0.3532	0.2600	0.1848
12	0.9840	0.9730	0.9573	0.9362	0.9091	0.8758	0.8364	0.7916	0.6887	0.5760	0.4631	0.3585	0.2676
13	0.9929	0.9872	0.9784	0.9658	0.9486	0.9261	0.8981	0.8645	0.7813	0.6815	0.5730	0.4644	0.3632
14	0.9970	0.9943	0.9897	0.9827	0.9726	0.9585	0.9400	0.9165	0.8540	0.7720	0.6751	0.5704	0.4657
15	0.9988	0.9976	0.9954	0.9918	0.9862	0.9780	0.9665	0.9513	0.9074	0.8444	0.7636	0.6694	0.5681
16	0.9996	0.9990	0.9980	0.9963	0.9934	0.9889	0.9823	0.9730	0.9441	0.8987	0.8355	0.7559	0.6641
17	0.9998	0.9996	0.9992	0.9984	0.9970	0.9947	0.9911	0.9857	0.9678	0.9370	0.8905	0.8272	0.7489
18	0.9999	0.9999	0.9997	0.9993	0.9987	0.9976	0.9957	0.9928	0.9823	0.9626	0.9302	0.8826	0.8195
19	1.0000	1.0000	0.9999	0.9997	0.9995	0.9989	0.9980	0.9965	0.9907	0.9787	0.9573	0.9235	0.8752
20			1.0000	0.9999	0.9998	0.9996	0.9991	0.9984	0.9953	0.9884	0.9750	0.9521	0.9170
21				1.0000	0.9999	0.9998	0.9996	0.9993	0.9977	0.9939	0.9859	0.9712	0.9469
22					1.0000	0.9999	0.9999	0.9997	0.9990	0.9970	0.9924	0.9833	0.9673
23						1.0000	0.9999	0.9999	0.9995	0.9985	0.9960	0.9907	0.9805
24							1.0000	1.0000	0.9998	0.9993	0.9980	0.9950	0.9888
25									0.9999	0.9997	0.9990	0.9974	0.9938
26									1.0000	0.9999	0.9995	0.9987	0.9967
27										0.9999	0.9998	0.9994	0.9983
28										1.0000	0.9999	0.9997	0.9991
29											1.0000	0.9999	0.9996
30												0.9999	0.9998
31												1.0000	0.9999
32													1.0000

TABLE 3 Cumulative Standardized Normal Probabilities

$P(-\infty < Z < z)$

Z	0.00	0.01	0.02	0.03	0.04	0.05	0.06	0.07	0.08	0.09
−3.0	0.0013	0.0013	0.0013	0.0012	0.0012	0.0011	0.0011	0.0011	0.0010	0.0010
−2.9	0.0019	0.0018	0.0018	0.0017	0.0016	0.0016	0.0015	0.0015	0.0014	0.0014
−2.8	0.0026	0.0025	0.0024	0.0023	0.0023	0.0022	0.0021	0.0021	0.0020	0.0019
−2.7	0.0035	0.0034	0.0033	0.0032	0.0031	0.0030	0.0029	0.0028	0.0027	0.0026
−2.6	0.0047	0.0045	0.0044	0.0043	0.0041	0.0040	0.0039	0.0038	0.0037	0.0036
−2.5	0.0062	0.0060	0.0059	0.0057	0.0055	0.0054	0.0052	0.0051	0.0049	0.0048
−2.4	0.0082	0.0080	0.0078	0.0075	0.0073	0.0071	0.0069	0.0068	0.0066	0.0064
−2.3	0.0107	0.0104	0.0102	0.0099	0.0096	0.0094	0.0091	0.0089	0.0087	0.0084
−2.2	0.0139	0.0136	0.0132	0.0129	0.0125	0.0122	0.0119	0.0116	0.0113	0.0110
−2.1	0.0179	0.0174	0.0170	0.0166	0.0162	0.0158	0.0154	0.0150	0.0146	0.0143
−2.0	0.0228	0.0222	0.0217	0.0212	0.0207	0.0202	0.0197	0.0192	0.0188	0.0183
−1.9	0.0287	0.0281	0.0274	0.0268	0.0262	0.0256	0.0250	0.0244	0.0239	0.0233
−1.8	0.0359	0.0351	0.0344	0.0336	0.0329	0.0322	0.0314	0.0307	0.0301	0.0294
−1.7	0.0446	0.0436	0.0427	0.0418	0.0409	0.0401	0.0392	0.0384	0.0375	0.0367
−1.6	0.0548	0.0537	0.0526	0.0516	0.0505	0.0495	0.0485	0.0475	0.0465	0.0455
−1.5	0.0668	0.0655	0.0643	0.0630	0.0618	0.0606	0.0594	0.0582	0.0571	0.0559
−1.4	0.0808	0.0793	0.0778	0.0764	0.0749	0.0735	0.0721	0.0708	0.0694	0.0681
−1.3	0.0968	0.0951	0.0934	0.0918	0.0901	0.0885	0.0869	0.0853	0.0838	0.0823
−1.2	0.1151	0.1131	0.1112	0.1093	0.1075	0.1056	0.1038	0.1020	0.1003	0.0985
−1.1	0.1357	0.1335	0.1314	0.1292	0.1271	0.1251	0.1230	0.1210	0.1190	0.1170
−1.0	0.1587	0.1562	0.1539	0.1515	0.1492	0.1469	0.1446	0.1423	0.1401	0.1379
−0.9	0.1841	0.1814	0.1788	0.1762	0.1736	0.1711	0.1685	0.1660	0.1635	0.1611
−0.8	0.2119	0.2090	0.2061	0.2033	0.2005	0.1977	0.1949	0.1922	0.1894	0.1867
−0.7	0.2420	0.2389	0.2358	0.2327	0.2296	0.2266	0.2236	0.2206	0.2177	0.2148
−0.6	0.2743	0.2709	0.2676	0.2643	0.2611	0.2578	0.2546	0.2514	0.2483	0.2451
−0.5	0.3085	0.3050	0.3015	0.2981	0.2946	0.2912	0.2877	0.2843	0.2810	0.2776
−0.4	0.3446	0.3409	0.3372	0.3336	0.3300	0.3264	0.3228	0.3192	0.3156	0.3121
−0.3	0.3821	0.3783	0.3745	0.3707	0.3669	0.3632	0.3594	0.3557	0.3520	0.3483
−0.2	0.4207	0.4168	0.4129	0.4090	0.4052	0.4013	0.3974	0.3936	0.3897	0.3859
−0.1	0.4602	0.4562	0.4522	0.4483	0.4443	0.4404	0.4364	0.4325	0.4286	0.4247
−0.0	0.5000	0.4960	0.4920	0.4880	0.4840	0.4801	0.4761	0.4721	0.4681	0.4641

TABLE **3** (*Continued*)

$P(-\infty < Z < z)$

Z	0.00	0.01	0.02	0.03	0.04	0.05	0.06	0.07	0.08	0.09
0.0	0.5000	0.5040	0.5080	0.5120	0.5160	0.5199	0.5239	0.5279	0.5319	0.5359
0.1	0.5398	0.5438	0.5478	0.5517	0.5557	0.5596	0.5636	0.5675	0.5714	0.5753
0.2	0.5793	0.5832	0.5871	0.5910	0.5948	0.5987	0.6026	0.6064	0.6103	0.6141
0.3	0.6179	0.6217	0.6255	0.6293	0.6331	0.6368	0.6406	0.6443	0.6480	0.6517
0.4	0.6554	0.6591	0.6628	0.6664	0.6700	0.6736	0.6772	0.6808	0.6844	0.6879
0.5	0.6915	0.6950	0.6985	0.7019	0.7054	0.7088	0.7123	0.7157	0.7190	0.7224
0.6	0.7257	0.7291	0.7324	0.7357	0.7389	0.7422	0.7454	0.7486	0.7517	0.7549
0.7	0.7580	0.7611	0.7642	0.7673	0.7704	0.7734	0.7764	0.7794	0.7823	0.7852
0.8	0.7881	0.7910	0.7939	0.7967	0.7995	0.8023	0.8051	0.8078	0.8106	0.8133
0.9	0.8159	0.8186	0.8212	0.8238	0.8264	0.8289	0.8315	0.8340	0.8365	0.8389
1.0	0.8413	0.8438	0.8461	0.8485	0.8508	0.8531	0.8554	0.8577	0.8599	0.8621
1.1	0.8643	0.8665	0.8686	0.8708	0.8729	0.8749	0.8770	0.8790	0.8810	0.8830
1.2	0.8849	0.8869	0.8888	0.8907	0.8925	0.8944	0.8962	0.8980	0.8997	0.9015
1.3	0.9032	0.9049	0.9066	0.9082	0.9099	0.9115	0.9131	0.9147	0.9162	0.9177
1.4	0.9192	0.9207	0.9222	0.9236	0.9251	0.9265	0.9279	0.9292	0.9306	0.9319
1.5	0.9332	0.9345	0.9357	0.9370	0.9382	0.9394	0.9406	0.9418	0.9429	0.9441
1.6	0.9452	0.9463	0.9474	0.9484	0.9495	0.9505	0.9515	0.9525	0.9535	0.9545
1.7	0.9554	0.9564	0.9573	0.9582	0.9591	0.9599	0.9608	0.9616	0.9625	0.9633
1.8	0.9641	0.9649	0.9656	0.9664	0.9671	0.9678	0.9686	0.9693	0.9699	0.9706
1.9	0.9713	0.9719	0.9726	0.9732	0.9738	0.9744	0.9750	0.9756	0.9761	0.9767
2.0	0.9772	0.9778	0.9783	0.9788	0.9793	0.9798	0.9803	0.9808	0.9812	0.9817
2.1	0.9821	0.9826	0.9830	0.9834	0.9838	0.9842	0.9846	0.9850	0.9854	0.9857
2.2	0.9861	0.9864	0.9868	0.9871	0.9875	0.9878	0.9881	0.9884	0.9887	0.9890
2.3	0.9893	0.9896	0.9898	0.9901	0.9904	0.9906	0.9909	0.9911	0.9913	0.9916
2.4	0.9918	0.9920	0.9922	0.9925	0.9927	0.9929	0.9931	0.9932	0.9934	0.9936
2.5	0.9938	0.9940	0.9941	0.9943	0.9945	0.9946	0.9948	0.9949	0.9951	0.9952
2.6	0.9953	0.9955	0.9956	0.9957	0.9959	0.9960	0.9961	0.9962	0.9963	0.9964
2.7	0.9965	0.9966	0.9967	0.9968	0.9969	0.9970	0.9971	0.9972	0.9973	0.9974
2.8	0.9974	0.9975	0.9976	0.9977	0.9977	0.9978	0.9979	0.9979	0.9980	0.9981
2.9	0.9981	0.9982	0.9982	0.9983	0.9984	0.9984	0.9985	0.9985	0.9986	0.9986
3.0	0.9987	0.9987	0.9987	0.9988	0.9988	0.9989	0.9989	0.9989	0.9990	0.9990

TABLE 4
Critical Values of the Student t Distribution

Degrees of Freedom	$t_{.100}$	$t_{.050}$	$t_{.025}$	$t_{.010}$	$t_{.005}$
1	3.078	6.314	12.706	31.821	63.657
2	1.886	2.920	4.303	6.965	9.925
3	1.638	2.353	3.182	4.541	5.841
4	1.533	2.132	2.776	3.747	4.604
5	1.476	2.015	2.571	3.365	4.032
6	1.440	1.943	2.447	3.143	3.707
7	1.415	1.895	2.365	2.998	3.499
8	1.397	1.860	2.306	2.896	3.355
9	1.383	1.833	2.262	2.821	3.250
10	1.372	1.812	2.228	2.764	3.169
11	1.363	1.796	2.201	2.718	3.106
12	1.356	1.782	2.179	2.681	3.055
13	1.350	1.771	2.160	2.650	3.012
14	1.345	1.761	2.145	2.624	2.977
15	1.341	1.753	2.131	2.602	2.947
16	1.337	1.746	2.120	2.583	2.921
17	1.333	1.740	2.110	2.567	2.898
18	1.330	1.734	2.101	2.552	2.878
19	1.328	1.729	2.093	2.539	2.861
20	1.325	1.725	2.086	2.528	2.845
21	1.323	1.721	2.080	2.518	2.831
22	1.321	1.717	2.074	2.508	2.819
23	1.319	1.714	2.069	2.500	2.807
24	1.318	1.711	2.064	2.492	2.797
25	1.316	1.708	2.060	2.485	2.787
26	1.315	1.706	2.056	2.479	2.779
27	1.314	1.703	2.052	2.473	2.771
28	1.313	1.701	2.048	2.467	2.763
29	1.311	1.699	2.045	2.462	2.756
30	1.310	1.697	2.042	2.457	2.750
35	1.306	1.690	2.030	2.438	2.724
40	1.303	1.684	2.021	2.423	2.704
45	1.301	1.679	2.014	2.412	2.690
50	1.299	1.676	2.009	2.403	2.678
55	1.297	1.673	2.004	2.396	2.668
60	1.296	1.671	2.000	2.390	2.660
65	1.295	1.669	1.997	2.385	2.654
70	1.294	1.667	1.994	2.381	2.648
75	1.293	1.665	1.992	2.377	2.643
80	1.292	1.664	1.990	2.374	2.639
85	1.292	1.663	1.988	2.371	2.635
90	1.291	1.662	1.987	2.368	2.632
95	1.291	1.661	1.985	2.366	2.629
100	1.290	1.660	1.984	2.364	2.626
110	1.289	1.659	1.982	2.361	2.621
120	1.289	1.658	1.980	2.358	2.617
130	1.288	1.657	1.978	2.355	2.614
140	1.288	1.656	1.977	2.353	2.611
150	1.287	1.655	1.976	2.351	2.609
160	1.287	1.654	1.975	2.350	2.607
170	1.287	1.654	1.974	2.348	2.605
180	1.286	1.653	1.973	2.347	2.603
190	1.286	1.653	1.973	2.346	2.602
200	1.286	1.653	1.972	2.345	2.601
∞	1.282	1.645	1.960	2.326	2.576

TABLE 5 Critical Values of the χ^2 Distribution

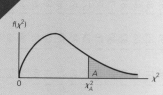

Degrees of Freedom	$\chi^2_{.995}$	$\chi^2_{.990}$	$\chi^2_{.975}$	$\chi^2_{.950}$	$\chi^2_{.900}$	$\chi^2_{.100}$	$\chi^2_{.050}$	$\chi^2_{.025}$	$\chi^2_{.010}$	$\chi^2_{.005}$
1	0.000039	0.000157	0.000982	0.00393	0.0158	2.71	3.84	5.02	6.63	7.88
2	0.0100	0.0201	0.0506	0.103	0.211	4.61	5.99	7.38	9.21	10.6
3	0.072	0.115	0.216	0.352	0.584	6.25	7.81	9.35	11.3	12.8
4	0.207	0.297	0.484	0.711	1.06	7.78	9.49	11.1	13.3	14.9
5	0.412	0.554	0.831	1.15	1.61	9.24	11.1	12.8	15.1	16.7
6	0.676	0.872	1.24	1.64	2.20	10.6	12.6	14.4	16.8	18.5
7	0.989	1.24	1.69	2.17	2.83	12.0	14.1	16.0	18.5	20.3
8	1.34	1.65	2.18	2.73	3.49	13.4	15.5	17.5	20.1	22.0
9	1.73	2.09	2.70	3.33	4.17	14.7	16.9	19.0	21.7	23.6
10	2.16	2.56	3.25	3.94	4.87	16.0	18.3	20.5	23.2	25.2
11	2.60	3.05	3.82	4.57	5.58	17.3	19.7	21.9	24.7	26.8
12	3.07	3.57	4.40	5.23	6.30	18.5	21.0	23.3	26.2	28.3
13	3.57	4.11	5.01	5.89	7.04	19.8	22.4	24.7	27.7	29.8
14	4.07	4.66	5.63	6.57	7.79	21.1	23.7	26.1	29.1	31.3
15	4.60	5.23	6.26	7.26	8.55	22.3	25.0	27.5	30.6	32.8
16	5.14	5.81	6.91	7.96	9.31	23.5	26.3	28.8	32.0	34.3
17	5.70	6.41	7.56	8.67	10.1	24.8	27.6	30.2	33.4	35.7
18	6.26	7.01	8.23	9.39	10.9	26.0	28.9	31.5	34.8	37.2
19	6.84	7.63	8.91	10.1	11.7	27.2	30.1	32.9	36.2	38.6
20	7.43	8.26	9.59	10.9	12.4	28.4	31.4	34.2	37.6	40.0
21	8.03	8.90	10.3	11.6	13.2	29.6	32.7	35.5	38.9	41.4
22	8.64	9.54	11.0	12.3	14.0	30.8	33.9	36.8	40.3	42.8
23	9.26	10.2	11.7	13.1	14.8	32.0	35.2	38.1	41.6	44.2
24	9.89	10.9	12.4	13.8	15.7	33.2	36.4	39.4	43.0	45.6
25	10.5	11.5	13.1	14.6	16.5	34.4	37.7	40.6	44.3	46.9
26	11.2	12.2	13.8	15.4	17.3	35.6	38.9	41.9	45.6	48.3
27	11.8	12.9	14.6	16.2	18.1	36.7	40.1	43.2	47.0	49.6
28	12.5	13.6	15.3	16.9	18.9	37.9	41.3	44.5	48.3	51.0
29	13.1	14.3	16.0	17.7	19.8	39.1	42.6	45.7	49.6	52.3
30	13.8	15.0	16.8	18.5	20.6	40.3	43.8	47.0	50.9	53.7
40	20.7	22.2	24.4	26.5	29.1	51.8	55.8	59.3	63.7	66.8
50	28.0	29.7	32.4	34.8	37.7	63.2	67.5	71.4	76.2	79.5
60	35.5	37.5	40.5	43.2	46.5	74.4	79.1	83.3	88.4	92.0
70	43.3	45.4	48.8	51.7	55.3	85.5	90.5	95.0	100	104
80	51.2	53.5	57.2	60.4	64.3	96.6	102	107	112	116
90	59.2	61.8	65.6	69.1	73.3	108	113	118	124	128
100	67.3	70.1	74.2	77.9	82.4	118	124	130	136	140

TABLE **6(a)** Critical Values of the *F*-Distribution: *A* = .05

ν_2 \ ν_1	1	2	3	4	5	6	7	8	9	10	11	12	13	14	15	16	17	18	19	20
												NUMERATOR DEGREES OF FREEDOM							
1	161	199	216	225	230	234	237	239	241	242	243	244	245	245	246	246	247	247	248	248
2	18.5	19.0	19.2	19.2	19.3	19.3	19.4	19.4	19.4	19.4	19.4	19.4	19.4	19.4	19.4	19.4	19.4	19.4	19.4	19.4
3	10.1	9.55	9.28	9.12	9.01	8.94	8.89	8.85	8.81	8.79	8.76	8.74	8.73	8.71	8.70	8.69	8.68	8.67	8.67	8.66
4	7.71	6.94	6.59	6.39	6.26	6.16	6.09	6.04	6.00	5.96	5.94	5.91	5.89	5.87	5.86	5.84	5.83	5.82	5.81	5.80
5	6.61	5.79	5.41	5.19	5.05	4.95	4.88	4.82	4.77	4.74	4.70	4.68	4.66	4.64	4.62	4.60	4.59	4.58	4.57	4.56
6	5.99	5.14	4.76	4.53	4.39	4.28	4.21	4.15	4.10	4.06	4.03	4.00	3.98	3.96	3.94	3.92	3.91	3.90	3.88	3.87
7	5.59	4.74	4.35	4.12	3.97	3.87	3.79	3.73	3.68	3.64	3.60	3.57	3.55	3.53	3.51	3.49	3.48	3.47	3.46	3.44
8	5.32	4.46	4.07	3.84	3.69	3.58	3.50	3.44	3.39	3.35	3.31	3.28	3.26	3.24	3.22	3.20	3.19	3.17	3.16	3.15
9	5.12	4.26	3.86	3.63	3.48	3.37	3.29	3.23	3.18	3.14	3.10	3.07	3.05	3.03	3.01	2.99	2.97	2.96	2.95	2.94
10	4.96	4.10	3.71	3.48	3.33	3.22	3.14	3.07	3.02	2.98	2.94	2.91	2.89	2.86	2.85	2.83	2.81	2.80	2.79	2.77
11	4.84	3.98	3.59	3.36	3.20	3.09	3.01	2.95	2.90	2.85	2.82	2.79	2.76	2.74	2.72	2.70	2.69	2.67	2.66	2.65
12	4.75	3.89	3.49	3.26	3.11	3.00	2.91	2.85	2.80	2.75	2.72	2.69	2.66	2.64	2.62	2.60	2.58	2.57	2.56	2.54
13	4.67	3.81	3.41	3.18	3.03	2.92	2.83	2.77	2.71	2.67	2.63	2.60	2.58	2.55	2.53	2.51	2.50	2.48	2.47	2.46
14	4.60	3.74	3.34	3.11	2.96	2.85	2.76	2.70	2.65	2.60	2.57	2.53	2.51	2.48	2.46	2.44	2.43	2.41	2.40	2.39
15	4.54	3.68	3.29	3.06	2.90	2.79	2.71	2.64	2.59	2.54	2.51	2.48	2.45	2.42	2.40	2.38	2.37	2.35	2.34	2.33
16	4.49	3.63	3.24	3.01	2.85	2.74	2.66	2.59	2.54	2.49	2.46	2.42	2.40	2.37	2.35	2.33	2.32	2.30	2.29	2.28
17	4.45	3.59	3.20	2.96	2.81	2.70	2.61	2.55	2.49	2.45	2.41	2.38	2.35	2.33	2.31	2.29	2.27	2.26	2.24	2.23
18	4.41	3.55	3.16	2.93	2.77	2.66	2.58	2.51	2.46	2.41	2.37	2.34	2.31	2.29	2.27	2.25	2.23	2.22	2.20	2.19
19	4.38	3.52	3.13	2.90	2.74	2.63	2.54	2.48	2.42	2.38	2.34	2.31	2.28	2.26	2.23	2.21	2.20	2.18	2.17	2.16
20	4.35	3.49	3.10	2.87	2.71	2.60	2.51	2.45	2.39	2.35	2.31	2.28	2.25	2.22	2.20	2.18	2.17	2.15	2.14	2.12
22	4.30	3.44	3.05	2.82	2.66	2.55	2.46	2.40	2.34	2.30	2.26	2.23	2.20	2.17	2.15	2.13	2.11	2.10	2.08	2.07
24	4.26	3.40	3.01	2.78	2.62	2.51	2.42	2.36	2.30	2.25	2.22	2.18	2.15	2.13	2.11	2.09	2.05	2.05	2.04	2.03
26	4.23	3.37	2.98	2.74	2.59	2.47	2.39	2.32	2.27	2.22	2.18	2.15	2.12	2.09	2.07	2.05	2.03	2.02	2.00	1.99
28	4.20	3.34	2.95	2.71	2.56	2.45	2.36	2.29	2.24	2.19	2.15	2.12	2.09	2.06	2.04	2.02	2.00	1.99	1.97	1.96
30	4.17	3.32	2.92	2.69	2.53	2.42	2.33	2.27	2.21	2.16	2.13	2.09	2.06	2.04	2.01	1.99	1.98	1.96	1.95	1.93
35	4.12	3.27	2.87	2.64	2.49	2.37	2.29	2.22	2.16	2.11	2.07	2.04	2.01	1.99	1.96	1.94	1.92	1.91	1.89	1.88
40	4.08	3.23	2.84	2.61	2.45	2.34	2.25	2.18	2.12	2.08	2.04	2.00	1.97	1.95	1.92	1.90	1.89	1.87	1.85	1.84
45	4.06	3.20	2.81	2.58	2.42	2.31	2.22	2.15	2.10	2.05	2.01	1.97	1.94	1.92	1.89	1.87	1.86	1.84	1.82	1.81
50	4.03	3.18	2.79	2.56	2.40	2.29	2.20	2.13	2.07	2.03	1.99	1.95	1.92	1.89	1.87	1.85	1.83	1.81	1.80	1.78
60	4.00	3.15	2.76	2.53	2.37	2.25	2.17	2.10	2.04	1.99	1.95	1.92	1.89	1.86	1.84	1.82	1.80	1.78	1.76	1.75
70	3.98	3.13	2.74	2.50	2.35	2.23	2.14	2.07	2.02	1.97	1.93	1.89	1.86	1.84	1.81	1.79	1.77	1.75	1.74	1.72
80	3.96	3.11	2.72	2.49	2.33	2.21	2.13	2.06	2.00	1.95	1.91	1.88	1.84	1.82	1.79	1.77	1.75	1.73	1.72	1.70
90	3.95	3.10	2.71	2.47	2.32	2.20	2.11	2.04	1.99	1.94	1.90	1.86	1.83	1.80	1.78	1.76	1.74	1.72	1.70	1.69
100	3.94	3.09	2.70	2.46	2.31	2.19	2.10	2.03	1.97	1.93	1.89	1.85	1.82	1.79	1.77	1.75	1.73	1.71	1.69	1.68
120	3.92	3.07	2.68	2.45	2.29	2.18	2.09	2.02	1.96	1.91	1.87	1.83	1.80	1.78	1.75	1.73	1.71	1.69	1.67	1.66
140	3.91	3.06	2.67	2.44	2.28	2.16	2.08	2.01	1.95	1.90	1.86	1.82	1.79	1.76	1.74	1.72	1.70	1.68	1.66	1.65
160	3.90	3.05	2.66	2.43	2.27	2.16	2.07	2.00	1.94	1.89	1.85	1.81	1.78	1.75	1.73	1.71	1.69	1.67	1.65	1.64
180	3.89	3.05	2.65	2.42	2.26	2.15	2.06	1.99	1.93	1.88	1.84	1.81	1.77	1.75	1.72	1.70	1.68	1.66	1.64	1.63
200	3.89	3.04	2.65	2.42	2.26	2.14	2.06	1.98	1.93	1.88	1.84	1.80	1.77	1.74	1.72	1.69	1.67	1.66	1.64	1.62
∞	3.84	3.00	2.61	2.37	2.21	2.10	2.01	1.94	1.88	1.83	1.79	1.75	1.72	1.69	1.67	1.64	1.62	1.60	1.59	1.57

DENOMINATOR DEGREES OF FREEDOM

NUMERATOR DEGREES OF FREEDOM

ν_2 \ ν_1	22	24	26	28	30	35	40	45	50	60	70	80	90	100	120	140	160	180	200	∞
1	249	249	249	250	250	251	251	251	252	252	252	253	253	253	253	253	254	254	254	254
2	19.5	19.5	19.5	19.5	19.5	19.5	19.5	19.5	19.5	19.5	19.5	19.5	19.5	19.5	19.5	19.5	19.5	19.5	19.5	19.5
3	8.65	8.64	8.63	8.62	8.62	8.60	8.59	8.59	8.58	8.57	8.57	8.56	8.56	8.55	8.55	8.55	8.54	8.54	8.54	8.53
4	5.79	5.77	5.76	5.75	5.75	5.73	5.72	5.71	5.70	5.69	5.68	5.67	5.67	5.66	5.66	5.65	5.65	5.65	5.65	5.63
5	4.54	4.53	4.52	4.50	4.50	4.48	4.46	4.45	4.44	4.43	4.42	4.41	4.41	4.41	4.40	4.39	4.39	4.39	4.39	4.37
6	3.86	3.84	3.83	3.82	3.81	3.79	3.77	3.76	3.75	3.74	3.73	3.72	3.72	3.71	3.71	3.70	3.70	3.69	3.69	3.67
7	3.43	3.41	3.40	3.39	3.38	3.36	3.34	3.33	3.32	3.30	3.29	3.29	3.28	3.27	3.27	3.26	3.26	3.25	3.25	3.23
8	3.13	3.12	3.10	3.09	3.08	3.06	3.04	3.03	3.02	3.01	2.99	2.99	2.98	2.97	2.97	2.96	2.96	2.95	2.95	2.93
9	2.92	2.90	2.89	2.87	2.86	2.84	2.83	2.81	2.80	2.79	2.78	2.77	2.76	2.76	2.75	2.74	2.74	2.73	2.73	2.71
10	2.75	2.74	2.72	2.71	2.70	2.68	2.66	2.65	2.64	2.62	2.61	2.60	2.59	2.59	2.58	2.57	2.57	2.57	2.56	2.54
11	2.63	2.61	2.59	2.58	2.57	2.55	2.53	2.52	2.51	2.49	2.48	2.47	2.46	2.46	2.45	2.44	2.44	2.43	2.43	2.41
12	2.52	2.51	2.49	2.48	2.47	2.44	2.43	2.41	2.40	2.38	2.37	2.36	2.36	2.35	2.34	2.33	2.33	2.33	2.32	2.30
13	2.44	2.42	2.41	2.39	2.38	2.36	2.34	2.33	2.31	2.30	2.28	2.27	2.27	2.26	2.25	2.25	2.24	2.24	2.23	2.21
14	2.37	2.35	2.33	2.32	2.31	2.28	2.27	2.25	2.24	2.22	2.21	2.20	2.19	2.19	2.18	2.17	2.17	2.16	2.16	2.13
15	2.31	2.29	2.27	2.26	2.25	2.22	2.20	2.19	2.18	2.16	2.15	2.14	2.13	2.12	2.12	2.11	2.10	2.10	2.10	2.07
16	2.25	2.24	2.22	2.21	2.19	2.17	2.15	2.14	2.12	2.11	2.09	2.08	2.07	2.07	2.06	2.05	2.05	2.04	2.04	2.01
17	2.21	2.19	2.17	2.16	2.15	2.12	2.10	2.09	2.08	2.06	2.05	2.03	2.03	2.02	2.01	2.00	2.00	1.99	1.99	1.96
18	2.17	2.15	2.13	2.12	2.11	2.08	2.06	2.05	2.04	2.02	2.00	1.99	1.98	1.98	1.97	1.96	1.96	1.95	1.95	1.92
19	2.13	2.11	2.10	2.08	2.07	2.05	2.03	2.01	2.00	1.98	1.97	1.96	1.95	1.94	1.93	1.92	1.92	1.91	1.91	1.88
20	2.10	2.08	2.07	2.05	2.04	2.01	1.99	1.98	1.97	1.95	1.93	1.92	1.91	1.91	1.90	1.89	1.88	1.88	1.88	1.84
22	2.05	2.03	2.01	2.00	1.98	1.96	1.94	1.92	1.91	1.89	1.88	1.86	1.86	1.85	1.84	1.83	1.82	1.82	1.82	1.78
24	2.00	1.98	1.97	1.95	1.94	1.91	1.89	1.88	1.86	1.84	1.83	1.82	1.81	1.80	1.79	1.78	1.78	1.77	1.77	1.73
26	1.97	1.95	1.93	1.91	1.90	1.87	1.85	1.84	1.82	1.80	1.79	1.78	1.77	1.76	1.75	1.74	1.73	1.73	1.73	1.69
28	1.93	1.91	1.90	1.88	1.87	1.84	1.82	1.80	1.79	1.77	1.75	1.74	1.73	1.73	1.71	1.71	1.70	1.69	1.69	1.65
30	1.91	1.89	1.87	1.85	1.84	1.81	1.79	1.77	1.76	1.74	1.72	1.71	1.70	1.70	1.68	1.68	1.67	1.66	1.66	1.62
35	1.85	1.83	1.82	1.80	1.79	1.76	1.74	1.72	1.70	1.68	1.66	1.65	1.64	1.63	1.62	1.61	1.61	1.60	1.60	1.56
40	1.81	1.79	1.77	1.76	1.74	1.72	1.69	1.67	1.66	1.64	1.62	1.61	1.60	1.59	1.58	1.57	1.56	1.55	1.55	1.51
45	1.78	1.76	1.74	1.73	1.71	1.68	1.66	1.64	1.63	1.60	1.59	1.57	1.56	1.55	1.54	1.53	1.52	1.52	1.51	1.47
50	1.76	1.74	1.72	1.70	1.69	1.66	1.63	1.61	1.60	1.58	1.56	1.54	1.53	1.52	1.51	1.50	1.49	1.49	1.48	1.44
60	1.72	1.70	1.68	1.66	1.65	1.62	1.59	1.57	1.56	1.53	1.52	1.50	1.49	1.48	1.47	1.46	1.45	1.44	1.44	1.39
70	1.70	1.67	1.65	1.64	1.62	1.59	1.57	1.55	1.53	1.50	1.49	1.47	1.46	1.45	1.44	1.42	1.42	1.41	1.40	1.35
80	1.68	1.65	1.63	1.62	1.60	1.57	1.54	1.52	1.51	1.48	1.46	1.45	1.44	1.43	1.41	1.40	1.39	1.38	1.38	1.33
90	1.66	1.64	1.62	1.60	1.59	1.55	1.53	1.51	1.49	1.46	1.44	1.43	1.42	1.41	1.39	1.38	1.37	1.36	1.36	1.30
100	1.65	1.63	1.61	1.59	1.57	1.54	1.52	1.49	1.48	1.45	1.43	1.41	1.40	1.39	1.38	1.36	1.35	1.35	1.34	1.28
120	1.63	1.61	1.59	1.57	1.55	1.52	1.50	1.47	1.46	1.43	1.41	1.39	1.38	1.37	1.35	1.34	1.33	1.32	1.32	1.26
140	1.62	1.60	1.57	1.56	1.54	1.51	1.48	1.46	1.44	1.41	1.39	1.38	1.36	1.35	1.33	1.32	1.31	1.30	1.30	1.23
160	1.61	1.59	1.57	1.55	1.53	1.50	1.47	1.45	1.43	1.40	1.38	1.36	1.35	1.34	1.32	1.31	1.30	1.29	1.28	1.22
180	1.60	1.58	1.56	1.54	1.52	1.49	1.46	1.44	1.42	1.39	1.37	1.35	1.34	1.33	1.31	1.30	1.29	1.28	1.27	1.20
200	1.60	1.57	1.55	1.53	1.52	1.48	1.46	1.43	1.41	1.39	1.36	1.35	1.33	1.32	1.30	1.29	1.28	1.27	1.26	1.19
∞	1.54	1.52	1.50	1.48	1.46	1.42	1.40	1.37	1.35	1.32	1.29	1.28	1.26	1.25	1.22	1.21	1.19	1.18	1.17	1.00

DENOMINATOR DEGREES OF FREEDOM

TABLE **6(b)** Values of the F-Distribution: A = .025

ν_2 \ ν_1	1	2	3	4	5	6	7	8	9	10	11	12	13	14	15	16	17	18	19	20
1	648	799	864	900	922	937	948	957	963	969	973	977	980	983	985	987	989	990	992	993
2	38.5	39.0	39.2	39.2	39.3	39.3	39.4	39.4	39.4	39.4	39.4	39.4	39.4	39.4	39.4	39.4	39.4	39.4	39.4	39.4
3	17.4	16.0	15.4	15.1	14.9	14.7	14.6	14.5	14.5	14.4	14.4	14.3	14.3	14.3	14.3	14.2	14.2	14.2	14.2	14.2
4	12.2	10.6	10.0	9.60	9.36	9.20	9.07	8.98	8.90	8.84	8.79	8.75	8.71	8.68	8.66	8.63	8.61	8.59	8.58	8.56
5	10.0	8.43	7.76	7.39	7.15	6.98	6.85	6.76	6.68	6.62	6.57	6.52	6.49	6.46	6.43	6.40	6.38	6.36	6.34	6.33
6	8.81	7.26	6.60	6.23	5.99	5.82	5.70	5.60	5.52	5.46	5.41	5.37	5.33	5.30	5.27	5.24	5.22	5.20	5.18	5.17
7	8.07	6.54	5.89	5.52	5.29	5.12	4.99	4.90	4.82	4.76	4.71	4.67	4.63	4.60	4.57	4.54	4.52	4.50	4.48	4.47
8	7.57	6.06	5.42	5.05	4.82	4.65	4.53	4.43	4.36	4.30	4.24	4.20	4.16	4.13	4.10	4.08	4.05	4.03	4.02	4.00
9	7.21	5.71	5.08	4.72	4.48	4.32	4.20	4.10	4.03	3.96	3.91	3.87	3.83	3.80	3.77	3.74	3.72	3.70	3.68	3.67
10	6.94	5.46	4.83	4.47	4.24	4.07	3.95	3.85	3.78	3.72	3.66	3.62	3.58	3.55	3.52	3.50	3.47	3.45	3.44	3.42
11	6.72	5.26	4.63	4.28	4.04	3.88	3.76	3.66	3.59	3.53	3.47	3.43	3.39	3.36	3.33	3.30	3.28	3.26	3.24	3.23
12	6.55	5.10	4.47	4.12	3.89	3.73	3.61	3.51	3.44	3.37	3.32	3.28	3.24	3.21	3.18	3.15	3.13	3.11	3.09	3.07
13	6.41	4.97	4.35	4.00	3.77	3.60	3.48	3.39	3.31	3.25	3.20	3.15	3.12	3.08	3.05	3.03	3.00	2.98	2.96	2.95
14	6.30	4.86	4.24	3.89	3.66	3.50	3.38	3.29	3.21	3.15	3.09	3.05	3.01	2.98	2.95	2.92	2.90	2.88	2.86	2.84
15	6.20	4.77	4.15	3.80	3.58	3.41	3.29	3.20	3.12	3.06	3.01	2.96	2.92	2.89	2.86	2.84	2.81	2.79	2.77	2.76
16	6.12	4.69	4.08	3.73	3.50	3.34	3.22	3.12	3.05	2.99	2.93	2.89	2.85	2.82	2.79	2.76	2.74	2.72	2.70	2.68
17	6.04	4.62	4.01	3.66	3.44	3.28	3.16	3.06	2.98	2.92	2.87	2.82	2.79	2.75	2.72	2.70	2.67	2.65	2.63	2.62
18	5.98	4.56	3.95	3.61	3.38	3.22	3.10	3.01	2.93	2.87	2.81	2.77	2.73	2.70	2.67	2.64	2.62	2.60	2.58	2.56
19	5.92	4.51	3.90	3.56	3.33	3.17	3.05	2.96	2.88	2.82	2.76	2.72	2.68	2.65	2.62	2.59	2.57	2.55	2.53	2.51
20	5.87	4.46	3.86	3.51	3.29	3.13	3.01	2.91	2.84	2.77	2.72	2.68	2.64	2.60	2.57	2.55	2.52	2.50	2.48	2.46
22	5.79	4.38	3.78	3.44	3.22	3.05	2.93	2.84	2.76	2.70	2.65	2.60	2.56	2.53	2.50	2.47	2.45	2.43	2.41	2.39
24	5.72	4.32	3.72	3.38	3.15	2.99	2.87	2.78	2.70	2.64	2.59	2.54	2.50	2.47	2.44	2.41	2.39	2.36	2.35	2.33
26	5.66	4.27	3.67	3.33	3.10	2.94	2.82	2.73	2.65	2.59	2.54	2.49	2.45	2.42	2.39	2.36	2.34	2.31	2.29	2.28
28	5.61	4.22	3.63	3.29	3.06	2.90	2.78	2.69	2.61	2.55	2.49	2.45	2.41	2.37	2.34	2.32	2.29	2.27	2.25	2.23
30	5.57	4.18	3.59	3.25	3.03	2.87	2.75	2.65	2.57	2.51	2.46	2.41	2.37	2.34	2.31	2.28	2.26	2.23	2.21	2.20
35	5.48	4.11	3.52	3.18	2.96	2.80	2.68	2.58	2.50	2.44	2.39	2.34	2.30	2.27	2.23	2.21	2.18	2.16	2.14	2.12
40	5.42	4.05	3.46	3.13	2.90	2.74	2.62	2.53	2.45	2.39	2.33	2.29	2.25	2.21	2.18	2.15	2.13	2.11	2.09	2.07
45	5.38	4.01	3.42	3.09	2.86	2.70	2.58	2.49	2.41	2.35	2.29	2.25	2.21	2.17	2.14	2.11	2.09	2.07	2.04	2.03
50	5.34	3.97	3.39	3.05	2.83	2.67	2.55	2.46	2.38	2.32	2.26	2.22	2.18	2.14	2.11	2.08	2.06	2.03	2.01	1.99
60	5.29	3.93	3.34	3.01	2.79	2.63	2.51	2.41	2.33	2.27	2.22	2.17	2.13	2.09	2.06	2.03	2.01	1.98	1.96	1.94
70	5.25	3.89	3.31	2.97	2.75	2.59	2.47	2.38	2.30	2.24	2.18	2.14	2.10	2.06	2.03	2.00	1.97	1.95	1.93	1.91
80	5.22	3.86	3.28	2.95	2.73	2.57	2.45	2.35	2.28	2.21	2.16	2.11	2.07	2.03	2.00	1.97	1.95	1.92	1.90	1.88
90	5.20	3.84	3.26	2.93	2.71	2.55	2.43	2.34	2.26	2.19	2.14	2.09	2.05	2.02	1.98	1.95	1.93	1.91	1.88	1.86
100	5.18	3.83	3.25	2.92	2.70	2.54	2.42	2.32	2.24	2.18	2.12	2.08	2.04	2.00	1.97	1.94	1.91	1.89	1.87	1.85
120	5.15	3.80	3.23	2.89	2.67	2.52	2.39	2.30	2.22	2.16	2.10	2.05	2.01	1.98	1.94	1.92	1.89	1.87	1.84	1.82
140	5.13	3.79	3.21	2.88	2.66	2.50	2.38	2.28	2.21	2.14	2.09	2.04	2.00	1.96	1.93	1.90	1.87	1.85	1.83	1.81
160	5.12	3.78	3.20	2.87	2.65	2.49	2.37	2.27	2.19	2.13	2.07	2.03	1.99	1.95	1.92	1.89	1.86	1.84	1.82	1.80
180	5.11	3.77	3.19	2.86	2.64	2.48	2.36	2.26	2.19	2.12	2.07	2.02	1.98	1.94	1.91	1.88	1.85	1.83	1.81	1.79
200	5.10	3.76	3.18	2.85	2.63	2.47	2.35	2.26	2.18	2.11	2.06	2.01	1.97	1.93	1.90	1.87	1.84	1.82	1.80	1.78
∞	5.03	3.69	3.12	2.79	2.57	2.41	2.29	2.19	2.11	2.05	1.99	1.95	1.90	1.87	1.83	1.80	1.78	1.75	1.73	1.71

NUMERATOR DEGREES OF FREEDOM

DENOMINATOR DEGREES OF FREEDOM

NUMERATOR DEGREES OF FREEDOM

ν_2 \ ν_1	22	24	26	28	30	35	40	45	50	60	70	80	90	100	120	140	160	180	200	∞
1	995	997	999	1000	1001	1004	1006	1007	1008	1010	1011	1012	1013	1013	1014	1015	1015	1015	1016	1018
2	39.5	39.5	39.5	39.5	39.5	39.5	39.5	39.5	39.5	39.5	39.5	39.5	39.5	39.5	39.5	39.5	39.5	39.5	39.5	39.5
3	14.1	14.1	14.1	14.1	14.1	14.1	14.0	14.0	14.0	14.0	14.0	14.0	14.0	14.0	13.9	13.9	13.9	13.9	13.9	13.9
4	8.53	8.51	8.49	8.48	8.46	8.43	8.41	8.39	8.38	8.36	8.35	8.33	8.33	8.32	8.31	8.30	8.30	8.29	8.29	8.26
5	6.30	6.28	6.26	6.24	6.23	6.20	6.18	6.16	6.14	6.12	6.11	6.10	6.09	6.08	6.07	6.06	6.06	6.05	6.05	6.02
6	5.14	5.12	5.10	5.08	5.07	5.04	5.01	4.99	4.98	4.96	4.94	4.93	4.92	4.92	4.90	4.90	4.89	4.89	4.88	4.85
7	4.44	4.41	4.39	4.38	4.36	4.33	4.31	4.29	4.28	4.25	4.24	4.23	4.22	4.21	4.20	4.19	4.18	4.18	4.18	4.14
8	3.97	3.95	3.93	3.91	3.89	3.86	3.84	3.82	3.81	3.78	3.77	3.76	3.75	3.74	3.73	3.72	3.71	3.71	3.70	3.67
9	3.64	3.61	3.59	3.58	3.56	3.53	3.51	3.49	3.47	3.45	3.43	3.42	3.41	3.40	3.39	3.38	3.38	3.37	3.37	3.33
10	3.39	3.37	3.34	3.33	3.31	3.28	3.26	3.24	3.22	3.20	3.18	3.17	3.16	3.15	3.14	3.13	3.13	3.12	3.12	3.08
11	3.20	3.17	3.15	3.13	3.12	3.09	3.06	3.04	3.03	3.00	2.99	2.97	2.96	2.96	2.94	2.94	2.93	2.92	2.92	2.88
12	3.04	3.02	3.00	2.98	2.96	2.93	2.91	2.89	2.87	2.85	2.83	2.82	2.81	2.80	2.79	2.78	2.77	2.77	2.76	2.73
13	2.92	2.89	2.87	2.85	2.84	2.80	2.78	2.76	2.74	2.72	2.70	2.69	2.68	2.67	2.66	2.65	2.64	2.64	2.63	2.60
14	2.81	2.79	2.77	2.75	2.73	2.70	2.67	2.65	2.64	2.61	2.60	2.58	2.57	2.56	2.55	2.54	2.54	2.53	2.53	2.49
15	2.73	2.70	2.68	2.66	2.64	2.61	2.59	2.56	2.55	2.52	2.51	2.49	2.48	2.47	2.46	2.45	2.44	2.44	2.44	2.40
16	2.65	2.63	2.60	2.58	2.57	2.53	2.51	2.49	2.47	2.45	2.43	2.42	2.40	2.40	2.38	2.37	2.37	2.36	2.36	2.32
17	2.59	2.56	2.54	2.52	2.50	2.47	2.44	2.42	2.41	2.38	2.36	2.35	2.34	2.33	2.32	2.31	2.30	2.29	2.29	2.25
18	2.53	2.50	2.48	2.46	2.44	2.41	2.38	2.36	2.35	2.32	2.30	2.29	2.28	2.27	2.26	2.25	2.24	2.23	2.23	2.19
19	2.48	2.45	2.43	2.41	2.39	2.36	2.33	2.31	2.30	2.27	2.25	2.24	2.23	2.22	2.20	2.19	2.19	2.18	2.18	2.13
20	2.43	2.41	2.39	2.37	2.35	2.31	2.29	2.27	2.25	2.22	2.20	2.19	2.18	2.17	2.16	2.15	2.14	2.13	2.13	2.09
22	2.36	2.33	2.31	2.29	2.27	2.24	2.21	2.19	2.17	2.14	2.13	2.11	2.10	2.09	2.08	2.07	2.06	2.05	2.05	2.00
24	2.30	2.27	2.25	2.23	2.21	2.17	2.15	2.12	2.11	2.08	2.06	2.05	2.03	2.02	2.01	2.00	1.99	1.99	1.98	1.94
26	2.24	2.22	2.19	2.17	2.16	2.12	2.09	2.07	2.05	2.03	2.01	1.99	1.98	1.97	1.95	1.94	1.94	1.93	1.92	1.88
28	2.20	2.17	2.15	2.13	2.11	2.08	2.05	2.03	2.01	1.98	1.96	1.94	1.93	1.92	1.91	1.90	1.89	1.88	1.88	1.83
30	2.16	2.14	2.11	2.09	2.07	2.04	2.01	1.99	1.97	1.94	1.92	1.90	1.89	1.88	1.87	1.86	1.85	1.84	1.84	1.79
35	2.09	2.06	2.04	2.02	2.00	1.96	1.93	1.91	1.89	1.86	1.84	1.82	1.81	1.80	1.79	1.77	1.77	1.76	1.76	1.70
40	2.03	2.01	1.98	1.96	1.94	1.90	1.88	1.85	1.83	1.80	1.78	1.76	1.75	1.74	1.72	1.71	1.70	1.70	1.69	1.64
45	1.99	1.96	1.94	1.92	1.90	1.86	1.83	1.81	1.79	1.76	1.74	1.72	1.70	1.69	1.68	1.66	1.66	1.65	1.64	1.59
50	1.96	1.93	1.91	1.89	1.87	1.83	1.80	1.77	1.75	1.72	1.70	1.68	1.67	1.66	1.64	1.63	1.62	1.61	1.60	1.55
60	1.91	1.88	1.86	1.83	1.82	1.78	1.74	1.72	1.70	1.67	1.64	1.63	1.61	1.60	1.58	1.57	1.56	1.55	1.54	1.48
70	1.88	1.85	1.82	1.80	1.78	1.74	1.71	1.68	1.66	1.63	1.60	1.59	1.57	1.56	1.54	1.53	1.52	1.51	1.50	1.44
80	1.85	1.82	1.79	1.77	1.75	1.71	1.68	1.65	1.63	1.60	1.57	1.55	1.54	1.53	1.51	1.49	1.48	1.47	1.47	1.40
90	1.83	1.80	1.77	1.75	1.73	1.69	1.66	1.63	1.61	1.58	1.55	1.53	1.52	1.50	1.48	1.47	1.46	1.45	1.44	1.37
100	1.81	1.78	1.76	1.74	1.71	1.67	1.64	1.61	1.59	1.56	1.53	1.51	1.50	1.48	1.46	1.45	1.44	1.43	1.42	1.35
120	1.79	1.76	1.73	1.71	1.69	1.65	1.61	1.59	1.56	1.53	1.50	1.48	1.47	1.45	1.43	1.42	1.41	1.40	1.39	1.31
140	1.77	1.74	1.72	1.69	1.67	1.63	1.60	1.57	1.55	1.51	1.48	1.46	1.45	1.43	1.41	1.39	1.38	1.37	1.36	1.28
160	1.76	1.73	1.70	1.68	1.66	1.62	1.58	1.55	1.53	1.50	1.47	1.45	1.43	1.42	1.39	1.38	1.36	1.35	1.35	1.26
180	1.75	1.72	1.69	1.67	1.65	1.61	1.57	1.54	1.52	1.48	1.46	1.43	1.42	1.40	1.38	1.36	1.35	1.34	1.33	1.25
200	1.74	1.71	1.68	1.66	1.64	1.60	1.56	1.53	1.51	1.47	1.45	1.42	1.41	1.39	1.37	1.35	1.34	1.33	1.32	1.23
∞	1.67	1.64	1.61	1.59	1.57	1.52	1.49	1.46	1.43	1.39	1.36	1.33	1.31	1.30	1.27	1.25	1.23	1.22	1.21	1.00

DENOMINATOR DEGREES OF FREEDOM

TABLE **6(c)** Values of the *F*-Distribution: *A* = .01

ν_2 \ ν_1	1	2	3	4	5	6	7	8	9	10	11	12	13	14	15	16	17	18	19	20
1	4052	4999	5403	5625	5764	5859	5928	5981	6022	6056	6083	6106	6126	6143	6157	6170	6181	6192	6201	6209
2	98.5	99.0	99.2	99.2	99.3	99.3	99.4	99.4	99.4	99.4	99.4	99.4	99.4	99.4	99.4	99.4	99.4	99.4	99.4	99.4
3	34.1	30.8	29.5	28.7	28.2	27.9	27.7	27.5	27.3	27.2	27.1	27.1	27.0	26.9	26.9	26.8	26.8	26.8	26.7	26.7
4	21.2	18.0	16.7	16.0	15.5	15.2	15.0	14.8	14.7	14.5	14.5	14.4	14.3	14.2	14.2	14.2	14.1	14.1	14.0	14.0
5	16.3	13.3	12.1	11.4	11.0	10.7	10.5	10.3	10.2	10.1	9.96	9.89	9.82	9.77	9.72	9.68	9.64	9.61	9.58	9.55
6	13.7	10.9	9.78	9.15	8.75	8.47	8.26	8.10	7.98	7.87	7.79	7.72	7.66	7.60	7.56	7.52	7.48	7.45	7.42	7.40
7	12.2	9.55	8.45	7.85	7.46	7.19	6.99	6.84	6.72	6.62	6.54	6.47	6.41	6.36	6.31	6.28	6.24	6.21	6.18	6.16
8	11.3	8.65	7.59	7.01	6.63	6.37	6.18	6.03	5.91	5.81	5.73	5.67	5.61	5.56	5.52	5.48	5.44	5.41	5.38	5.36
9	10.6	8.02	6.99	6.42	6.06	5.80	5.61	5.47	5.35	5.26	5.18	5.11	5.05	5.01	4.96	4.92	4.89	4.86	4.83	4.81
10	10.0	7.56	6.55	5.99	5.64	5.39	5.20	5.06	4.94	4.85	4.77	4.71	4.65	4.60	4.56	4.52	4.49	4.46	4.43	4.41
11	9.65	7.21	6.22	5.67	5.32	5.07	4.89	4.74	4.63	4.54	4.46	4.40	4.34	4.29	4.25	4.21	4.18	4.15	4.12	4.10
12	9.33	6.93	5.95	5.41	5.06	4.82	4.64	4.50	4.39	4.30	4.22	4.16	4.10	4.05	4.01	3.97	3.94	3.91	3.88	3.86
13	9.07	6.70	5.74	5.21	4.86	4.62	4.44	4.30	4.19	4.10	4.02	3.96	3.91	3.86	3.82	3.78	3.75	3.72	3.69	3.66
14	8.86	6.51	5.56	5.04	4.69	4.46	4.28	4.14	4.03	3.94	3.86	3.80	3.75	3.70	3.66	3.62	3.59	3.56	3.53	3.51
15	8.68	6.36	5.42	4.89	4.56	4.32	4.14	4.00	3.89	3.80	3.73	3.67	3.61	3.56	3.52	3.49	3.45	3.42	3.40	3.37
16	8.53	6.23	5.29	4.77	4.44	4.20	4.03	3.89	3.78	3.69	3.62	3.55	3.50	3.45	3.41	3.37	3.34	3.31	3.28	3.26
17	8.40	6.11	5.18	4.67	4.34	4.10	3.93	3.79	3.68	3.59	3.52	3.46	3.40	3.35	3.31	3.27	3.24	3.21	3.19	3.16
18	8.29	6.01	5.09	4.58	4.25	4.01	3.84	3.71	3.60	3.51	3.43	3.37	3.32	3.27	3.23	3.19	3.16	3.13	3.10	3.08
19	8.18	5.93	5.01	4.50	4.17	3.94	3.77	3.63	3.52	3.43	3.36	3.30	3.24	3.19	3.15	3.12	3.08	3.05	3.03	3.00
20	8.10	5.85	4.94	4.43	4.10	3.87	3.70	3.56	3.46	3.37	3.29	3.23	3.18	3.13	3.09	3.05	3.02	2.99	2.96	2.94
22	7.95	5.72	4.82	4.31	3.99	3.76	3.59	3.45	3.35	3.26	3.18	3.12	3.07	3.02	2.98	2.94	2.91	2.88	2.85	2.83
24	7.82	5.61	4.72	4.22	3.90	3.67	3.50	3.36	3.26	3.17	3.09	3.03	2.98	2.93	2.89	2.85	2.82	2.79	2.76	2.74
26	7.72	5.53	4.64	4.14	3.82	3.59	3.42	3.29	3.18	3.09	3.02	2.96	2.90	2.86	2.81	2.78	2.75	2.72	2.69	2.66
28	7.64	5.45	4.57	4.07	3.75	3.53	3.36	3.23	3.12	3.03	2.96	2.90	2.84	2.79	2.75	2.72	2.68	2.65	2.63	2.60
30	7.56	5.39	4.51	4.02	3.70	3.47	3.30	3.17	3.07	2.98	2.91	2.84	2.79	2.74	2.70	2.66	2.63	2.60	2.57	2.55
35	7.42	5.27	4.40	3.91	3.59	3.37	3.20	3.07	2.96	2.88	2.80	2.74	2.69	2.64	2.60	2.56	2.53	2.50	2.47	2.44
40	7.31	5.18	4.31	3.83	3.51	3.29	3.12	2.99	2.89	2.80	2.73	2.66	2.61	2.56	2.52	2.48	2.45	2.42	2.39	2.37
45	7.23	5.11	4.25	3.77	3.45	3.23	3.07	2.94	2.83	2.74	2.67	2.61	2.55	2.51	2.46	2.43	2.39	2.36	2.34	2.31
50	7.17	5.06	4.20	3.72	3.41	3.19	3.02	2.89	2.78	2.70	2.63	2.56	2.51	2.46	2.42	2.38	2.35	2.32	2.29	2.27
60	7.08	4.98	4.13	3.65	3.34	3.12	2.95	2.82	2.72	2.63	2.56	2.50	2.44	2.39	2.35	2.31	2.28	2.25	2.22	2.20
70	7.01	4.92	4.07	3.60	3.29	3.07	2.91	2.78	2.67	2.59	2.51	2.45	2.40	2.35	2.31	2.27	2.23	2.20	2.18	2.15
80	6.96	4.88	4.04	3.56	3.26	3.04	2.87	2.74	2.64	2.55	2.48	2.42	2.36	2.31	2.27	2.23	2.20	2.17	2.14	2.12
90	6.93	4.85	4.01	3.53	3.23	3.01	2.84	2.72	2.61	2.52	2.45	2.39	2.33	2.29	2.24	2.21	2.17	2.14	2.11	2.09
100	6.90	4.82	3.98	3.51	3.21	2.99	2.82	2.69	2.59	2.50	2.43	2.37	2.31	2.27	2.22	2.19	2.15	2.12	2.09	2.07
120	6.85	4.79	3.95	3.48	3.17	2.96	2.79	2.66	2.56	2.47	2.40	2.34	2.28	2.23	2.19	2.15	2.12	2.09	2.06	2.03
140	6.82	4.76	3.92	3.46	3.15	2.93	2.77	2.64	2.54	2.45	2.38	2.31	2.26	2.21	2.17	2.13	2.10	2.07	2.04	2.01
160	6.80	4.74	3.91	3.44	3.13	2.92	2.75	2.62	2.52	2.43	2.36	2.30	2.24	2.20	2.15	2.11	2.08	2.05	2.02	1.99
180	6.78	4.73	3.89	3.43	3.12	2.90	2.74	2.61	2.51	2.42	2.35	2.28	2.23	2.18	2.14	2.10	2.07	2.04	2.01	1.98
200	6.76	4.71	3.88	3.41	3.11	2.89	2.73	2.60	2.50	2.41	2.34	2.27	2.22	2.17	2.13	2.09	2.06	2.03	2.00	1.97
∞	6.64	4.61	3.78	3.32	3.02	2.80	2.64	2.51	2.41	2.32	2.25	2.19	2.13	2.08	2.04	2.00	1.97	1.94	1.91	1.88

NUMERATOR DEGREES OF FREEDOM

DENOMINATOR DEGREES OF FREEDOM

NUMERATOR DEGREES OF FREEDOM

ν_1 → / ν_2 ↓	22	24	26	28	30	35	40	45	50	60	70	80	90	100	120	140	160	180	200	∞
1	6223	6235	6245	6253	6261	6276	6287	6296	6303	6313	6321	6326	6331	6334	6339	6343	6346	6348	6350	6366
2	99.5	99.5	99.5	99.5	99.5	99.5	99.5	99.5	99.5	99.5	99.5	99.5	99.5	99.5	99.5	99.5	99.5	99.5	99.5	99.5
3	26.6	26.6	26.6	26.5	26.5	26.5	26.4	26.4	26.4	26.3	26.3	26.3	26.3	26.2	26.2	26.2	26.2	26.2	26.2	26.1
4	14.0	13.9	13.9	13.9	13.8	13.8	13.7	13.7	13.7	13.7	13.6	13.6	13.6	13.6	13.6	13.5	13.5	13.5	13.5	13.5
5	9.51	9.47	9.43	9.40	9.38	9.33	9.29	9.26	9.24	9.20	9.18	9.16	9.14	9.13	9.11	9.10	9.09	9.08	9.08	9.02
6	7.35	7.31	7.28	7.25	7.23	7.18	7.14	7.11	7.09	7.06	7.03	7.01	7.00	6.99	6.97	6.96	6.95	6.94	6.93	6.88
7	6.11	6.07	6.04	6.02	5.99	5.94	5.91	5.88	5.86	5.82	5.80	5.78	5.77	5.75	5.74	5.72	5.72	5.71	5.70	5.65
8	5.32	5.28	5.25	5.22	5.20	5.15	5.12	5.09	5.07	5.03	5.01	4.99	4.97	4.96	4.95	4.93	4.92	4.92	4.91	4.86
9	4.77	4.73	4.70	4.67	4.65	4.60	4.57	4.54	4.52	4.48	4.46	4.44	4.43	4.41	4.40	4.39	4.38	4.37	4.36	4.31
10	4.36	4.33	4.30	4.27	4.25	4.20	4.17	4.14	4.12	4.08	4.06	4.04	4.03	4.01	4.00	3.98	3.97	3.97	3.96	3.91
11	4.06	4.02	3.99	3.96	3.94	3.89	3.86	3.83	3.81	3.78	3.75	3.73	3.72	3.71	3.69	3.68	3.67	3.66	3.66	3.60
12	3.82	3.78	3.75	3.72	3.70	3.65	3.62	3.59	3.57	3.54	3.51	3.49	3.48	3.47	3.45	3.44	3.43	3.42	3.41	3.36
13	3.62	3.59	3.56	3.53	3.51	3.46	3.43	3.40	3.38	3.34	3.32	3.30	3.28	3.27	3.25	3.24	3.23	3.23	3.22	3.17
14	3.46	3.43	3.40	3.37	3.35	3.30	3.27	3.24	3.22	3.18	3.16	3.14	3.12	3.11	3.09	3.08	3.07	3.06	3.06	3.01
15	3.33	3.29	3.26	3.24	3.21	3.17	3.13	3.10	3.08	3.05	3.02	3.00	2.99	2.98	2.96	2.95	2.94	2.93	2.92	2.87
16	3.22	3.18	3.15	3.12	3.10	3.05	3.02	2.99	2.97	2.93	2.91	2.89	2.87	2.86	2.84	2.83	2.82	2.81	2.81	2.75
17	3.12	3.08	3.05	3.03	3.00	2.96	2.92	2.89	2.87	2.83	2.81	2.79	2.78	2.76	2.75	2.73	2.72	2.72	2.71	2.65
18	3.03	3.00	2.97	2.94	2.92	2.87	2.84	2.81	2.78	2.75	2.72	2.70	2.69	2.68	2.66	2.65	2.64	2.63	2.62	2.57
19	2.96	2.92	2.89	2.87	2.84	2.80	2.76	2.73	2.71	2.67	2.65	2.63	2.61	2.60	2.58	2.57	2.56	2.55	2.55	2.49
20	2.90	2.86	2.83	2.80	2.78	2.73	2.69	2.67	2.64	2.61	2.58	2.56	2.55	2.54	2.52	2.50	2.49	2.49	2.48	2.42
22	2.78	2.75	2.72	2.69	2.67	2.62	2.58	2.55	2.53	2.50	2.47	2.45	2.43	2.42	2.40	2.39	2.38	2.37	2.36	2.31
24	2.70	2.66	2.63	2.60	2.58	2.53	2.49	2.46	2.44	2.40	2.38	2.36	2.34	2.33	2.31	2.30	2.29	2.28	2.27	2.21
26	2.62	2.58	2.55	2.53	2.50	2.45	2.42	2.39	2.36	2.33	2.30	2.28	2.26	2.25	2.23	2.22	2.21	2.20	2.19	2.13
28	2.56	2.52	2.49	2.46	2.44	2.39	2.35	2.32	2.30	2.26	2.24	2.22	2.20	2.19	2.17	2.15	2.14	2.13	2.13	2.07
30	2.51	2.47	2.44	2.41	2.39	2.34	2.30	2.27	2.25	2.21	2.18	2.16	2.14	2.13	2.11	2.10	2.09	2.08	2.07	2.01
35	2.40	2.36	2.33	2.30	2.28	2.23	2.19	2.16	2.14	2.10	2.07	2.05	2.03	2.02	2.00	1.98	1.97	1.96	1.96	1.89
40	2.33	2.29	2.26	2.23	2.20	2.15	2.11	2.08	2.06	2.02	1.99	1.97	1.95	1.94	1.92	1.90	1.89	1.88	1.87	1.81
45	2.27	2.23	2.20	2.17	2.14	2.09	2.05	2.02	2.00	1.96	1.93	1.91	1.89	1.88	1.85	1.84	1.83	1.82	1.81	1.74
50	2.22	2.18	2.15	2.12	2.10	2.05	2.01	1.97	1.95	1.91	1.88	1.86	1.84	1.82	1.80	1.79	1.77	1.76	1.76	1.68
60	2.15	2.12	2.08	2.05	2.03	1.98	1.94	1.90	1.88	1.84	1.81	1.78	1.76	1.75	1.73	1.71	1.70	1.69	1.68	1.60
70	2.11	2.07	2.03	2.01	1.98	1.93	1.89	1.85	1.83	1.78	1.75	1.73	1.71	1.70	1.67	1.65	1.64	1.63	1.62	1.54
80	2.07	2.03	2.00	1.97	1.94	1.89	1.85	1.82	1.79	1.75	1.71	1.69	1.67	1.65	1.63	1.61	1.60	1.59	1.58	1.50
90	2.04	2.00	1.97	1.94	1.92	1.86	1.82	1.79	1.76	1.72	1.68	1.66	1.64	1.62	1.60	1.58	1.57	1.55	1.55	1.46
100	2.02	1.98	1.95	1.92	1.89	1.84	1.80	1.76	1.74	1.69	1.66	1.63	1.61	1.60	1.57	1.55	1.54	1.53	1.52	1.43
120	1.99	1.95	1.92	1.89	1.86	1.81	1.76	1.73	1.70	1.66	1.62	1.60	1.58	1.56	1.53	1.51	1.50	1.49	1.48	1.38
140	1.97	1.93	1.89	1.86	1.84	1.78	1.74	1.70	1.67	1.63	1.60	1.57	1.55	1.53	1.50	1.48	1.47	1.46	1.45	1.35
160	1.95	1.91	1.88	1.85	1.82	1.76	1.72	1.68	1.66	1.61	1.58	1.55	1.53	1.51	1.48	1.46	1.45	1.43	1.42	1.32
180	1.94	1.90	1.86	1.83	1.81	1.75	1.71	1.67	1.64	1.60	1.56	1.53	1.51	1.49	1.47	1.45	1.43	1.42	1.41	1.30
200	1.93	1.89	1.85	1.82	1.79	1.74	1.69	1.66	1.63	1.58	1.55	1.52	1.50	1.48	1.45	1.43	1.42	1.40	1.39	1.28
∞	1.83	1.79	1.76	1.73	1.70	1.64	1.59	1.56	1.53	1.48	1.44	1.41	1.38	1.36	1.33	1.30	1.28	1.26	1.25	1.00

DENOMINATOR DEGREES OF FREEDOM

TABLE **6(d)** Values of the *F*-Distribution: *A* = .005

ν_1	1	2	3	4	5	6	7	8	9	10	11	12	13	14	15	16	17	18	19	20
ν_2										NUMERATOR DEGREES OF FREEDOM									
1	16211	19999	21615	22500	23056	23437	23715	23925	24091	24224	24334	24426	24505	24572	24630	24681	24727	24767	24803	24836
2	199	199	199	199	199	199	199	199	199	199	199	199	199	199	199	199	199	199	199	199
3	55.6	49.8	47.5	46.2	45.4	44.8	44.4	44.1	43.9	43.7	43.5	43.4	43.3	43.2	43.1	43.0	42.9	42.9	42.8	42.8
4	31.3	26.3	24.3	23.2	22.5	22.0	21.6	21.4	21.1	21.0	20.8	20.7	20.6	20.5	20.4	20.4	20.3	20.3	20.2	20.2
5	22.8	18.3	16.5	15.6	14.9	14.5	14.2	14.0	13.8	13.6	13.5	13.4	13.3	13.2	13.1	13.1	13.0	13.0	12.9	12.9
6	18.6	14.5	12.9	12.0	11.5	11.1	10.8	10.6	10.4	10.3	10.1	10.0	9.95	9.88	9.81	9.76	9.71	9.66	9.62	9.59
7	16.2	12.4	10.9	10.1	9.52	9.16	8.89	8.68	8.51	8.38	8.27	8.18	8.10	8.03	7.97	7.91	7.87	7.83	7.79	7.75
8	14.7	11.0	9.60	8.81	8.30	7.95	7.69	7.50	7.34	7.21	7.10	7.01	6.94	6.87	6.81	6.76	6.72	6.68	6.64	6.61
9	13.6	10.1	8.72	7.96	7.47	7.13	6.88	6.69	6.54	6.42	6.31	6.23	6.15	6.09	6.03	5.98	5.94	5.90	5.86	5.83
10	12.8	9.43	8.08	7.34	6.87	6.54	6.30	6.12	5.97	5.85	5.75	5.66	5.59	5.53	5.47	5.42	5.38	5.34	5.31	5.27
11	12.2	8.91	7.60	6.88	6.42	6.10	5.86	5.68	5.54	5.42	5.32	5.24	5.16	5.10	5.05	5.00	4.96	4.92	4.89	4.86
12	11.8	8.51	7.23	6.52	6.07	5.76	5.52	5.35	5.20	5.09	4.99	4.91	4.84	4.77	4.72	4.67	4.63	4.59	4.56	4.53
13	11.4	8.19	6.93	6.23	5.79	5.48	5.25	5.08	4.94	4.82	4.72	4.64	4.57	4.51	4.46	4.41	4.37	4.33	4.30	4.27
14	11.1	7.92	6.68	6.00	5.56	5.26	5.03	4.86	4.72	4.60	4.51	4.43	4.36	4.30	4.25	4.20	4.16	4.12	4.09	4.06
15	10.8	7.70	6.48	5.80	5.37	5.07	4.85	4.67	4.54	4.42	4.33	4.25	4.18	4.12	4.07	4.02	3.98	3.95	3.91	3.88
16	10.6	7.51	6.30	5.64	5.21	4.91	4.69	4.52	4.38	4.27	4.18	4.10	4.03	3.97	3.92	3.87	3.83	3.80	3.76	3.73
17	10.4	7.35	6.16	5.50	5.07	4.78	4.56	4.39	4.25	4.14	4.05	3.97	3.90	3.84	3.79	3.75	3.71	3.67	3.64	3.61
18	10.2	7.21	6.03	5.37	4.96	4.66	4.44	4.28	4.14	4.03	3.94	3.86	3.79	3.73	3.68	3.64	3.60	3.56	3.53	3.50
19	10.1	7.09	5.92	5.27	4.85	4.56	4.34	4.18	4.04	3.93	3.84	3.76	3.70	3.64	3.59	3.54	3.50	3.46	3.43	3.40
20	9.94	6.99	5.82	5.17	4.76	4.47	4.26	4.09	3.96	3.85	3.76	3.68	3.61	3.55	3.50	3.46	3.42	3.38	3.35	3.32
22	9.73	6.81	5.65	5.02	4.61	4.32	4.11	3.94	3.81	3.70	3.61	3.54	3.47	3.41	3.36	3.31	3.27	3.24	3.21	3.18
24	9.55	6.66	5.52	4.89	4.49	4.20	3.99	3.83	3.69	3.59	3.50	3.42	3.35	3.30	3.25	3.20	3.16	3.12	3.09	3.06
26	9.41	6.54	5.41	4.79	4.38	4.10	3.89	3.73	3.60	3.49	3.40	3.33	3.26	3.20	3.15	3.11	3.07	3.03	3.00	2.97
28	9.28	6.44	5.32	4.70	4.30	4.02	3.81	3.65	3.52	3.41	3.32	3.25	3.18	3.12	3.07	3.03	2.99	2.95	2.92	2.89
30	9.18	6.35	5.24	4.62	4.23	3.95	3.74	3.58	3.45	3.34	3.25	3.18	3.11	3.06	3.01	2.96	2.92	2.89	2.85	2.82
35	8.98	6.19	5.09	4.48	4.09	3.81	3.61	3.45	3.32	3.21	3.12	3.05	2.98	2.93	2.88	2.83	2.79	2.76	2.72	2.69
40	8.83	6.07	4.98	4.37	3.99	3.71	3.51	3.35	3.22	3.12	3.03	2.95	2.89	2.83	2.78	2.74	2.70	2.66	2.63	2.60
45	8.71	5.97	4.89	4.29	3.91	3.64	3.43	3.28	3.15	3.04	2.96	2.88	2.82	2.76	2.71	2.66	2.62	2.59	2.56	2.53
50	8.63	5.90	4.83	4.23	3.85	3.58	3.38	3.22	3.09	2.99	2.90	2.82	2.76	2.70	2.65	2.61	2.57	2.53	2.50	2.47
60	8.49	5.79	4.73	4.14	3.76	3.49	3.29	3.13	3.01	2.90	2.82	2.74	2.68	2.62	2.57	2.53	2.49	2.45	2.42	2.39
70	8.40	5.72	4.66	4.08	3.70	3.43	3.23	3.08	2.95	2.85	2.76	2.68	2.62	2.56	2.51	2.47	2.43	2.39	2.36	2.33
80	8.33	5.67	4.61	4.03	3.65	3.39	3.19	3.03	2.91	2.80	2.72	2.64	2.58	2.52	2.47	2.43	2.39	2.35	2.32	2.29
90	8.28	5.62	4.57	3.99	3.62	3.35	3.15	3.00	2.87	2.77	2.68	2.61	2.54	2.49	2.44	2.39	2.35	2.32	2.28	2.25
100	8.24	5.59	4.54	3.96	3.59	3.33	3.13	2.97	2.85	2.74	2.66	2.58	2.52	2.46	2.41	2.37	2.33	2.29	2.26	2.23
120	8.18	5.54	4.50	3.92	3.55	3.28	3.09	2.93	2.81	2.71	2.62	2.54	2.48	2.42	2.37	2.33	2.29	2.25	2.22	2.19
140	8.14	5.50	4.47	3.89	3.52	3.26	3.06	2.91	2.78	2.68	2.59	2.52	2.45	2.40	2.35	2.30	2.26	2.22	2.19	2.16
160	8.10	5.48	4.44	3.87	3.50	3.24	3.04	2.88	2.76	2.66	2.57	2.50	2.43	2.38	2.33	2.28	2.24	2.20	2.17	2.14
180	8.08	5.46	4.42	3.85	3.48	3.22	3.02	2.87	2.74	2.64	2.56	2.48	2.42	2.36	2.31	2.26	2.22	2.19	2.15	2.12
200	8.06	5.44	4.41	3.84	3.47	3.21	3.01	2.86	2.73	2.63	2.54	2.47	2.40	2.35	2.30	2.25	2.21	2.18	2.14	2.11
∞	7.88	5.30	4.28	3.72	3.35	3.09	2.90	2.75	2.62	2.52	2.43	2.36	2.30	2.24	2.19	2.14	2.10	2.07	2.03	2.00

DENOMINATOR DEGREES OF FREEDOM

NUMERATOR DEGREES OF FREEDOM

ν_1 \ ν_2	22	24	26	28	30	35	40	45	50	60	70	80	90	100	120	140	160	180	200	∞
1	24892	24940	24980	25014	25044	25103	25148	25183	25211	25253	25283	25306	25323	25337	25359	25374	25385	25394	25401	25464
2	199	199	199	199	199	199	199	199	199	199	199	199	199	199	199	199	199	199	199	199
3	42.7	42.6	42.6	42.5	42.5	42.4	42.3	42.3	42.2	42.1	42.1	42.1	42.0	42.0	42.0	42.0	41.9	41.9	41.9	41.8
4	20.1	20.0	20.0	19.9	19.9	19.8	19.8	19.7	19.7	19.6	19.6	19.5	19.5	19.5	19.5	19.4	19.4	19.4	19.4	19.3
5	12.8	12.8	12.7	12.7	12.7	12.6	12.5	12.5	12.5	12.4	12.4	12.3	12.3	12.3	12.3	12.3	12.2	12.2	12.2	12.1
6	9.53	9.47	9.43	9.39	9.36	9.29	9.24	9.20	9.17	9.12	9.09	9.06	9.04	9.03	9.00	8.98	8.97	8.96	8.95	8.88
7	7.69	7.64	7.60	7.57	7.53	7.47	7.42	7.38	7.35	7.31	7.28	7.25	7.23	7.22	7.19	7.18	7.16	7.15	7.15	7.08
8	6.55	6.50	6.46	6.43	6.40	6.33	6.29	6.25	6.22	6.18	6.15	6.12	6.10	6.09	6.06	6.05	6.04	6.03	6.02	5.95
9	5.78	5.73	5.69	5.65	5.62	5.56	5.52	5.48	5.45	5.41	5.38	5.36	5.34	5.32	5.30	5.28	5.27	5.27	5.26	5.19
10	5.22	5.17	5.13	5.10	5.07	5.01	4.97	4.93	4.90	4.86	4.83	4.80	4.79	4.77	4.75	4.73	4.72	4.71	4.71	4.64
11	4.80	4.76	4.72	4.68	4.65	4.60	4.55	4.52	4.49	4.45	4.41	4.39	4.37	4.36	4.34	4.32	4.31	4.30	4.29	4.23
12	4.48	4.43	4.39	4.36	4.33	4.27	4.23	4.19	4.17	4.12	4.09	4.07	4.05	4.04	4.01	4.00	3.99	3.98	3.97	3.91
13	4.22	4.17	4.13	4.10	4.07	4.01	3.97	3.94	3.91	3.87	3.84	3.81	3.79	3.78	3.76	3.74	3.73	3.72	3.71	3.65
14	4.01	3.96	3.92	3.89	3.86	3.80	3.76	3.73	3.70	3.66	3.62	3.60	3.58	3.57	3.55	3.53	3.52	3.51	3.50	3.44
15	3.83	3.79	3.75	3.72	3.69	3.63	3.58	3.55	3.52	3.48	3.45	3.43	3.41	3.39	3.37	3.36	3.34	3.34	3.33	3.26
16	3.68	3.64	3.60	3.57	3.54	3.48	3.44	3.40	3.37	3.33	3.30	3.28	3.26	3.25	3.22	3.21	3.20	3.19	3.18	3.11
17	3.56	3.51	3.47	3.44	3.41	3.35	3.31	3.28	3.25	3.21	3.18	3.15	3.13	3.12	3.10	3.08	3.07	3.06	3.05	2.99
18	3.45	3.40	3.36	3.33	3.30	3.25	3.20	3.17	3.14	3.10	3.07	3.04	3.02	3.01	2.99	2.97	2.96	2.95	2.94	2.87
19	3.35	3.31	3.27	3.24	3.21	3.15	3.11	3.07	3.04	3.00	2.97	2.95	2.93	2.91	2.89	2.87	2.86	2.85	2.85	2.78
20	3.27	3.22	3.18	3.15	3.12	3.07	3.02	2.99	2.96	2.92	2.88	2.86	2.84	2.83	2.81	2.79	2.78	2.77	2.76	2.69
22	3.12	3.08	3.04	3.01	2.98	2.92	2.88	2.84	2.82	2.77	2.74	2.72	2.70	2.69	2.66	2.65	2.63	2.62	2.62	2.55
24	3.01	2.97	2.93	2.90	2.87	2.81	2.77	2.73	2.70	2.66	2.63	2.60	2.58	2.57	2.55	2.53	2.52	2.51	2.50	2.43
26	2.92	2.87	2.84	2.80	2.77	2.72	2.67	2.64	2.61	2.56	2.53	2.51	2.49	2.47	2.45	2.43	2.42	2.41	2.40	2.33
28	2.84	2.79	2.76	2.72	2.69	2.64	2.59	2.56	2.53	2.48	2.45	2.43	2.41	2.39	2.37	2.35	2.34	2.33	2.32	2.25
30	2.77	2.73	2.69	2.66	2.63	2.57	2.52	2.49	2.46	2.42	2.38	2.36	2.34	2.32	2.30	2.28	2.27	2.26	2.25	2.18
35	2.64	2.60	2.56	2.53	2.50	2.44	2.39	2.36	2.33	2.28	2.25	2.22	2.20	2.19	2.16	2.15	2.13	2.12	2.11	2.04
40	2.55	2.50	2.46	2.43	2.40	2.34	2.30	2.26	2.23	2.18	2.15	2.12	2.10	2.09	2.06	2.05	2.03	2.02	2.01	1.93
45	2.47	2.43	2.39	2.36	2.33	2.27	2.22	2.19	2.16	2.11	2.08	2.05	2.03	2.01	1.99	1.97	1.95	1.94	1.93	1.85
50	2.42	2.37	2.33	2.30	2.27	2.21	2.16	2.13	2.10	2.05	2.02	1.99	1.97	1.95	1.93	1.91	1.89	1.88	1.87	1.79
60	2.33	2.29	2.25	2.22	2.19	2.13	2.08	2.04	2.01	1.96	1.93	1.90	1.88	1.86	1.83	1.81	1.80	1.79	1.78	1.69
70	2.28	2.23	2.19	2.16	2.13	2.07	2.02	1.98	1.95	1.90	1.86	1.84	1.81	1.80	1.77	1.75	1.73	1.72	1.71	1.62
80	2.23	2.19	2.15	2.11	2.08	2.02	1.97	1.94	1.90	1.85	1.82	1.79	1.77	1.75	1.72	1.70	1.68	1.67	1.66	1.57
90	2.20	2.15	2.12	2.08	2.05	1.99	1.94	1.90	1.87	1.82	1.78	1.75	1.73	1.71	1.68	1.66	1.64	1.63	1.62	1.52
100	2.17	2.13	2.09	2.05	2.02	1.96	1.91	1.87	1.84	1.79	1.75	1.72	1.70	1.68	1.65	1.63	1.61	1.60	1.59	1.49
120	2.13	2.09	2.05	2.01	1.98	1.92	1.87	1.83	1.80	1.75	1.71	1.68	1.66	1.64	1.61	1.58	1.57	1.55	1.54	1.43
140	2.11	2.06	2.02	1.99	1.96	1.89	1.84	1.80	1.77	1.72	1.68	1.65	1.62	1.60	1.57	1.55	1.53	1.52	1.51	1.39
160	2.09	2.04	2.00	1.97	1.93	1.87	1.82	1.78	1.75	1.69	1.65	1.62	1.60	1.58	1.55	1.52	1.51	1.49	1.48	1.36
180	2.07	2.02	1.98	1.95	1.92	1.85	1.80	1.76	1.73	1.68	1.64	1.61	1.58	1.56	1.53	1.50	1.49	1.47	1.46	1.34
200	2.06	2.01	1.97	1.94	1.91	1.84	1.79	1.75	1.71	1.66	1.62	1.59	1.56	1.54	1.51	1.49	1.47	1.45	1.44	1.32
∞	1.95	1.90	1.86	1.82	1.79	1.72	1.67	1.63	1.59	1.54	1.49	1.46	1.43	1.40	1.37	1.34	1.31	1.30	1.28	1.00

DENOMINATOR DEGREES OF FREEDOM

TABLE **7(a)** Critical Values of the Studentized Range, $\alpha = .05$

v										k									
	2	3	4	5	6	7	8	9	10	11	12	13	14	15	16	17	18	19	20
1	18.0	27.0	32.8	37.1	40.4	43.1	45.4	47.4	49.1	50.6	52.0	53.2	54.3	55.4	56.3	57.2	58.0	58.8	59.6
2	6.08	8.33	9.80	10.9	11.7	12.4	13.0	13.5	14.0	14.4	14.7	15.1	15.4	15.7	15.9	16.1	16.4	16.6	16.8
3	4.50	5.91	6.82	7.50	8.04	8.48	8.85	9.18	9.46	9.72	9.95	10.2	10.3	10.5	10.7	10.8	11.0	11.1	11.2
4	3.93	5.04	5.76	6.29	6.71	7.05	7.35	7.60	7.83	8.03	8.21	8.37	8.52	8.66	8.79	8.91	9.03	9.13	9.23
5	3.64	4.60	5.22	5.67	6.03	6.33	6.58	6.80	6.99	7.17	7.32	7.47	7.60	7.72	7.83	7.93	8.03	8.12	8.21
6	3.46	4.34	4.90	5.30	5.63	5.90	6.12	6.32	6.49	6.65	6.79	6.92	7.03	7.14	7.24	7.34	7.43	7.51	7.59
7	3.34	4.16	4.68	5.06	5.36	5.61	5.82	6.00	6.16	6.30	6.43	6.55	6.66	6.76	6.85	6.94	7.02	7.10	7.17
8	3.26	4.04	4.53	4.89	5.17	5.40	5.60	5.77	5.92	6.05	6.18	6.29	6.39	6.48	6.57	6.65	6.73	6.80	6.87
9	3.20	3.95	4.41	4.76	5.02	5.24	5.43	5.59	5.74	5.87	5.98	6.09	6.19	6.28	6.36	6.44	6.51	6.58	6.64
10	3.15	3.88	4.33	4.65	4.91	5.12	5.30	5.46	5.60	5.72	5.83	5.93	6.03	6.11	6.19	6.27	6.34	6.40	6.47
11	3.11	3.82	4.26	4.57	4.82	5.03	5.20	5.35	5.49	5.61	5.71	5.81	5.90	5.98	6.06	6.13	6.20	6.27	6.33
12	3.08	3.77	4.20	4.51	4.75	4.95	5.12	5.27	5.39	5.51	5.61	5.71	5.80	5.88	5.95	6.02	6.09	6.15	6.21
13	3.06	3.73	4.15	4.45	4.69	4.88	5.05	5.19	5.32	5.43	5.53	5.63	5.71	5.79	5.86	5.93	5.99	6.05	6.11
14	3.03	3.70	4.11	4.41	4.64	4.83	4.99	5.13	5.25	5.36	5.46	5.55	5.64	5.71	5.79	5.85	5.91	5.97	6.03
15	3.01	3.67	4.08	4.37	4.59	4.78	4.94	5.08	5.20	5.31	5.40	5.49	5.57	5.65	5.72	5.78	5.85	5.90	5.96
16	3.00	3.65	4.05	4.33	4.56	4.74	4.90	5.03	5.15	5.26	5.35	5.44	5.52	5.59	5.66	5.73	5.79	5.84	5.90
17	2.98	3.63	4.02	4.30	4.52	4.70	4.86	4.99	5.11	5.21	5.31	5.39	5.47	5.54	5.61	5.67	5.73	5.79	5.84
18	2.97	3.61	4.00	4.28	4.49	4.67	4.82	4.96	5.07	5.17	5.27	5.35	5.43	5.50	5.57	5.63	5.69	5.74	5.79
19	2.96	3.59	3.98	4.25	4.47	4.65	4.79	4.92	5.04	5.14	5.23	5.31	5.39	5.46	5.53	5.59	5.65	5.70	5.75
20	2.95	3.58	3.96	4.23	4.45	4.62	4.77	4.90	5.01	5.11	5.20	5.28	5.36	5.43	5.49	5.55	5.61	5.66	5.71
24	2.92	3.53	3.90	4.17	4.37	4.54	4.68	4.81	4.92	5.01	5.10	5.18	5.25	5.32	5.38	5.44	5.49	5.55	5.59
30	2.89	3.49	3.85	4.10	4.30	4.46	4.60	4.72	4.82	4.92	5.00	5.08	5.15	5.21	5.27	5.33	5.38	5.43	5.47
40	2.86	3.44	3.79	4.04	4.23	4.39	4.52	4.63	4.73	4.82	4.90	4.98	5.04	5.11	5.16	5.22	5.27	5.31	5.36
60	2.83	3.40	3.74	3.98	4.16	4.31	4.44	4.55	4.65	4.73	4.81	4.88	4.94	5.00	5.06	5.11	5.15	5.20	5.24
120	2.80	3.36	3.68	3.92	4.10	4.24	4.36	4.47	4.56	4.64	4.71	4.78	4.84	4.90	4.95	5.00	5.04	5.09	5.13
∞	2.77	3.31	3.63	3.86	4.03	4.17	4.29	4.39	4.47	4.55	4.62	4.68	4.74	4.80	4.85	4.89	4.93	4.97	5.01

TABLE 7(b) Critical Values of the Studentized Range, $\alpha = .01$

ν	2	3	4	5	6	7	8	9	10	11	12	13	14	15	16	17	18	19	20
										k									
1	90.0	135	164	186	202	216	227	237	246	253	260	266	272	277	282	286	290	294	298
2	14.0	19.0	22.3	24.7	26.6	28.2	29.5	30.7	31.7	32.6	33.4	34.1	34.8	35.4	36.0	36.5	37.0	37.5	37.9
3	8.26	10.6	12.2	13.3	14.2	15.0	15.6	16.2	16.7	17.1	17.5	17.9	18.2	18.5	18.8	19.1	19.3	19.5	19.8
4	6.51	8.12	9.17	9.96	10.6	11.1	11.5	11.9	12.3	12.6	12.8	13.1	13.3	13.5	13.7	13.9	14.1	14.2	14.4
5	5.70	6.97	7.80	8.42	8.91	9.32	9.67	9.97	10.2	10.5	10.7	10.9	11.1	11.2	11.4	11.6	11.7	11.8	11.9
6	5.24	6.33	7.03	7.56	7.97	8.32	8.61	8.87	9.10	9.30	9.49	9.65	9.81	9.95	10.1	10.2	10.3	10.4	10.5
7	4.95	5.92	6.54	7.01	7.37	7.68	7.94	8.17	8.37	8.55	8.71	8.86	9.00	9.12	9.24	9.35	9.46	9.55	9.65
8	4.74	5.63	6.20	6.63	6.96	7.24	7.47	7.68	7.87	8.03	8.18	8.31	8.44	8.55	8.66	8.76	8.85	8.94	9.03
9	4.60	5.43	5.96	6.35	6.66	6.91	7.13	7.32	7.49	7.65	7.78	7.91	8.03	8.13	8.23	8.32	8.41	8.49	8.57
10	4.48	5.27	5.77	6.14	6.43	6.67	6.87	7.05	7.21	7.36	7.48	7.60	7.71	7.81	7.91	7.99	8.07	8.15	8.22
11	4.39	5.14	5.62	5.97	6.25	6.48	6.67	6.84	6.99	7.13	7.25	7.36	7.46	7.56	7.65	7.73	7.81	7.88	7.95
12	4.32	5.04	5.50	5.84	6.10	6.32	6.51	6.67	6.81	6.94	7.06	7.17	7.26	7.36	7.44	7.52	7.59	7.66	7.73
13	4.26	4.96	5.40	5.73	5.98	6.19	6.37	6.53	6.67	6.79	6.90	7.01	7.10	7.19	7.27	7.34	7.42	7.48	7.55
14	4.21	4.89	5.32	5.63	5.88	6.08	6.26	6.41	6.54	6.66	6.77	6.87	6.96	7.05	7.12	7.20	7.27	7.33	7.39
15	4.17	4.83	5.25	5.56	5.80	5.99	6.16	6.31	6.44	6.55	6.66	6.76	6.84	6.93	7.00	7.07	7.14	7.20	7.26
16	4.13	4.78	5.19	5.49	5.72	5.92	6.08	6.22	6.35	6.46	6.56	6.66	6.74	6.82	6.90	6.97	7.03	7.09	7.15
17	4.10	4.74	5.14	5.43	5.66	5.85	6.01	6.15	6.27	6.38	6.48	6.57	6.66	6.73	6.80	6.87	6.94	7.00	7.05
18	4.07	4.70	5.09	5.38	5.60	5.79	5.94	6.08	6.20	6.31	6.41	6.50	6.58	6.65	6.72	6.79	6.85	6.91	6.96
19	4.05	4.67	5.05	5.33	5.55	5.73	5.89	6.02	6.14	6.25	6.34	6.43	6.51	6.58	6.65	6.72	6.78	6.84	6.89
20	4.02	4.64	5.02	5.29	5.51	5.69	5.84	5.97	6.09	6.19	6.29	6.37	6.45	6.52	6.59	6.65	6.71	6.76	6.82
24	3.96	4.54	4.91	5.17	5.37	5.54	5.69	5.81	5.92	6.02	6.11	6.19	6.26	6.33	6.39	6.45	6.51	6.56	6.61
30	3.89	4.45	4.80	5.05	5.24	5.40	5.54	5.65	5.76	5.85	5.93	6.01	6.08	6.14	6.20	6.26	6.31	6.36	6.41
40	3.82	4.37	4.70	4.93	5.11	5.27	5.39	5.50	5.60	5.69	5.77	5.84	5.90	5.96	6.02	6.07	6.12	6.17	6.21
60	3.76	4.28	4.60	4.82	4.99	5.13	5.25	5.36	5.45	5.53	5.60	5.67	5.73	5.79	5.84	5.89	5.93	5.98	6.02
120	3.70	4.20	4.50	4.71	4.87	4.99	5.12	5.21	5.30	5.38	5.44	5.51	5.56	5.61	5.66	5.71	5.75	5.79	5.83
∞	3.64	4.12	4.40	4.60	4.76	4.88	4.99	5.08	5.16	5.23	5.29	5.35	5.40	5.45	5.49	5.54	5.57	5.61	5.65

Source: From E. S. Pearson and H. O. Hartley, *Biometrika Tables for Statisticians*, 1: 176–77. Reproduced by permission of the Biometrika Trustees.

TABLE **8(a)** Critical Values for the Durbin-Watson Statistic, $\alpha = .05$

n	d_L (k=1)	d_U (k=1)	d_L (k=2)	d_U (k=2)	d_L (k=3)	d_U (k=3)	d_L (k=4)	d_U (k=4)	d_L (k=5)	d_U (k=5)
15	1.08	1.36	.95	1.54	.82	1.75	.69	1.97	.56	2.21
16	1.10	1.37	.98	1.54	.86	1.73	.74	1.93	.62	2.15
17	1.13	1.38	1.02	1.54	.90	1.71	.78	1.90	.67	2.10
18	1.16	1.39	1.05	1.53	.93	1.69	.82	1.87	.71	2.06
19	1.18	1.40	1.08	1.53	.97	1.68	.86	1.85	.75	2.02
20	1.20	1.41	1.10	1.54	1.00	1.68	.90	1.83	.79	1.99
21	1.22	1.42	1.13	1.54	1.03	1.67	.93	1.81	.83	1.96
22	1.24	1.43	1.15	1.54	1.05	1.66	.96	1.80	.86	1.94
23	1.26	1.44	1.17	1.54	1.08	1.66	.99	1.79	.90	1.92
24	1.27	1.45	1.19	1.55	1.10	1.66	1.01	1.78	.93	1.90
25	1.29	1.45	1.21	1.55	1.12	1.66	1.04	1.77	.95	1.89
26	1.30	1.46	1.22	1.55	1.14	1.65	1.06	1.76	.98	1.88
27	1.32	1.47	1.24	1.56	1.16	1.65	1.08	1.76	1.01	1.86
28	1.33	1.48	1.26	1.56	1.18	1.65	1.10	1.75	1.03	1.85
29	1.34	1.48	1.27	1.56	1.20	1.65	1.12	1.74	1.05	1.84
30	1.35	1.49	1.28	1.57	1.21	1.65	1.14	1.74	1.07	1.83
31	1.36	1.50	1.30	1.57	1.23	1.65	1.16	1.74	1.09	1.83
32	1.37	1.50	1.31	1.57	1.24	1.65	1.18	1.73	1.11	1.82
33	1.38	1.51	1.32	1.58	1.26	1.65	1.19	1.73	1.13	1.81
34	1.39	1.51	1.33	1.58	1.27	1.65	1.21	1.73	1.15	1.81
35	1.40	1.52	1.34	1.58	1.28	1.65	1.22	1.73	1.16	1.80
36	1.41	1.52	1.35	1.59	1.29	1.65	1.24	1.73	1.18	1.80
37	1.42	1.53	1.36	1.59	1.31	1.66	1.25	1.72	1.19	1.80
38	1.43	1.54	1.37	1.59	1.32	1.66	1.26	1.72	1.21	1.79
39	1.43	1.54	1.38	1.60	1.33	1.66	1.27	1.72	1.22	1.79
40	1.44	1.54	1.39	1.60	1.34	1.66	1.29	1.72	1.23	1.79
45	1.48	1.57	1.43	1.62	1.38	1.67	1.34	1.72	1.29	1.78
50	1.50	1.59	1.46	1.63	1.42	1.67	1.38	1.72	1.34	1.77
55	1.53	1.60	1.49	1.64	1.45	1.68	1.41	1.72	1.38	1.77
60	1.55	1.62	1.51	1.65	1.48	1.69	1.44	1.73	1.41	1.77
65	1.57	1.63	1.54	1.66	1.50	1.70	1.47	1.73	1.44	1.77
70	1.58	1.64	1.55	1.67	1.52	1.70	1.49	1.74	1.46	1.77
75	1.60	1.65	1.57	1.68	1.54	1.71	1.51	1.74	1.49	1.77
80	1.61	1.66	1.59	1.69	1.56	1.72	1.53	1.74	1.51	1.77
85	1.62	1.67	1.60	1.70	1.57	1.72	1.55	1.75	1.52	1.77
90	1.63	1.68	1.61	1.70	1.59	1.73	1.57	1.75	1.54	1.78
95	1.64	1.69	1.62	1.71	1.60	1.73	1.58	1.75	1.56	1.78
100	1.65	1.69	1.63	1.72	1.61	1.74	1.59	1.76	1.57	1.78

Source: From J. Durbin and G. S. Watson, "Testing for Serial Correlation in Least Squares Regression, II," *Biometrika* 30 (1951): 159–78. Reproduced by permission of the Biometrika Trustees.

TABLE **8(b)** Critical Values for the Durbin-Watson Statistic, $\alpha = .01$

n	d_L (k=1)	d_U (k=1)	d_L (k=2)	d_U (k=2)	d_L (k=3)	d_U (k=3)	d_L (k=4)	d_U (k=4)	d_L (k=5)	d_U (k=5)
15	.81	1.07	.70	1.25	.59	1.46	.49	1.70	.39	1.96
16	.84	1.09	.74	1.25	.63	1.44	.53	1.66	.44	1.90
17	.87	1.10	.77	1.25	.67	1.43	.57	1.63	.48	1.85
18	.90	1.12	.80	1.26	.71	1.42	.61	1.60	.52	1.80
19	.93	1.13	.83	1.26	.74	1.41	.65	1.58	.56	1.77
20	.95	1.15	.86	1.27	.77	1.41	.68	1.57	.60	1.74
21	.97	1.16	.89	1.27	.80	1.41	.72	1.55	.63	1.71
22	1.00	1.17	.91	1.28	.83	1.40	.75	1.54	.66	1.69
23	1.02	1.19	.94	1.29	.86	1.40	.77	1.53	.70	1.67
24	1.04	1.20	.96	1.30	.88	1.41	.80	1.53	.72	1.66
25	1.05	1.21	.98	1.30	.90	1.41	.83	1.52	.75	1.65
26	1.07	1.22	1.00	1.31	.93	1.41	.85	1.52	.78	1.64
27	1.09	1.23	1.02	1.32	.95	1.41	.88	1.51	.81	1.63
28	1.10	1.24	1.04	1.32	.97	1.41	.90	1.51	.83	1.62
29	1.12	1.25	1.05	1.33	.99	1.42	.92	1.51	.85	1.61
30	1.13	1.26	1.07	1.34	1.01	1.42	.94	1.51	.88	1.61
31	1.15	1.27	1.08	1.34	1.02	1.42	.96	1.51	.90	1.60
32	1.16	1.28	1.10	1.35	1.04	1.43	.98	1.51	.92	1.60
33	1.17	1.29	1.11	1.36	1.05	1.43	1.00	1.51	.94	1.59
34	1.18	1.30	1.13	1.36	1.07	1.43	1.01	1.51	.95	1.59
35	1.19	1.31	1.14	1.37	1.08	1.44	1.03	1.51	.97	1.59
36	1.21	1.32	1.15	1.38	1.10	1.44	1.04	1.51	.99	1.59
37	1.22	1.32	1.16	1.38	1.11	1.45	1.06	1.51	1.00	1.59
38	1.23	1.33	1.18	1.39	1.12	1.45	1.07	1.52	1.02	1.58
39	1.24	1.34	1.19	1.39	1.14	1.45	1.09	1.52	1.03	1.58
40	1.25	1.34	1.20	1.40	1.15	1.46	1.10	1.52	1.05	1.58
45	1.29	1.38	1.24	1.42	1.20	1.48	1.16	1.53	1.11	1.58
50	1.32	1.40	1.28	1.45	1.24	1.49	1.20	1.54	1.16	1.59
55	1.36	1.43	1.32	1.47	1.28	1.51	1.25	1.55	1.21	1.59
60	1.38	1.45	1.35	1.48	1.32	1.52	1.28	1.56	1.25	1.60
65	1.41	1.47	1.38	1.50	1.35	1.53	1.31	1.57	1.28	1.61
70	1.43	1.49	1.40	1.52	1.37	1.55	1.34	1.58	1.31	1.61
75	1.45	1.50	1.42	1.53	1.39	1.56	1.37	1.59	1.34	1.62
80	1.47	1.52	1.44	1.54	1.42	1.57	1.39	1.60	1.36	1.62
85	1.48	1.53	1.46	1.55	1.43	1.58	1.41	1.60	1.39	1.63
90	1.50	1.54	1.47	1.56	1.45	1.59	1.43	1.61	1.41	1.64
95	1.51	1.55	1.49	1.57	1.47	1.60	1.45	1.62	1.42	1.64
100	1.52	1.56	1.50	1.58	1.48	1.60	1.46	1.63	1.44	1.65

Source: From J. Durbin and G. S. Watson, "Testing for Serial Correlation in Least Squares Regression, II," *Biometrika* 30 (1951): 159–78. Reproduced by permission of the Biometrika Trustees.

TABLE 9 Critical Values for the Wilcoxon Rank Sum Test

(a) $\alpha = .025$ one-tail; $\alpha = .05$ two-tail

n_2 \ n_1	3 T_L	3 T_U	4 T_L	4 T_U	5 T_L	5 T_U	6 T_L	6 T_U	7 T_L	7 T_U	8 T_L	8 T_U	9 T_L	9 T_U	10 T_L	10 T_U
4	6	18	11	25	17	33	23	43	31	53	40	64	50	76	61	89
5	6	11	12	28	18	37	25	47	33	58	42	70	52	83	64	96
6	7	23	12	32	19	41	26	52	35	63	44	76	55	89	66	104
7	7	26	13	35	20	45	28	56	37	68	47	81	58	95	70	110
8	8	28	14	38	21	49	29	61	39	63	49	87	60	102	73	117
9	8	31	15	41	22	53	31	65	41	78	51	93	63	108	76	124
10	9	33	16	44	24	56	32	70	43	83	54	98	66	114	79	131

(b) $\alpha = .05$ one-tail; $\alpha = 10$ two-tail

n_2 \ n_1	3 T_L	3 T_U	4 T_L	4 T_U	5 T_L	5 T_U	6 T_L	6 T_U	7 T_L	7 T_U	8 T_L	8 T_U	9 T_L	9 T_U	10 T_L	10 T_U
3	6	15	11	21	16	29	23	37	31	46	39	57	49	68	60	80
4	7	17	12	24	18	32	25	41	33	51	42	62	52	74	63	87
5	7	20	13	27	19	37	26	46	35	56	45	67	55	80	66	94
6	8	22	14	30	20	40	28	50	37	61	47	73	57	87	69	101
7	9	24	15	33	22	43	30	54	39	66	49	79	60	93	73	107
8	9	27	16	36	24	46	32	58	41	71	52	84	63	99	76	114
9	10	29	17	39	25	50	33	63	43	76	54	90	66	105	79	121
10	11	31	18	42	26	54	35	67	46	80	57	95	69	111	83	127

Source: From F. Wilcoxon and R. A. Wilcox, "Some Rapid Approximate Statistical Procedures" (1964), p. 28. Reproduced with the permission of American Cyanamid Company.

TABLE **10**
Critical Values for the
Wilcoxon Signed Rank
Sum Test

	(a) $\alpha = .025$ one-tail; $\alpha = .05$ two-tail		(b) $\alpha = .05$ one-tail; $\alpha = .10$ two-tail	
n	T_L	T_U	T_L	T_U
6	1	20	2	19
7	2	26	4	24
8	4	32	6	30
9	6	39	8	37
10	8	47	11	44
11	11	55	14	52
12	14	64	17	61
13	17	74	21	70
14	21	84	26	79
15	25	95	30	90
16	30	106	36	100
17	35	118	41	112
18	40	131	47	124
19	46	144	54	136
20	52	158	60	150
21	59	172	68	163
22	66	187	75	178
23	73	203	83	193
24	81	219	92	208
25	90	235	101	224
26	98	253	110	241
27	107	271	120	258
28	117	289	130	276
29	127	308	141	294
30	137	328	152	313

Source: From F. Wilcoxon and R. A. Wilcox, "Some Rapid Approximate Statistical Procedures" (1964), p. 28. Reproduced with the permission of American Cyanamid Company.

TABLE **11** Critical Values for the Spearman Rank Correlation Coefficient

The α values correspond to a one-tail test of $H_0 : \rho_s = 0$.
The value should be doubled for two-tail tests.

n	$\alpha = .05$	$\alpha = .025$	$\alpha = .01$
5	.900	—	—
6	.829	.886	.943
7	.714	.786	.893
8	.643	.738	.833
9	.600	.683	.783
10	.564	.648	.745
11	.523	.623	.736
12	.497	.591	.703
13	.475	.566	.673
14	.457	.545	.646
15	.441	.525	.623
16	.425	.507	.601
17	.412	.490	.582
18	.399	.476	.564
19	.388	.462	.549
20	.377	.450	.534
21	.368	.438	.521
22	.359	.428	.508
23	.351	.418	.496
24	.343	.409	.485
25	.336	.400	.475
26	.329	.392	.465
27	.323	.385	.456
28	.317	.377	.448
29	.311	.370	.440
30	.305	.364	.432

Source: From E. G. Olds, "Distribution of Sums of Squares of Rank Differences for Small Samples," *Annals of Mathematical Statistics* 9 (1938). Reproduced with the permission of the Institute of Mathematical Statistics.

TABLE **12** Control Chart Constants

Sample Size n	A_2	d_2	D_3	D_4	B_3	B_4
2	1.880	1.128	0	3.267	0	3.267
3	1.023	1.693	0	2.574	0	2.568
4	0.729	2.059	0	2.282	0	2.266
5	0.577	2.326	0	2.114	0	2.089
6	0.483	2.534	0	2.004	0.030	1.970
7	0.419	2.704	0.076	1.924	0.118	1.882
8	0.373	2.847	0.136	1.864	0.185	1.815
9	0.337	2.970	0.184	1.816	0.239	1.761
10	0.308	3.078	0.223	1.777	0.284	1.716
11	0.285	3.173	0.256	1.744	0.321	1.679
12	0.266	3.258	0.283	1.717	0.354	1.646
13	0.249	3.336	0.307	1.693	0.382	1.618
14	0.235	3.407	0.328	1.672	0.406	1.594
15	0.223	3.472	0.347	1.653	0.428	1.572
16	0.212	3.532	0.363	1.637	0.448	1.552
17	0.203	3.588	0.378	1.622	0.466	1.534
18	0.194	3.640	0.391	1.608	0.482	1.518
19	0.187	3.689	0.403	1.597	0.497	1.503
20	0.180	3.735	0.415	1.585	0.510	1.490
21	0.173	3.778	0.425	1.575	0.523	1.477
22	0.167	3.819	0.434	1.566	0.534	1.466
23	0.162	3.858	0.443	1.557	0.545	1.455
24	0.157	3.895	0.451	1.548	0.555	1.445
25	0.153	3.931	0.459	1.541	0.565	1.435

Source: From E. S. Pearson, "The Percentage Limits for the Distribution of Range in Samples from a Normal Population," *Biometrika* 24 (1932): 416. Reproduced by permission of the Biometrika Trustees.

TABLE 12 Control Chart Constants

Sample Size n	A	A_2	D_3	D_4	B_3	B_4
2	1.880	1.128	0	3.267	0	3.267
3	1.023	1.693	0	2.574	0	2.568
4	0.729	2.059	0	2.282	0	2.266
5	0.577	2.326	0	2.114	0	2.089
6	0.483	2.534	0	2.004	0.030	1.970
7	0.419	2.704	0.076	1.924	0.118	1.882
8	0.373	2.847	0.136	1.864	0.185	1.815
9	0.337	2.970	0.184	1.816	0.239	1.761
10	0.308	3.078	0.223	1.777	0.284	1.716
11	0.285	3.173	0.256	1.744	0.321	1.679
12	0.266	3.258	0.283	1.717	0.354	1.646
13	0.249	3.336	0.307	1.693	0.382	1.618
14	0.235	3.407	0.328	1.672	0.406	1.594
15	0.223	3.472	0.347	1.653	0.428	1.572
16	0.212	3.532	0.363	1.637	0.448	1.552
17	0.203	3.588	0.378	1.622	0.466	1.534
18	0.194	3.640	0.391	1.608	0.482	1.518
19	0.187	3.689	0.403	1.597	0.497	1.503
20	0.180	3.735	0.415	1.585	0.510	1.490
21	0.173	3.778	0.425	1.575	0.523	1.477
22	0.167	3.819	0.434	1.566	0.534	1.466
23	0.162	3.858	0.443	1.557	0.545	1.455
24	0.157	3.895	0.451	1.548	0.555	1.445
25	0.153	3.931	0.459	1.541	0.565	1.435

APPENDIX C

A Guide to Statistical Techniques

Problem Objectives

DATA TYPES	Describe a Population	Compare Two Populations	Compare Two or More Populations	Analyze Relationship between Two Variables	Analyze Relationship among Two or More Variables
Interval	Histogram **Section 3-1** Line chart **Section 3-2** Mean, median, and mode **Section 4-1** Range, variance, and standard deviation **Section 4-2** Percentiles and quartiles **Section 4-3** t-test and estimator of a mean **Section 12-1** Chi-squared test and estimator of a variance **Section 12-2**	Equal-variances t-test and estimator of the difference between two means: independent samples **Section 13-1** Unequal-variances t-test and estimator of the difference between two means: independent samples **Section 13-1** t-test and estimator of mean difference **Section 13-3** F-test and estimator of ratio of two variances **Section 13-4** Wilcoxon rank sum test **Section 19-1** Wilcoxon signed rank sum test **Section 19-2**	One-way analysis of variance **Section 14-1** LSD multiple comparison method **Section 14-2** Tukey's multiple comparison method **Section 14-2** Two-way analysis of variance **Section 14-4** Two-factor analysis of variance **Section 14-5** Kruskal-Wallis test **Section 19-3** Friedman test **Section 19-3**	Scatter diagram **Section 3-3** Covariance **Section 4-4** Coefficient of correlation **Section 4-4** Coefficient of determination **Section 4-4** Least squares line **Section 4-4** Simple linear regression and correlation **Chapter 16** Spearman rank correlation **Section 19-4**	Multiple regression **Chapters 17 and 18**
Nominal	Frequency distribution **Section 2-2** Bar chart **Section 2-2** Pie chart **Section 2-2** Z-test and estimator of a proportion **Section 12-3** Chi-squared goodness-of-fit test **Section 15-1**	Z-test and estimator of the difference between two proportions **Section 13-5** Chi-squared test of a contingency table **Section 15-2**	Chi-squared test of a contingency table **Section 15-2**	Chi-squared test of a contingency table **Section 15-2**	Not covered
Ordinal	Median **Section 4-1** Percentiles and quartiles **Section 4-3**	Wilcoxon rank sum test **Section 19-1** Sign test **Section 19-2**	Kruskal-Wallis test **Section 19-3** Friedman test **Section 19-3**	Spearman rank correlation **Section 19-4**	Not covered

C-1

APPENDIX D

Index of Excel Output and Instructions

APPENDIX E

MANAGEMENT AND ECONOMIC APPLICATIONS

APPLICATION BOXES

APPLICATION SECTIONS

APPLICATION SUBSECTION

INDEX